PHYSICS
for Science and Engineering

PHYSICS
for Science and Engineering

Dudley Williams

John Spangler

KANSAS STATE UNIVERSITY

D. VAN NOSTRAND COMPANY

New York ● Cincinnati ● Toronto ● London ● Melbourne

ACKNOWLEDGMENTS

We thank the following publishers for granting us permission to reproduce diagrams and photographs from the sources listed.

Figure 9.10   Gerald Holton and Stephen G. Brush. *Introduction to Concepts and Theories in Physical Science,* 2nd ed. Copyright © 1973 by Addison-Wesley Publishing Company, Inc., Reading, MA, Fig. 11.4.

Figure 9.11(b)   Vernon D. Barger and Martin G. Olsson. *Classical Mechanics: A Modern Perspective.* Copyright © 1973 by McGraw-Hill Book Company, New York, Fig. 7.3.

Figure 18.3   Frank S. Crawford, Jr. *Waves,* Berkeley Physics Course, Vol. 3. Copyright © 1968 by Educational Development Center, Inc., Newton MA, Fig. 4.2.

Figures 18.10 and 20.10   David Halliday and Robert Resnick. *Physics,* 3rd ed. Copyright © 1978 by John Wiley & Sons, Inc., New York, Figs. 19.5(a) and 26.3.

Figures 21.8 and 30.3   Edward M. Purcell. *Electricity and Magnetism,* Berkeley Physics Course, Vol. 2. Copyright © 1965 by Educational Development Center, Inc., Newton, MA, Figs. 1.11 and 10.9.

Figures 22.10   Francis W. Sears, Mark W. Zemansky, and Hugh D. Young. *University Physics,* 5th ed. Copyright © 1976 by Addison-Wesley Publishing Company, Inc., Reading, MA, Fig. 26–7.

Figure 28.5   A. B. Arons. *Development of Concepts of Physics.* Copyright © 1965 by Addison-Wesley Publishing Company, Inc., Reading, MA, Fig. 23.7.1.

Figure 30.11   S. Chikazumi. *Physics of Magnetism.* Copyright © 1964 by John Wiley & Sons, Inc., New York, Figs. 6.18 and 6.19(a).

Figures 32.3 and 32.4   John M. Stone. *Radiation and Optics.* Copyright © 1963 by McGraw-Hill Book Company, New York, Figs. 5–2 and 5–3.

Figure 32.5   H. H. Skilling. *Fundamentals of Electric Waves,* 2nd ed. Copyright © 1948 by H. H. Skilling. Published by John Wiley & Sons, Inc., New York, Fig. 60.

Figures 33.6, 35.1, and 36.3   Harvey E. White. *Modern College Physics,* 6th ed. Copyright © 1972 by Litton Educational Publishing, Inc., New York, Figs. 35H, 35I, 47B, and 37Q(c).

Figures 35.4, 35.11, 35.14, and 35.17   Michael Cagnet, Maurice Francon, and Jean Claude Thrierr. *Atlas of Optical Phenomena.* Copyright © 1962 by Springer-Verlag, New York, pp. 16 and 18.

Figures 35.6, 35.8, and 35.9   R. W. Ditchburn. *Light,* 2nd ed. Copyright © 1963 by R. W. Ditchburn. Published by Blackie and Son Limited, Glasgow, Plate III (c), (d), (e); Plate II (g), (k).

Figure 36.2   Gerhard Herzberg. *Molecular Spectra and Molecular Structure I. Spectra of Diatomic Molecules.* Copyright © 1950 by Van Nostrand Reinhold Company, New York, Fig. 6.

Cover photograph by Reginald Wickham

PREFACE

Physics for Science and Engineering is a textbook for beginning physics courses like the one normally taken by serious students of science and engineering. We attempt to give a rigorous but lucid introduction to physics that is free of ideas that have to be "unlearned" in later advanced courses. The book is designed to provide a firm foundation upon which subsequent courses can be based. We have tried throughout to keep in mind the interests and abilities of the students in our own course.

Our primary purpose is to provide students with a clear understanding of the fundamental principles of physics, of how they evolved from careful observation and quantitative experiment, and of how they can be applied. We seek to develop a deeper appreciation of the fundamental principles by using rigorous logical reasoning in deriving important secondary relationships from the principles. Former students in our course have reported that developing the ability to employ logical and quantitative thinking has made a major contribution to their later professional careers.

Our extended discussions in the first chapters of the book are intentional, because we feel that full and careful discussion of basic ideas is essential to students in the early stages of their studies. Once basic ideas have been fully introduced, we express the principles in mathematical form since mathematics is the language in which physical science is expressed and applied. We emphasize that mathematical relationships express ideas and are not mysterious "formulas" that provide a magic key to arcane knowledge.

The typical student beginning our course has completed the first course and is currently enrolled in the second course of a four-course sequence covering analytic geometry and calculus. Even though many students have not mastered all the techniques involved, they are familiar with the processes of differentiation and integration, which we employ early in the text. For the benefit of students just beginning their study of calculus, we have included sections in the Appendix that introduce the basic ideas involved in differentiation and integration and have also been careful early in the text to express important relationships in algebraic form so that they can be used directly in solving problems. In the first twelve chapters we have identified by asterisks problems that require calculus.

Although we attempt to make optimum use of the students mathematical knowledge of students, we make no attempt to "teach mathematics" as such. However, students in our course tell us that early use of their newly acquired mathematical knowledge of calculus gives them a deeper understanding and appreciation of the beauty and power of mathematical thinking.

In order to permit students to concentrate on basic principles, we have employed a single coherent system of units throughout the text. Because it has been adopted by major scientific societies throughout the world, by the American engineering institutes, and by U.S. governmental laboratories and other agencies, we have chosen the *Système International* (SI). We attempt to give students an understanding of dimensional analysis by careful attention to the SI units used in all key relationships. Comparison of the SI units with those employed in other systems is provided by an extensive set of conversion tables in the Appendix.

The order of topics is the traditional and logical sequence: mechanics, heat and thermodynamics, wave motion and sound, electromagnetism, light, and modern physics. In our course we cover mechanics and heat in the first semester and the remaining parts of the book in the second semester. However, provided mechanics is covered first, the order of the remaining topics can be altered without serious difficulty; for example, in a three-quarter sequence the second quarter could be devoted to heat, sound, and light and the third quarter could be devoted to electromagnetism and modern physics. Other divisions of subject matter by quarter or by semester are also possible.

Our treatment of classical physics is rigorous throughout. In shorter courses, it is possible to omit some of the material in the closing sections of various chapters without loss of continuity. In the final part of the book, which is devoted to modern physics, we focus on discussions of the two major theoretical developments of the 20th century: quantum mechanics and relativity. We note how classical theory failed when applied to the emission and absorption of radiation and to matter on an atomic scale, and we show how some of the basic quantum ideas evolved. We make no attempt to set up and solve the Schrodinger equation. In the final chapter, we give a brief but rigorous treatment of special relativity; we make no attempt to treat general relativity.

The Question set at the end of each chapter is intended to elucidate the ideas that have been presented and to provide bases for discussion. Many of these Questions do not have simple, clear-cut answers. The Problem sets include both simple, "confidence-building" problems that involve single concepts and problems of greater difficulty and sophistication in which several concepts are involved. The book contains many more problems than would normally be assigned in a one-year introductory course. It has been our experience that 15 to 20 properly selected problems per week are sufficient to keep the average student busy and that superior students frequently go on to solve more of the challenging problems. Answers to odd-numbered problems are given in the text, with numerical results given to three-figure accuracy. A Solutions Manual containing detailed solutions to every problem in the text is available to instructors from the publisher.

A Study Guide accompanies this text and provides additional aid in mastery of the material and in problem solving. Each unit reviews the basic concepts and laws introduced in the corresponding chapter and provides further worked examples to supplement those in the text. The Study Guide also includes a short quiz on each chapter that students can use to test their understanding of the basic concepts.

We should like to express our deepest appreciation to our colleagues for the encouragement and support that they have given us while this volume was being written and prepared for publication. We also gratefully acknowledge the valuable suggestions made by the following reviewers of the manuscript: Allen K. Garrison, Emory University; Philip C. Peters, University of Washington; William H. Parker, University of California at Irvine; H. R. Brewer, Georgia Institute of Technology; Mario Iona, University of Denver; Victor A. Stanionis, Iona College; William R. Riley, Ohio State University. One of us (D. W.) would like to offer special thanks to his earlier coauthor, the late George Shortley and to Logan Campbell and his associates at Prentice-Hall for their generous permission to adapt to the needs of the student of the 1980s some materials from an earlier text first published in 1953 and in its fifth edition in 1971. We further express our appreciation to Emil Wolf for suggestions regarding our introduction to quantum physics and to Dow Smith for suggesting several problems dealing with classical barrier penetration. We offer thanks to the staff at D. Van Nostrand Company for its excellent editorial work and to our typists for the preparation of the typescript.

Dudley Williams
John Spangler

CONTENTS

PART 1

MECHANICS

CHAPTER 1

Physics: A Quantitative Science

Throughout most of the period of mankind's existence on earth the activity of every individual was devoted to a constant struggle for mere survival. Gathering roots and berries and hunting wild animals for their flesh and pelts was a full-time activity. Although the domestication of certain animals had occurred somewhat earlier, the development of agriculture some 7000 years ago represented the first major change in man's adaptation to his environment. With a food supply ensured, nomadic life was no longer necessary; settlement in permanent communities became possible—in villages, in towns, and finally in cities. Social organization in settled communities was, of course, quite different from that of the wandering tribe.

With the development of the early cities, not *all* people had to devote their entire attention to the process of securing the food, clothing, and shelter required for survival. There were numerous new problems involved in community life: construction of permanent buildings, laying out of streets, provision for water supplies and sewage disposal, accurate surveying of land tracts, heating of dwellings, etc. New groups of specialists in handling these problems appeared; these specialists were the first *engineers*. These engineers played important roles in both military and civil affairs. Most of their operations were based on useful experience gathered on a trial-and-error basis and were handed down from generation to generation. We continue to be impressed today with many of these engineers' accomplishments, such as the pyramids of Egypt, the Roman roads, and the elaborate systems of aqueducts in various parts of the world.

In contrast to the practical knowledge developed and employed by the engineers, there were other individuals in a period beginning 2500 years ago who were interested in the nature of the physical world itself. The early Greek philosophers were interested in this subject and attempted to devise extremely general philosophic systems in terms of which natural phenomena could be interpreted and explained. These systems were based on data obtained from *qualitative* observations and experiments; with limited qualitative data, the Greek philosophers were inclined to make very broad generalizations. In terms of their systems, the philosophers were chiefly interested in explaining WHY the physical world behaves as it does. Greek science did not, in general, provide the practical engineer with knowledge useful to his profession. There were, of course, notable exceptions to this statement; for example, Archimedes of Syracuse (287–212 B.C.) was himself both a philosopher *and* an engineer. For more than 1000 years Greek science as formulated by Aristotle (384–322 B.C.) dominated European thought regarding the physical world.

For the past 400 years science and, to an ever-increasing extent, engineering have operated on an entirely new and different basis. Since the days of Galileo Galilei (1564–1642), Isaac Newton (1642–1727), and Robert Boyle (1627–1691), the methods of physical science have changed completely. Whereas the Greeks were interested in answering questions of WHY the physical world behaves as it does on the basis of broad philosophical generalizations based on qualitative data, modern scientists have more modest aims; their goal is to provide a quantitative description of HOW the universe behaves. The *quantitative* data employed by modern scientists involve carefully *measured* physical quantitites that have been defined clearly; all acceptable data must be subject to repeated checks by independent investigators making careful observations or performing carefully controlled experiments.

Once acceptable data have been amassed, the modern scientist makes generalizations involving *quantitative* relationships among measured quantities. These generalizations and scientific theories in general are stated in mathematical form. An acceptable theory must give a satisfactory account of known facts or data and must provide a basis for *predictions* that can be tested by observation or experiment. The procedures of mathematics have proved the most powerful way to make predictions based on a theory. Whereas the Greek philosophers sought for ultimate truths, the modern scientist is content with developing theories that provide valid predictions. The validity of its predictions is the ultimate test of any scientific theory.

Whereas the Greeks tended to make broad generalizations, the modern scientist usually proceeds more cautiously. He is initially content with generalizations having limited ranges of validity, which we shall call *rules*. Generalizations with wider ranges of validity we shall call *laws*. Generalizations that appear to have universal validity we shall call *principles*. One ultimate goal of science is the development of theories that have complete generality and that provide valid predictions for *all* physical situations; although this goal has not been achieved, science is nonetheless useful. We must point out that *all* scientific knowledge should be regarded as tentative; the discovery and verification of a single new fact that does not bear out a prediction can lead to the modification or downfall of even the most cherished general principle.

Modern science has made enormous contributions to engineering practice. By making predictions on the basis of scientific generalizations the modern engineer can eliminate many of the cut-and-try techniques that were employed in the prescientific age. Many of the newer branches of engineering have been based from the outset on scientific knowledge; older branches of engineering have been revolutionized by modern science. The time interval between a scientific discovery and its engineering application has become increasingly brief. In fact, much of the research conducted in engineering laboratories is essentially applied science, and the engineers involved are themselves acting as applied scientists. The practicing professional engineer, however, within the limits of what is scientifically possible, makes valuable use of other types of knowledge that have been developed on the basis of practical experience. The modern engineer's genius is in making applications of scientific knowledge available to society within the existing economic, environmental, social, and political constraints of the modern world.

In this volume we shall give a presentation of the science of physics designed to provide a basis for subsequent courses in engineering and physical science. We shall employ mathematics as a language in the same way that it is employed by modern professional engineers and scientists. Physics has a definite structure that will be presented in various parts: *Mechanics, Heat and Thermodynamics, Wave Motion, Electromagnetism, Light,* and *Modern Physics,* which deals with the quantum and relativistic developments of the present century. Each of these parts provides a foundation for what follows; for example, our discussion of electromagnetism is based on a clear understanding of mechanics.

In the present chapter we shall discuss the processes involved in measurement and shall discuss the development of the international system of units that has been adopted throughout most of the world today. Starting with the accepted base unit for the measurement of length as a fundamental physical quantity, we shall show how derived physical quantities such as areas, volumes, and angles can be measured without the introduction of additional arbitrary units. We close the chapter with a discussion of how length units are employed in specifying positions in various coordinate systems or frames of reference.

1.1 MEASUREMENTS

As we have indicated, modern physical science is based on quantitative data involving the careful measurement of physical quantities such as lengths, areas, and volumes. Making a measurement involves comparing the quantity of interest with some established standard unit for that quantity. At the beginning of the age of modern science some 400 years ago, scientists used the existing systems of "weights and measures" that had been adopted for use in commercial transactions. These systems used units based on arbitrary standards for each quantity to be measured; for example, length standards, area standards, and volume standards were entirely separate and bore no apparent relation to one another. Multiples and submultiples of the basic units usually involved halving or doubling but sometimes employed other strange numbers like those encountered in the familiar British length units: 12 inches = 1 foot; 3 feet = 1 yard; 5280 feet = 1 mile. Additional British length measures such as the ell, the rod, and the furlong were also employed. Each country maintained its own system of "weights and measures" with different sets of multiples and submultiples of the arbitrary units. It is easy to imagine the confusion involved not only in international commercial transactions but also in transactions within each country, where each merchant maintained his own set—or sets!—of weights and measures supposedly copied from national standards.

Abuses were so widespread that they constituted a major grievance at the time of the French Revolution in 1789, when the French national assembly appointed a committee of scientists to set up a system of base units based on clearly defined

Table 1.1   Fundamental Physical Quantities and SI Base Units

Fundamental Quantity	Base Unit
Length	meter
Mass	kilogram
Time	second
Quantity of substance	mole
Absolute temperature	kelvin
Electric current	ampere

standards, with decimal multiples and submultiples of the base units. The original French metric system gradually gained international acceptance and, after extensive refinement, has been adopted throughout the world today.

The formal name of the system of units adopted by the General Conference of Weights and Measures in the 1960s is the International Systems of Units; in recognition of its French origin the abbreviation SI (for *Système International*) is used in all languages. The SI units have been employed for some years by the US National Bureau of Standards and in government reports and publications. They have been adopted by the American professional engineering societies and scientific societies for use in their publications. The SI units will eventually be employed in general commercial transactions in the United States and are at present employed in American commercial transactions with foreign countries. The relationships between SI units and the units employed in other systems are given in a set of tables of Conversion Factors in the Appendix to this book.

1.2   THE INTERNATIONAL SYSTEM OF UNITS: SI

Any system of measurement is based on the arbitrary selection of certain base units; in the older systems an arbitrary base unit was employed for every physical quantity to be measured. In the SI a different procedure is employed. A relatively small number of *fundamental physical quantities* not definable in terms of other quantities has been selected to form the nucleus of the system; an arbitrary but internationally accepted *base unit* is selected for each fundamental quantity. The operational procedures to be used in establishing the base units are carefully described so that, in principle, the standards laboratory for each nation can fabricate an accurate set of standard measuring devices, replicas of which can be supplied to industry and to the general public. The fundamental quantities and their base units are listed in Table 1.1.

All physical quantities other than those listed in Table 1.1 are called *derived quantities*. The units in terms of which derived quantities are measured are *not* arbitrary, but represent combinations of base units. In contrast to the older systems, the SI employs only six arbitrary base units; once these are carefully established, *all* physical quantities can be measured. This is an enormous simplification over earlier systems!

In order to understand the operational procedures involved in the establishment

Table 1.2   SI Prefixes

Prefix	Pronunciation	Symbol	Factor
tera-	tear'ah	T	10^{12}
giga-	jig'ah	G	10^{9}
mega-	meg'ah	M	10^{6}
kilo-	kill'oh	k	10^{3}
hecto-	heck'toh	h	10^{2}
deka-	deck'ah	da	10^{1}
deci-	dess'ih	d	10^{-1}
centi-	cent'ih	c	10^{-2}
milli-	mill'ih	m	10^{-3}
micro-	mike'roh	μ	10^{-6}
nano-	nan'oh	n	10^{-9}
pico-	pee'koh	p	10^{-12}
femto-	fem'toh	f	10^{-15}
atto-	att'oh	a	10^{-18}

of the base units, we must first gain an understanding of various physical phenomena. The *meter, second,* and *mole* are based on certain atomic properties, which are believed to be invariable. The *kelvin* is based on the temperature at which water, ice, and water vapor exist in equilibrium. The *ampere* is based on the measurement of forces between current-carrying wires a definite distance apart. Only the *kilogram* is completely arbitrary in the older sense of this word; it is defined in terms of a metal cylinder that is carefully preserved in an underground laboratory at Sèvres, a suburb of Paris. In this book we shall later discuss at the appropriate points the operational procedures used in establishing the SI base units; for the present, we shall assume that the base units have been validly established and shall learn how to use them.

Because we shall use the same SI units for measuring very large quantities and very small quantities, it is necessary to consider decimal multiples and submultiples of the SI units. Just as in the American decimal coinage system we give names such as the mil, the cent, and the dime to decimal submultiples of the dollar and names such as the eagle to decimal multiples of the dollar, we also give names to decimal multiples and submultiples of SI units. A list of the names and their abbreviations is given in Table 1.2. Most multiples are given Greek names with single letters for their abbreviations; the submultiples are given Latin names with lowercase letters for their abbreviations.

1.3   DERIVED QUANTITIES: AREA, VOLUME

As a first and perhaps trivial example of a derived physical quantity, let us consider *area.* Consider the rectangle shown in Fig. 1.1 having height h and base length l. The height and base length are both measured in meters (m) in SI units. Because the area A of the rectangle is equal to the product hl, we may write the equation

$$A = hl. \qquad \begin{Bmatrix} A \text{ in m}^2 \\ h \text{ in m} \\ l \text{ in m} \end{Bmatrix} \qquad (1.1)$$

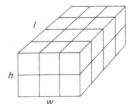

Fig. 1.1 The area of the surface is equal to the product hl.

Fig. 1.2 The volume of the body is equal to hlw.

In order for any equation to be valid, the physical dimensions of the two sides must be the same; if the dimensions of the two sides were *not* the same, we would be using the equation to assert some absurdity like setting oranges equal to apples. Since area is equal to the product of two lengths, the units used for measurement of area must be square meters (m²).

Example.	If, in Fig. 1.1, the height of the rectangle $h = 2$ m and the length $l = 3$ m, what is the area of the rectangle? From (1.1), we write $A = (2 \text{ m})(3 \text{ m}) = 6$ m², where we note that the area unit comes out quite "naturally" in m² in the SI.

We note that the SI unit for measuring area came out painlessly, without our having to set up any special unit for area by constructing a special standard area. In using a rectangle for our discussion we have considered a very simple case. If we consider a circle of radius R with $A = \pi R^2$, we must note that the numerical factor π is a pure number without physical dimensions; the area of the circle thus also comes out to be expressed in m².

Example.	What is the area of a circle with radius $R = 2$ m? The area is $A = \pi R^2 = \pi R \cdot R$; thus, $A = \pi(2 \text{ m})(2 \text{ m}) = 4\pi$ m², where we note again that both 4 and π are pure numbers without physical dimensions.

As a second example of a derived quantity, consider *volume,* for which so many strange and independent standards like drams, pints, gallons, and bushels were established in earlier systems of weights and measures. In Fig. 1.2 we show a rectangular body of length l, width w, and height h. The volume V of the body is given by the product

$$V = lwh. \quad \left\{ \begin{array}{c} V \text{ in m}^3 \\ l,\ w,\ h \text{ in m} \end{array} \right\} \quad (1.2)$$

In order for this equation to balance dimensionally, the volume V must be expressed in m³ because the right-hand side of the equation is the product of three lengths, each of which is expressed in m. The SI volume unit thus comes out as the cubic meter without the complications of devising special standards as had been usual in earlier systems of measurement.

Example.   If in Fig. 1.2, $l = 4$ m, $w = 3$ m, and $h = 2$ m, what is the volume of the solid?
From (1.2), $V = (4 \text{ m})(3 \text{ m})(2 \text{ m}) = 24$ m³, which clearly gives the cubic meter (m³) as the SI unit of volume.

Example.   What is the volume of a sphere having a radius $R = 2$ m?
We recall that the volume of a sphere is given by the relation $V = \frac{4}{3}\pi R^3$, where $\frac{4}{3}$ and π are pure numbers without physical dimensions. Therefore, $V = \frac{4}{3}\pi(2 \text{ m})(2 \text{ m})(2 \text{ m}) = \frac{32}{3}\pi$ m³.

1.4   MEASUREMENT OF ANGLES

We now come to a derived quantity that offers some practical difficulty in fitting into our SI system of units in the same way that we have employed for area and volume. The area unit and the volume unit came out as m² and m³, respectively, without any numbers other than unity appearing in the equations that relate them to the base unit of length. Now any angle* like θ between the intersecting lines in Fig. 1.3 can readily be defined by drawing a circle of arbitrary radius R with its center at the point at which the lines intersect and then defining the angle θ as the ratio of the arc length S to the radius R:

$$\theta = S/R. \quad \left\{\begin{matrix} \theta \text{ in rad} \\ S \text{ and } R \text{ in m} \end{matrix}\right\} \tag{1.3}$$

Here θ is expressed in a unit called the *radian,* which is the angle for which the arc length S is equal to the radius R. Because an angle in radians is defined as the ratio of two lengths, it is actually a pure number without any physical dimensions; however, we state the values of angles in units of *radians* to indicate clearly that an angle is being represented. Although we indicated that S and R in (1.3) are expressed in m, the value of θ in radians is uniquely determined when S and R are expressed in any length units provided the units are the same for both S and R. Why? Further-

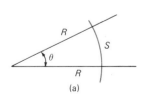

(a)

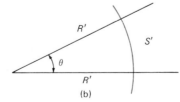

(b)

Fig. 1.3   The angle θ in radians is given by the ratio $S/R = S'/R'$.

---

* Physical scientists and engineers use Greek letters like theta (θ) to represent angles and many other quantities. A complete Greek alphabet is given in the Appendix; learn to recognize both lower case and capital Greek letters and remember their names.

more, we note that the value of θ given in (1.3) is independent of the magnitude of the radius R. Why?

Because no constants other than unity are involved in the definition given in (1.3), it is convenient to use angles in radians in equations. Unless we note otherwise, we shall always express angles in radians in all equations.

Thus far, there would seem to be no difficulties in our definition of angles and their measurement in radians. However, we remember that it is necessary to construct instruments for the actual measurement of angles. These instruments are always based on divided circles such as those employed by surveyors; a divided circle is an ideal device for measuring angles because if the maker of the circle makes a slight error in one part of the circle, the error is compensated in another part of the circle. Angles can be measured very accurately by comparing them with the divisions at several positions on the circle and taking the average of the results.

The total angle θ subtended by the entire circumference of a circle, called a revolution, is given by $\theta = S/R = 2\pi R/R = 2\pi$ radians. Because of the irrational nature of π, it is impossible to divide a circle into equal segments each having a rational number of radians. Recognizing this fact, those in charge of the International System of Units have decided for the present to retain the *degree* as the unit for the actual practical measurement of angles. The relation between degrees and radians is

$$1 \text{ revolution} = 2\pi \text{ radians} = 360°.$$

The relative sizes of these angles are given in Fig. 1.4. It is convenient to remember the *approximate* relation

$$1 \text{ radian} \cong 57.3°.$$

In this volume we shall express angles smaller than 1 degree as decimal fractions of the degree rather than in terms of *minutes* and *seconds* of arc as in the original Babylonian System of angle measurement. Relations between the various units used in angle measurement are given in the Table of Conversion Factors in the Appendix.

Example. What is the magnitude of the geometer's *right angle* in degrees? in radians?

The right angle or "square corner" has been useful since the days when the early Egyptian surveyors began to make land divisions following the annual overflow of the Nile; it was these surveyors who devised the 3–4–5 triangle for the construction of right angles. Because there are four right angles in a revolution, we can write 1 right angle $= 360°/4 = 90°$ and 1 right angle $= 2\pi/4$ rad $= \pi/2$ rad.

Example. What angle θ is "swept out" by the hour hand of a clock as the hand moves from 12 to 1 on the clock face?

In moving from 12 to 1 on the dial, the clock hand makes $\frac{1}{12}$ of a revolution. Therefore, $\theta = 360°/12 = 30°$ and $\theta = 2\pi/12$ rad $= \pi/6$ rad.

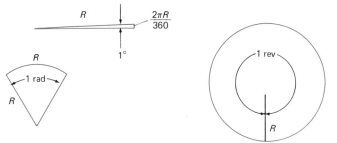

Fig. 1.4 Angular units.

1.5 COORDINATE SYSTEMS

As one of our major problems in mechanics will be a quantitative description of the motion of bodies, we now show how lengths and angles can be used in specifying positions. Initially we shall show how coordinate systems can be used for the location of a *particle*. The general schemes are already familiar to those who have studied analytic geometry and have learned how to indicate the location of a *point*. Because physicists deal with the material world, we use the term *particle* to indicate that matter is involved; the physicist's particle corresponds to the mathematician's point. As long as an object is small compared with the distances involved in specifying its position in the coordinate system, we can treat it as a particle. Thus, if we are locating an airplane traveling from New York to Los Angeles, we can in good approximation treat the airplane as a particle. In treating an extended body like an airplane as a particle, we must agree to ignore the problems of specifying the orientation of the airplane in the coordinate system; we shall learn to specify the orientation of an extended body when we later come to a discussion of rotational motion.

There is one other difference between the mathematician's use of coordinate systems and the physicist's use. The mathematician is content with stating positions in terms of undefined "units" of length. Engineers and physicists must use well-defined length units—meters in the SI.

When we wish to specify the position of a particle in a plane, we need to specify two numbers with respect to a coordinate system. Two types of coordinate system are in common use for this purpose. The first of these is the rectangular or Cartesian frame shown in Fig. 1.5, which makes use of two straight-line axes labeled X and

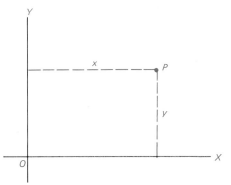

Fig. 1.5 A plane Cartesian system of coordinates.

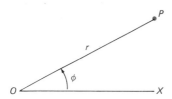

Fig. 1.6 A plane polar coordinate system.

Y that intersect at the origin O of the coordinate system and form right angles with each other. In this system we can specify the position of any particle P by giving its coordinates x and y, which represent the signed distances of the particle from the axes. The coordinate x is the distance of the point P from the Y axis measured along a line parallel to the X axis; it is positive if the movement from the Y axis to P is in the positive direction of the X axis and is negative if the movement from the Y axis to P is in the negative direction of the X axis. The coordinate y is the distance of the point P from the X axis measured along a line parallel to the Y axis; it is positive if the movement from the X axis to P is in the positive direction of the Y axis and is negative if the movement from the X axis to P is in the negative direction of the Y axis.

The second common coordinate system is the polar coordinate system shown in Fig. 1.6, which employs a single axis usually taken parallel to the X axis of Fig. 1.5. In the plane polar coordinate system, the position of a particle P is specified by stating its radial distance r from the origin O and the angle ϕ, measured in a counterclockwise sense, between the X axis and the line joining O to P; thus, the particle's position in Fig. 1.6 is given unambiguously by stating r and ϕ.

Example. If we know the coordinates x, y of a particle in Fig. 1.5, what are its corresponding polar coordinates in Fig. 1.6?

We note that the particle's radial distance r from the origin O is given by the Pythagorean theorem: $r^2 = x^2 + y^2$ or $r = \sqrt{x^2 + y^2}$. We can then determine ϕ in terms of any of the trigonometric functions of the angle: $\sin \phi = y/r$, $\cos \phi = x/r$, and $\tan \phi = y/x$.

Example. If we know the polar coordinates r and ϕ in Fig. 1.6, what are the Cartesian coordinates x,y of the particle in Fig. 1.5?

These are easily determined by noting that the values of x and y are merely the projections of r on the axes of the Cartesian coordinate system. Thus, $x = r \cos \phi$ and $y = r \sin \phi$. Note that in both these examples we have assumed that the origins O of the two systems are the same and that the X axes of the two systems coincide.

If we wish to specify the position of a particle in three-dimensional space, we must specify three numbers. In the Cartesian coordinate system shown in Fig. 1.7, we can locate the particle by giving its coordinates x, y, and z with respect to the X, Y, and Z axes of the frame. As indicated in the figure, x is the perpendicular

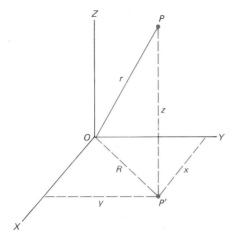

Fig. 1.7 A Cartesian coordinate system.

distance between the particle P and the YZ plane; y is the perpendicular distance between the particle and the ZX plane; and z is the perpendicular distance between the particle and the XY plane.

Example. Show that the radial distance of particle P from the origin O in Fig. 1.7 is given by the expression $r = \sqrt{x^2 + y^2 + z^2}$.

We can readily do this by using the Pythagorean theorem twice. First, we note that the length of the line R connecting O and P' in the XY plane is by the Pythagorean theorem simply $R = \sqrt{x^2 + y^2}$. Next we note that r is the hypoteneuse of the right triangle $OP'P$, the legs of which are R and z. Applying the Pythagorean theorem to triangle $OP'P$ gives: $r^2 = R^2 + z^2 = x^2 + y^2 + z^2$, or $r = \sqrt{x^2 + y^2 + z^2}$.

Various forms of polar coordinate systems can be employed to give the location of a particle in three-dimensional space. One commonly used coordinate system, called a *spherical polar coordinate system,* is shown in Fig. 1.8 imposed on a frame similar

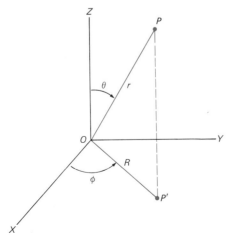

Fig. 1.8 A spherical polar coordinate system.

to the rectangular one shown in Fig. 1.7. The coordinates of particle P in the frame in Fig. 1.8 are given by radial distance r from O to P; by the polar angle θ between line r and the positive Z axis, which is called the polar axis; and by the angle ϕ, which is the angle between the positive X axis and line R, which is the projection of line r on the XY plane. We note that θ will lie in the range from 0 to π radians, and ϕ will lie in the range from 0 to 2π radians. The angle ϕ is measured in a counterclockwise sense from the positive X axis as seen by an observer looking down on the XY plane from the positive Z axis.

| Example. | If we know the rectangular coordinates x, y, and z of a particle in Fig. 1.7, what are the corresponding polar coordinates of the particle in Fig. 1.8? |

    We have shown that $r = \sqrt{x^2 + y^2 + z^2}$. We can obtain θ by noting that z is merely the projection of r on the polar axis; thus, $\cos \theta = z/r$. We next note that R in the XY plane is given by $R = r \sin \theta$. We then note that in the XY plane, $\cos \phi = x/R = x/(r \sin \theta)$. These relations enable us to determine θ in terms of its cosine expressed in terms of x, y, z, and ϕ in terms of its cosine in terms of x, y, and z.

    Another coordinate system that is often convenient, called a *cylindrical coordinate system*, is shown in Fig. 1.9. In this system the coordinates used to locate the particle P are z, the perpendicular distance between the particle and the XY plane; ρ, the perpendicular distance from the Z axis to the particle; and ϕ, the angle between the X axis and line R, which is the projection of line r on the XY plane and has length equal to ρ; the magnitude of R is equal to that of ρ. The angle ϕ is the

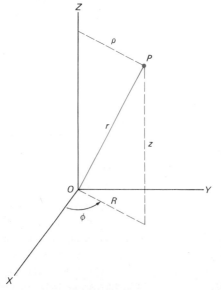

Fig. 1.9 A cylindrical coordinate system.

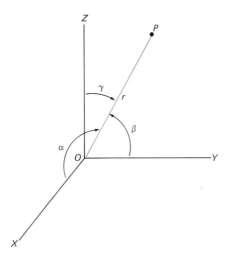

Fig. 1.10 The quantities cos α, cos β, and cos γ are called *direction cosines.*

same as the corresponding angle in spherical polar coordinates; the distance z is the same as the corresponding Cartesian coordinate. It is readily seen from Fig. 1.9 that the cylindrical coordinates ρ and ϕ are expressed in terms of the Cartesian coordinates of the particle by the following relations:

$$\rho = \sqrt{x^2 + y^2} \quad \text{and} \quad \cos\phi = x/\rho.$$

It is sometimes useful to specify the position of a particle by the scheme shown in Fig. 1.10. In this scheme r is the length of the straight line from the origin O to particle P. Angle α is the angle between line r and the X axis; β is the angle between line r and the Y axis; and γ is the angle between line r and the Z axis. It is easy to see that $x = r\cos\alpha$, $y = r\cos\beta$, and $z = r\cos\gamma$; $\cos\alpha$, $\cos\beta$, and $\cos\gamma$ are called the *direction cosines* of the line r from O to P. We note that we have specified the position of particle P by stating *four* numbers r, α, β, and γ. We leave it as a problem to prove that the angles are not all independent; once we have specified two of them, the cosine of the third is determined except for sign.

QUESTIONS

1. Discuss differences between the science of the Greek natural philosophers and modern science as regarding aims and methods of procedure.

2. How do physical laws differ from the civil laws passed by a legislature?

3. It has been stated that the purpose of science is "to discover the laws of nature." Discuss this statement.

4. What are the criteria for the success of a scientific theory? Do such abstract values as beauty and simplicity have a role in the evaluation of scientific theories?

5. What is the relationship between physical laws and the concept of cause and effect?

6. Operationalists take the view that the definition of any physical quantity must consist of a description of the actual *operations* involved in its measurement. Some scientists do not agree with this idea. Can a quantity have a role in science if we cannot specify

a means by which the quantity can be *measured?*

7. Why is it desirable to have a universally accepted system of physical units for use in commercial transactions?

8. Why is it unnecessary to have independent base units for area and volume? Would it be possible to introduce such base units if we so desired?

9. Why is the definition of the radian independent of the radius R of the circle involved? What restrictions must we place on the units used in the measurements of S and R?

10. What characteristics are desirable for a phys-

ical system that is used to define a base unit? (Definitions of the SI base units are given in the Appendix, Section III.)

11. When a base unit is defined, a standard is thereby established with which measurements of the particular quantity are to be compared. Is it meaningful to talk about possible changes in the standard under various conditions? By the nature of a "standard," are not such changes ruled out by definition?

12. What kinds of considerations are likely to be important in choosing a coordinate system in terms of which to describe a particular physical situation?

PROBLEMS

1. Considering the earth as a perfect sphere with a radius of 6400 km, compute the earth's circumference, area, and volume. Express the results of the three computations in terms of m, m^2, and m^3, respectively.

2. A rectangular solid has a width of 36 in., a height of 24 in., and a length of 36 in. Express these measurements in centimeters. Compute the surface area of the solid in cm^2 and in m^2. Compute the volume of the solid in cm^3 and in m^3.

3. Express the following angles in radians: 30°, 45°, 60°, 90°, 120°, 135°, 150°, 180°, 210°, 225°, 240°, 270°, 300°, 315°, 330°, and 360°.

4. Compute the angle that has been "swept out" by the minute hand of a clock during the intervals beginning at 4:00 PM and ending at 4:10 PM, 4:20 PM, 4:30 PM, 4:45 PM, and 4:55 PM.

5. If the value of S in Fig. 1.3a is 50 cm and the value of R is 2.0 m, what is the value of θ in radians? in degrees? in revolutions?

6. The radius of the sun is approximately 697,000 km and its mean distance from the

earth is approximately 150,000,000 km. The radius of the moon is approximately 1740 km and its mean distance from the earth is approximately 384,000 km. Compare the approximate angular diameters of the sun and moon as observed from the earth. Comment on the significance of the near equality of the two results with regard to eclipses.

7. Particles in a two-dimensional Cartesian coordinate system like the one in Fig. 1.5 have the following coordinates: (1) $x = 3$ m, $y = 4$ m; (2) $x = -3$ m, $y = 4$ m; (3) $x = -3$ m, $y = -4$ m; and (4) $x = 3$ m, $y = -4$ m. Express the position of each of these particles in terms of a polar coordinate system like the one in Fig. 1.6.

8. The coordinates of several particles in a two-dimensional polar coordinate system like the one in Fig. 1.6 are (1) $r = 10$ m, $\phi = 45°$; (2) $r = 10$ m, $\phi = 135°$; (3) $r = 10$ m, $\phi = 225°$; and (4) $r = 10$ m, $\phi = 315°$. What are their coordinates in the rectangular coordinate system shown in Fig. 1.5?

9. The coordinates of a particle in a rectangular coordinate system like the one in Fig. 1.7

are $x = 1$ m, $y = 1$ m, and $z = 1$ m. (1) What are the coordinates of this particle in terms of r, θ, and ϕ in the system shown in Fig. 1.8? (2) What is the location of the particle in terms of r, α, β, and γ in Fig. 1.10? (3) Show that your results satisfy the relation $\cos^2 \alpha + \cos^2 \beta + \cos^2 \gamma = 1$. (4) Prove that this relation is true in general.

10. Repeat Problem 9 for a particle with rectangular coordinates $x = 1$ m, $y = 2$ m, and $z = 3$ m.

11. A particle is located in the coordinate system of Fig. 1.10 by the coordinates $r = 10$ m, $\alpha = 45°$, and $\beta = 60°$. (1) What are possible values of γ as shown in the system of Fig. 1.10? (2) Give the coordinates r, θ, and ϕ of the particle in the system of Fig. 1.8. (3) Give the coordinates x, y, and z of the particle in the system of Fig. 1.7.

12. Because the earth is approximately spherical, positions on its surface are usually expressed by geographers and navigators in terms of latitude and longitude. Regarding the earth as a sphere of radius $R = 6400$ km, find the lengths of the paths traversed by an airplane traveling (1) from the north pole to the equator along any meridian; (2) northward from a point 40°N latitude on the prime meridian to the north pole and then southward along the 180° meridian to a point with 40°N latitude; (3) eastward along the 40° parallel of latitude from a point having the position with latitude 40°N and 0° longitude on the prime meridian to a point 40°N latitude, 180° longitude near the international date line.

13. Treating the earth as a perfect sphere with $R = 6400$ km, we can easily find the earth's present circumference, surface area, and total volume as in Problem 1. Suppose that the radius of the earth were increased by exactly 1 m. What would be the corresponding increases in the earth's circumference, surface area, and volume? Note: For a sphere of radius R, the surface area $A = 4\pi R^2$ and volume $V = (\frac{4}{3})\pi R^3$.

14. The coordinates of a point P in the spherical polar coordinate system shown in Fig. 1.8 are $r = 1.8$ m, $\theta = 0.8$ rad, and $\phi = 1.3$ rad. What are the coordinates of x, y, and z of this point in the Cartesian system shown in Fig. 1.7? Draw a diagram showing the location of the point P.

15. Repeat Problem 14 for a case where $r = 2.6$ m, $\theta = 0.95$ rad, and $\phi = 2.1$ rad.

16. The coordinates of a point P in the Cartesian coordinate system shown in Fig. 1.7 are $x = 0.24$ m, $y = -1.05$ m, and $z = -0.84$ m. What are the coordinates r, θ, and ϕ of this point in the spherical polar coordinate system shown in Fig. 1.8? Draw a diagram showing the location of the point P.

17. Find the coordinates ρ, ϕ, and z of the point P described in Problem 16 with respect to the cylindrical coordinate system shown in Fig. 1.9.

18. The coordinates of a point P in the cylindrical coordinate system shown in Fig. 1.9 are $\rho = 3.25$ m, $\phi = 100°$, and $z = 2.25$ m. What are the coordinates r, θ, and ϕ of this point in the spherical polar coordinate system shown in Fig. 1.8? Draw a diagram showing the location of the point P.

19. What are the angles α, β, and γ as defined in Fig. 1.10 for the point P that is described in Problem 18?

20. The coordinates of a point P in the coordinate system shown in Fig. 1.10 are $r = 4.6$ m, $\alpha = 100°$, $\beta = 267°$, and $\gamma = 10.5°$. What are its coordinates in the Cartesian system shown in Fig. 1.7?

21. A point in the Cartesian coordinate system shown in Fig. 1.7 has coordinates $x = 0.55$ m, $y = -1.0$ m, and $z = 1.48$ m. What are its coordinates in the cyclindrical coordinate system shown in Fig. 1.9?

22. A point P has coordinates r, θ, and ϕ in the coordinate system shown in Fig. 1.8. What is its coordinates in the system shown in Fig. 1.9?

23. A point has coordinates $x = 2.0$ m, $y = 0.91$ m, and $z = -1.6$ m in the Cartesian system shown in Fig. 1.7. What are its coordinates in the system shown in Fig. 1.10?

24. A sphere of radius R has a surface area given by $A = 4\pi R^2$ and a volume given by $V = (\frac{4}{3})\pi R^3$. Find the ratio of the new area and volume to the original area and volume (a) if the radius is doubled and (b) if the radius is reduced to one-quarter of its original value.

25. The area of a circle of radius R is given by $A = \pi R^2$. What is the volume of a right circular cylinder of radius 0.25 m and height 0.25 m?

26. The area of a circle of radius R is given by $A = \pi R^2$. A circular pie of radius 8 cm has had one piece cut out. The cuts were made along radii of the circle; the piece removed has an angular width of 0.26 radians. What is the ratio of the surface area of the remaining pie to the original surface area? What is the new ratio if a second piece the same size as the first is cut from the pie?

27. A prism has a base lying in the XY-plane that is an equilateral triangle of side length $b = 4.5$ cm and vertical sides parallel to the Z axis of length $h = 10$ cm. What is the volume of the prism? If b is doubled while h is unchanged, what is the *change* in the volume of the prism?

28. The volume of a sphere of radius R is given by $V = (\frac{4}{3})\pi R^3$. Two *concentric* spheres have radii R_1 and R_2, respectively, where $R_1 > R_2$. What should be the ratio R_1/R_2 if the volume between the two spheres is to equal half the volume of the inner sphere?

29. A certain cube has a volume that is three times the volume of a second cube. What is the ratio of the length of an edge of the first cube to the length of an edge of the second cube? What is the ratio of the total surface area of the first cube to the total surface area of the second cube?

30. Consider a cube of edge a with its center at the origin. Let V be the volume of the largest sphere with center at the origin that can be inscribed inside the cube. Let V' be the volume of the smallest sphere with center at the origin such that the cube is wholly within the sphere. What is the ratio V'/V? The volume of a sphere of radius R is given by $V = (\frac{4}{3})\pi R^3$.

CHAPTER 2

Displacement: A Vector Quantity

One problem that we shall treat in some detail in physics is a quantitative description of motion. In Chapter 1 we discussed various methods of specifying the position of a particle in appropriate coordinate systems. Our next step will involve a study of *changes* in position. In this chapter we shall show how changes in position can be described in terms of *displacements*. A displacement has the properties of a class of mathematical quantities called *vectors*. In this chapter we shall discuss briefly some of the mathematical properties of vectors; vector quantities will be very useful to us in our future treatments of both mechanics and electromagnetism.

2.1   DISPLACEMENT

In order to understand some of the problems involved in describing changes of position, consider the map shown in Fig. 2.1. A motorist wishes to travel from an initial position in city *J* to nearby city *M*. In making this journey he may wish to travel along the direct route, which passes through a large military reservation *R*, where speed limits are low and strictly enforced; he may wish to travel southward from *J* to the interstate highway and then eastward along the interstate highway until he reaches another road at the airport and along this road to *M;* or he may elect to go southward to the interstate and then travel directly eastward along the interstate to a major intersection and then take a major highway northward to *M*.

Regardless of his selection of route, the motorist at the end of his journey has made a change of position from *J* to *M*. This change of position is described by the arrow labeled **D** in Fig. 2.2; the tail of the arrow is at the motorist's initial position *J* and the point of the arrow is at his final position *M*. The change of position as described by arrow **D** is the motorist's *displacement*.

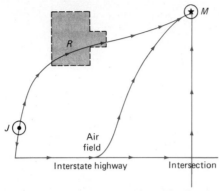

Fig. 2.1   Map showing possible paths taken by a motorist from *J* to *M*.

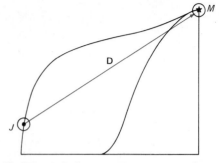

Fig. 2.2   A displacement **D** represents a change in position.

A DISPLACEMENT is a change of position; it is characterized by a magnitude and a direction.

We note that by stating the motorist's final displacement from his starting point we give no information about the path actually taken. The displacement merely states two things: (1) the *magnitude* of straight-line separation of his initial and final positions, given by the *length* of the arrow **D** in Fig. 2.2, and (2) the *direction* of his change of position as given by the orientation of the arrow in Fig. 2.2. Any displacement is characterized by a magnitude and a direction. Even if displacements start from different points, they are regarded as equal if their magnitudes and directions are the same.

Example.   On the map in Fig. 2.1 city *M* is 20 km east and 8 km north of city *J*. What is the magnitude of the motorist's displacement in going from *J* to *M*? What is the direction of his displacement?

If we use a coordinate frame with the $+X$ axis eastward and the $+Y$ axis northward, we see that *D* is merely the hypotenuse of a right triangle with legs $x = 20$ km and $y = 8$ km. From the Pythagorean theorem $D^2 = x^2 + y^2$, or $D = \sqrt{x^2 + y^2} = \sqrt{(20 \text{ km})^2 + (8 \text{ km})^2} = \sqrt{464 \text{ km}^2} = 21.5$ km. The direction of the displacement as represented by the angle between *D* and the *X* axis is given by: $\tan \phi = y/x = 8 \text{ km}/20 \text{ km} = 0.40$, whence $\phi = 21.8°$. Thus, the motorist's displacement is in a direction $21.8°$ north of east. We note that *x* and *y* are called the *rectangular components* of the motorist's displacement; they can be expressed as $x = D \cos \phi$ and $y = D \sin \phi$ in the coordinate frame that we have employed.

2.2   ADDITION OF DISPLACEMENTS

We now consider the problem of adding displacements. Consider Fig. 2.3, which shows the path a motorist travels along a curving road first from city *A* to nearby city *B* and then along another curving road from city *B* to city *C*. We can consider his final displacement $\mathbf{D}_R$ from *A* to *C* as being the *sum* or *resultant* of his first

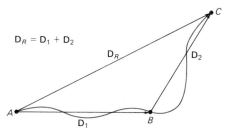

Fig. 2.3   The vector addition of displacements $\mathbf{D}_1$ and $\mathbf{D}_2$ gives a resultant displacement $\mathbf{D}_R$.

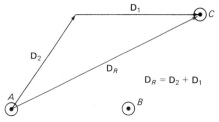

Fig. 2.4   Vector addition of displacements $\mathbf{D}_2$ and $\mathbf{D}_1$ gives resultant $\mathbf{D}_R$.

displacement $\mathbf{D}_1$ from A to B and his second displacement $\mathbf{D}_2$ from B to C. The final displacement $\mathbf{D}_R$ is given by the arrow in the figure that is drawn from the tail of the first displacement arrow $\mathbf{D}_1$ to the point of the second displacement arrow $\mathbf{D}_2$. The addition of the two displacements $\mathbf{D}_1$ and $\mathbf{D}_2$ is represented by the expression

$$\mathbf{D}_R = \mathbf{D}_1 + \mathbf{D}_2; \tag{2.1}$$

we use boldface type to indicate that the addition involves more than the mere addition of the magnitudes D_1 and D_2 of the two displacements.

Recalling that the statement of a displacement like $\mathbf{D}_R$ gives no information regarding the actual path traversed by the motorist in moving from A to C, we find a very interesting fact regarding the addition of displacements: The order of the displacements can be reversed without changing the results. In other words,

$$\mathbf{D}_R = \mathbf{D}_2 + \mathbf{D}_1. \tag{2.2}$$

As suggested in Fig. 2.4, in determining the motorist's final displacement $\mathbf{D}_R$ we can assume that the motorist first experienced a displacement $\mathbf{D}_2$ toward the northeast and then a displacement $\mathbf{D}_1$ toward the east. If we drew these two displacements on an actual map, we would have our motorist traversing territory that he did not visit at all in his actual journey from A to C. This need not bother us, because we have already agreed that by stating a displacement we give only information regarding the initial and final locations, not the actual path traversed.

In view of these considerations, we can state another procedure for adding two displacements. As in Fig. 2.5, we can draw displacement arrows $\mathbf{D}_1$ and $\mathbf{D}_2$ from the initial position A and complete the parallelogram as shown in the figure. The sum or resultant $\mathbf{D}_R$ of $\mathbf{D}_1$ and $\mathbf{D}_2$ is then given by the diagonal of the parallelogram. This method of adding displacements is called addition by the *parallelogram rule*.

If we have more than two displacements, we can add them graphically as indicated in Fig. 2.6 by drawing the displacement arrows tip-to-tail and then drawing a resultant displacement arrow $\mathbf{D}_R$ from the tail of the first displacement arrow $\mathbf{D}_1$ to the point of the final displacement arrow $\mathbf{D}_4$. It is easy to demonstrate graphically that we get the same final value for $\mathbf{D}_R$ regardless of the order in which we place $\mathbf{D}_1$, $\mathbf{D}_2$, $\mathbf{D}_3$, and $\mathbf{D}_4$ in the diagram. It should also be noted that we can get the same value for $\mathbf{D}_R$ by successive applications of the parallelogram rule; for example, we can first find the resultant of $\mathbf{D}_1$ and $\mathbf{D}_2$ by the parallelogram rule, then add this resultant

$$D_R = D_1 + D_2 + D_3 + D_4$$

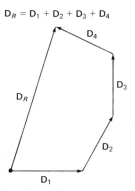

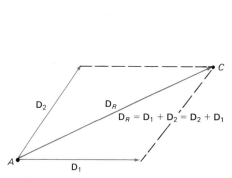

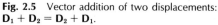

Fig. 2.5 Vector addition of two displacements: $\mathbf{D_1} + \mathbf{D_2} = \mathbf{D_2} + \mathbf{D_1}$.

Fig. 2.6 Graphical addition of several displacements.

to $\mathbf{D_3}$ by the parallelogram rule, etc. The same result is obtained if we first find the resultant of $\mathbf{D_2}$ and $\mathbf{D_3}$ by the parallelogram rule, then add this resultant to $\mathbf{D_1}$, etc.

2.3   VECTORS

Displacement is our first example of a class of mathematical quantities that are known as *vectors*. In our study of physics we shall have occasion to use many vector quantities. Therefore, we need to say a few words about the general mathematical properties of vectors.

In most of our early studies of arithmetic, algebra, and calculus the mathematical procedures are applied to a class of mathematical quantities known as *scalars*. A scalar quantity has magnitude only; it can be completely specified in terms of a number and a unit. For example, we can specify a man's height as 6 ft 2 in. or as 1.76 m; we can specify the area of his farm as 400 acres or as 1.65 square kilometers; we can specify his gross income as $15,000 or £8000. Quantities like height, area, and income are scalars; each is specified completely by the statement of a number and a unit. Scalar quantities can, of course, be negative as well as positive; thus, if a man's annual net income is −$2500, we know that he ended the year with a $2500 deficit.

Vector quantities have both magnitude and direction; for example, we can state a displacement as 20 km, northeastward. We specify a vector by stating a number, a unit, and a *direction*.

A VECTOR is a quantity that has both magnitude and direction; vectors are added by the parallelogram rule.

Thus, a vector quantity must have both magnitude and direction and must obey the same rule of addition that we have described for displacements. We shall now summarize some of the other mathematical properties of vectors. Since several of these properties, such as the addition rule, are different from those of scalars, we must clearly designate vector quantities. We do this in print by boldface type and

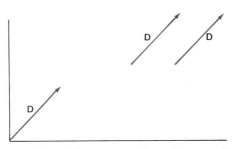

Fig. 2.7 All displacements shown have equal magnitudes and directions.

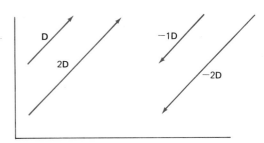

Fig. 2.8 Multiplication of a vector by a scalar.

in writing by underlining or placing an arrow over the symbol. For example, in this text we denote a displacement by **D**; in writing we might use $\underline{D}$ or $\vec{D}$. The magnitude of the displacement will be denoted by $|\mathbf{D}|$ or, when there is no danger of confusion, more simply by D. In our statements of the mathematical properties of vectors, we shall, in order to be specific, deal with displacements; however, all vector quantities have the same mathematical properties.*

First of all, as far as their mathematical nature is concerned, we note that vectors can be moved about on a diagram just as we have moved displacements $\mathbf{D}_1$ and $\mathbf{D}_2$ in Figs. 2.3 and 2.4. We emphasize this in Fig. 2.7, where we show several presentations of a single vector **D**. The vectors shown in Fig. 2.7 are mathematically the same because *they are all characterized by the same magnitude and the same direction.*

Next we indicate that the multiplication of a vector by a scalar changes only the magnitude of the vector and not its orientation in space, as indicated graphically in Fig. 2.8. Of special importance is the multiplication of a vector by -1; this operation reverses the sense of the vector without changing the orientation of the vector in space; in other words, multiplication by -1 merely reverses the positions of the point and tail of the arrow representing the vector. Algebraically, the multiplication of a vector such as **D** by a scalar a can be written as

$$a\mathbf{D} = \mathbf{D}a. \tag{2.3}$$

We can easily demonstrate by drawing some diagrams that multiplication by a scalar is distributive with respect to vector addition; that is,

$$a(\mathbf{D}_1 + \mathbf{D}_2) = a\mathbf{D}_1 + a\mathbf{D}_2.$$

There are two different types of multiplication of two vector quantities, which we shall introduce in later chapters when we need to employ them. The division of one vector by another is not a mathematically defined operation.

---

* Analytical systems that were forerunners of vector analysis were developed in the mid-19th century by Sir William Rowan Hamilton (1805–1865) and Hermann Günther Grassmann (1809–1877). Modern vector analysis originated with Josiah Willard Gibbs (1839–1903) and Oliver Heaviside (1850–1925). These two physicists, working independently, developed essentially identical systems of vector analysis during the late 1870s and early 1880s. Many prominent contemporary physicists were not favorably disposed toward vector methods; this is somewhat surprising in view of the great analytical power and economy that vector methods bring to the expression of physical laws.

In our earlier discussion of the addition of displacements we have indicated in (2.1) and (2.2) that the order of the addition makes no difference in the resultant. We formalize this statement by the expression

$$\mathbf{D}_1 + \mathbf{D}_2 = \mathbf{D}_2 + \mathbf{D}_1. \tag{2.4}$$

We have also seen that vector addition is associative:

$$\mathbf{D}_1 + (\mathbf{D}_2 + \mathbf{D}_3) = (\mathbf{D}_1 + \mathbf{D}_2) + \mathbf{D}_3.$$

Thus far, we have not considered the subtraction of one vector from another. Now that we have stated that the multiplication of a vector by -1 reverses the direction of the vector, we can define the process of vector subtraction by the expression

$$\mathbf{D}_1 - \mathbf{D}_2 = \mathbf{D}_1 + (-1)\mathbf{D}_2. \tag{2.5}$$

We merely reverse the direction of the vector to be subtracted and add the reversed vector to the other vectors involved. For example, if we wished to subtract $\mathbf{D}_2$ from $\mathbf{D}_1$ in Fig. 2.4, we would merely reverse the direction of $\mathbf{D}_2$ and add this reversed vector to $\mathbf{D}_1$. This is illustrated in Fig. 2.9.

One other mathematical process that should be mentioned is the resolution of one vector into two or more vectors that can be added to replace the original vector. In a sense this is the reverse process of vector addition; in the process of addition we find a single resultant vector that will be the equivalent of two vectors, and in the process of resolution we replace a single vector by two or more vectors. This process is demonstrated graphically in Fig. 2.10a, in which we have replaced a single original vector $\mathbf{D}$ by two component vectors $\mathbf{D}_1$ and $\mathbf{D}_2$, the sum of which is equal to the original vector $\mathbf{D}$. Because the two component vectors $\mathbf{D}_1$ and $\mathbf{D}_2$ *replace* the original vector, we cross out the original vector in the figure. As suggested in the diagram, it is frequently desirable to resolve the original vector into component vectors that are parallel to the axes of some conveniently oriented coordinate system.

The vectors produced by the process of resolution are not unique. For example, in Fig. 2.10b we show the original vector $\mathbf{D}$ resolved into components $\mathbf{D}_1'$ and $\mathbf{D}_2'$ that are not the same as vectors $\mathbf{D}_1$ and $\mathbf{D}_2$ in Fig. 2.10a.

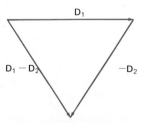

Fig. 2.9 Vector subtraction. The vectors $\mathbf{D}_1$ and $\mathbf{D}_2$ are as in Fig. 2.4.

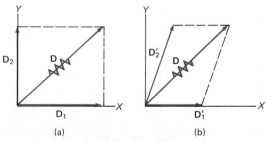

(a)   (b)

Fig. 2.10 Resolution of a vector $\mathbf{D}$ into component vectors.

2.4   THE SCALAR COMPONENTS OF A VECTOR

The general properties of vectors that we have discussed are independent of any coordinate system that we may wish to employ. Thus far, we have used geometrical methods of addition and subtraction of vectors. It is, however, desirable to use *analytical methods* of addition and subtraction that involve familiar algebraic processes that are applicable to scalars. In order to use analytical methods, we must note that a vector can be specified by stating its *scalar components* in some conveniently chosen coordinate system. For example, if as in Fig. 2.11 we choose a coordinate system with its origin at the tail of the arrow representing the vector, it is easy to see that we can uniquely identify the vector in terms of its scalar components $D_x = D \cos \phi$ and $D_y = D \sin \phi$. Thus, we can completely specify vector **D** with respect to our coordinate system by stating its rectangular components in the system:

$$\mathbf{D} : D_x = D \cos \phi, \quad \text{and} \quad D_y = D \sin \phi. \tag{2.6}$$

No vector lying in the XY plane other than **D** can have these stated scalar components.

Example.   A particle in a horizontal plane experiences a displacement of 10 m in a direction of 30° north of east. What are the rectangular components of this displacement?

Using a coordinate system like that in Fig. 2.11 with the $+X$ axis eastward and the $+Y$ axis northward, we obtain $D_x = D \cos 30° = (10 \text{ m})(0.866) = 8.66 \text{ m}$ and $D_y = D \sin 30° = (10 \text{ m})(0.5) = 5 \text{ m}$.

In our earlier discussion of the geometrical addition and subtraction of vectors, we have considered only vectors in a single plane. We can always add two vectors by simple graphical methods because two arrows—or "directed line segments"—always lie in some single plane. How do we proceed if we have three or more vectors that are not in a single plane? One geometrical method would be repeated addition of two vectors at a time by the parallelogram rule. The resultant $\mathbf{D}_{R\,12} = \mathbf{D}_1 + \mathbf{D}_2$ of the first two vectors could readily be determined. This resultant $\mathbf{D}_{R\,12}$ and the third vector $\mathbf{D}_3$ will both lie in another plane; the parallelogram rule could then be

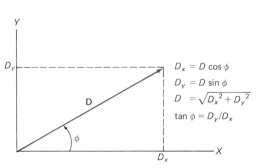

Fig. 2.11   The rectangular components of a vector **D**: D_x, D_y.

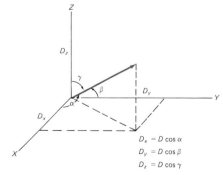

Fig. 2.12   The rectangular components of a vector **D**: D_x, D_y, D_z.

used to determine the resultant $\mathbf{D}_R = \mathbf{D}_{R\,12} + \mathbf{D}_3$, and so on. This process is cumbersome if we wish to add a large number of noncoplanar vectors. Alternatively, we could add the noncoplanar vectors by building a three-dimensional contraption utilizing short, stiff, tipped arrows and arranging these in space as the three-dimensional analogue of Fig. 2.6; mechanical devices to hold the arrows in position would have to be constructed. The resulting contraption would be even more cumbersome than repeated graphical addition by successive applications of the parallelogram rule.

Obviously, we need an analytical scheme for vector addition. In order to develop this much needed scheme, we must employ scalar components of the vectors that we wish to add. The general method employed is suggested in Fig. 2.12, where we show vector $\mathbf{D}$ in a three-dimensional coordinate system. The rectangular components with respect to this system can be easily stated in terms of the direction cosines of $\mathbf{D}$; thus, $D_x = D\cos\alpha$, $D_y = D\cos\beta$, and $D_z = D\cos\gamma$, where we recall that α, β, and γ are the angles between $\mathbf{D}$ and the X, Y, and Z axes, respectively. In the system shown in Fig. 2.12, vector $\mathbf{D}$ can be uniquely described in terms of its rectangular components D_x, D_y, and D_z. Thus,

$$\mathbf{D}: \quad D_x = D\cos\alpha, \quad D_y = D\cos\beta, \quad \text{and} \quad D_z = D\cos\gamma. \tag{2.6a}$$

A notation that is sometimes convenient is

$$\mathbf{D} = (D_x,\, D_y,\, D_z). \tag{2.6b}$$

2.5 ANALYTIC ADDITION OF VECTORS

Now that we have seen that a vector can be uniquely characterized by a statement of its rectangular scalar components, we can show how vectors can be added analytically. If $\mathbf{D}_R$ is the resultant of several vectors $\mathbf{D}_1$, $\mathbf{D}_2$, and $\mathbf{D}_3$, each of its scalar components must be equal to the sum of the corresponding scalar components of the vectors to be added. Thus, in the case of coplanar vectors $\mathbf{D}_1$, $\mathbf{D}_2$, and $\mathbf{D}_3$ as shown in Fig. 2.13, we can express the scalar components of the resultant $\mathbf{D}_R$ as

$$\begin{aligned} D_{Rx} &= D_{1x} + D_{2x} + D_{3x}, \\ D_{Ry} &= D_{1y} + D_{2y} + D_{3y}. \end{aligned} \tag{2.7}$$

The magnitude of the resultant is then

$$D_R = \sqrt{D_{Rx}^2 + D_{Ry}^2}. \tag{2.8}$$

Its direction as established by the angle ϕ between $\mathbf{D}_R$ and the X axis can then be determined by any one of the relations: $\tan\phi = D_{Ry}/D_{Rx}$, $\sin\phi = D_{Ry}/D_R$, or $\cos\phi = D_{Rx}/D_R$.

Because we can move displacement vectors about as in Fig. 2.7, we can start vectors $\mathbf{D}_1$, $\mathbf{D}_2$, and $\mathbf{D}_3$ at the origin O of the coordinate system as in Fig. 2.13b and add them vectorially to obtain the same resultant displacement $\mathbf{D}_R$; note that the rectangular components of each vector in Fig. 2.13b are equal to those of the corresponding vector in Fig. 2.13a.

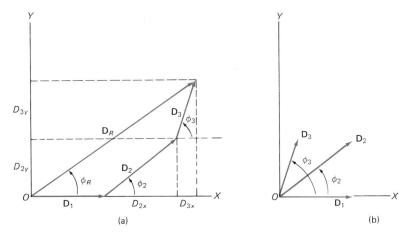

Fig. 2.13 Addition of several vectors.

Example. If the displacements shown in Fig. 2.13 have magnitudes $D_1 = 6$ m, $D_2 = 10$ m, and $D_3 = 8$ m and directions characterized by $\phi_1 = 0$, $\phi_2 = 30°$, and $\phi_3 = 60°$, what is the magnitude of the resultant $\mathbf{D}_R$ and what is its direction as given by ϕ_R?

We can make use of the arguments given in connection with (2.7), remembering that the scalar components of each vector in the frame are given by the general relations $D_x = D \cos \phi$ and $D_y = D \sin \phi$. Thus, we can write

$$D_{Rx} = (6 \text{ m})(1) + (10 \text{ m})(0.866) + (8 \text{ m})(0.5) = 18.66 \text{ m},$$
$$D_{Ry} = (6 \text{ m})(0) + (10 \text{ m})(0.5) + (8 \text{ m})(0.866) = 11.93 \text{ m}.$$

Knowing the values of D_{Rx} and D_{Ry}, we can now determine the magnitude of the resultant from (2.8): $D_R = \sqrt{(18.66 \text{ m})^2 + (11.93 \text{ m})^2} = \sqrt{348 \text{ m}^2 + 142 \text{ m}^2} = \sqrt{490 \text{ m}^2} = 22.1$ m. The direction of $\mathbf{D}_R$ can be obtained from $\tan \phi_R = D_{Ry}/D_{Rx} = (11.93 \text{ m}/18.66 \text{ m}) = 0.639$, corresponding to a value of $\phi_R = 32.6°$. The results can be checked geometrically by the scheme suggested in Fig. 2.13a.

The procedure that we have described for the addition of vectors in a single plane can be immediately extended to the addition of noncoplanar vectors. In the case of noncoplanar vectors, we must recognize that each vector involved has three scalar components D_x, D_y, and D_z. The analytic addition of three noncoplanar vectors is thus given by

$$\begin{aligned} D_{Rx} &= D_{1x} + D_{2x} + D_{3x}, \\ D_{Ry} &= D_{1y} + D_{2y} + D_{3y}, \\ D_{Rz} &= D_{1z} + D_{2z} + D_{3z}, \end{aligned} \tag{2.7a}$$

with

$$D_R = \sqrt{D_{Rx}^2 + D_{Ry}^2 + D_{Rz}^2}. \tag{2.8a}$$

The direction of $\mathbf{D}_R$ can be expressed in terms of its direction cosines: $\cos \alpha = D_{Rx}/D_R$, $\cos \beta = D_{Ry}/D_R$, and $\cos \gamma = D_{Rz}/D_R$.

The advantages of analytic addition of vectors over the corresponding geometrical addition are obvious.

2.6   RESOLUTION OF A VECTOR; UNIT VECTORS

In our discussion of the general characteristics of vectors in Sec. 2.3 we pointed out that it is possible to resolve a vector into two or even more component vectors. The process of resolution of a vector actually involves the replacement of the *original* vector by vector components of the vector. The components *replace* the original vector; they do not *augment* it.

Very frequently it is desirable to replace a vector by a set of components that are parallel to the axes of a rectangular coordinate system. This can easily be done by means of what are called *unit vectors*. In general, a unit vector has magnitude one, no dimensions, and serves to define a particular direction in space. Unit vectors that define the directions of the axes of a rectangular Cartesian coordinate system are usually denoted by $\mathbf{i}$, $\mathbf{j}$, and $\mathbf{k}$, where $\mathbf{i}$ is a unit vector parallel to the X axis, $\mathbf{j}$ is a unit vector parallel to the Y axis, and $\mathbf{k}$ is a unit vector parallel to the Z axis. Recalling from (2.3) that the product of a vector $\mathbf{D}$ by a scalar a has the magnitude aD and the direction of $\mathbf{D}$, we can obtain a vector of magnitude a and direction parallel to the X axis by multiplying the unit vector $\mathbf{i}$ by a scalar a: $\mathbf{i}a$; similarly, $\mathbf{j}b$ gives a vector of magnitude b with a direction parallel to the Y axis, and $\mathbf{k}c$ gives a vector of magnitude c with a direction parallel to the Z axis.

By using the unit vectors $\mathbf{i}$, $\mathbf{j}$, and $\mathbf{k}$ we can easily resolve a given vector into component vectors parallel to the axes of a rectangular coordinate system. Any vector $\mathbf{D}$ can be characterized by its scalar components D_x, D_y, and D_z. Using the unit vectors $\mathbf{i}$, $\mathbf{j}$, and $\mathbf{k}$, we can immediately obtain new vectors $\mathbf{i}D_x$, $\mathbf{j}D_y$, and $\mathbf{k}D_z$. The sum of these new vectors is just equal to the original vector $\mathbf{D}$:

$$\mathbf{D} = \mathbf{i}D_x + \mathbf{j}D_y + \mathbf{k}D_z. \tag{2.9}$$

Therefore, we can replace $\mathbf{D}$ by the component vectors $\mathbf{i}D_x$, $\mathbf{j}D_y$, and $\mathbf{k}D_z$.

It is sometimes convenient to express an arbitrary vector $\mathbf{D}$ in terms of its magnitude and a unit vector that denotes its direction. To do this we define a vector $\hat{\mathbf{D}} = \mathbf{D}/|\mathbf{D}|$ that has unit magnitude and points in the direction of $\mathbf{D}$. Here we have introduced the caret symbol (^) that is often used to denote that a particular vector is a unit vector. In terms of this unit vector we have $\mathbf{D} = D\,\hat{\mathbf{D}}$.

2.7   POSITION VECTORS

A vector can be used to indicate the position of a particle in a coordinate system. For example, consider the particle P in the rectangular coordinate system in Fig. 2.14; if its position in the system is given by the coordinates x, y, z, the position of

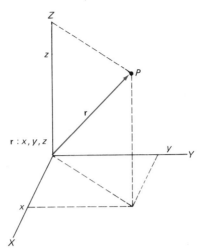

Fig. 2.14 The rectangular components of position vector **r** are x, y, and z.

the particle relative to the origin O can be specified by the vector **r** shown in the figure, where

$$\mathbf{r} = x\mathbf{i} + y\mathbf{j} + z\mathbf{k}. \quad \textit{(Position Vector)} \qquad (2.10)$$

This vector has the magnitude $r = \sqrt{x^2 + y^2 + z^2}$, where x, y, and z are the scalar components of **r**. The vector **r** given in (2.10) is called the *position vector* of the particle relative to the origin of the coordinate frame.

The position vector provides a very convenient way to describe displacements. Suppose that at time t_1 a certain particle has position vector $\mathbf{r}_1$ and at some later time t_2 it has position vector $\mathbf{r}_2$, as shown in Fig. 2.15. The displacement $\mathbf{D}_{2,1}$ of the particle during the time interval $\Delta t = t_2 - t_1$ is the vector running from position ① to position ②. We can see from the figure that $\mathbf{r}_2 = \mathbf{r}_1 + \mathbf{D}_{2,1}$, or

$$\mathbf{D}_{2,1} = \mathbf{r}_2 - \mathbf{r}_1. \qquad (2.11)$$

Thus, the displacement of a particle during a certain time interval is just the vector difference between the final and initial position vectors of the particle. This representa-

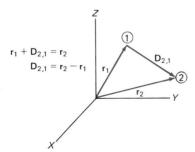

Fig. 2.15 The displacement $\mathbf{D}_{2,1}$ from ① to ② is the difference between position vectors $\mathbf{r}_2$ and $\mathbf{r}_1$: $\mathbf{D}_{2,1} = \mathbf{r}_2 - \mathbf{r}_1.$

tion of displacements will be useful to us in the next chapter when we discuss the motion of particles as a function of time.

We shall sometimes wish to represent the position vector in the form

$$\mathbf{r} = r\hat{\mathbf{r}}, \tag{2.12}$$

where $\hat{\mathbf{r}}$ is a unit vector having the same direction as the position vector $\mathbf{r}$.

Example.   The rectangular coordinates of a particle are $x = 2$ m, $y = 3$ m, and $z = 4$ m. What is the magnitude of the particle's position vector? Express the unit vector $\hat{\mathbf{r}}$ in terms of the unit vectors $\mathbf{i}$, $\mathbf{j}$, and $\mathbf{k}$.

The magnitude of the position vector is $r = \sqrt{x^2 + y^2 + z^2} = 5.39$ m. Using (2.10) and (2.12) we can express r in the form

$$r\hat{\mathbf{r}} = x\mathbf{i} + y\mathbf{j} + z\mathbf{k};$$

from this relation, we obtain

$$\hat{\mathbf{r}} = (x/r)\mathbf{i} + (y/r)\mathbf{j} + (z/r)\mathbf{k} \quad \text{or} \quad \hat{\mathbf{r}} = 0.371\mathbf{i} + 0.0557\mathbf{j} + 0.743\mathbf{k}.$$

We recognize the terms x/r, y/r, and z/r as the direction cosines of $\mathbf{r}$.

We note that the position vectors $\mathbf{r}_1$ and $\mathbf{r}_2$ must be drawn from the origin of the coordinate system being used and cannot be moved about arbitrarily. However, we also note that the displacement $\mathbf{D}_{2,1} = \mathbf{r}_2 - \mathbf{r}_1$ does *not* depend on the choice of the coordinate system.

QUESTIONS

1. Give several examples of scalar quantities. Can a scalar quantity be negative?

2. Can you think of any physical quantities that have both magnitude and a sense of direction and yet are *not* vectors?

3. Can two vectors of equal magnitude be added to give a zero resultant? Can three vectors of equal magnitude be added to give a zero resultant?

4. Can two vectors of unequal magnitude be added to give a zero resultant? Can three vectors of unequal magnitude be added to give a zero resultant?

5. Can any of the rectangular components of a vector have a magnitude greater than the magnitude of the vector itself?

6. Can a vector be resolved into two vectors, each of which has a magnitude greater than that of the original vector?

7. A particle experiences a displacement from point ① to point ②. Can the actual path length traversed between the two points ever be smaller than the magnitude of the displacement?

8. Is it possible for a zero vector to have nonzero components?

9. Is it ever possible for the magnitude of a vector to be negative?

10. Why doesn't a unit vector have dimensions?

11. We have stated that the mathematical nature of a vector is determined by its magnitude and direction. However, the physical significance of a vector may also depend on its location in space. Are two position vectors having the same magnitudes and directions really equivalent if they locate points relative to different origins?

12. We can order events in time; there is a sense of direction of time distinguishing past, present, and future. If time has both a magnitude and a sense of direction, why isn't time a vector quantity?

PROBLEMS

1. A ship sails 8 km directly eastward and then sails 6 km due northward. What is the final displacement of the ship from its starting point?

2. A ship sails 10 km directly eastward and then sails 10 km exactly northeast. What is the final displacement of the ship from its starting point?

3. The displacement of a ship from its home port is 40 km in a direction 30° north of east. In a coordinate system with the $+X$ axis eastward and the $+Y$ axis northward, what are the scalar components of the ship's displacement?

4. The parallelogram rule for the addition of two vectors $\mathbf{D}_1 + \mathbf{D}_2$ is illustrated in Fig. 2.5, in which the resultant is given by the "long diagonal" of the parallelogram. Show that the vector corresponding to the subtraction $\mathbf{D}_1 - \mathbf{D}_2$ is given by the "short diagonal" of the parallelogram in Fig. 2.5. How would you represent the subtraction $\mathbf{D}_2 - \mathbf{D}_1$ in terms of the parallelogram?

5. A particle experiences the following displacements: 2 m, eastward; 3 m, northward; and 4 m, vertically upward. Using a coordinate system with the $+X$ axis eastward, the $+Y$ axis northward, and the $+Z$ axis vertically upward, find the scalar components of the particle's final displacement. What is the magnitude of the particle's final displacement? What are the angles α, β, and γ between the particle's final displacement and the X, Y, and Z axes, respectively?

6. Repeat Problem 5 for a particle experiencing the following displacements: 2 m eastward, 2 m northward, and 2 m vertically downward.

7. Using the unit vectors $\mathbf{i}$, $\mathbf{j}$, and $\mathbf{k}$, resolve the final displacement vectors in the two preceding problems into components parallel to the coordinate axes.

8. Show that the vector addition $\mathbf{D}_R = \mathbf{D}_1 + \mathbf{D}_2 + \mathbf{D}_3 + \mathbf{D}_4$ illustrated in Fig. 2.6 yields the same resultant vector $\mathbf{D}_R$ regardless of the order in which $\mathbf{D}_1$, $\mathbf{D}_2$, $\mathbf{D}_3$, and $\mathbf{D}_4$ are considered. Do this graphically and also analytically in terms of the scalar components of the vectors being added. How must your proofs be changed if the vectors being added do not all lie in the same plane?

9. An airplane takes off in the northeast direction at an angle of 10° above the horizontal and flies in a straight line for 10 km. Find the eastward, the northward, and the vertical components of its final displacement. If the X axis is eastward, the Y axis is northward, and the Z axis is vertically upward, what are the angles α, β, and γ between the plane's displacement and the axes?

10. Suppose that $\mathbf{C} = \mathbf{A} + \mathbf{B}$. With the aid of the rules of vector algebra, show that $C^2 = A^2 + B^2 + 2AB \cos \phi$, a trigonometric relation called the *law of cosines*, and that $(\sin \alpha)/A = (\sin \beta)/B = (\sin \gamma)/C$, a trigono-

metric relation called the *law of sines,* where the angles are defined in the accompanying figure.

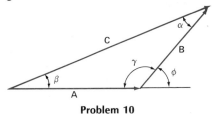

Problem 10

11. A particle moves from an initial position $x_0 = 2$ m, $y_0 = 3$ m, $z_0 = 4$ m to a final position $x = 6$ m, $y = 4$ m, and $z = 6$ m. What is the magnitude of the particle's displacement **D**? Specify the direction of the displacement in terms of the direction angles α, β, and γ between **D** and the X, Y, and Z axes.

12. A particle moves from an initial position $x_0 = 3$ m, $y_0 = 4$ m, $z_0 = 2$ m to a final position $x = 6$ m, $y = -2$ m, $z = 4$ m. What is the magnitude of the particle's displacement **D**? Specify the direction of the particle's displacement in terms of the direction angles α, β, and γ between **D** and the X, Y, and Z axes.

13. Express the displacement **D** of the particle in Problem 11 in terms of a unit vector $\hat{\mathbf{D}}$ in the direction of the displacement. Express $\hat{\mathbf{D}}$ in terms of the unit vectors **i**, **j**, and **k**.

14. Repeat Problem 13 for the particle in Problem 12.

15. A particle has a position given by $x = 3$ m, $y = 4$ m, and $z = 5$ m. Write an expression giving the position vector **r** of the particle. Express the position vector **r** in terms of a unit vector $\hat{\mathbf{r}}$. Express $\hat{\mathbf{r}}$ in terms of **i**, **j**, and **k**.

16. Repeat Problem 15 for a particle at $x = 4$ m, $y = 5$ m, and $z = 6$ m.

17. An airplane flies due eastward from a point on the prime meridian having latitude 40°N to a point on the 180° meridian at the same latitude. What is the length of the path traversed by the plane? What is the displacement of the plane? (The radius of the earth is 6400 km.)

18. A plane flies due southward from a point having a latitude of 30°N to a point with latitude 30°S. What is the length of the path traversed by the plane? What is the magnitude of the plane's displacement? (The radius of the earth is 6400 km.)

19. A horizontal line is one that is tangential to the earth's surface. If a plane were able to take off horizontally and fly for 200 km in a straight line, what would be the altitude of the plane above the earth's surface at the end of this trip? (The radius of the earth is 6400 km.)

20. An airplane flying at constant altitude starts at the equator and flies due northward for 2000 km, then flies 2000 km due eastward, then 2000 km due southward, and finally 2000 km due westward. What is the final displacement of the plane from its starting point? (The radius of the earth is 6400 km.)

21. Subtract a displacement of 20 m due southeast from a displacement of 20 m due northeast. What is the resulting displacement?

22. A displacement has a magnitude of 10 m and a direction 30° north of east. From this displacement subtract a displacement of 30 m with a direction of 45° north of west.

23. A displacement has scalar components $D_x = 10$ m, $D_y = 15$ m, and $D_z = 20$ m. What is the magnitude of this displacement? If this displacement were reversed in direction, what would be its magnitude and what would be the values of its scalar components?

24. Show that multiplication of a vector by -1 merely reverses the algebraic signs of its scalar components.

25. The initial position of a particle in the XY plane of a coordinate system is $x_1 = 2$ m and $y_1 = 3$ m. Its final position following a

displacement is $x_2 = 4$ m and $y_2 = 6$ m. What is the magnitude of the particle's displacement? What are the scalar components of the particle's displacement?

26. If the initial and final positions of the particle in Problem 25 were specified with respect to a second coordinate system with its origin at a point $x_0 = 3$ m and $y_0 = 6$ m relative to the first coordinate system, what would be the coordinates of its initial and final positions in the second system? What would be the magnitude of its displacement? What would be the scalar components of its displacement?

27. A particle is initially at a point $x_1 = 3$ m, $y_1 = 2$ m, and $z_1 = 1$ m in a certain coordinate system. At a later time the particle has moved to a point $x_2 = -1$ m, $y_2 = 4$ m, and $z_2 = -5$ m. (a) What is the initial position vector $\mathbf{r}_1$ of the particle? (b) What is the final position vector $\mathbf{r}_2$ of the particle? (c) What is the displacement $\mathbf{D}_{2,1}$ of the particle? Express your answers in terms of the unit vectors $\mathbf{i}$, $\mathbf{j}$, and $\mathbf{k}$.

28. What are the magnitudes of $\mathbf{r}_1$, $\mathbf{r}_2$, and $\mathbf{D}_{2,1}$ for the particle described in Problem 27?

29. A particle is located initially at the origin of a rectangular coordinate system XY. It first moves to a point $x_1 = 4$ m, $y_1 = 0$ and then to a point $x_2 = 6$ m, $y_2 = 3$ m. Express the first displacement $\mathbf{D}_{1,0}$, the second displacement $\mathbf{D}_{2,1}$, and the resultant displacement $\mathbf{D}_{2,0}$ in vector form by using the unit vectors $\mathbf{i}$ and $\mathbf{j}$.

30. What are the magnitudes of the displacements $\mathbf{D}_{1,0}$, $\mathbf{D}_{2,1}$, and $\mathbf{D}_{2,0}$ in Problem 29?

31. A particle initially at the origin undergoes a displacement of 25 m in a direction 20° east of north and 15° above the horizontal. What are the Cartesian coordinates of the position vector of the particle's new location? Use a coordinate system with the X axis to the east, the Y axis to the north, and the Z axis vertically upward. What subsequent

displacement is required to bring the particle to the position $\mathbf{r}_P = (0, 0, 40$ m$)$, which is 40 m directly above the origin? What is the magnitude of this displacement?

32. The following displacements in a horizontal plane are made in sequence: 201 m at 12° south of east, 175 m due north, 197 m at 39° south of west, 378 m at 24° east of north. What are the magnitude and direction of the resultant displacement? Draw a diagram representing the vector addition of these displacements.

33. Repeat Problem 32 for the following displacements: 6.4 m at 30° north of east, 4.6 m due west, 5.7 m at 20° south of west, 3.7 m at 5° east of south.

34. With the aid of appropriate diagrams, prove that multiplication by a scalar is distributive with respect to vector addition: $a(\mathbf{D}_1 + \mathbf{D}_2) = a\mathbf{D}_1 + a\mathbf{D}_2$. First consider the case when a is a positive scalar, then consider the case when a is a negative scalar.

35. What are the direction cosines of the position vector $\mathbf{r} = (4.5$ m, -3.8 m, 2.7 m$)$?

36. What are the direction cosines of the position vector $\mathbf{r} = (26.2$ cm, 31.5 cm, -62.1 cm$)$?

37. What are the magnitude and the direction cosines of the displacement that takes a particle from position $\mathbf{r}_1 = (82$ cm, 21 cm, -5 cm$)$ to $\mathbf{r}_2 = (17$ cm, 63 cm, -29 cm$)$?

38. A certain pocket watch keeping accurate time lies on a horizontal surface. Take the origin at the center of the watch face and let the Y axis extend through the numeral 12 and the X axis through the numeral 3 on the watch face. What are the magnitude and the direction of the displacement of the tip of the minute hand between 1:04 P.M. and 2:38 P.M. if the minute hand is 2.2 cm long?

39. A particle initially having spherical polar coordinates $r_1 = 1.45$ m, $\theta_1 = 28°$, $\phi_1 = 102°$ is displaced to a location having spherical

polar coordinates $r_2 = 2.32$ m, $\theta_2 = 98°$, $\phi_2 = 10°$. What are the magnitude and direction cosines of the displacement?

40. A particle initially having spherical polar coordinates $r_1 = 2.75$ m, $\theta_1 = 36°$, $\phi_1 = 40°$ is given a displacement having magnitude 3.5 m and the following direction cosines: $\cos \alpha = 0.111$, $\cos \beta = -0.111$, $\cos \gamma = 0.988$. What are the spherical polar coordinates of the particle's final location?

CHAPTER 3

Kinematics of a Particle

Kinematics is the branch of mechanics that deals with the *quantitative description of motion*. We note that kinematics involves only the description of motion and is *not* concerned with the *causes* of motion, which we shall consider initially in Chapter 4. In this chapter we shall give a quantitative description of the motion of a particle in terms of a continuous change in its position. The central problem to be considered is the development of relationships that will give *the position of a particle as a function of time*. Time is a fundamental physical quantity. Its measurement has long presented problems to man; the development of *clocks* of various kinds constitutes an interesting story in itself.

3.1 TIME INTERVALS

A central problem of time measurement is to find some repetitive process that provides a standard unit with which other time intervals can be compared. In his attempt to measure time intervals man has made use of what he regarded as "natural time units" such as the *day,* defined as the interval between successive noons; the *month,* defined as the interval between successive full moons; and the *year,* defined as the interval between successive summer solstices, the times when the noon sun observed in the northern hemisphere is highest above the southern horizon. These natural units are actually incommensurable; the lunar month does not consist of a whole number of days, and the year does not consist of a whole number of lunar months or a whole number of days. The fact that these natural units are incommensurable made it difficult to establish a calendar; the story of the development of our present calendar is interesting, but is not of crucial importance to our present study.

Although the day as the shortest natural astronomical time interval served the needs of early man, the development of civilization following the agricultural revolution

35

of 7000 years ago made it necessary to divide the day into smaller time intervals. The subdivision of the day into hours, minutes, and seconds is of Babylonian origin; these subdivisions are so widely accepted throughout the world that all proposals of decimal time divisions have met with failure. With regard to public time measurements mankind is very "set in its ways."

There have been marked improvements in the precisions of the clocks developed for the measurement of time intervals. The first satisfactory clock was the sundial, which measured the passing hours by means of shadows on an appropriately designed dial. The first mechanical clocks, developed during the middle ages, consisted of large elaborate mechanisms designed to operate at a constant rate; these devices were powered by means of a suspended weight that gradually descended and had to be raised again periodically. The early mechanical clocks were extremely expensive and could be afforded only by large cathedrals or by cities; these clocks indicated time by the movement of hour hands and minute hands moving on "clock faces" mounted on high towers. The arbitrary choice made by the designers of these early clock faces provides the basis for the "senses" of rotary motion that we use today: *clockwise* and *counterclockwise*. The early clocks were checked and adjusted on the basis of daily observations of the noon sun.

The next development in time measurement was the pendulum clock, which is based on Galileo's discovery of the relationship between the length of a pendulum and the time required for the pendulum to make a complete to-and-fro swing. Pendulum clocks were powered either by gradually falling weights or by wound springs. Although less expensive than the earlier mechanical clocks, pendulum clocks could be afforded only by the wealthy; installed in beautiful cabinets, they became known as "grandfather clocks."

Further development in clock design was made in response to navigational needs recognized during the European voyages of discovery when it became imperative to have some method of determining longitude. If a sea captain possessed an accurate clock reading Greenwich time, which is the local time on the prime meridian, he could establish his longitude by noting the Greenwich time at which his own local noon occurred. As a result of the pitch and roll of a ship, pendulum clocks will not work at sea. The British Admiralty in 1760 offered a large prize for the development of a *chronometer* not subject to mechanical motions of its mount. The prize-winning device was a springdriven clock that employed a small oscillating "balance wheel" acted upon by tiny restoring springs known as "hair springs." This chronometer was the forerunner of our common alarm clocks and wristwatches. We can now adjust precision clocks and watches by comparison with time signals provided by government radio stations such as the US National Bureau of Standards (NBS) station WWV and the BBC.

For many years clocks at the national standards laboratories have employed vibrating quartz crystals as timing devices; these devices are the forerunners of modern watches based on vibrating crystals. With the development of these precision crystal-controlled clocks, it was clearly established early in the present century that the astronomical motions of the earth—rotation on its own axis and revolution in its orbit about the sun—were subject to irregularities not recognized earlier. This discovery indicated that crystal-controlled clocks were capable of measuring time intervals more accurately than the earth–sun astronomical clock that long provided the earth's time standards. Improved clock accuracy was actually needed for practical engineering purposes in connection with radio and television broadcasting systems.

Because the vibrating quartz crystals have to be fabricated by shaping and polishing procedures that are not readily duplicated to high precision in different laboratories, they constitute man-made devices that are not satisfactory as international standards. Therefore, the 12th General Conference of Weights and Measures in 1964 decided to adopt a time standard based on atomic properties. The SI unit of time is the *second* (s) and is defined as the time required for the cesium atom (Cs) to send out a certain number of wavelengths of one of its characteristic electromagnetic radiations; in other words, the time for the cesium atom to make a specified number of electrical "oscillations" or "vibrations." These oscillations are imparted electrically to the so-called "atomic clocks" at the standards laboratories of various nations. In order to maintain civil time for use in everyday affairs, the civil-time clocks at national observatories such as the U.S. Naval Observatory and the Greenwich Royal Observatory are appropriately corrected by the insertion or omission of a "leap second" whenever the irregular astronomical motions differ by as much as one second from the standard atomic clock.

In the tables of conversion factors in the Appendix, we list relationships between various time units that are in common use. Here we note that

$$1 \text{ minute} = 60 \text{ s}; \quad 1 \text{ hour} = 3600 \text{ s}; \text{ and } 1 \text{ day} = 86,400 \text{ s}.$$

These relations will be useful in solving some of the problems at the end of this chapter.

3.2 SPEED

The kinematical quantity most familiar to all of us is *speed,* the quantity that is registered by the speedometer of every automobile. A driver relies on the speedometer to tell him how fast his car is moving, but recognizes that the instrument gives no information at all about the direction in which the car is moving. Speed is thus a scalar quantity.

SPEED is path length traversed per unit time.

It is a derived quantity involving both length and time. The SI unit of speed is m/s; its relations to other speed units are given in the Table of Conversion Factors in the Appendix.

In order to understand what is actually involved in the measurement of speed, consider the motion of a car along a roadway between J and M as suggested in Fig. 3.1. We can measure the length L of the path being traversed by the car by means of the car's odometer, which we shall for reasons of convenience set to zero at position J; we can measure the elapsed travel time t by means of a stopwatch, which we can start at $t = 0$ when the car leaves J.

If the total length of the car's path from J to M is L_T as indicated by the odometer or as measured by surveyor's chains, and the total time required for the total journey

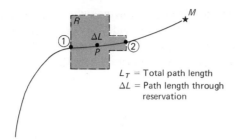

L_T = Total path length
ΔL = Path length through
     reservation

Fig. 3.1 Average speed is the path traversed per unit time.

is t_T as measured by the stopwatch, the average speed for the entire trip is simply the total path length traversed by the car divided by the total time required: $\bar{s} = L_T/t_T$, where we use the bar over s to indicate the *time average*.

We can similarly measure the average speed of the car for the path length between points ① and ② in its passage through military reservation R by dividing the length of path ΔL indicated in the figure by the time Δt required for the car to move from ① to ② ; $\bar{s} = \Delta L/\Delta t$ for the passage from ① to ②. We note that ΔL is just the difference between the odometer reading L_2 at ② and the odometer reading L_1 at ① and that Δt is just the difference in the stopwatch readings t_2 and t_1 at these points: $\Delta L = L_2 - L_1$ and $\Delta t = t_2 - t_1$. The average speeds involved in other parts of the journey from J to M can be obtained in similar fashion in terms of odometer and stopwatch readings.

Now let us see how the *instantaneous speed* of the car at some point such as P in Fig. 3.1 can be determined; the instantaneous speed of the car is what is purportedly registered by the car's speedometer. In Fig. 3.2 we show an enlarged drawing of the roadway in the vicinity of point P; ΔL represents a small path length that includes point P. The average speed $\bar{s}$ of the car in the part of the path indicated in Fig. 3.2 is just $\bar{s} = \Delta L/\Delta t$. We define the instantaneous speed s of the car at point P to be the limiting value of $\Delta L/\Delta t$ as Δt approaches zero and as ΔL also approaches zero but always includes point P:

$$s = \lim_{\Delta t \to 0} \frac{\Delta L}{\Delta t} \quad \text{or} \quad s = \frac{dL}{dt}, \begin{cases} s \text{ in m/s} \\ L \text{ in m} \\ t \text{ in s} \end{cases} \quad (Speed) \qquad (3.1)$$

where we recognize the limiting value of $\Delta L/\Delta t$ as the derivative dL/dt.* If we have any method of expressing L as a differentiable function of t, we can obtain the value of the instantaneous speed s by differentiating L with respect to t. Otherwise, we could make a plot of odometer reading L as a function of stopwatch reading and obtain the instantaneous speed of the car at any point by determining the limiting slope $\Delta L/\Delta t$ of the curve at the point in question.

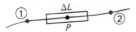

Fig. 3.2 Instantaneous speed is the limiting value of $\Delta L/\Delta t$ as $\Delta t \to 0$.

---

* In an Appendix, we give a brief discussion of derivatives and integrals for the benefit of students who are only beginning their study of calculus.

Now that we have expressed instantaneous speed as a derivative in (3.1), let us show that this relation leads to the same values for average speed as were stated earlier. We define the average value of any time-dependent quantity such as the speed $s(t)$ over the interval from time t_1 to time t_2 by the relation

$$\bar{s} = \left(\int_{t_1}^{t_2} s(t)\, dt \right) / (t_2 - t_1). \tag{3.2}$$

Since $s = dL/dt$, this becomes

$$\bar{s} = \left(\int_{t_1}^{t_2} (dL/dt)\, dt \right) / (t_2 - t_1)$$

$$= \left(\int_{L_1}^{L_2} dL \right) / (t_2 - t_1) = (L_2 - L_1)/(t_2 - t_1), \tag{3.2'}$$

which agrees with the relationship $\bar{s} = \Delta L / \Delta t$ stated earlier.

Example.   The total distance traveled as a function of time during a certain time interval for an ant crawling on a picnic table is given by the relation $L = (10^{-5}\ \text{m/s}^3)t^3 + (2 \times 10^{-3}\ \text{m/s}^2)t^2 + (3 \times 10^{-2}\ \text{m/s})t$. What is the speed with which the ant is crawling at $t = 0$ s, at $t = 1$ s, and at $t = 10$ s? What is the average speed of the ant during the interval from $t = 0$ s to $t = 10$ s?

From (3.1) we have $s = dL/dt = 3(10^{-5}\ \text{m/s}^3)t^2 + 2(2 \times 10^{-3}\ \text{m/s}^2)t + (3 \times 10^{-2}\ \text{m/s})$. Evaluating this expression at the given values of t, we find the following:

$$s(t = 0\ \text{s}) = 3 \times 10^{-2}\ \text{m/s},$$
$$s(t = 1\ \text{s}) = 3 \times 10^{-5}\ \text{m/s} + 4 \times 10^{-3}\ \text{m/s} + 3 \times 10^{-2}\ \text{m/s}$$
$$= 3.4 \times 10^{-2}\ \text{m/s},$$

and

$$s(t = 10\ \text{s}) = 3 \times 10^{-3}\ \text{m/s} + 4 \times 10^{-2}\ \text{m/s} + 3 \times 10^{-2}\ \text{m/s}$$
$$= 7.3 \times 10^{-2}\ \text{m/s}.$$

From the expression for L we have $L(t = 0\ \text{s}) = 0$ m and $L(t = 10\ \text{s}) = 10^{-2}\ \text{m} + 2 \times 10^{-1}\ \text{m} + 3 \times 10^{-1}\ \text{m} = 0.51$ m.

Therefore, from (3.2') we have for the average speed

$$\bar{s} = (0.51\ \text{m} - 0\ \text{m})/(10\ \text{s} - 0\ \text{s}) = 5.1 \times 10^{-2}\ \text{m/s}.$$

Although speed is a useful physical quantity for many purposes, its use in kinematics is very limited. The main problem in the kinematics of particles is specifying the position of a particle as a function of time. Knowing only the speed of a particle, we can give the length of the path traversed by the particle in a given time, but the speed by itself says nothing regarding the direction in which the particle has traveled. We obviously need a quantity related to speed but with vector properties.

Example.   A particle initially at point O travels in a plane at a constant speed of 30 km/h for one hour. What can be said regarding the position of the particle at the end of the hour?

If the particle traveled in a straight line for one hour, the magnitude of the particle's displacement from O could be as great as 30 km, but we have no information regarding the direction of the particle's displacement. If the particle moved around a closed race track, its displacement at the end of one hour might actually be zero. If the particle moved along some curved but unclosed path, the magnitude of the particle's displacement could have any value between zero and 30 km. All that we can say about the particle's final position relative to point O is that the particle is somewhere within a circle with center at O and a radius of 30 km. Speed alone is not very useful in kinematics!

3.3   VELOCITY

The vector quantity that we need is called velocity **v**; it is related to displacement **D** in the same way that speed is related to path length.

VELOCITY is the time rate of change in position.

In order to indicate what is involved in this definition we have in Fig. 3.3 redrawn the map shown in Fig. 3.1 with the motorist's position vectors for different parts of his journey indicated on the map. On the basis of the definition of velocity and the fact that the initial displacement of the motorist from J is zero at time $t = 0$, we can immediately write down the average velocity $\bar{\mathbf{v}}$ of the car for various parts of the trip from J to M. For the part of the trip from J to point ①, $\bar{\mathbf{v}} = \mathbf{r}_1/t_1$; for the trip through the military reservation from ① to ②, $\bar{\mathbf{v}} = \Delta\mathbf{r}/\Delta t = (\mathbf{r}_2 - \mathbf{r}_1)/(t_2 - t_1)$; for the final portion of the journey from ② to final destination M, $\bar{\mathbf{v}} = (\mathbf{r}_M - \mathbf{r}_2)/(t_M - t_2)$; and for the complete trip, $\bar{\mathbf{v}} = \mathbf{r}_M/t_M$, where t_M is the total elapsed time for the journey.

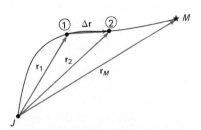

Fig. 3.3   Velocity is the change in position per unit time, the time rate of displacement.

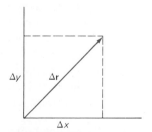

Fig. 3.4   The rectangular components of a change in position.

In order to understand what is meant by the term *instantaneous velocity,* we use arguments similar to those used earlier in connection with instantaneous speed; we define instantaneous velocity as the limiting value of $\Delta r/\Delta t$ as Δt approaches zero. Thus, in Fig. 3.4 we show $\Delta \mathbf{r}$ as the small displacement of a particle in time Δt and obtain the instantaneous velocity $\mathbf{v}$ as the limiting value

$$\mathbf{v} = \lim_{\Delta t \to 0} \frac{\Delta \mathbf{r}}{\Delta t}.$$

We recognize this limit as the derivative $d\mathbf{r}/dt$:

$$\mathbf{v} = d\mathbf{r}/dt. \quad \left\{ \begin{array}{l} v \text{ in m/s} \\ r \text{ in m} \\ t \text{ in s} \end{array} \right\} \quad (Velocity) \qquad (3.3)$$

Since $\mathbf{r}$ is a vector and t is a scalar, we see that velocity $\mathbf{v}$ is a vector having both a magnitude, measured in m/s, and a direction. Because a change in position is a displacement, we note that *velocity is displacement per unit time;* it does not depend on the location of the origin of the coordinate system employed. The vector relation between velocity and displacement in (3.3) is the analogue of the scalar relation in (3.1) between speed and path length traversed.

Remembering that a vector can be characterized by a statement of its scalar components, let us consider the scalar components of $\mathbf{v}$. Consider first motion that occurs in the XY plane. We note, as suggested in Fig. 3.4, that $\Delta \mathbf{r}$ is characterized by the scalar components $\Delta r_x = \Delta x$ and $\Delta r_y = \Delta y$. Thus we have the limiting values $v_x = dx/dt$ and $v_y = dy/dt$. Therefore, we can characterize $\mathbf{v}$ in terms of its scalar components as follows:

$$\mathbf{v} = d\mathbf{r}/dt: \quad v_x = dx/dt \quad \text{and} \quad v_y = dy/dt. \qquad (3.4)$$

The magnitude of $\mathbf{v}$ is given by $v = \sqrt{v_x^2 + v_y^2}$ and the direction of $\mathbf{v}$ is specified by the relation $\tan \phi = v_y/v_x$, where ϕ is the angle between $\mathbf{v}$ and the X axis of the coordinate system employed.

Example. A particle moving in a horizontal plane experiences a displacement of 10 m in a direction 30° north of east. If the time required for the displacement is 5 s, what is the average velocity of the particle? What are the scalar components of the displacement? What are the scalar components of the particle's average velocity?

The average velocity of the particle is given by the ratio of the total displacement to elapsed time: $\bar{\mathbf{v}} = \mathbf{D}/t = (10 \text{ m}, 30° \text{ N of E})/5 \text{ s} = 2 \text{ m/s}, 30° \text{ N of E}$. The scalar components of the displacement are $D_x = D \cos \phi = (10 \text{ m})(0.866) = 8.66$ m and $D_y = D \sin \phi = (10 \text{ m})(0.500) = 5$ m. The scalar components of the average velocity of the particle are given by $\bar{v}_x = D_x/t = (8.66 \text{ m})/(5 \text{ s}) = 1.73$ m/s and $\bar{v}_y = (5 \text{ m})/(5 \text{ s}) = 1.00$ m/s. To check these results, we can compute $\bar{v}$ from the relation $\bar{v} = \sqrt{\bar{v}_x^2 + \bar{v}_y^2}$ and compare the results with our earlier value of $\bar{v}$.

In our discussion of (3.4) we have limited ourselves to the motion of a particle in the XY plane. The discussion can easily be generalized for a particle in three-dimensional space. We then have the following relations:

$$\mathbf{v} = d\mathbf{r}/dt: \quad v_x = dx/dt, \; v_y = dy/dt, \; v_z = dz/dt. \tag{3.4'}$$

In this case, the magnitude of the velocity $\mathbf{v}$ is given by $v = \sqrt{v_x^2 + v_y^2 + v_z^2}$, and the direction of $\mathbf{v}$ can be specified in terms of the direction cosines: $\cos \alpha = v_x/v$, $\cos \beta = v_y/v$, and $\cos \gamma = v_z/v$.

The scalar components of velocity are subject to the familiar operations of ordinary algebra and calculus. Therefore, if the velocity of a particle is known, we can use (3.4') to determine its displacement in any time interval $t - t_0$. We obtain relations of the type

$$\int_{x_0}^{x} dx = \int_{t_0}^{t} v_x \, dt \quad \text{or} \quad x = x_0 + \int_{t_0}^{t} v_x \, dt,$$

with similar relations for the y and z rectangular components. The corresponding integrals of the vector relation $d\mathbf{r} = \mathbf{v} \, dt$ can be written formally as

$$\int_{\mathbf{r}_0}^{\mathbf{r}} d\mathbf{r} = \int_{t_0}^{t} \mathbf{v} \, dt \quad \text{or} \quad \mathbf{r} = \mathbf{r}_0 + \int_{t_0}^{t} \mathbf{v} \, dt. \tag{3.5}$$

This is completely characterized by the scalar equations

$$x = x_0 + \int_{t_0}^{t} v_x \, dt, \quad y = y_0 + \int_{t_0}^{t} v_y \, dt, \quad \text{and} \quad z = z_0 + \int_{t_0}^{t} v_z \, dz. \tag{3.6}$$

The results can be simplified by choosing the origin of the coordinate system at the initial position, with the result that $\mathbf{r}_0$, x_0, y_0, and z_0 are all zero.

Before concluding our discussion of velocity, we must note that *all* velocities are relative.

The velocity of a particle can be specified only with respect to other matter in the universe; there is no way in which absolute velocity can be specified. In our earlier discussion of velocity we have characterized the velocity of a particle in terms of its time rate of change of position relative to some coordinate system attached to the earth. We have thus been stating velocities relative to the earth and shall continue to do so. However, the earth itself is certainly not at rest; it is rotating on its own axis; it is revolving in its orbit about the sun; the sun is moving relative to the center of our own galaxy at enormous speed; and our own galaxy is moving relative to other galaxies at still larger speeds. In spite of many attempts, some of which we shall discuss in later chapters, no one has devised a way in which *absolute velocity* relative to "space itself" can be measured; absolute velocity is therefore a meaningless concept.

We must be careful, however, to specify the coordinate systems in which we *are* specifying velocities. Most velocities used in engineering and physics laboratories are velocities stated relative to the earth. If a particle's velocity $\mathbf{v}_{PA}$ is stated in some coordinate system A moving relative to the earth E with velocity $\mathbf{v}_{AE}$, the velocity $\mathbf{v}_{PE}$ of the particle relative to the earth is given by

$$\mathbf{v}_{PE} = \mathbf{v}_{PA} + \mathbf{v}_{AE}. \tag{3.7}$$

This "transformation" of velocities from coordinate system A to coordinate system E can be illustrated by the motion of an airplane. The pilot has reliable methods of measuring the velocity $\mathbf{v}_{PA}$ of his plane relative to the surrounding air. If the air providing his coordinate system A is moving at a velocity $\mathbf{v}_{AE}$ relative to the earth's surface, which provides system E, the plane's velocity $\mathbf{v}_{PE}$ relative to the earth is equal to the vector sum of $\mathbf{v}_{PA}$ and $\mathbf{v}_{AE}$ as indicated in (3.7). The vector addition of velocities is similar to the vector addition of displacements that we have already considered in some detail. In a later chapter we shall show the simple relation given in (3.7) must be modified for high velocities that are comparable in magnitude with the speed of light.

Example. The indicated air speed of a high-altitude jet airplane is 600 km/h at a time when the stratospheric wind is blowing eastward at a speed of 200 km/h relative to the earth's surface. What is the velocity of the plane relative to the ground if the plane is headed directly east? directly west?

When the plane is headed east, the velocity of the plane relative to the air is $\mathbf{v}_{PA} = 600$ km/h, eastward. The velocity of the air relative to the ground is $\mathbf{v}_{AE} = 200$ km/h, eastward. Because both velocities have the same direction, we may use the eastward scalar components of (3.7) to obtain $\mathbf{v}_{PE} = (600 + 200)$ km/h, eastward $= 800$ km/h, eastward. The pilot in this case says that he has a tail wind. When the plane is headed westward relative to the air, the value of $\mathbf{v}_{PA}$ is 600 km/h, westward; the velocity of the air is 200 km/h, eastward, or -200 km/h, westward. Making use of (3.7) to obtain $\mathbf{v}_{PE}$, we thus obtain $\mathbf{v}_{PE} = (600 - 200)$ km/h, westward $= 400$ km/h, westward. The pilot in this case reports a head wind.

Example. If the pilot in the preceding example heads his plane due north, what is his velocity $\mathbf{v}_{PE}$ relative to the earth? In which direction should the pilot head the plane if he wishes to *travel* due north?

In the first case, the value of $\mathbf{v}_{PA}$ is 600 km/h, northward, and the value of $\mathbf{v}_{AE}$ is 200 km/h, eastward, as indicated in Fig. 3.5a. The magnitude of $\mathbf{v}_{PE}$ is given by $v_{PE} = \sqrt{v_{PA}^2 + v_{AE}^2} = \sqrt{(600)^2 + (200)^2}$ km/h $= \sqrt{(36 + 4) \times 10^4}$ km/h $= \sqrt{40} \times 100$ km/h $= 6.32 \times 100$ km/h $= 632$ km/h. The direction of $\mathbf{v}_{PE}$ can be obtained from $\cos \phi = v_{AE}/v_{PE} = (200$ km/h$)/(632$ km/h$) = 0.316$; the value ϕ in Fig. 3.5a is 71.6°. Thus, we can express $\mathbf{v}_{PE}$ as 632 km/h in a direction 71.6° north of east.

In order to fly due north, the pilot must head the plane in a direction ϕ' deg

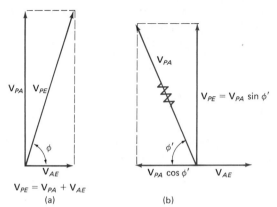

$$v_{PE} = v_{PA} + v_{AE}$$
(a)   (b)

Fig. 3.5   The vector addition of velocities.

north of west so that his westward velocity component relative to the air, $v_{PA} \cos \phi'$, is equal in magnitude to v_{AE}, as suggested in Fig. 3.5b. Thus we have $v_{PA} \cos \phi' = v_{AE}$ or $\cos \phi' = v_{AE}/v_{PA} = (200 \text{ km/h})/(600 \text{ km/h}) = 0.333$; the value of ϕ' is 70.5°. The pilot must head his plane in a direction 70.5° north of west. The magnitude of the northward velocity of the plane relative to the earth is $v_{PE} = v_{PA} \sin \phi' = (600 \text{ km/h}) \sin 70.5° = (600 \text{ km/h})(0.943) = 566 \text{ km/h}$.

3.4   ACCELERATION

In addition to velocity, another kinematical quantity must be defined. This quantity is *acceleration,* a quantity that will have great importance to our subsequent study of dynamics.

ACCELERATION is the time rate of change in velocity.

Because velocity is a vector quantity and time is a scalar quantity, acceleration is a vector quantity. Acceleration is related to velocity in the same way that velocity is related to position:

$$\mathbf{a} = d\mathbf{v}/dt. \quad \left\{ \begin{array}{l} a \text{ in m/s}^2 \\ v \text{ in m/s} \\ t \text{ in s} \end{array} \right\} \quad (Acceleration) \qquad (3.8)$$

We note that the SI unit for acceleration is written m/s², which we should read as "m/s each s" until we become fully familiar with what is involved; change in velocity is itself measured in m/s and acceleration is defined as the time rate of change of velocity. Like all vector quantities, acceleration has direction as well as magnitude.

In order to clarify our ideas about acceleration, let us consider the diagrams in Fig. 3.6. Part (a) of the figure shows the path being traversed by an automobile. At time t_1 the automobile is at point ① and has velocity $\mathbf{v}_1$; at time t_2 the automobile is at point ② and has velocity $\mathbf{v}_2$. The change in velocity $\Delta\mathbf{v} = \mathbf{v}_2 - \mathbf{v}_1$ is indicated by the vector $\Delta\mathbf{v}$ in part (b) of the figure; we note that $\Delta\mathbf{v}$ is the vector that must

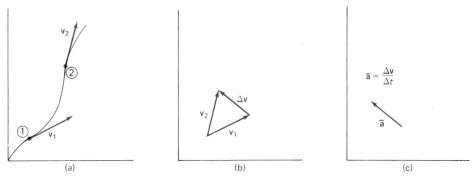

Fig. 3.6 Acceleration is the change in velocity per unit time, the time rate of velocity change.

be *added* to v_1 to give velocity v_2; that is, $v_2 = v_1 + \Delta v$. In part (c) of the figure we show the average acceleration $\bar{a}$ during the time interval $\Delta t = t_2 - t_1$; $\bar{a} = \Delta v/\Delta t$. We note that $\bar{a}$ has the same direction as Δv. The instantaneous acceleration defined by Eq. (3.8) represents the limiting value of $\bar{a}$ as the time interval Δt becomes arbitrarily small. If there is a change in either the magnitude or the direction of the velocity of a particle, the particle is accelerated.

Example. A particle is initially moving at a velocity $v_1 = 2$ m/s, eastward, and 2 s later is moving at a velocity $v_2 = 4$ m/s, eastward, as suggested in Fig. 3.7a. What is the average acceleration of the particle during this time interval?

We note that the change in velocity $\Delta v = v_2 - v_1 = (4$ m/s, eastward$) - (2$ m/s, eastward$) = 2$ m/s, eastward. The average acceleration $\bar{a} = \Delta v/\Delta t = (2$ m/s, eastward$)/2$ s $= 1$ m/s², eastward.

Example. A particle is initially moving at a velocity of 2 m/s, eastward, and 2 s later is moving with a velocity of 2 m/s, northward. What is its average acceleration during this time interval?

This situation is shown in Fig. 3.7b. The change in velocity $\Delta v = v_2 - v_1$ is the change in velocity that must be added to v_1 to produce v_2; that is, $v_2 = v_1 + \Delta v$. The magnitude of Δv can be obtained from the Pythagorean theorem: $|\Delta v| = \sqrt{v_1^2 + v_2^2} = \sqrt{(2 \text{ m/s})^2 + (2 \text{ m/s})^2} = \sqrt{8 \text{ m}^2/\text{s}^2} = 2.83$ m/s. The average acceleration has magnitude $\bar{a} = |\Delta v|/\Delta t = (2.83$ m/s$)/(2$ s$) = 1.41$ m/s². The direction of Δv can be obtained from tan $\phi = v_2/v_1 = 1$; thus $\phi = 45°$; $\bar{a}$ has the same direction as Δv. Therefore, we may state that $\bar{a} = 1.41$ m/s² in a direction 45° north of west.

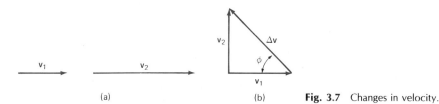

Fig. 3.7 Changes in velocity.

The acceleration **a** of a particle can be specified in terms of its rectangular scalar components:

$$\mathbf{a} = d\mathbf{v}/dt \quad : \quad a_x = dv_x/dt, \quad a_y = dv_y/dt, \text{ and } a_z = dv_z/dt. \tag{3.9}$$

In view of (3.4′), we could also write the above relations in the form

$$\mathbf{a} = d^2\mathbf{r}/dt^2 : \quad a_x = d^2x/dt^2, \ a_y = d^2y/dt^2, \text{ and } a_z = d^2z/dt^2. \tag{3.9′}$$

In other words, the acceleration **a** of a particle is the second derivative of the particle's position vector **r** with respect to time.

If we know the acceleration of a particle, we can find the velocity of the particle by means of integrals similar to those in (3.5). Thus,

$$\int_{\mathbf{v_0}}^{\mathbf{v}} d\mathbf{v} = \int_{t_0}^{t} \mathbf{a} \ dt \quad \text{or} \quad \mathbf{v} = \mathbf{v_0} + \int_{t_0}^{t} \mathbf{a} \ dt. \tag{3.10}$$

This integral involving vector quantities can be characterized by rectangular scalar-component integrals of the type

$$\int_{v_{x0}}^{v_x} dv_x = \int_{t_0}^{t} a_x \ dt \quad \text{or} \quad v_x = v_{x0} + \int_{t_0}^{t} a_x \ dt, \tag{3.11}$$

with corresponding integrals for the y and z components.

We shall have occasion to apply these equations in the following sections of this chapter.

3.5   RECTILINEAR MOTION

We now consider a special type of motion, *rectilinear motion,* which is merely motion in a straight line. Positions, velocities, and accelerations in straight-line motion can change in magnitude and sign, but are always along a single axis; thus, we can use one set of scalar equations like those in (3.6) and (3.11) to describe rectilinear motion. For example, if we choose our coordinate system in such a way that the straight line corresponds to the X axis, we can immediately describe rectilinear motion in terms of x, v_x, and a_x.

For the case of rectilinear motion *at constant acceleration* the motion can be described without making use of the calculus. Thus, for the case of motion in the X direction, the displacement is given by $x = x_0 + \bar{v}_x t$, where $\bar{v}_x$ is the average velocity and x_0 is the location at the initial time $t = 0$. Because the acceleration a_x is *constant,* the velocity v_x at time t is given by the relation

$$v_x = v_{x0} + a_x t, \quad (Constant \ Acceleration) \tag{3.12}$$

where v_{x0} is the initial velocity. In the *special case of constant acceleration,* the average velocity is given by $\bar{v}_x = (v_{x0} + v_x)/2$. By using (3.12) for v_x we obtain $\bar{v}_x =$

$v_{x0} + a_x t/2$, which is equal to the instantaneous velocity v_x at time $t/2$. Substituting this expression for $\bar{v}_x$ in the general expression for x leads to the relation

$$x = x_0 + v_{x0}t + (\tfrac{1}{2})a_x t^2 \quad \textit{(Constant Acceleration)} \tag{3.13}$$

for the position x at time t. By replacing t in (3.13) by $t = (v_x - v_{x0})/a_x$, we obtain another useful kinematic relationship:

$$v_x^2 = v_{x0}^2 + 2a_x(x - x_0), \quad \textit{(Constant Acceleration)} \tag{3.14}$$

which gives the final velocity v_x in terms of the initial velocity v_{x0} and the displacement $(x - x_0)$. Note that (3.12), (3.13), and (3.14) hold only for *constant acceleration*.

We now apply the general theory we have developed to a set of special cases.

Example. A car moving at a constant velocity of 2 m/s, eastward, is initially 30 m east of a crossroad. What is the change in the position of the car during the first 10 s of motion? What is the final location of the car?

We can choose a coordinate system with its origin located at the crossroad and with its $+X$ axis directed eastward from the origin. In this frame the initial position of the car at $t = 0$ is $x_0 = 30$ m. The displacement of the car after t seconds is simply $\Delta x = v_x t$ because v_x has a *constant* value $v_x = 2$ m/s; hence, $\Delta x = (2 \text{ m/s}) \times (10 \text{ s}) = 20$ m. The final position of the car is thus $x = x_0 + v_x t = 30 \text{ m} + 20 \text{ m} = 50$ m; the final location of the car is 50 m east of the crossroad. The equations we have used can be obtained by the integration in (3.6) with $x_0 = 30$ m and $\int_0^t v_x \, dt = v_x \int_0^t dt = v_x t$, where v_x is constant. The result of the integration is thus $x = x_0 + v_x t$. Substitution of $x_0 = 30$ m and $v_x = 2$ m/s leads to $x = 30 \text{ m} + (2 \text{ m/s})(10 \text{ s}) = 50$ m.

Example. A car with a initial velocity $v_{x0} = 3$ m/s, eastward, and initially at a point $x_0 = 6$ m east of a certain street intersection moves for 10 s at a constant acceleration $a_x = 2$ m/s², eastward. What is the velocity of the car at the end of 10 s? What is the position of the car at the end of 10 s? What is the average velocity of the car during the 10 s of motion?

On the basis of (3.10) with the acceleration taken as constant and $t_0 = 0$, we can express the car's velocity v_x at time t as $v_x = v_{x0} + a_x t$, just (3.12); thus, at the end of 10 s, $v_x - v_{x0} = (2 \text{ m/s}^2)(10 \text{ s}) = 20$ m/s. The final velocity at the end of t seconds is $v_x = v_{x0} + a_x t = (3 \text{ m/s}) + (20 \text{ m/s}) = 23$ m/s, eastward. The final position of the car can be obtained by the integration in (3.6):

$$x = x_0 + \int_0^t (v_{x0} + a_x t)dt.$$ The result is $x = x_0 + v_{x0}t + a_x t^2/2$, just (3.13). Thus,

$x = (6 \text{ m}) + (3 \text{ m/s})(10 \text{ s}) + \tfrac{1}{2}(2 \text{ m/s}^2)(100 \text{ s}^2) = 136$ m, east of the intersection. The average velocity is given by $\bar{v}_x = D_x/\Delta t = (v_{x0}t + \tfrac{1}{2}a_x t^2)/t = (3 \text{ m/s}) + \tfrac{1}{2}(2 \text{ m/s}^2)(10 \text{ s}) = 13$ m/s, eastward. Note that $\bar{v}_x$ is equal to the instantaneous value of v_x at $t/2$ and also $\bar{v}_x = (v_{x0} + v_{x \text{ final}})/2$; these special relations for $\bar{v}_x$ hold only for constant acceleration.

Example. A car is moving at an initial velocity of 10 m/s, eastward, when the driver applies the brake in such a way as to bring the car to rest after 5 s. What is the car's average acceleration as it comes to rest? If the car's acceleration is *constant,* how far does the car move before it comes to rest?

The car's initial velocity is $v_{x0} = 10$ m/s and its final velocity v_{xf} after 5 s is zero. The average acceleration of the car is $\bar{a}_x = (v_{xf} - v_{x0})/\Delta t = (-10$ m/s, eastward$)/(5$ s$) = -2$ m/s^2, eastward. A negative acceleration of this kind that involves a slowing down is sometimes called a *deceleration.* If the acceleration is constant, the displacement Δx of the car as it comes to rest is

$$\Delta x = \int_0^t v_x dt = \int_0^t (v_{x0} + a_x t)dt = v_{x0}t + \tfrac{1}{2}a_x t^2,$$

as given by (3.13). Substituting $v_{x0} = 10$ m/s, eastward, and $a_x = -2$ m/s^2, eastward gives $\Delta x = (10$ m/s, eastward$)(5$ s$) + \tfrac{1}{2}(-2$ m/s^2, eastward$)(25$ s$^2) = (50{-}25)$ m, eastward $= 25$ m, eastward. We remember that for constant acceleration the average velocity $\bar{v}_x = (v_{x0} + v_{xf})/2 = (10$ m/s $+ 0$ m/s$)/2 = 5$ m/s. We can thus write $\Delta x = \bar{v}_x t = (5$ m/s$)(5$ s$) = 25$ m, eastward, as a check of our earlier result.

3.6   FREELY FALLING BODIES

As we all know, an object released above the earth's surface falls to the surface. According to Aristotle's physics, heavy bodies move downward more rapidly than light bodies. This view is borne out by casual observation; a coin or a marble falls more rapidly than a feather or a sheet of paper. In a series of famous experiments, Galileo Galilei (1564–1642), who can well be regarded as the first experimental physicist, concluded that in the absence of air resistance *all* falling bodies have the same kind of motion—a uniformly accelerated motion. His experiments involved observing the motion of marbles rolling down inclined planes; by using inclined planes Galileo was able to "dilute the downward motion" sufficiently to enable him to measure the distance moved as a function of time. According to legend, he also demonstrated the validity of his conclusions by dropping objects from the top of the leaning Tower of Pisa. Because his conclusions differed with the views of Aristotle, which had gained the sanction of the Church during the Middle Ages, Galileo was prosecuted for his views and eventually ended his life under house arrest. His defiance of officially authorized doctrines could not be tolerated in the political climate of the time.

Galileo was aware that large and small lead spheres dropped together will not strike the ground at *exactly* the same time; the slight difference in the times of arrival he attributed to the effects of air resistance. He maintained that the times of free fall would be the same if the experiment were performed in vacuum. As another Aristotelian tenet maintained that "nature abhors a vacuum," Galileo's argument carried little weight with the churchmen of the time, who regarded the creation of a vacuum as an impossibility.

Since Galileo's day his experiments on freely falling bodies have been repeatedly verified and his conclusions have been fully confirmed. Nowadays it is easy to produce a vacuum and to show that in the vacuum a light feather and a heavy coin do indeed have the same downward acceleration. Even in air a small dense object has approximately uniformly accelerated motion for the first few seconds of fall. After the downward velocity of a falling body in air becomes sufficiently large, the body no longer obeys the simple laws of freely falling bodies formulated by Galileo. In the present chapter we shall deal with free fall, which is approximated by objects like steel balls, lead shots, and golf balls; objects like ping pong balls, tennis balls, and feathers falling in air do not qualify as good approximations of freely falling objects.

Under conditions of free fall, all objects near the earth's surface have the same downward acceleration **g**, which is approximately 9.8 m/s², downward. Although the exact value of g varies slightly with latitude and with altitude above sea level, we shall for the present ignore these variations and regard the so-called gravitational acceleration of free fall as a constant with the nominal value

$$g = 9.8 \text{ m/s}^2.$$

By a variety of laboratory experiments a student can with care find a more exact value of g that is applicable to his own geographical location.

Example.   A steel ball is dropped from rest at the top of a tall building. Assuming that the ball falls freely, make a table showing the downward velocity and downward displacement of the ball at the end of each of the first 5 s of motion.

In this problem we shall use a coordinate system with its origin at the point at which the ball is released and regard downward displacements h as positive. We recognize that the initial velocity of the ball is zero because the ball falls from rest: $v_0 = 0$. Because of our choice of coordinate system the initial displacement of the ball is also zero: $h_0 = 0$. Because the falling ball has rectilinear motion with the constant acceleration $g = 9.8$ m/s², downward, we can make use of the arguments used in Section 3.5 in connection with (3.11) and (3.6) to write $v = gt$ and $h = gt^2/2$, which represent special cases of (3.12) and (3.13). From these two relations we can construct the table requested.

Time (s)	Downward Velocity v (m/s)	Downward Displacement h (m)
0	0	0
1	9.8	4.9
2	19.6	19.6
3	29.4	44.1
4	39.2	78.4
5	49.0	122.5

In Fig. 3.8 we show the positions and velocities of a freely falling body at the times indicated in the table.

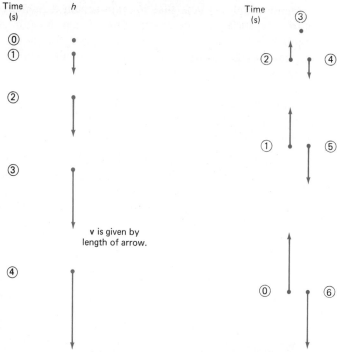

Fig. 3.8 Positions and velocities of a ball falling from rest.

Fig. 3.9 Positions and velocities of a ball thrown vertically upward.

Example. A baseball player throws a baseball directly upward. The initial upward velocity of the ball as it leaves his hand is 29.4 m/s. How long will the ball continue to rise? How high will the ball rise above its point of release? Make a table giving the position and velocity of the ball at one second intervals during its flight.

We choose a coordinate system with its origin at the point at which the player releases the ball and with positive displacements h measured upward. In this system, the initial velocity of the ball is $v_0 = 29.4$ m/s and the constant acceleration of the ball is $a = -g = -9.8$ m/s². On the basis of (3.11) we can write $v = v_0 - gt$ to obtain the upward velocity of the ball at any time t; on the basis of (3.6) we can write $h = v_0 t - \frac{1}{2}gt^2$. These relationships are special cases of (3.12) and (3.13). In order to obtain the time when the ball is at its maximum height, we ask for the time when v is instantaneously zero. This is given by $t_m = v_0/g = (29.4 \text{ m/s})/(9.8 \text{ m/s}^2) = 3.0$ s. The maximum height itself is then given by $h_m = (29.4 \text{ m/s})(3 \text{ s}) - \frac{1}{2}(9.8 \text{ m/s}^2)(3 \text{ s})^2 = 44.1$ m. The following table gives values of v and of h at one second intervals.

Time (s)	Upward Velocity v (m/s)	Upward Displacement h (m)
0	29.4	0
1	19.6	24.5
2	9.8	39.2
3	0	44.1
4	− 9.8	39.2
5	−19.6	24.5
6	−29.4	0

These values are shown schematically in Fig. 3.9. We note that the total time of rise is equal to the total time of descent; the reader should show algebraically that this must be true. Note that the positions of the ball at various time intervals *after* it reaches its highest point are the same as its positions at the same time intervals before it reaches the highest point. What can be said regarding the relationship between the *speed* of the ball and the height of the ball? What is the acceleration of the ball at the highest point in its trajectory?

3.7 PROJECTILES: FREE-FALL APPROXIMATION

When an object is *projected* horizontally, like a cannonball from the muzzle of a cannon, the object traverses a curved path or *trajectory* like the one shown in Fig. 3.10. In the absence of air resistance, the motion of the projectile can be regarded as the combination of a *horizontal motion with constant velocity* and a *vertical motion with constant downward acceleration g*. The vertical motion is in all respects similar to the motion of a body dropped from rest at the level of the muzzle of the cannon; in other words, it is simply the motion of free fall from rest. We have considered this motion in the first example in the preceding section. The horizontal motion of the projectile is the kind of motion that we considered in the first example of Section 3.5. If we use a coordinate system with its origin at the muzzle of the gun and the

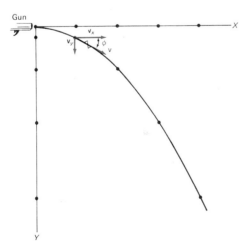

Fig. 3.10 The trajectory of a projectile fired horizontally.

$+Y$ axis directed vertically downward, as in Fig. 3.10, we can immediately give the position of the projectile t seconds after it has left the gun muzzle by stating its coordinates: $x = v_m t$ and $y = gt^2/2$, where v_m is the horizontal muzzle velocity of the projectile as it emerges from the muzzle of the cannon. These relations are based on the assumption that air resistance can be neglected; during the early stages of the motion they provide a good approximation of the actual position of the projectile provided the muzzle velocity is not too great. They provide a good description of the motion of a shell from a howitzer, a gun used to lob projectiles over limited horizontal ranges.

Example.   A howitzer is used to fire a shell horizontally with a muzzle velocity of 40 m/s from the top of a high cliff, as suggested in Fig. 3.10. Find the location of the shell at the end of its first 5 s of flight. Obtain an expression for the velocity of the shell as a function of time.

The X component of the shell's velocity is given by $v_x = dx/dt = v_m$ and is constant; the Y component of the shell's acceleration is $dv_y/dt = g$; the Y component of the shell's velocity is given by $v_y = dy/dt = gt$. (Note that $v_{y0} = 0$.) The shell's X coordinates are given by $x = v_m t$. At $t = 0$, $x = 0$; at $t = 1$ s, $x = 40$ m; at $t = 2$ s, $x = 80$ m; at $t = 3$ s, $x = 120$ m; at $t = 4$ s, $x = 160$ m; and at $t = 5$ s, $x = 200$ m. The shell's Y coordinates are given by $y = gt^2/2$; because the Y coordinates are those of any object in free fall, they are the same as those given for h in the table in the first example of Section 3.6. The magnitude of the shell's velocity is given by the expression $v = \sqrt{v_x^2 + v_y^2}$; the direction of the shell's velocity is given by the relation $\tan \phi = v_y/v_x$, where ϕ is the angle measured downward from the horizontal.

Now consider the free-fall approximation of the trajectory of a projectile fired at an elevation angle ϕ above the horizontal, as suggested in Fig. 3.11. In this case we have chosen the direction of the $+Y$ axis to be vertically upward. The horizontal component of the muzzle velocity $\mathbf{v}_m$ is $v_x = v_m \cos \phi$. The X component of projectile's motion is simply motion at constant velocity; the X coordinate of the particle is therefore given by $x = v_x t = (v_m \cos \phi)t$. The Y component of the projectile's motion

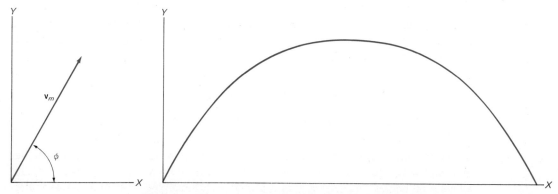

Fig. 3.11   The trajectory of a projectile near the earth's surface.

is like that of an object projected vertically upward with an initial velocity $v_{y0} = v_m \sin \phi$; we have considered motion of this type in the second example of Section 3.6.

Example.   A shell is fired with a muzzle velocity of 58.8 m/s from a howitzer aimed at an angle of 30° above the horizontal. Describe the trajectory of the shell by giving the X and Y components of its displacement from the muzzle of the howitzer as functions of time. What is the magnitude of the velocity of the shell at the highest point in its trajectory? What is the total horizontal range of the shell?

The X component of the shell's velocity is given by $v_x = v_m \cos \phi = (58.8 \text{ m/s}) \times (0.866) = 50.9$ m/s. Because in the absence of air resistance v_x is constant, we can determine the X component of the shell's displacement from the relation $x = v_x t$. Thus, at $t = 0$, $x = 0$; at $t = 1$ s, $x = 50.9$ m; at $t = 2$ s, $x = 102$ m; at $t = 3$ s, $x = 153$ m; at $t = 4$ s, $x = 204$ m; at $t = 5$ s, $x = 255$ m; at $t = 6$ s, $x = 306$ m; etc. The Y component of the shell's muzzle velocity is given by $v_m \sin \phi = (58.8 \text{ m/s})(0.5) = 29.4$ m/s; this is just the *initial* value v_{y0}. The value of v_y decreases as the shell progresses upward along its trajectory; at any time t we have $v_y = v_{y0} - gt = (29.4 \text{ m/s}) - (9.8 \text{ m/s}^2)t$, as we have seen from (3.11) and (3.12). As we have seen from (3.6) and (3.13), $y = v_{y0}t - \frac{1}{2}gt^2$; in the present case, $y = (29.4 \text{ m/s})t - \frac{1}{2}(9.8 \text{ m/s}^2)t^2$. We have already obtained both v_y and y for this situation in the second example of Section 3.6, where the values of the vertical velocity and heights $h = y$ have been tabulated. The shell is at the highest point in the trajectory when the vertical velocity is *zero*, which is at $t = 3$ s. Thus, the total velocity of the shell at the highest point in the trajectory is equal to the constant horizontal component of the shell's velocity; at the highest point, $\mathbf{v} = 50.9$ m/s, in a horizontal direction. To find the total horizontal range R of the shell, we note that the shell has returned to ground level, $y = 0$, at $t = 6$ s; at this time $x = 306$ m, which is the total range R.

In selecting data for use in the above examples, we have intentionally taken projectiles having low muzzle velocities so that we could more realistically neglect the effects of air resistance, which becomes increasingly important as muzzle velocities increase. The trajectory of a projectile computed on the basis of free fall represents a limiting case of real trajectories. The maximum height and the maximum horizontal range actually attained by a real projectile are both lower than those given by our simple treatment.

3.8   MOTION IN A CIRCULAR PATH

The motion of a particle in a circular path at constant speed, or "uniform circular motion," was regarded as the ideal motion by the Aristotelians. They believed that all celestial bodies—moon, stars, and planets—had this type of motion. We are interested at this point in examining the kinematical properties of this type of motion where the moving particle has an acceleration of constant magnitude without any change of speed, in contrast to rectilinear motion where the particle's acceleration involves a change in speed but no change in direction except for possible reversal of the sense of the motion.

In describing the motion of a particle in a circular path, we find it convenient to use polar coordinates of the type shown in Fig. 3.12. We recall that the position of a particle in such a frame can be specified by a statement of R, the radial distance of the particle from the origin O, and a statement of the angle ϕ. When a particle moves in a circular path, R is constant but ϕ changes; in fact, if the particle is moving at constant speed along the circular path, ϕ has a constant time rate of change. The velocity $\mathbf{v}$ of the particle at any time has a magnitude equal to the speed of the particle and a direction that is tangential to the circle; this direction is always perpendicular to the radius from the origin to the particle, along which R is measured, as indicated in the figure. As the particle moves along the path, the direction of $\mathbf{v}$ continually changes. Because of this change in the direction of $\mathbf{v}$, the particle has an acceleration.

In order to see how this occurs, consider the particle moving at a constant speed in the circular path in Fig. 3.13a. When the particle is at point ①, its velocity $\mathbf{v}_1$ is perpendicular to radius $\mathbf{R}_1$; at a later time t the particle is at point ② and its velocity $\mathbf{v}_2$ is perpendicular to radius $\mathbf{R}_2$. In Fig. 3.13b we show the triangle representing the change in the position of the particle during its movement from ① to ② during time interval Δt; $\mathbf{R}_1$ is the position vector of the particle when it is at ①, $\mathbf{R}_2$ is the position vector of the particle when it is at point ②, and $\Delta \mathbf{r} = \bar{\mathbf{v}} \Delta t$ is the displacement of the particle as it moves from ① to ②, where $\bar{\mathbf{v}}$ is the average velocity of the particle during the time interval Δt. Because $\mathbf{R}_1$ and $\mathbf{R}_2$ are of equal magnitude, the triangle in Fig. 3.13b is an isosceles triangle with small side $\bar{v}\Delta t$. In Fig. 3.13c we show a triangle representing the velocity change of the particle in the same time interval Δt; $\mathbf{v}_1$ is the velocity of the particle at point ①, $\mathbf{v}_2$ is the velocity of the particle at point ②, and $\Delta \mathbf{v} = \bar{\mathbf{a}} \Delta t$ is the change of the particle's velocity during time Δt, where $\bar{\mathbf{a}}$ is the average acceleration of the particle during this interval. Because $\mathbf{v}_1$ and $\mathbf{v}_2$ are equal in magnitude, the velocity triangle is an isosceles triangle with small side $\bar{a}\Delta t$.

Because the sides of the displacement triangle in Fig. 3.13b and the sides of the

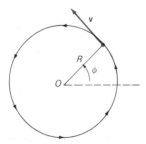

Fig. 3.12 The velocity of a body moving in a circular path at constant speed continually changes in direction.

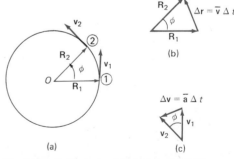

Fig. 3.13 Uniform circular motion: A particle moving in a circular path at constant speed has centripetal acceleration.

velocity triangle in Fig. 3.13c are mutually perpendicular, the two triangles are similar, and we can write

$$\frac{\bar{a}\Delta t}{v} = \frac{\bar{v}\Delta t}{R}.$$

In the limit $\Delta t \to 0$ we have $\bar{v} \to v$ and $\bar{a} \to a$; thus we have

$$a_C = v^2/R. \quad \textit{(Centripetal Acceleration)} \quad\quad\quad (3.15)$$

Here a_C is the magnitude of the instantaneous value of the particle's acceleration, which is directed radially inward toward the center of the circle, and v is the magnitude of the instantaneous velocity of the particle and equal to the speed of the particle in its circular path. Because $\mathbf{a}_C$ is directed toward the center of the circle, it is called the *centripetal* (center-seeking) acceleration of the particle.

Whenever a car moves around a curve at constant speed, it has an acceleration toward the "inside" of the curve that is equal to the centripetal acceleration given in (3.15); this situation is demonstrated in Fig. 3.14. A curving roadway has at any point a local radius of curvature R as indicated by the circles in the figure.

Example.   A car is moving at a speed of 30 m/s around a curve having a radius of curvature of 400 m. What is the centripetal acceleration of the car?

As indicated by (3.15) as applied to Fig. 3.14, the centripetal acceleration is $a_C = v^2/R = (900 \text{ m}^2/\text{s}^2)/(400 \text{ m}) = 2.25 \text{ m/s}^2$.

In the case of a particle moving at nonconstant speed in a circular path, the particle has, in addition to the centripetal acceleration a_C, a tangential component of acceleration $a_T = dv_T/dt$, where v_T is the *magnitude* of the particle's velocity; in other words, the magnitude of a_T is equal to the time rate of change of the particle's speed. A way to prove this assertion, based on an extension of the reasoning illustrated in Fig. 3.13, is suggested in one of the problems at the end of the chapter. This situation is indicated by Fig. 3.15, which shows $a_C = v_T^2/R$ directed toward the center of the

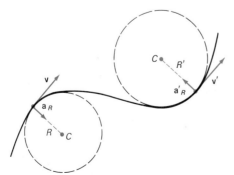

Fig. 3.14 Acceleration of a body moving at constant speed along a curved path.

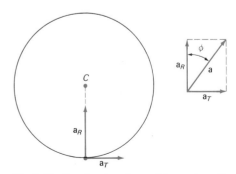

Fig. 3.15 Acceleration of a particle moving with changing speed in a circular path.

circle and $a_T = dv_T/dt$ tangential to the circle. As indicated in the figure, the resultant instantaneous acceleration **a** of the particle has a magnitude $a = \sqrt{a_C^2 + a_T^2}$ and has a direction at angle ϕ with respect to the radius, where $\tan \phi = a_T/a_C$.

QUESTIONS

1. Why are there not *exactly* 365 days in one year?

2. Following the French revolution, clocks were constructed with 10 "decimal hours" instead of the 12 hours in use today; each decimal hour was divided into 100 decimal minutes. Why isn't such decimal time a part of the metric system of units? What is the length of your class period in "decimal minutes"?

3. How could you explain the meaning of the term *clockwise* to another person on earth without any use of diagrams or gestures? Would the same explanation be valid for a person on another planet?

4. Discuss various methods that might be used to measure path length along an arbitrarily curved path. A practical device for use in such a measurement is called an *odometer;* explain in detail how an odometer might be constructed by use of a wheel of known diameter along with a revolution counter.

5. Can the magnitude of a car's instantaneous velocity ever be greater than the car's instantaneous speed? If not, explain why not; if so, give an example of such a situation.

6. In the course of a trip from one city to another, is a motorist's average speed equal to the magnitude of the average velocity? If the speed is constant, is the average speed equal to the magnitude of the instantaneous velocity?

7. If the speed of a car is constant, can the car have *acceleration*? If the velocity of a car is constant, can the car have *acceleration*?

8. In the rectilinear motion of a particle, the average velocity can sometimes be set equal to $\frac{1}{2}$ ($v_{\text{final}} + v_{\text{initial}}$). Explain in detail the conditions for which this relation is valid.

9. Can a particle have an eastward velocity and a westward acceleration at the same time? Can a particle with zero instantaneous velocity have acceleration?

10. Under what circumstances might the use of the term deceleration be justified? Is this terminology *necessary* for a complete description of motion?

11. A person throws one ball vertically upward and a second ball vertically downward with equal initial speeds. Over the times required for the balls to reach the ground, which ball has the greater average velocity? Which ball has the greater final velocity? Which ball has the greater final acceleration? In the course of the motion, is the instantaneous acceleration of either ball ever equal to zero?

12. In the absence of air resistance, the horizontal component of a bullet's velocity is constant. Does the bullet have acceleration?

13. Is it possible for an automobile to have both constant speed and an acceleration of constant nonzero magnitude? If so, what can you say about the path being traversed by the automobile?

14. A passenger in a railway car traveling at constant velocity tosses a ball vertically upward. Can the passenger catch the ball without movement of the hands? Is the situation different if the train is accelerating? Describe the path of the ball in each case from the point of view of an observer standing on the ground beside the tracks.

PROBLEMS

Problems or parts of problems marked with an asterisk * require the use of calculus for their solution.

1. A motorist travels due eastward at a speed of 60 km/h for 3 hours and then due northward at a speed of 80 km/h for 2 hours. What is the average speed for this journey? What is the average velocity for the journey?

2. City B is 120 km west of city A. In traveling from A to B a motorist takes 3 hours, but it takes only 2 hours to make the return trip from B to A. What is the motorist's average velocity during the trip from A to B? What is the average velocity during the return trip from B to A? What is the average speed for the round trip? What is the average velocity for the complete round trip?

3. A ship travels due eastward for 4 hours at a speed of 30 km/h and then due northeastward for 6 hours at a speed of 20 km/h. What is the ship's final displacement from its starting point? What is the ship's average velocity for the trip? What is the ship's average speed for the trip?

4. A ship sails 30 km, eastward, in 3 hours and then sails 40 km, northward, in 2 hours. What is the ship's average velocity for the trip? What is the ship's average speed for the trip?

5. The speedometers on American cars give readings in miles per hour. Using the tables of conversion units for length and time given in the Appendix, express 60 mi/h in km/h and in m/s.

6. European speedometers give readings in km/h. When a European speedometer registers 60 km/h, what is the car's speed in mi/h? in m/s?

7. A particle moving in the XY plane moves with a constant velocity of 2 m/s along a line that makes an angle of 30° with the X axis. What are the scalar components of the particle's velocity? Express the particle's velocity in terms of the unit vectors **i** and **j** and in terms of a unit vector $\hat{v}$ in the direction of the particle's velocity; express $\hat{v}$ in terms of **i** and **j**.

8. If the particle in Problem 7 is at the origin of the coordinate system at time $t = 0$, write expressions for the particle's coordinates x and y as functions of time. Express the particle's position in terms of a position vector **r**. Express the unit vector $\hat{r}$ in terms of **i** and **j**.

9. Consider a boat moving at velocity $\mathbf{v}_{BW}$ relative to the water in a river, in which the water has a velocity $\mathbf{v}_{WE}$ relative to the earth. The velocity of the boat relative to the earth is given by $\mathbf{v}_{BE}$. What is the magnitude of $\mathbf{v}_{BE}$ if the boat heads directly upstream? What is the magnitude of $\mathbf{v}_{BE}$ if the boat travels directly downstream? For a case with $v_{BW} > v_{WE}$ in which the velocity $\mathbf{v}_{BE}$ is perpendicular to $\mathbf{v}_{WE}$, show that $v_{BE} = \sqrt{v_{BW}^2 - v_{WE}^2}$.

10. A boat travels at speed v_{BW} relative to the water in a river of width d, in which the water is moving at speed v_{WE} relative to the earth. On the assumption that $v_{BW} > v_{WE}$, show that the time t_1 required to cross the river to a point exactly opposite the starting point and then to return to the starting point is

$$t_1 = \frac{2d}{\sqrt{v_{BW}^2 - v_{WE}^2}} = \frac{2d/v_{BW}}{\sqrt{1 - v_{WE}^2/v_{BW}^2}},$$

and that the time t_2 for the boat to travel a distance d directly upstream and then to return to its starting point is

$$t_2 = \frac{2d/v_{BW}}{1 - v_{WE}^2/v_{BW}^2}.$$

Compare these two times with the time $t_0 = 2d/v_{BW}$ required to traverse the distance $2d$ in still water for the cases: $v_{WE}/v_{BW} = 0.1, 0.5,$ and 0.9. (In Chapter 37, we describe a famous experiment first performed by Michelson in 1881 and repeated with greater precision by Michelson and Morley in 1887; they found that the times required for *light* to travel round trips of length $2d$ parallel and perpendicular to the earth's orbital velocity were exactly the same, in contrast to what one would expect from reasoning like that used for this problem if light moved relative to "space" like a boat relative to water. Note that because of its orbital motion the earth is moving through "space"; from the point of view of the earth observer "space" is flowing past like a river moving relative to its banks. The Michelson–Morley experiment showed that this point of view is not correct for describing the motion of light. A point of view about light propagation that is in agreement with experiment is provided by Einstein's theory of relativity.)

11. Consider a river 4 km wide in which the water has a velocity of 3 km/h, eastward. A man wishes to cross directly from the south bank to the north bank in a boat that has a speed of 5 km/h in still water. At what angle upstream should he head the boat? What is the resulting speed of the boat relative to the earth? How long is required to reach the north bank of the river?

12. An airplane has an air speed of 400 km/h. The pilot wishes to fly due northwest on a day when the wind is blowing from due west with a wind speed of 100 km/h relative to the ground. In what direction should the pilot head the plane? What will be the speed of the plane relative to the ground?

13. A car starting from rest attains a velocity of 16 m/s, eastward, in 8 s; at the end of the eighth second the driver applies the brakes and brings the car to rest in 4 s. What is the average acceleration of the car during the first 8 s of motion? What is the average acceleration of the car during the final 4 s of motion?

14. A car starting from rest and moving eastward along a straight street attains a speed of 36 km/h in 10 s. What is the final speed of the car in m/s? What is the average acceleration of the car?

15. A car initially at rest has a constant acceleration of 2 m/s², eastward. At the end of 10 s: (1) What is the velocity of the car? (2) What is the total displacement of the car from its starting point? (3) What is the average velocity of the car during its first 10 s of motion?

16. A particle initially at rest at the origin of a Cartesian coordinate system moves with a constant acceleration of 1 m/s² in a direction making an angle of 30° with the X axis. What are the scalar components a_x and a_y of the particle's acceleration $\mathbf{a}$? Construct a table giving the values of the scalar components v_x and v_y of the particle's velocity $\mathbf{v}$ and the coordinates x and y of the particle at the end of each second during the first 10 s of motion. At the end of the tenth second, what is the position vector $\mathbf{r}$ of the particle and what is the velocity $\mathbf{v}$ of the particle? (Express these vectors in terms of $\mathbf{i}$ and $\mathbf{j}$.)

17. A steel ball is dropped from rest by a man who extends his arm over the side of a building 160 m high. What is the downward velocity of the ball at the end of the first, second, and third seconds of motion? What is the downward displacement of the ball from its starting point at these times? How long is required for the ball to reach the sidewalk outside the building? What is the average velocity of the ball during its down-

ward motion to the sidewalk? What is the corresponding average acceleration?

18. Answer all questions in Problem 17 for a case in which the man throws the ball directly downward with an initial speed of 8 m/s.

19. A large cannon fires a cannonball horizontally eastward from the top of a high cliff. The muzzle velocity of the cannonball is 100 m/s. Give the horizontal and vertical components of the cannonball's displacement at the end of each of the first 5 seconds of motion.

20. What is the velocity of the cannonball in Problem 19 at the end of 3 seconds? at the end of 10 seconds?

21. A ball is thrown vertically upward with an initial speed of 30 m/s. How long does the ball continue to rise? What is the ball's maximum height above its point of release? What is the velocity of the ball at the highest point in its trajectory? What is the ball's acceleration at this point?

22. A gun at ground level fires a shell eastward in a direction 30° above the horizontal; the muzzle velocity of the shell is 296 m/s. What are the horizontal and vertical components of the shell's initial velocity? How long will the shell continue to rise? What is the maximum height attained by the shell? What is the horizontal range of the shell?

23. A car moving at a constant speed of 30 m/s goes around a curve in a roadway. If the radius of curvature of the roadway is 200 m, what is the magnitude of the car's acceleration?

24. A car is moving around a circular racetrack with a radius of 300 m. At an instant when the speed of the car is 30 m/s and is increasing at the rate of 2 m/s², what are the centripetal and tangential components of the car's acceleration? What are the magnitude

and direction of the car's resultant acceleration?

25. Returning to our approximation of the earth as a sphere with a radius of 6400 km, consider the rotational motion of the earth in a coordinate system with the X axis along the line connecting the earth to the sun. With respect to such a system the earth makes one complete rotation every 24 hours. Find the speed of a particle located on the equator, at 30° N latitude, at 60° N latitude, and at the north pole.

26. Find the magnitudes of the accelerations of the particles mentioned in the preceding problem. What is the direction of their accelerations?

27. In what directions and at what ground speeds should a pilot fly his airplane in order to maintain local noon throughout his flight at latitudes 0°, 30° N, and 60° N?

28. An artillery piece at ground level fires a shell with muzzle velocity v_0 at an angle θ above the horizontal. In terms of v_0, θ, and g derive an expression for the horizontal range R, where R represents the horizontal displacement of the shell when it returns to ground level. Prove that R is a maximum for $t = 45°$. Show that the range R is the same for θ and for $90° - \theta$.

29. The water in a river 2 km wide flows due eastward at a speed of 10 km/h. A boat can travel at 6 km/h in still water. A man who can walk at a speed of 4 km/h starts from a point O on the south side of the river and wishes to reach a point P directly opposite on the north bank of the river. Because the speed of his boat is less than the speed of the water in the river, he cannot land at point P but must land downstream and walk back to P along the north bank. Find his time of crossing, his time of walking, and his total travel time from O to P (a) if he heads the boat due northward to minimize the time of crossing and (b) if

he heads his boat directly northwestward ($\theta = 45°$). (c) *In what direction θ should he head his boat in order to minimize his total travel time from O to P? In this case find his time of crossing, his walking time, and his total time of travel.

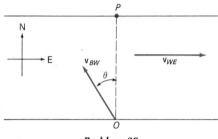

Problem 29

30. Show algebraically that, for an object thrown vertically upward with an initial velocity v_0, the time of rise is equal to the time of descent in the absence of air resistance.

31. An artillery piece at ground level fires shells with a muzzle velocity of 980 m/s at an angle of 30° above the horizontal. What is the maximum height attained by the shell? What is the horizontal range attained? What is the acceleration of the shell at the highest point in its trajectory? Ignore air resistance; assume that the ground is level over the range of the shell.

32. Solve Problem 31 for cases in which the artillery piece is aimed in directions of 45° above the horizontal and 60° above the horizontal.

Problems 33–39. By analyzing motion pictures of a particle moving along the X axis of a coordinate system, an observer finds that during the 6 s of the motion between $t = 0$ s and $t = 6$ s the position x of the particle can be expressed as

$$x = 3 + 2t + 3t^2 - 0.5t^3,$$

where x is in m and t in s.

33. What is the average velocity of the particle in the X direction during the first 3 s of

motion? During the first 6 s of motion? Make a plot showing x as a function of time t.

34. What is the average velocity of the particle during the first second of motion? During the sixth second of motion?

*35. What is the instantaneous velocity v_{x0} of the particle at time $t = 0$? What is the instantaneous velocity v_x of the particle at the end of each of the first six seconds of motion?

*36. Derive a general expression giving velocity v_x as a function of time. Make a plot of v_x as a function of time t.

*37. What is the initial acceleration a_{x0} of the particle? What is the instantaneous acceleration a_x of the particle at the end of each of the first 6 s of motion?

*38. Derive a general expression giving acceleration a_x as a function of time. Make a plot of a_x as a function of time t.

*39. At what time t during the interval when the equation for x holds is the velocity v_x of the particle zero? Is its acceleration a_x zero at this time, when the particle is momentarily at rest? Discuss.

Problems 40–45. The position of a particle moving in the XY-plane of a coordinate system is given by the expressions:

$$x = 4t + 2t^2 - 0.2t^3$$
$$y = 2t + 4t^2 - 0.5t^3,$$

where x and y are in m and t is in s. These expressions are valid for the 4 s of motion between $t = 0$ s and $t = 4$ s.

40. What is the initial position of the particle? What is the magnitude of the particle's average velocity $\bar{v}$ during the 4 s of motion? Express this average velocity $\bar{v}$ of the particle in terms of the unit vectors $\mathbf{i}$ and $\mathbf{j}$.

41. Make plots of x as a function of t and y as a function of t. On the basis of these

plots make an estimate of the particle's instantaneous velocity **v** at the end of the third second of motion. Express your estimated value of **v** in terms of the unit vectors **i** and **j**.

*42. Obtain an expression for the components v_x and v_y of the particle's velocity as a function of time.

*43. What is the magnitude of the particle's velocity **v** at the end of the third second? Express the instantaneous velocity **v** in terms of **i** and **j**.

*44. What is the instantaneous acceleration of the particle at the end of the third second of motion? Express your answer in terms of the unit vectors **i** and **j**.

*45. What is the average acceleration **ā** of the particle during the first four seconds of motion?

Problems 46–48. The coordinates of a particle during the time interval from $t = 0$ s to $t = 4$ s are given by the following expressions with x, y, and z in m and t in s:

$$x = 2 + 6t - 2t^2 + 0.2t^3,$$
$$y = 3 + 4t + 3t^2 - 0.3t^3,$$
$$z = 1 + 4t + 4t^2 - 0.4t^3.$$

46. What is the average velocity **v̄** of the particle during the first four seconds of motion? Express your result in terms of **i**, **j**, and **k**.

*47. What is the velocity **v** of the particle as a function of time t?

*48. What is the acceleration **a** of the particle as a function of time t?

*49. Using your knowledge of the meaning of "average" for discrete quantities like test scores or points scored per game in athletic contests, discuss why (3.2) is a sensible way to define the average value of a quantity $s(t)$ that can very continuously with the time t. Imagine the time span from t_1 to t_2 to be divided into a large number of intervals of width δt. Let $s(t_i)$ be a representative value of the quantity s for the ith interval. Consider the ordinary average of these representative values in the limit where δt becomes arbitrarily small.

*50. Consider (3.2′) for a particle following a curved path such that at time t_2 it has returned to the location it occupied at time t_1. If we set $L_2 = L_1$ in (3.2′), we obtain $\bar{s} = 0$. However, throughout the motion the speed of the particle is non-negative, which is not consistent with an average speed $\bar{s}$ of zero. What is the flaw in the reasoning leading to $\bar{s} = 0$?

*51. Consider two coordinate systems A and B in two dimensions. Assume that the axes X_A and X_B and the axes Y_A and Y_B of the two systems are parallel and remain parallel. Suppose that the origin of system B has coordinates $x_{BA}(t)$ and $y_{BA}(t)$ relative to system A, where we assume that these coordinates can depend on the time t. A certain particle P is observed to have coordinates $x_{PA}(t)$ and $y_{PA}(t)$ relative to system A and coordinates $x_{PB}(t)$ and $y_{PB}(t)$ relative to system B. Show that $x_{PA} = x_{PB} + x_{BA}$ and $y_{PA} = y_{PB} + y_{BA}$. Using these results, show that $\mathbf{v}_{PA} = \mathbf{v}_{PB} + \mathbf{v}_{BA}$, where $\mathbf{v}_{PA}$ is the velocity of the particle relative to system A, $\mathbf{v}_{PB}$ is the velocity of the particle relative to system B, and $\mathbf{v}_{BA}$ is the velocity of the origin of system B relative to system A.

*52. The particle shown in Fig. 3.12 moves around the circumference of the circle of radius R with constant speed v. How does the angle ϕ change with time? Show that $d\phi/dt$ is equal to a constant; express that constant in terms of R and v.

*53. Consider a particle moving around a circular path of radius R with non-constant speed. In this case the velocity vectors $\mathbf{v}_1$ and $\mathbf{v}_2$ shown in Fig. 3.13 have different magnitudes. Let the magnitude of $\mathbf{v}_1$ be v and that of $\mathbf{v}_2$ be $v + \Delta v$. Replace Fig. 3.13c by the diagram shown for this problem. Resolve $\Delta \mathbf{v} = \bar{\mathbf{a}} \Delta t$ into components $\Delta \mathbf{v} =$

$\Delta \mathbf{v}_C + \Delta \mathbf{v}_T$, where $\Delta \mathbf{v}_C = \bar{\mathbf{a}}_C \Delta t$ is the chord of an arc of radius v as indicated in the diagram and $\Delta \mathbf{v}_T = \bar{\mathbf{a}}_T \Delta t$ is parallel to $\mathbf{v}_2$ and has magnitude Δv. Figure 3.13b remains valid as drawn. By an argument involving similar triangles analogous to the argument given in the text for the case of constant particle speed show that $a_C = v^2/R$, where a_C is the magnitude of the component of the instantaneous acceleration that is directed toward the center of the circle. Also show that $a_T = dv/dt$, where a_T is the magnitude of the component of

the instantaneous acceleration that is directed tangent to the circle.

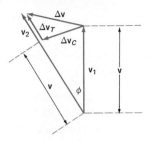

Problem 53

CHAPTER 4

Newton's Principles of Motion

Having learned something of kinematics, we are now ready to tackle the subject of *dynamics: The influence of forces on motion.* In this chapter we present Newton's Principles of Motion, a set of generalizations developed by Isaac Newton (1642–1727) while he was still in his twenties. These principles form the basis not only of *classical dynamics,* but of classical physics in general. Although they involve certain definitions and can in a sense be regarded as axioms, Newton asserted that they are based on quantitative observation and experiment; certainly they cannot be derived from other more basic relationships. The test of their validity involves predictions, arrived at by logical, mathematical derivations of other relationships from the principles themselves; these predictions can be tested by actual experiments. The validity of such predictions was verified in every case for more than two centuries. During the 20th century, it has been discovered that phenomena involving very small particles like electrons, atoms, and molecules must be treated by *quantum* methods and that motions of particles moving at speeds comparable with the speed of light must be treated by *relativistic* methods. However, Newton's principles still provide the basis for most of the "everyday," "practical" problems encountered by the physicist and engineer; when quantum and relativistic mechanics are applied to problems involving things like bullets, baseballs, automobiles, aircraft, and rockets, they reduce to the classical mechanics directly based on Newton's principles. Newton's principles thus continue to form the basis of much present-day physics and engineering and will continue to do so. A clear understanding of classical mechanics is necessary for a proper appreciation of quantum physics and relativistic physics, which we shall treat briefly in later chapters of this book.

Although even primitive man, as a result of the muscular exertion involved in pushing and pulling bodies about, probably developed some ideas regarding force, the influence of force on motion was never clearly understood until Newton's time. In order to understand and to appreciate Newton's revolutionary contributions, we must first review briefly Aristotle's ideas regarding the relationships between force and motion and must recall that Aristotle's views had met with general acceptance for more than 1000 years. Aristotle carefully distinguished two types of motion: "natural motion" and "forced motion." The natural state of any object was regarded as a state of rest at the proper position of the body. Because all terrestrial matter was supposed to consist of the elements earth, water, air, and fire, in order of decreasing "heaviness," the proper place of the heaviest bodies, those containing the most earth, was lowest in the scheme of things. Forced motions resulted when some human agent disturbed the natural state of affairs by exerting forces on various objects. Thus, by exerting an upward force a man could raise a stone above the surface of the ground by forced motion; as soon as he ceased to exert the upward force, the stone would *of its own accord* return to its proper position by natural motion and then come to rest. According to this scheme, a body could be kept in motion only by applying a force; a man could push a cart at constant speed in forced motion along a horizontal roadway by exerting a horizontal force but, as soon as he ceased applying the force, the cart would come to rest as a result of natural motion. In certain cases, such as those of projectiles, the Aristotelians had to invoke the concept of "mixed motion," which represented a combination of forced motion and natural motion.

The Aristotelian theories should not be regarded as trivial; they gave a satisfactory account of terrestrial mechanics based on qualitative observation. The only predictions that could be based on them were qualitative predictions. However, as soon as Galileo began making quantitative measurements of position as a function of time, it was obvious that some better theory was necessary if quantitative predictions were to be made. Galileo made careful observations of marbles of different sizes moving along inclined planes; he noted that the marbles were accelerated in rolling down an inclined plane, were decelerated in moving up an inclined plane, and moved with nearly constant velocity along a horizontal plane. He proposed what is called the law of inertia: *The natural state of an isolated particle is one of constant velocity.* By an *isolated* particle, Galileo meant a particle not interacting in any way with other bodies. The acceleration and deceleration of marbles moving along inclined planes he attributed to gravitational forces exerted on the marbles by the earth. To the extent that marbles moving along a horizontal plane do not interact with the plane itself, the marbles have constant velocities. Of course, a marble rolling along a horizontal surface does eventually come to rest; the resulting small deceleration Galileo attributed to small interactions between the marble and the horizontal surface itself. Galileo's conclusions embodied in his law of inertia thus involve not only careful quantitative observations but also an idealization of his results. A particle such as the marble *would* have constant velocity if there were no interactions between it and the rest of the universe.

4.1   MASS

In order to begin our discussion of Newton's principles, we need to introduce a third fundamental physical quantity called *mass*. Because mass is a fundamental quantity, we cannot define it in terms of simpler physical quantities but must describe a set of operations that can be used to measure masses in terms of some arbitrary standard mass. It will, however, be desirable for us to discuss some of the properties of mass.

One property of mass is that it is in some way related to "quantity of matter." Thus, Newton quite properly maintained that the mass of a body composed of a given material was directly proportional to the volume of the body; for example, two cubic meters of water have twice the mass of one cubic meter of water. Similarly, two cubic meters of gold have twice the mass of one cubic meter of gold. However, one cubic meter of gold has a much larger mass than one cubic meter of water. The mass of a body thus depends not only on the volume of the body but also on the chemical composition of the body. In terms of atoms we can say that the mass of a body composed of a given element is proportional to the number of atoms of the element in the body or, in other words, to the number of moles of material in the body. Although these statements are true, they do not provide a method of *defining* mass or even of selecting a standard of mass.

A logical resolution of these difficulties was proposed by Ernst Mach (1838–1916) nearly two centuries after Newton's formulation of his principles. In mechanics the mass of a body is a direct measure of the *inertia* of the body, where inertia is the tendency of the body to remain in motion if it is initially moving or the tendency of the body to remain at rest if it is initially at rest. Mach pointed out that whenever two particles interact *only with each other* in any way, they experience oppositely directed accelerations. For example, in Fig. 4.1 we show two "particles" on a horizontal "air track," which gives a nearly frictionless surface, so the particles interact essentially only with one another so far as their horizontal motion is concerned. The particles are connected by means of a light coil spring. By observing the motion of the particles we find that at any time the acceleration $\mathbf{a}_1$ of the first particle is opposite in direction to the acceleration $\mathbf{a}_2$ of the second particle; if the spring is stretched, as in Fig. 4.1a, the particles tend to be accelerated toward each other; if the spring is compressed, as in Fig. 4.1b, the particles tend to be accelerated away from each other. In either case, we find experimentally that for a given pair of particles the ratio $|a_1/a_2|$ is a constant.

This experimental result provides a basis for comparing masses. Suppose that in Fig. 4.2 we replace particle ② by some "particle" or body to which we arbitrarily assign the standard mass M_S. We can then determine the mass m_1 of particle ① in terms of a *defining relation:*

$$m_1 = |a_S/a_1| M_S. \tag{4.1}$$

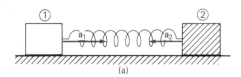

(a)

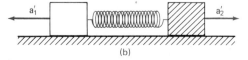

(b)

Fig. 4.1 The accelerations are always opposite in direction. The ratio of their magnitudes is a constant for a given pair of bodies.

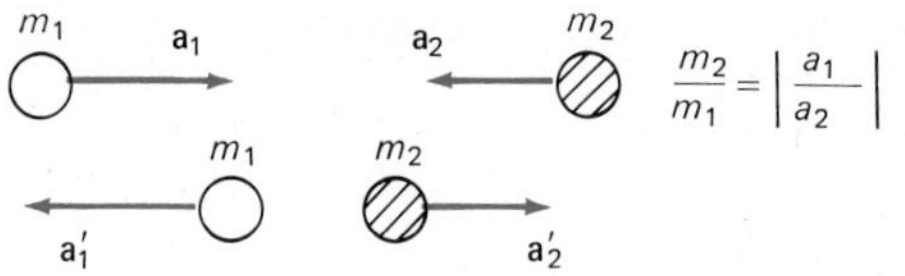

Fig. 4.2   Relation between masses and accelerations in an interaction.

The ratio $|a_S/a_1|$ can be determined experimentally in terms of length and time. Similarly, if we replace particle ① in Fig. 4.2 by our standard particle with mass M_S, we can determine the mass m_2 of particle ② by experimental measurement of $|a_S/a_2|$ and the defining relation

$$m_2 = |a_S/a_2|M_S. \tag{4.1'}$$

In a similar way we can determine the masses of other particles or bodies by letting them interact with our standard particle.

Having determined m_1 and m_2 in terms of M_S, we can now let particles ① and ② interact as shown in Fig. 4.2. Experiment shows that

$$m_1\mathbf{a}_1 = -m_2\mathbf{a}_2. \tag{4.2}$$

In terms of the magnitudes of the accelerations, we can write

$$m_1|\mathbf{a}_1| = m_2|\mathbf{a}_2| \quad \text{or} \quad m_1/m_2 = |a_2/a_1|. \tag{4.3}$$

Thus, in any interaction between two particles, the ratio of the masses of the particles is inversely proportional to the ratio of the magnitudes of the accelerations of the particles.

Although we have drawn a spring connecting the objects in Fig. 4.1, the precise nature of the interaction between the bodies is unimportant. The bodies could actually collide, and the mass ratios given in (4.2) and (4.3) would be the same. The interactions between the pairs of particles could be gravitational, electric, magnetic, or any other kind; the results given in (4.1), (4.2), and (4.3) would be the same, as suggested in Fig. 4.2. The measure of m_1 and m_2 in terms of M_S would remain valid and would be a measure of the *inertial* properties of the interacting particles.

In addition to being characterized in terms of its inertia, the mass of an object can be characterized in terms of certain *gravitational* properties, which we shall discuss in some detail in Chapter 9. The mass of a body as measured in terms of gravitational properties is identical with the mass of the same body measured in terms of its inertial properties, so far as can be determined from careful experiment.

The standard mass M_S employed in the International System of units, called the *kilogram,* is the mass of a platinum–iridium cylinder that is carefully preserved at the SI laboratory at Sèvres, near Paris. The secondary standard kilograms employed in various countries throughout the world must be compared periodically with the international standard at Sèvres. The comparisons actually involve careful weighing procedures that we shall describe later.

The technical problems involved in accurately preparing sets of masses that represent decimal multiples and submultiples of the kilogram were at first formidable, but have been solved satisfactorily. It is now possible for every well-equipped laboratory to possess a set of standard masses. Because a set of standard masses is frequently used in weighing procedures, it is sometimes called a set of "standard weights," which is something of a misnomer.

4.2 NEWTON'S FIRST PRINCIPLE

Newton's First Principle is essentially a reaffirmation of Galileo's law of inertia; we shall state it as follows:

NEWTON'S FIRST PRINCIPLE: A particle not acted on by forces moves with constant velocity.

A frame of reference in which this principle holds is called an *inertial frame of reference.* We recall that in discussing Galileo's law of inertia we spoke of an *isolated particle,* by which we meant a particle not interacting with other particles or bodies. Our statement of the First Principle thus implies that *interactions involve forces* and that forces are related in some way to *changes in velocity.* We note that in order for a particle to experience a change in velocity with respect to an inertial frame of reference, a force must act on the particle; the *force must be exerted on the particle by other particles or bodies.* A particle cannot change its own state of motion, as has been maintained by the Aristotelians in their considerations of "natural motion." If by natural motion we mean the motion of a particle or body not acted on by forces outside itself, we conclude that the natural state of a particle is one of constant velocity. If a particle is initially at rest in an inertial frame of reference with $v = 0$, it will remain at rest unless some force acts on it; if a particle is initially in motion with $v \neq 0$, its velocity will remain constant unless some force acts on it.

Because no particle in the universe is truly isolated, the First Principle is an idealization. It identifies forces from the outside as being responsible for changes in a particle's velocity relative to an inertial frame of reference. In addition, at the time of its enunciation the First Principle was important in affirming that Galileo had been right about motion and that, in spite of widespread general acceptance of his views, Aristotle had been wrong!

4.3 NEWTON'S SECOND PRINCIPLE

The Second Principle establishes precisely what we mean by a "force" acting on a particle; as we shall state it, the Second Principle also implies that forces are vector quantities.

NEWTON'S SECOND PRINCIPLE: The resultant force acting on a particle is directly proportional to the acceleration of the particle relative to an inertial frame of reference and to the mass of the particle.

This is shown pictorially in Fig. 4.3. If a net or resultant force $\mathbf{F}_R$ as in Fig. 4.3a

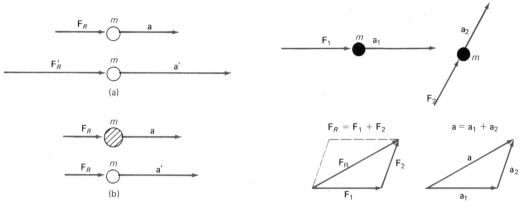

Fig. 4.3   Newton's Second Principle: $\mathbf{F}_R = m\mathbf{a}$.   **Fig. 4.4**   Forces are vector quantities.

acts on a particle, the acceleration **a** of the particle relative to an inertial frame of reference always has the same direction as the direction of the resultant force; if we increase the magnitude of the resultant force acting on the particle, the magnitude of the particle's acceleration increases in direct proportion. If as in Fig. 4.3b resultant forces of equal magnitude act on particles of mass m and mass M, where $m < M$, the magnitude of the acceleration of the particle with smaller mass will be the greater; in either case, the direction of the acceleration is the same as that of the resultant force.

We can summarize our statement of the Second Principle by the vector equation

$$\mathbf{F}_R \propto m\mathbf{a} \quad \text{or} \quad \mathbf{F}_R = km\mathbf{a}, \quad \textit{(Newton's Second Principle)} \qquad (4.4)$$

where k is a proportionality constant. This equation represents the actual definition of force. Because we have not yet selected the SI unit to be used in measuring force, we are at liberty to select a force unit that will make the proportionality constant $k = 1$ and write

$$\mathbf{F}_R = m\mathbf{a}. \quad \left\{ \begin{array}{l} \mathbf{F}_R \text{ in N} \\ m \text{ in kg} \\ a \text{ in m/s}^2 \end{array} \right\} \quad \textit{(Newton's Second Principle)} \qquad (4.5)$$

The resultant force $\mathbf{F}_R$ is measured in a unit called the newton (N). We note that 1 N is the magnitude of the resultant force acting on a particle with a mass of 1 kg when the particle has an acceleration with a magnitude of 1 m/s²; thus,

$$1 \text{ N} = 1 \text{ kg} \cdot \text{m/s}^2.$$

Example.   If a 2-kg particle has an acceleration of 3 m/s², eastward, what resultant force acts on the particle? If the magnitude of the resultant force was doubled, what would be the particle's acceleration?

From (4.5), we find $\mathbf{F}_R = m\mathbf{a} = (2 \text{ kg})(3 \text{ m/s}^2, \text{ eastward}) = 6 \text{ N}$, eastward. Doubling the magnitude of $\mathbf{F}_R$ gives a resultant force of 12 N, eastward; in this case (4.5) leads to an acceleration $\mathbf{a} = 12 \text{ N}/2 \text{ kg}$, eastward $= 6 \text{ m/s}^2$, eastward.

Our statement of Newton's Second Principle in terms of the resultant force implies that *force is a vector quantity.* This is indeed the case, as suggested in Fig. 4.4. Consider two forces F_1 and F_2 acting on a particle of mass m. If force F_1 alone acted on the particle, the particle would have acceleration a_1 given by $F_1 = ma_1$; if force F_2 alone acted on the particle, the particle would have acceleration a_2 given by $F_2 = ma_2$. If the two forces F_1 and F_2 act simultaneously, their resultant is $F_R = F_1 + F_2$; on the basis of Newton's Second Principle (4.5) the particle's resultant acceleration a is then given by $F_R = ma$. If forces are vectors, writing F_R as

$$F_R = F_1 + F_2$$

implies that

$$ma = ma_1 + ma_2 \quad \text{or} \quad a = a_1 + a_2.$$

The resultant acceleration a produced by F_R should be the vector sum of a_1 and a_2, the accelerations that forces F_1 and F_2 would produce if each acted alone. On the basis of experiment, this is found to be the case. We are therefore justified in treating forces as vectors. The value of F_R in (4.5) is indeed the resultant $F_1 + F_2 + F_3 + \cdots$ of *all* the forces acting on the particle; the value of a in (4.5) is equal to the vector sum $a_1 + a_2 + a_3 + \cdots$ of the accelerations that each applied force would produce if it acted alone.

4.4 NEWTON'S THIRD PRINCIPLE

The First and Second Principles tell us what happens to a particle when forces act on it. The Third Principle deals with an important property of the forces that each of a pair of interacting particles exerts on the other.

NEWTON'S THIRD PRINCIPLE: To every action there is always an equal and opposite reaction.

By the terms action and reaction Newton was referring to forces; the Third Principle thus states that forces always occur in pairs.

How this occurs is shown in Fig. 4.5, which gives an interpretation of Fig. 4.1 in terms of forces. In connection with Fig. 4.1 we noted that in any interaction between two particles the accelerations of the two particles are oppositely directed. Now that we have discussed the First and Second Principles we interpret the results of the experiments shown in Fig. 4.1 and generalized in Fig. 4.2 in terms of forces. Thus, because the force F_{12} exerted *on* particle ① *by* particle ② is $F_{12} = m_1 a_1$ and the force F_{21} exerted *on* particle ② *by* particle ① is $F_{21} = m_2 a_2$, we can rewrite (4.2) in the form

$$F_{12} = -F_{21}. \quad (\textit{Newton's Third Principle}) \tag{4.6}$$

Fig. 4.5 Newton's Third Principle: $F_{12} = -F_{21}$. Note that the forces are oppositely directed along the line between the particles.

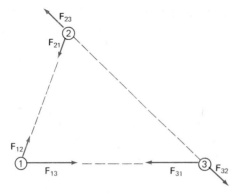

Fig. 4.6   Forces always occur in pairs.

Equation (4.6) asserts that $\mathbf{F}_{12}$ and $\mathbf{F}_{21}$ are equal in magnitude and opposite in direction. In addition, we shall assume that both $\mathbf{F}_{12}$ and $\mathbf{F}_{21}$ lie along the line joining the two particles. These two forces are the "action" and "reaction" mentioned in the statement of the Third Principle; it makes no difference which we call the "action" and which we call the "reaction." The important point is that particle ① cannot exert a force *on* particle ② without experiencing a force equal in magnitude and opposite in direction exerted on it *by* particle ②. Forces thus always occur in pairs; *note that each force in the pair treated by the Third Principle is exerted on a different particle.*

According to the Third Principle, no particle ever experiences a force without exerting an oppositely directed force on some other particle. Consider the isolated dynamical system consisting of three particles that is shown in Fig. 4.6. Because the group of particles is isolated, no outside forces are exerted on the particles in the system. As indicated in the figure, the forces $\mathbf{F}_{12}$ and $\mathbf{F}_{13}$ acting on particle ① are exerted by particles ② and ③, respectively; although the *resultant* force acting on particle ① is not directed toward either ② or ③, the resultant force has components in these directions. These components are the forces covered by the Third Principle.

Example.   A heavy man sits on a light chair in his garden. Considering the man, the chair, and the earth as particles, discuss the forces exerted on each of these particles. Why do these particles remain at rest?

First we consider the interaction between the man and the earth. The man has weight **w,** which if unopposed would cause him to be accelerated downward; as indicated in Fig. 4.7a, his weight is a gravitational force $\mathbf{F}_{ME}$ exerted by the earth. According to the Third Principle, the man exerts an upward gravitational force of magnitude $F_{EM} = w$ on the earth. Next we consider the interaction between the man and the chair. Because the man is not accelerated downward, we know by the Second Principle that the resultant force on the man is zero. Therefore, the chair must exert an upward force $\mathbf{F}_{MC}$ on the man, and the magnitude of $\mathbf{F}_{MC}$ must be equal to the magnitude of $\mathbf{F}_{ME}$. By the Third Principle we know that the man exerts a downward force $\mathbf{F}_{CM}$ on the chair with magnitude equal to that of $\mathbf{F}_{MC}$. Thus, the magnitude of $\mathbf{F}_{CM}$ is also equal to the magnitude of $\mathbf{F}_{ME}$. Finally, we consider the interaction between the chair and the earth. Since the chair is "light," we neglect the gravitational interaction between the chair and the earth. However, the surface of the earth exerts an upward force $\mathbf{F}_{CE}$ on the chair; because the chair is not accelerated we know that the magnitude of $\mathbf{F}_{CE}$ must be equal to the magnitude of $\mathbf{F}_{CM}$ and therefore to the magnitude of $\mathbf{F}_{ME}$. The Third Principle asserts that the chair exerts a downward force $\mathbf{F}_{EC}$ on the earth and that the magnitude of $\mathbf{F}_{EC}$ is just equal to the magnitude of $\mathbf{F}_{CE}$ and thus to the magnitude of $\mathbf{F}_{ME}$. We note that the resultant force on the man is $\mathbf{F}_M = \mathbf{F}_{ME} + \mathbf{F}_{MC} = 0$, the resultant force on the chair is $\mathbf{F}_C = \mathbf{F}_{CM} + \mathbf{F}_{CE} = 0$, and the resultant force on the earth is $\mathbf{F}_E = \mathbf{F}_{ME} + \mathbf{F}_{MC} = 0$. By specifying that the chair is "light" we have agreed to neglect the weight of the chair. If we had included the weight of the chair, how would this have changed our argument?

With our statement of the Third Principle, we have completed our presentation of the Newtonian system of mechanics. The three principles provide a complete system that is applicable to the motion of all particles in the universe providing the particles are not too tiny, in which case we must use quantum mechanics, and provided the particles do not move at speeds comparable to the speed of light, in which case we must use relativistic mechanics. Because large extended bodies are composed of particles, Newton's Principles also provide a method of treating the motions of extended bodies; we shall treat the motions of extended bodies in later chapters. With the exceptions we have mentioned, the Newtonian Principles provide a basis for our understanding of how the universe works; outside the quantum and relativistic domains, predictions based on the Newtonian Principles have proved to be valid. Newton's genius lay in devising a complete system of theory that gave us an understanding of how the world behaves; others including Galileo had made very significant discoveries, but it remained for Newton to formulate a complete system.

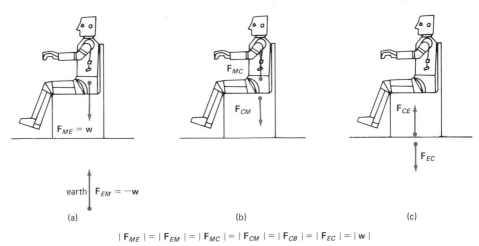

$$|\mathbf{F}_{ME}| = |\mathbf{F}_{EM}| = |\mathbf{F}_{MC}| = |\mathbf{F}_{CM}| = |\mathbf{F}_{CB}| = |\mathbf{F}_{EC}| = |\mathbf{w}|$$

Fig. 4.7 Action and reaction forces always occur in pairs that act on different bodies. (a) The earth exerts a downward gravitational force $\mathbf{F}_{ME}$ on the man; the man exerts an upward gravitational force $\mathbf{F}_{EM} = -\mathbf{F}_{ME}$ on the earth. (b) The chair exerts an upward force $\mathbf{F}_{MC}$ supporting the man; the man exerts a downward force $\mathbf{F}_{CM} = -\mathbf{F}_{MC}$ on the chair. (c) The surface of the earth exerts an upward force $\mathbf{F}_{CE}$ supporting the chair; the chair exerts a downward force $\mathbf{F}_{EC} = -\mathbf{F}_{CE}$ on the surface of the earth.

4.5   FRAMES OF REFERENCE

Now that we have presented Newton's Principles, we must say a few words about the frames of reference to be used in their application. Newton believed that there exists an absolute reference frame in which absolute positions, velocities, and accelerations can be determined with respect to space itself and that this provides a primary inertial frame of reference as defined by the First Principle. Newton showed that any reference frame moving with constant velocity relative to such a primary inertial frame is also an inertial reference frame; this conclusion is called the Newtonian Principle of Relativity.

Subsequent studies in other fields of physics have indicated that it is impossible to set up an absolute frame of reference. However, a frame at rest with respect to the fixed stars, which are the stars so far away that they *appear* to be "fixed" in position in space, for many practical purposes provides an approximate primary inertial frame with respect to which Newton's Principles are valid. It is such a frame that must be used in considering the astronomical motions of the moon, the planets, and modern space probes. However, fortunately we do not have to resort to this frame in most of our everyday work as laboratory scientists and engineers.

For the treatment of *small-scale* phenomena a coordinate system attached to the earth's surface is in excellent approximation an inertial frame; for example, the motions of objects inside a laboratory can be described in terms of a frame attached to one corner of the room. The motions of projectiles can be treated in terms of a frame fixed to the earth's surface provided the ranges of the projectiles are small as compared with the radius of the earth.

By application of the Newtonian Principle of Relativity, we can show that a frame moving at constant velocity relative to the earth's surface is also in good approximation an inertial frame for use in describing small-scale motions. However, use of a reference frame that is accelerated with respect to the earth's surface generally leads to difficulties in the use of Newton's Principles. For example, a frame attached to an airplane in flight at constant velocity relative to the earth's surface is approximately inertial; motions inside the cabin can be treated easily in terms of Newton's Principles. On the other hand, during the accelerated motions that occur during takeoff or landing or when the plane is encountering turbulence, a frame attached to the plane is definitely not an inertial frame. Objects observed inside the cabin of the accelerated plane have accelerations relative to the cabin that cannot be readily treated in terms of Newton's Principles; these accelerations can be attributed to accelerations of the noninertial reference frame itself relative to inertial frames.

Similarly, a frame rotating with respect to the earth's surface is not an inertial frame; for example, a frame attached to a merry-go-round is definitely not an inertial frame. It is possible to apply Newton's Principles to noninertial frames by introducing fictitious forces of one kind or another that represent the accelerations arising from the noninertial nature of the coordinate system. This should be done with great caution.

4.6   DENSITY

In our initial discussion of mass as a measure of the "quantity of matter" in a body, we indicated that for a body with a given chemical composition the mass of the body is proportional to the volume of the body. This is indeed correct, and we can determine the mass of a body in terms of a characteristic of materials called *density*.

DENSITY is mass per unit volume.

The average density ρ_{AV} of an object is defined as the total mass M of the object divided by the total volume of the object:

$$\rho_{AV} = M/V. \quad \left\{ \begin{array}{l} \rho \text{ in kg/m}^3 \\ M \text{ in kg} \\ V \text{ in m}^3 \end{array} \right\} \qquad (4.7)$$

From the average density of a body, which is a directly measurable quantity, it is often desirable to proceed to the concept of density at a point in a body or in a *material*. We do this by considering the procedure suggested in Fig. 4.8, in which we take the ratio of the mass ΔM inside a small volume ΔV containing the point P to the magnitude of ΔV. Mathematically, we could then define the density ρ at point P by

$$\rho = \lim_{\Delta V \to 0} \frac{\Delta M}{\Delta V}. \qquad (4.8)$$

This is a mathematical process that is familiar to all of us.

However, this elegant mathematical process will not work in physical science. We must remember that matter consists of atoms. An atom itself consists of a tiny nucleus that has most of the mass, a number of electrons, and mostly empty space; there is thus a physical difficulty involved in the mathematical process $\Delta V \to 0$. If point P in Fig. 4.8 happened to be at the center of a nucleus, the local density as given by (4.8) would be enormous; if P were at some other point, the local density would be very small or even zero. In either case, we would not obtain a value of ρ that would be of any use for our purposes.

The physical problem that faces us has a mathematically inexact solution, but one that is highly important; just as in our treatment of kinematics we have been indefinite about specifying the size of a "particle," we must be indefinite about the limit approached by ΔV in (4.8). In order to obtain useful values for density, we must define it by the expression

$$\rho = \lim_{\Delta V \to \delta V} \frac{\Delta M}{\Delta V} = \frac{\delta M}{\delta V}, \qquad (4.9)$$

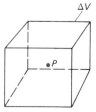

Fig. 4.8 Density ρ at point P is the limit of the ratio $\Delta M/\Delta V$ as ΔV becomes very small.

where δV is small as compared with the sizes of macroscopic bodies like bricks, baseballs, automobiles, *etc.*, but large as compared with the size of atoms. Density is useful as a *macroscopic* property of a material but not as a *microscopic* (atomic scale) property. This means that the limit δV must be small but still large enough to contain a quantity of matter that is a characteristic sample of the bulk material.

As an example of a typical size of δV, we might take 1 μm^3. A small volume of this size in ordinary air contains more than 10^7 molecules; in a solid or liquid it contains approximately 10^{10} molecules. Although we shall remain indefinite about the size of δV, it would appear that 1 $\mu m^3 = 10^{-12}$ cm^3 = 10^{-18} m^3 would be satisfactory in that it is small on a macroscopic scale but still large enough to provide a characteristic sample of the material. We note that 1 μm is approximately the smallest length that can be observed with an ordinary laboratory microscope. We have gone into some considerable detail in discussing the process $\Delta V \rightarrow \delta V$ because we shall need to make use of the process in subsequent discussions of other mechanical, thermal, electrical, and magnetic properties of materials.

In Table 4.1 we list typical densities ρ for various materials under common laboratory conditions. A macroscopic sample of a *homogeneous* material such as a liquid has a constant value of ρ throughout its entire volume; the liquids listed in the table can be regarded as homogeneous, as can most of the solid metals. Some of the nonmetallic solids such as concrete, packed earth, and woods are obviously hetero-

Table 4.1   Typical Mass Densities ρ of Liquids and Solids at 20°C and Normal Atmospheric Pressure[a]

Liquids	kg/m³	Solid metals	kg/m³
Water	1000	Aluminum	2700
Sea water	1030	Cast iron	7200
Benzene	879	Copper	8890
Carbon tetrachloride	1594	Gold	19 300
Ethyl alcohol	789	Lead	11 340
Gasoline	680	Magnesium	1740
Kerosene	800	Nickel	8850
Lubricating oil	900	Silver	10 500
Methyl alcohol	792	Steel	7800
Sulfuric acid, 100%	1831	Tungsten	19 000
Turpentine	873	Zinc	7140
Mercury (0°C)	13 595	Brass or bronze	8700
Nonmetallic solids		**Woods**	
Ice (0°C)	922	Balsa	130
Concrete	2300	Pine	480
Earth, packed	1500	Maple	640
Glass	2600	Oak	720
Granite	2700	Ebony	1200

[a] The exact value of the density will depend on the history of the particular sample and the conditions of temperature and pressure under which it is measured.

geneous; the typical densities listed for these materials are, however, useful for many practical purposes.

Example. The volume unit used in many commercial transactions throughout the world is the liter, where 1 liter = 10^{-3} m³ = 10^3 cm³. What is the mass of 1 liter of the following liquids: water, alcohol, gasoline, and mercury?

We can obtain these masses from the defining relation $M = \rho V$; because the liquids in question are homogeneous, we are justified in using ρ for ρ_{AV} in (4.7). Thus, we obtain

$$\begin{aligned}
\text{For water:} \quad & M = (10^3 \text{ kg/m}^3)(10^{-3} \text{ m}^3) && = 1.00 \text{ kg.} \\
\text{For alcohol:} \quad & M = (0.789 \times 10^3 \text{ kg/m}^3)(10^{-3} \text{ m}^3) && = 0.789 \text{ kg.} \\
\text{For gasoline:} \quad & M = (0.680 \times 10^3 \text{ kg/m}^3)(10^{-3} \text{ m}^3) && = 0.680 \text{ kg.} \\
\text{For mercury:} \quad & M = (13.6 \times 10^3 \text{ kg/m}^3)(10^{-3} \text{ m}^3) && = 13.6 \text{ kg.}
\end{aligned}$$

4.7 WEIGHT

Consider again a freely falling body. The only force acting on such a body is the gravitational attraction of the earth. We recall that Galileo concluded that all such bodies near the earth's surface have the same downward acceleration $g = 9.8$ m/s². According to Newton's Second Principle, any object experiencing an acceleration is subject to a resultant force. In the case of gravitational attraction, we call this resultant force the weight **w** of the body.

The WEIGHT of an object is the resultant force due to the gravitational attraction of the earth acting on the object.

Thus, we can write

$$w = mg. \qquad \left\{ \begin{array}{l} w \text{ in N} \\ m \text{ in kg} \\ g \text{ in m/s}^2 \end{array} \right\} \qquad (4.10)$$

Because, by definition, the direction of **w** is always vertically downward, we usually specify the weight of an object by stating its magnitude w.

Example. What is the weight of a large man whose mass is 100 kg? What is the weight of a petite model whose mass is 45 kg?

From (4.10) we have $w = (100 \text{ kg})(9.8 \text{ m/s}^2) = 980$ kg m/s² = 980 N for the man and $w = (45 \text{ kg})(9.8 \text{ m/s}^2) = 441$ kg m/s² = 441 N for the model. Note that, because g is constant, a person who wishes to reduce his or her weight must actually reduce his or her mass!

We note that in the case of projectile motion, in the absence of air resistance, the projectile is subject to a constant resultant force at all points in its trajectory: **w** = *m***g**. It experiences a constant downward acceleration **g**. In the absence of air resistance no horizontal forces act on the projectile once it has been launched; the horizontal component of the projectile's motion is therefore one of constant velocity.

The downward force **w** experienced by a body of mass *m* near the earth's surface is due to the gravitational attraction of the earth for the body. Although we shall postpone a detailed treatment of gravitational forces until Chapter 9, we should point out that Newton's Third Principle requires that the particle exert an upward force of equal magnitude on the earth. However, in view of the enormous mass M_E of the earth, the acceleration g' of the earth produced by the force exerted on the earth by the freely falling body is negligible, as indicated by the relation

$$M_E g' = -mg \quad \text{or} \quad g' = -(m/M_E)g.$$

The weight of a body can be measured by means of a spring scale, which makes use of the elastic properties of a metallic spring, as suggested in Fig. 4.9. It is found experimentally that within certain limits the elongation *e* of the suspended spring in Fig. 4.9a is directly proportional to the magnitude of the vertical forces acting on its ends. The spring can be calibrated by attaching known masses *m* of weight *w* = *mg* to its lower end; if the spring is not to experience a downward acceleration, the support at its upper end must exert an upward force of equal magnitude on the upper end of the spring. We assume for simplicity that the weight of the spring itself is negligible. By attaching a suitable device to the spring, the resulting elongation can be registered by a pointer on a scale; because the elongation of the spring is directly proportional to the magnitude of the forces acting on its ends, the scale can be arranged to give a direct reading of weight. The spring in Fig. 4.9b supported by a table or floor can be used in similar fashion; its compression *c* is directly proportional to the magnitude of the compressional forces acting on its ends. The suspended spring in Fig. 4.9a is the device used in the suspended "spring scale" sometimes used in grocery stores. The supported spring in Fig. 4.9b is the element employed in the "spring platform scale" like the so-called "bathroom scales" used daily by

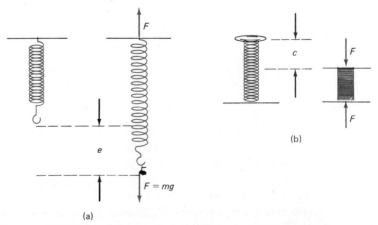

(a)   (b)

Fig. 4.9   Measurement of weight by means of a spring.

weight-conscious people to measure their weight. Although more accurate weighing procedures are possible, spring scales are widely used for commercial purposes; if the spring is properly calibrated, a spring scale can give reasonably reliable results. It is worthwhile to note that while in commercial transactions we measure "weight," the physical quantity of interest is in fact mass. Thus, when we in the United States eventually "go metric" in our daily commerce, we will purchase bulk items in units of kilograms.

If a person regards the reading of his bathroom scale as a true measure of his weight, he can get some surprising results by placing the scale in the cage of an elevator. We shall call the scale reading the person's "apparent weight" and show in the following example how this quantity varies when the elevator cage is accelerated.

Example. A 100-kg man stands on a bathroom scale in an elevator cage. What is the man's apparent weight when the cage (1) is at rest; (2) is moving upward at constant velocity; (3) is moving downward at constant velocity; (4) has an acceleration of 4.9 m/s², upward; (5) has an acceleration of 9.8 m/s², upward; (6) has an acceleration of 4.9 m/s², downward; and (7) has an acceleration of 9.8 m/s², downward?

In solving this problem we shall make use of the diagram in Fig. 4.10; we consider the forces exerted on the *man*. The only pertinent forces acting on the man are his true weight $\mathbf{w} = m\mathbf{g}$ exerted on him by the earth and the upward force $\mathbf{F}_{MS}$ exerted on the man by the scale. The reaction force $\mathbf{F}_{SM}$ exerted by the man on the scale has the same magnitude as $\mathbf{F}_{MS}$. This force is indicated on the scale dial and represents the man's apparent weight. Taking the upward direction as positive, we can write the resultant force on the man as: $F_R = F_{MS} - w = F_{MS} - mg$. By Newton's Second Principle, $F_R = ma$. In situations (1), (2), and (3) $a = 0$ so that $F_R = 0$, whence $F_{MS} = w$. Thus, when the man and cage are not accelerated, the man's apparent weight as indicated by the scale is equal to his actual weight: $F_{MS} = (100 \text{ kg})(9.8 \text{ m/s}^2) = 980$ N. (4) When the man has an upward acceleration $a = g/2 = 4.9$ m/s², Newton's Second Principle, $F_R = ma$, gives $F_{MS} - mg = mg/2$ or $F_{MS} = 3\ mg/2 = 3\ w/2 = 1470$ N. (5) When the man has an acceleration $a = g = 9.8$ m/s², upward, Newton's Second Principle, $F_R = ma$, gives $F_{MS} - mg = mg$ or $F_{MS} = 2\ mg = 2\ w = 1960$ N. In other words, when the upward acceleration is 9.8 m/s², the man's apparent weight is twice his actual weight. (6) With an acceleration of 4.9 m/s², downward, the value of a in the coordinate system of Fig. 4.10 is $a = -4.9$ m/s² $= -g/2$. Using Newton's Second Principle as before gives $F_{MS} - mg = -mg/2$ or $F_{MS} = mg/2 = (100 \text{ kg})(4.9 \text{ m/s}^2) = 490$ N. In other words, when the man and cage have an acceleration of $g/2$, downward, the man's apparent weight is half his actual weight. (7) Finally, we consider the case when man and cage are in free fall with acceleration 9.8 m/s², or $a = -g = -9.8$ m/s². In this condition, the expression for Newton's Second Principle is $F_{MS} - mg = -mg$ which gives $F_{MS} = 0$. The man's apparent weight is zero!

The final result obtained in this example is quite general. Whenever an object is inside a vehicle in free fall, its apparent weight as read on a scale inside the vehicle

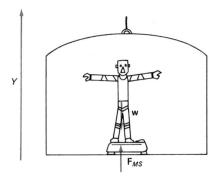

Fig. 4.10 The scale exerts an upward force $\mathbf{F}_{MS}$ on the man; by the Third Principle, the man exerts a downward force $\mathbf{F}_{SM}$ of equal magnitude on the scale. (The downward force exerted by the man is not shown in the figure.)

is zero. Astronauts inside a space vehicle circling the earth are "weightless" in this sense, because the vehicle and its contents are in a state of free fall toward the earth's surface.

4.8   RECTILINEAR MOTION

In Chapter 3 we discussed the kinematics of rectilinear motion, or motion in a straight line. The dynamics of this type of motion is very simple. In the coordinate system shown in Fig. 4.11, the resultant force $\mathbf{F}_R$ on the particle of mass m has only an X component. If $F_{Rx} = 0$, the motion of the particle of mass m in the figure is one of constant velocity. If $F_{Rx} \neq 0$, the particle has acceleration $a_x\mathbf{i} = (F_{Rx}/m)\mathbf{i}$. The case of free fall near the earth's surface is a special case in which the constant force $\mathbf{w}$ acts on the particle; in this case, the acceleration is constant. Similarly, if the horizontal force $F_{Rx}\mathbf{i}$ suggested in Fig. 4.11 is constant, we have a case of constant acceleration. Rectilinear motion at constant acceleration has been discussed in Chapter 3 on kinematics.

If the resultant force F_{Rx} varies with time, the particle's acceleration $a_x = F_{Rx}/m$ varies in a precisely similar fashion. The particle's velocity v_x must then be determined by integration: $v_x = v_{x_0} + \int_0^t a_x dt$; the particle's position must also be determined by integration: $x = x_0 + \int_0^t v_x dt$. Here x_0 is the position of the particle at time $t = 0$ and v_{x_0} is the velocity of the particle at time $t = 0$.

4.9   MOTION OF A PARTICLE IN A CIRCULAR PATH

We have studied the kinematics of a particle moving at constant speed of magnitude v_T in a circular path of radius $\mathscr{R}$—so-called uniform circular motion—and have shown that such a particle has an acceleration of constant magnitude $a_C = v_T^2/\mathscr{R}$ always directed toward the center of the circle, the so-called centripetal acceleration. In order for such a particle to have this acceleration a_C, it must, in accord with Newton's

$$O \vdash\!\!\!\!\!—\!\!\!—\!\!\!—\!\!\underset{m}{\oslash}\!\xrightarrow{\;F_R = F_{Rx}\mathbf{i}\;}—\!\!\!—\!\!\!—\!\!\!—X \quad \textbf{Fig. 4.11}$$

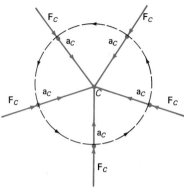

Fig. 4.12 Centripetal forces.

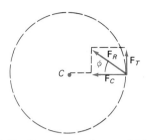

Fig. 4.13 Centripetal and tangential forces.

Second Principle, be acted on at all times by a resultant force $\mathbf{F}_C$ directed toward the center of the circle. This resultant force is called a *centripetal force:*

$$F_C = mv_T^2/\mathscr{R}. \quad \text{(Centripetal Force)} \tag{4.11}$$

As indicated in Fig. 4.12, the direction of this resultant force is toward the center of the circle at all points of the path.

If the tangential speed of the particle in its circular path is changing, the resultant force $\mathbf{F}_R$ acting on the particle must have not only a radially directed centripetal component $F_C = mv_T^2/\mathscr{R}$ but also a tangential component $F_T = m(dv_T/dt)$, where $dv_T/dt = a_T$ is the tangential component of the particle's acceleration. As indicated in Fig. 4.13, the magnitude of the resultant force $\mathbf{F}_R$ acting on the particle is $F_R = \sqrt{F_T^2 + F_C^2}$; the angle ϕ between the direction of the resultant force $\mathbf{F}_R$ and the radius is given by the relation $\tan \phi = F_T/F_C$. The magnitude of the particle's resultant acceleration is $a = F_R/m$ and its direction is the same as that of the resultant force $\mathbf{F}_R$. These results are consistent with the kinematical discussion given in Chapter 3.

4.10 FRICTION

We now return to a consideration of one of the phenomena that had a major influence on the formulation of Aristotelian physics. If we set a body in motion across a horizontal surface, the body sooner or later comes to rest. On this phenomenon we can all agree, but the Aristotelian and Newtonian explanations are different. The Aristotelians would hold that the body in executing "natural motion" comes to rest of its own accord because its natural state is one of rest. Because Newton's principles assert that the velocity of a body changes only when a resultant force acts on the body, Newtonians attribute the deceleration of the body to some force exerted on the body by the surface with which it is in contact. We call such a force a *frictional force.* We shall now consider the properties of such forces and shall discuss certain *empirical laws* that describe their behavior.

Consider a block lying on a level table as in Fig. 4.14a. By pulling on a string attached to the block and using a spring scale to measure the force $\mathbf{F}_{app}$ applied to

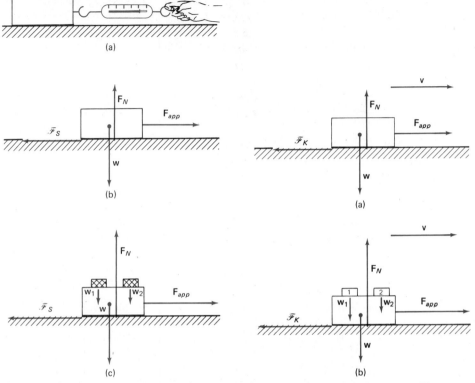

Fig. 4.14   Force of static friction $\mathscr{F}_S$.   **Fig. 4.15**   Force of kinetic friction $\mathscr{F}_K$.

the block, we can perform various experiments. When we apply a small horizontal force to the right, nothing happens; we conclude from Newton's Second Principle that there is no resultant force acting on the block. We interpret this result as meaning that the surface of the table must be exerting a horizontal frictional force $\mathscr{F}_S$ to the left, as shown in Fig. 4.14b. The magnitude of $\mathscr{F}_S$ is equal to the magnitude of the applied force $\mathbf{F}_{app}$, because the resultant of the two forces is zero. We call $\mathscr{F}_S$ a force of *static friction* because the block is at rest with respect to the table top. Forces of static friction always act to oppose the tendency of two surfaces to slide relative to one another under the influence of a resultant applied force. As we gradually increase the magnitude of the applied force $\mathbf{F}_{app}$, the magnitude of the force of static friction also increases up to a certain maximum value $\mathscr{F}_{S,\text{Max}}$. When the magnitude of our applied force, F_{app}, reaches the value $\mathscr{F}_{S,\text{Max}}$, the block suddenly begins to move to the right with accelerated motion; we can measure the magnitude of $\mathscr{F}_{S,\text{Max}}$ by noting that $|\mathbf{F}_{app}| = |\mathscr{F}_{S,\text{Max}}|$ when accelerated motion begins. As we are in the process of increasing the magnitude of the applied force, $|\mathbf{F}_{app}| = |\mathscr{F}_S|$ at all times until motion begins. Thus, the magnitude of *the force of static friction $\mathscr{F}_S$ can have any value from zero up to the maximum value $\mathscr{F}_{S,\text{Max}}$*, which is attained just as motion starts.

Experiment shows that the value of $\mathscr{F}_{S,\text{Max}}$ depends on the nature of the surfaces of the block and the table top but does not depend on the area of the surface of contact; we can turn the block on another side so that the area of contact is different and obtain the same value of $\mathscr{F}_{S,\text{Max}}$. The value of $\mathscr{F}_{S,\text{Max}}$ is, however, proportional to the magnitude of the force $\mathbf{F}_N$ in Fig. 4.14b exerted on the block by the table top; this force is called the *normal force* because its line of action is *perpendicular* or *normal* to the surface of the table top. In the situation shown in Fig. 4.14b, the net force on the block in the vertical direction is zero because there is no acceleration in the vertical direction, and therefore $F_N = w$. We can demonstrate the dependence of $\mathscr{F}_{S,\text{Max}}$ on F_N by placing "laboratory weights" on top of the block as indicated in Fig. 4.14c. In the case shown $F_N = w + w_1 + w_2$. By determining $\mathscr{F}_{S,\text{Max}}$ as we put successive additional loads on the block, we find experimentally that $\mathscr{F}_{S,\text{Max}}$ is directly proportional to F_N. We write this proportionality in the form of an equation:

$$\mathscr{F}_{S,\text{Max}} = \mu_S F_N, \tag{4.12}$$

where μ_S is called the *coefficient of static friction.* The coefficient of static friction depends on the nature of the surfaces in contact; typical values of μ_S for various materials are listed in Table 4.2.

Returning to our consideration of the block on the table top, we find experimentally that, once the block begins to slide across the table, we need to apply a smaller force $\mathbf{F}_{app}$ to *keep* the block moving at constant velocity than the force needed to *start* the block moving. We interpret this result in Fig. 4.15a as being due to the action of a force of *kinetic friction* $\mathscr{F}_K$ that is smaller in magnitude than $\mathscr{F}_{S,\text{Max}}$; whenever a body is sliding with velocity $\mathbf{v}$ across a surface, $\mathscr{F}_K$ always acts in a direction opposite to the direction of the velocity. In other words, $\mathscr{F}_K$ always tends to decelerate a moving body. As in the case of static friction, the force of kinetic friction is independent of the area of contact between the block and the table. It depends on the nature of the surfaces and its magnitude is directly proportional to F_N, as we can find by adding various additional weights as suggested in Fig. 4.15b. We again write this proportionality as an equation:

$$\mathscr{F}_K = \mu_K F_N, \tag{4.13}$$

Table 4.2   Typical Values of the Coefficients of Static Friction, μ_S, and of Kinetic Friction, μ_K[a]

Materials	μ_S	μ_K
Steel on steel	0.15	0.09
Steel on ice	0.03	0.01
Hemp rope on wood	0.5	0.4
Leather on wood	0.5	0.4
Oak on oak	0.5	0.3
Wrought iron on cast iron or bronze	0.19	0.18
Rubber tire on dry concrete road	1.0	0.7
Rubber tire on wet concrete road	0.7	0.5

[a] The exact values of μ_S and μ_K depend on the particular conditions of the surfaces that are in contact. The value of μ_K also depends on the relative velocity of the sliding surfaces.

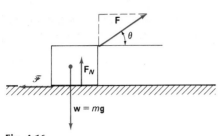

Fig. 4.16

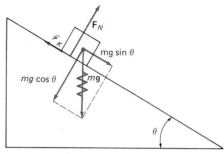

Fig. 4.17

where μ_K is called the *coefficient of kinetic friction*. Typical values of μ_K for various materials are listed in Table 4.2.

The values of μ_S and μ_K listed in Table 4.2 are given for reasonably smooth surfaces. The values would be considerably higher for very rough surfaces; higher values are also sometimes encountered for extremely smooth, highly polished surfaces that tend to cling together.

Equations (4.12) and (4.13) are formulations of relations sometimes called the "Laws of Friction." These empirical laws represent generalizations that have limited application; for example, the equations are limited to relatively small values of F_N because for large values of the normal force the surfaces in contact are permanently deformed. The proportionality "constants" μ_K and μ_S, which are not strictly constants, but can vary with the particular conditions of the surfaces in contact, are accurate only to within a few percent. There is evidence that μ_K varies with the velocity of the moving object; at high speeds the block tends to be separated from the table by a thin layer of air. The laws in (4.12) and (4.13) do not apply for lubricated surfaces, which are separated by a layer of oil or grease.

Empirical laws like the laws of friction are useful approximations that can be very valuable in practical work. They are usually not of fundamental importance to general theory. We should not confuse empirical relations of this kind with the *general principles* that form the basis of general physical theory. In *principle* it is possible to deduce these laws from the basic principles of physical theory, but despite the superficial simplicity of the laws, this is usually a complex and difficult task.

Example.   A man sets a 2-kg box in motion across a horizontal platform by pulling on a rope attached to the box. If the coefficients of friction between the box and the platform are $\mu_S = 0.4$ and $\mu_K = 0.3$ and if the rope makes an angle of 30° with the horizontal, what is the magnitude of the force that the man must exert in order to (1) start the box moving and (2) keep the box moving at constant speed? (3) If the man continued after motion began to exert the force required to start the box moving, what would be the acceleration of the box?

We begin by drawing the diagram in Fig. 4.16 showing all the pertinent forces exerted *on the box*. In parts (1) and (2), the acceleration of the box is zero, so that the resultant force on the box must be zero. Under this condition, the vertical force components must add to zero; in other words the sum of the upward force components must be equal to the sum of the downward force components:

$$F \sin \phi + F_N = mg. \qquad (i)$$

Similarly, the horizontal force components must add to zero; the sum of the force components to the right must be equal to the sum of the force components to the left:

$$F \cos \theta = \mathcal{F}. \qquad \text{(ii)}$$

Finally, we make use of the laws of friction:

$$\mathcal{F} = \mu F_N \qquad \text{(iii)}$$

We can now solve problems (1) and (2) by solving the simultaneous equations (i), (ii), and (iii) with $\mu = \mu_S$ for (1) and $\mu = \mu_K$ for (2). Try it!

In order to solve problem (3), we need to consider only horizontal motion; no vertical motion occurs. The resultant force on the box will be toward the right in Fig. 4.16 and will have a value $F_1 \cos \theta - \mathcal{F}_K$, where F_1 is the force that is obtained in part (1) and $\mathcal{F}_K$ is the kinetic friction in part (2). Use of Newton's Second Principle leads to

$$ma = F_1 \cos \theta - \mathcal{F}_K. \qquad \text{(iv)}$$

We merely solve (iv) for a; all other quantities in the equation are known.

Example.   A 2-kg block slides from rest down an inclined plane that makes an angle of 30° with the horizontal. What is the acceleration of the block (1) if the plane is frictionless and (2) if the coefficient of kinetic friction between the block and the plane is 0.2?

In this situation we first draw the diagram in Fig. 4.17 and then we resolve all forces acting *on the block* into components parallel to the incline and perpendicular to the incline, as shown in Fig. 4.17. The force components perpendicular to the incline always add to zero because no motion occurs in this direction; therefore,

$$F_N = mg \cos \theta. \qquad \text{(i)}$$

The resultant force acting on the block is down the plane and is equal to $mg \sin \theta - \mathcal{F}_K$; the block's acceleration down the plane can be obtained from Newton's Second Principle:

$$mg \sin \theta - \mathcal{F}_K = ma. \qquad \text{(ii)}$$

Finally, we use the laws of friction to obtain

$$\mathcal{F}_K = \mu_K F_N. \qquad \text{(iii)}$$

In problem (1) we have $\mu_K = 0$ so that $\mathcal{F}_K = 0$; in this case we need to solve only relation (ii) to obtain $a = g \sin \theta$. Note that for $\theta = 90°$, the block would be in free fall with $a = g$. In problem (2) we must solve (i), (ii), and (iii) simultaneously to obtain the value of the acceleration a, which is

$$a = g(\sin \theta - \mu_K \cos \theta).$$

4.11   MOMENTUM AND IMPULSE

In sharp contrast to the empirical "laws of friction" that we have been considering are Newton's Principles, which are the broad generalizations upon which classical physics is based. Although we have no reason to doubt their validity in macroscopic terrestrial physics, we sometimes encounter phenomena that cannot be readily treated by direct application of Newton's Principles. Such phenomena are often more readily treated in terms of secondary relationships that can be derived from Newton's Principles. As an example of such a phenomenon, consider a golf ball on its tee being hit by a golf club as in Fig. 4.18. The golf club exerts an enormous force on the ball for a very brief time interval. During this brief time interval, the ball is accelerated from rest to some very high final velocity; during this brief time interval the resultant force acting on the ball varies with time in both magnitude and direction. Such a force is sometimes called an *impulsive force*. While the club is in contact with the ball, it would be extremely dangerous if not impossible for us to sneak in with a spring scale to attempt measurements of the varying force so that we could determine the ball's varying acceleration from Newton's Second Principle; even with the aid of high-speed motion pictures, we would find it difficult to measure the instantaneous acceleration to check our results. Direct application of the Newtonian Principles seems hopelessly difficult.

The physical quantities that we *can* measure are the mass m of the ball and the final velocity $\mathbf{v}$ of the ball as it leaves the club; we can with the aid of a high-speed movie camera estimate the time interval Δt during which the club is in contact with the ball. How can we interpret the physics of the situation in terms of these measurable quantities?

We begin by introducing a new derived physical quantity called *momentum* $\mathbf{p}$, which Galileo first introduced and found useful in his work.

> The MOMENTUM of a particle is a vector defined as the product of the mass of the particle and the velocity of the particle.

Thus, we write

$$\mathbf{p} = m\mathbf{v}, \quad \left\{ \begin{array}{l} p \text{ in kg} \cdot \text{m/s} \\ m \text{ in kg} \\ \mathbf{v} \text{ in m/s} \end{array} \right\} \quad (Momentum) \qquad (4.14)$$

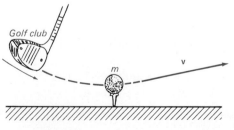

Fig. 4.18

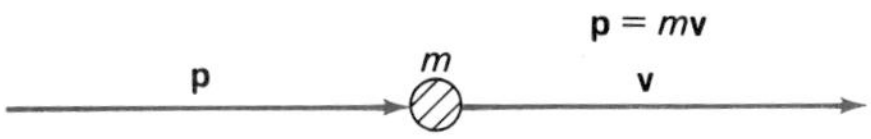

$$\mathbf{p} = m\mathbf{v}$$

Fig. 4.19 Momentum $\mathbf{p} = m\mathbf{v}$.

where we note in Fig. 4.19 that $\mathbf{p}$ is a vector quantity having the same direction as the particle's velocity $\mathbf{v}$. We can now express Newton's Second Principle in terms of momentum by noting that $d\mathbf{p}/dt = m\ d\mathbf{v}/dt = m\mathbf{a}$. Thus,

$$\mathbf{F}_R = d\mathbf{p}/dt. \quad \textit{(Newton's Second Principle*)} \qquad (4.15)$$

From this fundamental principle we can write

$$d\mathbf{p} = \mathbf{F}_R\ dt$$

and proceed to integrate this equation:

$$\int_{\mathbf{p}_0}^{\mathbf{p}_f} d\mathbf{p} = \int_{t_0}^{t_f} \mathbf{F}_R\ dt,$$

which gives

$$\mathbf{p}_f - \mathbf{p}_0 = \int_{t_0}^{t_f} \mathbf{F}_R\ dt. \qquad (4.16)$$

The integral $\int_{t_0}^{t_f} \mathbf{F}_R\ dt$ is called the *impulse* associated with the resultant force. Equation (4.16) thus asserts that the change in the momentum of the particle is equal to the impulse associated with the resultant force acting on the particle:

Change in momentum = Impulse of resultant force.

In order to gain some insight into the nature of impulse, consider the graph in Fig. 4.20a, which shows the X component F_x of the resultant force acting on the particle as a function of time. The X component of the impulse is $\int_{t_0}^{t_f} F_x\ dt$ and is just equal to the area under the curve in Fig. 4.20a. If we know this area, we can find the time average of the force F_x by constructing the rectangle shown in Fig. 4.20b so that $\bar{F}_x(t_f - t_0) = \bar{F}_x\Delta t = \int_{t_0}^{t_f} F_x\ dt$; in other words, by making the areas under the curves in Fig. 4.20 the same, we have obtained the value of $\bar{F}_x$.

By generalizing this argument we may rewrite (4.16) in the forms

$$\mathbf{p}_f - \mathbf{p}_0 = \bar{\mathbf{F}}(t_f - t_0) \quad \text{or} \quad \Delta\mathbf{p} = \bar{\mathbf{F}}\Delta t. \qquad (4.17)$$

We note that this gives us an alternative definition of impulse: *The impulse of a*

---

* We shall discover in a later chapter that for speeds that are an appreciable fraction of the speed of light the assumption of constant mass is no longer valid.

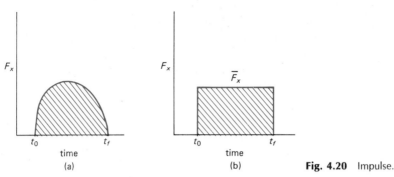

Fig. 4.20   Impulse.

force is the product of the time-average value of the force and the time interval during which the force acts.

How these relations can be used in the treatment of impulsive forces is demonstrated in the following examples.

Example.   A 50-g rubber ball is placed on a golf tee as suggested in Fig. 4.18 and struck by a club, which remains in contact with the ball for 0.1 s. The ball has a speed of 40 m/s just after breaking contact with the club. What is the magnitude of the average force exerted on the ball by the club?

The ball's initial momentum is zero; after leaving the club the ball has a momentum of magnitude $p_f = mv$. The change in the ball's momentum while in contact with club has a magnitude of $\Delta p = mv$. From relation (4.17), we note that the magnitude of this change in momentum is equal to the magnitude of the impulse $\overline{F}\Delta t$ associated with the average force exerted on the ball. Therefore, $\overline{F} = \Delta p/\Delta t = (5 \times 10^{-2}\text{ kg})(40\text{ m/s})/(10^{-1}\text{ s}) = 20\text{ kg m/s}^2 = 20\text{ N}$. The direction of $\overline{F}$ is the same as that of the final velocity of the ball.

Example.   A man leans over the side of a building and drops a 100-g ball to the sidewalk below. He notes that 4 s elapse between the time of release and the time the ball reaches the sidewalk. The ball striking the sidewalk bounces and moves upward for 2 s before reaching the highest point in its trajectory. If the time of contact between the ball and the sidewalk is 0.1 s, what average force is exerted on the ball by the sidewalk? Use the free-fall approximation.

We shall use a coordinate system with the + direction upward. This means that $a = -g = -9.8\text{ m/s}^2$. Because a time interval of $t_1 = 4$ s is required for the ball to reach the ground, its velocity v_1 just before it reaches the sidewalk is given by $v_1 = -gt_1 = (-9.8\text{ m/s}^2)(4\text{ s}) = -39.2\text{ m/s}$. Its momentum at this time is given by $p = mv = (0.1\text{ kg})(-39.2\text{ m/s}) = -3.92\text{ kg·m/s}$. Because the ball rises for $t_2 = 2$ s on its first bounce, its change in velocity as it moves upward is $v_{2f} - v_{20} = -gt = (-9.8\text{ m/s}^2)(2\text{ s}) = -19.6\text{ m/s}$; because its vertical velocity at the top of its first bounce is $v_{2f} = 0$, the ball's initial upward velocity as it leaves the sidewalk is $v_{20} = 19.6\text{ m/s}$, and its corresponding momentum is $p_{20} = mv_{20} = (0.1\text{ kg})(19.6\text{ m/s}) = 1.96\text{ kg·m/s}$. The change in the momentum of the ball during its collision with the sidewalk is given by $\Delta p = p_{20} - p_1 = (1.96 + 3.92)$ kg·m/s $= 5.88$ kg·m/s. By relation (4.17), the impulse $\bar{F}\Delta t$ associated with the average force $\bar{F}$ exerted on the ball is equal to Δp. Thus, $\bar{F}\Delta t = \Delta p$ and $\bar{F} = \Delta p / \Delta t = (5.88$ kg·m/s$)/(10^{-1}$ s$) = 58.8$ kg·m/s$^2 = 58.8$ N; because $\bar{F}$ is positive, the force on the ball has a vertically upward direction.

Example. A large artillery piece with a barrel 6 m long is used to fire a 2-kg shell. The muzzle velocity of the shell is 600 m/s. Assuming that the shell has constant acceleration, find the magnitude of the average force exerted on the shell as it passes through the gun barrel.

From kinematic considerations, the average velocity of the shell as it moves through the barrel is $\bar{v} = (v_f + v_0)/2 = 300$ m/s. The time t required for the shell's passage through length L of the barrel is $t = L/\bar{v} = 6$ m/$(3 \times 10^2$ m/s$) = 2 \times 10^{-2}$ s. The impulse involved is thus $\bar{F}t = (2 \times 10^{-2}$ s$)\bar{F}$; the impulse must be equal to the change in the shell's momentum $\Delta p = mv = (2$ kg$)(6 \times 10^{-2}$ m/s$) = 1200$ kg·m/s. Therefore, $\bar{F} = \Delta p/t = (12 \times 10^2$ kg·m/s$)/(2 \times 10^{-2}$ s$) = 6 \times 10^4$ kg·m/s$^2 = 6 \times 10^4$ N. Note: This can be checked by finding the shell's average acceleration and making direct use of Newton's Second Principle; an assumption of constant acceleration implies an assumption of constant force.

4.12 DYNAMICAL SYSTEMS: CONSERVATION OF MOMENTUM

Although we have introduced momentum to assist us in the treatment of problems involving impulsive forces, momentum is an extremely important physical quantity that is useful in solving many other kinds of dynamical problems. We shall now demonstrate some of the other properties of this interesting quantity.

First, however, we must formally define a concept that we have used earlier on an informal basis, the concept of a *dynamical system:*

A DYNAMICAL SYSTEM is any well-defined collection of matter.

Although we have been dealing with particles and have had occasion to deal with a dynamical system consisting of a single particle in discussing Newton's First and Second Principles and a dynamical system consisting of two particles in discussing the Third Principle, dynamical systems can be more generally defined. A dynamical system might be all the people in a room, all the water in the oceans, all the air in the atmosphere, etc. The important point is that *we define clearly what constitutes the system.*

Because all matter is composed of particles, the concept of a dynamical system as a collection of particles is an important one that we shall use frequently. In treating a dynamical system we shall have occasion to distinguish between *external forces,* which are exerted *on* the particles of the system *by* particles *outside the system,* and *internal forces,* which are forces exerted *on* the particles of the system *by* other particles *within the system.* An *isolated* dynamical system is one that is not subject to external forces.

Now consider the isolated dynamical system shown in Fig. 4.21 consisting of two particles ① and ② having momenta $\mathbf{p}_1 = m_1\mathbf{v}_1$ and $\mathbf{p}_2 = m_2\mathbf{v}_2$, respectively. We define the total momentum $\mathbf{P}$ of the system as the vector sum of the momenta of the particles constituting the system:

$$\mathbf{P} = \mathbf{p}_1 + \mathbf{p}_2. \tag{4.18}$$

We shall now prove that the total momentum of this isolated system is constant.

In any interaction between the particles, Newton's Third Principle assures us that $\mathbf{F}_{12} = -\mathbf{F}_{21}$, as suggested in Fig. 4.22. Using the statement of Newton's Second Principle in terms of momentum given in (4.15), we can write the Third Principle in the forms

$$\frac{d\mathbf{p}_1}{dt} = -\frac{d\mathbf{p}_2}{dt} \quad \text{or} \quad \frac{d\mathbf{p}_1}{dt} + \frac{d\mathbf{p}_2}{dt} = 0 \quad \text{or} \quad \frac{d}{dt}(\mathbf{p}_1 + \mathbf{p}_2) = 0.$$

Because $\mathbf{P} = \mathbf{p}_1 + \mathbf{p}_2$, the last expression tells us that $d\mathbf{P}/dt = 0$, and we conclude that the total momentum of our isolated dynamical system is constant:

$$\mathbf{P} = \text{constant.} \quad \textit{(Isolated Dynamical System)} \tag{4.19}$$

Because all interactions are between *pairs* of particles, we can extend our treatment directly to a system of any number of particles whatsoever. Thus, the statement in (4.19) is general and is applicable to any *isolated* dynamical system. It has such broad application that it is termed a *principle.*

PRINCIPLE OF THE CONSERVATION OF MOMENTUM: The total momentum of an isolated dynamical system is constant.

This is the first of several principles that deal with the *conservation* of various physical quantities; when a physical quantity remains constant in time, we say that the quantity is *conserved*. In the case of momentum we have proved that no combinations of internal forces can ever change the total momentum of a dynamical system. Note that this is a vector relation; the momentum-conservation principle can be applied separately to each of the components of the total momentum of the system.

Because we have derived the conservation-of-momentum principle directly from

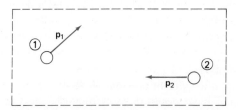

Fig. 4.21 The momentum $\mathbf{P}$ of an isolated dynamical system is defined as $\mathbf{P} = \mathbf{p}_1 + \mathbf{p}_2 + \cdots$

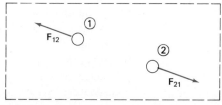

Fig. 4.22 Because $\mathbf{F}_{12} = -\mathbf{F}_{21}$ the momentum $\mathbf{P}$ of this isolated dynamical system is constant.

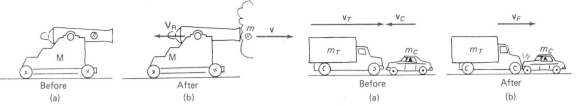

Fig. 4.23 Recoil of a gun when a projectile is fired.   **Fig. 4.24** Momentum is conserved in a collision.

Newton's Principles, we have every confidence that it applies rigorously to all situations covered by classical mechanics. Actually, it has even wider applications. This conservation principle holds rigorously in quantum physics and in relativistic physics and can be used as a guide to understanding the processes involved in the emission and absorption of electromagnetic radiation. So far as we know the principle is *never* violated.

The following examples show how the principle can be applied.

Example.   A 1000-kg cannon fires a 1-kg cannonball in a horizontal direction. If the muzzle velocity of the cannonball is 300 m/s, what is the magnitude of the recoil velocity of the cannon?

We begin by drawing the diagrams shown in Fig. 4.23. In Fig. 4.23a, we note that the initial total momentum of the cannon–cannonball–earth system is zero, because all bodies are at rest. According to the Conservation-of-Momentum Principle, the total momentum of the system remains zero after the cannon is fired. We assume that the horizontal forces acting between the wheels and the ground are negligibly small. This means that the momentum of the cannon MV_R toward the left in the diagram must be equal in magnitude to the momentum of the cannonball to the right in the diagram. Thus, we can write

$$MV_R = mv \quad \text{or} \quad V_R = mv/M.$$

The numerical value of the recoil velocity of the gun is thus $V_R = (1 \text{ kg})(3 \times 10^2 \text{ m/s})/(10^3 \text{ kg}) = 3 \times 10^{-1} \text{ m/s} = 0.3 \text{ m/s}$. Query: Why does a gun "kick" when it is fired?

Example.   A 5000-kg truck moving with an initial velocity of 30 m/s, eastward, has a head-on collision with a 1000-kg car moving with an initial velocity of 20 m/s, westward. During the collision the bumpers of the two vehicles become locked together. What is the common velocity of the two vehicles immediately after the collision? Assume that the horizontal forces between the wheels and the ground are negligible up to this time.

We begin by sketching the "before" and "after" diagrams in Fig. 4.24. Taking the eastward direction as positive, we note that the momentum P_B of the truck–car system before the collision is $m_T v_T - m_C v_C$ and that after the collision the total momentum of the system P_A is $(m_T + m_C)v_F$, where v_F is the common final velocity of the two vehicles. According to the Conservation-of-Momentum Principle, $P_A = P_B$. Therefore,

$$(m_T + m_C)v_F = m_T v_T - m_C v_C$$

or

$$v_F = (m_T v_T - m_C v_C)/(m_T + m_C).$$

Substitution of numerical values gives

$$v_F = \frac{(5000 \text{ kg})(30 \text{ m/s}) - (1000 \text{ kg})(20 \text{ m/s})}{(5000 + 1000) \text{ kg}} = 21.7 \text{ m/s}.$$

The direction of the final velocity is toward the east.

QUESTIONS

1. Compare the ideas of Aristotle with those of Galileo regarding the "natural state" of a body. On the basis of *your own experience,* does the point of view of Aristotle or that of Galileo appear more plausible?

2. Ernst Mach's definition of mass as described in Section 4.1 is an *operational definition* in the sense that definite operations are prescribed for the determination of the mass m of a particle in terms of a standard mass M_S. Other people have defined the mass of a body as a "measure of the inertia" of the body or as a "measure of the quantity of matter" in the body. Can such nonoperational statements provide a satisfactory alternative definition of mass?

3. The base units of length and time are defined in terms of atomic standards. (See the Appendix, Section III.) Discuss the possibility of using the mass of a single atom of ^{12}C as an atomic standard of mass. How could you define the kilogram in terms of this atomic standard?

4. Discuss the way in which Newton's First Principle actually *defines* an *inertial frame of reference.*

5. Under what circumstances can the interior of an airliner serve as the basis of an inertial

frame of reference? An observer attaches her frame of reference to a "merry-go-round;" describe the motion of a nearby tree as reported by the observer. Is this frame of reference likely to be an *inertial frame?*

6. If a particle has an acceleration relative to an inertial frame of reference, what can you conclude on the basis of Newton's Second Principle? How is the situation different if the reference frame is not inertial?

7. Is it possible to provide a direct experimental verification of Newton's Second Principle? If so, describe such an experiment. If not, why should we accept the Second Principle as a valid statement?

8. A donkey pulls a cart along a level road. By Newton's Third Principle, the force exerted on the cart by the donkey is equal in magnitude but opposite in direction to the force exerted on the donkey by the cart. In view of this, how is any motion possible? Will not the two forces exactly balance one another? Explain in detail how the donkey is able to move the cart.

9. Explain carefully why the densities listed in Table 4.1 are not applicable to matter on an atomic scale.

10. If your apparent weight is the reading registered by a set of spring scales attached to the ceiling of an elevator cage, under what circumstances would your apparent weight be less than your actual weight? Under what circumstances would your apparent weight be greater than your actual weight? Under what circumstance would your apparent weight be zero?

11. Why are astronauts in a space capsule "weightless" when the capsule is in a circular orbit about the earth? Does the word "weightless" provide a good description of the situation?

12. Sherlock Holmes and Professor Moriarty have equal weights and cling near opposite ends of the rope to a massless rope passing over a frictionless pulley. If they are initially at the same level and face each other, is it possible for the evil professor to escape from Holmes (a) by climbing up the rope, (b) by sliding down the rope, or (c) by releasing the rope? Discuss each possibility.

13. If the Greeks had understood the nature of friction, how might the Aristotelian views regarding the "natural state" of a body have been modified?

14. Explain why Newton's Principles are more basic in giving us an understanding of dynamics than the laws of friction.

15. Could a person on the *perfectly frictionless* surface of a frozen pond ever reach the shore by self-propulsion?

16. A nonoperational dictionary definition of momentum is "the quantity of motion of a moving body." Discuss the usefulness of this statement as a definition.

17. What is meant by the *conservation* of a physical quantity? Is the momentum of a single body conserved during a collision?

PROBLEMS

A number of additional problems that involve the application of Newton's principles can be found at the end of Chapter 5.

1. In an interaction between a 1-kg body and a second body, the acceleration of the 1-kg body is 1 m/s² and that of the second body is 4 m/s². What is the mass of the second body?

2. In an interaction between a 2-kg body and a 4-kg body the acceleration of the 2-kg body is 2 m/s². What is the acceleration of the 4-kg body?

3. A resultant force of 4 N, eastward, is exerted for 5 s on a 2-kg body, which was initially at rest. What is the acceleration of the body? What is the velocity of the body at the end of the fifth second? What is the displacement of the body during the 5 s of motion?

4. A 1000-kg car is moving with an initial velocity of 8 m/s, eastward, when the driver applies the brakes in such a way as to bring the car to rest in 4 s with constant acceleration. What is the acceleration of the car? What resultant force acts on the car? How far does the car move while it is coming to rest? What exerts the force on the car?

5. A 2000-kg car is advertised as being able to attain a speed of 108 km/h along a straight road in seven seconds after starting from rest. What is the magnitude of the average acceleration of the car during this period? What is the magnitude of the average resultant force acting on the car during the seven seconds?

6. A resultant external force of 12 N, westward, acts on a 6-kg body having an initial velocity of 16 m/s, eastward. What is the velocity of the body at the end of 10 s?

What is the displacement of the body from its initial position at the end of 10 s? What is the average velocity of the body during the 10-s period? What is the total path length traversed by the body during the 10-s period?

7. In the case of the accelerating car in Problem 5, what are the magnitude and direction of the average force exerted on the roadway by the car? What is the average acceleration of the road?

8. A 4-kg body lies at rest on the surface of the earth. What is the gravitational force exerted on the earth by the body? What force does the body exert on the surface of the earth? What resultant force is exerted on the body by the earth? on the earth by the body?

9. A horizontal force of 4 N, eastward, and a vertical force of 3 N, upward, act on a 2.5-kg body initially at rest. Assuming that these two forces are the only forces acting on the body, find the acceleration of the body.

10. Consider the situation in the preceding problem in terms of a rectangular coordinate system with its X axis toward the east and its Y axis vertically upward. Express the resultant force acting on the body and the acceleration of the body in terms of the unit vectors $\mathbf{i}$ and $\mathbf{j}$. If the body was initially at a point $x_0 = 1$ m and $y_0 = 2$ m, what will be the velocity $\mathbf{v}$, the displacement $\mathbf{D}$, and the position $\mathbf{r}$ of the body after 3 s? Express all of these quantities in terms of $\mathbf{i}$ and $\mathbf{j}$.

11. A 50-liter pail has a mass of 500 g. What upward force is required to lift this pail when it is completely filled with water?

12. What is the volume of a block of ice that has exactly the same mass as 2 m³ of water?

13. A 1000-kg car moves around a circular racetrack at a speed of 30 m/s; the radius of the racetrack is 400 m. What is the magnitude of the resultant force acting on the car? What exerts this force?

14. A 1200-kg car moves around a circular racetrack with a radius of curvature of 200 m. At a certain time the speed of the car is 20 m/s and is increasing at the rate of 3 m/s². What is the tangential component of the force acting on the car? What is the radial component of the force acting on the car? What is the magnitude of the resultant force acting on the car?

15. A man pulls horizontally with a gradually increasing force on a rope attached to a 6-kg body initially at rest on a horizontal surface. Nothing happens until the force attains a magnitude of 29.4 N, at which point the block suddenly moves with accelerated motion. The man finds that he can keep the body in motion at constant velocity by applying a force of only 14.7 N. What is the coefficient of static friction between the body and the surface? What is the coefficient of kinetic friction?

16. The coefficient of static friction between a crate and a horizontal loading platform is 0.6, and the corresponding coefficient of kinetic friction is 0.2. A man finds that by applying a horizontal force of at least 1200 N he can set the crate into motion. What is the mass of the crate? If the man continues to exert a force of 1200 N after the crate begins to move, what will be the magnitude of the crate's acceleration?

17. A 10-kg box is initially at rest on a plane that is inclined at an angle of 30° with the horizontal. (a) If the plane were frictionless: (1) what normal force would be exerted on the box by the plane? (2) What resultant force would act on the box? (3) What would be the acceleration of the box down the incline? (b) If the coefficient of static friction between the box and the plane were 0.4 and the corresponding coefficient of kinetic friction were 0.2: (1) What resultant force would act on the box? (2) What would be

the acceleration of the box down the incline?

18. Under the conditions of Problem 17b, (1) what would be the magnitude of the minimum force acting parallel to the incline required to hold the box at rest on the incline? What would be the magnitude of the force acting parallel to the incline required (2) to start the box moving up the incline, (3) to keep the box moving at constant velocity up the incline, and (4) to keep the box moving at constant velocity down the incline?

19. A constant resultant force of 10 N, eastward, acts on body for 5 s. At what rate is the momentum of the body changing? If the body has a mass of 2 kg and was initially at rest, what is the momentum of the body at the end of 5 s? What is the final velocity of the body at the end of 5 s?

20. A 50-g ball, initially at rest, is struck with a golf club and acquires a velocity of 60 m/s, northward. What is the total impulse associated with the force exerted on the ball by the club? If the club was in contact with the ball for 0.04 s, what is the average force exerted on the ball?

21. A 50-g ball dropped from a height of 44.1 m strikes a sidewalk and rebounds to a height of 19.6 m. What is the total change in momentum of the ball during its collision with the sidewalk? If the ball remains in contact with the sidewalk for 0.08 s, what is the average force exerted on the ball by the sidewalk?

22. A 100-g ball is dropped from rest at a certain height above a concrete roadway. If the ball falls for 3 s before striking the surface of the road and after striking the surface takes 2 s to attain its maximum height on the first bounce, what is the total change in the momentum of the ball during its collision with the road? If the contact between the ball and the surface lasted for 0.04 s,

what was the average resultant force acting on the ball during the collision?

23. A 2-kg shell is fired horizontally from a 2000-kg gun aimed toward the east; the muzzle velocity of the shell is 400 m/s. What was the total momentum of the shell–gun system before the gun was fired? What is the total momentum of the system after the gun is fired? What is the momentum of the shell as it emerges from the gun barrel? What is the momentum of the gun as the shell emerges from the barrel? What is the initial recoil velocity of the gun? If the gun were mounted on a frictionless track, how far would it move in 10 s after the gun was fired?

24. Answer all questions in Problem 23 for situations in which the mass of the gun is 1000 kg, 500 kg, and 100 kg.

25. A light bulb with a mass of 50 g falls from its socket located at a height of 4.9 m above the floor of an elevator cage. If the elevator cage is at rest, how long does it take for the bulb to reach the floor? What is the weight of the bulb? If the elevator is moving upward at a velocity of 4.9 m/s, what is the motion of the bulb as seen by (1) a man inside the moving elevator cage and (2) a man at rest with respect to the shaft of the elevator?

*26. Generalize the results of the preceding problem by considering the situation shown in the figure, which shows a coordinate system $X' Y'$ moving at constant velocity $V_x \mathbf{i}$ with respect to a coordinate system XY fixed with respect to the earth's surface. Suppose that the origins O and O' coincided at time $t = 0$. The location of a particle of mass m at the time t is (x', y') with respect to the moving frame. Show that its location in the fixed frame at time t is given by $y = y'$ and $x = x' + V_x t$. Find expressions for the velocity and acceleration of the particle relative to the XY frame in terms of the velocity and acceleration as observed in the $X'Y'$ frame. Is $X'Y'$ an inertial frame?

*27. Consider the situation shown in the figure if the $X'Y'$ frame moves at a constant acceleration $A_x\mathbf{i}$ with respect to the XY frame. Assume that the origins O and O' coincided at time $t = 0$ and that the primed frame had a velocity $V_{0x}\mathbf{i}$ relative to the unprimed frame at that time. The location of a particle of mass m at the time t is (x',y') with respect to the primed frame. Find expressions for its position, velocity, and acceleration relative to the unprimed frame in terms of x',y', and its velocity and acceleration as observed in the primed frame. Is the $X'Y'$ frame an inertial frame?

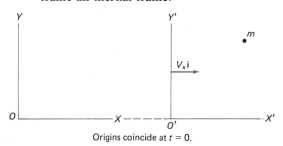

Origins coincide at $t = 0$.

Problems 26 and 27

28. An oak block with a mass of 500 g is started at an initial speed of 8 m/s up an oak board inclined at an angle of 60° with the horizontal. What resultant force acts on the block as it moves upward along the incline? What resultant force acts on the block as it slides back down along the incline? How long will the block continue to move upward along the incline? How long will be required for the block to slide back down the incline? What will be the speed of the block as it returns to its starting point?

29. Repeat Problem 28 for a case in which the inclined plane makes an angle of 45° with the horizontal.

30. For a situation similar to that described in Problem 28, what is the maximum angle of the incline at which the block would come to rest and not slide back down the incline? What would be the resultant force acting on the block as it moves up this incline? If the block had an initial velocity of 8 m/s upward along the incline, how far would it move before coming to rest?

31. A 1200-kg racing car moves at a speed of 20 m/s around a flat, horizontal concrete race track having a radius of 200 m. What is the acceleration of the car? What is the magnitude of the resultant force acting on this car? What is the minimum value of the coefficient of static friction between the tires and the track that would be required to make the motion possible?

32. Using the coefficients of friction in Table 4.2 find the maximum speed at which a rubber-tired race car could move around the track described in Problem 31 (a) if the concrete were wet and (b) if the concrete were dry. Why are real race tracks "banked" so that they slope "inward" along the curved portions of the track?

33. Explain in detail why a coordinate system attached to the earth's surface like the one used by geographers is *not* a good approximation of an inertial frame for large-scale motions. Suppose that we select as an approximately inertial frame a reference frame with its origin at the earth's center, with its Z axis parallel to the axis of the earth, and with its X and Y axes fixed in space with respect to the distant *stars*, a so-called *sidereal frame*. In this frame the earth rotates on its axis once in 24 h. What is the tangential speed of a point on the equator in this frame? What is its centripetal acceleration? What resultant force is required to keep a 2-kg body at the equator in motion about the Z axis of our coordinate system? The radius of the earth is approximately 6400 km.

34. Repeat Problem 33 for points with latitudes of 30°, 45°, 60°, and 90°.

35. Although the sidereal reference frame described in Problem 33 might seem to meet the requirements of an inertial frame, we

must remember that the earth itself is moving in an orbit around the sun. If we choose a sidereal frame with its origin at the center of the sun and with its Z axis perpendicular to the earth's orbit and consider the earth as moving about the sun in a circular orbit of radius $R = 150 \times 10^6$ km, what is the tangential speed of the earth as it moves in its orbit? What is the centripetal acceleration of the earth? What is the magnitude of the resultant force acting on the earth? (Use the astronomical data given in the Appendix.)

36. A *solar day* is the time interval between local noons, where local noon is defined as the time at which an observer sees the sun cross his meridian. Instead of using *solar time,* astronomers find it more convenient to use *sidereal time* with one *sidereal day* defined as the time interval between the successive passages of a distant star across an observer's meridian. Make a diagram of the earth in its orbit about the sun to show that the solar day is slightly longer than a sidereal day (actually about 4 minutes longer). Show that a sidereal year is one full sidereal day longer than a solar year.

37. If a 1-kg block of aluminum is dropped into a large vessel initially filled to the brim with water, some of the water flows over the brim. What is the total volume of this overflow?

38. Generalize Problem 37 to show how the densities of heavy objects with irregular shapes can be determined in terms of the known density of water.

39. A 1000-kg car moving eastward at a speed of 20 m/s has a head-on collision with a second 1000-kg car moving westward at a speed of 20 m/s along the same horizontal roadway. The road is ice-covered in the region of the collision, so frictional effects are negligible. As a result of the collision the bumpers of the two cars become locked

together. Considering the cars as a single dynamical system, find the resultant force acting on the system. What is the momentum of the system immediately after the collision? What is the change in the momentum of the first car? Of the second car?

40. Answer all questions of the preceding problem for a case in which the car moving eastward has a mass of 2000 kg.

41. An automobile with a mass of 2000 kg is moving at an initial velocity of 12 m/s eastward along a horizontal road. If a constant resultant horizontal force of 1000 N, eastward, is applied to the car for 20 s, what will be the final velocity of the car? What will be the change in the momentum of the automobile during this time interval? What will be the displacement of the automobile during this time interval?

42. By applying his brakes carefully the driver of the car in the preceding problem brings the automobile to rest in 10 s with constant deceleration. What resultant force acts on the automobile? What exerts this force? What is the displacement of the car during this 10 s interval? What is the change in the momentum of the car?

43. A 1200-kg car equipped with a spring-operated bumper and initially moving eastward at a speed of 20 m/s strikes the wall of a rigid concrete building and rebounds westward at the same speed. What is the change in the momentum of the car? If the car's bumper remains in contact with the wall for 0.2 s, what average resultant force $\bar{\mathbf{F}}$ acts on the car during the collision?

44. What average resultant force $\bar{\mathbf{F}}$ does the car exert on the building during the collision described in Problem 43? Why is the building not observably accelerated? Discuss.

*45. The position of a 500-g "particle" moving along the X axis of a coordinate system is given by the expression $x = 4 + 3t + 2t^2$, with x in m and t in s. What is the momentum of the particle at the end of the 4th second of motion? What is the time rate of change of the particle's momentum of this time? What is the magnitude of the resultant force acting on the particle at this time?

*46. With reference to the particle in Problem 45, what is the total change in the particle's momentum during the first 4 seconds of motion? What is the average force $\bar{F}_x$ acting on the particle during this time interval? What is the magnitude of the resultant force F_x acting on the particle at the end of the third second?

*47. The location of a 400-g "particle" during its first 6 seconds of motion is given by the expressions $x = 3 + 2t + 2t^2 - 0.2t^3$ and $y = 2 + 3t + 3t^2 - 0.1t^3$ with x and y in m and t in s. What is the momentum of the particle at the end of the 4th second? What is the resultant force acting on the particle at this time? Express your answers in terms of the unit vectors $\mathbf{i}$ and $\mathbf{j}$.

*48. With regard to the particle in Problem 47, what are the average velocity $\bar{\mathbf{v}}$ and average momentum $\bar{\mathbf{p}}$ of the particle during the first four seconds of the motion? What are the average value of the acceleration $\bar{\mathbf{a}}$ and the average resultant force $\bar{\mathbf{F}}$ acting on the particle during the first four seconds. Express

your answers in terms of the unit vectors $\mathbf{i}$ and $\mathbf{j}$.

*49. The location of a 500-g particle during its first 6 s of motion is given by the following equations: $x = 1 + 2t + 3t^2 + 0.1t^3$; $y = -2 + 2t + 4t^2 - 0.2t^3$, and $z = -3 + 3t + 2t^2 - 0.2t^3$ with x, y, and z in m and t in s. What is the momentum $\mathbf{p}$ of the particle at the end of the fourth second? What is the resultant force $\mathbf{F}_R$ acting on the particle at this time?

*50. With regard to the particle in Problem 49, what is the average velocity $\bar{\mathbf{v}}$ during the first 4 seconds of motion? What is the average acceleration $\bar{\mathbf{a}}$ during this time interval? What is the average resultant force $\bar{\mathbf{F}}_R$ acting on the particle during this time interval?

*51. The acceleration a_x of a 500-g "particle" moving along the X axis of a Cartesian coordinate system is given by the relation $a_x = 2 + 0.3t$ with a_x in m/s² and t in s. The particle is initially at rest at the origin of the system. What is the resultant force acting on the particle at the end of the 4th second? What is the change in momentum p_x during the first 4 seconds? What is the average value of the resultant force $\bar{F}_x$ during this time interval? What is the total displacement and what is the average velocity of the particle during this time interval? What is its average momentum?

CHAPTER 5

Translational Motion of Extended Bodies

In the preceding chapters we have talked a great deal about "particles" and have indeed stated Newton's Principles in terms of these entities. Yet in the examples and problems we have dealt with things like blocks, cannonballs, automobiles, etc., as if they were particles, even though they are obviously extended bodies. In this chapter we shall justify our earlier practice by showing that the motion of an extended body from place to place can be described in terms of the motion of a hypothetical particle with mass equal to the mass of the body and located at a certain point called the *center of mass* of the body. We shall begin our discussion with some extremely general theorems concerning dynamical systems consisting of sets of individual particles.

After proving these general dynamical theorems, we shall apply the results to the *pure translational motion* of a *rigid body,* which can be considered as made up of particles having fixed positions relative to one another. We shall state the condition for the *translational equilibrium* of a rigid body, one of the two important relations on which the branch of mechanics known as *statics* is based. Rotational equilibrium will be considered in a later chapter.

We close the chapter with a discussion of a subject called *dimensional analysis* that is of great importance in providing a check of the validity of various equations expressing relationships between physical quantities. Dimensional analysis provides a formal expression of derived quantities in terms of fundamental physical quantities.

5.1 CENTER OF MASS

Consider the dynamical system shown in Fig. 5.1, which consists of N particles with masses m_1, m_2, m_3, ..., m_N. The total mass M of the system is simply the sum of the masses of the individual particles:

$$M = m_1 + m_2 + m_3 + \cdots + m_N. \tag{5.1}$$

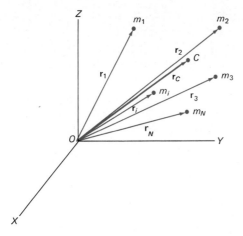

Fig. 5.1   The center of mass of a dynamical system.

We can express this sum by the expression

$$M = \sum_{i=1}^{N} m_i,$$

(5.1')

where the symbol "Σ" indicates a summation and the limits 1 and N indicate that the sum includes all particle masses m_i with i running from $i = 1$ to $i = N$.

For many purposes we can treat the motion of the entire dynamical system in terms of the motion of a single particle with mass M. The position of this hypothetical particle is called the *center of mass* of the dynamical system. Its location is defined by means of the position vector $\mathbf{r}_C$ shown in Fig. 5.1, where

$$M\mathbf{r}_C = m_1\mathbf{r}_1 + m_2\mathbf{r}_2 + m_3\mathbf{r}_3 + \cdots + m_N\mathbf{r}_N$$

(5.2)

or

$$M\mathbf{r}_C = \sum_{i=1}^{N} m_i\mathbf{r}_i.$$

(5.2')

In the figure we have located each particle by means of a position vector $\mathbf{r}_i$ drawn from the origin O of a conveniently selected coordinate system to the location of the particle. The center of mass C of the dynamical system is given by the point of the vector $\mathbf{r}_C$, where

$$\mathbf{r}_C = \frac{m_1\mathbf{r}_1 + m_2\mathbf{r}_2 + m_3\mathbf{r}_3 + \cdots + m_N\mathbf{r}_N}{M}$$

(5.3)

or

$$\mathbf{r}_C = \left(\sum_{i=1}^{N} m_i\mathbf{r}_i \right) \Big/ M.$$

(5.3')

Here, M represents the total mass of the dynamical system as given by (5.1) and (5.1'). We shall see that we can characterize the entire dynamical system in terms of a single "big particle" of mass M located at the center of mass C.

If our dynamical system is an extended body consisting of N particles, we can by Eqs. (5.1), (5.2), and (5.3) or by the equivalent "shorthand" equations (5.1'), (5.2'), and (5.3') locate the center of mass of the extended body. By characterizing the extended body by its total mass M located at its center of mass C we shall be able to justify our earlier practice of treating the extended body as a particle.

5.2 THE MOMENTUM OF A DYNAMICAL SYSTEM

By differentiating (5.2) and (5.2') with respect to time we obtain an interesting result:

$$M\frac{d\mathbf{r}_C}{dt} = m_1\frac{d\mathbf{r}_1}{dt} + m_2\frac{d\mathbf{r}_2}{dt} + \cdots + m_N\frac{d\mathbf{r}_N}{dt}$$

or

$$M\frac{d\mathbf{r}_C}{dt} = \sum_{i=1}^{N} m_i\frac{d\mathbf{r}_i}{dt}.$$

Because the derivatives of the position vectors with respect to time are by definition velocities, these equations can be written

$$M\mathbf{v}_C = m_1\mathbf{v}_1 + m_2\mathbf{v}_2 + \cdots + m_N\mathbf{v}_N \quad \text{or} \quad M\mathbf{v}_C = \sum_{i=1}^{N} m_i\mathbf{v}_i. \tag{5.4}$$

The terms on the right-hand sides of these equations are immediately recognizable as the momenta $\mathbf{p}_i$ of the individual particles; these add to give the total momentum of the system $\mathbf{P}$, in accord with Eq. (4.18) of Chapter 4. Thus, we conclude that

The total momentum of a dynamical system is equal to the product of the total mass of the system by the velocity of the center of mass of the system:

$$\mathbf{P} = M\mathbf{v}_C. \tag{5.5}$$

Because an extended body such as an automobile can be regarded as a dynamical system, we have been justified in expressing its momentum as the product of the body's mass by the body's velocity, which is also the velocity of its center of mass. We now recognize that our earlier treatment actually involves the motion of a "big particle" of mass M located at the body's center of mass.

In Chapter 4 we pointed out that, because *internal forces* between particles always cancel in pairs, the total momentum of an isolated dynamical system is constant. In view of this, relation (5.5) tells us that

When no external forces act on a dynamical system, the center of mass of the system moves at constant velocity.

On the assumption that a dynamical system is equivalent to a single hypothetical particle of mass M located at the center of mass of the system, this is what we would expect. Because a single particle cannot exert forces on itself, the absence of external forces implies that no resultant force acts on our hypothetical particle. Therefore, in accord with Newton's First and Second Principles, the motion of the hypothetical particle is one of constant velocity.

5.3   THE EFFECT OF EXTERNAL FORCES ON A DYNAMICAL SYSTEM

Now let us differentiate (5.4) with respect to time. We obtain

$$M\frac{d\mathbf{v}_C}{dt} = m_1\frac{d\mathbf{v}_1}{dt} + m_2\frac{d\mathbf{v}_2}{dt} + m_3\frac{d\mathbf{v}_3}{dt} + \cdots + m_N\frac{d\mathbf{v}_N}{dt}.$$

In view of the definition of acceleration $\mathbf{a} = d\mathbf{v}/dt$, we recognize that each derivative is simply an acceleration; we can rewrite the equation in the form*

$$M\mathbf{a}_C = m_1\mathbf{a}_1 + m_2\mathbf{a}_2 + m_3\mathbf{a}_3 + \cdots + m_N\mathbf{a}_N \qquad (5.6)$$

or, in shorthand form,

$$M\mathbf{a}_C = \sum_{i=1}^{N} m_i\mathbf{a}_i.$$

However, by Newton's Second Principle $\mathbf{F}_R = M\mathbf{a}$, we can write

$$M\mathbf{a}_C = \mathbf{F}_1 + \mathbf{F}_2 + \mathbf{F}_3 + \cdots + \mathbf{F}_N \text{ or } M\mathbf{a}_C = \sum_{i=1}^{N} \mathbf{F}_i, \qquad (5.7)$$

where each term on the right-hand side of the equation represents the resultant force on the corresponding individual particle. Each of these forces can be divided into two parts: (a) *external forces* exerted on the particle by particles outside the dynamical system and (b) *internal forces* exerted on the particle by other particles within the dynamical system.

Newton's Third Principle requires that the sum over all the particles of the internal forces is zero because oppositely directed forces of equal magnitude are associated with the interaction between each pair of particles inside the dynamical system; hence,

$$(\mathbf{F}_1 + \mathbf{F}_2 + \mathbf{F}_3 + \cdots + \mathbf{F}_N)_{\text{internal}} = 0 \quad \text{or} \quad \sum_{i=1}^{N} \mathbf{F}_{i(\text{internal})} = 0.$$

---

* The same symbol $\mathbf{a}_C$ has been used for the centripetal acceleration of a particle undergoing circular motion. No confusion should arise if the context of the discussion is kept in mind.

Therefore, the right-hand side of (5.7) can be rewritten in the form

$$\mathbf{F}_R = (\mathbf{F}_1 + \mathbf{F}_2 + \mathbf{F}_3 + \cdots + \mathbf{F}_N)_{\text{external}} \quad \text{or} \quad \mathbf{F}_R = \sum_{i=1}^{N} \mathbf{F}_{i(\text{external})}. \qquad (5.8)$$

This relation states that the resultant force acting on a dynamical system is simply the vector sum of the external forces acting on the individual particles of the system.

From (5.7) and (5.8) we see that we can apply Newton's Second Principle to the hypothetical particle of mass M located at the center of mass of the dynamical system; we can write

$$\mathbf{F}_R = M\mathbf{a}_C. \qquad (5.9)$$

In view of what we have said regarding the origin of $\mathbf{F}_R$, this force is sometimes called the *resultant external force* acting on the system.

> Regardless of the forces that act between the individual particles of a system, the center of mass of the system moves with acceleration $\mathbf{a}_C = \mathbf{F}_R/M$, where $\mathbf{F}_R$ is the resultant external force acting on the system and M is the total mass of the system.

One interesting application of this theorem involves the motion of dynamical systems in free fall near the earth's surface, where the resultant external force on the system is merely the weight of the system $\mathbf{w} = M\mathbf{g}$. The center of mass of the system moves with the gravitational acceleration $\mathbf{g}$ directed vertically downward. We can now treat the cannonball, which we have considered earlier in Section 7 of Chapter 3, as a dynamical system; we now recognize that the parabolic trajectory that we obtained earlier is actually the path followed by the center of mass of the projectile. Its height y above its starting point is given by $y = (V_M \sin \theta)t - \frac{1}{2}gt^2$; its horizontal coordinate is $x = (V_M \cos \theta)t$, where V_M is the muzzle velocity of the cannonball and θ is the elevation angle of the gun barrel above the horizontal.

Now let us apply the above theorem to an exploding shell like the one shown in Fig. 5.2. The dashed parabola given in this figure represents the parabolic path that we obtained for the cannonball; during the early stages of its motion the shell follows the parabolic trajectory, provided air resistance is negligible. At some point in its trajectory the shell explodes, sending out shell fragments in all directions. However,

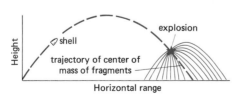

Fig. 5.2 Trajectory of an explosive shell in the absence of air resistance.

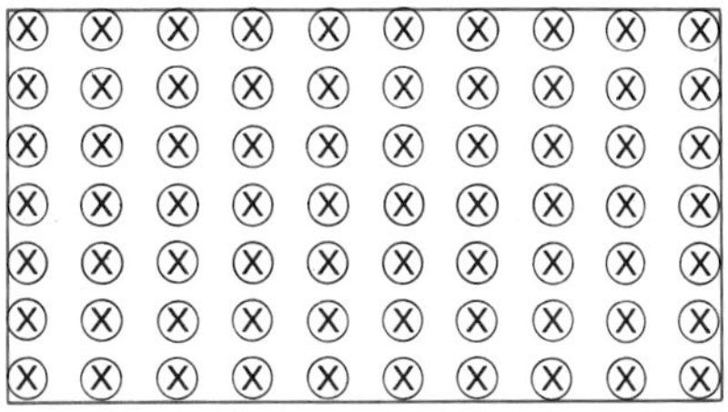

Fig. 5.3 The particles making up a rigid body maintain their positions *relative to one another.*

we note that *the process of explosion involves only internal forces.* Although the shell fragments have a variety of trajectories following the explosion, as suggested in Fig. 5.2, the theorem that we have proved asserts that the center of mass of the shell fragments continues to move along the dotted parabolic path. If the artilleryman wishes to concentrate his shell fire in the immediate vicinity of the target, he will set the shell to explode late in its trajectory; if, on the other hand, he wishes to spray the entire countryside in the vicinity of the target, he will use a shell timed to explode earlier in the trajectory. In either case, the center of mass of the fragments will "land" directly on target if the gun has been properly aimed.

5.4   RIGID BODIES

We shall have many opportunities to apply the general dynamical theorems proved in the earlier sections of this chapter. Initially we shall apply them to a special class of bodies called rigid bodies. A rigid body is a body that has a definite shape and definite volume; neither shape nor volume changes when external forces are applied to the body. Another way of saying this is to define a rigid body as a dynamical system consisting of particles as suggested in Fig. 5.3 that maintain their positions *relative to one another* even when external forces are applied to the body.

Like the particle itself, the rigid body is something of an abstraction. No real body is truly rigid. Every real body can be altered in volume and in shape if sufficiently large external forces are applied; a real body can be twisted or bent so that the particles in it no longer maintain their original relative positions. If sufficiently large forces are applied to a real body, the body will actually break into pieces.

Although completely rigid bodies do not exist, many real bodies are excellent approximations of rigid bodies provided the external forces acting on them are not too large. We can learn many things by considering their dynamical properties as approximately those of completely rigid bodies. In a later chapter dealing with elasticity we shall discuss the ways in which real bodies change their shapes and sizes when subjected to external forces. For the present we shall ignore such changes and treat solid bodies as if they were rigid.

5.5   THE CENTER OF MASS OF A RIGID BODY

If we have a regular solid consisting of a material of constant density, the center of mass of the solid always coincides with the center of symmetry of the body. We can illustrate this by considering a few examples. Although for many purposes we can regard a rigid body as consisting of particles, it is usually desirable to treat such a body as continuous and to use the calculus in determining the location of its center of mass. In this case it is necessary to replace the summation in (5.3) and (5.3′) with the corresponding integration:

$$\mathbf{r}_C = (\int \mathbf{r}\, dm)/M, \qquad (5.10)$$

where dm can be regarded as the mass of an infinitesimal particle and the limits of the integral include the entire body. We usually express dm as the product of the density ρ and a volume element dV. The single integral sign in (5.10) symbolically represents all three of the integration operations that are required to cover the variations in the three spatial coordinates and include contributions from all the volume elements in the summation. If the object has sufficient symmetry, it may not be necessary to perform all three integrations explicitly. This is illustrated in the following examples.

Example.   Show that the center of mass of a rectangular parallelopiped coincides with its geometrical center provided its density ρ is constant.

   We can do this by considering the steel block of length l, width w, and height h shown in Fig. 5.4a, in which we have aligned the edges of the body with the axes of a rectangular coordinate system. We proceed to find the X coordinate of the center of mass of the solid. We imagine the block to be divided into a very large number of infinitesimal particles of mass dm. The position vector locating the particle with coordinates (x,y,z) is $\mathbf{r} = x\mathbf{i} + y\mathbf{j} + z\mathbf{k}$. If we insert this vector into (5.10), we see that the X component of the position vector locating the center of mass is $X_C = (\int x\,dm)/M$. Consider now the slab of height h, width w, and thickness dx shown in Fig. 5.4b. All the mass elements in this slab have the same X coordinate. Therefore, in computing the summation represented by $\int x\,dm$ we can group the contributions from these mass elements; their total contribution to the sum is $x\rho hw\,dx$. To complete the summation we have to add the contributions of all such slabs from $x = 0$ to $x = l$. This gives

$$X_C = \left(\int_0^l x\rho hw\,dx \right) \Big/ M = \left(\rho hw \int_0^l x\,dx \right) \Big/ \rho hwl$$

$$= \tfrac{1}{2} l^2 / l = \tfrac{1}{2} l.$$

In similar fashion we can show that $Y_C = \tfrac{1}{2} w$ and $Z_C = \tfrac{1}{2} h$. The center of mass thus corresponds to the center of the slab; midway between the ends, midway between top and bottom, and midway between the left and right faces in Fig. 5.4.

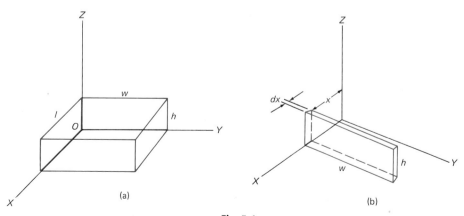

(a)   (b)

Fig. 5.4

Example.   Show that the center of mass of a homogeneous circular brass disk is at the center of the disk.

Suppose that the disk has radius R and thickness τ. Choose coordinates with origin at the center of the bottom face of the disk and Z axis coincident with the symmetry axis of the disk, as shown in Fig. 5.5a. Imagine the disk to be divided into a very large number of infinitesimal particles of mass dm. These particles are chosen in the following way, which is "natural" to the shape of the disk. Divide the disk into thin slabs oriented perpendicular to the Z axis, each slab of thickness dz. Then divide each slab into segments of surface area $r\,d\phi\,dr$ as indicated in Fig. 5.5b. These area elements are natural for plane polar coordinates. By this means we have divided the disk into small elements of volume $dV = r\,d\phi\,dr\,dz$. The mass dm is given by $dm = \rho r\,d\phi\,dr\,dz$, where ρ is the density of the disk.

In order to sum over all such volume elements in the disk, we must allow ϕ to range from 0 to 2π, r to range from 0 to R, and z to range from 0 to τ. Three integration processes are required to cover the variations of the three variables. Thus, for the X coordinate of the center of mass we have

$$X_C = (\textstyle\int x\,dm)/M = \left(\int_{r=0}^{R} \int_{\phi=0}^{2\pi} \int_{z=0}^{\tau} r(\cos \phi)\rho r\,d\phi\,dr\,d\tau \right) \Big/ \rho\pi R^2 \tau$$

$$= \left(\rho \int_{0}^{R} r^2 dr \int_{0}^{2\pi} \cos \phi\, d\phi \int_{0}^{\tau} dz \right) \Big/ \rho\pi R^2 \tau.$$

We need evaluate only the integral $\displaystyle\int_{0}^{2\pi} \cos \phi\, d\phi = \sin \phi \, \Big|_{0}^{2\pi} = 0$ in order to see that $X_C = 0$. Using $y = r \sin \phi$ we can similarly show that $Y_C = 0$ because $\displaystyle\int_{0}^{2\pi} \sin \phi\, d\phi = 0$. By applying the method of the preceding example we find that $Z_C = \frac{1}{2}\tau$, midway between the faces of the disk.

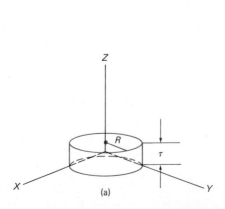
(a)

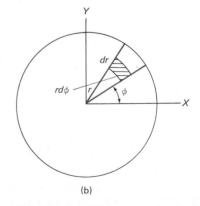
(b)

Fig. 5.5

We should point out that the center of mass of a body does not necessarily lie inside the material of which the body is composed. For example, the center of mass of a ring, a doughnut, or an automobile tire lies in the geometric center, where there is no matter at all.

By recognizing that a rigid body can be characterized by a single particle of mass M located at its center of mass, we can sometimes locate the center of mass of a complex body by dividing the body into smaller parts, the centers of mass of which can be located by considerations of symmetry. This is illustrated in the following example.

Example. A "carpenter's square" has the dimensions and shape shown in Fig. 5.6 and is made of flat sheet steel. Where is its center of mass?

We can use the rectangular coordinate system shown in Fig. 5.6 with its axes coinciding with the outer edges of the "square." It will be convenient to use the mass per unit area $\sigma = \rho\tau$, where τ is the thickness of the sheet steel, in solving the problem. The total mass of the carpenter's square can be written as $M = \sigma A$, where A is the total area of the square. We now divide the square into two rectangular sections with masses $M_1 = \sigma A_1$ and $M_2 = \sigma A_2$; these are shown by the shaded rectangles in the figure. The centers of mass of these two rectangles are located at their geometrical centers; for rectangle ①, $X_{1C} = 2.5$ cm, $Y_{1C} = 25$ cm; for rectangle ②, $X_{2C} = 15$ cm, $Y_{2C} = 2.5$ cm. Treating these two rectangles as particles located at their centers of mass, we can find the coordinates of the center of mass of the carpenter's square from the following relations:

$$X_C = \frac{M_1 X_{1C} + M_2 X_{2C}}{M} = \frac{\sigma A_1 X_{1C} + \sigma A_2 X_{2C}}{\sigma A} = \frac{A_1 X_{1C} + A_2 X_{2C}}{A}$$

$$= \frac{(250 \text{ cm}^2)(2.5 \text{ cm}) + (100 \text{ cm}^2)(15 \text{ cm})}{350 \text{ cm}^2} = 6.07 \text{ cm},$$

$$Y_C = \frac{M_1 Y_{1C} + M_2 Y_{2C}}{M} = \frac{\sigma A_1 Y_{1C} + \sigma A_2 Y_{2C}}{\sigma A} = \frac{A_1 Y_{1C} + A_2 Y_{2C}}{A}$$

$$= \frac{(250 \text{ cm}^2)(25 \text{ cm}) + (100 \text{ cm}^2)(2.5 \text{ cm})}{350 \text{ cm}^2} = 18.6 \text{ cm}.$$

These values give the coordinates of the center of mass of the entire carpenter's square. Note that the dimensions come out correctly in centimeters. Note also that the center of mass of the body is actually outside of the square itself.

In a later chapter we shall suggest certain experimental procedures that can be used to find the location of the center of mass of a body.

5.6 PURE TRANSLATIONAL MOTION OF A RIGID BODY

A rigid body undergoes pure translational motion provided its orientation in space does not change. Consider, for example, a body that moves in or parallel to the XY

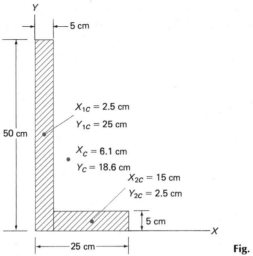

Fig. 5.6

plane from Site *A* to Site *B* as shown in Fig. 5.7. The rectangular coordinate system *XY* can be regarded as "space-fixed"; for our purposes we can imagine it as firmly attached to the earth's surface, like the corner of a room or the southwest corner of a football field. Now we can set up another coordinate system $X'Y'$ attached firmly to the rigid body, a so-called "body-fixed" coordinate system. If the body-fixed coordinate system does not change its orientation with respect to the space-fixed coordinate system during the course of the motion from Site *A* to Site *B*, the motion of the body is one of pure translation. This is the case for the motion of the body in Fig. 5.7; at all times the *X'* axis remains parallel to the *X* axis and the *Y'* axis remains parallel to the *Y* axis. Similarly, the *Z'* axis and the *Z* axis, both of which are directed toward the reader in Fig. 5.7, remain parallel during the translation of the body from Site *A* to Site *B*.

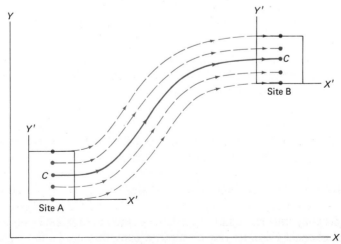

Fig. 5.7 Pure translation of a rigid body.

The paths traversed by representative particles in the rigid body are shown by the dotted curves in Fig. 5.7. It will be noted that the path traversed by each particle in the body is similar to the path traversed by the center of mass of the body, which is shown by the heavily dashed curve. At any instant all particles in the body have the same velocity as the center of mass. If the velocity of the center of mass changes, the velocity of each particle in the body changes in exactly the same manner.

The rigid body represents an important special case of the general dynamical systems that we have considered in the first three sections of this chapter. If the resultant external force acting on a rigid body is zero, the velocity of the center of mass of the body is constant; provided the motion of the body is one of pure translation, the velocity of each particle in the body is also constant and is equal to the velocity of the center of mass. If a rigid body is subjected to a nonzero resultant force $\mathbf{F}_R$, the acceleration $\mathbf{a}_C$ of the center of mass has the value $\mathbf{a}_C = \mathbf{F}_R/M$ in accord with (5.9); if the motion of the rigid body is one of pure translation, each particle in the body also has an acceleration equal to $\mathbf{a}_C$.

Pure translation is a very special type of motion of a rigid body. More frequently motion of a rigid body involves not only translation but also rotation. When rotation occurs, the body-fixed coordinate system $X'Y'$ does not maintain its orientation with respect to the space-fixed coordinate axes XY, in contrast to the situation of Fig. 5.7. Any motion of a rigid body can be considered as a combination of translation and rotation. We shall postpone consideration of rotation to a later chapter; we now proceed to an important special case of the translational portion of the motion of a rigid body.

5.7 TRANSLATIONAL EQUILIBRIUM

We now come to a situation of great practical importance to architects and mechanical engineers: *translational equilibrium. A dynamical system is in translational equilibrium when the acceleration $\mathbf{a}_C$ of its center of mass is zero.* Since $\mathbf{a}_C = \mathbf{F}_R/M$, we see that the resultant external force acting on the system must be zero. Because this condition is one of the relationships on which the branch of mechanics known as *statics* is based, we give the following formal statement:

CONDITION FOR TRANSLATIONAL EQUILIBRIUM: The vector sum of all external forces acting on a dynamical system with center of mass at rest or in motion at constant velocity must be zero.

Although this condition is quite general and applies to elastic solids, to liquids, to gases, and to any well-defined collection of matter, we shall restrict our present application to rigid bodies. The condition for translational equilibrium applies to every structural member of a building or of a complex piece of machinery; it is therefore of special importance to architects and to design engineers. Although the term *statics* implies that the body involved is *at rest,* we note that the condition also applies to a body moving with constant velocity; in either case the acceleration of the body's center of mass is zero.

Example.   A suspended signboard consists of a rectangular piece of wood with a mass of 2 kg. It is supported at rest as indicated in Fig. 5.8 by two flexible wires, one of which makes an angle $\theta_1 = 30°$ with the horizontal; the other wire makes an angle $\theta_2 = 45°$ with the horizontal. What forces $\mathbf{F}_1$ and $\mathbf{F}_2$ do the wires exert on the signboard?

Because the board is at rest, we can apply the condition for translational equilibrium:

$$\mathbf{F}_1 + \mathbf{F}_2 + \mathbf{w} = 0,$$

where $\mathbf{w} = M\mathbf{g}$. This is a single equation with two unknowns, $\mathbf{F}_1$ and $\mathbf{F}_2$, so at first glance we might conclude that it is impossible to determine the two unknowns. However, we note that the equation involves vector quantities, each of which has scalar components. Taking the coordinate system as suggested in the figure, we can write

$X:$ $-F_1 \cos \theta_1 + F_2 \cos \theta_2 = 0$ or $F_1 \cos \theta_1 = F_2 \cos \theta_2.$ (i)

$Y:$ $F_1 \sin \theta_1 + F_2 \sin \theta_2 - Mg = 0$ or $F_1 \sin \theta_1 + F_2 \sin \theta_2 = Mg.$ (ii)

The first of these equations shows that $F_1 = F_2(\cos \theta_2 / \cos \theta_1)$. Substituting this value for F_1 in the second equation gives

$$F_2[(\cos \theta_2 / \cos \theta_1)\sin \theta_1 + \sin \theta_2] = Mg.$$

Substituting the numerical values of the sines and cosines, we obtain

$$F_2[(0.707/0.866)0.500 + 0.707] = (2 \text{ kg})(9.8 \text{ m/s}^2).$$

Because $1 \text{ N} = 1 \text{ kg m/s}^2$, $F_2 = 17.6 \text{ N}$ and $F_1 = (0.707/0.866)F_2 = 14.3 \text{ N}$.

We note that we were able to find $\mathbf{F}_1$ and $\mathbf{F}_2$ only because the two forces had both horizontal and vertical components. If both these forces had been directed vertically upward, we would have been unable to solve the problem because we would have had only the single relation $F_1 + F_2 = Mg$. We would have been able to obtain the value of their sum, but would have been unable to obtain unique values for F_1 and F_2 separately.

One other important point should be noted. In solving this problem we have obtained two forces $\mathbf{F}_1$ and $\mathbf{F}_2$ that will give a zero resultant force $\mathbf{F}_R$ on the signboard so that $\mathbf{a}_C = 0$. However, we have no assurance that the sign board would actually remain suspended horizontally without rotation as suggested in Fig. 5.8. As we shall see later when we consider rotational equilibrium, we *could* use the two forces that we have obtained to support the signboard in a horizontal position if we properly selected the points at which the flexible wires are attached to the board. (See page 193.)

As suggested in the example, the condition for translational equilibrium alone merely gives us the values of forces that must be applied to a body to make the acceleration $\mathbf{a}_C$ of the body's center of mass zero. It gives us no information about where the forces must be applied to the body. This is an important question that can be answered only after we have considered rotation. As a simple example of what is involved,

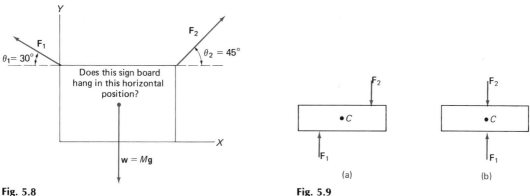

Fig. 5.8

Fig. 5.9

consider the situation shown in Fig. 5.9, which shows horizontal forces F_1 and F_2 applied to a rigid body on a horizontal frictionless surface as seen from above. In order for the body to remain in translational equilibrium, the magnitudes F_1 and F_2 must be equal. However, if we apply the two forces as in Fig. 5.9a, the rigid body will begin to rotate; if we apply the two forces as in Fig. 5.9b, there is no tendency for the body to rotate. We shall treat rotation in Chapters 7 and 8.

5.8 APPLICATION OF NEWTON'S PRINCIPLES TO LINEAR MOTION WITH CONSTANT FORCES

In many applications of Newton's Principles we have several objects connected by strings or rods and arranged so that during the time of interest each object moves in a straight line under the influence of constant forces. In this section we consider a particular example of such motion in order to illustrate the kind of logical reasoning that is useful in treating such a system. We shall also introduce several idealizations concerning strings and pulleys that are frequently valid approximations that simplify the application of Newton's Principles.

Let us consider the system shown in Fig. 5.10. Three objects of masses $m_1 = 0.6$ kg, $m_2 = 0.8$ kg, and $m_3 = 1.1$ kg are connected by flexible, inextensible strings of negligible mass as shown in the figure. The strings do not break under the conditions being considered. At time $t = 0$ the system is released from rest and objects ①

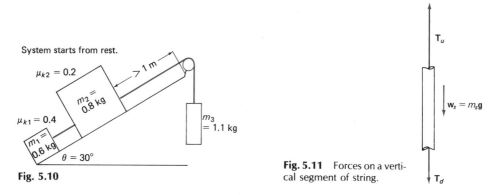

Fig. 5.10

Fig. 5.11 Forces on a vertical segment of string.

and ② begin to move up the incline. The coefficient of kinetic friction between the bottom of object ② and the surface of the incline is $\mu_{k2} = 0.2$; the coefficient of kinetic friction between the bottom of object ① and the surface of the incline is $\mu_{k1} = 0.4$. The angle of the incline with the horizontal is $\theta = 30°$; the pulley at the end of the incline has negligible friction in its bearings and negligible mass. What are the accelerations of the three objects? What are the tension forces in the strings? Assuming that the front edge of object ② is initially more than 1 m from the upper end of the incline, find the time required for object ② to move 1 m along the incline.

We must comment on several of the conditions regarding the strings and the pulley. The strings in our problem serve to transmit forces from one object to another. When we say that a string is "inextensible," we simply mean that it does not stretch. When we say that a string is "flexible," we imply that it can exert only a "pull" on an object to which it is attached and that the pull must be along the direction of the string. The internal structure of the string does not allow it to transmit a push or a force component perpendicular to its own direction. A rigid rod, on the other hand, has both of these possibilities. We shall return to the properties of flexibility and rigidity in Chapter 10.

The force that one part of a string exerts on an adjacent part of the string is called the *tension* in the string. Consider the segment of string shown in Fig. 5.11. The portion of the string above the segment exerts a tension force T_u on the segment shown; the portion of the string below the segment exerts a tension force T_d on the segment shown. If the mass of the string segment is m_s and the upward acceleration of the segment is **a**, by Newton's Second Principle we must have $T_u - T_d - m_s g = m_s a$. If the mass of the string is negligible, this requires that $T_u = T_d$. This is a general result; *if the mass of a straight piece of string is negligible, the tension in the string has the same magnitude everywhere along its length.* For the time being, we shall usually assume that strings are inextensible, flexible, and of negligible mass.

A pulley serves to change the direction of the tensional force exerted by a string while allowing the string to move either way around the corner. We shall assume that there is sufficient friction that the string does not slip relative to the rim of the pulley wheel. If the inertia of the pulley wheel with respect to rotational motion and the friction in the bearings are not negligible, the tensions in the string at the two places where it leaves the pulley will not have equal magnitudes. By specifying a pulley of negligible mass and frictionless bearings we imagine an ideal device that serves to *change the direction of the tension of a string without changing the magnitude of the tension.* We shall be able to consider the properties of real pulleys after we have discussed rotational motion in Chapter 7; for the time being we shall assume that all pulleys are ideal, being both light and frictionless.

We now consider the questions posed in the example. In order to treat such a problem successfully, we must organize our thinking in a systematic way. First, *draw a diagram* and label that diagram with the information that is known. In the present example this is done for us in Fig. 5.10.

Second, *identify the unknown quantities of interest and the conditions under which they are to be found.* The problem asks for three kinds of quantities: (1) the accelerations of the three objects, (2) the tension forces in the strings, and (3) the time required

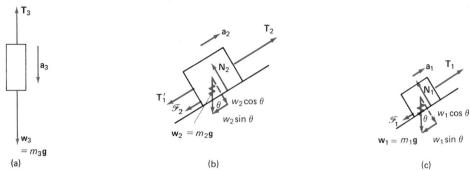

Fig. 5.12 (a) Forces on object three of Fig. 5.10. (b) Forces on object two of Fig. 5.10. (c) Forces on object one of Fig. 5.10.

for object ② to move 1 m. We are given conditions that the strings are flexible, inextensible, have negligible mass, and do not break; that the pulley has negligible mass and negligible bearing friction; and that there is room on the incline for the proposed 1 m displacement. Frequently conditions are not stated so explicitly, and common sense must be used to identify the context in which the problem is to be treated. For example, in the present problem we assume that the incline is strong enough to support the system. Further, the motion of objects ① and ② will be along the surface of the incline; they will not jump up off of the slope.

The third step in our solution is to *consider separately each of the bodies of interest and to identify the forces acting on each body.* In this problem there are three bodies of interest, objects ①, ②, and ③. The forces acting on each separate object are indicated in Fig. 5.12. The forces on object ③ are the weight $\mathbf{w}_3$ downward and the upward tension force $\mathbf{T}_3$ exerted by the string. The forces on object ② are the tension force $\mathbf{T}_2$ up the incline exerted by the string passing over the pulley, the tension force $\mathbf{T}_1'$ down the incline exerted by the string joining objects ① and ②, the weight $\mathbf{w}_2$ directed downward, the force $\mathbf{N}_2$ normal to the incline exerted by the surface of the incline, and the friction force $\mathscr{F}_2$ down the incline opposing the sliding of object ② up the incline. The forces on object ① are the tension force $\mathbf{T}_1$ up the incline exerted by the string joining objects ① and ②, the weight $\mathbf{w}_1$ directed downward, the force $\mathbf{N}_1$ normal to the incline exerted by the surface of the incline, and the friction force $\mathscr{F}_1$ down the incline opposing the sliding of object ① up the incline.

As our fourth step, *we apply Newton's Second Principle to each object in turn.* To do this, we introduce a coordinate system for each object. For objects ① and ② the natural coordinate system has axes parallel and perpendicular to the incline. All forces on these objects except their weights are parallel to one of these axes. In Figs. 5.12b and 5.12c, we show the weights $\mathbf{w}_1$ and $\mathbf{w}_2$ resolved into components perpendicular and parallel to the incline. For object ① there is no acceleration perpendicular to the incline. Therefore, by Newton's Second Principle $N_1 = w_1 \cos \theta$, and this in turn means that $\mathscr{F}_1 = \mu_{k1} N_1 = \mu_{k1} w_1 \cos \theta$. Similarly, for object ② we have $N_2 = w_2 \cos \theta$ so that $\mathscr{F}_2 = \mu_{k2} N_2 = \mu_{k2} w_2 \cos \theta$. Then by applying Newton's Second Principle to the components of the forces *on* the object that are parallel to the incline we obtain for object $\textcircled{1}$

$$m_1a_1 = T_1 - \mu_{k1}w_1 \cos \theta - w_1 \sin \theta \tag{i}$$

and for object $\textcircled{2}$

$$m_2a_2 = T_2 - T_1' - \mu_{k2}w_2 \cos \theta - w_2 \sin \theta. \tag{ii}$$

By applying Newton's Second Principle to the vertical forces on object $\textcircled{3}$ we obtain

$$m_3a_3 = w_3 - T_3. \tag{iii}$$

Since the strings do not stretch or break, the three objects must move together. This means that the magnitudes of the three accelerations must be the same: $a_1 = a_2 = a_3$. We shall call this common acceleration magnitude simply a. From our discussion of strings and pulleys we know that $T_1 = T_1'$ and $T_2 = T_3$. We also use the relations $w_1 = m_1g$, $w_2 = m_2g$, and $w_3 = m_3g$. Then our equations take the forms

$$m_1a = T_1 - \mu_{k1}m_1g \cos \theta - m_1g \sin \theta, \tag{i$'$}$$
$$m_2a = T_2 - T_1 - \mu_{k2}m_2g \cos \theta - m_2g \sin \theta, \tag{ii$'$}$$
and
$$m_3a = m_3g - T_2. \tag{iii$'$}$$

The fifth step of our solution is to solve these equations algebraically for the unknown quantities, which in this case are a, T_1, and T_2, and then to substitute the given numerical values in the resulting relations. We see that if we simply add the three equations written above we eliminate the tensions. Thus, we have

$$(m_1 + m_2 + m_3)a = m_3g - \mu_{k1}m_1g \cos \theta - \mu_{k2}m_2g \cos \theta - m_1g \sin \theta - m_2g \sin \theta,$$

which we can immediately solve for a. Upon substitution of the given numerical values we obtain

$$a = \frac{[(1.1 \text{ kg}) - (0.4)(0.6 \text{ kg}) \cos 30° - (0.2)(0.8 \text{ kg}) \cos 30° - (0.6 \text{ kg}) \sin 30° - (0.8 \text{ kg}) \sin 30°](9.8 \text{ m/s}^2)}{(0.6 \text{ kg} + 0.8 \text{ kg} + 1.1 \text{ kg})} = 0.21 \text{ m/s}^2.$$

In order to find the tensions in the strings, we return to equations (i$'$) and (iii$'$). From (iii$'$) we have

$$T_2 = m_3(g - a) = (1.1 \text{ kg})(9.8 \text{ m/s}^2 - 0.21 \text{ m/s}^2) = 10.6 \text{ N},$$

and from (i$'$) we have

$$T_1 = m_1a + \mu_{k1}m_1g \cos \theta + m_1g \sin \theta$$
$$= (0.6 \text{ kg})(0.21 \text{ m/s}^2) + (0.4)(0.6 \text{ kg})(9.8 \text{ m/s}^2) \cos 30° + (0.6 \text{ kg})(9.8 \text{ m/s}^2) \sin 30°$$
$$= 5.1 \text{ N}.$$

With the acceleration known, the time for object ② to move a distance D up the incline can be found from $D = v_0t + \frac{1}{2}at^2$. Since $v_0 = 0$, this gives

$$t = \sqrt{2D/a} = \sqrt{2(1 \text{ m})/(0.21 \text{ m/s}^2)} = 3.1 \text{ s.}$$

5.9 DIMENSIONAL ANALYSIS

At this point we introduce a subject that is of importance not only to mechanics but to physics in general and also to engineering. It is a subject that we have already introduced implicitly by ensuring that every equation that we have employed must have dimensional balance in the sense that the SI units of all terms on the left-hand side of the equation must be the same as the SI units of all terms on the right-hand side of the equation. We have also indicated that the units used for all derived quantities must be clearly expressed in terms of the *base units* used for the fundamental quantities; i.e., in terms of the *meter,* the *kilogram,* and the *second.*

The subject of dimensional analysis presents these ideas in a formal manner that is more general in the sense that it can be applied to physical quantities expressed in terms of any consistently organized system of units. The general method is to express all *derived quantities* in terms of *fundamental quantities,* which for mechanics are length *(L),* mass *(M),* and time *(T).* For example, speed and velocity are both derived quantities expressed as ratios of length L to time T and are thus dimensionally expressed as L/T or LT^{-1}. Similarly, acceleration is defined as the ratio of velocity change to elapsed time and can be expressed dimensionally as $(L/T)/T = L/T^2 = LT^{-2}$. Force is defined as the product of mass and acceleration and can be expressed dimensionally as $M(L/T^2) = MLT^{-2}$. In any valid physical relation, each term must give the same result when expressed dimensionally in terms of the fundamental quantities.

In Table 5.1 we give the dimensional analysis of all quantities that we have thus far employed. The reader would do well to check the analysis of each quantity by going back to its formal definition.

Because we are employing only SI units in this book, we shall continue our insistence on correct dimensional analysis by indicating the proper SI units in each defining equation. It is to be noted that M, L, and T suffice for the dimensional analysis of all mechanical quantities. Additional fundamental quantities are required for the treatment of heat and electromagnetism.

Table 5.1 Dimensional Analysis of Physical Quantities

Length	L	Speed	LT^{-1}
Mass	M	Velocity	LT^{-1}
Time	T	Acceleration	LT^{-2}
Volume	L^3	Force	MLT^{-2}
Angle	(Pure number)	Momentum	MLT^{-1}
Area	L^2	Impulse	MLT^{-1}
		Density	ML^{-3}

Dimensional analysis is an extremely valuable technique to employ in checking the possible validity of proposed relationships between physical quantities. If some newly proposed discovery or relationship is stated in the form of an equation that does not balance dimensionally, we know at once that the proponent of the relationship is talking nonsense. If the proponent's equations *do* balance dimensionally, we know that his proposal *may* be valid and *may* deserve further serious consideration. Many engineers and physicists practice dimensional analysis on every mathematical statement that confronts them; to them the use of dimensional analysis has become habitual and almost automatic. The development of a habit of this kind is valuable to anyone employing quantitative thinking.

Example. Somebody reports that the velocity of a body is equal to the product of the resultant force acting on the body and the time that the force acts; that is, $\mathbf{v} = \mathbf{F}_R t$. Discuss this statement from the point of view of dimensional analysis.

In considering the equation $\mathbf{v} = \mathbf{F}_R t$, we note that the dimensions of velocity are given by LT^{-1}, those by force by MLT^{-2}, and those of time by T. Thus, the dimensional analysis of the proposed relationship gives: $LT^{-1} = MLT^{-1}$. Because the two sides of this equation do not have the same dimensions, we know at once that the proposed relation is invalid.

QUESTIONS

1. Give several examples of dynamical systems. Can a dynamical system *really* be isolated so that no external forces act on it?

2. Is it necessary for any mass actually to be located at the center of mass of a dynamical system?

3. In Chapter 4 we applied Newton's principles to *bodies* like automobiles and treated these bodies as if they were particles. To what extent is this treatment valid?

4. What is a *rigid body?* Are any real bodies truly rigid? Why is it convenient to introduce the concept of a completely rigid body?

5. Explain why the forces acting between particles making up a dynamical system cannot change the momentum of the system.

6. Two people are at rest together on the frictionless surface of a frozen river. Suggest a way in which they can both reach the same bank of the river without outside aid.

7. Is the pure translational motion of a rigid body necessarily a form of rectilinear motion?

8. If the center of mass of a rigid body has rectilinear motion, does the body as a whole necessarily have pure translational motion?

9. What is the condition for the translational equilibrium of a rigid body? If this condition is satisfied, is the center of mass of the body necessarily at rest?

10. If a rigid body is at rest, can we say with certainty that no external forces act on the body?

11. Why does *dimensional analysis* provide a useful technique for scientists and engineers to employ?

PROBLEMS

Many of these problems represent further applications of Newton's principles and other ideas that were discussed in Chapter 4. The student should review the concepts in Chapter 4 as well as those in Chapter 5 before beginning work on these problems.

1. A man exerts a force of 10 N at one end of a string of negligible mass; the other end of the string is attached to a tree as suggested in the figure. What force is exerted on the tree? In answering this question, consider the two forces acting on the two ends of the string. Also consider the force exerted on the part of the string on the left of plane AA' by the part on the right; consider the force exerted on the part of the string on the right of plane AA' by the part on the left. Whenever forces exist across a boundary like AA', the string is said to be under a *tension* equal to the magnitude of the "transmitted" force. What is the tension in the cord between the man and the tree in the figure?

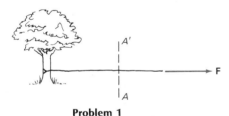

Problem 1

2. A man exerts a force of 10 N on a block by pulling on the end of a cord of negligible mass attached to the block as shown in the figure; the angle between the cord and the horizontal is 30°. The coefficient of static friction between the block and the surface is 0.4; the coefficient of kinetic friction is 0.2. What is the magnitude of the normal force exerted on the block by the surface? What is the tension in the cord? What is the acceleration of the block as it moves across the surface?

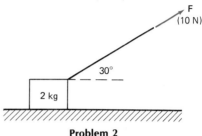

Problem 2

3. A man slowly raises one end of a board on which a 1-kg block lies at rest. When the angle θ in the figure reaches 30°, the block begins to slide down the board. What is the coefficient of static friction between the block and the plane?

4. The angle θ_S at which a block begins to slide from rest down an inclined plane is called the *angle of slip* or the *limiting angle of repose*. Write expressions (1) for the components of the weight parallel to and perpendicular to the plane, (2) for the normal force exerted on the block by the plane, and (3) for the force of friction acting on the block as a function of θ. Show that $\tan \theta_S = \mu_S$.

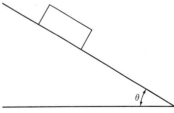

Problems 3 and 4

5. A car moves around a *flat* circular race track that has a radius of 100 m. If the

coefficient of static friction between the car tires and the race track is 0.6, what is the maximum speed the car can attain without skidding?

6. A small truck is equipped with a four-wheel drive. If the coefficient of static friction between the tires and a dry road is 0.8, what is the maximum acceleration that the truck can attain along a level portion of the roadway? If the level road is covered with ice so that the coefficient of friction is only 0.15, what is the maximum acceleration attainable by the truck?

7. A curve in a highway has a radius of curvature of 100 m. At what angle θ should the road be "banked" in order for a car moving at 30 m/s to go around the curve without any tendency to skid? (No "tendency to skid" means that no frictional forces contribute to the centripetal force acting on the car; the normal force exerted on the car by the road not only supports the weight of the car but also furnishes the required centripetal force.)

8. Generalize the results for Problem 7 by demonstrating that the correct angle of bank for a car moving at speed v around a curve of radius R is given by the relation: $\tan \theta = v^2/Rg$.

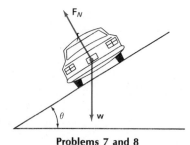

Problems 7 and 8

9. Returning to the truck mentioned in Problem 6, find the maximum acceleration attainable by the truck in going *up* a hill on a road that is inclined at an angle of 10° with the horizontal (1) when the road is dry and (2) when the road is covered with ice.

10. Find the maximum acceleration of the truck in Problem 9 in going *down* the hill along the road.

11. A 2-kg iron ball is supported at rest by cords of negligible mass as shown in the figure. What are the tensions T_1 and T_2 in the upper cords if $\phi_1 = 30°$ and $\phi_2 = 45°$?

12. For the situation of Problem 11, what would be the tensions T_1 and T_2 in the upper cords if $\phi_1 = 15°$ and $\phi_2 = 30°$?

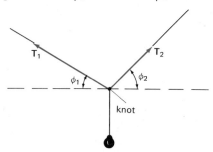

Problems 11 and 12

13. A pendulum consists of a 1-kg steel ball attached to the end of a light nylon cord 3 m long having negligible mass. At equilibrium the cord normally hangs vertically downward. What is the magnitude of the horizontal force **F** required to hold the pendulum 30° away from the vertical? With the pendulum in this position, what is the tension in the cord?

14. Find the magnitude of the horizontal force and the tension in the cord when the pendulum in Problem 13 is displaced 45° from the vertical. What is the tension in the cord when the pendulum hangs in its usual vertical position?

15. As shown in the figure, a body is suspended at the midpoint of a cord 2 m long. The cord has negligible mass. The ends of the cord are attached to rings that are free to move along a horizontal rod. If the coefficient of static friction between the rings and the rod is 0.4, what is the maximum separation that the rings can have without slipping?

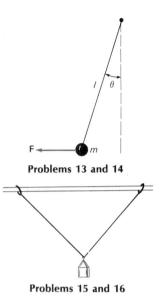

Problems 13 and 14

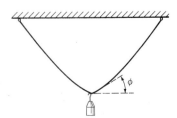

Problems 15 and 16

16. Solve Problem 15 for a cord 3 m in length when the coefficient of static friction between the rings and the rod is 0.5.

17. A flexible rope having a weight of 7 N is attached to two hooks in the ceiling, as indicated in the figure. At the midpoint of the rope is hung a body that weighs 3 N. The angle between the rope and the ceiling is 45°. What is the angle ϕ that the rope makes with the horizontal at the midpoint of the rope? Find the tension in the rope near the points of attachment to the ceiling and near the midpoint of the rope. Explain why the rope cannot be straight. *Hint:* The whole rope, each half of the rope, and the midpoint of the rope are all in equilibrium.

18. The rope considered in Problem 17 is rehung with the suspended body removed and an angle of 50° between the rope and the ceiling. Under this condition, find the ten-

sion in the rope at its midpoint and at the points of attachment to the ceiling.

19. A 2-kg lead ball is attached to a 3-m length of nylon cord of negligible mass hanging from the ceiling of a laboratory. By pulling the ball to one side and then pushing it in the proper direction, a student sets the ball into motion at constant speed in a horizontal circular path. If the radius of the circular path is 1 m, what is the speed of the ball? Find the magnitudes of the centripetal acceleration of the ball, the centripetal force acting on the ball, and the tension in the cord.

20. The student gives the ball in Problem 19 a lateral displacement R and then releases the ball; the ball then swings back and forth as a "simple pendulum." The speed of the ball when the ball is directly under the point of support is 1.64 m/s. What is the tension in the supporting cord when the ball is at the lowest point in its to-and-fro swing?

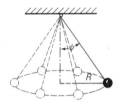

Problems 19 and 20

21. The device in the figure is known as Atwood's machine. Bodies of masses m_1 and m_2 are connected by means of cord of negligible mass. The cord passes over a *light, frictionless pulley.* If $m_1 = 2$ kg and $m_2 = 2.5$ kg, find the magnitude a of the accelerations of the bodies and the tension T in the string connecting the bodies. Show that $m_2 g > T > m_1 g$.

22. Solve Problem 21 for a case where $m_1 = 3$ kg and $m_2 = 2.8$ kg.

23. A block with 1 kg mass lying on a horizontal table top is attached to a cord of negligible mass that passes over a light, frictionless pulley to a suspended block with a mass of 2 kg that hangs vertically downward.

Problems 17 and 18

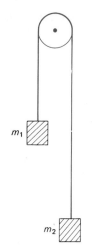

Problems 21 and 22

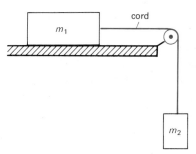

Problems 23 and 24

(1) If the table top were frictionless, what would be the common magnitude of the accelerations of the blocks and what would be the tension in the cord? (2) If the coefficient of kinetic friction between the block and the table top were 0.4, what would be the magnitude of the accelerations of the blocks and what would be the tension in the cord?

24. Answer the questions of Problem 23 above for a situation in which the mass of the block on the table is 2 kg, the mass of the suspended body is 3 kg, and the coefficient of kinetic friction is (1) 0, (2) 0.3.

25. In the experimental arrangement shown in the figure a body of mass $m_1 = 2$ kg lies at rest on an inclined plane making an angle $\theta = 30°$ with the horizontal. Assume that

the mass of the cord is negligible and that the pulley is light and frictionless. The coefficient of static friction between the body and the plane is 0.4 and the corresponding coefficient of kinetic friction is 0.2. (1) What is the minimum mass m_2 of a suspended body that will cause body one to move up the plane? (2) With a body of this minimum mass m_2 suspended, what will be the common magnitude of the bodies' accelerations, and what will be the tension in the cord connecting the bodies?

26. Repeat Problem 25 for an angle $\theta = 45°$ between the plane and the horizontal.

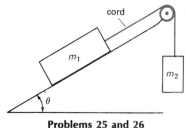

Problems 25 and 26

27. A flexible chain 1 m long lies initially extended and at rest on the horizontal top of a table. The coefficient of static friction between the chain and the table top is 0.4 and the corresponding coefficient of kinetic friction is 0.2. If the chain is pulled toward the edge of the table so that part of the chain hangs vertically, the chain tends to slide off the table. What fraction of the chain must hang over the side of the table in order to *start* the chain sliding? What will be the initial downward acceleration of the lower end of the chain as the chain begins to move?

28. What is the downward acceleration of the lower end of the chain considered in Problem 27 when the following fractions of the chain are hanging vertically downward: 0.4, 0.5, 0.6, 0.7, 0.8, 0.9, 1.0? Discuss the motion of the center of mass of the chain as it slides off the table.

29. It is sometimes useful to regard the moon

and the earth as a dynamical system. Using the astronomical data in the Appendix, compute the distance of the center of mass of the earth–moon system from the center of the earth when the earth and the moon have their mean separation.

30. Hydrogen has two isotopes: Normal hydrogen H and deuterium D. The mass of the deuterium atom D is approximately twice that of the lighter hydrogen atom H. In the HD molecule the atomic nuclei have an equilibrium separation R. In terms of R, what is the distance between the center of mass of the HD molecule and the nucleus of the H atom?

31. Jupiter is the largest planet in the solar system. It is sometimes useful to regard the Sun and Jupiter as constituting a dynamical system. If the distance between the Sun's center and Jupiter's center is R, what is the distance between the center of the Sun and the center of mass of the Sun–Jupiter system? (Use the astronomical data in the Appendix.)

32. If the equilibrium distance between the hydrogen nucleus and the fluorine nucleus in the HF molecule is R, what is the distance between the F nucleus and the center of mass of the HF molecule? The atomic mass of fluorine is approximately 19 times that of hydrogen.

33. The end of a 12-kg steel rod 3 m long is welded to the center of a second steel rod of mass 8 kg and length 2 m to form the letter "T." How far from the free end of the longer rod is the center of mass of the T?

34. For the "T" considered in Problem 33, what should be the mass of a short lead "foot" attached to the free end of the longer rod in order to make the center of mass of the resulting structure exactly 1.5 m from the originally free end of the longer steel rod? Assume that the lead foot has the form

of a flat plate 1 cm thick; the end of the steel rod is attached to the center of the lead plate.

35. What is the location of the center of mass of a system of five particles having masses of $m_1 = 2$ g, $m_2 = 3$ g, $m_3 = 7$ g, $m_4 = 0.5$ g, and $m_5 = 4.5$ g and the following position vectors: $r_1 = (2.6$ m, 0, 0), $r_2 = (1.4$ m, 0.8 m, 0.5 m), $r_3 = (0, 1.2$ m, -0.9 m), $r_4 = (-1.7$ m, -2.3 m, 1.6 m), $r_5 = (1.5$ m, -2.1 m, 3.1 m)?

36. Suppose that each of the particles in Problem 35 is acted on by an external force of the form $\mathbf{F} = k\hat{\mathbf{r}}/r^2$, where r is the distance of the particle from the origin, $\hat{\mathbf{r}}$ is a unit vector pointing radially away from the origin, and k is a constant that is the same for all the particles. The force $\mathbf{F}$ on each particle is in newtons when r is in meters. What is the acceleration of the center of mass of the system at the instant when the particles have the position vectors given in Problem 35?

37. What are the SI units of the constant k in Problem 36? Express these units in terms of the fundamental quantities of mass, length, and time.

38. In Table 5.1 it is indicated that the dimensions of angle are simply a pure number. Yet we have introduced a *unit* for angles, the radian. Is it logically consistent for a physical quantity to have units but no dimensions? Discussion this question. What is the status of the degree for the measurement of angles? Is it a unit, a dimension, or some other kind of quantity?

39. The following equations are proposed for the range R of a projectile fired horizontally with initial velocity v_0 from the top of a cliff of height h: $R = 2v_0 h\sqrt{g}$, $R = v_0/2hg$, $R = 2h\sqrt{v_0/g}$, $R = v_0 h/2g$, $R = v_0\sqrt{2h/g}$, $R = g/\sqrt{2v_0 h}$. On the basis of dimensional analysis, which of these relations has a possibility of being correct?

40. The velocity of propagation v of a wave on a stretched string depends on the mass per unit length μ of the string and the tension F with which the string is stretched. Assuming that the propagation velocity does not depend on any other quantities, use dimensional analysis to determine how v depends on F and μ to within a dimensionless numerical factor.

*41. A certain homogeneous solid object has the shape of a hemisphere of radius R. Choose a coordinate system such that the hemisphere has its flat face in the XY plane with its curved surface extending in the positive Z direction. Take the origin at the center of the flat face. What are the coordinates of the center of mass of the hemisphere?

*42. A homogeneous pyramid has a square base with side of length l and an apex that is a distance h above the center of the base. Choose a coordinate system with origin at the center of the base and Z axis through the apex. What is the Z coordinate of the center of mass of the pyramid in terms of l and h? The volume of the pyramid is $(\frac{1}{3})l^2h$.

43. In the example at the end of Section 5.5 we locate the center of mass of a complex body by dividing the body into smaller parts, the centers of mass of which can be located simply. We replace each part by a particle located at the center of mass of the part with mass equal to the total mass of the part. Show in detail that this process is justified and that the center of mass of the complex body coincides with the center of mass of the collection of particles just defined as determined by (5.3).

CHAPTER 6

Work,
Energy,
Power

Work, energy, and power are words that are a part of our everyday language; each is employed with a variety of meanings and connotations, not all of which are clearly defined. In modern physical science we use these words as the names of precisely defined physical quantities. These physical quantities are scalars that can be used in solving many problems that we have treated earlier by means of the vector quantities, force and momentum; the mathematics of scalars is simpler than that of vectors, as we have seen in earlier chapters. Many physical phenomena can be handled more simply in terms of work and energy than by the direct application of Newton's Principles.

The importance of what we now call kinetic energy was noted by Christian Huygens (1629–1695), a somewhat older contemporary of Newton, and by Gottfried Wilhelm Leibniz (1646–1716), an intense rival of Newton who independently invented the calculus. The general relationships between work and mechanical energy were developed during the 18th and 19th centuries by many scientists. The Irish mathematician and scientist Sir William Rowan Hamilton (1805–1865) emphasized the importance of the total mechanical energy in his system of analytical dynamics. In the course of the 19th century the energy concept was broadened to include thermal, chemical, electric, and magnetic energy, all of which we shall consider in later chapters. The energy concept is useful in all branches of physics, in chemistry, and in engineering; as we shall see in later chapters, the total energy in any isolated system appears to be constant. During the present century, Einstein's development of relativistic mechanics has led to an extension of earlier ideas to include mass–energy relationships that form the basis for practical uses of nuclear energy.

In this chapter we present the classical definitions of work and mechanical energy and discuss mechanical energy transformations. After we have shown how these ideas can be applied to several kinds of problems, we introduce the concept of power and discuss power transmission, a subject of major importance in engineering.

6.1   WORK

In common language we use the term *work* to denote any type of purposeful activity involving muscular or mental effort. In the language of physics, the term *work* has a precise definition and is used only in the restricted sense of this definition. In order for work in the physical sense to be done, it is necessary for a *force* to act on a body and for the body to undergo a *displacement* that has a component parallel to the direction in which the force is acting. Another way of saying this is that the applied force must have a component parallel to the displacement if it is to do work.

Figure 6.1 shows a body undergoing a displacement **D** along a horizontal surface in a direction along the X axis of a frame of reference. A constant force **F** acts on the body at an angle ϕ relative to the direction of the displacement. The work done is defined in the following way:

The WORK done by a constant force acting on a body while the body experiences a displacement along a straight line is a scalar quantity defined as the product of the magnitude of the displacement by the component of the force in the direction of the displacement.

Thus, the work done in Fig. 6.1 is $(F \cos \phi)D$. Because we have chosen the displacement **D** parallel to the X axis, and the body has moved a distance X along this axis, we can write

$$W = (F \cos \phi)X = F_x X, \quad \textit{(Work)} \tag{6.1}$$

where we recognize that the X component of the force is given by $F_x = F \cos \phi$. No work is done by the force component F_y because the displacement has no Y component. In the special case where $\phi = 0$ in Fig. 6.1, we can write $W = FD = FX$. In the case when $\phi = 90°$, no work is done because then $F_x = 0$. If the angle between **F** and **D** in Fig. 6.1 is greater than $90°$, the work is negative because $\cos \phi$ is negative. This is the case when a force is applied to retard the motion of a body already moving with a positive velocity in the X direction.

We note that, regardless of how large a force may act on a body, no work is done by that force unless there is a displacement with a component parallel to the direction of the force. Similarly, regardless of how large the displacement of a body, no work is done unless there is a force component parallel to the displacement.

Because work is defined as the *product* of a force component and the magnitude

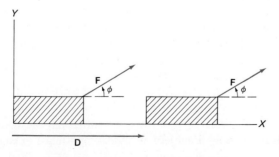

Fig. 6.1 The work done is given by $W = FD \cos \phi$.

of a displacement, the derived unit used in measuring work involves the product of a force unit and a length unit. The SI unit is called the joule (J) in honor of the English physicist James Prescott Joule (1818–1889), whose work we shall discuss in a later chapter. The SI work unit is defined as follows:

> One JOULE is the work done when a constant force of one newton acts on a body while the body moves a distance of one meter in the direction of the force: $1 \text{ J} = 1 \text{ N} \cdot 1 \text{ m} = 1 \text{ Nm}$.

We close this section by indicating that the arguments used in connection with Fig. 6.1 can be generalized for the case of a constant force **F** acting on a body that experiences a displacement **D** along *any* straight line. The result is that

$$W = F_x D_x + F_y D_y + F_z D_z, \qquad \left\{ \begin{array}{l} W \text{ in J} \\ F \text{ in N} \\ D \text{ in m} \end{array} \right\} \tag{6.2}$$

Because we shall have occasion to use (6.2) in later discussions, we shall give a formal derivation of it in the following section.

6.2 THE SCALAR PRODUCT OF TWO VECTORS

The definition of work given in the preceding section involves a type of product of two vectors, *force* and *displacement,* to obtain a scalar quantity, *work.* This type of product of two vector quantities is called a *scalar product* or *dot product:*

> The SCALAR PRODUCT of two vectors is defined as a scalar quantity equal to the product of the magnitudes of the two vectors and the cosine of the smaller angle between their positive directions.

The scalar product of two vectors is denoted by placing a dot between the two vectors. Thus, for the constant force **F** acting on a body undergoing the straight-line displacement **D** as suggested in Fig. 6.2, the work W done is

$$W = FD \cos \theta = \mathbf{F} \cdot \mathbf{D}. \tag{6.3}$$

The expression $\mathbf{F} \cdot \mathbf{D}$ is simply a shorthand notation for $FD \cos \theta$.

Because the scalar product is used frequently in physics and modern engineering, it is desirable to summarize some of its mathematical properties. By its definition, the scalar product is clearly *commutative:*

$$\mathbf{A} \cdot \mathbf{B} = \mathbf{B} \cdot \mathbf{A}. \tag{6.4}$$

Furthermore, it is *associative:*

$$(\mathbf{A} + \mathbf{B}) \cdot \mathbf{C} = \mathbf{A} \cdot \mathbf{C} + \mathbf{B} \cdot \mathbf{C}. \tag{6.5}$$

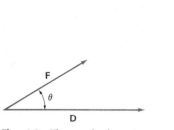

Fig. 6.2 The work done is $W = FD \cos \theta = \mathbf{F} \cdot \mathbf{D}$.

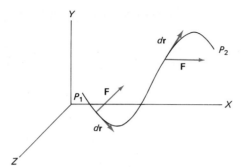

Fig. 6.3 The work done in moving a particle from P_1 to P_2 is given by the line integral

$$\int_{P_1}^{P_2} \mathbf{F} \cdot d\mathbf{r}.$$

To prove the associative property (6.5), consider a coordinate system having the X axis parallel to $\mathbf{C}$. Then, the right-hand side of (6.5) becomes $A_x C + B_x C$. The left-hand side of (6.5) is the X component of $(\mathbf{A} + \mathbf{B})$ multiplied by C. We have shown earlier in our treatment of vector addition (p. 26) that the X component of the vector $(\mathbf{A} + \mathbf{B})$ is simply $A_x + B_x$; therefore, the left-hand side of (6.5) is also $A_x C + B_x C$. Thus, (6.5) is indeed correct. Logical extension of (6.4) and (6.5) shows that for any number of vectors

$$(\mathbf{A} + \mathbf{B} + \cdots) \cdot (\mathbf{D} + \mathbf{E} + \cdots) = \mathbf{A} \cdot \mathbf{D} + \mathbf{A} \cdot \mathbf{E} + \cdots + \mathbf{B} \cdot \mathbf{D} + \mathbf{B} \cdot \mathbf{E} + \cdots. \qquad (6.6)$$

Now consider a vector $\mathbf{A}$ resolved into rectangular vector components:

$$\mathbf{A} = \mathbf{i}A_x + \mathbf{j}A_y + \mathbf{k}A_z,$$

where $\mathbf{i}$, $\mathbf{j}$, and $\mathbf{k}$ are, respectively, unit vectors along the positive X, Y, and Z axes. Similarly, a vector $\mathbf{B}$ can be written

$$\mathbf{B} = \mathbf{i}B_x + \mathbf{j}B_y + \mathbf{k}B_z.$$

Then the scalar product of $\mathbf{A}$ and $\mathbf{B}$ becomes by (6.6)

$$\mathbf{A} \cdot \mathbf{B} = A_x B_x + A_y B_y + A_z B_z \qquad (6.7)$$

because $\mathbf{i} \cdot \mathbf{i} = \mathbf{j} \cdot \mathbf{j} = \mathbf{k} \cdot \mathbf{k} = 1$ and $\mathbf{k} \cdot \mathbf{j} = \mathbf{i} \cdot \mathbf{k} = \mathbf{j} \cdot \mathbf{k} = 0$. Our general argument in connection with (6.7) thus justifies our earlier equation (6.2).

The expressions for work given in (6.1) and (6.2) were stated for the simple case in which the applied force is constant and the motion of the body is rectilinear. Now consider the more general case of motion of a body along an arbitrary path like the one from initial point P_1 to final point P_2 in Fig. 6.3. We consider an applied force that may vary from point to point along the path. In order to determine the total work done by the agent exerting the applied force $\mathbf{F}$, we must divide the path followed by the body into small increments and compute the work done for each separate increment of the path. Let $d\mathbf{r} = \mathbf{i} \, dx + \mathbf{j} \, dy + \mathbf{k} \, dz$ represent the displacement of the body as it moves along a small increment of the path. The increment of work dW done during the displacement $d\mathbf{r}$ is $dW = \mathbf{F} \cdot d\mathbf{r}$. In view of (6.7) we can write this as

$$dW = \mathbf{F} \cdot d\mathbf{r} = F_x\,dx + F_y\,dy + F_z\,dz. \tag{6.8}$$

The total work W done during the motion from point P_1 to point P_2 is the *sum* of all such increments; mathematically this is represented by the integral

$$W = \int_{P_1}^{P_2} \mathbf{F} \cdot d\mathbf{r}. \tag{6.9}$$

Such an integral is called a *line integral* because it is evaluated along a particular path or line from P_1 to P_2. In general, the value of a line integral will depend on the particular path followed as well as the end points of the path. In view of (6.8), the line integral (6.9) can be expressed as the sum of three ordinary integrals:

$$W = \int_{X_1}^{X_2} F_x\,dx + \int_{Y_1}^{Y_2} F_y\,dy + \int_{Z_1}^{Z_2} F_z\,dz, \tag{6.10}$$

where the subscript 1 refers to the coordinates of P_1 and the subscript 2 refers to those of P_2. We shall frequently make use of line integrals; in certain special cases they can be evaluated rather easily.

We now make use of the ideas just introduced to prove an important theorem:

If several forces act on a particle or body in translational motion along a path, the total work done by all the forces is equal to the work done by the resultant force.

By definition the resultant force is $\mathbf{F}_R = \mathbf{F}_1 + \mathbf{F}_2 + \cdots$. The work done by the resultant force is by (6.9)

$$\int_{P_1}^{P_2} \mathbf{F}_R \cdot d\mathbf{r} = \int_{P_1}^{P_2} (\mathbf{F}_1 + \mathbf{F}_2 + \cdots) \cdot d\mathbf{r} = \int_{P_1}^{P_2} \mathbf{F}_1 \cdot d\mathbf{r} + \int_{P_1}^{P_2} \mathbf{F}_2 \cdot d\mathbf{r} + \cdots.$$

The first term on the right-hand side is the work done by $\mathbf{F}_1$, the second term is the work done by $\mathbf{F}_2$, and so on. Thus, our theorem is proved.

6.3 MECHANICAL ENERGY

In physics the term energy has a precise meaning:

The ENERGY of a body is the capacity or ability of the body to perform work. Energy is a scalar quantity and is measured in the same units as work.

On the basis of this definition we can think immediately of many examples of bodies that possess energy because of their motion. Thus, a moving automobile, a moving freight car, and a moving bullet all have the ability to do work during the process of being brought to rest. *The energy possessed by a body as a result of its motion is called kinetic energy.* We consider at this point the kinetic energy of a moving particle and the kinetic energy of a body in pure translational motion—the so-called *translational kinetic energy* of the body. Kinetic energy is also associated with the rotational motion of a body such as a flywheel; we shall consider rotational kinetic energy in Chapter 7.

In order to set a body into motion we must do work to the body. The amount of work required is a measure of the kinetic energy associated with the moving body:

The KINETIC ENERGY of a moving body is equal to the work required in order to change the body from a state of rest to its state of motion.

We now derive an expression for the kinetic energy E_K of a particle, which we shall find can be expressed in terms of its mass m and the magnitude of its velocity v. In order to do this we must compute the work done in accelerating the particle from a state of rest to velocity **v.** If a constant resultant force $\mathbf{F}_R$ acts on the particle, the acceleration **a** is constant and the displacement **D** is in the direction of the force. In applying Newton's Second Principle $\mathbf{F}_R = m\mathbf{a}$ to the problem, we may choose the direction of the $+X$ axis of the coordinate system in the direction of $\mathbf{F}_R$, as shown in Fig. 6.4. In accord with the Second Principle, $F_x = ma_x$ and, by the definition of work, $W = F_x x = ma_x x$. If the particle starts from rest at $t = 0$, its displacement at any time t is $x = \frac{1}{2} at^2$, and our equation becomes

$$W = (ma_x)(\tfrac{1}{2} a_x t^2) = \tfrac{1}{2} m(a_x t_x)^2 = \tfrac{1}{2} mv_x^2,$$

since the velocity $v_x = a_x t$ for constant acceleration.

Because the kinetic energy E_K of a particle moving at velocity **v** is defined as the work W required to accelerate the particle from rest to velocity **v,** we can write

$$E_K = \tfrac{1}{2} mv^2. \quad \left\{ \begin{array}{l} E_K \text{ in J} \\ m \text{ in kg} \\ v \text{ in m/s} \end{array} \right\} \quad \textit{(Translational Kinetic Energy)} \qquad (6.11)$$

As we have shown earlier, an extended body in pure translational motion can be considered as a "big particle" located at the body's center of mass. Therefore, the expression $E_K = \frac{1}{2} mv^2$ in (6.11) also gives the *translational kinetic energy* of a moving extended body of mass m; in this case, v is the speed of the center of mass of the body.

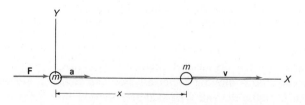

Fig. 6.4

In our derivation of (6.11) we have used a constant resultant force $\mathbf{F}$ to obtain the expression $E_K = \frac{1}{2}mv^2$. However, by use of (6.10) it is easy to show that our expression for E_K is independent of the way in which the particle acquired its speed. In using (6.10) we start at some point P_1 at which the particle is at rest with $v_{1x} = v_{1y} = v_{1z} = 0$ and assume that the resultant force on the particle is $\mathbf{F}_R = F_x\mathbf{i} + F_y\mathbf{j} + F_z\mathbf{k}$. Under the influence of this resultant force the particle moves to the point P_2. By Newton's Second Principle $\mathbf{F}_R = m\mathbf{a}$; therefore, the first of the integrals in (6.10) can be written

$$\int_{X_1}^{X_2} F_x \, dx = m \int_{X_1}^{X_2} a_x \, dx.$$

Now $dx = v_x \, dt$. Since $a_x = dv_x/dt$, the above integrand can be expressed as $a_x \, dx = (dv_x/dt)v_x \, dt = v_x \, dv_x$. The value of v_x at P_1 is 0; if we let v_{2x} represent the value of v_x at P_2, the above integral can be written

$$\int_{X_1}^{X_2} F_x \, dx = m \int_0^{v_{2x}} v_x \, dv_x = \frac{1}{2} mv_{2x}^2.$$

The second and third integrals in (6.10) similarly give $\frac{1}{2} mv_{2y}^2$ and $\frac{1}{2} mv_{2z}^2$, respectively. The sum of the three integrals is

$$\frac{1}{2} m(v_{2x}^2 + v_{2y}^2 + v_{2z}^2) = \frac{1}{2} mv_2^2,$$

where v_2 is the magnitude of the particle's velocity and therefore the particle's speed at point 2. Thus, our result $E_K = \frac{1}{2} mv^2$ in (6.11) is general; it depends in no way on how the particle acquired its speed.*

Example. How much work must be done by the resultant force in accelerating a 5000-kg truck from rest to a speed of 30 m/s?

As no information is given regarding the forces acting on the truck or the displacement of the truck during the period of its acceleration, we cannot solve

* It is interesting to compare the work–energy relations of this chapter with the impulse–momentum relations discussed in Chapter 4. In the case of a resultant force $\mathbf{F}_R$ acting on a particle initially at rest, the momentum $\mathbf{p}$ of the particle is given by the relation $\mathbf{p} = \int \mathbf{F}_R \, dt$ and the kinetic energy of the particle E_K is given by the relation $E_K = \int \mathbf{F}_R \cdot d\mathbf{r}$. The early adherents of Newton regarded the first of these relations as "fundamental"; the adherents of Huygens and Leibnitz took an opposing view and based their system of mechanics on work–energy relations. The word energy had not then been invented; the Huygens–Leibnitz school referred to the quantity mv^2 as *vis viva* ("living force"). We recognize today that impulse–momentum relations and work–energy relations are both of great importance; the validity of one approach to a problem in no way implies the invalidity of the other!

this problem directly in terms of the definition of work. We do know, however, that the work done by the resultant force is equal to the final kinetic energy of the truck. Thus, $W = E_K = \frac{1}{2}mv^2 = \frac{1}{2}(5000 \text{ kg})(900 \text{ m}^2/\text{s}^2) = 2.25 \times 10^6 \text{ kg·m}^2/\text{s}^2 = 2.25 \times 10^6 \text{ N·m} = 2.25 \times 10^6 \text{ J}$ since $1 \text{ N} = 1 \text{ kg·m/s}^2$ and $1 \text{ J} = 1 \text{ N·m}$.

Note: If we had been given the total displacement **D** of the truck during its period of acceleration, we could have obtained the average value $\mathbf{F}_{AV}$ of the resultant force in the direction of the displacement: $W = \mathbf{F}_{AV} \cdot \mathbf{D} = E_K$. Note that $\mathbf{F}_{AV}$ is a "space-average" force and may be quite different from the time-average force $\overline{\mathbf{F}}$ we have used in earlier discussions.

The other type of mechanical energy that can readily be recognized is called *potential energy;* this is energy that a particle or body possesses as a result of its position or configuration. It is easily recognized that a body raised above the earth's surface is capable of doing work on other bodies at the earth's surface. For example, even a nonexplosive bomb high above the earth in an airplane is capable of doing much destructive work to a building on the ground if the bomb is allowed to fall. Similarly, water at the top of a waterfall is capable of doing work to a turbine at the foot of the waterfall. These are examples of *gravitational potential energy.* Another type of potential energy is involved when we change the configuration of an elastic body. For example, when we bend a bow, the bow acquires elastic potential energy that can be used to shoot an arrow. Similarly, elastic potential energy can be stored in a spring and can be used to operate the mechanism of an alarm clock or a "wind-up toy."

We shall discuss elastic potential energy in Chapter 10, which deals with elasticity; here we shall consider only gravitational potential energy.

The GRAVITATIONAL POTENTIAL ENERGY of a particle or body at a given height above the earth's surface is equal to the work done *against gravitational forces* in raising the particle or body to this height.

A body thus has gravitational potential energy because of its position above the earth's surface; this energy represents the work that it can do to other bodies located at the earth's surface.

In order to find an expression for the potential energy E_P of a particle at a height h above the earth's surface, we need to compute the work required to raise the particle vertically at constant velocity so that we do not change the kinetic energy of the particle. The downward gravitational force on the particle is simply the weight of the particle; close to the surface of the earth this is given by $w = mg$. In order to raise the particle vertically at constant velocity, we must exert an upward force of equal magnitude. In raising the body to height h under these conditions, we must do work $W = mgh$. By definition, this work is just equal to the gravitational potential energy of the particle, so

$$E_P = mgh. \quad \left\{\begin{array}{l} E_P \text{ in J} \\ m \text{ in kg} \\ g \text{ in m/s}^2 \\ h \text{ in m} \end{array}\right\} \quad \textit{(Gravitational Potential Energy)} \quad (6.12)$$

This expression for E_P is valid for values of h that are small as compared with the radius of the earth; a more general discussion of gravitational potential energy will be given in Chapter 9.

The above expression for the gravitational potential energy of a particle also gives the value of E_P for an extended body if h is interpreted as the vertical height of the center of mass of the body above its initial position at the surface of the earth.

The expression for E_P in (6.12) was obtained on the assumption that we raised the body vertically upward. Now let us compute the work we would do against gravitational forces if we raised it by pulling it along the ramp or inclined plane shown in Fig. 6.5. In order to pull the body a distance l along the plane at constant speed we must apply a force $\mathbf{F}_{\text{app}}$ upward along the inclined plane; this force must be equal in magnitude to the component of the body's weight acting downward along the incline, which is $w_{\parallel} = mg \sin \phi$, as indicated in Fig. 6.5. The work that we must do against gravitational forces in raising the body to height h is therefore $W = F_{\text{app}} l = (mg \sin \phi) l$; but $l \sin \phi$ is equal to h, and thus the work we do is $W = mgh$. By definition then $E_P = mgh$, which is the value given in (6.12). We can show that this result holds in general by considering the work against gravitational forces that we must do in dragging or pushing the body up an incline of variable slope; this will be considered in a problem. Note that we have considered only the work done *against gravitational forces* in computing E_P; because frictional forces always oppose motion, the *total* work required to drag a body up an incline is always greater than the work mgh required to increase the potential energy of the body.

Energy is always measured relative to some arbitrary reference state or level. This is easily understood in the case of gravitational potential energy. In the cases we have described, the height h in our expression $E_P = mgh$ is always measured from a reference level that we have taken as ground level; our expression gives the work a body of mass m at height h above the ground is capable of doing to objects at ground level. The body could do no work at all to other objects at the same height h; on the other hand, it could do more work than mgh to objects below ground level at the bottom of a vertical mine shaft.

The expression $E_K = \frac{1}{2} mv^2$ represents the work that a moving object could do to other objects at rest in the same inertial reference frame. The value $v = 0$ relative to the reference frame thus represents an arbitrary level from which we measure kinetic energies. Thus, an object at rest with respect to a railroad car moving at constant velocity $\mathbf{v}$ relative to a level track has no kinetic energy relative to other objects at rest with respect to the car. However, the body has kinetic energy $\frac{1}{2} mv^2$ relative to the track. The object could thus do no work to other objects at rest with respect to the car but could do work $\frac{1}{2} mv^2$ to objects at rest on the ground beside the track. Note that kinetic energy is measured relative to a level established by the reference frame used to describe the motion.

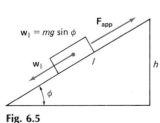

Fig. 6.5

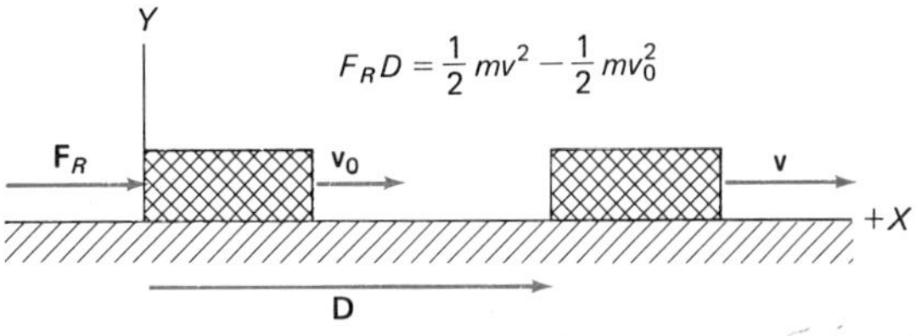

$$F_R D = \frac{1}{2} mv^2 - \frac{1}{2} mv_0^2$$

Fig. 6.6 The work done by a resultant force is equal to the increase in kinetic energy.

The sum of the kinetic energy and the potential energy of a body is called the total mechanical energy of the body.

6.4   WORK DONE BY FRICTION: DISSIPATION OF MECHANICAL ENERGY

Let us consider the application of work–energy relations to the problem of the rectilinear motion of a body as suggested in Fig. 6.6, which shows a constant resultant force $\mathbf{F}_R$ acting on a body of mass m initially moving at a velocity $\mathbf{v}_0$ along a horizontal surface in the $+X$ direction. The body experiences an acceleration in accord with Newton's Second Principle $\mathbf{F}_R = m\mathbf{a}$ and attains velocity $\mathbf{v}$ after the body has undergone a displacement $\mathbf{D}$. *The work W done to the body is $\mathbf{F}_R \cdot \mathbf{D}$ and is equal to the change in the kinetic energy of the body;* because the body moves along a horizontal surface, only the kinetic energy of the body changes. Therefore, $W = E_K - E_{K0}$, where E_K is the final kinetic energy of the body and E_{K0} is the initial value of its kinetic energy. This leads to the relation

$$F_R D = \tfrac{1}{2} mv^2 - \tfrac{1}{2} mv_0^2. \tag{6.13}$$

Recalling that $F_R = ma$, we can obtain the useful kinematic relation

$$maD = \tfrac{1}{2} mv^2 - \tfrac{1}{2} mv_0^2 \quad \text{or} \quad v^2 = v_0^2 + 2aD, \tag{6.14}$$

which applies to a body subject to a constant resultant force acting in the direction of motion. This useful relation was derived in Chapter 3 in an indirect way from purely kinematic considerations by the elimination of time factors.

Now consider the situation in Fig. 6.7 in which the resultant force acting on a sliding body is the force of kinetic friction $\mathscr{F}_K$, which, we recall, always opposes motion. The work done by this force $W = \mathscr{F}_K \cdot \mathbf{D}$ is *negative* because $\mathscr{F}_K$ and the displacement $\mathbf{D}$ are in opposite directions, and the angle θ between them is 180°: $\mathscr{F}_K D \cos \theta = -\mathscr{F}_K D$. Negative work takes mechanical energy away from a body; therefore, with $\mathscr{F}_K$ as the resultant force (6.13) becomes

$$-\mathscr{F}_K D = \tfrac{1}{2} mv^2 - \tfrac{1}{2} mv_0^2 \quad \text{or} \quad \mathscr{F}_K D = \tfrac{1}{2} mv_0^2 - \tfrac{1}{2} mv^2. \tag{6.15}$$

As the displacement D increases, the mechanical energy of the body will decrease until the velocity of the moving body becomes zero. When the body comes to rest with $v = 0$, (6.15) no longer applies because there is no force of *kinetic* friction on a body at rest.

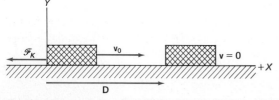

Fig. 6.7   The work done by a force of kinetic friction reduces the mechanical energy of a body.

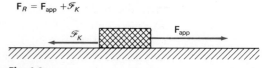

Fig. 6.8

Thus, if we set a body in motion across a horizontal surface, the force of kinetic friction will bring the body to rest after it has experienced a final displacement $\mathbf{D}_f$ at the end of which $\mathbf{v} = 0$. In this situation (6.15) assumes the form

$$\mathscr{F}_K D_f = \tfrac{1}{2} m v_0^2. \tag{6.15'}$$

The kinematic relation corresponding to (6.14) becomes

$$v_0^2 = 2 a D_f, \tag{6.16}$$

where a is the magnitude of the acceleration produced by the resultant force $\mathscr{F}_K$.

Example.   A small wooden disk moving at an initial speed of 2 m/s across a highly polished horizontal floor comes to rest after moving a distance of 10 m. What is the coefficient of kinetic friction between the disk and the floor?

As we have no information regarding the mass of the disk, we shall start with the kinematic relation (6.16). Solving this equation for a gives $a = v_0^2/2D = (4 \text{ m}^2/\text{s}^2)/2(10 \text{ m}) = 0.2$ m/s². The magnitude of the resultant force acting on the disk is $\mathscr{F}_K = ma$. The coefficient of kinetic friction is defined as $\mu_K = \mathscr{F}_K/F_N$, where F_N is the normal force exerted on the disk by the floor; the magnitude of F_N is equal to the weight of the disk mg. Thus, $\mu_K = ma/mg = a/g = (0.2 \text{ m/s}^2)/(9.8 \text{ m/s}^2) = 0.02$.

We note that the kinetic energy E_K of the body in Fig. 6.7 has entirely vanished when the body comes to rest as a result of the frictional force $\mathscr{F}_K$. We say that *mechanical energy has been dissipated;* forces of *kinetic* friction *always* result in the dissipation of mechanical energy; thus, a sliding body always comes to rest, losing all of its kinetic energy. We note, however, that forces of *static* friction *never* cause the dissipation of mechanical energy because no relative motion of the surfaces in contact is involved; i.e., the body on which the force of static friction acts has no displacement relative to the surface exerting the frictional force.

Now we return to a consideration of a general resultant force $\mathbf{F}_R$. In Fig. 6.8 we show the resultant force as made up of an "applied" force $\mathbf{F}_{\text{app}}$ acting in the $+X$ direction and a force of kinetic friction acting in the opposite direction. In this case the work done by the resultant force is

$$F_R D = F_{\text{app}} D - \mathscr{F}_K D. \tag{6.17}$$

Note that the work done by the applied force $F_{\text{app}} D$ adds mechanical energy to the body and the work done by the frictional force $-\mathscr{F}_K D$ removes mechanical energy from the body. Note also that the work done by the resultant force $F_R D$ is the algebraic sum of the work done by $\mathbf{F}_{\text{app}}$ and the work done by $\mathscr{F}_K$, in accord with a theorem stated in Sec. 6.2. If $F_{\text{app}} > \mathscr{F}_K$, the work done by $\mathbf{F}_R$ is positive and the mechanical energy of the body increases; if $\mathscr{F}_K > F_{\text{app}}$, the work done by $\mathbf{F}_R$ is negative and the mechanical energy of the body decreases.

Now consider the situation in which the applied force $\mathbf{F_{app}}$ in Fig. 6.8 is equal in magnitude to the frictional force $\mathscr{F}_K$. In this case, the resultant force $\mathbf{F}_R$ is zero and the body moves with constant velocity $\mathbf{v}$ in accord with Newton's Second Principle. The mechanical energy of the moving body remains constant. Thus, $F_R D$ in (6.17) is zero and we can write

$$F_{app}D = \mathscr{F}_K D, \tag{6.18}$$

a relation that states that the magnitude of the work done by the applied force is equal to the magnitude of the work done by the frictional force. Because the mechanical energy of the body does not change, it is sometimes said that the agent exerting the applied force is merely *doing work against friction!*

Example. A 2 kg body slides from rest down an inclined plane making an angle of 30° with the horizontal, as shown in Fig. 6.9. After the body has moved a distance of 4 m along the plane, its speed is 3 m/s. (i) What is the final kinetic energy of the body? (ii) What is the initial potential energy of the body relative to the body's final position? (iii) How much mechanical energy has been dissipated? (iv) What is the magnitude of the frictional force acting on the body as it moves down the plane?

(i) The final kinetic energy of the body is $E_f = \frac{1}{2}mv^2 = \frac{1}{2}(2 \text{ kg})(9 \text{ m}^2/\text{s}^2) = 9$ J. (ii) The initial potential energy of the body is $mgh = mgD \sin \theta = (2 \text{ kg})(9.8 \text{ m/s}^2)(4 \text{ m}) \sin 30° = 39.2$ J. (iii) If no work had been done to the body, its total mechanical energy would have remained constant. However, because of friction the final mechanical energy $E_K = \frac{1}{2}mv^2 = 9$ J is less than the initial mechanical energy $E_P = mgh = 39.2$ J. The mechanical energy dissipated is thus $(39.2 - 9.0)$ J $= 30.2$ J. (iv) The mechanical energy has been dissipated as a result of the work done by friction: $\mathscr{F}_K D = $ mechanical energy dissipated. Thus, $\mathscr{F}_K = E_{dis}/D = (30.2 \text{ J})/(4 \text{ m}) = 7.55$ N.

6.5   MECHANICAL ENERGY TRANSFORMATIONS

From Newton's Principles it is possible to prove the following theorem:

CONSERVATION OF MECHANICAL ENERGY: The total mechanical energy of any system of bodies remains constant provided there are no forces of kinetic friction and no dissipative (inelastic) collisions between the bodies and provided all forces are mechanical or gravitational in nature.

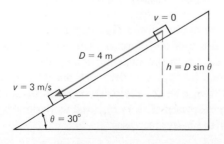

Fig. 6.9

By mechanical forces we mean forces exerted because of contact between two objects, either directly or through intermediary strings, ropes, rods, etc.

Because any system of real bodies is subject to frictional forces of one kind or another and because any collision between bodies usually causes slight permanent distortions that dissipate mechanical energy, the theorem just stated would appear to be of limited value. However, in certain cases the theorem can be used to advantage in providing approximate results. In using it, however, we must remember that frictional and other dissipative effects always tend to *reduce* the total mechanical energy of any system.

As the first example of the application of this theorem, consider the case of free fall to the earth's surface. In this problem, we assume that the falling object of mass m is subject *only* to the gravitational force $w = mg$. Consider an apple initially at some height h above the earth's surface; let us find the final downward velocity v_f of the apple as it reaches the earth's surface. Its final mechanical energy is entirely kinetic with $E_{Kf} = \frac{1}{2} mv_f^2$; its initial mechanical energy is entirely potential, $E_{P0} = mgh$. According to the conservation theorem the final and initial mechanical energies are equal; therefore,

$$\tfrac{1}{2} mv_f^2 = mgh \quad or \quad v_f = \sqrt{2gh}.$$

This is exactly the same result that is obtained from direct application of Newton's principles—and it is obtained with much less effort! We note that our result is also the result stated in (6.14) for a case in which $F_R = mg$ downward and the displacement $D = h$ downward. We note that the dynamical system involved consists of the apple and the earth. The theorem can also be applied to an object thrown vertically upward with initial speed v_0; we leave this application as a problem.

When we apply the energy-conservation theorem to the case of a projectile, we must recall that only the vertical component v_V of the velocity changes, the horizontal component v_H of the velocity remains unchanged. Therefore, the kinetic energy at the highest point in the trajectory where $v_V = 0$ is $\frac{1}{2} mv_H^2$. Setting the initial mechanical energy of the projectile $\frac{1}{2} mv_M^2$ equal to the mechanical energy at the highest point in the trajectory, we obtain

$$\tfrac{1}{2} mv_H^2 + mgh_{\max} = \tfrac{1}{2} mv_M^2;$$

here v_M is the magnitude of the muzzle velocity. Because $v_M^2 = v_H^2 + v_{V0}^2$, where v_{V0} is the vertical component of the muzzle velocity v_M, we conclude that kinetic energy $\frac{1}{2} mv_{V0}^2$ has been transformed into potential energy $mgh_{\max}$ by the time the projectile has reached the highest point $h_{\max}$ in its trajectory.

In any dynamical system to which our theorem can be applied, kinetic energy can be *transformed* into an equal amount of potential energy and potential energy can be *transformed* into an equal amount of kinetic energy, provided the *total* mechanical energy of the system does not change. If the total mechanical energy of a dynamical system decreases, we say that mechanical energy has been dissipated. In any case, the amount of energy transformed or dissipated is equal to the work done by some force. Work represents a transfer of energy.

Example.   A body slides from rest down a frictionless plane inclined at an angle θ with the horizontal as shown in Fig. 6.10. (i) Show that after the body has descended through a vertical distance h it has the same speed that it would have had if it had fallen vertically downward. (ii) How does the magnitude of the actual acceleration of the body along the frictionless slope depend on θ? (iii) How would the presence of friction influence the motion of the body?

(i) In the absence of friction the total mechanical energy of the system is constant. Thus, the total mechanical energy at the end of the incline is equal to the total mechanical energy at the top; i.e., $E_{Kf} = E_{P0}$, $\frac{1}{2}mv_f^2 = mgh$, or $v_f = \sqrt{2gh}$, which is just the speed attained by a body in free fall from height h as given directly from Newton's Principles.

(iii) The actual displacement of the body along the slope is l. Therefore, we can use (6.14) to obtain the acceleration a; $v_f^2 = 2al$ or $a = v_f^2/2l$. Thus, the longer the slope, the smaller the acceleration. We note that $\sin \theta = h/l$ or $l = h/\sin \theta$. Hence, $a = v_f^2 \sin \theta/2h$. Since from (i) $v_f^2 = 2gh$, we can write $a = g \sin \theta$. For $\theta = 90°$, $a = g$, as expected since free fall would be involved. On the other hand, a approaches zero as θ approaches zero, at which angle the plane is horizontal.

(iii) If friction were present, energy would be dissipated and for $\theta < 90°$ we would have v_f less than $\sqrt{2gh}$. Similarly, a would be less than $g \sin \theta$ for $\theta < 90°$. As $\theta \to 0$, we would find that at some stage the body would not slide at all. Why?

We close the present discussion by pointing out that nothing has been said about what happens to mechanical energy that has been dissipated by friction. This energy is not destroyed; although mechanical energy disappears, an equal amount of energy appears in another form. We shall discuss the fate of dissipated mechanical energy in the part of this book dealing with heat.

The conservation of mechanical energy is a special case of the general *Conservation-of-Energy Principle* that we shall state formally in Section 14.10. Mechanical energy is conserved only under certain conditions. The general conservation principle *always* applies. Thus far we have discussed only the mechanical energy associated with the motions and the positions of bodies. Whenever the kinetic energy of a body decreases as the result of friction, the body becomes warmer. That work done against friction produces heat was recognized by primitive man when he first became a "fire maker!"

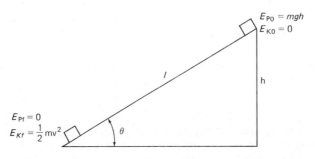

Fig. 6.10

Heat is associated with a form of energy called thermal energy that is discussed fully in Chapter 14. Along with *thermal energy*, we now recognize *chemical energy, electrical energy, magnetic energy* and *nuclear energy* in addition to the mechanical energy that we are now considering. The Conservation-of-Energy Principle asserts that the total energy of an isolated system never changes. The developments that led to this broad generalization are discussed in Chapter 14.

The general Conservation-of-Energy Principle is one of the most important generalizations in physics; it has important implications in *all* of modern physical science. Energy is a physical quantity that we shall employ not just in mechanics but in *all* of the other divisions of physics to be considered in subsequent parts of this book.

6.6 COLLISIONS

As an example of the ways in which energy and momentum relations can be applied, we now consider the problem of collisions between particles and between rigid bodies in translational motion. The treatment we present has practical applications in modern research work in atomic and nuclear physics and in our later studies of the kinetic theory of gases. We restrict our treatment to only two limiting cases: A. *Perfectly Inelastic Collisions,* in which the colliding particles stick together following collisions, and B. *Perfectly Elastic Collisions,* in which mechanical energy is conserved. We consider "head-on" collisions in detail and derive relationships to cover certain other cases.

Perfectly Inelastic Collisions

In perfectly inelastic collisions mechanical energy is always dissipated; therefore, we cannot apply mechanical energy-conservation relations. However, so long as the dynamical system is isolated, the *conservation-of-momentum principle can be applied to all types of collisions.*

We first consider head-on collisions in which the colliding particles move in a straight line before and after collision as suggested in Fig. 6.11; we choose a reference frame so that the motion is along the X axis. The velocities of the particles of mass m_1 and m_2 before collision are u_1 and u_2, respectively. Because the particles stick together after collision, they have a common final velocity v. Considering the two particles as an isolated dynamical system, we use the conservation-of-momentum principle to state that

$$\text{Momentum Before Collision} = \text{Momentum After Collision,}$$
$$m_1 u_1 + m_2 u_2 = (m_1 + m_2)v.$$

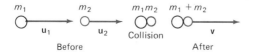

Fig. 6.11 In a perfectly inelastic collision the particles stick together following the collision; momentum is conserved.

Therefore, the common velocity v of the particles after impact is

$$v = (m_1 u_1 + m_2 u_2)/(m_1 + m_2). \qquad (6.19)$$

As a consequence of this equation, we can show that mechanical energy is always dissipated in such a collision; i.e. the total kinetic energy following collision is always less than the total kinetic energy before collision.

Example.   A 100-g lead ball moving with an initial velocity of 10 m/s, eastward, strikes a 100-g ball of putty, which is initially at rest. If the two balls stick together after collision, what is their common velocity? How much mechanical energy is dissipated in the collision?

Using the results given in (6.19), we obtain $v = m_1 u_1/(m_1 + m_2) = (0.1 \text{ kg})(10 \text{ m/s})/(0.2 \text{ kg}) = 5$ m/s. The initial mechanical energy of the system is $E_{K0} = \frac{1}{2} m_1 u_1^2 = \frac{1}{2}(0.1 \text{ kg})(100 \text{ m}^2/\text{s}^2) = 5$ J; the final mechanical energy of the system is $E_{Kf} = \frac{1}{2}(m_1 + m_2)v^2 = \frac{1}{2}(0.2 \text{ kg})(25 \text{ m}^2/\text{s}^2) = 2.5$ J. The mechanical energy dissipated is

$$E_{K0} - E_{Kf} = 5 \text{ J} - 2.5 \text{ J} = 2.5 \text{ J}.$$

In the more general case of inelastic collisions of particles not traveling along the same line, the conservation-of-momentum principle still provides sufficient information to find the final common velocity of the particles following collision. Consider the vector equation for the momenta of the particles before and after collision:

$$\mathbf{p}_{\text{final}} = (\mathbf{p}_1 + \mathbf{p}_2)_{\text{before}}, \qquad (6.20)$$

which is represented graphically in Fig. 6.12. Momentum vectors $\mathbf{p}_{\text{final}}$, $\mathbf{p}_1$, and $\mathbf{p}_2$ are in a single plane. Why? We can consider this to be the XY plane of some coordinate system. We can then write (6.20) in terms of its scalar components in the form

$$(m_1 + m_2)v_x = m_1 u_{1x} + m_2 u_{2x},$$

$$(6.20')$$

$$(m_1 + m_2)v_y = m_1 u_{1y} + m_2 u_{2y}.$$

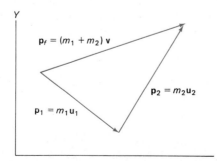

Fig. 6.12   Conservation of momentum in an inelastic collision.

These two simultaneous equations can be solved for v_x and v_y. The magnitude of the final common velocity then is $v = \sqrt{v_x^2 + v_y^2}$. The direction of $\mathbf{v}$ can be specified in terms of the angle ϕ between $\mathbf{v}$ and the X axis, where $\tan \phi = v_y/v_x$.

Perfectly Elastic Collisions

A perfectly elastic collision is by definition a collision in which no mechanical energy is dissipated. Therefore, treating the two colliding particles as a dynamical system, we can set the total mechanical energy before collision equal to the total mechanical energy after collision. For the head-on collision shown in Fig. 6.13, the energy relation becomes

$$\tfrac{1}{2} m_1 u_1^2 + \tfrac{1}{2} m_2 u_2^2 = \tfrac{1}{2} m_1 v_1^2 + \tfrac{1}{2} m_2 v_2^2. \tag{6.21}$$

The momentum-conservation relation holds for *all* collisions of isolated dynamical systems and in the present case can be written

$$m_1 u_1 + m_2 u_2 = m_1 v_1 + m_2 v_2. \tag{6.22}$$

From the simultaneous equations (6.21) and (6.22) we can get a very interesting result:

$$u_1 - u_2 = v_2 - v_1. \tag{6.23}$$

The derivation of (6.23) is left as a problem. Equation (6.23) has a very interesting interpretation: *In a head-on perfectly elastic collision between particles, the relative speed of approach before collision is equal to the relative speed of separation after collision.*

In order to find v_1 and v_2 in terms of u_1 and u_2, the easiest procedure is to solve the simultaneous linear equations (6.22) and (6.23). Several cases are of special interest. In a case where $m_1 = m_2$, it turns out that $v_1 = u_2$ and $v_2 = u_1$, which states that in a head-on perfectly elastic collision between two particles of equal mass, the particles simply exchange velocities during impact.

Another case of special interest is that in which the second particle is at rest ($u_2 = 0$) and thus forms a *target* for the first particle. This is indeed the case of interest to the nuclear physicist when he fires fast-moving particles from a particle accelerator at nuclei at rest in a thin foil, which serves as the target. With $u_2 = 0$, (6.22) and (6.23) become

$$m_1 u_1 = m_1 v_1 + m_2 v_2 \quad \text{and} \quad u_1 = v_2 - v_1.$$

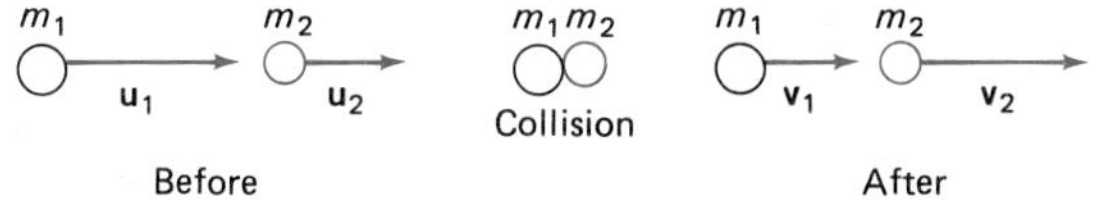

Fig. 6.13   In a perfectly elastic collision momentum and mechanical energy are conserved.

These two equations are easily solved for v_1 and v_2 in terms of u_1 with the result

$$v_1 = \frac{m_1 - m_2}{m_1 + m_2}\, u_1 \quad \text{and} \quad v_2 = \frac{2m_1}{m_1 + m_2}\, u_1.$$

We note from these equations that for a massive target where $m_2 \gg m_1$, $v_1 \approx -u_1$ and $v_2 \ll u_1$. This approximates the case when we throw a golf ball against a massive wall attached rigidly to the earth; the ball rebounds with little change in speed and the wall remains at rest. We note that for $m_1 = m_2$, $v_2 = u_1$ and $v_1 = 0$ in accord with our earlier observation that for $m_1 = m_2$ the particles merely exchange velocities. What happens in the case when a heavy projectile makes a head-on elastic collision with a very light particle: $m_1 \gg m_2$?

Example. A 1-kg steel disk moving at a velocity of 10 m/s, eastward, across the nearly frictionless surface of a frozen pond makes a head-on elastic collision with a 200-g steel disk at rest on the surface of the ice. What are the velocities of the disks immediately after collision? What fraction of the initial kinetic energy is transferred to the 200-g target disk?

In this problem $m_1 = 1$ kg, $u_1 = 10$ m/s, eastward, and $m_2 = 0.2$ kg with $u_2 = 0$. From the last two equations above, we obtain

$$v_1 = \frac{m_1 - m_2}{m_1 + m_2}\, u_1 = \left(\frac{0.8 \text{ kg}}{1.2 \text{ kg}}\right)(10 \text{ m/s, eastward}) = 6.67 \text{ m/s, eastward};$$

$$v_2 = \frac{2m_1}{m_1 + m_2}\, u_1 = \left(\frac{2 \text{ kg}}{1.2 \text{ kg}}\right)(10 \text{ m/s, eastward}) = 16.7 \text{ m/s, eastward}.$$

The initial kinetic energy is the kinetic energy of the large disk prior to the collision: $E_{K1} = \frac{1}{2} m_1 u_1^2 = \frac{1}{2}(1 \text{ kg})(100 \text{ m}^2/\text{s}^2) = 50$ J. The kinetic energy of the 0.2-kg disk after the collision is $E_{K2} = \frac{1}{2} m_2 v_2^2 = \frac{1}{2}(0.2 \text{ kg})(16.7 \text{ m/s})^2 = 27.8$ J. Therefore, 27.8 J/50 J = 0.556 of the initial energy was transferred to the 200-g disk during the collision. What should we make the mass of a target disk in order for it to have *all* of the kinetic energy after collision?

The general problem of elastic collisions in three dimensions cannot be solved because we have more unknowns than applicable momentum and energy relationships. We can illustrate the difficulties by considering a simple but important case indicated in Fig. 6.14 where a projectile of mass m_1 moving at velocity $\mathbf{u}_1$ along the X axis

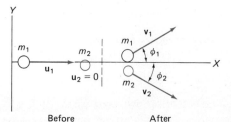

Before   After   **Fig. 6.14** A glancing ("non-head-on") collision.

of a coordinate system makes a glancing collision with a target of mass m_2 initially at rest. In this case, the momentum conservation equations become

$$X: \quad m_1 u_1 = m_1 v_1 \cos \phi_1 + m_2 v_2 \cos \phi_2,$$
$$Y: \quad 0 = m_1 v_1 \sin \phi_1 - m_2 v_2 \sin \phi_2.$$

These equations together with the energy conservation equation (6.21) provide us *three* equations in *four* unknowns: v_1, v_2, ϕ_1, and ϕ_2. The general problem can therefore not be solved. However, if we have some other independent method of determining one of the unknowns, we can determine the other three.

6.7 POWER

Now that we have defined and discussed mechanical energy and mechanical energy transformations and have shown how mechanical energy relationships can be used to advantage in treating certain kinds of problems, we return to further consideration of the performance of work. In the performance of work in accomplishing some task, we often are interested not only in the total amount of work required but also in how long a time is required for the performance of the task; in other words we are interested in the time rate at which the work is being done. The physical quantity giving a measure of the time-rate of doing work is a scalar quantity called *power P:*

POWER is the time rate at which work is done.

Thus, the power P supplied by any device in performing work W is given by the expression

$$P = dW/dt. \quad \left\{ \begin{array}{l} P \text{ in W} \\ W \text{ in W} \\ t \text{ in s} \end{array} \right\} \quad (Power) \tag{6.24}$$

Power is measured in a unit called the *watt* (W); this SI unit is named in honor of James Watt (1736–1819), the Scottish inventor of the reciprocating steam engine:

$$1 \text{ watt} = 1 \text{ joule/second}; \quad 1 \text{ W} = 1 \text{ J/s}.$$

If a device is able to perform an amount of work W measured in joules in time t measured in seconds, it is working with time-average power output $\bar{P}$ given by the relation

$$\bar{P} = W/t. \quad \left\{ \begin{array}{l} P \text{ in W} \\ W \text{ in J} \\ t \text{ in s} \end{array} \right\} \quad (Average \ Power) \tag{6.24'}$$

We can easily compute the power being delivered when work is being done on a moving body. Consider a resultant force F_x acting on a body moving in the $+X$

direction as suggested in Fig. 6.6. The element of work dW done while the body experiences displacement dx is $dW = F_x \, dx$. Therefore, the instantaneous power involved is given by the relation

$$P = dW/dt = F_x dx/dt = F_x v_x.$$

Thus, the time rate at which work is being done when a force $\mathbf{F}$ acts on a body moving at velocity $\mathbf{v}$ in the direction of the force is equal to the product of the force and the velocity of the body. If the force $\mathbf{F}$ and the velocity $\mathbf{v}$ are not in the same direction, the corresponding expression for the instantaneous power is from (6.8)

$$P = \mathbf{F} \cdot \mathbf{v} = Fv \cos \theta, \quad \begin{cases} P \text{ in W} \\ F \text{ in N} \\ v \text{ in m/s} \end{cases} \tag{6.25}$$

where θ is the angle between $\mathbf{F}$ and $\mathbf{v}$.

Example.   If a hoist is able to raise 2 m of water to a height of 30 m in 1 min, what is the average power output of the hoist?

The mass of 2 m³ of water is given by the relation $m = \rho V = (1000 \text{ kg/m}^3)(2 \text{ m}^3) = 2000$ kg. The work done in raising 2 m³ of water to a height of 30 m is $W = mgh = (2000 \text{ kg})(9.8 \text{ m/s}^2)(30 \text{ m}) = 58.8 \times 10^4$ J. The average power output of the hoist is $\bar{P} = W/t = (58.8 \times 10^4 \text{ J})/(60 \text{ s}) = 0.98 \times 10^4$ W $= 9.8$ kW.

Example.   When a resultant force $\mathbf{F}_R$ acts on a body, the kinetic energy E_K of the body increases provided the force has a component in the direction of motion. Show for the case where $\mathbf{F}_R$ is *in the direction of motion* that the power being delivered to the body is equal to the time rate of change of the body's kinetic energy.

The time rate of change of kinetic energy is given by $d(\frac{1}{2} mv^2)/dt = mvdv/dt = mva = F_R v$, which is equal to the expression for power given by (6.25) for the case in which $\mathbf{F}_R$ is in the same direction as $\mathbf{v}$. Note that we are able to set $dv/dt = a$ only because $\mathbf{F}_R$ is in the same direction as $\mathbf{v}$.

When an engine develops some power output P, the power can be used in a variety of ways in moving bodies about. The engine can be attached to a *power transmission device* consisting of a *gear-box* or a *set of pulleys* or a *fluid transmission* like the one used in many automobiles. This is suggested in Fig. 6.15. If the engine is capable of furnishing input power P_I of amount $P_I = F_I v_I$ to the input of an ideal transmission, the ideal transmission delivers an equal output power P_O by providing force F_O and velocity v_O with power $F_O v_O$. By proper arrangement of the pulleys or gear wheels inside the transmission, the ratio of F_O to F_I can be varied. For an ideal transmission

$$F_O v_O = F_I v_I \quad \text{or} \quad F_O/F_I = v_I/v_O.$$

Fig. 6.15 In any real power-transmission device the output power is less than the input power.

The ratio F_O/F_I is called the ideal mechanical advantage of the transmission and for an ideal device is equal to v_I/v_O.

In any real transmission device there are always frictional effects that result in energy dissipation, so that the output power P_O is always less than the input power P_I. The efficiency of any transmission is defined as the ratio of power output to the power input:

$$\text{Efficiency} = P_O/P_I.$$

The actual mechanical advantage of a transmission is less than the velocity ratio v_I/v_O; i.e., $F_O/F_I < v_I/v_O$.

Most transmissions in everyday use are operated with rotating shafts, which will be discussed further in Chapter 7.

6.8 PERFORMANCE OF WORK: PRIME MOVERS

In closing this chapter we need to say a few more words about *how* work is done. Although it is customary to speak of "the work done by the applied force," "the work done by the frictional force," etc., we must remember that some *object* must exert the applied force or the frictional force. When work is done, some *agent*—animate or inanimate—must do the work. Because the performance of work represents a transfer of energy, the agent can do the work only if it can make use of energy from some source. Unless energy is available, the agent can do no work.

It is usually easy to do negative work and reduce the mechanical energy of a body by forces of kinetic friction. The agent doing the required negative work actually transforms the mechanical energy already possessed by the body to heat. Once the mechanical energy of the body has been completely dissipated, the agent exerting the frictional force can no longer do any work. For example, an automobile moving along a horizontal roadway can be brought to rest as a result of an agent applying forces of kinetic friction; the agent may be either the braking mechanism attached to the rolling car, or the roadway if the car is sliding with its wheels locked. Once the car has been brought to rest, the agent can do no more work.

Increasing the mechanical energy of a body is quite a different matter. The agent doing the required positive work must obtain the energy that is transferred to the body from some source or reservoir. For example, in the case of an automobile on a level roadway, the kinetic energy of the automobile can be increased as a result of energy supplied, by the *engine*. The source of the energy supplied by the engine is the chemical energy associated with the fuel being burned. Once the fuel supply is gone, the engine can supply no more energy.

Note that there is no theorem that states that changes in the mechanical energy of a dynamical system such as the automobile must be the result of energy supplied by agents external to the system. Although the primary external force acting on a rolling car during acceleration or deceleration is exerted by the roadway, the kinetic energy gained during acceleration is supplied by the engine. During deceleration without sliding, kinetic energy is dissipated by the braking mechanism and by other sources of kinetic friction in the car. When the energy supplied by the engine and the energy dissipated by frictional forces are equal, the mechanical energy of the car is constant and the car moves at constant speed. The resultant external force exerted on the car is always equal to the mass times acceleration as required by Newton's Second Principle. When we employ work–energy relationships, we do not repeal Newton's Principles!

It is interesting to note that the total amount of work that an agent must do in performing a task often depends on the way in which the task is accomplished, as the following example will show.

Example.   A large crate weighing 100 N lies on the floor of a flat car attached to a railroad train moving horizontally westward at a speed of 10 m/s; the coefficient of kinetic friction between the crate and the floor is 0.4. By pulling in the forward direction on a rope of fixed length attached to the crate a man wishes to move the crate 2 m forward toward the locomotive pulling the train. How much work must the man do (i) if he stands on the freight car while pulling on the rope and (ii) if he runs along the track at a speed of 10.5 m/s westward while pulling on the rope.

The force of kinetic friction acting on the crate is $\mathscr{F}_k = \mu w = 0.4 \times 100$ N = 40 N. (i) In order to give the crate a displacement of 2 m without changing its kinetic energy, the man aboard the train must do work $W = (40$ N$)(2$ m$) = 80$ J. (ii) If the man is running along the track while moving the crate, he also must exert a force equal to 40 N; he must exert this force for 4 s in order to move the crate a distance of 2 m forward with respect to the floor. During this period the distance moved by the man relative to the track is $D = (10.5$ m/s$)(4$ s$) = 42$ m. Thus, the man running along the track must do work: $W = (40$ N$)(42$ m$) = 1680$ J. Show that the additional work $(1680 - 80)$ J = 1600 J actually goes into helping the locomotive keep the train moving.

In analyzing the ways in which man is able to accomplish useful work, we find that in any such operation there must be some sort of *prime mover,* a device that converts environmental energy of some kind into the ordered motion required for doing useful work. Throughout most of man's history, the prime movers he has employed have been *animate:* man himself and beasts of burden. Animate prime movers derive their energy from the chemical energy in *food.* Animate prime movers are capable of performing large amounts of work provided they have plenty of time to do it; however, animate prime movers have rather limited output powers $P = \mathbf{F} \cdot \mathbf{v}$ and always require the use of suitable power transmission devices for work in which large forces are needed.

Much larger output powers are available from *inanimate prime movers.* The earliest inanimate prime movers to be developed were those making use of the environmental energy associated with the *mass motion* of air and water. Thus, the sail and the windmill operate from "wind power," and the water wheel operates from "water power."

Example.   A waterfall is 30 m above the level of the river below the fall. Some of the water is used to operate a large waterwheel located below the fall. After passing over the wheel, water reaching the river level has a speed of 10 m/s; assume that the water speed at the top of the fall is negligible. Two cubic meters of water pass over the wheel each second. What is the maximum theoretical efficiency of the water wheel as operated? What is the maximum theoretical output power that can be expected from the wheel? Because of frictional effects the real values of both these quantities will actually be less than their maximum theoretical values.

In order to compute the efficiency of the wheel we use the general definition: Efficiency = (Work Done)/(Energy Supplied). For maximum efficiency, the work done is the difference between the energy mgh supplied to the wheel and the energy $\frac{1}{2}mv^2$ retained by the water leaving the wheel; thus, for the maximum theoretical efficiency (MTE) we obtain MTE $= (mgh - \frac{1}{2}mv^2)/(mgh) = 1 - v^2/2gh = 1 - (100 \text{ m}^2/\text{s}^2)/2(9.8 \text{ m/s}^2)(30 \text{ m}) = 1 - 0.17 = 0.83$. Thus, in the absence of friction 0.83 of *all* the input energy can be used to do useful work.

The energy supplied to the water wheel by each cubic meter of water is simply ρgh, where ρ is the density of water: Energy supplied per cubic meter $= (1000 \text{ kg/m}^3)(9.8 \text{ m/s}^2)(30 \text{ m}) = 294,000 \text{ J/m}^3$. With a flow or "flux" of 2 m³/s the maximum input power is $(294,000 \text{ J/m}^3)(2 \text{ m}^3/\text{s}) = 588,000 \text{ J/s} = 588,000 \text{ W} = 588 \text{ kW}$. For MTE $= 0.83$, the maximum theoretical output power $P_O = 0.83(588 \text{ kW}) = 488 \text{ kW}$.

Although greater power outputs are available from inanimate prime movers using mass motion of air and water than from animate prime movers, the development known as the industrial revolution would have never been possible without the development of another class of inanimate movers known as *heat engines,* which we consider in a later chapter. The environmental energy used by heat engines is usually the chemical energy of *coal, natural gas,* and *petroleum.* The rapid depletion of the world's supply of these so-called *fossil fuels* has resulted in the "energy crisis" facing mankind.

QUESTIONS

1. In solving a physics problem, do you do any "work" in the physical sense of this term?

2. According to the Conservation of Energy Principle, if we include *all* forms of energy, the total energy associated with any isolated system is constant. Can we conclude that the total energy content of the entire universe is constant?

3. Work is defined in terms of two vector quantities, force and displacement. Does this definition make work a vector quantity?

4. Under what conditions can the scalar product of two vectors be negative?

5. Explain why the line integral in (6.9) is independent of the path joining P_1 and P_2 for a case in which only gravitational forces are involved.

6. Show that a force of kinetic friction does negative work to a moving body, thereby reducing its kinetic energy.

7. Compare in detail the work–energy relations

of this chapter with the impulse–momentum relations of Chapter 4. Can you say that one of these sets of relations is more "fundamental" than the other?

8. What restrictions are involved in the expression $E_P = mgh$? Is it valid for all values of h?

9. If some agent drags a box across a level platform at constant speed, it does work to the box but does not increase its mechanical energy. It is sometimes said that the agent is merely "doing work against friction"; criticize this statement.

10. When a body initially in motion slides across a horizontal surface and comes to rest, what becomes of the body's initial kinetic energy?

11. Under what conditions is the total momentum of a dynamical system conserved? Under what conditions is the total mechanical energy of a dynamical system conserved? Under what conditions is the total energy of a system conserved?

12. What mechanical quantities are conserved in (a) perfectly elastic collisions and (b) perfectly inelastic collisions?

13. Imperfectly elastic head-on collisions of two particles can be treated in terms of an empirical constant e called the *coefficient of restitution,* which is defined as the ratio of the particles' relative velocity of approach before collision to the particles' relative velocity of separation after collision. Show how e can be used along with the conservation-of-momentum relation to obtain the velocities $\mathbf{v}_1$ and $\mathbf{v}_2$ after collision in terms of m_1, m_2, and the initial velocities $\mathbf{u}_1$ and $\mathbf{u}_2$. What is

the value of e for a perfectly elastic collision? for a perfectly inelastic collision?

14. When an automobile starts from rest, the external force responsible for its acceleration is exerted by the roadway. Does the road do work to the car? Discuss the mechanism by which chemical energy of the fuel becomes kinetic energy of the moving car.

15. Some commercial utilities refer to the central locations where prime movers are located as "energy centers"; other companies refer these locations as "power stations." Discuss these terms. Are they both appropriate?

16. When a consumer receives a statement from his local "power company," is the consumer billed for *power* or *energy?*

17. Why are long trains of freight cars usually employed when freight is to be moved over a pass in the mountains? This is usually done even though two locomotives must be used in moving the train uphill toward the pass.

18. If all the components of the velocity $\mathbf{v}$ of a particle are reversed, what change results in the kinetic energy of the particle?

19. Does the work done to an object by a force acting on the object depend on the particular inertial frame of reference that is used to observe the object?

20. Observers in different inertial frames of reference will in general assign different velocities and different kinetic energies to a given object. How is it possible for the conservation-of-energy principle to be true with respect to *all* inertial frames of reference?

PROBLEMS

1. By pulling on a rope attached to a crate a man drags the crate 20 m eastward at constant speed across a horizontal loading platform. The man exerts a force 30 N on the rope, which makes an angle of 30° with the horizontal. How much work does the man do?

2. How much work would the man in Problem 1 do in moving a second crate at con-

stant speed if the rope were horizontal and the man exerted a force of 30 N, eastward? Why are different amounts of work done in moving a crate a distance of 20 m in the two situations, even though the magnitudes of the applied forces are the same? If the coefficient of kinetic friction between the crate and the loading platform is 0.32 for both situations, what is the ratio of the masses of the two crates? Discuss the relative advantages of exerting the applied force at different angles with the horizontal.

3. A *resultant* force 12 N, eastward, acts on a 1000-kg automobile initially at rest on a horizontal roadway. What is the velocity of the automobile after it has moved a distance of 30 m along the roadway? What is the final kinetic energy of the automobile?

4. What is the translational kinetic energy of a 1200-kg car when it is moving at a speed of 15 m/s? What would be the kinetic energy of the car if its speed were doubled?

5. A 1200-kg car is at rest at the top of a hill 20 m high. What is its gravitational potential energy with respect to objects at the bottom of the hill? At what speed would the car have kinetic energy equal in magnitude to its potential energy when it is on the hill top?

6. How much work must be done against gravitational forces in raising 1 m³ of water vertically upward to a height of 30 m above its initial position? What would be the potential energy of the water at this height relative to objects at its initial level?

7. A 12-kg box with an initial speed of 8 m/s moves a distance of 6 m across a horizontal floor before coming to rest. What is the magnitude of the frictional force acting on the box? What is the coefficient of kinetic friction between the box and the floor?

8. By applying a horizontal force of 20 N, eastward, to an 8-kg box a man moves the box a distance of 30 m, eastward, across a horizontal floor. The box starts from rest and has a final velocity of 4 m/s, eastward. How much work does the man do? What fraction of the work done by the man has resulted in increasing the mechanical energy of the box? How much work has the man done "against friction"? What is the magnitude of the frictional force acting on the box? What is the coefficient of kinetic friction between the box and the floor?

9. A 2-kg block slides from rest down an inclined plane making an angle of 45° with the horizontal. After the block has moved 7 m along the incline, its speed is 6 m/s. How much mechanical energy has been dissipated? What is the magnitude of the frictional force acting on the block? What is the coefficient of kinetic friction between the block and the incline?

10. An object of mass m is to be pushed at constant speed up an inclined plane like the one shown in the figure. The applied force F_{app} is parallel to the incline. Show that the work done in moving the object a distance l along the incline is given by the expression

$$W = (mg \sin \phi + \mu_K mg \cos \phi)l,$$

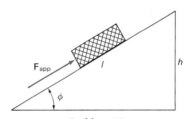

Problem 10

where μ_K is the coefficient of kinetic friction between the object and the incline. Show that the fraction of the work done that goes into increasing the mechanical energy of the block is given by the expression $\sin \phi / (\sin \phi + \mu_K \cos \phi)$. For what angle ϕ would the work required for a given mechanical energy increase be a minimum? Why are ramps used for loading purposes?

11. A hockey puck moving with an initial speed of 8 m/s moves a distance of 6 m across

a horizontal floor before coming to rest. What is the coefficient of kinetic friction between the puck and the floor?

12. A force of static friction of 20 N, eastward, acts for 12 s on a 4-kg body. How much energy is dissipated by this force? Discuss the role of static friction in the dissipation of mechanical energy.

13. A baseball is thrown vertically upward. If the initial speed of the ball is 30 m/s, to what height above its point of release will the ball rise? What will be the speed of the ball when it has reached half this height? Regard the effects of air resistance as negligible.

14. An object slides from rest down a frictionless plane inclined at an angle of 30° with the horizontal. What is its speed after it has moved a distance of 9.8 m along the incline?

15. A body with mass $m_1 = 4$ kg lying on a table top is connected to a second body with mass $m_2 = 2$ kg by a light cord passing over a light frictionless pulley as shown in the diagram; both bodies are initially at rest. (1) If the table top were frictionless, what would be the common speed of the bodies after m_2 has undergone a vertical downward displacement of 2 m? (2) What would be their common speed in this situation if the coefficient of kinetic friction between m_1 and the table top were 0.2? How much mechanical energy would be dissipated?

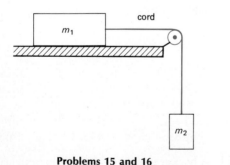

Problems 15 and 16

16. If we stopped the motion of the bodies of Problem 15 when the second body is 2 m below its initial position, what horizontal force must be applied to m_1 in order to pull the two bodies at *constant speed* back to their initial positions if the coefficient of kinetic friction between m_1 and the table top is 0.2? How much work is required to return the bodies to their initial positions? How much of this work goes into increasing the mechanical energy of the bodies?

17. A 30-g bullet moving horizontally eastward at a speed of 200 m/s strikes a 4-kg log lying at rest on the frozen surface of a pond, which can be regarded as frictionless. The bullet becomes embedded in the log. What is the common velocity of the two bodies following the collision? How much momentum is dissipated in the collision? How much mechanical energy is dissipated?

18. A 2000-kg car moving eastward at a speed of 20 m/s makes a "rear-end" collision with a 1200-kg car moving eastward at a speed of 10 m/s. During the collision the bumpers of the two cars become "locked" so that the two cars have a common velocity immediately following the collision. What is this common velocity? How much mechanical energy is dissipated in the collision?

19. Repeat Problem 18 for a case in which the 1200-kg car is moving westward so that a direct "head-on" collision is involved.

20. A 500-g ball is dropped from a height of 19.6 m to a sidewalk. If the ball rebounds from the sidewalk to a height of 12 m, how much mechanical energy is dissipated in the collision? What is the ball's momentum just before it strikes the sidewalk? What is its momentum as it leaves the sidewalk? Is momentum conserved in the collision? Discuss.

21. A 2-kg body moving at a velocity of 10 m/s, eastward, makes a perfectly elastic head-on collision with a 1-kg body moving at a

velocity of 4 m/s, eastward. What are the velocities of the two bodies following the collision? How much mechanical energy is transferred from the first body to the second during the collision?

22. Repeat Problem 21 for a case in which the initial velocity of the 1-kg body is 4 m/s, westward.

23. A 1-kg body moving at a velocity of 20 m/s, eastward, makes a perfectly elastic head-on collision with a 20-kg body that is initially at rest. What are the velocities of the two bodies after the collision? What fraction of the 1-kg projectile's initial mechanical energy is transferred to the 20-kg target?

24. Repeat Problem 23 for a situation in which the 20-kg body has an initial velocity of 20 m/s, eastward, and the 1-kg body is initially at rest.

25. What is the average power output of a motor-operated hoist if it is used to raise a 200-kg bale a vertical distance of 12 m in 3 min?

26. If the hoist in Problem 25 were powered by a one-half horsepower (373 W) motor, what is the minimum time that would be required to raise the 200-kg load a vertical distance of 12 m at constant speed?

27. Three cubic meters of water per second pass over a waterfall 25 m high. If *all* of the potential energy of the water could be used in operating a large waterwheel, what would be the output power of the waterwheel? If the water enters the wheel at a speed of 2 m/s and leaves the wheel at the base of the fall at a speed of 12 m/s, what is the maximum efficiency to be expected of the wheel?

28. Water moving through a pipe at a speed of 20 m/s enters a turbine and leaves the turbine through a larger pipe at a speed of 8 m/s. Two cubic meters of water flow through the turbine each second. What is

the efficiency of the turbine? What is the maximum power output to be expected from the turbine?

*29. A projectile particle of mass m_1 makes a perfectly elastic head-on collision with a stationary target particle of mass m_2 initially at rest. Show that the fraction f of the initial kinetic energy of the projectile that is transferred to the target is given by $f = 4m_1m_2/(m_1 + m_2)^2$. Show that f becomes small for $m_1 \ll m_2$ and for $m_1 \gg m_2$. Show by differentiation that f is a maximum when $m_1 = m_2$. Hint: Write f as a function of the single variable $x = m_1/m_2$.

30. Derive Eq. (6.23) for a head-on perfectly elastic collision.

*31. Use Eq. (6.9) to show that the work against gravitational forces required to push an object at constant speed up a frictionless incline of variable slope is just the increase in gravitational potential energy mgh, where h is the vertical distance between the initial and final positions.

32. In the text it is asserted that the potential energy of an extended body near the earth's surface is given by $E_P = Mgh_C$, where h_C is the height of the center of mass above the reference level and M is the mass of the body. Present a proof of this statement by considering an extended body as a collection of particles and setting the potential energy of the body equal to the sum of the potential energies of the particles.

*33. By consideration of the line integrals involved, show that the work done against frictional forces in moving an object from one place to another on a horizontal surface with constant coefficient of kinetic friction is directly proportional to the length of the path traversed. Assume that the applied force is horizontal. Discuss the situation if the coefficient of kinetic friction varies with location.

*34. Prove that the work done against gravitational forces in raising an object from one height to another is independent of the path traversed.

35. Consider a sled sliding from rest along the frictionless runway shown in the figure. What will be the speed of the sled at points B, C, and D in the figure?

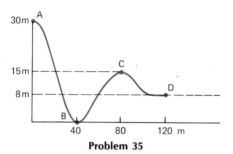

Problem 35

36. A box is to be moved from position ① in the figure to position ②. The coefficients of kinetic friction μ_K between the box and the floor and between the box and the ramp are the same. Compare the work required to drag the box at constant speed directly from ① to ② along the ramp with the work required to drag the box at constant speed horizontally along the floor from ① to ③ and then raise the box vertically from ③ to ②. Assume in each case that the applied force is parallel to the displacement. Why is the ramp useful?

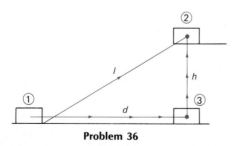

Problem 36

37. Consider a uniform, flexible chain with length $l = 1$ m being moved over a *thin* barrier of height $h = 1$ m. Assume that the chain conforms to the contour of the

barrier as suggested in the diagram. If we drag end ① of the chain to the top of the barrier, what is the height h_C of the chain's center of mass? If we drag end ① of the chain over the top of the barrier so that equal lengths of chain hang on each side of the barrier, what is the height of the center of mass of the chain? If we continue moving the chain until end ② is at the top of the barrier, and end ① is at the base of the barrier, what is the height of the chain's center of mass? What is the maximum height h_{max} attained by the center of mass? Discuss the path traversed by its center of mass as the chain moves over the barrier. Discuss the work that must be done against gravity in dragging the chain up over the barrier.

38. Repeat Problem 37 for chains of lengths 50, 20, 10, and 1 cm. Note that the shorter the chain, the more it behaves like a particle.

39. Repeat Problem 37 for chains of lengths 2, 4, and 8 m.

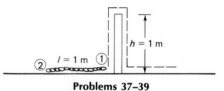

Problems 37–39

40. The figure shows a barrier of height $h = 1$ m and width $w = 1$ m over which we wish to pull a chain of length $l = 1$ m under the conditions of Problem 37. What is the maximum height h_{max} attained by the center of mass of the chain as the chain is pulled over the barrier? Discuss the work that must be done against gravity in dragging the chain up over the barrier.

41. Repeat Problem 40 for a barrier of height $h = 1$ m and a chain of length $l = 1$ m for barrier widths of $w = 2, 0.5, 0.2,$ and 0.1 m? Note that for all values of $l \leq w$, h_{max} is the same as that for a particle, but

as l becomes progressively larger than w, h_{max} becomes progressively smaller than for a particle.

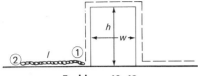

Problems 40–42

42. Derive an equation representing the general relationship between the maximum height h_{max} attained by the center of mass of a uniform, flexible object being pulled over a barrier and the values of the length l of the object and the height h and width w of the barrier. Assume that the object conforms to the contour of the barrier and that $w \leq l \leq h$.

43. A small 500-g object is attached to one end of a light string 1 m in length. A student holds the other end of the string and swings the object in a circular path in a vertical plane. What is the minimum possible speed that the object can have at the highest point in its circular path? Under this condition, what is the tension in the string when the object is at the lowest point in its circular path?

44. A 2-kg lead ball is attached to one end of a string 2 m long and the other end of the string is attached to the ceiling of a laboratory room. If the ball is pulled to one side so that the supporting string makes an angle of 60° with the vertical and then released, the object and supporting string swing as a pendulum. What is the tension in the string when the ball is immediately below the point of support? at maximum displacement of the pendulum from the vertical?

45. An object slides without friction along the track of the "loop-the-loop" shown in the figure. In terms of radius R, what is the minimum height h from which the object can be released and still move around the loop? If the object is released from this

height, what is its speed at the top of the loop? What is its final speed? Express the speeds in terms of R and g.

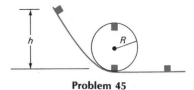

Problem 45

*46. Reconsider Problem 36 for a case where the ramp from ① to ② does not have constant slope along its length. Assume that the applied force is always parallel to the incline and that the speed of the box is constant. Show that the work required to drag the box from ① to ② along the ramp is not the same as for the case of a ramp of constant slope. Is the least work done for a convex ramp, a ramp of constant slope, or a concave ramp? Explain your reasoning.

*47. If **A** and **B** are vectors that depend on the time t, prove that the time derivative of their scalar product is given by

$$\frac{d}{dt}(\mathbf{A} \cdot \mathbf{B}) = \frac{d\mathbf{A}}{dt} \cdot \mathbf{B} + \mathbf{A} \cdot \frac{d\mathbf{B}}{dt}.$$

*48. For the pendulum described in Problem 44, find the tension in the string, the time rate of change of the kinetic energy, and the time rate of change of the potential energy for an arbitrary displacement of the pendulum from the vertical.

*49. Suppose that the force **F** in Fig. 6.1 is constant and the box is being dragged at constant speed along a horizontal surface where the coefficient of kinetic friction between the bottom of the box and the surface is μ_K. Show that the angle ϕ for which the magnitude F of the required force is a minimum is given by $\phi = \arctan \mu_K$. At what angle ϕ is the minimum power required to pull the box at a given constant speed v?

50. Prove that in a head-on perfectly elastic collision between two particles of equal

mass the particles simply exchange velocities.

51. Prove that when an object makes a perfectly elastic *glancing* collision with another body of equal mass that is initially at rest, the angle between the final velocities of the objects is 90°.

52. Two objects of masses m_1 and m_2 and initial velocities u_1 and u_2 undergo a perfectly in-elastic collision. Derive a formula for the kinetic energy that is dissipated in the collision in terms of m_1, m_2, u_1, and u_2.

53. An object of mass 4.5 kg traveling with a velocity 0.38 m/s at 20° north of east has a perfectly inelastic collision with an object of mass 3.8 kg traveling with a velocity 0.65 m/s due east. What is the velocity of the composite object after the collision?

CHAPTER 7

Rotational Motion

As we have noted in our earlier discussion of translational motion, a rigid body is essentially a collection of particles with fixed positions relative to one another. When a rigid body undergoes pure translation from one place to another, the particles composing the body move in parallel paths. When a rigid body has a motion of pure rotation about a fixed axis, all particles in the body move along circular paths centered at the axis of rotation. To visualize this type of motion, consider a wheel free to rotate on a fixed *axle;* as the wheel rotates, all particles making up the wheel move in circular paths. Each of these paths is centered at the center of the axle; a line along the center of the axle thus represents the axis of rotation.

In this chapter we first consider in detail the pure rotational motion of a rigid body about a *fixed axis.* We shall define *angular displacement, angular velocity, angular acceleration,* and *torque.* We shall show that the *angular acceleration* of a body is directly proportional to the *resultant torque* acting on the body; thus, in rotational motion torque plays a role corresponding to that of force in translational motion. The rotational quantity corresponding to mass in translational motion is called *moment of inertia* or *rotational inertia;* we shall show how this quantity is determined. We then discuss how rotational motion can be used for *power transmission.*

After completing our discussion of the pure rotational motion of a rigid body about a fixed axis, we proceed to a more general discussion of rotational motion. We shall discuss the vector properties of torque and angular momentum and show how they can conveniently be computed by means of the *vector product,* sometimes called the *cross product,* of two vector quantities. In our treatment of electromagnetism, we shall make extensive use of vector products. At the end of this chapter, we state some general theorems regarding rotational motion of dynamical systems including the principle of *conservation of angular momentum.*

7.1 KINEMATICS OF PURE ROTATION

Consider Fig. 7.1, which shows the cross section of a rigid body mounted so that its only possible motion is that of rotation about a fixed axis through O perpendicular

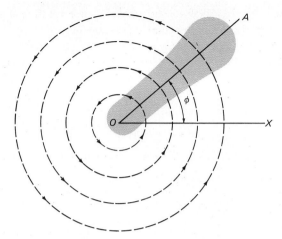

Fig. 7.1   All particles in a rigid body move in circular paths when the body has a motion of *pure rotation*.

to the plane of the diagram. All points in the body move in circles with their centers on the axis *O*. The orientation of the body in space is determined by the angle ϕ between a radial reference line *OA marked on the body* and some direction *OX* fixed in space relative to the walls of the laboratory room. The angle ϕ also can be used in specifying the positions of all particles in the rotating rigid body because the positions of the particles in the rigid body do not change *relative* to one another.

The angle ϕ between *OX* and *OA* gives the orientation of the *body as a whole*. If *OA* initially coincides with *OX* and later turns through angle ϕ, the angle ϕ can be considered the *angular displacement* of the body from its initial orientation.

The ANGULAR DISPLACEMENT of a rigid body in pure rotation is the angle through which any radius in the body turns about an axis fixed in space.

Note that the angular displacement can be greater than 2π radians. We must know how many complete *turns* the body has made about the axis of rotation as well as its final angular position in order to specify the angular displacement. The axis fixed in space can be considered the axis of a plane-polar coordinate system, with which we are already familiar. In accord with the usual convention used with such a coordinate system, we regard counterclockwise (CCW) angular displacements as positive and clockwise (CW) angular displacements as negative; we measure angular displacements in radians.

The *angular velocity** ω of a rotating rigid body is defined in terms of the angular displacement $\Delta\phi$ in time Δt in accord with the relation

$$\omega = \lim_{\Delta t \to 0} \frac{\Delta\phi}{\Delta t} = \frac{d\phi}{dt} \cdot \left\{ \begin{array}{l} \omega \text{ in rad/s} \\ \phi \text{ in rad} \\ t \text{ in s} \end{array} \right\} \qquad (7.1)$$

With ϕ in radians and t in seconds, angular velocity ω is measured in rad/s; ω is positive for CCW rotations and is negative for CW rotations.

---

* The vector properties of angular velocity and other rotational quantities are discussed in Section 7.8.

The ANGULAR VELOCITY of a rigid body in pure rotation is defined as the time rate of change in the body's angular displacement.

Thus, we can define the average angular velocity $\bar{\omega}$ in time interval $\Delta t = t - 0$ as $\bar{\omega} = (\phi - \phi_0)/t$, where ϕ_0 is the initial angular position. For constant angular velocity ω, the angular displacement at time t is

$$\phi - \phi_0 = \omega t \quad \text{or} \quad \phi = \phi_0 + \omega t \quad (\omega = \text{constant}). \tag{7.2}$$

The magnitude of a body's angular velocity is often called the *rotational speed* of the body.

If the angular velocity of a rotating rigid body is changing, the body has *angular acceleration*. In terms of the change $\Delta \omega$ in angular velocity in time interval Δt, angular acceleration α is defined as

$$\alpha = \lim_{\Delta t \to 0} \frac{\Delta \omega}{\Delta t} = \frac{d\omega}{dt} = \frac{d^2\phi}{dt^2} . \quad \begin{cases} \alpha \text{ in rad/s}^2 \\ \omega \text{ in rad/s} \\ \phi \text{ in rad} \\ t \text{ in s} \end{cases} \tag{7.3}$$

With ω measured in rad/s and t in s, angular acceleration is measured in rad/s *per second;* i.e., in rad/s^2.

The ANGULAR ACCELERATION of a rigid body in pure rotation is defined as the time rate of change in the body's angular velocity.

If the body is rotating CCW (ω positive) and its angular acceleration α is positive, the body's angular velocity is increasing; if its angular acceleration is negative, the angular velocity of the body is decreasing.

From the above definitions of ϕ, ω, and α, we note that there is an exact mathematical analogy with the definitions of position x, velocity v_x, and acceleration a_x that we have used earlier in our discussions of rectilinear motion. It is therefore not surprising that the mathematical form of the equations used to describe the kinematics of rotation is the same as the form of the equations used earlier to describe the kinematics of rectilinear motion.

Thus, for the case of *constant angular acceleration* α, the angular velocity ω of a rotating body at time t is

$$\omega = \omega_0 + \alpha t, \tag{7.4}$$

where ω_0 is value of the body's angular velocity at $t = 0$. The angular displacement $d\phi$ of the body in time dt is $d\phi = \omega dt$; integration of this relation leads to

$$\phi = \phi_0 + \omega_0 t + \tfrac{1}{2}\alpha t^2, \tag{7.5}$$

where ϕ_0 gives the angular position of the body at $t = 0$. If $\phi_0 = 0$, we may write

$$\phi = \omega_0 t + \tfrac{1}{2}\alpha t^2. \tag{7.5'}$$

By elimination of t from (7.4) and (7.5'), we obtain the useful relation

$$\omega^2 = \omega_0^2 + 2\alpha\phi; \tag{7.6}$$

we shall later derive this relation directly by using work–energy relations.

Note that Eqs. (7.4)–(7.6) are valid only for the case of constant angular acceleration α. The mathematical form of these equations is exactly the same as the mathematical form of the equations describing rectilinear motion. In fact, we can adapt *any* of the kinematical equations employed earlier to describe motion along the X axis for use in describing the kinematics of the rotation of a rigid body about a fixed axis by making the following replacements: $\phi \rightarrow x$, $\omega \rightarrow v_x$, and $\alpha \rightarrow a_x$. We shall note still further analogies between pure rotation and rectilinear motion when we study the dynamics of pure rotational motion.

Example.   A motor-driven grinding wheel starts from rest and moves with a constant acceleration of 2 rad/s², CCW, for 10 s. What is the wheel's angular velocity at the end of this time? What is the wheel's angular displacement?

The constant angular acceleration gives the wheel a final angular velocity $\omega = \alpha t = (2 \text{ rad/s}^2, \text{CCW}) (10 \text{ s}) = 20 \text{ rad/s}$, CCW, in accord with (7.4); thus, $\omega = +20 \text{ rad/s}$. From (7.5') the angular displacement ϕ of the wheel is $\phi = \frac{1}{2}\alpha t^2 = \frac{1}{2}(2 \text{ rad/s}^2, \text{CCW}) (100 \text{ s}^2) = 100 \text{ rad}$, CCW; thus, $\phi = +100 \text{ rad}$.

Example.   A motor-driven grinding wheel is rotating at the rate of 40 rad/s, CW, when the motor is turned off. After the motor has been turned off, the wheel comes to rest after making 200 complete revolutions. Assume that *constant* angular acceleration is involved. What is the wheel's angular acceleration?

First we note that the angular acceleration is CCW because the clockwise angular velocity is decreasing. The angular displacement of the wheel is $\phi = 2\pi \times 200 = 1257 \text{ rad}$, CW (i.e., $\phi = -1257 \text{ rad}$) during the period of deceleration. We can make use of (7.6) to write $\alpha = -\omega_0^2/2\phi = (1600 \text{ rad}^2/\text{s}^2)/2(1257 \text{ rad}) = +0.636 \text{ rad/s}^2$.

7.2   MOTION OF A PARTICLE IN A ROTATING RIGID BODY

The angular displacement ϕ, angular velocity ω, and angular acceleration α describe the motion of an entire rigid body in pure rotational motion. Now we shall show how these quantities can be used to describe the motion of any particle P of the body at radial distance r from the axis of rotation, as shown in Fig. 7.2. The relations we develop will be important later in treating rotational kinetic energy. If the particle radius OP coincides with OX at time $t = 0$, then when the body undergoes an angular displacement ϕ the particle moves a distance S along a circular path given by the expression

$$S = r\phi \tag{7.7}$$

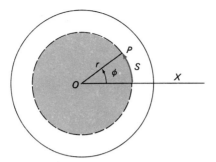

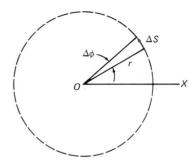

Fig. 7.2 Angular displacement ϕ of a rigid body rotating about an axis through O. Note that ϕ can have any value and is not limited to angles smaller than 2π radians.

Fig. 7.3

since S is merely the arc of a circle at radius r and, by definition, $\phi = S/r$. If we use the polar coordinate system suggested in Fig. 7.2, the position of the particle is uniquely determined by its polar coordinates r and ϕ.

As noted in Fig. 7.3, in time Δt the particle moves a distance ΔS along its circular path; ΔS is positive if ϕ is increasing with time and negative if ϕ is decreasing. At any instant the velocity vector of the particle is tangent to the circle in which the particle moves, as suggested in Fig. 7.4. The tangential component of the velocity is given by the relation

$$v_T = \lim_{\Delta t \to 0} \frac{\Delta S}{\Delta t} = \frac{dS}{dt}.$$

Because the radius of the particle's path is constant, we have from (7.7) that

$$\frac{dS}{dt} = \frac{d}{dt}(r\phi) = r\frac{d\phi}{dt} = r\omega.$$

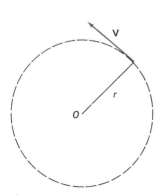

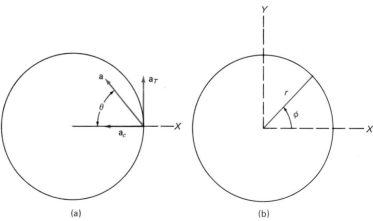

Fig. 7.4 A particle's tangential velocity $v_T = dS/dt$; $v_T = r\omega$.

Fig. 7.5 (a) $\mathbf{a} = \mathbf{a}_c + \mathbf{a}_T$ with $a_c = v_T^2/r = r\omega^2$ and $a_T = r\alpha$; $\tan \theta = a_T/a_c$. (b) $x = r\cos\phi$, $y = r\sin\phi$; $v_x = -r\sin\phi\,(d\phi/dt)$, $v_y = r\cos\phi\,(d\phi/dt)$.

Thus, we have for the tangential component of the particle's velocity

$$v_T = r\omega. \quad \text{(Tangential Velocity)} \tag{7.8}$$

Because the radial distance r of the particle does not change with time, the radial component of the particle's velocity is always zero.

The tangential component of the particle's acceleration is given by the expression

$$a_T = dv_T/dt = rd\omega/dt = r\alpha. \quad \text{(Tangential Acceleration)} \tag{7.9}$$

Because the particle is moving in a circular path, it also has a centripetal acceleration *directed radially inward* toward the axis of rotation. As was discussed in Chapter 3, $a_C = v_T^2/r$. Thus, from (7.8) we have

$$a_C = v_T^2/r = (r\omega)^2/r = r\omega^2. \quad \text{(Centripetal Acceleration)} \tag{7.10}$$

The resultant acceleration **a** of the particle is given by the vector sum

$$\mathbf{a} = \mathbf{a}_T + \mathbf{a}_C. \tag{7.11}$$

The magnitude of the resultant acceleration is $a = \sqrt{a_T^2 + a_C^2}$. The angle θ between the resultant acceleration **a** and the radius of the particle's path as shown in Fig. 7.5a is given by $\tan \theta = a_T/a_C$. When the rotating body has constant angular velocity, $\mathbf{a} = \mathbf{a}_C$ and is directed toward the axis of rotation because $\mathbf{a}_T = 0$ and $\theta = 0$ in Fig. 7.5a.

If we need to describe the particle's motion in the XY coordinate system indicated by the dotted lines in Fig. 7.5b we note that $x = r \cos \phi$ and $y = r \sin \phi$; $v_x = dx/dt$ and $v_y = dy/dt$; $a_x = dv_x/dt$ and $a_y = dv_y/dt$. The results of these differentiations show that v_x and v_y are merely the projections of $\mathbf{v}_T$ on the X and Y axes of the Cartesian coordinates system, $v_x = -v_T \sin \phi$ and $v_y = v_T \cos \phi$, and that, similarly, a_x and a_y are the projections of **a** on the X and Y axes. Ordinarily, use of the plane polar coordinate system gives a clearer insight into the motion of a particle in a rotating body.

Example.   A small grinding wheel has a radius of 10 cm and is attached to the shaft of a motor. The shaft of the motor moves with an angular velocity of 1800 rev/min. What is the tangential velocity of a point on the rim of the wheel? What is the acceleration of the point?

We note first that 1800 rev/min = 30 rev/s; this gives an angular velocity $\omega = 2\pi(30 \text{ rad/s}) = 60 \pi \text{ rad/s} = 188 \text{ rad/s}$. Use of (7.8) gives $v_T = r\omega = (0.1 \text{ m}) (188 \text{ rad/s}) = 18.8 \text{ m/s}$. When the motor shaft is operating at a constant speed, the acceleration is directed radially inward and has the magnitude given by (7.10): $a_C = r\omega^2 = (0.1 \text{ m}) (188 \text{ rad/s})^2 = 3.53 \times 10^3 \text{ m/s}^2$.

Example. An entertainment park includes among its attractions a circular horizontal rotating platform that has an angular velocity of 2 rad/s. If the coefficient of static friction between a man's shoes and the platform is 0.4, how far from the center of the platform can the man stand without sliding?

The man will have a centripetal acceleration $a_C = v_T^2/r = r\omega^2$. The maximum frictional force on the man before he begins to slide is $\mu_S F_N = \mu_S mg$. Since the frictional force is the only horizontal force, its magnitude must equal the centripetal force ma_C required to keep the man moving in a circular path around the axis of rotation: $\mathscr{F} = mr\omega^2$. Thus the greatest value of r occurs when $\mathscr{F}$ has its maximum value. The greatest value of r is obtained from $r\omega^2 = \mu_S g$ or $r = \mu_S g/\omega^2 = 0.4\ (9.8\ \text{m/s}^2)/(2\ \text{rad/s})^2 = 0.98$ m. At all radii smaller than this, the man is "safe"; at this radius the man begins to slide.

7.3 WORK, POWER, TORQUE

We now begin our discussion of the dynamics of rotational motion. Consider the wheel in Fig. 7.6 mounted to rotate about a horizontal axis through O perpendicular to the plane of the diagram. A string is wound around the rim of the wheel. When a constant force **F** to the left in the diagram is exerted on the string, the string exerts a tangential force $F_T = F$ on the wheel. When the end of the string moves to the left, work $W = FS$ is done when the end of the string has the displacement S as indicated in the figure. During this displacement of the string, the wheel turns through an angle $\phi = S/R$, so that $S = R\phi$. We assume that the string does not slip relative to the wheel. We can write the work done by the tangential force as the wheel turns through angle ϕ as

$$W = FS = F_T R\phi.$$

The quantity

$$\tau = F_T R \quad \begin{cases} \tau \ \ \text{in N} \cdot \text{m} \\ F_T \ \text{in N} \\ R \ \ \text{in m} \end{cases} \quad (Torque) \qquad (7.12)$$

is called the torque exerted by the tangential force F_T.

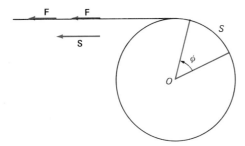

Fig. 7.6

The TORQUE associated with a tangential force acting on a rotating body is the product of the magnitude of the force and the radial distance from the axis to the point at which the force is applied.

Torque is measured in N · m. We regard a torque as positive if it tends to cause counterclockwise rotation and negative if it tends to cause clockwise rotation. The radial component of a force acting on a rotating body has no tendency to change the state of rotational motion of the body. Therefore, no torque is associated with the radial components of forces. A more general discussion of torque is given later in this chapter.

Using torque in our earlier expression for the work done by the tangential force, we can write

$$W = \tau\phi. \quad \begin{cases} W \text{ in J} \\ \tau \text{ in N} \cdot \text{m} \\ \phi \text{ in rad} \end{cases} \quad \textit{(Work)} \qquad (7.13)$$

When the wheel experiences an angular displacement $d\phi$, work $dW = \tau d\phi$ is done. Because power $P = dW/dt$, we can write $P = \tau \, d\phi/dt$. However, $d\phi/dt = \omega$ and hence we can write

$$P = \tau\omega. \quad \begin{cases} P \text{ in W} \\ \tau \text{ in N} \cdot \text{m} \\ \omega \text{ in rad/s} \end{cases} \quad \textit{(Power)} \qquad (7.14)$$

Thus, power is given by the product of torque and angular velocity.

In comparing the expressions for work and power given in (7.13) and (7.14) with the corresponding expressions $W = F_x x$ and $P = F_x v_x$ for rectilinear motion, we note that *torque* is the rotational analogue of force.

7.4   ROTATIONAL KINETIC ENERGY; ROTATIONAL INERTIA

Now consider the kinetic energy of a rigid body in pure rotation about a fixed axis. It is a matter of experience that work must be done in setting a body like a flywheel into rotational motion, even when frictional torques are negligible, and that work must be done in stopping a flywheel. The work done in setting a flywheel into rotational motion is stored as *kinetic energy of the rotation.*

The kinetic energy of a body rotating about a stationary, fixed axis is the sum of the kinetic energies of the particles of which the body is composed. To obtain an expression for the rotational kinetic energy of an extended body, we consider first the kinetic energy of a typical particle in the body such as the ith particle indicated in Fig. 7.7. The mass of this particle is m_i and its kinetic energy is $E_{Ki} = \frac{1}{2} m_i v_i^2$, where v_i is the magnitude of the particle's velocity. The velocity $\mathbf{v}_i$ is tangential to

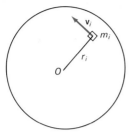

Fig. 7.7 $E_{Ki} = \frac{1}{2} m_i v_i^2 = \frac{1}{2} m_i r_i^2 \omega^2.$

the circle of radius r_i traversed by the particle as the body rotates. As we have seen earlier, the tangential velocity of a particle at radial distance r_i is given by the expression $v_i = r_i \omega$, where ω is the angular velocity of the rigid body in its rotation. Therefore, the kinetic energy E_{Ki} of the particle i is simply $E_{Ki} = \frac{1}{2} m_i r_i^2 \omega^2$. We get the total kinetic energy of the body by summing the kinetic energies of *all* the particles in the body:

$$E_K = \sum_{i=1}^{N} \frac{1}{2} m_i r_i^2 \omega^2.$$

Because ω is the same for all particles in the body, we can rewrite the above expression in the form

$$E_K = \frac{1}{2} \left[\sum_{i=1}^{N} m_i r_i^2 \right] \omega^2.$$

This equation is analogous to the equation $E_K = \frac{1}{2} m v^2$ for the translational kinetic energy of a particle or rigid body. We have already noted that ω is the rotational analogue of velocity **v**. Just as the mass M is said to be a measure of the *inertia* of a particle or a rigid body in translational motion, the quantity in brackets $[\Sigma \, m_i r_i^2]$ is called the *rotational inertia* or *moment of inertia* of the rigid body in its rotational motion about axis O in Fig. 7.7. Rotational inertia is denoted by the letter I; i.e.,

$$I = \sum_{i=1}^{N} m_i r_i^2. \quad \text{(Rotational Inertia)} \tag{7.15}$$

It is measured in kg · m².

> The ROTATIONAL INERTIA of a body about an axis of rotation is defined as the summation $\Sigma \, m_i r_i^2$, where m_i is the mass of a typical particle in the body, r_i is the radial distance of the particle from the axis of rotation, and the summation includes *all* the particles in the body.

The rotational inertia of a body depends on the total mass of the body and on the way the mass is distributed about the particular axis of rotation.

With this definition of I, the expression for the rotational kinetic energy of a body becomes

$$E_K = \tfrac{1}{2} I \omega^2. \quad \left\{ \begin{array}{l} E_k \text{ in J} \\ I \ \text{ in kg} \cdot \text{m}^2 \\ \omega \text{ in rad/s} \end{array} \right\} \quad (\textit{Kinetic Energy}) \qquad (7.16)$$

For a continuous distribution of mass the summation in (7.15) is replaced by an integration covering all mass elements dm in the body. Thus, we can write (7.15) in the symbolic form

$$I = \int_0^M r^2 \, dm, \qquad (7.15')$$

where r is the radial distance of mass element dm from the axis of rotation. Writing $dm = \rho \, dV$, where ρ is the density of the material of which the body is composed and dV is an element of volume, we obtain $I = \int_0^V r^2 \rho \, dV$. Note that the integral is actually a triple integral; that is, three integration operations are required to cover the variations in the three spatial coordinates and include contributions from all the volume elements of the body.

In Fig. 7.8 we give the rotational inertias I_C of several types of uniform rigid bodies about certain axes of rotation passing through their centers of mass. In every

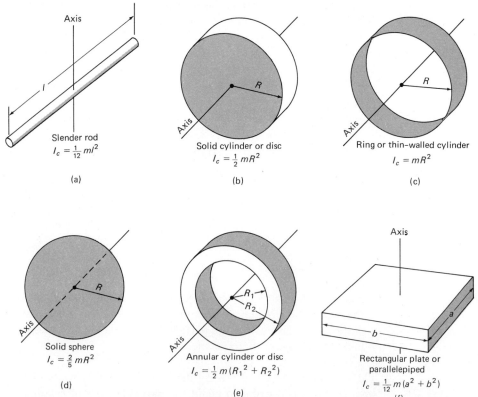

Fig. 7.8 The rotational inertias I_C of various rigid bodies about certain axes through their centers of mass.

case we note that I_C depends on the total mass M of the body and on the distribution of mass about the axis of rotation. This is readily seen in the case of the thin-walled hollow cylinder or ring, in which case *all* of the mass **M** is at the *same* radial distance R from the axis so that $I_C = MR^2$.

For any body it is possible to define a *radius of gyration k* such that $I = Mk^2$. For example, in the case of the solid cylinder in Fig. 7.8 the rotational inertia $I_C = \frac{1}{2}MR^2$ can be written as $I_C = Mk_C^2$ if we set $k_C = R/\sqrt{2}$. The radius of gyration is convenient for stating the rotational inertia of a complex object like a spoked wheel.

Example.   Verify by integration that a uniform solid cylinder like that in Fig. 7.8 has rotational inertia $I_C = MR^2/2$ about its axis of symmetry.

Suppose that the cylinder has thickness T. Choose coordinates with origin at the center of the cylinder and Z axis coincident with the symmetry axis; choose volume elements by dividing the cylinder into thin slabs oriented perpendicular to the Z axis, each slab of thickness dz, and then dividing each slab into elements of area $r\,d\phi\,dr$ as shown in Fig. 7.9. In this way the cylinder is divided into elements of volume $dV = r\,d\phi\,dr\,dz$. The element of mass dm for this volume element is $dm = \rho r\,d\phi\,dr\,dz$, where ρ is the density of the material, and its contribution to the rotational inertia is $dI = r^2\,dm = \rho r^3\,dr\,d\phi\,dz$. In order to include all volume elements we must allow ϕ to range from 0 to 2π, r to range from 0 to R, and z to range from $-T/2$ to $T/2$. Three integrations are required to cover the variations of the three variables. Thus, for the rotational inertia of the cylinder we have

$$I_C = \int_{r=0}^{R} \int_{\phi=0}^{2\pi} \int_{z=-T/2}^{T/2} \rho r^3\,dr\,d\phi\,dz = \rho \int_0^R r^3\,dr \int_0^{2\pi} d\phi \int_{-T/2}^{T/2} dz$$

$$= \rho \cdot (r^4/4)\Big|_0^R \cdot \phi\Big|_0^{2\pi} \cdot z\Big|_{-T/2}^{T/2} = \rho(R^4/4)2\pi T$$

$$= (\rho\pi R^2 T)R^2/2 = MR^2/2,$$

where we recognize that $\rho\pi R^2 T$ is the total mass M of the cylinder and, therefore, $I_C = MR^2/2$ as stated in Fig. 7.8.

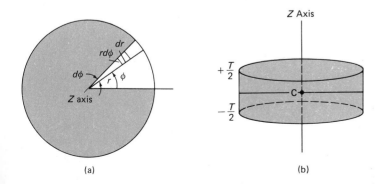

(a)

(b)

Fig. 7.9 A solid cylinder. (a) The Z axis is perpendicular to the plane of the diagram. (b) A "side view" of the cylinder.

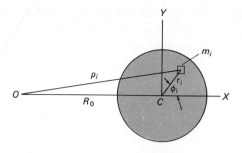

Fig. 7.10 The parallel axis theorem: $I_O = I_C + MR_O^2$.

The values of the rotational inertia about axes through the center of mass are of special importance because, if we know I_C, we can find very simply the rotational inertia I_O about any axis that is parallel to the axis through C. To see how this is done, consider Fig. 7.10, which shows an axis through O parallel to the axis through C, with both axes perpendicular to the plane of the diagram. The perpendicular distance between the axes is R_O. We choose a coordinate system with origin at the center of mass and X axis oriented as shown in Fig. 7.10. We divide the body into thin slices oriented perpendicular to the Z axis. The computation of I_C or I_O can then be carried out by first finding the contribution to $\Sigma\ m_i r_i^2$ for each slice and then summing over all the slices. The situation for a particular one of the slices is shown in Fig. 7.10. The distance of a typical particle in the slice from the axis through O is ρ_i. By the law of cosines $\rho_i^2 = R_O^2 + r_i^2 + 2R_O r_i \cos\ \phi_i = R_O^2 + r_i^2 + 2R_O x_i$. The rotational inertia of the slice about the axis through O is

$$\delta I_O = \Sigma\ m_i \rho_i^2 = R_O^2\ \Sigma\ m_i + \Sigma\ m_i r_i^2 + 2R_O\ \Sigma\ m_i x_i,$$

where the summations include all particles in the slice. The first term $R_O^2\ \Sigma\ m_i = \delta M R_O^2$, where δM is the total mass of the slice. The second term $\Sigma\ m_i r_i^2$ is by definition simply δI_C, the rotational inertia of the slice about the axis through the center of mass of the body. We next sum over all the slices, which gives

$$\Sigma\ \delta I_O = R_O^2\ \Sigma\ \delta M + \Sigma\ \delta I_C + \Sigma\ (2R_O\ \Sigma\ m_i x_i).$$

Now $\Sigma\ \delta I_O = I_O$, $\Sigma\ \delta M = M$, and $\Sigma\ \delta I_C = I_C$. Furthermore, the final term is just $2R_O\ \Sigma_{tot}\ m_i x_i$, where Σ_{tot} represents a summation over *all* particles of the body. By our choice of coordinates and the definition of the center of mass, $\Sigma_{tot}\ m_i x_i = 0$. Thus we have as our final result

$$I_O = MR_O^2 + I_C. \tag{7.17}$$

This relationship is known as the

PARALLEL AXIS THEOREM: The rotational inertia of a rigid body about any axis equals the rotational inertia about a parallel axis through the center of mass plus the mass of the body times the square of the perpendicular distance between the axes.

Since MR_0^2 is necessarily positive, the rotational inertia I_C of a body about an axis passing through its center of mass is smaller than its rotational inertia I_0 about any parallel axis.

Example.   A metal ring is suspended from a nail at point O in Fig. 7.11. If the ring is displaced to one side and then released, it will swing as a pendulum about an axis through O. What is the rotational inertia I_0 about this axis? What is the radius of gyration of the ring about the axis through O?

From the figure we note that the perpendicular distance between the axis through O and a parallel axis through C is equal to the radius R of the ring. Thus, by the parallel-axis theorem $I_0 = I_C + MR^2$, where M is the mass of the ring. According to Fig. 7.8, $I_C = MR^2$; thus, $I_0 = MR^2 + MR^2 = 2MR^2$. The radius of gyration of the ring about the axis through O is determined from the relation $Mk^2 = 2MR^2$, which gives $k = \sqrt{2}\,R$.

7.5   THE DYNAMICS OF PURE ROTATION

The dynamics of translational motion is based directly on Newton's Second Principle: $\mathbf{F}_R = m\mathbf{a}$. In this section we use Newton's Second Principle to derive an analogous expression for the rotational motion of a rigid body.

We start by considering the simple situation in Fig. 7.12, which shows a particle of mass m constrained by a light rigid "connecting rod" of length R to move in a circular path about an axis through O. If the total tangential force on the particle is F_T, the particle will have tangential acceleration a_T which by Newton's Second Principle is

$$F_T = ma_T.$$

From (7.9) we have $a_T = R\alpha$, where α is the angular acceleration of the particle in its rotational motion about the axis through O. The torque τ associated with tangential force F_T is by (7.12) $F_T R$. Thus, multiplication of both sides of the above equation by R gives

$$F_T R = mR^2\alpha \quad \text{or} \quad \tau = I_0\alpha, \tag{7.18}$$

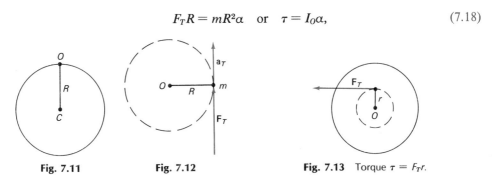

Fig. 7.11   **Fig. 7.12**   **Fig. 7.13**   Torque $\tau = F_T r$.

where we have replaced a_T by $R\alpha$ and have noted that mR^2 is simply the rotational inertia I_0 of a particle of mass m at a distance R from the axis of rotation through O. For the case of a single particle moving in a circular path, we have derived the rotational analogue of Newton's Second Principle with $\tau \to F$, $I_0 \to m$, and $\alpha \to a$.

We now apply this result to a rigid body. We write the relation $\tau_i = [m_i r_i^2]\alpha$ for a typical mass particle and then sum both sides of the equation over all particles in the body. Since $\tau = \Sigma \tau_i$ and $I_0 = \Sigma m_i r_i^2$, we obtain the result $\tau = I_0\alpha$ in accord with (7.18). We must note that the rigid body is a dynamical system in which all internal forces cancel in pairs; in the evaluation of $\tau = \Sigma \tau_i$ only torques that are due to *external forces* as suggested in Fig. 7.13 contribute to the final result. (See Section 4.12.) Thus, τ is the algebraic sum of all torques about the axis through O exerted by external forces and can be regarded as the *resultant external torque* acting on the rotating body.

A rigorous derivation of the desired relation can also be obtained by noting that the power furnished by the resultant torque τ must equal the rate of change of the rotational kinetic energy of the body: $P = \tau\omega = d/dt \ (E_K)$ so that

$$\tau\omega = \frac{d}{dt}(\tfrac{1}{2}I\omega^2) = I\omega\frac{d\omega}{dt} = I\omega\alpha.$$

Dividing both sides of this equation by ω gives

$$\tau = I\alpha \cdot \quad \left\{ \begin{array}{l} \tau \text{ in N } \cdot \text{ m} \\ I \text{ in kg } \cdot \text{ m}^2 \\ \alpha \text{ in rad/s}^2 \end{array} \right\} \begin{array}{l} \textit{(Rotational Analogue of} \\ \textit{Newton's Second Principle)} \end{array} \qquad (7.19)$$

The rotational analogue of linear momentum $p_x = mv_x$ is *angular momentum*. If I is the rotational inertia of a rigid body rotating at angular velocity ω about a fixed axis, the angular momentum about the fixed axis is $L = I\omega$. It is readily seen that, because $\tau = d/dt \ (I\omega) = I\alpha$, we have

$$\tau = dL/dt, \qquad (7.20)$$

where τ is the resultant external torque exerted on the rotating rigid body. If $\tau = 0$, $L = $ constant, and we have derived the *conservation-of-angular-momentum* theorem for the case of a rigid body rotating about a fixed axis:

If no resultant torque acts on a rigid body mounted on a fixed axis, the angular momentum of the body is constant.

If an impulsive torque acts, which might occur for example when the spoke of a wheel is struck with a hammer, we may not be able to determine the torque τ as a function of time. However, we can rewrite (7.20) in the form $dL = \tau dt$ and integrate to obtain

$$\Delta L = \bar\tau \Delta t$$
Change in Angular Momentum = Angular Impulse. $\qquad (7.21)$

Table 7.1 Analogues Between Rectilinear Motion and Rotational Motion about a Fixed Axis

Quantity or Relation	Rectilinear Motion	Rotational Motion
Displacement	x	ϕ (angular)
Velocity	$v_x = dx/dt$	$\omega = d\phi/dt$ (angular)
Acceleration	$a_x = dv_x/dt$	$\alpha = d\omega/dt$ (angular)
Inertia	m (mass)	I (rotational inertia)
Force, torque	F (force)	τ (torque)
Newton's principle	$F_x = ma_x$	$\tau = I\alpha$
Element of work	$dW = F_x dx$	$dW = \tau d\phi$
Kinetic energy	$\frac{1}{2}mv^2$	$\frac{1}{2}I\omega^2$
Power	$F_x v_x$	$\tau\omega$
Momentum	$p_x = mv_x$	$L = I\omega$ (angular)
Impulse	$F_x\Delta t$	$\bar{\tau}\Delta t$ (angular)

This relation is the rotational analogue of Eq. (4.17).

We have now defined all physical quantities and relations needed for the treatment of the rotational motion of a rigid body about a fixed axis. We note a complete set of analogues of these with the quantities and relations used earlier in our treatment of the rectilinear motion of a particle. Table 7.1 gives a convenient summary of the analogous quantities and relations.

Example. A flywheel with a rotational inertia of 2 kg·m² is rotating counterclockwise at a rotational speed of 30 rad/s at the time the driving motor is turned off. The flywheel comes to rest as a result of a constant frictional torque after 1 min. Find the angular acceleration of the wheel and the torque acting on the flywheel.

Since the constant resultant torque implies constant angular acceleration, we can write $\alpha = \Delta\omega/\Delta t = (0 - \omega_0)/(t - 0) = (-30 \text{ rad/s})/(60 \text{ s}) = -0.5 \text{ rad/s}^2$. We then employ the rotational analogue of Newton's Second Principle (7.19) to obtain the torque acting on the wheel: $\tau = I\alpha = (2 \text{ kg·m}^2)(-0.5 \text{ rad/s}^2) = -1.0 \text{ kg·m}^2/\text{s}^2 = -1 \text{ N·m}$; i.e., 1 N·m, CW.

Example. An electric motor exerting a constant torque is used to set a flywheel into rotational motion. The flywheel has a rotational inertia of 3 kg·m². If the flywheel starts from rest and attains a final rotational speed of 40 rad/s in 45 s, what is the magnitude of the flywheel's angular acceleration? What is the average power delivered to the wheel? What is the effective power output of the motor (a) as the wheel starts from rest and (b) as the wheel attains its final rotational speed?

Since no information is given regarding the sense of the wheel's rotation, we shall assume that the motion is in the CCW sense, so that all quantities in our equations will be positive. First, we find the constant angular acceleration: $\alpha = (\omega_{\text{final}} - \omega_0)/(t - 0) = (40 \text{ rad/s} - 0)/45 \text{ s} = 0.889 \text{ rad/s}^2$. Using (7.19) to find the torque, we write $\tau = I\alpha = (3 \text{ kg·m}^2)(0.889 \text{ rad/s}^2) = 2.67 \text{ N·m}$. The effective power output of the motor has gone into increasing the kinetic energy of the wheel so that we can write $\bar{P} = W/t = E_K/t = \frac{1}{2}I\omega^2/t = \frac{1}{2}(3 \text{ kg}\cdot\text{m}^2)(40 \text{ rad/s})^2/45 \text{ s} = 2400 \text{ J}/45 \text{ s} = 53.3 \text{ W}$ as the average power delivered to the wheel.

In finding the instantaneous useful power output of the motor we can use the power relation (7.14), which can also be obtained by noting that $P = dE_K/dt = d/dt(\frac{1}{2}I\omega^2) = I\omega\alpha = \tau\omega$. Thus, as the wheel starts, $P_0 = \tau\omega_0 = (2.67 \text{ N}\cdot\text{m})(0) = 0$. The final useful power output is $P_f = \tau\omega_f = (2.67 \text{ N}\cdot\text{m})(40 \text{ rad/s}) = 107 \text{ N}\cdot\text{m/s} = 107 \text{ W}$. *Note:* Once the wheel has attained its final speed, the only power required from the motor is that needed to compensate for frictional power losses, which we hope are small.

7.6   POWER-TRANSMISSION DEVICES

Power from a prime mover such as an automobile engine is usually made available by a rotating crankshift; similarly, the power supplied directly by an electric motor also involves a rotating shaft. In using the power it is frequently desired to operate a machine employing a drive shaft rotating at quite a different rotational speed. The transmission of power at the required rotational speed can be accomplished by a transmission device with input power $\tau_{in}\omega_{in}$ from the prime mover and with output power $\tau_{out}\omega_{out}$, where the output rotational speed ω_{out} is that required by the machine to be operated. Because of frictional energy losses, the output power $\tau_{out}\omega_{out}$ is always less than the input power $\tau_{in}\omega_{in}$. Their ratio gives the *efficiency* of the transmission device:

$$\text{Efficiency} = \frac{\text{Power Output}}{\text{Power Input}} = \frac{\tau_{out}\omega_{out}}{\tau_{in}\omega_{in}}. \tag{7.22}$$

In any mechanical device like the gear wheels in Fig. 7.14a or the nonslipping pulley drive in Fig. 7.14b, the ratio of the rotational speeds of the shafts ω_{out}/ω_{in} is determined by strictly geometric considerations in terms of the radii of the input and output wheels, both of which are attached to shafts. For example, in Fig. 7.14, if the radius of the output wheel is $2R$ and that of the input wheel is R, the output wheel will rotate once for every two complete rotations of the input wheel; thus $\omega_{out} = \omega_{in}/2$. In the case of the cog wheels the same result can be obtained by "counting the

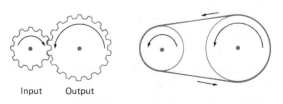

Input   Output

(a)   (b)   **Fig. 7.14** Power transmission devices.

teeth" on each wheel and taking the ratio. Therefore, the *speed ratio* of the shafts is given unambiguously by the relation

$$\frac{\omega_{out}}{\omega_{in}} = \frac{R_{in}}{R_{out}}.$$

In an ideal transmission device with no dissipative energy losses

$$P_{out} = P_{in}, \quad \tau_{out}\omega_{out} = \tau_{in}\omega_{in}, \quad \frac{\tau_{out}}{\tau_{in}} = \frac{\omega_{in}}{\omega_{out}}.$$

In other words, the torque ratio τ_{out}/τ_{in} is exactly equal to the speed ratio ω_{in}/ω_{out}. In any real transmission device, the torque ratio τ_{out}/τ_{in} is always less than the speed ratio ω_{in}/ω_{out}. It is easily seen from (7.22) that the efficiency of a transmission device is given by the expression

$$\text{Efficiency} = \frac{\text{Torque Ratio}}{\text{Speed Ratio}} = \frac{\tau_{out}/\tau_{in}}{\omega_{in}/\omega_{out}}.$$

For mechanical devices employing gears or nonslipping belts between pulley wheels of different sizes, the speed ratio can always be determined geometrically in the manner just described; the torque ratio in these devices is equal to the speed ratio times the efficiency. In the case of the so-called *hydraulic torque converters* and *fluid transmission devices,* in which the only contact between the driving and driven members is by means of a liquid, neither the speed ratio nor the torque ratio is geometrically determined. However, in all kinds of transmissions $\tau_{out}\omega_{out}$ is always less than $\tau_{in}\omega_{in}$ because mechanical energy is always being dissipated.

Example.   In a belt-driven transmission device like the one shown in Fig. 7.14b, the input wheel is 5 cm in diameter and is attached directly to the shaft of a motor rotating at a speed of 1800 rev/min. The motor delivers 600 W of power to the input wheel. What is the speed of the output shaft if the output wheel has a diameter of 25 cm? What can we say about the torque transmitted by a shaft attached to the output wheel?

First, we find the value of ω_{in} in rad/s: $\omega_{in} = 1800$ rev/min $= 30$ rev/s $= (30)(2\pi)$ rad/s $= 188.5$ rad/s. Since we know the power delivered by the motor, we can make use of the power relation $P = \tau_{in}\omega_{in}$ to obtain the input torque: $\tau_{in} = P/\omega_{in} = (600 \text{ W})/(188.5 \text{ rad/s}) = 3.18$ N·m.

The rotational speed of the output wheel is, by geometrical considerations, $\omega_{out} = \omega_{in}/(D_{out}/D_{in}) = (188.5 \text{ rad/s})/(25 \text{ cm}/5 \text{ cm}) = 37.7$ rad/s, where D_{out} and D_{in} are the diameters of the output and input wheels, respectively. The output torque τ_{out} can be obtained from power considerations. If the transmission device were ideal, the output power would equal the input power: $\tau_{out}\omega_{out} = \tau_{in}\omega_{in}$, whence $\tau_{out} = \tau_{in}\omega_{in}/\omega_{out} = (3.18 \text{ N·m})(5) = 15.9$ N·m. Because the real device shown in Fig. 7.14b is not ideal, the actual value of the output torque τ_{out} is less than 15.9 N·m and is given by $\omega_{out} = $ (efficiency of the device)(15.9 N·m). The efficiency depends on the details of the particular device.

7.7   THE TORQUE VECTOR: VECTOR PRODUCT OF TWO VECTORS

In our discussion of the rotational motion of a rigid body about a fixed axis, we have not referred to torque as a vector. However, we have seen that torque is not an ordinary scalar because we have had to specify whether it was clockwise or counterclockwise. In fact, torque has the properties of a vector, and in the general case where the rotation axis is not fixed, a vector representation of torque is essential. In the case of torque about a fixed axis, the torque vector τ is drawn along the axis in the sense shown in Fig. 7.15. This sense is given by the right-hand rule: *If one encircles the axis with the fingers of his right hand to indicate the direction of the tendency to rotate, the thumb points in the direction of the torque vector.* Another way of saying this is that if we use a screw driver to exert a torque on a screw with a right-hand thread, the torque vector points in the direction that the screw advances.

The torque vector is our first example of the *vector product* of two vectors; the representation of torque as a vector product is accomplished as follows. In Fig. 7.16a we draw a radius vector **R** perpendicular to the axis through *O* to the point at which force **F** is applied. On the basis of our earlier discussion in Section 7.3, we know that only the tangential component of **F** exerts a torque about the axis through *O*. We note from the figure that $F_T = F \sin \theta$, where θ is the angle between the force **F** and the radius vector **R**. Therefore, the magnitude of the torque is $FR \sin \theta$; its sense is in the counterclockwise direction about the axis through *O*.

The correct direction for the torque vector is shown in Fig. 7.16b, in which **R** and **F** have been placed tail to tail and the direction of τ is given by the circled point $\odot$ representing the point of an arrow directed toward the reader. The direction of the torque vector τ corresponds to a counterclockwise torque. Note that the torque vector τ is perpendicular to both **R** and **F**. This torque vector corresponds to a "product" of **R** and **F** that is called the *vector product* and is symbolized by the expression

$$\tau = \mathbf{R} \times \mathbf{F}. \tag{7.23}$$

The VECTOR PRODUCT $\mathbf{A} \times \mathbf{B}$ of two vectors **A** and **B** is a vector having magnitude $AB \sin \theta$, where θ is the smaller angle between the positive directions of the two vectors when they are placed tail to tail. The direction of $\mathbf{A} \times \mathbf{B}$ is

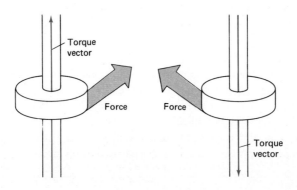

Torque vector

Force   Force

Torque vector

Fig. 7.15 The torque vector has the direction in which the torque would tend to advance a right-hand screw.

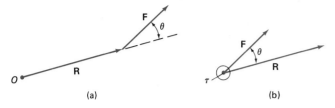

Fig. 7.16 The magnitude of the torque is $\tau = RF \sin \theta$. The torque vector, τ, which has both magnitude and direction, is given by the cross or vector product: $\tau = \mathbf{R} \times \mathbf{F}$.

perpendicular to the plane containing vectors **A** and **B** and is directed in the sense that a right-hand screw would advance if **A** were rotated through angle θ into **B**.

The rotation of **A** into **B** through angle θ is illustrated in Fig. 7.17. Because it is denoted by a cross, this product is sometimes called the *cross product* of two vectors.

Note that the vector product $\mathbf{A} \times \mathbf{B}$ is a *vector* quantity having magnitude $AB \sin \theta$, whereas the scalar product $\mathbf{A} \cdot \mathbf{B}$ is a *scalar* quantity of magnitude $AB \cos \theta$, as pointed out on p. 123. We shall make use of both of these kinds of products not only in our study of mechanics but also in later chapters dealing with electromagnetism.

We note that the vector product of two vectors is *not* commutative. Instead, by definition of the operation we have

$$\mathbf{A} \times \mathbf{B} = -(\mathbf{B} \times \mathbf{A}), \qquad (7.24)$$

as we can readily understand from Fig. 7.17. In the product $\mathbf{B} \times \mathbf{A}$, the magnitude has the same value $BA \sin \theta$ as the magnitude $AB \sin \theta$ of $\mathbf{A} \times \mathbf{B}$. However, according to our definition the direction of $\mathbf{B} \times \mathbf{A}$ is a vector directed *downward* in Fig. 7.17— thus, in the direction opposite to the direction of $\mathbf{A} \times \mathbf{B}$. Some additional properties of vector products are considered in the problems.

7.8   VECTOR PROPERTIES OF ROTATIONAL QUANTITIES: RIGID BODIES

Now that we have noted that torque has vector properties, let us consider other rotational quantities that we have introduced in connection with the rotation of a rigid body about a *fixed axis*. Because we have indicated that torque is a vector quantity, and I is a scalar quantity, we expect from (7.19) that

$$\tau = I\alpha;$$

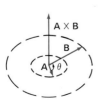

Fig. 7.17 The vector product $\mathbf{A} \times \mathbf{B}$: Its magnitude is $AB \sin \theta$; its direction, obtained by rotating **A** through angle θ into **B**, is the direction in which such a rotation would advance a right-hand screw.

we anticipate that angular acceleration α should be a vector quantity because it is equal to the product of a vector by a scalar.

Because angular velocity can be defined in terms of α by the relation

$$\boldsymbol{\omega} = \int \boldsymbol{\alpha} \, dt,$$

we can conclude that $\boldsymbol{\omega}$ should also be a vector quantity. Similarly, because $L = I\omega$ for a fixed axis, we expect that angular momentum $\mathbf{L}$ is also a vector quantity satisfying

$$\mathbf{L} = I\boldsymbol{\omega}.$$

From the relation (7.1) we might next conclude that an infinitesimal angular displacement is also a vector quantity,

$$d\boldsymbol{\theta} = \boldsymbol{\omega} \, dt.$$

However, this chain of reasoning based on our results for a single, fixed axis of rotation meets difficulties for general rotations. When we come to *finite* angular displacements in three dimensions, we find that *finite angular displacements are not vector quantities.* If we consider angular displacements about more than one axis, we find that they do not add at all in the way that vector quantities add. This fact can easily be demonstrated by considering a particular example. Suppose that we place a meterstick on the X axis of an XYZ coordinate system as shown in Fig. 7.18a. First we give it a rotation to align it with the Y axis as shown in Fig. 7.18b;

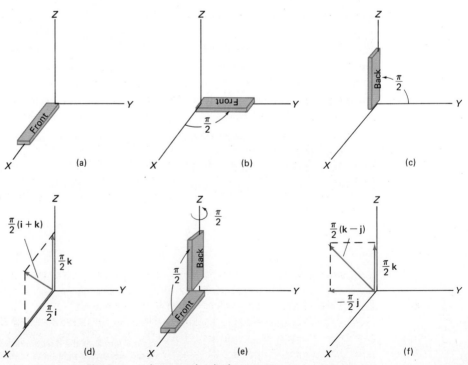

Fig. 7.18   A finite angular displacement is *not* a vector quantity.

if we assume that angular displacement *is* a vector, we could describe this first displacement as $\mathbf{k}\pi/2$. Next, we rotate the stick so that it is in alignment with the *Z* axis of the coordinate system as shown in Fig. 7.18c; on the assumption that angular displacement is a vector, we would write the second displacement as $\mathbf{i}\pi/2$. The vector sum of these two assumed vector angular displacements would be a vector lying in the *XZ* plane midway the *X* and *Z* axes as shown in Fig. 7.18d, not aligned with any axis of the coordinate system. However, we note that the result of the two angular displacements is also obtained by a rotation about the *Y* axis followed by a rotation about the *Z* axis, as shown in Fig. 7.18e. Assuming again that angular displacement is a vector, we could describe the result of these two displacements as the vector sum $-\mathbf{j}\pi/2 + \mathbf{k}\pi/2$ shown in Fig. 7.18f. Because $\mathbf{k}\pi/2 + \mathbf{i}\pi/2 \neq -\mathbf{j}\pi/2 + \mathbf{k}\pi/2$, we can conclude that our assumption that finite angular displacements have vector properties is wrong. Thus, we conclude that *a finite angular displacement is not a vector quantity.*

It also turns out that for general rotations the rotational inertia cannot be treated as a simple scalar quantity but must be regarded as a more complex quantity called a tensor. These facts make the general treatment of the rotation of a rigid body a very complex subject. In the following section we shall consider some of the general rotational properties of dynamical system, and in the final section we return to a special problem involving rigid bodies.

7.9 THE ANGULAR MOMENTUM OF A DYNAMICAL SYSTEM

In Sec. 7.5 dealing with the rotation of a rigid body about a fixed axis we defined angular momentum about the fixed axis as $L = I\omega$ and noted that this angular momentum is constant provided the resultant torque acting on the rotating body is zero. In this section we shall discuss the angular momentum of a *dynamical system* and the conditions under which it remains constant. Because a dynamical system consists of particles, we first consider the angular momentum of a single particle. Since for a general dynamical system there may not be a single axis of rotation, we shall be discussing the angular momentum and the torque about a *point* rather than about a line axis.

The angular momentum l of a particle about a point *O* is defined as the vector product $\mathbf{r} \times \mathbf{p}$, where $\mathbf{r}$ is the position vector from *O* to the particle and $\mathbf{p}$ is the linear momentum $m\mathbf{v}$ of the particle as indicated in Fig. 7.19. Note from the definition of the vector product that l is a vector perpendicular to both $\mathbf{r}$ and $\mathbf{p}$. Thus, in general,

$$\mathit{l} = \mathbf{r} \times \mathbf{p}. \tag{7.25}$$

It is easy to see that l is constant for a particle moving at constant velocity $\mathbf{v}$. Consider Fig. 7.20, where the axes have been chosen so that the particle moves in the *XY* plane at constant velocity $\mathbf{v}$ along a line parallel to the *Y* axis. As the particle crosses the *X* axis at point ①, its angular momentum about the point *O* has a magnitude $\mathit{l} = r_o p = m r_o v$ and a direction parallel to the *Z* axis. At point ② its angular momentum has a magnitude of $rp \sin\theta = rp \cos\phi = r_o p = m r_o v$, the same magnitude as at ①, and its direction is again parallel to the *Z* axis. Thus, l is constant for a

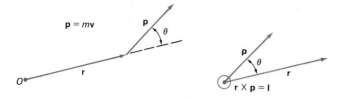

Fig. 7.19   The angular momentum $\mathbf{l}$ of a particle about an axis through O is given by $\mathbf{l} = \mathbf{r} \times \mathbf{p}$, where $p = mv$ is the momentum of the particle.

particle m moving at constant velocity $\mathbf{v}$. From Newton's Second Principle, we know the condition that $\mathbf{v}$ be constant means that there is no resultant force $\mathbf{F}$ acting on the particle. The resultant torque about the point O acting on the particle is defined to be $\boldsymbol{\tau} = \mathbf{r} \times \mathbf{F}$. Thus, the absence of a resultant force means that there is no resultant torque $\boldsymbol{\tau}$ acting on the particle.

This example illustrates a result that we can derive in general as follows. The time rate of change of the angular momentum of the particle about O is given by

$$\frac{d\mathbf{l}}{dt} = \frac{d}{dt}(\mathbf{r} \times \mathbf{p}).$$

Now in general the time derivative of the vector product of two vectors is given by

$$\frac{d}{dt}(\mathbf{A} \times \mathbf{B}) = \frac{d\mathbf{A}}{dt} \times \mathbf{B} + \mathbf{A} \times \frac{d\mathbf{B}}{dt}. \tag{7.26}$$

The reasoning by which this can be proved is suggested in one of the problems. If we take $\mathbf{r} = \mathbf{A}$ and $\mathbf{p} = \mathbf{B}$, and note that $d\mathbf{r}/dt = \mathbf{v}$ and $\mathbf{p} = m\mathbf{v}$, we obtain

$$\frac{d\mathbf{l}}{dt} = \frac{d\mathbf{r}}{dt} \times \mathbf{p} + \mathbf{r} \times \frac{d\mathbf{p}}{dt} = \mathbf{v} \times m\mathbf{v} + \mathbf{r} \times \frac{d\mathbf{p}}{dt} = 0 + \mathbf{r} \times \frac{d\mathbf{p}}{dt} = \mathbf{r} \times \mathbf{F},$$

where we have noted that the vector product of two parallel vectors is zero and in the last step have used Newton's Second Principle. But $\mathbf{r} \times \mathbf{F}$ is just the resultant torque $\boldsymbol{\tau}$ about O acting on the particle. Thus,

$$\tag{7.27}$$

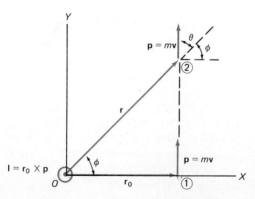

Fig. 7.20   In the absence of a resultant force the angular momentum of the particle about an axis through O is constant.

Our derivation of (7.27) is valid in any inertial frame of reference. Therefore we can conclude that

A particle has constant angular momentum $\mathbf{l}$ about a point O provided there is no resultant torque τ about O.

Now consider a dynamical system consisting of n particles. The total angular momentum of the system $\mathbf{L}$ about any point O is defined as the vector sum of the angular momenta $\mathbf{l}$ of the individual particles as given by (7.25). Thus, relative to any point O,

$$\mathbf{L} = \mathbf{l}_1 + \mathbf{l}_2 + \cdots + \mathbf{l}_n = \sum_{i=1}^{N} \mathbf{l}_i. \qquad (7.28)$$

If we differentiate each term in (7.28) with respect to time, we obtain for the time rate of change of the total angular momentum

$$\frac{d\mathbf{L}}{dt} = \frac{d\mathbf{l}_1}{dt} + \frac{d\mathbf{l}_2}{dt} + \cdots + \frac{d\mathbf{l}_n}{dt} = \sum_{i=1}^{n} \frac{d\mathbf{l}_i}{dt}.$$

However, we have shown in (7.27) that for each particle $d\mathbf{l}_i/dt = \tau_i$, where τ_i is the torque acting on the ith particle. Therefore,

$$\frac{d\mathbf{L}}{dt} = \tau_1 + \tau_2 + \cdots + \tau_n = \sum_{i=1}^{n} \tau_i = \tau, \qquad (7.29)$$

where τ turns out to be the *resultant external torque* exerted on the system by particles or bodies external to the system. We have stated in Section 4.12 that the internal forces due to oppositely directed forces between particles inside the system cancel in pairs, but it is not obvious that the resultant of the internal torques produced by internal forces should also be zero. However, it is easy to verify that this occurs for the simple system treated in the following example.

Example. A dynamical system consists of two mutually attracting particles ① and ②. Show that the forces of attraction have a zero resultant torque about any point O.

Particles ① and ② and point O are in a common plane as shown in Fig. 7.21. The forces of attraction $\mathbf{F}_1$ and $\mathbf{F}_2$ act in opposite directions along the dotted line joining the particles. The torques are by definition $\tau_1 = \mathbf{r}_1 \times \mathbf{F}_1$ and $\tau_2 = \mathbf{r}_2 \times \mathbf{F}_2$. The magnitude of τ_1 is $\tau_1 = r_1 F_1 \sin \theta_1$ and its sense is clockwise as indicated in the diagram; the magnitude of τ_2 is $\tau_2 = r_2 F_2 \sin \theta_2$ and its sense is counterclockwise. From Newton's Third Principle, the magnitudes of the forces are equal: $F_1 = F_2 = F$.

In Fig. 7.21 the line of length λ is the perpendicular distance from O to the dotted line between ① and ②. We note that θ_1 is the exterior angle of triangle OP① and, by a well-known theorem of plane geometry, is equal to the sum of the opposite interior angles: $\theta_1 = \pi/2 + \alpha$. Similarly, $\theta_2 = \pi/2 + \beta$. Thus,

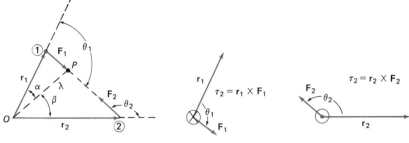

Fig. 7.21 In the absence of *external* forces the total angular momentum of a system is constant. Internal forces cannot change the angular momentum of an isolated system.

$\sin \theta_1 = \sin (\pi/2 + \alpha) = \cos \alpha$ and $\sin \theta_2 = \sin (\pi/2 + \beta) = \cos \beta$. Therefore, $\tau_1 = Fr_1 \cos \alpha = F\lambda$, clockwise, and $\tau_2 = Fr_2 \cos \beta = F\lambda$, counterclockwise, from which $\tau_1 + \tau_2 = 0$.

The line of length λ in Fig. 7.21, which is drawn from O perpendicular to the line of action of a force, is called the *lever arm* of the force. Any torque associated with a force has a magnitude $F\lambda$. Pairs of equal but oppositely directed internal forces that act along the same line have the same lever arm λ and thus have equal but opposite torques. Note that the lever arm of a radial force is zero.

We can generalize the result obtained on the basis of Newton's Third Principle in this example to any dynamical system by considering the internal forces of attraction or repulsion between each pair of particles in the system. Thus, in (7.29) the contributions to the sum on the right-hand side from internal torques cancel in pairs. Only torques due to external forces give a nonvanishing result after the summation. We can conclude that for any dynamical system the time rate of change of its total angular momentum L is given by the relation

$$\frac{d\mathbf{L}}{dt} = \tau_{\text{ext}}, \tag{7.30}$$

where τ_{ext} is the resultant of all external torques exerted on the system. In the case where τ_{ext} is zero, we conclude that the angular momentum of the system is constant. This important conclusion is called the Conservation-of-Angular-Momentum Principle, which can be stated as follows:

CONSERVATION OF ANGULAR MOMENTUM: The total angular momentum of any isolated dynamical system is constant.

We recall that by an *isolated system* we mean a system not subject to external forces exerted by particles or bodies not included in the system. The principle also applies to a nonisolated system provided there is no resultant torque associated with the external forces acting on the system.

Example.   In a lecture demonstration, a college professor stands on a "friction-free" rotating platform as in Fig. 7.22a with a heavy 'laboratory weight' in each extended arm. A student standing on the floor beside the platform sets the professor into rotational motion about a vertical axis at a small angular velocity ω_0. If the professor pulls the "laboratory weights" in toward the axis of rotation, his angular velocity increases

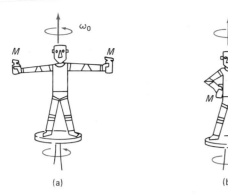

Fig. 7.22 Conservation of angular momentum: $I_0\omega_0 = I\omega$.

(a)   (b)

enormously to some value ω as shown in Fig. 7.22b. Explain this phenomenon.

Because of the friction-free support, the professor, the laboratory weights, and the platform itself approximate a dynamical system isolated from external torques about the axis of rotation. Once the system has been set into motion, its angular momentum **L** remains constant. In Fig. 7.22a, the angular momentum about a vertical axis has the magnitude $I_0\omega_0$, where I_0 is the rotational inertia of the system when the professor's arms are extended. After he has brought the laboratory weights inward toward the axis of rotation, as in Fig. 7.22b, the rotational inertia of the system has been reduced to some value $I < I_0$. However, the angular momentum of the system remains constant with

$$I\omega = I_0\omega_0. \quad \textit{(Conservation of Angular Momentum)}$$

Because $I < I_0$, $\omega = (I_0/I)\omega_0$ is greater than ω_0. *Suggestion:* Compare the kinetic energy of the system in part a of the figure with that of the system in part b of figure. Account for any difference.

7.10 GYROSCOPIC MOTION

Although the general treatment of the rotational motion of an unconstrained rigid body in three-dimensional motion is difficult and is far beyond the scope of our present studies, we can under certain simplifying assumptions treat one extremely interesting case: *gyroscopic motion.* A gyroscope consists of a wheel of some kind rotating at a high angular speed about an axis through its center of mass; the rotational inertia of the wheel is usually quite large. Such a device has a large angular momentum $L_S = I\omega_S$ about its axis of rotation as a result of its *spin* velocity ω_S, as suggested in Fig. 7.23. Just as a body such as a moving bullet with a large translational momentum $\mathbf{p} = m\mathbf{v}$ tends to continue its motion in a straight line, so also the gyroscope with large spin angular momentum $L_S = I\omega_S$ tends to maintain its *orientation in space* and will maintain this orientation unless subjected to large external torques. A *free gyroscope,* not subject to external torques, will continue to have constant $\mathbf{L}_S$ in any inertial frame of reference such as the one provided by the fixed stars. Although a truly free gyroscope cannot be devised, it can be closely approximated by the multiple gimbal mount shown in Fig. 7.24 and by certain types of magnetic suspensions.

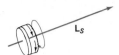

Fig. 7.23 A gyroscope has a large spin angular momentum: $L_S = I\omega_S$.

The free gyroscope has an important practical application as a *gyrocompass*. If we align a "free gyroscope" like the one shown in Fig. 7.24 so that its spin angular momentum vector $\mathbf{L}_S$ is parallel to the earth's axis of rotation and thus points toward the North Star, $\mathbf{L}_S$ will continue to point in this direction regardless of what may happen to the gimbal mount. If we attach the mount to the hull of an ocean vessel or to the body of an airplane, the direction of $\mathbf{L}_S$ remains pointed toward the North Star and the horizontal component of $\mathbf{L}_S$ thus points geographically northward. For navigational purposes, the gyrocompass has many advantages over the common magnetic compass, a device having shortcomings that we shall discuss later. Because a gyrocompass has a constant orientation with respect to the fixed stars, it can be used as a means of "inertial guidance."

Now we consider the motion of an incompletely gimbaled gyroscope like the one shown schematically in Fig. 7.25. The rotating wheel is attached to an axle that is supported by low-friction bearings at A and A', which are attached to the frame. Also attached to the frame is a shaft which terminates in a ball bearing that can be placed in a cup at the top of the vertical support mounted on a table top. As the center of mass of the gyroscope wheel, mount, and shaft are not directly above the top of the support, gravitational forces have a resultant torque τ about the point of support; the direction of the torque vector τ is horizontal and in Fig. 7.25 is directed away from the reader. If the gyrowheel were not spinning, the torque τ would cause the entire device to rotate clockwise in the figure so that the wheel and its frame would move downward.

However, what happens if the wheel has a large angular momentum $\mathbf{L}_S$ as shown in Fig. 7.26? At the instant shown $\mathbf{L}_S$ is directed horizontally to the right in the figure and the torque vector τ is directed horizontally away from the reader. In accord with (7.30)

$$\tau = \frac{d\mathbf{L}}{dt} \quad \text{or} \quad d\mathbf{L} = \tau\, dt.$$

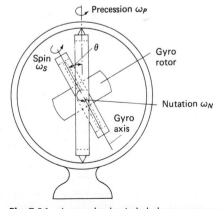

Fig. 7.24 A completely gimbaled gyroscope approximates a "free gyroscope."

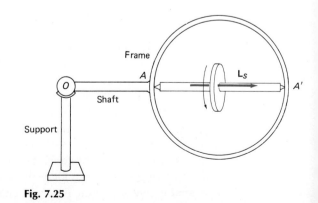

Fig. 7.25

Fig. 7.26

We note that $d\mathbf{L}$ is a vector having the same direction as the torque vector $\boldsymbol{\tau}$. This means that in Fig. 7.26 $d\mathbf{L}$ is perpendicular to $\mathbf{L}_S$ and thus serves to change the *direction* but not the magnitude of $\mathbf{L}_S$. The result is shown diagrammatically in Fig. 7.27; $\mathbf{L}_S$ remains constant in magnitude and remains in a horizontal plane but changes its direction by $d\phi$, where

$$d\phi = dL/L_S = \tau\, dt/L_S.$$

Because $\mathbf{L}_S$ is changing in orientation by $d\phi$ in time dt, it has an *angular velocity of precession* $\omega_P = d\phi/dt$ about the vertical axis in Fig. 7.27. Because $d\phi/dt = \tau/L_S$, we can write

$$\omega_P = \tau/L_S. \quad \textit{(Precession)} \tag{7.31}$$

We note that a torque $\boldsymbol{\tau}$ about one axis causes the angular momentum $\mathbf{L}_S$ about a second axis perpendicular to the first to have an angular velocity or percession about a third axis; not at all what we might expect from intuition!

There will be a component of angular momentum along the vertical axis associated with the precessional motion. The appearance of this angular momentum component is not consistent with (7.30) if $\mathbf{L}_S$ remains in a horizontal plane. Actually, the direction of $\mathbf{L}_S$ initially will dip below the horizontal so that the total angular momentum component along the vertical axis remains zero. The motion proceeds with a vertical oscillation known as *nutation* ("nodding") in addition to precession.

We have assumed that L_S due to the spin of the gyro on its axis is very large. If the magnitude of $\mathbf{L}_S$ decreases, the angular velocity of precession ω_P increases. This can be observed in the precessional motion of a spinning top as suggested in Fig. 7.28. In the case of the top $\tau = mgl \sin\theta$, where l is the distance between the center of mass of the top and the point of the top touching the ground. We shall show in Chapter 8 that for the purpose of computing the resultant gravitational torque the entire weight can be assumed to act at the center of mass of the top.

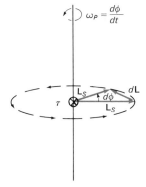

Fig. 7.27 Precession of a gyroscope: $\omega_P = d\phi/dt = \tau/L_S$.

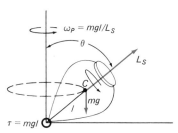

Fig. 7.28 Precessional motion of a spinning top.

The horizontal component of the top's angular momentum, corresponding to L_S as shown in Fig. 7.26, is $L_S \sin \theta$; thus, for the top, in accord with (7.31), $\omega_P = mgl \sin \theta / L_S \sin \theta = mgl / L_S$. As L_S decreases as a result of frictional torques, the precessional velocity of the top increases. As the top spins, the value of angle θ in Fig. 7.28 slowly increases. As every youngster knows, ω_P is greatest just at the end of the period during which spinning occurs.

Gyroscopic actions are involved in the explanation of why a rolling wheel does not quickly tip over on its side; how it is possible to balance a bicycle or a motorcycle; how the spin of a rifle bullet keeps the bullet from tumbling; and how the earth's axis maintains its orientation in space, with a very slow precessional motion called the precession of the equinoxes, which occurs because the earth is not a perfect sphere.

QUESTIONS

1. What is angular velocity of the second hand of an accurate watch? What are the angular velocities of the minute hand and the hour hand?

2. How would forms of (7.1)–(7.6) be changed if we measured angles in degrees rather than in radians? What are the advantages of using radians rather than degrees?

3. Under what conditions does a point on the rim of a wheel rotating with angular velocity ω have a tangential acceleration? Under what conditions does the point have a radial acceleration? Can the point have both kinds of acceleration simultaneously?

4. Can a point on the rim of a rotating wheel ever have a tangential acceleration but no radial acceleration? Can a point on the rim ever have a radial velocity?

5. What are the dimensions of angular velocity, angular acceleration, rotational inertia, torque, and angular momentum in terms of mass, length, and time?

6. Show that angular momentum can be measured in J·s as well as in kg·m²/s.

7. During glacial eras, sea level is lowered and large quantities of ice are accumulated in the form of glaciers in the north and south polar regions. What effect does this have on the earth's angular velocity of rotation?

8. Show that the rotational inertia of a rigid body about an axis through its center of mass is smaller than its rotational inertia about any parallel axis.

9. Discuss the physical processes involved when a child in a swing sets the swing into motion by "pumping." Is energy conserved in this operation?

10. When the pilot of a helicopter sets the supporting blades into motion in one sense, why doesn't the cabin of the helicopter rotate in the opposite sense, as might be expected on the basis of the conservation of angular momentum?

11. A man stands on a rotating platform as suggested in Fig. 7.22. If he is set into rotational motion when his arms are extended and he is holding "weights" in his hands as in Fig. 7.22a and he then drops the weights to the floor, what happens to his rotational speed? Is this operation different in its effects from having him pull the weights in to his sides? Can the man do anything to the weights that will bring him to rest?

12. Two persons A and B stand on opposite edges of a rotating platform. If A throws a ball that he aims directly toward B, what will be the path of the ball (a) as seen by an observer on the ground beside the platform and (b) as seen by an observer using a refer-

ence frame attached to the rotating platform? Does the ball thrown directly toward *B* actually reach *B?*

13. The French physicist J. B. L. Foucault (1819–1868) used a pendulum to demonstrate the rotation of the earth. To understand the operation of a Foucault pendulum, consider a pendulum suspended directly above the north pole. In the course of its to-and-fro motion, what is the angular momentum of the pendulum about the rotation axis of the earth? The pendulum will continue to swing in a fixed plane in an inertial frame. Why? What will be its motion relative to a reference frame attached to the earth's surface?

PROBLEMS

1. A grinding wheel starting from rest experiences a constant angular acceleration of 3 rad/s², counterclockwise (CCW), for 12 s. What is the angular velocity of the wheel at the end of this time? What is its angular displacement?

2. A flywheel with an initial angular velocity of 24 rad/s, clockwise (CW), comes to rest after 8 s. On the assumption that the motion involves constant angular acceleration, find the value of the constant angular acceleration and the total angular displacement of the wheel. What is the average angular velocity of the wheel in the course of its motion?

3. A wheel starting from rest has a constant angular acceleration of 4 rad/s², CCW, while it undergoes an angular displacement of 20 revolutions, CCW. What is the final angular velocity of the wheel? What is the time required for the wheel to attain this angular velocity? What is the average angular velocity $\bar{\omega}$ of the wheel during this time interval?

4. A flywheel with an initial angular velocity of 120 rad/s, CW, comes to rest after undergoing 200 revolutions, CW. Assuming the motion to involve constant angular acceleration, find the value of the angular acceleration, the time required for the flywheel to come to rest, and the average angular velocity of the wheel during this time interval.

5. What is the speed of a particle on the rim of a flywheel 40 cm away from the axis of rotation of the flywheel when the wheel has a rotational speed of 240 revolutions per minute? What is the centripetal acceleration of the particle?

6. What is the speed of a particle 30 cm away from the axis of rotation of a flywheel when the flywheel has an angular velocity of 60 rad/s and an angular acceleration of 3 rad/s², each in the CCW sense? What is the radial component of the particle's acceleration? What is the tangential component of its acceleration? What is the magnitude of the resultant acceleration of the particle?

7. A cord is wrapped around the rim of a grinding wheel in the manner suggested in Fig. 7.6 while the wheel is at rest; the radius of the wheel is 30 cm. If a force of 12 N is applied to the end of the string, how much work is done while 2 m of string unwind from the rim of the wheel? What torque is exerted on the wheel? What is the angular displacement of the wheel?

8. A constant resultant torque of 2 N·m, CCW, acts on a flywheel while the wheel makes 12 revolutions, CCW. How much work is done to the wheel? What is the result of this work? At a time when the wheel is moving at an angular velocity of 2 rad/s, CCW, how much power is being delivered to the wheel by the agent exerting the torque?

9. A 4-kg grinding wheel has a radius of 30 cm and is dynamically equivalent to a solid disk rotating about an axis through its center of mass. What is the rotational inertia of the wheel? If the rotational speed of this wheel is 60 rad/s, what is its rotational kinetic energy? What would be the speed of the center of mass of the wheel if the wheel had an equal amount of translational kinetic energy?

10. A flywheel has a mass of 100 kg and a radius of gyration of 1.5 m. What is the rotational inertia of the flywheel? What is the rotational kinetic energy of this wheel when it is rotating at a rotational speed of 600 revolutions per minute? What would be the speed of the center of mass of this wheel if the wheel had an equal amount of translational kinetic energy?

11. A flywheel with a radius of 60 cm and a rotational inertia of 2 kg·m² is driven by a belt like the one shown in the diagram. At a time when the flywheel has an angular velocity of 30 rad/s, CCW, at what rate is energy being delivered to the wheel when the tensions T_1 and T_2 in the parts of the belt are equal? At what rate is energy being delivered when $T_1 - T_2 = 2$ N? When $T_1 - T_2 = 4$ N?

12. If the belt drive in the figure were used to set the wheel into motion and it were possible to maintain a tension difference $T_1 - T_2 = 40$ N in the belt, at what rate would energy be delivered to the wheel (a) as the wheel is starting from rest and (b) as the wheel is attaining its final rotational speed of 30 rad/s?

13. As indicated in Fig. 7.8, the rotational inertia of a slender rod about an axis through its center of mass is $ml^2/12$. Show that the rotational inertia of the rod about a parallel axis through one end of the rod is $ml^2/3$. What are the radii of gyration k of the rod about the two axes?

14. What is the rotational inertia of a solid cylinder with radius R and mass M about an axis O through the rim of the disk if the axis is parallel to the axis through the center of mass as shown in Fig. 7.8? State the result in terms of M and R.

15. What is the angular acceleration of the flywheel in Problem 11 when the tension difference $T_1 - T_2$ in the belts is 2 N? When the tension difference $T_1 - T_2$ is 4 N?

16. A 2-kg grinding wheel (a solid cylinder) with a radius of 30 cm has an angular velocity of 40 rad/s, CCW. If the driving motor is turned off, the wheel comes to rest after 15 s as a result of a constant frictional torque. What are the magnitude and sense of the frictional torque?

17. A cord of negligible mass is wound around the outer surface of a 12-kg solid cylinder with a radius of 40 cm mounted on a friction-free axis through the center of mass of the cylinder. If a 300-g block of steel is attached to one end of the cord, what will be the downward acceleration of the block if it is released from rest and allowed to move downward? What will be the tension in the cord? Assume that the cord

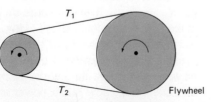

Problems 11 and 12

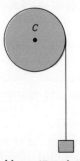

Problems 17 and 18

around the cylinder does not slip with respect to the surface of the cylinder.

18. After the downward motion of the block in Problem 17 has proceeded for 8 s, what is the angular velocity of the cylinder? At this time what is the rotational kinetic energy of the cylinder? What is the translational kinetic energy of the block?

19. In the so-called Atwood's machine shown in the figure two masses M_1 and M_2 are connected by a cord of negligible mass passing over the rim of a wheel. The wheel has a radius of 40 cm and a rotational inertia of 2 kg·m². Assume that there is no slipping between the cord and the wheel and that there is no friction in the bearings of the wheel; find the magnitude of the common acceleration of the masses when they are released if $M_1 = 1$ kg and $M_2 = 0.5$ kg. What are the tensions T_1 and T_2 in the two parts of the cord?

20. What is the total kinetic energy of the system of Problem 19 when mass M_1 has a downward displacement of 2 m from its initial position? Assume that the masses are released from rest. What is the rotational kinetic energy of the wheel at this time? What are the translational kinetic energies of the suspended bodies?

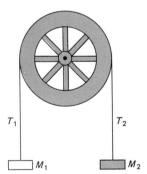

T_1 T_2

M_1 M_2

Problems 19 and 20

21. A large flywheel has a rotational inertia of 4 kg·m² and is initially at rest. A constant external torque of 8 N·m, CW, is applied to the wheel for 0.2 s. What is the angular impulse associated with this torque? What is the final angular velocity of the wheel?

22. When the flywheel in Problem 21 is rotating at an initial angular velocity of 30 rad/s, CW, a brakeshoe is applied to the rim of the wheel and brings the wheel to rest in 15 s with constant deceleration. What constant frictional torque is exerted by the brakeshoe? How much mechanical energy is dissipated as the wheel is brought to rest?

23. In a belt drive mechanism like the one considered in Problem 11, the radius of the small wheel is 3 cm and the radius of the large wheel is 18 cm. If the small wheel, which is mounted on the shaft of an electric motor, is rotating at a speed of 30 rad/s, what is the rotational speed of the large wheel if there is no slipping between the wheel rims and the belt? At a time when the motor is supplying 200 W of power to the small wheel, what is the *maximum* torque that could be expected from the large wheel in the absence of frictional losses?

24. If the large wheel in Problem 23 actually exerts a torque of 38 N·m on the shaft to which it is attached, what is the power output of the belt-drive transmission device? What is the efficiency of the device? How much mechanical energy is dissipated in the device in 1 min?

25. The diagram in the figure represents a 2-kg steel rod 2 m in length and hinged so that it can rotate about a horizontal axis through O. What gravitational torque about O acts on the rod when it is in the position shown in the figure? What force **F** exerted at the end of the rod at angle $\phi = 30°$ above the horizontal would be required to hold the rod in its horizontal position? What is the magnitude of the force exerted on the rod by the hinge and what torque about O is associated with this force? Note: Assume that, for the purpose of computing

torques, the weight of the rod can be applied at the rod's center of mass. This assumption will be justified in Chapter 8.

26. Answer all questions in Problem 25 for cases where the force **F** is vertical and is exerted at distances of 1.5 m, 1 m, and 0.5 m from the hinge. (See Note in Problem 25.)

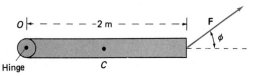

Problems 25 and 26

27. In the figure a 2-kg uniform piece of lumber 2 m long is hinged about a horizontal axis through O with $I_0 = Ml^2/3$, as found in Problem 13. When the piece of lumber is hanging vertically, a 30-g bullet moving horizontally at a speed of 100 m/s strikes the piece of lumber at a point 10 cm above its lower end and becomes embedded in the wood. Immediately following the collision, what is the angular velocity of the piece of lumber with the embedded bullet?

28. What would have been the angular velocity immediately following the collision for the situation in Problem 27 if the bullet had struck the piece of lumber 1 m below the axis of rotation? Compare the losses in mechanical energy in the two cases.

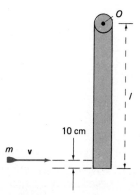

Problems 27 and 28

29. A man stands with 1-kg masses in his hands on a rotating platform like the one shown in Fig. 7.22. When his arms are stretched fully outward, the rotational inertia of the man and platform is 2.5 kg·m²; after he has pulled the masses inward toward the axis of rotation, this rotational inertia is 0.5 kg·m². If the system is given an angular velocity of 2 rad/s when the man's arms are extended, what will be his angular velocity after he has pulled the masses inward? What is the difference between the final kinetic energy and the initial kinetic energy? Because the platform is mounted on "frictionless" bearings, no external torques about the axis of rotation act on the man and platform; how can you account for the difference in the initial and final kinetic energies of rotation?

30. An isolated spherically symmetric dynamical system has a rotational inertia I_0 and angular momentum L. (1) Derive an expression for the rotational kinetic energy of the system in terms of I_0 and L. (2) Suppose that a rotating spherical star of initial radius R_0 undergoes "gravitational collapse" to a smaller radius $R = R_0/2$. What are the effects of collapse on its average density, on its angular velocity, and on its kinetic energy of rotation? Is mechanical energy conserved by this system?

31. Consider a system consisting of two particles of masses m_1 and m_2, respectively, connected by a rigid rod of negligible mass that keeps them separated by a definite distance ρ as suggested in the figure. (a) Show that the relation between the masses of the particles and their distances r_1 and r_2 from the center of mass of the system is given by the expression $m_1 r_1 = m_2 r_2$, where $r_1 + r_2 = \rho$. (b) Show that the rotational inertia of the system about an axis through the center of mass and perpendicular to the rod connecting the particles is given by the expression $I_C = \mu \rho^2$, where $\mu = m_1 m_2/(m_1 + m_2)$; μ is called the *reduced*

mass of such a system. A system like the one considered in this problem is called a *rigid rotator;* its rotational motion is equivalent to that of a particle of mass μ moving in a circular orbit of radius ρ.

32. For many purposes diatomic molecules can be regarded as *rigid rotators* as defined in Problem 31. The separation ρ between the nuclei of the various isotopic hydrogen molecules H_2, HD, and D_2 is the same for all three molecules. Consider an axis through the center of mass and perpendicular to the internuclear axis of a molecule. What is the ratio of the rotational inertia of HD to that of H_2? What is the ratio of the rotational inertia of D_2 to that of H_2? What is the separation r_D of the nucleus of the deuterium atom from the center of mass of the HD molecule in terms of the internuclear separation ρ of H and D? The mass of the deuterium atom D is approximately twice the mass of the lighter hydrogen atom H.

33. Hydrogen H_2 and deuterium D_2 molecules in a gas are free to rotate about axes perpendicular to the internuclear axes of the molecules, which are the straight lines between the atomic nuclei in the molecules. If the kinetic energies of rotation of an H_2 molecule and a D_2 molecule about axes through the center of mass and perpendicular to the internuclear axis of the respective molecules are equal, what is the ratio of the angular velocity of the H_2 molecule to the angular velocity of the D_2 molecule? Under similar circumstances, what is the ratio of the angular velocity of an H_2 molecule to the angular velocity of an HD molecule? See Problems 31 and 32.

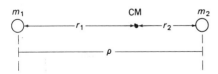

Problems 31–33

34. On the basis of Newton's First Principle, show that the angular momentum of a free particle about any axis fixed in an inertial frame of reference is constant.

*35. A grinding wheel with a rotational inertia of 0.4 kg·m² starts from rest and has a counterclockwise angular acceleration given by $\alpha = 3 - 0.2t$, where α is in rad/s² and t is in s. What resultant torque τ acts on the wheel at the end of the third second of motion? What is the angular momentum of the wheel at the end of the third second? What is the kinetic energy of the wheel at the end of the third second?

*36. If the angular displacement $\phi - \phi_0$ of a wheel is directly proportional to the time t of motion, what can you conclude about the initial angular velocity ω_0 and the angular acceleration α of the wheel? If $\phi - \phi_0$ is directly proportional to t^2, what can you conclude about ω_0 and α? If $\phi - \phi_0$ is directly proportional to t^3, what can you conclude about ω_0 and α?

*37. An observer reports that the angular displacement of a rotating wheel can be described by the relation $\phi - \phi_0 = k\sqrt{t}$, where ϕ and ϕ_0 are in rad, t in s, and k is a constant. What are the SI units in which k must be measured? What is the predicted angular velocity ω of the wheel at time t? What is the predicted angular acceleration α of the wheel at time t? Is the reported relationship physically valid?

38. A particle of mass m moves at constant speed v_0 in a circular orbit of radius R_0 about a fixed axis through O. What is the kinetic energy associated with this orbital motion? What is the angular momentum? What centripetal force acts on the particle? State your answers in terms of m, v_0, and R_0.

39. If the particle in Problem 38 is drawn radially inward toward the axis through O until the radius R of its new orbit is $R_0/2$, what will be its orbital speed and its kinetic

energy? What centripetal force is now required for the motion?

40. A student holds one end of a string of length l and a ball of mass m is attached to the other end of the string. The student then sets the ball into motion in a circular path in a vertical plane. If the tangential speed of the ball is the minimum speed required to keep the ball moving in a circular path, what is the speed of the ball at the uppermost point in its path? At the lowest point in its path?

41. In the situation described in Problem 40, is mechanical energy conserved? Is angular momentum conserved? In view of the Conservation-of-Angular-Momentum Principle, is the result a valid result? Discuss.

*42. The angular velocity ω of a rotating wheel with rotational inertia I_C about an axis through its center of mass is given by the expression $\omega = \omega_0 e^{-\beta t}$, where ω and ω_0 are in rad/s, t is in s, and β is a constant. In what units must β be measured? Obtain expressions for angular acceleration α and angular displacement $\phi - \phi_0$ as functions of time t.

43. Under what conditions could the relation given in Problem 42 be physically valid? What are the initial and final values of α and ϕ? Check the dimensions of the expressions for angular velocity, angular acceleration, and angular displacement.

44. Prove the distributive law for vector products: $\mathbf{A} \times (\mathbf{B} + \mathbf{C}) = (\mathbf{A} \times \mathbf{B}) + (\mathbf{A} \times \mathbf{C})$. To do this, set up a coordinate system with origin at the tail of $\mathbf{A}$ and Z-axis in the direction of $\mathbf{A}$. The vector $\mathbf{A} \times \mathbf{B}$ can be constructed by the following sequence of operations: (a) Project $\mathbf{B}$ onto the XY-plane. If θ is the angle between $\mathbf{A}$ and $\mathbf{B}$,

this projection gives a vector $\mathbf{B}'$ of magnitude $B \sin \theta$. (b) Rotate $\mathbf{B}'$ by 90° in a right-hand sense about $\mathbf{A}$. This gives a vector $\mathbf{B}''$. (c) Multiply $\mathbf{B}''$ by the magnitude of $\mathbf{A}$. The resulting vector $\mathbf{AB}''$ by its construction has the magnitude and direction of $\mathbf{A} \times \mathbf{B}$. Apply the same operations to the other two sides of the triangle representing the vector sum $\mathbf{B} + \mathbf{C} = (\mathbf{B} + \mathbf{C})$. The desired conclusion can be reached from the properties of the resulting triangle.

45. Show that the unit vectors $\mathbf{i}$, $\mathbf{j}$, and $\mathbf{k}$ satisfy $\mathbf{i} \times \mathbf{j} = \mathbf{k}$, $\mathbf{j} \times \mathbf{k} = \mathbf{i}$, $\mathbf{k} \times \mathbf{i} = \mathbf{j}$, $\mathbf{i} \times \mathbf{i} = 0$, $\mathbf{j} \times \mathbf{j} = 0$, and $\mathbf{k} \times \mathbf{k} = 0$.

46. Use the results of Problems 44 and 45 to deduce an expression for $\mathbf{A} \times \mathbf{B}$ in terms of the Cartesian components of the vectors $\mathbf{A}$ and $\mathbf{B}$.

47. If $\mathbf{A} = (3,-1,2)$, $\mathbf{B} = (2,1,-1)$, and $\mathbf{C} = (1,-2,2)$, find $\mathbf{A} \times \mathbf{B}$, $\mathbf{A} \cdot \mathbf{B}$, $\mathbf{B} \times \mathbf{C}$, and $\mathbf{A} \cdot (\mathbf{B} \times \mathbf{C})$.

*48. Derive Eq. (7.26). One way to proceed is to use the result of Problem 46 to express the vector product in terms of the Cartesian components of the two vectors. An alternative method is to work directly with relations of the form

$$\frac{d\mathbf{A}}{dt} = \lim_{\delta t \to 0} \left(\frac{\mathbf{A}(t + \delta t) - \mathbf{A}(t)}{\delta t} \right).$$

In this case the distributive law of Problem 44 will be needed.

*49. Derive the result shown in Fig. 7.8 for the rotational inertia of a uniform annular cylinder.

*50. Derive the result shown in Fig. 7.8 for the rotational inertia of a slender rod.

*51. Derive the result shown in Fig. 7.8 for the rotational inertia of a uniform solid sphere.

CHAPTER 8

Two-Dimensional Motion of Rigid Bodies

In Chapter 5 we used Newton's Principles to derive some general theorems regarding the *translational motions* of dynamical systems, and in Chapter 7 we similarly derived additional theorems regarding the *rotational motions* of dynamical systems. In this chapter we shall apply these theorems in a study of both the translational and the rotational motions of *rigid bodies,* which constitute a special class of dynamical system. Because the general three-dimensional motion of a rigid body is a very complex subject beyond the scope of this book, we shall content ourselves with treating the *two-dimensional motion* of a rigid body. In two-dimensional motion all particles making up a rigid body move in parallel planes—for example, in planes parallel to the *XY* plane of a rectangular coordinate system.

We begin the chapter with a résumé of some of the pertinent theorems developed in the earlier chapters dealing with pure translational and pure rotational motion of rigid bodies. Next we shall state the conditions of translational and rotational equilibrium of a rigid body and show how these conditions can be applied; we note that this provides an introduction to the branch of mechanics known as *statics,* a subject of a special importance to mechanical and architectural engineers. We show how our treatment of statics can easily be extended from two to three dimensions.

The general motion of a rigid body can be described in terms of a displacement of the body's center of mass together with a rotation of the body about an axis through its center of mass. We shall apply these ideas to rolling motion, a subject of considerable importance to every engineer. Although the wheel was invented several millenia ago, the details of its motion remain something of a mystery to many people living in the 20th century. Perhaps we can dispel some of the mystery!

8.1 PURE TRANSLATIONAL MOTION OF A RIGID BODY

In Chapter 5 we showed that the pure translational motion of a dynamical system is equivalent to that of a single hypothetical particle located at the center of mass of the system. The mass M of the hypothetical particle is the total mass of the entire system. Thus, if we consider as our dynamical system a rigid body of mass M, we can treat the translational motion of the rigid body in terms of the motion of a hypothetical particle of mass M located at the center of mass of the rigid body.

The hypothetical particle, in accord with Newton's Second Principle, has acceleration when subjected to a resultant force. Therefore, for a rigid body we can write

$$\mathbf{F}_R = M\mathbf{a}_C, \tag{8.1}$$

where $\mathbf{F}_R$ is the resultant external force exerted on the body and $\mathbf{a}_C$ is the acceleration of the body's center of mass.* We recall that external forces are exerted *on* a dynamical system by particles or bodies outside the system; thus, $\mathbf{F}_R$ in (8.1) is the vector sum or resultant of all forces exerted *on* the rigid body *by* other bodies.

Because the translational motion of a rigid body can be described in terms of a hypothetical particle of mass M located at the center of mass, we can immediately write expressions for the mechanical energy of the body. Its *translational kinetic energy* E_{KT} is given by

$$E_{KT} = \tfrac{1}{2} M v_C^2, \tag{8.2}$$

where v_C is the magnitude of the velocity of the body's center of mass. Similarly, the gravitational potential energy E_P of the body is given by

$$E_P = M g h_C, \tag{8.3}$$

where h_C is the height of the body's center of mass above some arbitrary reference level.

8.2   PURE ROTATIONAL MOTION OF A RIGID BODY

In the early sections of Chapter 7 we discussed the rotational motion of a rigid body about a fixed axis and developed a rotational analogue of Newton's Second Principle, which states that $\tau = I\alpha$, where the resultant external torque τ and rotational inertia I are taken about any arbitrary fixed axis. For an axis through the center of mass of the rigid body, this relation becomes

$$\tau_C = I_C \alpha. \tag{8.4}$$

In this chapter rotational motion about an axis through the center of mass C assumes special importance.

In Chapter 7 we also discussed the mechanical energy possessed by a rigid body as a result of rotational motion. This energy is called the *rotational kinetic energy*

---

* The same symbol a_C has been used for centripetal acceleration of a *particle* undergoing circular motion. No confusion should arise if the context of the discussion is kept in mind.

E_{KR} and, for the case of rotation about a fixed axis through the body's center of mass, can be expressed as

$$E_{KR} = \tfrac{1}{2} I_C \omega^2. \tag{8.5}$$

Later in this chapter we shall show how (8.4) and (8.5) can be used together with (8.1), (8.2), and (8.3) in the treatment of the two-dimensional motion of a rigid body.

8.3 EQUILIBRIUM OF A RIGID BODY: STATICS

In Sec. 7 of Chapter 5 we gave a general discussion of the translational equilibrium of a dynamical system. By definition, a dynamical system is in translational equilibrium provided the acceleration $\mathbf{a}_C$ of its center of mass is zero. This occurs when the resultant external force acting on the system is zero: $\mathbf{F}_R = 0$. In view of the fact that $\mathbf{F}_R = d\mathbf{P}/dt$, where $\mathbf{P}$ is the momentum of the system, we see that the momentum $\mathbf{P}$ of a dynamical system is constant provided the resultant external force acting on the system is zero. Therefore, we might give an equivalent definition of translational equilibrium:

A dynamical system is in TRANSLATIONAL EQUILIBRIUM provided the momentum $\mathbf{P}$ of the system is constant.

In analogy we can state that

A dynamical system in translational equilibrium is in addition in
                     provided the angular momentum $\mathbf{L}$ of the system about any point
O is constant.

In Eq. (7.29) we showed that $d\mathbf{L}/dt = \boldsymbol{\tau}_R$, where $\boldsymbol{\tau}_R$ represents the *resultant external torque* acting on the system; if $\boldsymbol{\tau}_R = 0$, $d\mathbf{L}/dt = 0$ and thus $\mathbf{L} = $ constant. Thus, *the condition for the rotational equilibrium of a dynamical system is that the resultant external force and the resultant external torque acting on the system be zero:* $\mathbf{F}_R = 0$ and $\boldsymbol{\tau}_R = 0$.

By considering a rigid body as a dynamical system, we can use the foregoing discussion to formulate the general conditions for the equilibrium of a rigid body:

CONDITION FOR TRANSLATIONAL EQUILIBRIUM: The resultant of all external forces must be zero: $\mathbf{F}_R = 0$.

CONDITION FOR ROTATIONAL EQUILIBRIUM: The resultant of all external torques about any point O must be zero: $\boldsymbol{\tau}_R = 0$.

These conditions have general application to three dimensions. Thus, we can state them in terms of the scalar components of $\mathbf{F}_R$ and $\boldsymbol{\tau}_R$ in a rectangular coordinate system. If $\mathbf{F}_R = 0$, then $F_{Rx} = 0$, $F_{Ry} = 0$, and $F_{Rz} = 0$. Similarly, if $\boldsymbol{\tau}_R = 0$, then

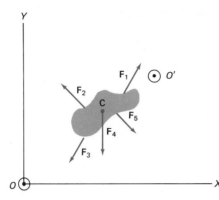

Fig. 8.1 Equilibrium of a rigid body. Axes through O, C, and O' are perpendicular to the plane of the diagram.

$\tau_{Rx} = 0$, $\tau_{Ry} = 0$, and $\tau_{Rz} = 0$. Application of these relations constitutes the important branch of mechanics known as *statics,* which involves a study of the forces acting on bodies at rest or on bodies with constant velocity and constant angular velocity.

In this chapter we shall concentrate our attention on forces with lines of action confined to or parallel to a single plane, such as the XY plane in Fig. 8.1. This restriction to coplanar forces simplifies the applications of the general conditions of translational and rotational equilibrium and also lays the basis for the treatment of forces and torques that we shall need later in this chapter when we consider the two-dimensional motions of rigid bodies. The methods used for this introductory treatment of equilibrium can easily be extended to three dimensions if one is interested in a more general treatment of statics.

When all forces on a rigid body are confined to or parallel to a single plane, the general condition $\mathbf{F}_R = 0$ for translational equilibrium reduces to two simple equations involving scalar components of the individual forces. For the case shown in Fig. 8.1 where forces $\mathbf{F}_1$, $\mathbf{F}_2$, . . . , $\mathbf{F}_N$ act on the rigid body, we obtain the following equations:

$$\begin{aligned} F_{Rx} &= F_{1x} + F_{2x} + \cdots + F_{Nx} = 0, \\ F_{Ry} &= F_{1y} + F_{2y} + \cdots + F_{Ny} = 0. \end{aligned} \quad \textit{(Translational Equilibrium)} \quad (8.6)$$

Some people get more physical insight into the meaning of these two equations if we state them in a different way:

$$\left[\begin{array}{c} \text{Sum of the force components} \\ \text{in the } +X \text{ direction} \end{array} \right] = \left[\begin{array}{c} \text{Sum of the force components} \\ \text{in the } -X \text{ direction} \end{array} \right], \quad (8.6')$$

$$\left[\begin{array}{c} \text{Sum of the force components} \\ \text{in the } +Y \text{ direction} \end{array} \right] = \left[\begin{array}{c} \text{Sum of the force components} \\ \text{in the } -Y \text{ direction} \end{array} \right].$$

The statement of the condition for translational equilibrium given in (8.6') shows that the applied forces always "balance out"; in fact, statics is sometimes referred to as a study of the "balance of forces."

The general condition for rotational equilibrium $\tau_R = 0$ is also simplified in the case of coplanar forces satisfying (8.6) because for such forces we need consider only torques about axes that are perpendicular to the plane in which the applied forces act. The rotational equilibrium condition can be applied to any such axis. For example, in Fig. 8.1 the forces with lines of action in the XY plane have torques about axes through O, O', and C that are perpendicular to the XY plane and therefore parallel to the Z axis. The various torques about any of these axes can be classified as clockwise or counterclockwise. Using our customary practice of regarding CCW torques as positive and CW torques as negative, we can express the condition for rotational equilibrium about any of these axes as

$$\tau_R = \tau_1 + \tau_2 + \cdots + \tau_N = 0. \quad \textit{(Rotational Equilibrium)} \qquad (8.7)$$

We note that condition (8.7) holds for any axis perpendicular to the plane of the forces such as axes through O, O', and C in Fig. 8.1. If the body has zero angular acceleration about one axis such as the one through center of mass C, its angular acceleration is also zero about other axes such as the ones through O and O'.

The condition for rotational equilibrium expressed in (8.7) can also be stated in another way: About any axis,

$$[\text{sum of the clockwise torques}] = [\text{sum of the counterclockwise torques}]. \quad (8.7')$$

This statement displays the "balance" among the torques applied to the rigid body. When we use the statements (8.6') and (8.7') in solving problems, we begin to develop some physical intuition regarding the equilibrium of rigid bodies.

The best way to understand the conditions for equilibrium is to apply them to specific problems. It is important to realize that we are free to choose the particular axis about which torques are computed and the orientation of the coordinate axes. In solving these problems, we try to select the coordinate system and the axis of rotation in such a way as to simplify the mathematical computations as much as possible; for example, if we let the axis of rotation pass through the point at which one of the forces is applied to the body, we make the torque associated with that force zero. This will reduce the number of terms in (8.7).

Commonly, one of the forces acting on a rigid body will be the force of gravity. The resultant gravitational force is just the weight of the body, $\mathbf{w} = M\mathbf{g}$, downward. However, the gravitational force actually is applied to each mass element of the body. This requires that we think about how to compute the torques produced by such a distributed force. We are almost always concerned with a *uniform* gravitational field where the value of $\mathbf{g}$ is the same throughout the region occupied by the body. In this case, we can prove the following convenient relation:

> For the purpose of computing torques on a body in a uniform gravitational field, the distributed gravitational force can be replaced by the weight of the body applied at the center of mass of the body.

The point at which we can consider the resultant gravitational force on a body to be applied is sometimes called its *center of gravity*. What we prove, then, is that in a uniform gravitational field the center of gravity of a body coincides with its center of mass.

In order to prove the above assertion, we imagine the body to be divided into a

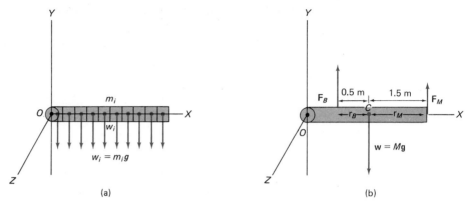

Fig. 8.2   The gravitational forces acting on a rigid body can be considered as a single force $M\mathbf{g}$ acting at the center of mass of the body.

large number N of particles of masses $m_1, m_2, m_3, \ldots, m_N$, respectively, as suggested in Fig. 8.2a. The gravitational force on a typical one of these particles is $\mathbf{w}_i = m_i\mathbf{g}$, where the vector $\mathbf{g}$ is directed vertically downward. Let us consider the resultant torque about a horizontal axis. Choose coordinates so that the $-Z$ axis coincides with the axis about which torques are to be computed and the XY plane is vertical. Then the gravitational torque about the $-Z$ axis due to the ith particle is $\tau_i = m_i g x_i$, where x_i is the X coordinate of the ith particle. The resultant torque about the $-Z$ axis due to the gravitational forces on all the particles is

$$\tau_R = \sum_{i=1}^{N} m_i g x_i = g \sum_{i=1}^{N} m_i x_i,$$

and from the definition of the center of mass this is just

$$\tau_R = gMx_C,$$

which is the torque that would be obtained if the entire gravitational force $\mathbf{w} = M\mathbf{g}$ were applied at the center of mass. This argument is readily extended to an axis that is not horizontal.

Example.   A cruel employer enlists the help of his small apprentice in lifting a 20-kg uniform board that is 3 m in length. In accomplishing this task he supports the board at one end and tells the apprentice to support the board in a horizontal position by lifting the board at a point 1 m from the other end. What upward force does the employer exert? What upward force does the poor apprentice exert?

We choose the coordinate system shown in Fig. 8.2b with the Y axis vertically upward and the X axis horizontally to the right; by choosing this coordinate system, we avoid having any forces with X or Z components. The force F_B exerted by the boy and the force F_M exerted by the man are vertically upward and thus parallel to the Y axis; the weight of the board $w = Mg$ is downward and thus also parallel to the Y axis. Using the statement of the condition for translational equilibrium given in (8.6'), we write

The sum of the upward forces = The sum of the downward forces,

or

$$F_M + F_B = w. \tag{i}$$

If we choose an axis of rotation through C and use the condition for rotational equilibrium given in (8.7′), we write

Sum of the CCW torques = Sum of the CW torques,

or

$$r_M F_M = r_B F_B, \tag{ii}$$

where r_M and r_B are the radial distances shown in Fig. 8.2b.

We note that $w = Mg = (20 \text{ kg})(9.8 \text{ m/s}^2) = 196$ N. Substitution in equations (i) and (ii) yields

$$F_M + F_B = 196 \text{ N}, \tag{i′}$$

and

$$(1.5 \text{ m})F_M = (0.5 \text{ m})F_B. \tag{ii′}$$

Solution of these two equations gives $F_M = 49$ N and $F_B = 147$ N. Note that we can check our answer by using our numerical results to compute torques about an axis through O at the boy's end of the board: The CCW torque about this axis is $(3 \text{ m})(49 \text{ N}) + (1 \text{ m})(147 \text{ N}) = 294$ N·m. The CW torque is $(1.5 \text{ m})(196\text{N}) = 294$ N·m. Thus, our numerical answers are consistent.

Questions: (a) If the man had been a kind employer, he would have let the boy lift one end of the board. In this case, where would the man lift the board in order to make $F_M = 2F_B$? (b) If the man had been an overindulgent employer, where would he have lifted the board in order to make the boy's force zero?

Example.   A uniform 3-m board weighing 196 N is hinged at one end as shown in Fig. 8.3. By pulling on a cord attached to the other end of the board a man is able to support the board in a horizontal position. What is the magnitude of the force **F** exerted by the man if the cord makes an angle of 30° with the horizontal? What force is exerted on the board by the hinge? Draw a diagram showing the lever arm λ of the force exerted by the man, where the length of λ is *defined* by the relation $\tau = \lambda F$.

In solving the problem let us begin with the relation (8.7′) and take the axis of rotation through O in Fig. 3. This choice means that the force exerted by the hinge does not appear in the torque equation. The torque associated with **F** is given by the relation $\tau = rF \sin \theta$ and is counterclockwise; the torque associated with the weight w of the board is $\tau = (r/2)w$ and is clockwise. Thus, by (8.7′): $rF \sin \theta = (r/2)w$. Solution gives $F = w/2 \sin \theta = (196 \text{ N})/2 \sin 30° = 196$ N.

In order to find the force **F′** exerted on the board by the hinge, we first use the translational equilibrium conditions (8.6′) to find the vertical F_V and horizontal

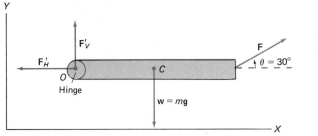

Fig. 8.3   **Fig. 8.4**

F'_H components: $F'_H = F \cos \theta$, giving $F'_H = (196 \text{ N})(\cos 30°) = 170 \text{ N}$; $F'_V + F \sin \theta = w$, giving $F'_V = w - F \sin \theta = 196 \text{ N} - (196 \text{ N})(\sin 30°) = 98 \text{ N}$. The magnitude of $\mathbf{F}'$ is given by $F' = \sqrt{F'^2_H + F'^2_V} = \sqrt{(170 \text{ N})^2 + (98 \text{ N})^2} = 196 \text{ N}$. What can we say about the *direction* of $\mathbf{F}'$?

The magnitude of the *lever arm* of the force $\mathbf{F}$ exerted on the board by the cord is given by the torque relation $F\lambda = rF \sin \theta$ or $\lambda = r \sin \theta$. The meaning of lever arm is shown graphically in Fig. 8.4; the lever arm is the length of the line λ drawn from the axis through O and perpendicular to the line of action of the force. Note that to exert a maximum torque, a force F should be applied in such a way as to make λ as large as possible. To do this, what should be the value of θ in Fig. 8.4?

Example.   Figure 8.5a shows a straight ladder 7 m long leaning against the smooth wall of a building at an angle of 30°. The mass of the ladder is 10 kg and the center of mass of the ladder is midway between its ends. A 90-kg man has climbed the ladder a distance of 5 m measured along the ladder. The smooth wall can exert only a horizontal push $\mathbf{P}$ on the ladder. Find the magnitude of this push $\mathbf{P}$ and also the magnitude and direction of the force $\mathbf{F}$ exerted on the ladder by the ground.

In solving the problem we shall use the coordinate system shown in Fig. 8.5b; all pertinent forces applied *to* the ladder are shown on the sketch. All quantities are known except for P, F, and the angle θ between the force $\mathbf{F}$ and the ground. We resolve $\mathbf{F}$ into a horizontal component $F_x = F \cos \theta$ and a vertical component $F_y = F \sin \theta$. Using the condition for translational equilibrium, we can write

$$F_x = P \qquad \qquad \text{(i)}$$

$$F_y = w_L + w_M, \qquad \qquad \text{(ii)}$$

where w_M and w_L are the weights of the man and the ladder, respectively. Using the condition for rotational equilibrium with an axis through the point at which the ladder touches the ground, we can write

$$Pl \sin \phi = w_L l_L \cos \phi + w_M l_M \cos \phi, \qquad \qquad \text{(iii)}$$

where l is the length of the ladder, l_L is the length of the part of the ladder between the axis and the center of mass of the ladder, and l_M is the distance the

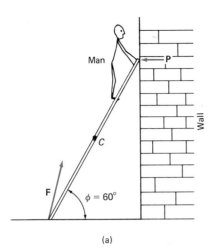
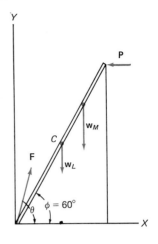

(a)

Fig. 8.5

man has climbed along the ladder. Note that because of our choice of axis the components of **F** do not appear in the torque equation. We solve Eqs. (i)–(iii) for P and for F_x and F_y.

With $w_L = m_L g = (10 \text{ kg})(9.8 \text{ m/s}^2) = 98 \text{ N}$ and with $w_M = m_M g = (90 \text{ kg})(9.8 \text{ m/s}^2) = 882 \text{ N}$, we can write

$$F_x = P, \tag{i'}$$

$$F_y = 98 \text{ N} + 882 \text{ N} = 980 \text{ N}, \tag{ii'}$$

$$(7 \text{ m}) \sin 60° \, P = (98 \text{ N})(3.5 \text{ m}) \cos 60° + (882 \text{ N})(5 \text{ m}) \cos 60°. \tag{iii'}$$

Solving (iii') for P gives $P = 392 \text{ N}$. By (i') $F_x = 392 \text{ N}$. To find F, we remember that $F = \sqrt{F_x^2 + F_y^2} = \sqrt{(392 \text{ N})^2 + (980 \text{ N})^2} = 1055 \text{ N}$, and $\tan \theta = F_y/F_x = 980 \text{ N}/392 \text{ N} = 2.50$. Thus, $\theta = 68.2°$.

Example. Let us return to the example on p. 108 in which we have a suspended signboard consisting of a rectangular piece of wood with a mass of 2 kg suspended by two flexible wires; one of the wires makes an angle of $\theta_1 = 30°$ with the horizontal and the other wire makes an angle of $\theta_2 = 45°$ with the horizontal. We have found that the wires exert forces of magnitudes $F_1 = 17.6 \text{ N}$ and $F_2 = 14.3 \text{ N}$. Now we shall assume that the sign board is 2 m long and 1 m high as indicated in Fig. 8.6. If we attach the first wire to one corner of the board, where should we attach the other wire in order to make the signboard hang so that the lettering is horizontal?

Let x be the distance from the corner of the board to where the wire is attached, as indicated in the figure. In applying the condition for rotational equilibrium, we shall use an axis through O at the upper left corner of the board. Setting CCW and CW torques about the axis through O equal to each other, we have

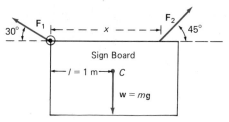

Fig. 8.6   This signboard hangs properly only if force F_2 is applied at the proper point.

$$(F_2 \sin 45°)x = mgl,$$
$$x = mgl/F_2 \sin 45°,$$
$$x = (2 \text{ kg})(9.8 \text{ m/s}^2)(1 \text{ m})/(14.3 \text{ N})(\sin 45°) = 1.94 \text{ m}.$$

Therefore, the signboard will be horizontal if we attach the second wire 1.94 m from the upper-left-hand corner of the sign; i.e., 6 cm from the upper right-hand corner.

The conditions for translational and rotational equilibrium can generally be applied to coplanar forces in the manner illustrated in the above examples. As these examples illustrate, in working problems dealing with statics it is essential to *start with a clearly drawn diagram* showing all the forces that are applied *to* the rigid body at the points where the forces act.

The general methods of treating noncoplanar forces are similar to the ones that we have outlined. The basic equilibrium conditions are just the ones we have stated on p. 187. However, with noncoplanar forces, the forces shown in Fig. 8.1 must be regarded as the *projections* of the actual forces on the XY plane. We would need to draw similar diagrams of the projections of the forces on the YZ plane and on the ZX plane of a rectangular coordinate system. By use of such diagrams we easily can write equations for translational equilibrium. However, writing the equations for rotational equilibrium is considerably more difficult, because noncoplanar forces parallel to the XY plane can produce torques about axes parallel to the X and Y axes as well as about axes parallel to the Z axis. An example of this kind of complication is given in Problem 35.

8.4   TWO-DIMENSIONAL MOTION

The general description of the kinematics and dynamics of a rigid body in three-dimensional motion is mathematically complex and is usually considered only in advanced texts dealing with analytical dynamics. The complexity of three-dimensional motion arises because in such motion a rigid body has six *degrees of freedom;* its motion involves translation along three perpendicular axes XYZ and also rotation about each of these axes. We shall not attempt to treat three-dimensional motion.

We can, however, give a general treatment of the special case of *two-dimensional motion* of a rigid body in which all particles in the body move in paths that are parallel to a single plane. The kinematical and dynamical treatment of this important type of motion is not difficult because the moving body has only three degrees of freedom: translation along two axes, which we can take as X and $Y,$ and rotation about a third axis parallel to $Z.$ The reader should remain aware throughout the following sections that the ideas developed apply to the important *special case* of two-dimensional motion. Some nontrivial extensions are required to treat general motion of a rigid body in three dimensions.

The final results of the motion of a rigid body from one place to another can always be described in terms of a displacement of the center of mass of the body together with a rotation of the body about an axis through the center of mass. Consider two-dimensional motion such as that shown in Fig. 8.7. If a rigid body moves from Position ① to Position ②, the change in position can be described in terms of a displacement **D** of the body's center of mass from its initial position at x_1, y_1 to its final position at x_2, y_2 along with an angular displacement ϕ about an axis through the body's center of mass C. Note that the axis of rotation is perpendicular to the XY plane and is thus parallel to the Z axis of the coordinate system.

We must remember that the actual path of the center of mass C does not necessarily coincide with the vector **D** giving its final displacement. The actual path l traversed by C while the body is being displaced will depend on the initial velocity of C and on the subsequent acceleration of C. We recall from our early discussion of the kinematics of a particle that the velocity $\mathbf{v}_C$ of a hypothetical particle at C has components

$$v_{Cx} = dx_C/dt \quad \text{and} \quad v_{Cy} = dy_C/dt. \tag{8.8}$$

Similarly, the acceleration $\mathbf{a}_C$ of C has components

$$a_{Cx} = dv_{Cx}/dt \quad \text{and} \quad a_{Cy} = dv_{Cy}/dt. \tag{8.9}$$

Because the angular displacement ϕ of the body is about an axis through C that maintains its orientation in space parallel to the Z axis in Fig. 8.7, we can express the body's angular velocity ω and angular acceleration α as

$$\omega = d\phi/dt \quad \text{and} \quad \alpha = d\omega/dt, \tag{8.10}$$

where positive values of ϕ, ω, and α are usually assigned to the counterclockwise sense of rotation about the axis.

Thus, we have a means of describing the change in position of a rigid body in terms of a displacement of its center of mass, with velocity $\mathbf{v}_C$ and acceleration $\mathbf{a}_C$ having components given by (8.8) and (8.9), respectively, along with an angular dis-

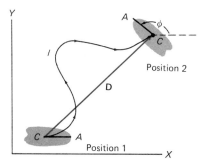

Fig. 8.7 Any two-dimensional motion of a rigid body is equivalent to a displacement of the center of mass of the body together with a rotation about an axis through its center of mass.

placement ϕ of the body about an axis through C. Changes of ϕ in the course of the motion can be expressed in terms of ω and α given in (8.10). In this way we can give a *kinematical description* of the motion of a rigid body in terms of the *translational motion of the center of mass* together with *rotational motion of the body about an axis through the center of mass.*

8.5 THE KINETIC ENERGY OF A BODY IN TWO-DIMENSIONAL MOTION

Because we can describe the *kinematics* of two-dimensional motion of a rigid body as the combination of a *translation* of the center of mass along with a *rotation* of the body about an axis through the center of mass, it would seem possible to make a corresponding simplification of the *dynamics* of two-dimensional motion. This is indeed the case.

We begin our treatment of dynamics by stating a theorem dealing with kinetic energy:

The kinetic energy of a rigid body of mass M in two-dimensional motion is equal to the kinetic energy of a particle of mass M moving with the center of mass plus the rotational kinetic energy of the body computed as if the body were in pure rotation about the center of mass.

We can prove this theorem by summing the kinetic energies of all the particles making up the rigid body and in the summation describing the motion of each particle in terms of the motion of the center of mass plus the motion of the particle relative to the center of mass. The details of this general proof are considered in Problem 47. At this point we shall content ourselves with a simple proof for the case of rotation about a fixed axis, in which we shall make use of the parallel axis theorem proved on p. 162. Consider a rigid body in the two-dimensional motion shown in Fig. 8.8, which is pure rotation about an axis through O perpendicular to the XY plane. From our earlier treatment of pure rotation on p. 160, we recall that the total rotational kinetic of the body can be expressed as

$$E_K = \tfrac{1}{2} I_O \omega^2,$$

where I_O is the rotational inertia of the body about the axis through O. However,

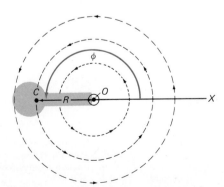

Fig. 8.8 Pure rotation of a rigid body.

the parallel-axis theorem tells us that $I_O = I_C + MR^2$, where I_C is the rotational inertia of the body about a parallel axis through its center of mass, M is the total mass of the body, and R is the perpendicular distance between the parallel axes through O and through C. Therefore, we can substitute $I_C + MR^2$ for I_O in the above equation:

$$E_K = \tfrac{1}{2} I_C \omega^2 + \tfrac{1}{2} MR^2 \omega^2.$$

In this expression, $R\omega$ is just equal to the tangential velocity v_C of the center of mass about the axis through O. Thus, we obtain the relation

$$E_K = \tfrac{1}{2} Mv_C^2 + \tfrac{1}{2} I_C \omega^2. \tag{8.11}$$

The term $\tfrac{1}{2} Mv_C^2$ represents the *translational kinetic energy* E_{KT} of the rigid body, and the term $\tfrac{1}{2} I_C \omega^2$ represents the *rotational kinetic energy* E_{KR} of the body in pure rotation with angular velocity ω about an axis through its center of mass. Thus, (8.11) can be written

$$E_K = E_{KT} + E_{KR}. \tag{8.12}$$

This expression indicates that we have been able to express the total kinetic of a body in rotation about a fixed axis in terms of the translational motion of the body's center of mass and its rotational motion about an axis through its center of mass.

In our interpretation of (8.11) we used a fact that may not be immediately obvious when we assumed that the angular velocity about the moving axis through C is equal to the angular velocity ω about the fixed axis through O. That this is the case can be seen from Fig. 8.9, which shows that the actual change in position in part (a) of the figure can be considered as the sum of a translation of the body's center of mass in part (b) of the figure and a rotation ϕ_C about the axis through C in part (c) of the figure. We see that ϕ_C is exactly equal to ϕ_O, the actual rotation about the fixed axis through O. Although Fig. 8.9 has been drawn for an easily identified rotation $\phi_C = \phi_O = 90°$, it is readily seen that at every instant $\phi_C = \phi_O$. The time derivatives of ϕ_C and ϕ_O are thus also equal. Therefore, $\omega_C = \omega_O$ and $\alpha_C = \alpha_O$, and we can write ϕ, ω, and α without using subscripts.

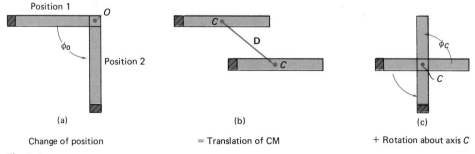

| (a) | (b) | (c) |
| Change of position | = Translation of CM | + Rotation about axis C |

Fig. 8.9

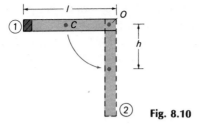

Fig. 8.10

Example.   Consider a 2-kg rod of length $l = 3$ m hinged with no friction at one end so that it can rotate about an axis through O as indicated in Fig. 8.10. If the rod is initially at rest in a horizontal Position ① and then released, what is its angular velocity ω as it reaches vertical Position ②? What is the total kinetic energy of the rod at Position ②? What fraction of its kinetic energy can be attributed to the translational motion of its center of mass? What fraction of its kinetic energy can be attributed to rotational motion about an axis through its center of mass?

First we note that as the rod swings from Position ① to Position ②, potential energy $Mgh = (2 \text{ kg})(9.8 \text{ m/s}^2)(1.5 \text{ m}) = 29.4$ J is, in the absence of friction, transformed into kinetic energy. Thus, the total kinetic energy of the rod at ② is 29.4 J.

This energy E_K can be considered associated with the rotational kinetic energy of the rod in its motion about the axis through O at the hinge; i.e., $E_K = \frac{1}{2} I_O \omega^2$. By the parallel axis theorem, $I_O = I_C + Mh^2$, where $h = l/2$ is the distance between O and C. From p. 160, we note that $I_C = Ml^2/12$, so that $I_O = Ml^2/3 = (2 \text{ kg})(9 \text{ m}^2)/3 = 6 \text{ kg} \cdot \text{m}^2$. Thus, $\omega^2 = 2E_K/I_O = 2(29.4 \text{ J})/6 \text{ kg} \cdot \text{m}^2 = 9.8 \text{ rad}^2/\text{s}^2$ and $\omega = 3.13$ rad/s.

The velocity v_C of the center of mass is $v_C = h\omega = l\omega/2 = (3 \text{ m})(3.13 \text{ rad/s})/2 = 4.69$ m/s. The translational kinetic energy of the rod is therefore $E_{KT} = \frac{1}{2} M v_C^2 = \frac{1}{2}(2 \text{ kg})(4.69 \text{ m/s})^2 = 22.0$ J. The kinetic energy of rotation about C is $E_{KR} = \frac{1}{2} I_C \omega^2 = \frac{1}{2}(Ml^2/12)\omega^2 = \frac{1}{2}(2 \text{ kg} \cdot 9 \text{ m}^2/12)(9.8 \text{ rad}^2/\text{s}^2) = 7.35$ J. Note that $E_K = E_{KT} + E_{KR} = 22.05 \text{ J} + 7.35 \text{ J} = 29.4$ J.

Therefore, the fraction $E_{KT}/E_K = 22.0 \text{ J}/29.4 \text{ J} = 0.75$ of the total kinetic energy can be attributed to E_{KT}, and the fraction $E_{KR}/E_K = 7.35 \text{ J}/29.4 \text{ J} = 0.25$ of the total kinetic energy can be attributed to E_{KR}.

8.6   THE DYNAMICS OF A BODY IN TWO-DIMENSIONAL MOTION

Now we shall consider the relation between the resultant force exerted on a rigid body and the acceleration of the body. In the case of translational motion we showed in Sec. 6 of Chapter 5 that the relation between the resultant external force $\mathbf{F}_R$ acting on the body and the acceleration $\mathbf{a}_C$ of the center of mass of the body is similar to Newton's Second Principle for a particle:

$$\mathbf{F}_R = M\mathbf{a}_C. \tag{8.13}$$

As far as translational motion is concerned, a rigid body behaves like a big particle of mass M located at the body's center of mass.

In Sec. 9 of Chapter 7 we showed that the time rate of change of angular momentum $d\mathbf{L}/dt$ of a dynamical system is equal to the resultant external torque τ_R acting on the system. This result holds in any inertial frame of reference. We shall now make use of the energy relation (8.11) to prove that an analogous relation holds for a rigid body in two-dimensional motion if all rotational quantities are measured relative to an axis through the center of mass, regardless of whether or not the center of mass is at rest in any inertial system. This illustrates another way in which the center of mass holds a priviledged position for the description of the motion of a dynamical system.

We shall compute the power P delivered to a rigid body by external forces and set this power equal to dE_K/dt, the time rate of change of the kinetic energy of the body. Consider the power $P_i = \mathbf{F}_i \cdot \mathbf{v}_i$ delivered to the rigid body by a single external force $\mathbf{F}_i$ acting at point i in the body, as shown in Fig. 8.11. In the inertial system with origin at O shown in Fig. 8.11 we have $\mathbf{v}_i = d\mathbf{R}_i/dt$. Because $\mathbf{R}_i = \mathbf{R}_C + \mathbf{r}_i$, where $\mathbf{R}_C$ is the position vector of the center of mass C of the body and $\mathbf{r}_i$ is the position vector of point i relative to the center of mass, we can write $d\mathbf{R}_i/dt = d\mathbf{R}_C/dt + d\mathbf{r}_i/dt = \mathbf{v}_C + d\mathbf{r}_i/dt$. We can thus set $P_i = \mathbf{F}_i \cdot \mathbf{v}_C + \mathbf{F}_i \cdot (d\mathbf{r}_i/dt)$. We must remember that the magnitude of $\mathbf{r}_i$ for any point in a rigid body is constant, so that $d\mathbf{r}_i/dt$ represents the tangential velocity $v_{Ti} = r_i\omega$ of the point, where ω is the angular velocity of the body about an axis through C. Only the tangential component F_{Ti} of the external force delivers power to the body as a result of tangential velocity v_{Ti}. Therefore we can write P_i in the form

$$P_i = \mathbf{F}_i \cdot \mathbf{v}_C + F_{Ti}r_i\omega.$$

However, $F_{Ti}r_i$ is simply the torque τ_i about an axis through C perpendicular to the plane of the diagram in Fig. 8.11; therefore,

$$P_i = \mathbf{F}_i \cdot \mathbf{v}_C + \tau_i\omega.$$

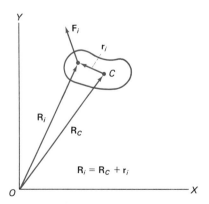

Fig. 8.11 An external force $\mathbf{F}_i$ acts at the point i located by position vectors $\mathbf{R}_i = \mathbf{R}_C + \mathbf{r}_i$.

If several external forces act on the body, we can express the total power P delivered to the body in the form

$$P = \Sigma\, P_i = (\Sigma\, \mathbf{F}_i) \cdot \mathbf{v}_C + (\Sigma\, \tau_i)\omega.$$

However, $\Sigma\, \mathbf{F}_i = \mathbf{F}_R$, the resultant external force, and $\Sigma\, \tau_i$ is the resultant external torque τ_{RC} about the axis through C. Thus, because $\mathbf{F}_R = M\mathbf{a}_C$, we can write

$$P = \mathbf{F}_R \cdot \mathbf{v}_C + \tau_{RC}\omega = M\mathbf{a}_C \cdot \mathbf{v}_C + \tau_{RC}\omega,$$

where τ_{RC} and ω can be clockwise or counterclockwise.

This power is equal to the time rate of change dE_K/dt of the kinetic energy of the body. We write (8.11) in the form $E_K = \tfrac{1}{2} M(\mathbf{v}_C \cdot \mathbf{v}_C) + \tfrac{1}{2} I_C\omega^2$. Then

$$\frac{dE_K}{dt} = \tfrac{1}{2} M\left(\frac{d\mathbf{v}_C}{dt} \cdot \mathbf{v}_C\right) + \tfrac{1}{2} M\left(\mathbf{v}_C \cdot \frac{d\mathbf{v}_C}{dt}\right) + I_C\omega\,\frac{d\omega}{dt}$$

$$= M\frac{d\mathbf{v}_C}{dt} \cdot \mathbf{v}_C + I_C\omega\,\frac{d\omega}{dt}.$$

Because $d\mathbf{v}_C/dt = \mathbf{a}_C$ and $\alpha = d\omega/dt$, we have upon setting $P = dE_K/dt$ that

$$\tau_{RC} - I_C\alpha. \tag{8.14}$$

Equations (8.13) and (8.14) provide the basis for the dynamical treatment of the two-dimensional motion of a rigid body. We emphasize that in the analysis just completed we have assumed that the motion is two dimensional, and the result (8.14) is valid only for this type of motion. However, for two-dimensional motion (8.14) is true regardless of how the center of mass is moving; the axis through C does not have to be at rest in any inertial frame of reference.

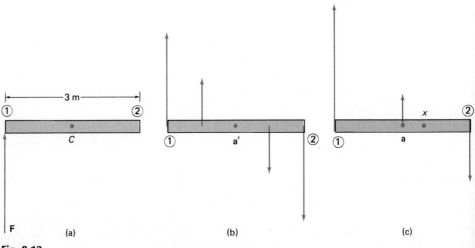

Fig. 8.12

Equations (8.13) and (8.14) form the basis of the system of dynamics applicable to the two-dimensional motion of a rigid body; (8.13) governs the translational motion of the center of mass and (8.14) governs the rotational motion about the center of mass. The application of (8.13) and (8.14) to bodies in two-dimensional motion is illustrated in the following examples.

Example. A 2-kg slender rod of length $l = 3$ m lies at rest on the horizontal surface of a frozen pond as indicated in Fig. 8.12a. If a horizontal force of 6 N, northward, is applied to one end of the rod as indicated in the figure, what will be the acceleration of the body's center of mass and what will be the initial angular acceleration of the rod about a vertical axis through C? Combine the translational and rotational motions to find the total initial acceleration of the ends of the rod in two-dimensional motion.

First we use (8.13) and (8.14) to find $\mathbf{a}_C$ and α: $\mathbf{F}_R = M\mathbf{a}_C$ or $\mathbf{a}_C = \mathbf{F}_R/M =$ (6 N, northward)/2 kg $= 3$ m/s², northward, and $\tau_C = I_C\alpha$ or $\alpha_C = \tau_C/I_C = (F_R l/2)/(Ml^2/12) = 6F_R/Ml = 36$ N/2 kg · 3 m $= 6$ rad/s², clockwise about the vertical axis through C.

Associated with this angular acceleration about C, each point in the rod will have tangential acceleration $a' = r\alpha$, as suggested in Fig. 8.12b. Since the rod is at rest when the force is applied, the initial radial component of the acceleration of any point relative to the center of mass is zero. Thus, the left end ① of the rod has acceleration $a' = (l/2)\alpha = (1.5$ m$)(6$ rad/s²$) = 9$ m/s², northward; similarly, the right end of the rod has acceleration $a' = 9$ m/s², southward.

The initial resultant acceleration $\mathbf{a}$ of any particle in the rod is $\mathbf{a} = \mathbf{a}_C + \mathbf{a}'$. Thus, for end ① $\mathbf{a}_1 = (3$ m/s², northward$) + (9$ m/s², northward$) = 12$ m/s², northward; for end ② $\mathbf{a}_2 = (3$ m/s², northward$) + (9$ m/s², southward$) = 6$ m/s², southward. The resultant initial accelerations $\mathbf{a}$ for various points in the rod are shown pictorially in Fig. 8.12c. Show that the acceleration $\mathbf{a}$ is zero for a point x that is 0.5 m to the right of C in Fig. 8.12c.

Example. A 2-kg slender rod of length $l = 3$ m is hinged at one end as shown in Fig. 8.13 and is held in a horizontal position. If the rod is suddenly released, what is the initial acceleration $\mathbf{a}_C$ of its center of mass? What is the initial angular acceleration of the rod about a horizontal axis through C? What upward force $\mathbf{F}$ is exerted on the rod by the hinge?

First, we note that $I_C = Ml^2/12 = (2$ kg$)(9$ m²$)/12 = 1.5$ kg·m². Taking downward forces and accelerations as positive and counterclockwise rotations as positive, we can use (8.13) to give

$$Mg - F = Ma_C \qquad \text{(i)}$$

and (8.14) to give

$$Fr = I_C\alpha, \qquad \text{(ii)}$$

with $r = l/2$. We recall from the discussion on p. 197 that $\alpha_C = \alpha_0$. Furthermore,

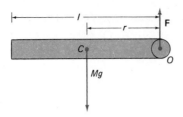

Fig. 8.13

we note the following kinematic relation between tangential and angular accelerations about O:

$$\alpha = a_C/r = a_C/(l/2). \tag{iii}$$

Substitution of (iii) into (ii) and subsequent solution of (i) and (ii) give $\mathbf{a}_C = 7.35$ m/s², downward; $\alpha = 4.90$ rad/s², CCW; and $\mathbf{F} = 4.90$ N, upward. *Note:* Try checking the result for α by considering the motion as one of pure rotation about an axis through O with $\tau_R = I_O\alpha$ and $\tau_R = Mgr = Mgl/2$.

8.7   ROLLING MOTION

An interesting and very important example of two dimensional motion is that of bodies that roll on a surface without slipping. We shall consider the rolling of such uniform circular bodies as wheels, cylinders, and spheres, in which the center of mass is at the center of the circular cross section of the body.

The condition that the body roll without slipping imposes a *definite kinematical relation between the translational motion and the rotational motion of the body.* The condition of "no slipping" means that there is no relative sliding motion at the point of contact between the body and the surface on which it is rolling. The contact point of the body is instantaneously at rest relative to the surface, although it is accelerated; the frictional force acting between the body and the surface is a force of *static friction.* Figure 8.14 shows a cross section of a wheel with radius R rolling to the right along a surface that is flat but is not necessarily horizontal. Let the initial position of the axis of rotation through C be at the origin O of the XY coordinate system. If the wheel rotates in a clockwise sense until one complete revolution, $\phi = 2\pi$ rad, has taken place, the center of the wheel has a displacement of $2\pi R$ in the $+X$ direction; i.e., the wheel makes one complete revolution when its center moves a distance equal to the circumference of the wheel. Thus, when the clockwise

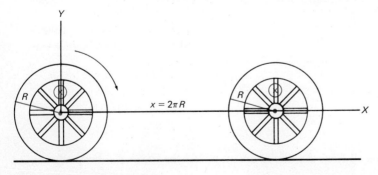

Fig. 8.14   Rolling motion.

angular displacement of the wheel ϕ is 2π rad, the linear displacement of the wheel's center is $2\pi R$. Hence, for the rolling wheel, we can write

$$x = R\phi. \tag{8.15}$$

From this relation and from the definition $v_x = dx/dt$, we find by differentiation that

$$v_x = R\omega, \tag{8.16}$$

where v_x is the X component of the velocity of the center of the wheel. Similarly, in view of the definition $a_x = dv_x/dt$, differentiation of (8.16) with respect to time gives

$$a_x = R\alpha, \tag{8.17}$$

where a_x is the X component of the acceleration of the center of the wheel.

Equations (8.15), (8.16), and (8.17) provide the kinematical relations between (i) the displacement x, the velocity v_x, and the acceleration a_x of the center of mass C of the wheel and (ii) the angular displacement ϕ, the angular velocity ω, and the angular acceleration α of the wheel about an axis through the center of mass of the wheel. Note that in these kinematical relations, the rotational quantities ϕ, ω, and α are shown in the diagram as positive in the clockwise sense rather than in the usual counterclockwise sense. This change in the convention for rotation is convenient for situations involving rolling bodies because it allows the X axis to be directed as usual from left to right in a diagram and at the same time has a positive angular displacement associated with a positive linear displacement of the center of mass.

The kinematical relations in conjunction with the dynamical relations (8.13) and (8.14) provide a basis for the treatment of the rotational motion of a uniform wheel that rolls without slipping when external forces are applied.

Example. Find the translational acceleration of a hollow cylinder of radius R when horizontal external force $\mathbf{F}$ acts through the cylinder's center of mass as indicated on Fig. 8.15; also find the magnitude of the frictional force $\mathscr{F}$ acting on the cylinder. Assume that the cylinder rolls without slipping.

In Fig. 8.15 are shown *all* the pertinent external forces acting *on* the cylinder. Because there is no acceleration of C in the Y direction, the weight $\mathbf{w}$ of the cylinder and the normal force $\mathbf{N}$ must be of equal magnitude but have opposite directions; because $\mathbf{w}$ and $\mathbf{N}$ both act on a line through C, they exert no torque about C. Therefore, we can ignore $\mathbf{w}$ and $\mathbf{N}$ in our treatment of the problem and consider only forces with components in the X direction.

As shown in Fig. 8.15, the force of static friction $\mathscr{F}$ acting on the cylinder will be in such a direction as to oppose the tendency of the surfaces in contact to slide relative to one another. Equation (8.13), $\mathbf{F}_R = M\mathbf{a}_C$, as applied to the problem becomes

$$F - \mathscr{F} = Ma_{Cx}. \tag{i}$$

Equation (8.14), $\tau_C = I_C\alpha$, as applied to the problem becomes

$$\mathscr{F}R = I_C\alpha. \tag{ii}$$

Kinematical relation (8.17) gives us a third equation:

$$\alpha = a_{Cx}/R. \tag{iii}$$

For a hollow cylinder $I_C = MR^2$; substitution of this value of I_C along with $\alpha = a_{Cx}/R$ into (ii) gives

$$\mathscr{F}R = (MR^2)a_{Cx}/R \quad \text{or} \quad \mathscr{F} = Ma_{Cx}.$$

Substitution of $\mathscr{F} = Ma_{Cx}$ into (i) gives

$$F = 2Ma_{Cx} \quad \text{or} \quad a_{Cx} = F/2M.$$

This relation shows that a_{Cx} *has only one-half the value it would have if the cylinder were sliding without friction. The frictional force has the magnitude* $\mathscr{F} = Ma_{Cx} = MF/2M = F/2$, just one-half the value of the applied force.

Although the situation shown in Fig. 8.15 is a special case, it illustrates several points that should be noted. The relation between the frictional force $\mathscr{F}$ and the force $\mathbf{F}$ applied with its line of action through C will depend on the rotational inertia of the rolling body—such as a solid cylinder, a sphere, or a wheel—that is being accelerated. However, the value of $\mathscr{F}$ required for rolling is always proportional to the magnitude of the applied force. When the acceleration a_{Cx} of the rolling body is zero, the resultant force $\mathbf{F} + \mathscr{F}$ on the body is zero. Neither an applied force $\mathbf{F}$ nor a frictional force $\mathscr{F}$ is needed to keep the body rolling with $v_C = $ constant. This is a familiar phenomenon to automobile drivers on a level icy road; friction is needed to start the wheels rolling, but once the car is moving at constant velocity no friction is needed to keep the wheels rolling.

As we shall see in some of the problems at the end of the chapter, the magnitude and also the direction of the frictional force $\mathscr{F}$ depend in an interesting way on the line of action of the applied force $\mathbf{F}$, which need not necessarily pass through the center of mass of the rolling body.

As we have noted, a body that is rolling without slipping and the surface on which it rolls are momentarily at rest with respect to each other at the point of contact. Therefore, the force $\mathscr{F}$ exerted on the rolling body is a *force of static friction*. It can have any magnitude from zero up to some maximum value $\mathscr{F}_{max} = \mu_S N$. For the case shown in Fig. 8.15 involving a hollow cylinder we have $\mathscr{F} = F/2$ or

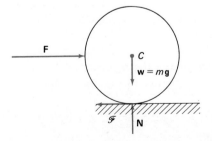

Fig. 8.15

$F = 2\mathscr{F}$, therefore, there is a maximum value of the applied force $F_{max} = 2\mathscr{F}_{max} = 2\mu_S N$ that is consistent with the condition of rolling. For an applied force greater than F_{max}, the cylinder begins to slip along the surface.

No mechanical energy is dissipated by a force of static friction $\mathscr{F}_{\!\!s}$. This makes it possible to use the kinematic relations (8.15), (8.16), and (8.17) with the energy relation (8.11) and work relations in studying rolling motion. If a rolling body is set in motion and then the applied force is removed, the total mechanical energy of the body should remain constant. Actually, of course, a rolling body eventually comes to rest because its mechanical energy is dissipated as a result of small inelastic distortions of the rolling body and the surface on which it rolls. In the case of a wheel with an inflated rubber tire, energy is dissipated as a result of the continual "flexing" of the tire. The gradual loss of mechanical energy by rolling bodies is sometimes attributed to "forces of rolling friction."

Example.   Using the results of the previous example, show that if the cylinder in Fig. 8.15 starts from rest and moves a distance D to the right, the work done by the applied force F equals the increase in the kinetic energy of the rolling cylinder.

The total work done by F is FD; the force of static friction does no work. The translational velocity acquired by the cylinder is given by $v^2 = 2aD = 2FD/2M = FD/M$. The cylinder's translational kinetic energy is $E_{KT} = \frac{1}{2}Mv^2 = FD/2$. The angular velocity of the cylinder is $\omega = v/R$. The rotational kinetic energy of the cylinder is given by $E_{KR} = \frac{1}{2}I\omega^2 = \frac{1}{2}(MR^2)(v/R)^2 = \frac{1}{2}Mv^2$; however, we have just shown that $\frac{1}{2}Mv^2 = FD/2$. Thus, $E_{KR} = FD/2$. The total kinetic energy E_K of the rolling cylinder is $E_K = E_{KT} + E_{KR} = FD$, which is just equal to the work done by the applied force. We note that in the case of a hollow cylinder or ring we will always have $E_{KT} = E_{KR}$.

Note: We have omitted subscripts on a, v, and D which are in the $+X$ direction and represent the motion of the center of mass. Similarly, the forces F and $\mathscr{F}$ are parallel to the X axis. We shall omit subscripts in the following examples where there should be no confusion as to the precise meaning of the symbols.

Example.   The hollow cylinder in Fig. 8.16 rolls without slipping down an inclined plane. Use the energy relation (8.11) along with the kinematical relations (8.15), (8.16), and (8.17) to find the speed of the cylinder's center of mass after the cylinder has descended a vertical distance h. What is the acceleration of the center of mass of the cylinder?

During the cylinder's descent potential energy Mgh has been transformed into kinetic energy: $E_{KT} + E_{KR} = Mgh$. Thus, we can write

$$\tfrac{1}{2}Mv^2 + \tfrac{1}{2}I_C\omega^2 = Mgh.$$

Substitution of $I_C = MR^2$ and $\omega^2 = v^2/R^2$ yields

$$Mv^2 = Mgh \quad \text{or} \quad v = \sqrt{gh},$$

where v is the final speed of the center of mass. This speed $v = \sqrt{gh}$ is less than

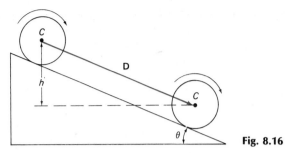

Fig. 8.16

the corresponding speed $v = \sqrt{2gh}$ of a body that has undergone free fall from a height h because in the present case one-half the initial potential energy has been transformed into the kinetic energy of rotation, while in the case of free fall all the initial potential energy is transformed into kinetic energy of translation.

In order to find the acceleration a of the body parallel to the slope, we make use of the relation $v^2 = 2aD$ or $a = v^2/2D$, which is valid because the resultant external force is constant. This leads to $a = gh/2D$. Because $\sin\theta = h/D$, we can express the acceleration in the form $a = (g\sin\theta)/2$. We note that this acceleration is one-half as great as that of a body sliding down a frictionless inclined plane.

Example.   Again consider a hollow cylinder rolling down an inclined plane. Use the dynamical relations (8.13) and (8.14) along with our kinematical relations (8.15), (8.16), and (8.17) to find the acceleration of the cylinder's center of mass in its motion down the plane. What must be the value of the coefficient of static friction between the cylinder and the plane if the cylinder is to roll without slipping?

The forces acting on the cylinder are shown in Fig. 8.17. In the figure we have resolved the body's weight $\mathbf{w} = m\mathbf{g}$ into one component $w\sin\theta$ parallel to the incline and a second component $w\cos\theta$ perpendicular to the incline. Because there is no component of acceleration perpendicular to the incline, the weight

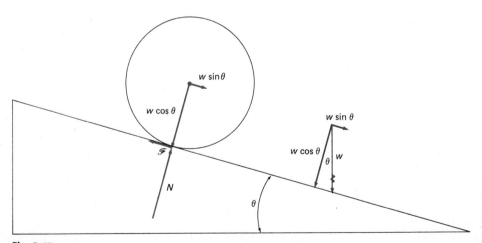

Fig. 8.17

component perpendicular to the incline is equal in magnitude to the normal force N exerted on the cylinder by the plane: $N = Mg \cos \theta$.

The net force down the plane is $Mg \sin \theta - \mathscr{F}$. By (8.13) we can write

$$Mg \sin \theta - \mathscr{F} = Ma, \tag{i}$$

where a is the acceleration down the plane.

The clockwise torque τ_C about the axis through center of mass of the cylinder is $\mathscr{F}R$, and we use (8.14) to write

$$\mathscr{F}R = I_C \alpha. \tag{ii}$$

For a hollow cylinder $I_C = MR^2$, because $\alpha = a/R$, we can rewrite (ii) in the form

$$\mathscr{F} = Ma. \tag{ii'}$$

Adding (i) and (ii') gives $Mg \sin \theta = 2Ma$, which yields the value $a = (g \sin \theta)/2$, in agreement with the result obtained in the preceding example.

With $a = (g \sin \theta)/2$, we see from (ii') that $\mathscr{F} = (Mg \sin \theta)/2$. Since $N = Mg \cos \theta$, we have $\mathscr{F}/N = \frac{1}{2} \tan \theta$. Since $\mathscr{F}_{max} = \mu_s N$, the coefficient of static friction must be equal to or greater than $\frac{1}{2} \tan \theta$ if the cylinder is to roll without slipping.

We note that all of our examples have dealt with the rolling of a hollow cylinder and with an applied force whose line of action passes through the center of mass C. The specific results will be different for other types of rolling bodies and also for cases in which the line of action of the applied force does not pass through C; however, the basic relations we have used are applicable to any uniform body with circular cross section that is rolling without slipping.

Now we consider the instantaneous velocity of various points on a wheel rolling in the X direction in Fig. 8.18. We can regard the rolling motion as a combination of *translation* and *rotation about the axis through the center*. If we consider *translation only*, all points on the wheel have the same velocity v_C as the center of mass of the wheel as shown in Fig. 8.18a. If we consider *rotation only*, the center of the wheel is at rest with $v = 0$ while points of the wheel at a radius r have tangential velocity $v_T = r\omega$. For points on the circumference, $v_T = R\omega = v_C$, as shown in Fig. 8.18b. The rolling motion of the wheel is a combination of translation and rotation; the

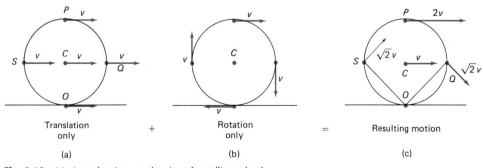

Translation only (a)   +   Rotation only (b)   =   Resulting motion (c)

Fig. 8.18 Motion of points on the rim of a rolling wheel.

resultant velocity of any point is the vector sum of its velocities due to translation and due to rotation. The resultant velocity components of points O, C, P, Q, and S are, for example,

$$\text{Point } O: v_x = v_C - R\omega = 0, \qquad v_y = 0,$$
$$\text{Point } C: v_x = v_C, \qquad v_y = 0,$$
$$\text{Point } P: v_x = v_C + R\omega = 2v_C, \quad v_y = 0,$$
$$\text{Point } Q: v_x = v_C \qquad\qquad v_y = -R\omega = -v_C,$$
$$\text{Point } S: v_x = v_C \qquad\qquad v_y = +R\omega = v_C.$$

These results are shown schematically in Fig. 8.18c.

We note that at any instant the point of the rolling wheel in contact with the road is at rest with $v = 0$ with respect to the road. It is possible to regard the entire motion of the wheel as one of pure rotation about an instantaneous axis through O. The speed of any point in the wheel is given by the relation $v = \rho\omega = \rho v_C/R$, where ρ is the radial distance from the axis through O to the point. Note that the velocity $\mathbf{v}$ of any point is perpendicular to ρ. It is easy to check these results by comparison with Fig. 8.18c.

Example.   An automobile moves at a constant speed of 30 m/s along a horizontal roadway. What is the instantaneous speed of the center of each wheel of the car? The bottom point of each wheel? The top of each wheel?

Because the axle is attached to the frame of the car, the speed of the center of each wheel is $v_C = 30$ m/s. The point of the wheel in contact with the roadway is at rest with respect to the road with $v_O = 0$. In accord with our discussion of Fig. 8.18, the top of each wheel must move at twice the speed of the wheel's center: $v_P = 2v_C = 60$ m/s.

8.8   THE EQUILIBRIUM OF A DYNAMICAL SYSTEM

Earlier in the present chapter we discussed the equilibrium of a rigid body. At this point we wish to broaden our discussion to the case of the equilibrium of a dynamical system. Consider a dynamical system consisting of the earth and the pendulum shown in Fig. 8.19. The earth exerts forces on the pendulum by gravitational attraction and by contact at the point of support O. We note that there are two positions of equilibrium. One of these is shown in part (a) of the figure, where the center of mass C of the pendulum is directly *below* the point of support O; in this case the resultant force and the resultant torque exerted by the earth on the pendulum are both zero. The second position of equilibrium is shown in part (b) of the figure, where the center of mass is directly *above* the point of support; in this case also the resultant force and torque exerted on the pendulum by the earth are both zero.

The two equilibrium configurations of the earth–pendulum system are different in an important way. Any small change in configuration (a) will result in forces and torques that tend to return the system to its initial configuration, which we

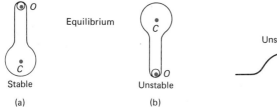

Fig. 8.19 A rigid body in two positions of equilibrium.

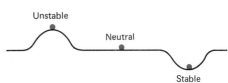

Fig. 8.20 Equilibrium of a ball on a supporting surface.

therefore call a configuration of *stable equilibrium*. In sharp contrast, any small change in configuration (b) will result in forces and torques that tend to move the system still further away from its initial configuration, which we therefore call a configuration of *unstable equilibrium*.

In terms of potential energy, we can define stable and unstable equilibrium in the following way:

A dynamical system in equilibrium is in STABLE EQUILIBRIUM when any small change in configuration resulting from forces exerted by bodies external to the system *increases* the potential energy of the system. A dynamical system in equilibrium is in UNSTABLE EQUILIBRIUM when any small change in configuration resulting from forces exerted by bodies external to the system *decreases* the potential energy of the system. If such small changes in configuration neither increase nor decrease the potential energy of the system, the system is in *neutral equilibrium*.

Examples of stable, unstable, and neutral equilibrium are given in Fig. 8.20, which shows balls at rest on a curved surface. It is easy to list other examples. A circular cone is in unstable equilibrium when it is balanced on its point, neutral equilibrium when it lies on its side, and stable equilibrium when sitting on its base.

Because no dynamical system is truly isolated, there is always a tendency for a dynamical system to change from configurations of high potential energy to configurations of lower potential energy as a result of small random external forces. Thus, a *small* external force to the right in Fig. 8.20 might well cause a ball to move from the position of unstable equilibrium through the position of neutral equilibrium to the position of stable equilibrium. A *small* external force would never cause the ball to roll uphill from the position of stable equilibrium in Fig. 8.20 to the position of unstable equilibrium.

Example.   Considerations of equilibrium are important to the design of the beam balances used for the accurate comparison of masses. Discuss the design of accurate chemical balances.

The unknown mass M of a body can be determined by means of an equal-arm beam balance as shown in Fig. 8.21. At equilibrium the unknown weight Mg produces a counterclockwise torque $\tau = Mgl$ computed about a horizontal axis O passing through the "knife-edge" that is exactly equal to the clockwise torque

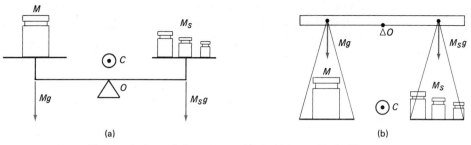

Fig. 8.21   The equilibrium of a beam balance is unstable in (a) but stable in (b).

$\tau_S = M_S gl$ produced by a set of standard masses. For rotational equilibrium we have $Mgl = M_S gl$ or $M = M_S$. However, the arrangement shown in Fig. 8.21a is never employed. The center of mass of the system consisting of M, M_S, pans, and beam is well *above* the point of support O at the knife edge. At balance, the dynamical system is in *unstable equilibrium*.

The precision "chemical balance" in actual use is shown schematically in Fig. 8.21b. The torques are equal, $Mgl = M_S gl$, and thus $M = M_S$ when the beam is balanced, as in part (a) of the figure. However, the balance in part (b) has the advantage of being in *stable equilibrium* because the center of mass of the system consisting of M, M_S, pans, and beam is *below* the point of support at the knife edge.

QUESTIONS

1. If two external forces equal in magnitude and opposite in direction act on a rigid body, is the body necessarily in equilibrium?

2. Three coplanar external forces of equal magnitude act on a rigid body. If the body is in equilibrium, where are the forces applied?

3. Two external forces that are equal in magnitude and opposite in direction are applied to a rigid body at two points 1 m apart. Show that the torque about any point associated with these forces does not depend on the positions of the two points on the body.

4. The coefficient of static friction between the surface of a hollow cylinder and an inclined plane is μ_S. What condition determines the maximum angle between the incline and the horizontal that can be given the plane without having the cylinder slide instead of rolling down the plane?

5. Explain why a wooden cone of circular cross section is in unstable equilibrium when it stands on its point, is in neutral equilibrium when it lies on its side, and is in stable equilibrium when it stands on its base.

6. Explain the difference between the center of mass and the center of gravity of an object. Under what conditions is this difference significant?

7. Give several examples of bodies for which the condition for translational equilibrium is satisfied but the condition for rotational equilibrium is not satisfied.

8. Give several examples of bodies for which the resultant torque about the center of mass is zero but the condition for translational equilibrium is not satisfied.

9. Suggest several ways in which the rotational

inertia of an object about some arbitrary axis could be determined experimentally. Is there any static measurement by which I could be determined, or is a dynamic measurement required?

10. Discuss the way in which a diver or gymnast can control the body's orientation by adjust-

ing the rotational inertia relative to an axis through the center of mass.

11. How can a cat that is held upside down and dropped land on its feet while conserving angular momentum? Is it possible that cats are not required to conserve angular momentum?

PROBLEMS

1. A 6-kg tapered pole 2 m long is hinged at the small end as indicated in the figure. When the pole is supported horizontally by a rope attached to the center of the large end at an angle of 30° with the horizontal, the force exerted on the pole by the rope has a magnitude of 50 N. What is the horizontal distance between the hinge and the center of gravity of the pole? What is the magnitude of the force exerted on the pole by the hinge?

2. In the situation of Problem 1, if the rope were detached from the end of the pole and attached to the pole at a point 40 cm from the hinge, what vertical force would be required to support the pole in a horizontal position? What force would the hinge exert on the pole?

Problems 1 and 2

3. A uniform rod with a length of 2 m and a mass of 2 kg is supported in a horizontal position by vertical cords attached to the ends of the rod. A 4-kg body is suspended from the rod at a distance of 30 cm from the right end of the rod. Find the tensions in the supporting cords.

4. Verify that the resultant torque acting on the rod of Problem 3 is zero about axes through O, C, O', and O'', where O'' is 40 cm beyond the right end of the rod.

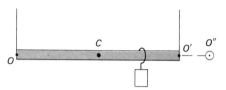

Problems 3 and 4

5. When the front wheels of an empty truck are placed on the scale platform at a weighing station, the scale reads 25,000 N; with the rear wheels on the platform, the scale reads 15,000 N. If the distance between the front and rear axles of the truck is 3 m, what is the weight of the truck and what is the horizontal location of its center of mass?

6. After the truck in Problem 5 has been loaded, the scale reads 35,000 N with the front wheels on the platform and 45,000 N with the rear wheels on the platform. What is the weight of the load and what is the horizontal location of its center of mass?

7. In the figure a uniform 2-kg bar 1 m long carries the two weights indicated in the figure and is supported in a horizontal position by two cords. If $\phi_1 = 60°$, find F_1, F_2, and ϕ_2 for equilibrium.

8. Repeat Problem 7 for a situation in which the second cord is attached to the bar at a distance of 20 cm from the right end of the bar.

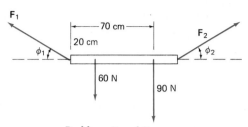

Problems 7 and 8

9. A cubical 10-kg box 1 m on each edge rests on the floor with one edge against a *small* cleat as shown in the diagram. The center of mass of the box is at the geometrical center of the box. At what height above the floor must a horizontal 80-N force be applied to just tip the box?

10. What horizontal force applied 85 cm above the floor will just tip the box of Problem 9?

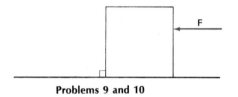

Problems 9 and 10

11. The box shown in the figure is 1 m high and 50 cm wide; it weighs 200 N and its center of mass coincides with its geometrical center. The coefficient of static friction between the box and the floor is 0.4. What horizontal force **F** is required to set the box in motion? What is the maximum height *h* at which this force could be applied without causing the box to tip over?

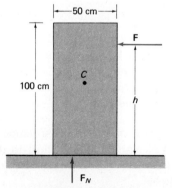

Problems 11 and 12

12. If no horizontal force is applied to the box of Problem 11, where does the *effective* normal force $\mathbf{F}_N$ of the floor act on the box? If a horizontal force of 80 N acts on the box, locate the position of $\mathbf{F}_N$ when the horizontal force is applied at heights $h =$ 10 cm, 20 cm, 30 cm, 40 cm, 50 cm, and 60 cm. At what height would a horizontal force of 50 N have to be applied to make the box tip over?

13. A 500-g stick ($I_C = ml^2/12$) 2 m long lies at rest on the frictionless surface of a frozen pond as in Fig. 8.12. If a lateral force of 2 N is applied to the left end of the stick, what will be the initial accelerations of the ends and the center of mass C of the stick?

14. At what distance from the center of mass could the 2-N force be applied to the stick of Problem 13 in order to make the acceleration of the right end equal to zero?

15. If the left end of the stick in Problem 13 is attached to a frictionless horizontal hinge and supported at rest in a horizontal position, what will be the initial downward accelerations of C and the right end if the stick is suddenly released? What initial upward force is exerted on the stick by the hinge?

16. After the stick in Problem 15 has swung downward so that its center of mass is directly below the hinge, what is the total kinetic energy of the stick? What fraction of the kinetic energy can be associated with translational motion of the center of mass and what fraction can be associated with rotational motion about an axis through the center of mass? What is the speed of the far end of the stick when it is directly below the hinge?

17. A solid cylinder ($I_C = MR^2/2$) rolls from rest down an inclined plane making an angle of 30° with the horizontal. What is the acceleration of its center of mass as the cylinder rolls without slipping down the incline? What is the velocity of its center of

mass after the cylinder has moved a distance of 9.8 m along the incline?

18. Repeat Problem 17 for a solid sphere ($I_C = \frac{2}{5}MR^2$) and for a hollow cylinder ($I_C = MR^2$). Compare your results with the acceleration and the final velocity of a block sliding without friction along the incline.

19. A 50-kg lawn roller consists of a solid cylinder with a radius of 40 cm that is mounted on a frictionless axle to which a handle of negligible mass is attached. With the handle making an angle of 30° with the horizontal, a man exerts a force **F** of magnitude 100 N as shown in the diagram. Assuming that the cylinder rolls without slipping, find the acceleration of its center of mass and the frictional force acting on the cylinder.

20. Repeat Problem 19 for a situation in which the handle is horizontal, with $\theta = 0$ in the diagram.

21. After the roller in Problem 19 has a displacement of 2 m to the right along the horizontal surface in the diagram, what is its total kinetic energy? Assume that the roller starts from rest. How much kinetic energy is associated with the translational motion of the roller? How much is associated with the rotational motion of the roller about its axle?

22. Repeat Problem 21 for the situation considered in Problem 20.

23. If the coefficient of kinetic friction between the roller shown in the diagram and the horizontal surface is 0.25 and the corresponding coefficient of static friction is 0.4, what is the maximum acceleration the center of mass of the roller can have for $\theta = 30°$ in the figure? What is the magnitude of the force **F** that must be applied to produce this maximum acceleration if the mass of the lawn roller is 50 kg?

24. Repeat Problem 23 for a situation in which $\theta = 0$.

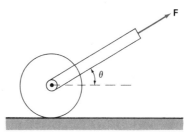

Problems 19–24

25. A child sets a 0.8-kg hoop ($I_C = MR^2$) into rolling motion along a horizontal surface by applying a horizontal force of magnitude 2 N to the upper rim of the hoop as shown in the diagram. If the hoop rolls without slipping, what is the magnitude of the acceleration of its center of mass? What is the frictional force exerted on the hoop by the horizontal surface?

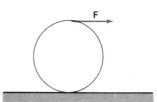

Problems 25 and 26

26. Solve Problem 25 for a 2-kg solid disk and for a 2-kg solid sphere.

27. The wheel with a heavy rim and light spokes shown in the diagram is dynamically equivalent to a hoop. The wheel has a mass of 3 kg and a radius of 50 cm. As shown in the diagram, the wheel is equipped with knobs to which horizontal forces are to be applied; the heights of these knobs above the horizontal surface are: A, 100 cm; B, 75 cm; C, 50 cm; D, 25 cm. What are the initial accelerations $\mathbf{a}_C$ of the wheel's center of mass if a horizontal force to the right in the diagram of magnitude 3 N is applied to each of the knobs in turn? What would be the magnitude and direction of the initial frictional force acting on the wheel in each case? Take the direction to the right in the diagram as positive.

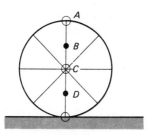

Problem 27

28. Repeat Problem 27 for a solid disk of the same mass and radius.

29. A flywheel rotating freely without friction on a horizontal shaft is "lopsided" with its center of mass 5 mm from the axis of rotation. The flywheel has a mass of 10 kg and a rotational inertia of 0.036 kg·m² relative to the axis of rotation. If the rotational speed of the wheel is 20 rad/s when the center of mass of the wheel is directly above the axis, what is its rotational speed when the center of mass is directly below the axis?

30. Find the forces exerted by the bearings on the flywheel in Problem 29 when its center of mass is directly above and directly below the axis of rotation.

31. A 2000-kg automobile with a rear-wheel drive has a 3-m wheel base; its center of mass is 140 cm ahead of the rear wheels and 70 cm above the ground. What is the maximum acceleration that the car can have along a horizontal roadway without having its front wheels leave the ground?

32. Suppose that the automobile in Problem 31 were loaded in such a way that the total mass of the vehicle and load was 2600-kg with its center of mass 1 m above the ground and 120 cm ahead of the rear wheels. What would be the maximum attainable acceleration without having its front wheels leave the ground?

33. A particle slides from rest down a frictionless track in the form of a "loop-the-loop" as shown in the figure. The particle first descends the vertical distance h and then rises the distance D as it traverses the circular loop. Determine the minimum height h required for the particle to remain in contact with the track at the top of the loop.

34. Solve Problem 33 for the case in which a sphere having a diameter small compared with D rolls without slipping around the loop-the-loop. Repeat for a solid cylinder and a hollow cylinder.

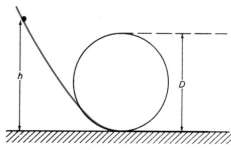

Problems 33 and 34

35. Three women support the wooden door in the figure in a horizontal position. The 8-kg door is 1 m in width and 2 m in length and its center of mass is at its geometrical center. If the women exert vertical forces at points A, B, and D, what are the magnitudes of the forces they must exert?

36. If the women supported the door in Problem 35 at points A, C, and D, what forces would each have to exert?

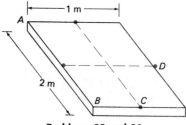

Problems 35 and 36

37. A solid cylinder of wood will roll from rest down an inclined plane for any angle θ of inclination with the horizontal provided $\frac{1}{3}\tan\theta < \mu_s$. However, if the cylinder is "loaded" with a lead slug in such a way that its center of mass is not at the geometri-

cal center of the cylinder, the cylinder will not roll from its position of stable equilibrium. Why? If the cylinder is held in a position of unstable equilibrium and then released, what happens? Discuss the motion of the cylinder after it is released.

38. A thin-walled hollow metal cylinder is filled with sand to one third of its total volume. The cylinder is placed on an inclined plane making a small angle of inclination with the horizontal and is released from rest. The cylinder does *not* roll down the inclined plane. Why? Explain this observation.

39. In our discussion of mass in Chapter 4, we showed how an unknown mass m can be measured in terms of a known standard mass m_S by allowing the two masses to interact and determining the magnitudes of their accelerations $\mathbf{a}$ and $\mathbf{a}_S$; we then have $m = m_S |\mathbf{a}_S| / |\mathbf{a}|$. Masses determined in this way are called *inertial masses*. In the comparison of masses by means of the weighing procedures suggested in Fig. 8.21, what properties of M and M_S are compared? Masses measured by weighing procedures are called *gravitational masses*. No difference between the inertial mass of an object and its gravitational mass has ever been detected.

40. In weighing procedures like those suggested in Fig. 8.21 the objects of masses M and M_S on the two pans of the balance do not interact directly. However, the individual interactions of the bodies on the pans with a third body are compared. What is the third body? Discuss the nature of the comparison. Note that none of the objects on the two pans is accelerated.

41. The diagram shows a 2-kg homogeneous solid cylinder having a radius of 50 cm and thickness 2 cm that is equipped with a small steel axle having a radius of 1 cm that protrudes 4 cm from each side of the cylinder and passes through the center of mass of the large cylinder. Strings are wound

around the axle; the upper ends of the strings are attached to the ceiling such that the axle is horizontal. When the cylinder is released from rest, it moves downward as the strings around the axle unwind without slipping. What is the downward acceleration of the center of mass of the solid cylinder?

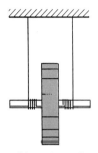

Problems 41 and 42

42. After the disk described in Problem 41 has moved downward 2 m from its initial position, what is its total kinetic energy? How much energy is associated with the rotational motion of the disk about an axis through its center of mass? At what rate is the total kinetic energy of the disk increasing?

43. The figure shows an Atwood's machine in which objects of masses $m_1 = 1$ kg and $m_2 = 2$ kg are attached to the ends of a string of negligible mass passing over a solid cylinder having a mass of 8 kg and a radius of 40 cm mounted on a horizontal frictionless axle passing through its center of mass. The string does not slip with respect to the surface of the cylinder. If the masses are released from rest, what is the downward acceleration of mass m_2 and what are the tensions T_1 and T_2 in the two parts of the string?

44. After the mass m_2 of Problem 43 has descended a distance of 2 m after being released, what is its speed? What fraction of the total kinetic energy of the system is associated with the rotational motion of the cylinder? At what rate is the kinetic energy

of the system increasing when m_2 is 2 m below its initial position?

45. Solve Problem 43 for a case in which the mass of the cylinder is 16 kg and its radius is 60 cm.

46. Solve Problem 44 for a case in which the mass of the cylinder is 16 kg and its radius is 60 cm.

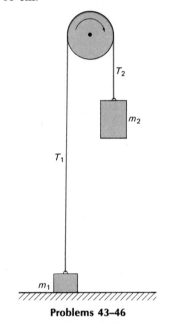

Problems 43–46

*47. By considering the motion of a typical particle of mass m_i in a rigid body and then

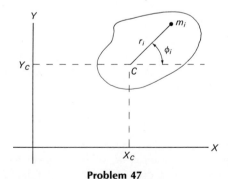

Problem 47

summing over all particles in the body, prove in general that the total kinetic energy of a rigid body of mass M in *two-dimen-*

sional motion is equal to the translational kinetic energy $\frac{1}{2}Mv_C^2$ of a particle of mass M moving with the center of mass plus the rotational kinetic energy $\frac{1}{2}I_C\omega^2$ of the body computed as if the body were in pure rotation about an axis through its center of mass. Suggestion: Choose the Z axis such that each particle of the body moves in a plane parallel to the XY-plane. Note as shown in the diagram that the coordinates of the ith particle can be written in the form $x_i = X_C + r_i \cos\phi$ and $y_i = Y_C + r_i \sin\phi$, where r_i is the radial distance of the particle from an axis through the center of mass C and parallel to the Z axis. Determine v_{ix} and v_{iy} for the particle and set $E_{Ki} = \frac{1}{2}m_iv_i^2$. Then set $E_K = \Sigma E_{Ki}$.

*48. Derive (8.14) by writing the angular momentum of the rigid body about the Z axis in Fig. 8.11 in terms of $\mathbf{R}_C$ and $\mathbf{r}_i$ as shown in the figure and then setting the time derivative of the angular momentum equal to the resultant torque about the Z axis. Remember that the body is rigid and is undergoing two-dimensional motion so that all particles of the body move parallel to the XY plane.

49. Prove the assertion that for the purpose of computing torques on a rigid body in a uniform gravitational field, the distributed gravitational force can be replaced by the weight of the body applied at the center of mass of the body for the case of a non-horizontal axis and a rigid body of arbitrary shape.

50. Show for a system in translational equilibrium that if the resultant torque about any point O is zero then the resultant torque about any other point is also zero.

51. Two identical ladders each 3.5 m long and each having a mass of 23 kg with center of mass 1.5 m from the bottom are hinged together at the top and stand on a smooth horizontal floor. To prevent slipping, they are joined by cords 60 cm long fastened

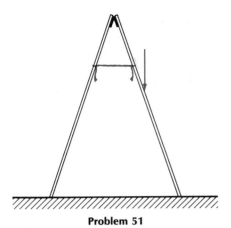

Problem 51

at points 1.0 m from the top ends of the ladders. A 62-kg man stands vertically on one ladder 1.5 m from the top, measured along the ladder. Find (a) the push of the floor on each ladder, (b) the tension in each of the two cords, and (c) the force exerted by each ladder on the other at the hinge. See the diagram.

CHAPTER 9

Gravitational Forces and Fields

In Chapter 4 we discussed the Aristotelian views of terrestrial physics and showed how they were superseded by the Newtonian view with its clearly stated principles that were capable not only of interpreting Galileo's "laws of falling bodies" but also of providing *quantitative predictions* of relations that had not been previously established. In Chapters 5–8 we have used the Newtonian Principles to define quantities like work and energy that we have used to advantage in describing the behavior of bodies near the earth's surface. Such bodies are subject to an ever-present force that we have called "weight" or the "force of gravity." Thus far, we have taken this force for granted and have said very little about its nature. In this chapter we shall elaborate our quantitative description of gravitational forces and shall discuss the influence of gravitational forces on the astronomical motions of the moon and the planets.

The Greeks regarded the matter making up the "heavenly bodies" like the sun, the moon, the planets, and the stars as being quite different from the matter composing ordinary terrestrial bodies. In fact, Aristotle regarded celestial matter as obeying quite different laws from the laws governing terrestrial matter. Whereas the natural state of terrestrial bodies was believed to be a state of rest, the Aristotelians believed the natural motion of a celestial body to be uniform circular motion, i.e., motion in a circular path at constant speed. The Greeks regarded celestial matter as ideal or perfect; for esthetic reasons they regarded the circle as the perfect geometrical figure and uniform circular motion as the ideal motion. The Aristotelian ideas culminated in the *geocentric model* of the universe developed by Claudius Ptolemy of Alexandria (*ca.* 140 AD). According to the Ptolemaic model, the earth is stationary at the center of the universe, and all heavenly bodies have circular motions relative to the earth. Thus, the sun, the moon, and the planets were believed to move in circular paths or orbits of different radii or in more complex paths that were circles about points that in turn themselves moved in circular paths relative to the earth. The stars were attached to a crystalline celestial sphere with the earth at its center; the celestial sphere, which was large enough to enclose all other bodies, rotated about the earth once each day.

The Ptolemaic model with some refinements was able to explain all astronomical motions to the accuracy with which they were known at the time. Just as Aristotelian physics gained approval by the Church during the Middle Ages, so also Ptolemaic astronomy was accepted by the Church and became entwined with Christian theology. Some of the theologians of the time even located heaven in the region just outside the celestial sphere. The geocentric theory of Ptolemy thus not only provided a ready explanation of astronomical observations but also fitted in comfortably with the theology of the time. Including all its refinements, the Ptolemaic model was, however, a fearsome contraption!

It is easy to imagine the horror and indignation of those in clerical authority when it was discovered by a Pole, Nicholas Copernicus (1473–1543), himself a member of the clergy, that it was possible to account equally well for all known astronomical facts by means of a simpler model with the sun at its center, the so-called *heliocentric model*. Copernicus retained the Greek principle of uniform circular motion but made the earth itself merely a planet moving about the sun. By allowing the earth to rotate on its own axis once a day, Copernicus was able to dispense with the large crystalline celestial sphere but had to place the fixed stars at enormous distances. Removing the earth from the center of the universe and having it revolve in a circular path about the sun once each year and rotate once each day on its own axis were highly unacceptable to the orthodox churchman of the time—but moving heaven away to some enormous distance while leaving hell immediately underground was even worse!

With two models, one geocentric and the other heliocentric, equally capable of explaining the then known planetary motions, the astronomers of the time were in a quandary. Observations in greater number and with increased accuracy were needed; these observations were supplied by the Danish astronomer Tycho Brahe (1546–1601). Whereas many of the earlier observations were of low precision and were often made only when exciting events such as eclipses were taking place, Tycho Brahe made painstaking and very careful observations of planetary motion on a nightly basis over a large number of years.

After Tycho's death, his extensive notebooks came into the possession of his assistant, a German named Johannes Kepler (1571–1630). Kepler found that Tycho's observations could be interpreted on the basis of three simple empirical laws.

KEPLER'S EMPIRICAL LAWS OF PLANETARY MOTION

First: The path of each planet is an ellipse with the sun at one focus.

Second: The radius vector from the sun to a moving planet sweeps out equal areas in equal times.

Third: The square of the time of revolution of any planet in its path about the sun is directly proportional to the cube of its average distance from the sun.

These laws summarize facts based on accurate observation. Despite the esthetic preferences of the Greeks, the planets do *not* move in circular paths; however, the eccentricities of the planetary orbital ellipses are extremely small—so in this regard the Greeks were almost right!

This was the state of affairs in astronomy when Isaac Newton began to give serious consideration to the subject. Clearly, it was desirable to understand the empirical Keplerian laws in terms of more general scientific principles. Newton found that by stating one additional principle—called the *Principle of Universal Gravitation*—he could treat both celestial motions and terrestrial motions by the same general methods. Philosophers now call this triumph the *Great Newtonian Synthesis.*

9.1   UNIVERSAL GRAVITATION

According to tradition, which he himself fostered, Newton at the age of 23 was sitting under an apple tree thinking about the orbital motion of the moon when he saw an apple fall to the earth. This set him wondering whether the gravitational force on the apple could extend as far as the moon's orbit and act as the centripetal force responsible for keeping the moon in its nearly circular orbit around the earth. He deduced that the force F_A exerted on the apple by the earth must have the form

$$F_A = G\frac{mM_E}{R_E^2} \quad \text{or} \quad mg = G\frac{mM_E}{R_E^2}, \tag{9.1}$$

where m is the mass of the apple, M_E is the mass of the earth, R_E is the distance between the center of the apple and the center of the earth, and G is a constant of proportionality, and that a similar relation holds for the moon:

$$F_M = G\frac{M_M M_E}{R_M^2} \quad \text{or} \quad M_M a_C = G\frac{M_M M_E}{R_M^2}, \tag{9.2}$$

where M_M is the mass of the moon, R_M is the distance between the center of the moon and the center of the earth, and a_C is the centripetal acceleration of the moon toward the earth.

Taking the ratio of the second equations in (9.1) and (9.2) shows that

$$\frac{a_C}{g} = \frac{R_E^2}{R_M^2} \quad \text{or} \quad a_C = g\frac{R_E^2}{R_M^2}. \tag{9.3}$$

Relation (9.3) gives the moon's centripetal acceleration a_C in terms of the known quantities g, R_E, and R_M. However, we also know from kinematics that a_C can be expressed as

$$a_C = v_T^2/R_M. \tag{9.4}$$

Here R_M is known and $v_T = 2\pi R_M/T$, where T is the well-known time for the moon to make a complete revolution in its orbit about the earth. The value of a_C given in

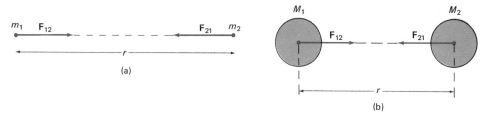

Fig. 9.1 Gravitational attraction.

(9.3) on the basis of an inverse-square relation for force and Newton's Second Principle is in excellent agreement with the value of a_c given in (9.4) on the basis of kinematics. Therefore, Newton concluded that his assumption of the force relations in (9.1) and (9.2) was indeed correct.

Newton then proceeded to generalize his assumption as a principle that applies to *all* particles:

PRINCIPLE OF UNIVERSAL GRAVITATION: Every particle in the universe attracts every other particle with a gravitational force. The magnitude of the gravitational force between a pair of particles is directly proportional to the masses of the particles and inversely proportional to the square of the distance between them. The gravitational forces of attraction between two particles act along the line joining the particles.

In symbols,

$$F \propto \frac{m_1 m_2}{r^2} . \quad \textit{(Universal Gravitation)} \tag{9.5}$$

We note that the principle applies strictly to *particles* as suggested in Fig. 9.1a. However, relation (9.5) also holds exactly for pairs of *spherically symmetric* bodies as indicated in Fig. 9.1b, where r is the distance between the centers of mass of the spheres. The basis for this conclusion will be discussed in Chapter 23. Although Newton assumed that this was correct when he first studied the moon's motion, he was unable to prove it to be so—because he had not yet invented the integral calculus! Actually, the inverse-square relation in (9.5) holds in good approximation for the gravitational force between two bodies of any shape provided the dimensions of the bodies are small as compared with the distance between their centers of mass. In his initial calculations of the moon's motion Newton was justified in applying relation (9.5) to the apple and the earth and to the moon and the earth. We note that he assumed that the moon moves about the earth in a circular orbit; this assumption was also justified as a valid first approximation.

Although Newton stated the Principle of Universal Gravitation as a *proportion*, we put a proportionality constant G into (9.1) and (9.2) to make his assumption an equation. This proportionality constant is not arbitrary, but must be determined experimentally and assigned dimensions to make the dimensions of the two sides of the equation the same. Thus, with SI units

$$F = G\frac{m_1 m_2}{r^2} \cdot \left\{\begin{array}{c} F \text{ in N} \\ m_1 \text{ and } m_2 \text{ in kg} \\ r^2 \text{ in m}^2 \\ G \text{ in N}\cdot\text{m}^2/\text{kg}^2 \end{array}\right\} \qquad (9.5')$$

The numerical value of the gravitational constant G was first determined experimentally by Henry Cavendish (1731–1810) in 1798 with apparatus similar to that shown schematically in Fig. 9.2. Two small balls of mass m are attached to the ends of a light rod that is supported in a horizontal position by a fine quartz fiber. Heavy lead balls can be moved close to the small balls by sliding them along the supporting rods. With the lead balls in the position shown they exert gravitational forces on the small balls that tend to twist the fiber in one direction. When the lead balls are moved into the positions shown by the dotted lines, the gravitational forces on the small balls tend to twist the fiber in the opposite direction. From a knowledge of the geometry of the apparatus and a knowledge of the elastic properties of the fiber, G can be determined in terms of the angles of twist. The gravitational force between objects of laboratory size is exceedingly small, and considerable experimental skill is required to produce unambiguous results. The most accurate value of G as determined by this general method is

$$G = 6.670 \times 10^{-11} \text{ N}\cdot\text{m}^2/\text{kg}^2$$

and was obtained by P. R. Heyl and P. Chrzanowski at the National Bureau of Standards in 1942.

A more accurate value of G can be obtained by a method originated by Jesse W. Beams (1898–1977) that involves measuring the angular acceleration of a "dumbbell" like the one in Fig. 9.2 when it is subjected to a constant torque τ produced by constant gravitational forces for a known length of time. In one form of this experiment the suspended dumbbell and the larger masses, shown schematically in Fig. 9.3, are supported by a rotating table. The angle θ between the large balls and the small balls is kept constant by an optical system that senses the tendency of the dumbbell

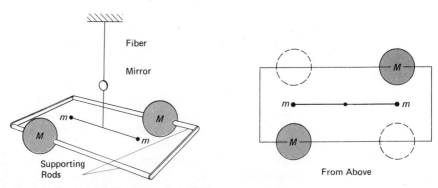

Fig. 9.2 The Cavendish measurement of G.

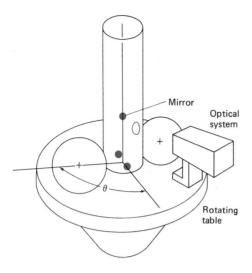

Fig. 9.3 A schematic diagram of an apparatus used by Beams and co-workers for the measurement of G. [Adapted from R. D. Rose, N. M. Parker, R. A. Lowry, A. R. Kuhlthan, and J. W. Beams, *Phys. Rev. Lett.* **23**, 655–657 (1969)]

to rotate toward alignment with a line joining the centers of the large masses in response to the gravitational attraction and operates servomechanisms. The most recent value obtained by this method is

$$G = (6.6699 \pm 0.0014) \times 10^{-11} \ \text{N} \cdot \text{m}^2/\text{kg}^2.$$

The actual measurement involves measuring the angle ϕ of rotation of the table in time t. For constant torques the motion is one of constant angular acceleration α so that $\phi = \frac{1}{2}\alpha t^2$; measurements last a number of hours.

9.2 PLANETARY MOTIONS

After his initial successful application of his principles to the motion of the moon around the earth, Newton next considered the motions of the planets in their orbits around the sun. He assumed that the major force acting on a planet was a gravitational force

$$F = G\, M_P M_S / r^2, \tag{9.6}$$

where M_P is the mass of the planet, M_S is the mass of the sun, and r is the radial distance between the planet and the sun as suggested in Fig. 9.4. The reference frame in Fig. 9.4 is an approximately inertial frame with its origin at the center of the sun and with its axes fixed sidereally.

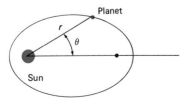

Fig. 9.4 Planets move in elliptical orbits around the sun.

By applying his general Principles of Motion to the planet Newton was able to show that the planet moved in a path described by the relation

$$r = l/(1 - e \cos \theta), \quad \text{(Conic Section)} \tag{9.7}$$

where l is the *semi-latus rectum* of a conic section and e is its eccentricity, as shown in Fig. 9.5. The geometrical parameters l and e depend on the energy and the orbital angular momentum of the planet. For an ellipse, the eccentricity can have values in the range $0 < e < 1$. If $e = 0$, (9.7) reduces to $r = l$, which is merely the equation for a circle with radius $R = l$. For all presently known planets, the value of e is very small. In fact, if we made accurate plots of the orbits, they would to the casual observer appear to be circles—with the possible exceptions of the orbits of Mercury and Pluto.

Newton's derivation of (9.7), which we omit, thus shows that any object moving about the sun in a closed path under the influence of an attractive force of magnitude given by (9.6) has an elliptical orbit with eccentricity e in the range $0 < e < 1$ and

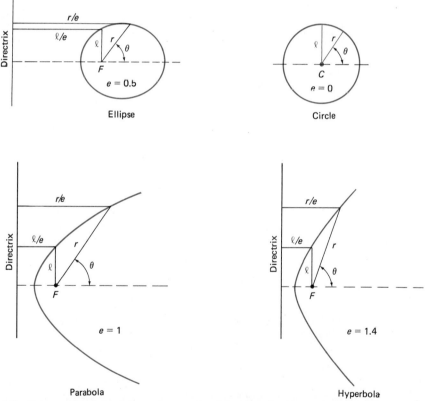

Fig. 9.5 Conic sections. A conic section can be defined as the locus of a point whose distance r from a fixed point F called the *focus* is e times its distance from a straight line called the *directrix*, where e is a constant called the *eccentricity*. We can see from the diagrams that $r/e = (l/e) + r \cos \theta$, where the length l from the focus to the curve measured on a line parallel to the directrix is called the *semi-latus rectum*. This equation when solved for r yields $r = l/(1 - e \cos \theta)$. For $0 < e < 1$ this is the equation of an *ellipse*, for $e = 1$ it is the equation of a *parabola*, and for $e > 1$ it is the equation of a *hyperbola*. For $e = 0$ the expression becomes the equation of the circle $r = l$.

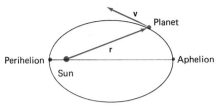

Fig. 9.6 The angular momentum of a planet is $\mathbf{L} = M_P \mathbf{r} \times \mathbf{v}$.

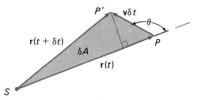

Fig. 9.7 As the planet moves from P to P' the area swept out by its position vector $\mathbf{r}$ is just the shaded triangle. The magnitude of this area is $\delta A = \frac{1}{2} r v \delta t \sin \theta = \frac{1}{2} |\mathbf{r} \times \mathbf{v}| \, \delta t$. Thus, the area swept out per unit time by its position vector is $\delta A / \delta t = \frac{1}{2} |\mathbf{r} \times \mathbf{v}|$.

the sun at one focus of the ellipse. By applying his general principles to the problem along with the Principle of Universal Gravitation, Newton thus was able to *derive* Kepler's empirical first law.

The derivation of Kepler's second law from Newton's principles is quite simple. If we assume that the sun–planet system is an isolated dynamical system, the total angular momentum of the system is constant. On the reasonable assumption that the angular momenta associated with the rotations of the sun and of the planet on their own axes can be neglected in considering the orbital motion, we can set the angular momentum associated with the orbital motion of the planet shown in Fig. 9.6 equal to a constant:

$$\mathbf{L} = \mathbf{r} \times \mathbf{p} = M_P \mathbf{r} \times \mathbf{v} = \text{constant orbital angular momentum.} \qquad (9.8)$$

We rewrite (9.8) in the form

$$\mathbf{r} \times \mathbf{v} = \mathbf{L}/M_P. \qquad (9.8')$$

Consideration of Fig. 9.7 shows that the magnitude of $\mathbf{r} \times \mathbf{v}$ is simply twice the time rate at which the radius vector is sweeping our area. Because $|\mathbf{r} \times \mathbf{v}|$ is constant and equal to L/M_P, we can write for the area A swept out by the position vector of the planet relative to the sun during the interval between times t_1 and t_2 that

$$A = \int_{t_1}^{t_2} (L/2M_P)dt = L/2M_P \int_{t_1}^{t_2} dt = (L/2M_P)(t_2 - t_1),$$

or

$$A = (L/2M_P)\Delta t. \quad \textit{(Kepler's Second Law)} \qquad (9.9)$$

Equation (9.9) tells us that for a given time interval Δt the radius vector from the sun to the planet sweeps out the same area A in any part of the orbit. This is merely Kepler's Second Law. In this way, Newton *derived* Kepler's second empirical law by applying general principles.

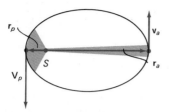

Fig. 9.8   The radius vector sweeps out equal areas in equal times.

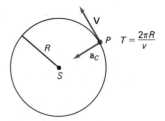

Fig. 9.9

Example.   In orbital motion the point at which the planet is closest to the sun is called *perihelion;* the point at which the planet is farthest from the sun is called *aphelion.* The corresponding points for an object in an orbit about the earth are called *perigee* and *apogee.** In Fig. 9.8, the radial distance of the planet from the sun at aphelion is r_a and the radial distance of the planet from the sun at perihelion is r_p. Noting that at perihelion and aphelion the orbital velocities are perpendicular to the radius vectors, use the conservation-of-angular-momentum principle as expressed in (9.8) to find a relation between v_a and v_p in terms of r_a and r_p.

From the angular-momentum principle in (9.8) we can write

$$M_P r_p v_p = M_P r_a v_a \quad \text{or} \quad r_p v_p = r_a v_a,$$

whence

$$v_p / v_a = r_a / r_p \quad \text{or} \quad v_p = (r_a / r_p) v_a.$$

In deriving Kepler's Third Law from Newton's principles, we shall make the circular-orbit approximation, which we can justify on the basis that the eccentricities of all known planetary orbits are extremely small. For the planet moving in the circular orbit in Fig. 9.9, we note that the planet experiences a radial gravitational force of constant magnitude $GM_S M_P / R^2$ that results in a centripetal acceleration $a_C = v_T^2 / R$. Thus, by Newton's Second Principle, we can write

$$M_P v^2 / R = GM_P M_S / R^2,$$

which gives the square of the planet's orbital speed as

$$v^2 = GM_S / R. \qquad (9.10)$$

The time T required for one complete trip by the planet around its orbit is given by $T = 2\pi R / v$. The square of this time is therefore $T^2 = 4\pi^2 R^2 / v^2$. By substituting the value of v^2 given in (9.10), we obtain

$$T^2 = 4\pi^2 R^2 / (GM_S / R) = 4\pi^2 R^3 / GM_S,$$

or

* These words come from the Greek: *ap*, away from; *peri*, near; *geos*, earth; *helios*, sun.

$$T^2 = (4\pi/GM_S)R^3. \quad \textit{(Kepler's Third Law)} \tag{9.11}$$

Because $4\pi^2/GM_S$ is a constant, we see that (9.11) is merely a statement of Kepler's Third Law. Following Newton, we have thus derived yet another previously known empirical law by arguments based on general principles.

We have now given a résumé of the way in which Newton showed how the empirical Keplerian laws can be understood quantitatively in terms of *basic principles,* which include the three Newtonian Principles of Motion together with the Principle of Universal Gravitation. We have regarded the gravitational force exerted on a planet by the sun as the *resultant force* acting on the planet. This is not quite true because, according to the Principle of Universal Gravitation, all the other planets and satellites in the solar system also exert forces on the planet in question. However, the forces exerted by other bodies in the solar system are so much smaller than the force exerted by the sun that they can contribute only minor *perturbations* to the planet's motion in its orbit. These perturbations are observable and have proved useful in advancing astronomy; the planet Neptune was actually discovered in 1846 on the basis of the perturbations it produces on the motions of Uranus.

Although the planets move in orbits that are nearly circular with very small eccentricities, the behavior of comets is quite different. The comets that are permanent members of the solar system have highly eccentric orbits, as indicated in Fig. 9.10 for one of the most famous comets. The eccentricity of the orbit of any object moving around the sun depends on the body's total energy and the body's angular momentum. If, when the body passes perihelion in Fig. 9.8, it has a speed much greater than the speed v_p required to keep it in a circular orbit of radius r_p, its orbit will be extremely eccentric; if it has a speed v_p only slightly greater than that required to keep it in a circular orbit of radius r_p, its orbit will have low eccentricity.

Returning to (9.7), which gives the orbit derived from Newton's principles, we note that it is not merely the equation of an *ellipse;* it is, in fact, the general equation for a so-called conic section. If an object is at rest with respect to the sun at infinite distance ($r = \infty$) from the sun, it will be attracted by the sun and pass around the sun along a *parabolic path* ($e = 1$) and, provided it does not collide with some member of the solar system, it will go back out to rest at infinite distance. If an object at infinite distance has some initial velocity relative to the sun, it will be attracted by the sun and pass around the sun in a *hyperbolic path* ($e > 1$) and, in the absence of collisions, will go back out to infinite distance. Thus, in general, any "object from

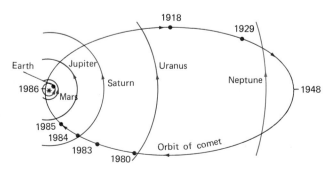

Fig. 9.10 The orbit of Halley's comet is a highly eccentric ellipse.

outer space" will pass through the solar system and then return to "outer space" provided it does not have a collision while inside the solar system.

The classical principles of mechanics can be used to predict the future behavior of the solar system. From a knowledge of the positions and the velocities of the planets at a given time, it is possible to make valid predictions of their positions and velocities for many years into the future. The planet Mercury is the only exception. The perihelion of Mercury's orbit precesses slowly in a way *not* predicted by classical theory, and relativistic mechanics must be invoked. In fact, accurate prediction of the rate of precession of the perihelion of mercury has been considered one of the principal tests of the general theory of relativity.

9.3   TIDAL MOTION

Although Newton was considering astronomical motions when he formulated the Universal Gravitation principle, he was able almost immediately to use it to solve a problem that had long puzzled mankind: the ocean tides. It had long been known that the tides were in some way associated with the moon. However, the nature of the "influence of the moon" on the sea had never been understood.

The basic tidal phenomenon can readily be explained in terms of gravitational forces exerted by the moon. For simplicity we initially consider a nonrotating, homogeneous, spherical earth that is entirely covered by ocean. In Fig. 9.11a we show a cross section of this earth covered by a layer of sea water with greatly exaggerated thickness. This represents the equilibrium situation if the moon were not present. The moon is off the diagram to the right at a distance R_M from the center of the earth, which has radius R_E. Let M_E and M_M represent the masses of the earth and the moon, respectively. Because of the presence of the moon, the situation shown

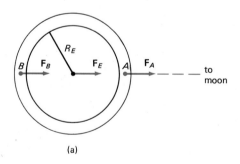

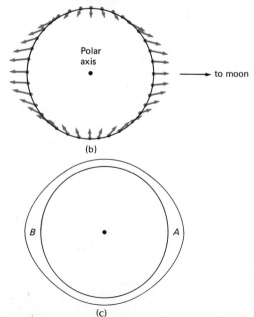

Fig. 9.11 (a) Equilibrium configuration of a non-rotating, spherical earth covered by ocean in the absence of gravitational forces due to the moon. (b) Effective tidal forces around the earth's equator due to the moon. (c) Tidal bulges produced by the gravitational effect of the moon.

in Fig. 9.11a does not represent equilibrium. Consider the gravitational forces $\mathbf{F}_A$ and $\mathbf{F}_B$ exerted by the moon on "particles" of water of mass m at points A and B in Fig. 9.11a. Both these forces are directed along the line joining the centers of the earth and the moon. We introduce an inertial frame of reference with the X-axis along this line. We can then write

$$F_A = m\frac{d^2x_A}{dt^2} = \frac{GmM_M}{(R_M - R_E)^2} \quad \text{and} \quad F_B = m\frac{d^2x_B}{dt^2} = \frac{GmM_M}{(R_M + R_E)^2}.$$

The gravitational force exerted on the solid earth by the moon is

$$F_E = M_E\frac{d^2x_E}{dt^2} = \frac{GM_EM_M}{R_M^2}.$$

We are interested in the relative motion of the sea water and the solid earth. Therefore, we want to have equations for the quantities $r_A = x_A - x_E$ and $r_B = x_B - x_E$ representing the coordinates of the particles of water relative to the center of the earth. By dividing the first pair of the above equations by m and the last equation by M_E and subtracting, we obtain

$$\frac{d^2r_A}{dt^2} = \frac{GM_M}{(R_M - R_E)^2} - \frac{GM_M}{R_M^2} \quad \text{and} \quad \frac{d^2r_B}{dt^2} = \frac{GM_M}{(R_M + R_E)^2} - \frac{GM_M}{R_M^2}.$$

Upon multiplying these expressions by m we obtain expressions for the effective tidal force on the particles of water due to the moon as seen by an observer on the solid earth, which is not an inertial reference frame.

These expressions can be algebraically simplified. We can treat both expressions simultaneously as follows:

$$\frac{1}{(R_M \pm R_E)^2} - \frac{1}{R_M^2} = \frac{1}{R_M^2}\left(\frac{1}{(1 \pm R_E/R_M)^2} - 1\right) =$$

$$\frac{1}{R_M^2}\left\{\frac{1 - (1 \pm 2R_E/R_M + (R_E/R_M)^2)}{1 \pm 2R_E/R_M + (R_E/R_M)^2}\right\} = \frac{1}{R_M^2}\left\{\frac{-(R_E/R_M)(\pm 2 + R_E/R_M)}{1 \pm 2R_E/R_M + (R_E/R_M)^2}\right\}$$

Now the ratio R_E/R_M has a value the order of 0.016. Therefore, the above expression can be written approximately as $\mp (2R_E/R_M^3)$. Thus, the effective tidal forces of the moon on the particles of water are

$$m\frac{d^2v_A}{dt^2} \simeq \frac{2GmM_MR_E}{R_M^3} \quad \text{and} \quad m\frac{d^2r_B}{dt^2} \simeq \frac{-2GmM_MR_E}{R_M^3}. \tag{9.12}$$

The water particle at A experiences a tidal force toward the moon and the water particle at B experiences a tidal force of equal magnitude away from the moon, both relative to an observer on the solid earth. If we perform a similar analysis for points around the earth's equator not on the X axis, we obtain the effective tidal forces indicated in Fig. 9.11b. We see that the effect of the presence of the moon is to produce two tidal bulges, as suggested in Fig. 9.11c. As the earth rotates, an observer on the solid earth sees each bulge once a day and therefore observes *two high tides daily*. Because of frictional effects, the tidal bulges are dragged eastward with the earth's rotation. As a result, the high tide due to the bulge at A does not occur when the moon is directly overhead but at a somewhat later time.

The discussion can be extended to predict the height of the tides, but the analysis is beyond the level of this book. In any event, the actual height of the tides at any location is strongly influenced by the detailed nature of the land masses that border the ocean.

Because the sun's mass M_S is enormously larger than the moon's mass M_M, we might expect the sun to have a larger tidal action than that exerted by the moon. However, the distance R_S to the sun is so much larger than the distance to the moon that the effective tidal force of the sun, which on the basis of the above theory we can represent by the quantity

$$F_A - F_B \cong 4GM_SmR_E/R_S^3, \quad \textit{(Tidal Force of Sun)} \tag{9.13}$$

is actually only about 0.46 times the corresponding tidal force of the moon in (9.12). In (9.13), A and B represent water particles on the line between the center of the earth and the center of the sun. Although smaller than those of the moon, the tidal effects of the sun are by no means negligible. The highest tides *(spring tides)* are observed at times of new moon and full moon when the earth, moon, and sun are situated on an approximately straight line; in this case the tidal effects of the moon and sun combine constructively. Lowest tides *(neap tides)* occur at first quarter and last quarter moons when the line from the earth to the moon makes a right angle with the line from the earth to the sun; in this case the tidal effects of the moon and sun tend to cancel each other.

A great deal of mechanical energy is associated with the motion of the tides. Ordinarily this energy is entirely dissipated in the waves and at shore lines. However, at certain localities it is possible to use this tidal energy to operate prime movers like waterwheels or turbines; we might note that such a prime mover could operate on both the "incoming" and "outgoing" tide. Though large on a human scale, tidal energy is extremely small compared with the enormously greater energies associated with the orbital motion of the moon and the earth. On an astronomical scale, the dissipation of tidal energy is almost negligibly small. The torque on the earth associated with forces of tidal friction causes an increase in the period of the earth's rotation that is estimated to be the order of 2×10^{-3} s per century.

9.4   WEIGHT

We now return to a consideration of the ever-present force acting on a body near the earth's surface: *weight*. In earlier chapters we merely accepted the existence of this force without further questions. Now that we have learned about universal gravitation, we can in good approximation attribute the weight mg of a body near the earth's surface to the gravitational force exerted on the body by a spherical earth:

$$G\frac{M_E m}{R_E^2} = mg, \qquad\qquad (9.14)$$

where R_E is the radius of the earth and M_E is its mass. This relation enables us to determine the mass of the earth in terms of measured quantities:

$$M_E = gR_E^2/G. \quad \textit{(Mass of Earth)} \qquad\qquad (9.15)$$

Although g is easily measured and R_E was well known in Newton's time, the mass of the earth became known from (9.15) only after Cavendish had measured G. The above equations would be exact for g determined at sea level on a nonrotating spherical earth.

At any height h above sea level on a nonrotating spherical earth, the value of g would be smaller than the value at sea level in accord with the expression

$$g = F_S/m = GM_E/(R_E + h)^2. \qquad\qquad (9.16)$$

A decrease in g with increasing height above sea level is actually observed when the values of g are measured at various heights above sea level. Values of g as a function of altitude are given in Table 9.1 for a latitude of 40°.

Now the earth is not really a perfect sphere but an *oblate spheroid* with a polar radius that is slightly smaller than its radius at the equator. We expect the value of g_P at the pole of a nonrotating oblate spheroidal earth to be slightly greater than g at the equator for measurements made at sea level because the earth's polar radius R_P is smaller than its equatorial radius R_E. Quantitative analysis of the variation of

Table 9.1   Values of the Gravitational Acceleration*

At sea level		At 40° latitude	
Latitude	g (m/s²)	Altitude (m)	g (m/s²)
0°	9.780 39	0	9.801 71
10°	9.781 95	500	9.800 17
20°	9.796 41	1 000	9.798 64
30°	9.793 29	2 000	9.795 54
40°	9.801 71	4 000	9.789 37
50°	9.810 71	8 000	9.777 02
60°	9.819 18	16 000	9.752 33
70°	9.826 08	32 000	9.702 96
80°	9.830 59		
90°	9.832 17		

* Accurate values of g are given for sea-level stations at various latitudes and for stations at various altitudes at 40° latitude. These values are only mean values, since there are local variations of smaller magnitude that depend on the particular character of the underlying earth.

g is complicated by the fact that (9.14) is strictly valid only for a spherically symmetric earth.

Furthermore, we must recognize the fact that the earth *is* rotating about its axis. Any coordinate system attached to the earth is therefore not really an inertial system. If we consider our easily measured value of g at the earth's surface in terms of a true inertial system, we must conclude that the weight $w = mg$ determined for a body at the earth's surface is really an *apparent weight* of the kind we discussed earlier (p. 77) in connection with weight measurements in a frame attached to an elevator with vertical acceleration.

The ideas involved can be understood in connection with Fig. 9.12, which shows a body of mass m supported on a platform scale at the equator, at the north pole, and at an intermediate latitude on a spherical earth rotating on its axis at angular velocity ω. A resultant force $\mathbf{F}_R$ directed perpendicular to the axis of rotation is required to provide the centripetal force $F_C = mv^2/r = mr\omega^2$ to keep the body in a circular path about the earth's axis: $\mathbf{F}_R = m\mathbf{a}_C$. This resultant force on the body is the vector sum of the gravitational force $\mathbf{F}_G$ toward the earth's center and the "upward" force $\mathbf{F}_S$ of magnitude $w = mg$ exerted on the body by the compressed spring of the weighing scale: $\mathbf{F}_R = m\mathbf{a}_C = \mathbf{F}_G + \mathbf{F}_S$. Thus, at the equator $\mathbf{F}_R = m\mathbf{a}_C$ leads to

$$GM_E m/R_E^2 - mg = mR_E\omega^2$$

and

$$g = GM_E/R_E^2 - R_E\omega^2. \quad \textit{(Equator)} \qquad (9.17)$$

At the pole, there is no centripetal acceleration because the body of mass m is *on* the axis of rotation. Therefore, $a_C = 0$ in the above equation and the resultant force $\mathbf{F}_R$ on the body is zero:

$$GM_E m/R_E^2 - mg = 0$$

and

$$g = GM_E/R_E^2. \quad \textit{(Pole)} \qquad (9.17')$$

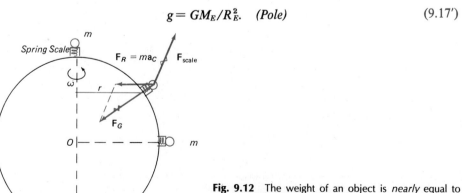

Fig. 9.12 The weight of an object is *nearly* equal to the gravitational force exerted by the earth. The rotational motion of the earth has a *slight* influence on the weight of object.

Therefore, the local value of g at the pole is greater than the corresponding value at the equator also because of the earth's rotation. The difference between the two values determined above is small: $g_{Pole} - g_{Eq} = R_E\omega^2$, where the value of $R_E\omega^2$ is only 0.034 m/s² or about 0.3% of the nominal value 9.8 m/s² that we have used. Thus, the value of g would show a small gradual increase as we move from the equator to the pole on a rotating spherical earth.

These considerations of the nonspherical shape of the earth and of the earth's rotational motion on its axis lead to predictions that g increases with increasing latitude as we move at sea level from the equator to the pole. The measured mean values of g at sea level as a function of latitude are listed in Table 9.1. We note that the difference in g between the pole and the equator amounts to only 0.5% of the nominal value $g = 9.8$ m/s² that we have been using. We also note that the measured weight differs from the value predicted by (9.14) for the gravitational force exerted on the body by the earth by at most about 0.4%. To this accuracy we can state that the measured weight of a body is equal to the gravitational force exerted on the body by the earth.

9.5   GRAVITATIONAL POTENTIAL ENERGY

At this point we must consider a more general expression for gravitational potential energy than the relation $E_P = mgh$, relative to a reference level $E_P = 0$ at the earth's surface, that we used successfully in dealing with many aspects of terrestrial physics. We recall that we derived this expression by computing the work required to raise a body from the earth's surface to some height h while the body was subject to a *constant* downward gravitational force of magnitude mg. It is now obvious from (9.16) that $E_P = mgh$ can remain valid only for values of h that are small compared with the earth's radius R_E.

In order to derive a more general expression for E_P we shall use an approximately inertial frame that has its origin at the earth's center. In using this frame, we must remember that we shall be stating displacements and velocities relative to the reference frame and not relative to the earth's surface. It will be convenient to use a polar coordinate system like the one shown in Fig. 1.8 (p. 13), in which the position of a particle is stated in terms of its radial distance r from the origin along with a polar angle θ and an azimuthal angle ϕ.

The gravitational force exerted on a particle or body of mass m at a radial distance $r > R_E$ from the center of the earth in Fig. 9.13 is a force of magnitude GM_Em/r^2 directed toward the earth's center of mass located at the origin of the coordinate system. We assume that the earth is a perfect sphere. In vector form, we can write this equation

$$\mathbf{F}_G = -(GM_Em/r^2)\hat{\mathbf{r}}, \tag{9.18}$$

where $\hat{\mathbf{r}}$ is a unit vector directed outward from the origin at C. We have noted that the gravitational force $\mathbf{F}_G$ is directed radially inward toward the center of the earth; its *magnitude* is the same for all points at the same radial distance r from C.

In order to find the gravitational potential energy of the body at distance R from

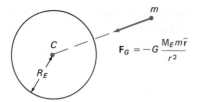

Fig. 9.13

the center of the earth *relative to $E_P = 0$ at the earth's surface,* we must calculate the work that we must do against gravitational forces in moving the body from radial distance R_E to some greater distance R. We note that the force $\mathbf{F}_A$ we must apply is just equal in magnitude but opposite in direction to $\mathbf{F}_G$; i.e., $\mathbf{F}_A = -\mathbf{F}_G = (GM_Em/r^2)\hat{\mathbf{r}}$.

If we move the body radially outward from a point on the surface of the earth to a point P at distance R from the earth's center as suggested in Fig. 9.14, we can compute the work to be done by means of a simple integral. The work done in moving the body a radial distance dr outward is $dW = F_A dr$, where F_A is the force we exert outward in the radial direction. The total amount of work we must do is given by the integral

$$W = \int_{R_E}^{R} F_A \, dr = GM_Em \int_{R_E}^{R} \frac{dr}{r^2} = GM_Em \left(-\frac{1}{r}\right)\Big|_{R_E}^{R} = GM_Em \left(\frac{1}{R_E} - \frac{1}{R}\right). \quad (9.19)$$

This amount of work is just equal to the increase in the potential energy of the body of mass m relative to a location *at the surface of the earth.*

We have obtained the expression given in (9.19) for a case in which we moved the body out radially from the earth's surface. However, we get the same expression regardless of how we raise the body from the earth's surface to a point at height $R - R_E$ above the earth's surface. For example, in Fig. 9.15 we show a curving path along which we shall move the body from any point B at the earth's surface to point P at a height $R - R_E$ above the earth's surface. The work required is given by the line integral

$$W = \int_{B}^{P} \mathbf{F}_A \cdot d\mathbf{l}$$

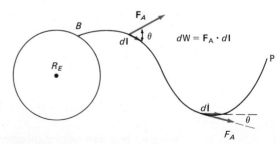

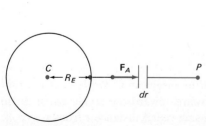

Fig. 9.14 $dW = F_A \, dr.$

Fig. 9.15 The work that we do in moving a body from B to P is given by the line integral $\int_{B}^{P} \mathbf{F}_A \cdot d\mathbf{l}$, where $\mathbf{F}_A$ is the force we apply to the body.

from point B to P along the curving path. However, at every point along the path $\mathbf{F}_A \cdot d\mathbf{l} = F_A \cos \theta \, dl$. Because $\mathbf{F}_A$ is always directed radially outward, $\cos \theta \, dl = dr$, which is the radial component of $d\mathbf{l}$. Therefore, $\int_B^P \mathbf{F}_A \cdot d\mathbf{l} = \int_{R_E}^R F_A \, dr$, which is just the integral considered in (9.19). Therefore, we conclude that the result given in (9.19) is quite general and does not depend on the particular path taken from the surface of the earth to the point P.

Because the gravitational potential energy E_P at a given position is equal to the work done against gravitational forces in placing the body at the position starting from some reference location, in this case the earth's surface, we use (9.19) to obtain a general expression for E_P:

$$E_P = GM_E m \left(\frac{1}{R_E} - \frac{1}{r} \right), \quad \text{(Potential Energy)} \qquad (9.20)$$

where E_P is the potential energy of a body of mass m at any radial distance $r > R_E$ *relative to a location at the earth's surface.*

Example.   Show that the expression in (9.20) reduces to the simple expression mgh at height h above the earth's surface, provided $h \ll R_E$.

We use (9.20) and set $r = R_E + h$. This gives

$$E_P = GM_E m \left(\frac{1}{R_E} - \frac{1}{R_E + h} \right) = GM_E m \left(\frac{R_E + h - R_E}{R_E(R_E + h)} \right)$$

$$= GM_E m \left(\frac{h}{R_E^2 + R_E h} \right) \cong \frac{GM_E m}{R_E^2} h,$$

where we can delete $R_E h$ in the denominator because it is negligibly small as compared with R_E^2. By (9.13) $GM_E m / R_E^2 = mg$ and therefore $E_P \cong mgh$.

How much work would we have to do in removing a body from the earth completely? Removing the body completely means moving the body an infinite distance from the earth, i.e., the distance r from the earth's center approaches infinity: $r \to \infty$. The *minimum* amount of work done in removing the body from the earth would be that required to move the body to infinite distance and leave it at rest in its final position. The entire final mechanical energy of the body would be potential, and the work required is merely equal to the body's final potential energy:

$$W = GM_E m / R_E, \qquad (9.21)$$

which is the form of (9.20) with $r \to \infty$.

Removal of an object from the earth can be achieved by using rocket propulsion to give the object an amount of kinetic energy at the earth's surface that is equal to the potential energy the body is to have at infinite distance from the earth. If no mechanical energy is dissipated, the total mechanical energy of the earth–body system is conserved, and we can equate the body's initial kinetic energy at the earth's surface to the body's final potential energy at infinite distance: $E_K(\text{at } R_E) = E_p(\text{at } \infty)$, or $\frac{1}{2}mv_E^2 = GM_Em/R_E$. Solving this equation for v_E gives

$$v_E = \sqrt{2GM_E/R_E}, \quad \textit{(Velocity of Escape)} \tag{9.22}$$

where v_E is called the *velocity of escape* from the earth.

Direct substitution into (9.22) gives the numerical value

$$v_E = \sqrt{2(6.67 \times 10^{-11}\ \text{N·m}^2/\text{kg}^2)(5.98 \times 10^{24}\ \text{kg})/(6.37 \times 10^6\ \text{m})}$$
$$= 11.2 \times 10^3\ \text{m/s} = 11.2\ \text{km/s}.$$

Alternatively, we might note that from (9.14) $GM_Em/R_E^2 = mg$ and write

$$v_E = \sqrt{2gR_E} = \sqrt{2(9.8\ \text{m/s}^2)(6.37 \times 10^6\ \text{m})} = 11.2 \times 10^3\ \text{m/s} = 11.2\ \text{km/s}.$$

The expression for the velocity of escape (9.22) was obtained on the assumption that no mechanical energy is dissipated. Because large amounts of mechanical energy *are* dissipated when an object like a rocket moves at high speed through the earth's atmosphere, a space probe would have to have a speed v_E *after* it had passed through the atmosphere in order to "escape" from the earth. We note that we have not said anything about the direction of $\mathbf{v}_E$. Its direction makes no difference—as long as the moving body does not go downward and strike the earth! So long as an object has energy $\frac{1}{2}mv_E^2$ at the top of the atmosphere, it will escape permanently from the earth, provided it is not moving back toward the earth.

Light molecules like H_2 and He in the upper levels of the earth's atmosphere sometimes have speeds as great or greater than the escape velocity v_E. Such gases gradually escape into space. For astronomical bodies less massive than the earth velocities of escape are smaller than v_E for the earth. Rapidly moving gas molecules readily escape from these bodies; this phenomenon accounts for the fact that the planet Mercury and our own moon have no atmosphere.

9.6   EARTH SATELLITES: SPACE PROBES

Since the beginning of the Space Age in 1957, amazing engineering developments have taken place in the field of rocket propulsion. It is now possible to launch fairly massive objects into orbital motion around the earth in practically any desired path. These artificial earth satellites are being used for a variety of purposes including *communications* (TV relay stations), *meteorology* (weather satellites), *land surveying* (photogrammetry, surface temperature studies, etc.), *military intelligence,* and many others. We shall consider briefly some of the space-engineering techniques involved. The actual problems of launching a satellite are complicated by the fact that the launching platform (the earth) has motions of its own—rotation on its axis and revolution in its orbit around the sun. We shall simplify our discussions by using an approximately inertial frame of reference with its origin at the center of the earth and axes that do not rotate with the earth.

In launching a space probe of any kind, we use several rocket stages. The large primary stage called the "booster" serves to raise the probe high above the earth's atmosphere. The secondary stage is a smaller rocket that is used to steer the probe into the desired orbit. Still further small rockets aboard the probe are used for minor course corrections. We shall consider only a greatly simplified launch pattern in which after "burn out" of the secondary rocket the probe at Point P in Fig. 9.16 is moving at a velocity $\mathbf{v}_P$ perpendicular to the radius vector from the center of the earth. The magnitude of the angular momentum probe at this Point P is given by $L = mv_Pr_P$, where r_P is the radial distance between the center of the earth C and the Point P. Once the value of the angular momentum L and the probe's total mechanical energy $E_P + E_K$ are established at Point P, we shall regard them as constant in subsequent motion and the orbit of the probe as firmly established.

It is convenient to express the total energy in terms of the total *equivalent initial kinetic energy* $E_{K0} = \frac{1}{2}mv_0^2$ that would be required at the launch pad on the earth's surface in order to place the probe at Point P with speed v_P on the assumption that there is no dissipation of mechanical energy. By using (9.20) we obtain

$$\tfrac{1}{2}mv_0^2 = \tfrac{1}{2}mv_P^2 + GM_Em(1/R_E - 1/r_P) \qquad (9.23)$$

We shall call v_0 the equivalent launch velocity.

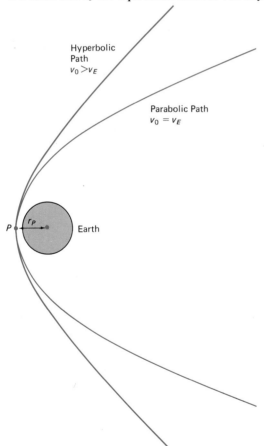

Fig. 9.16 A space probe moving with the velocity of escape v_E moves in a parabolic path; if its initial velocity is greater than v_E, the probe moves in a hyperbolic path.

If v_0 for a given probe is exactly equal to the escape velocity v_E, the probe will move along a *parabolic path* as shown in Fig. 9.16 and come to rest at infinite distance from the earth with its final kinetic energy $E_{Kf} = 0$. In this case, the final potential energy of the probe is just equal to $\frac{1}{2}mv_0^2 = \frac{1}{2}mv_E^2$, where v_E is the velocity of escape.

If v_0 for a given probe is greater than v_E, the probe will go into a hyperbolic path as shown in Fig. 9.16. In this case, the probe will continue to move out to infinite distance and will still have some kinetic energy remaining at infinite distance. Thus, for $v_0 \geq v_E$ an object will escape permanently from the earth. We should point out that for $v_0 \geq v_E$ a probe does not necessarily really go to infinite distance. We must remember that the sun also exerts a strong gravitational force on the probe; the sun can capture any probe now launched from the earth because of present limitations on v_0. With $v_0 \geq v_E$, a space probe does permanently escape from the earth, but it may go into some closed orbit around the sun. The other planets of the Solar System will also have some effect on the motion of the space probe, particularly if the probe passes close to some one of the planets.

Next we consider the important case in which the equivalent launch velocity v_0 is less than the velocity of escape v_E. In this case the probe goes into a closed elliptical orbit, in which it remains as a permanent *earth satellite;* this situation is shown in Fig. 9.17. For a given equivalent launch velocity v_0, we can use (9.23) to determine the object's velocity v_P at Point P, which in Fig. 9.17 represents the *perigee* of the elliptical orbit. We can express the velocity v_A of the object at *apogee*, represented by Point A in Fig. 9.17, from considerations of angular-momentum conservation: $v_A = v_P(r_p/r_A)$. (See Example on p. 226.) By substituting this expression for v_A into the mechanical-energy-conservation relation,

$$GM_E m \left(\frac{1}{R_E} - \frac{1}{r_A} \right) + \frac{1}{2}mv_A^2 = GM_E m \left(\frac{1}{R_E} - \frac{1}{r_P} \right) + \frac{1}{2}mv_P^2, \qquad (9.24)$$

         (Energy at Apogee)   (Energy at Perigee)

we can determine the value of r_A in terms of r_P and v_P. If we know both r_P and r_A, we can derive the actual equation of the ellipse (9.7).

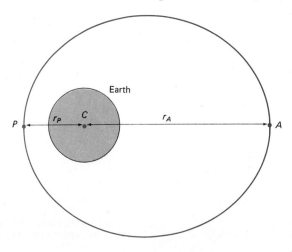

Fig. 9.17 An earth satellite moves in an elliptical path; in this case the equivalent launch velocity must be less than the velocity of escape.

We note that at perigee the satellite has a velocity v_P greater than that required by a body moving at a circular orbit of radius r_P and that at apogee the satellite has a velocity v_A smaller than that required by a body moving in a circular orbit of radius r_A. If we wish to place a satellite into a circular orbit like that required by a communications satellite, we must make v_p in Fig. 9.17 exactly that required by the centripetal force relation,

$$\frac{mv_P^2}{r_P} = \frac{GMm}{r_P^2} \quad \text{or} \quad v_P = \sqrt{\frac{GM}{r_P}}, \quad \text{(Circular Orbit)} \tag{9.25}$$

for an object moving in a circular orbit of radius r_P. A communications satellite that remains above a fixed point on the earth's surface moves in a circular orbit like that described by (9.25). (See problem 15.)

9.7 GRAVITATIONAL FIELDS

We now return to the picture of Sir Isaac Newton watching the apple and the moon both having acceleration toward the earth as a result of gravitational attraction. Newton was able to account for these effects and many others in terms of his principle of Universal Gravitation. This principle as the basis of a theory is scientifically acceptable; it gives straightforward explanation of previously known facts and serves as a basis of successful prediction. However, Newton was still left with questions as to just *how* the earth exerts forces on the moon and the apple!

As there is no visible material forming a mechanical link between the earth and the moon or even between the earth and the apple, he was puzzled as to *how* gravitational interactions take place. Fortunately, Newton in developing his system of mechanics did not become bogged down in speculations as to the nature of gravitational interactions. However, despite the success of Newton's Principle of Universal Gravitation as a basis for explanation and prediction, the question of a deeper understanding of how gravitational interactions occur cannot be totally ignored. It has long been recognized that there are two possible explanations of gravitational forces.

One of these is called *action at a distance*. This involves an assumption that through the vacuum of interplanetary and interstellar space gravitational forces act *instantaneously*. In other words, the action and reaction involved in our statement of Newton's Third Principle occur at the same instant when, for example, the sun exerts a force on the distant planet Pluto. This means that gravitational forces are transmitted at infinite speed. Although in Newton's time there was no reason to reject this as a possibility, modern relativity theory indicates that no speed of transmission of forces can be greater than the speed of light. Because, in our example, several hours are required for light to travel from the sun to Pluto, we recognize at once that *action-at-a-distance* explanations lead us into grave difficulties.

An alternative explanation of gravitational forces is that a body like the earth "does something" to the space in its vicinity. The earth itself causes alteration of space; the altered space, in turn, acts on the apple and the moon. The alteration in the space around the earth is called the earth's *gravitational field*. The gravitational field thus acts as an intermediary or "middle man" in the transmission of gravitational forces. As finite time may be required for the transmission of a force by the gravitational field, we no longer have the embarassment of infinite speeds of transmission of gravitational forces. We do, however, have to accept some modification of the Third Principle. In an interaction between the earth and the moon, for example, the "action" experienced by the earth "now" reflects the condition of the moon at least 1.3 s earlier, and the corresponding reaction experienced by the moon will not be noted until at least 1.3 s later, where 1.3 s is the time required for light to travel between the earth and the moon.

The real need for the concepts of force fields was not recognized until the 19th century when Michael Faraday (1791–1867) and James Clerk Maxwell (1831–1879) employed them in their interpretation of electric and magnetic forces. Electric and magnetic fields are *necessary* to an interpretation of the transmission of light itself. Because gravitational fields are in certain ways easier to visualize than electric and magnetic fields, we shall at this point give a brief discussion of gravitational fields. This will provide a useful foundation for later discussion of electric and magnetic fields.

Any point in space can be characterized by a gravitational vector $\mathscr{G}$ that can be determined by placing a small *test body* of known mass m at the point and measuring the resultant gravitational force $\mathbf{F}_G$ exerted on the test body as in Fig. 9.18.

The gravitational intensity $\mathscr{G}$ is defined as the ratio of the gravitational force acting on a test body to the mass of the test body.

$$\mathscr{G} = \mathbf{F}_G/m. \left\{ \begin{array}{l} \mathscr{G} \text{ in N/kg} \\ F_G \text{ in N} \\ m \text{ in kg} \end{array} \right\} \quad \textit{(Gravitational Intensity)} \qquad (9.26)$$

It is important that the test body be sufficiently small in mass that it does not exert significant forces on the masses that are the sources of $\mathscr{G}$ and therefore by its very presence possibly alter the field that is being determined. Various names are applied to the gravitational vector $\mathscr{G}$: the gravitational *field strength*, the gravitational *intensity*, or merely the gravitational *vector*. As indicated in (9.26), $\mathscr{G}$ is measured N/kg; however, because 1 N = 1 kg·m/s², we recognize that $\mathscr{G}$ also represents the acceleration that a body of mass m at the point in space would experience as a result of gravitational forces. If we know the value of $\mathscr{G}$ at all points in a given region of space, we have a complete description of the gravitational field in that region.

From our earlier discussion of the gravitational forces exerted by the earth, we can easily compute $\mathscr{G}$ associated with the earth. We know that the earth exerts a force of attraction

$$\mathbf{F}_G = \frac{-GM_E m}{r^2} \hat{\mathbf{r}} \qquad (9.27)$$

on a body of mass m at a distance r from the center of the earth with unit vector $\hat{\mathbf{r}}$

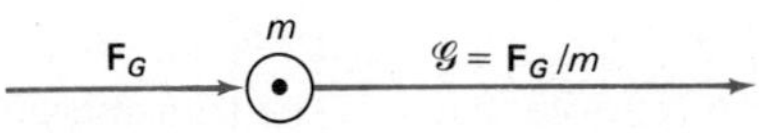

Fig. 9.18 The gravitational intensity vector $\mathscr{G} = \mathbf{F}_G/m$.

directed radially outward. By definition (9.26), we can find the gravitational intensity $\mathcal{G}$ of the *earth's field* by the relation

$$\mathcal{G} = \mathbf{F}_G/m = -\frac{GM_E}{r^2}\,\hat{\mathbf{r}}.\qquad(9.28)$$

The earth's gravitational field can be represented as illustrated in Fig. 9.19, which shows a central cross section of the earth along with $\mathcal{G}$ vectors at various points in the same plane. The corresponding situation in three dimensions involves $\mathcal{G}$ vectors pointing toward the center of the sphere representing the earth. We note that the magnitude of $\mathcal{G}$ at any point in the figure is inversely proportional to the square of the distance between the point and the center of the earth.

It is sometimes useful to visualize a gravitational field in terms of directed *gravitational lines* that are everywhere tangent to $\mathcal{G}$. Some of these lines are shown in Fig. 9.19; they begin at $r = \infty$ where $\mathcal{G} = 0$ and go inward parallel to $\mathcal{G}$ at every point.

We show the gravitational lines in Fig. 9.19 ending at the center of the earth, but we have not yet shown how to determine $\mathcal{G}$ at points below the earth's surface. Consider the force $\mathbf{F}_G$ exerted by the earth on a test body as we lower it down a long well toward the earth's center. When the test body is at the very center C of the earth, $\mathbf{F}_G$ is obviously zero because the test body is subject to equal gravitational forces in all directions, and the resultant force on it is zero. We have asserted that the gravitational force exerted on a particle outside a spherically symmetric distribution of mass is equal to that produced if all the mass of the sphere were located at the center of the sphere. Therefore, a particle on the dotted circle of radius $r < R_E$ in Fig. 9.20 experiences a gravitational force due to the mass *inside* a sphere of volume $\tfrac{4}{3}\pi r^3$ that is the same as if all this mass were at the center of the sphere. We now assert that the resultant force on this particle due to the mass *outside* the dotted circle of radius r is zero. Neither of these assertions is trivial; they depend on (9.5) involving exactly the inverse of the square of the distance between the particles.

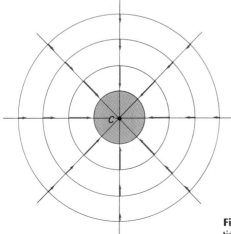

Fig. 9.19 The gravitational field of the earth. Gravitational lines are everywhere parallel to $\mathcal{G}$.

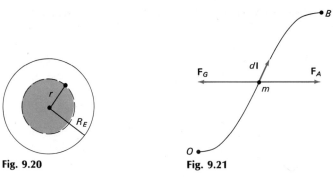

Fig. 9.20   Fig. 9.21

We shall present the basis for these assertions in Chapter 23 in connection with a similar result for electric fields. For a body in which the density depends only on r, F_G increases from zero at the center of the object to a maximum at the surface; $\mathscr{G} = F_G/m$ varies in the same manner inside the sphere. Therefore, we are justified in drawing gravitational lines in Fig. 19 that end at C. Note that the gravitational lines begin at points where $\mathscr{G} = 0$ at $r = \infty$ and end at a point where $\mathscr{G} = 0$ at C. It is possible to extend the definition of gravitational lines so that they represent the magnitude as well as the direction of $\mathscr{G}$; we consider this in Chapter 23.

Example. Show that for a sphere of uniform density $\mathscr{G}$ is directly proportional to r inside the sphere.

Consider a sphere like the one shown in Fig. 9.20; the gravitational intensity $\mathscr{G} = \mathbf{F}_G/m$ at a point on the dotted circle defining the small sphere depends only on the total mass $M = \tfrac{4}{3}\pi r^3 \rho$ *inside* the dotted sphere. Thus,

$$\mathscr{G} = \mathbf{F}_G/m = -(GM/r^2)\hat{\mathbf{r}} = -\tfrac{4}{3}(G\rho\pi r^3/r^2)\hat{\mathbf{r}} = -\tfrac{4}{3}G\pi\rho r\hat{\mathbf{r}}.$$

Thus, $\mathscr{G}$ is directed inward toward the sphere's center, increases linearly with r, and reaches a maximum at $r = R$.

We note that our calculations of $\mathscr{G}$ in the vicinity of the earth actually represent only the *gravitational field of the earth,* which is regarded as the *source* of the field. Although the value of $\mathscr{G}$ given in (9.28) is useful in considering motions of bodies near the earth, we must recognize that (9.28) gives only that part of $\mathscr{G}$ due to the earth; the actual value of $\mathscr{G}$ at points even in the near vicinity of the earth is the resultant $\mathscr{G}$ and should include not only on the earth's field but also fields produced by the sun, the moon, Jupiter, the other planets, and the stars, which also act as *sources.*

Another property of a gravitational field is a scalar quantity U called *gravitational potential,* which is a shortened term for "gravitational potential energy per unit mass." We can understand the meaning of this quantity by first defining the difference in potential between two points:

The DIFFERENCE IN GRAVITATIONAL POTENTIAL between two points is equal to the work done against gravitational forces in moving a test body of known mass from the first point to the second divided by the mass of the test body.

We recall that a test body has a very small mass so that it does not exert significant forces on the sources of $\mathscr{G}$ and thereby possibly alter the field. Thus, in Fig. 9.21, the difference in gravitational potential $U_B - U_O$ is given by the expression

$$U_B - U_O = \frac{\text{Work}_{O \to B}}{m} = \frac{\int_O^B \mathbf{F}_A \cdot d\mathbf{l}}{m} = \frac{-\int_O^B \mathbf{F}_G \cdot d\mathbf{l}}{m} = -\int_O^B \mathscr{G} \cdot d\mathbf{l}, \quad (9.29)$$

where $\mathbf{F}_A = -\mathbf{F}_G$ is the force *we* must apply to the test body of mass m. We note that the line integral $\int_O^B \mathbf{F}_A \cdot d\mathbf{l}$, in accord with our discussions in Sec. 5, is merely the difference between the potential energy of the test body E_{PB} at Point B and its potential energy E_{PO} at Point O. Therefore,

$$U_B - U_O = \frac{E_{PB} - E_{PO}}{m}. \quad (9.30)$$

Because E_P is always measured with respect to some arbitrary reference level, it is possible to define *the potential U* at any point relative to the arbitrary reference level. For example, we can easily use (9.20) together with (9.30) to obtain an expression for U if we remember that we have measured E_P in (9.20) relative to the earth's surface. Thus for the earth's gravitational field we can write

$$U = GM_E\left(\frac{1}{R_E} - \frac{1}{r}\right), \quad \begin{cases} U \text{ in J/kg} \\ M \text{ in kg} \\ r \text{ in m} \\ G \text{ in N·m}^2/\text{kg}^2 \end{cases} \left. \begin{array}{l} \textit{(Gravitational} \\ \textit{Potential of} \\ \textit{the Earth)} \end{array} \right\} \quad (9.31)$$

with $U = 0$ at $r = R_E$. In any statement of potential, the arbitrary reference level must be stated. On the basis of the last term in (9.29), we note that in general the expression for gravitational potential becomes

$$U_P = -\int_{\text{Ref}}^P \mathscr{G} \cdot d\mathbf{l}, \quad [\textit{Potential (General)}] \quad (9.31')$$

where the line integral is taken over a path from the reference level to the Point P at which U is to be evaluated.

From (9.31') it follows that $dU = -\mathscr{G} \cdot d\mathbf{l}$. In a case like (9.28) for the earth in which $\mathscr{G}$ has only a radial component we can write $dU = -\mathscr{G}_r dr$, whence $\mathscr{G}_r = -dU/dr$, or

$$\mathscr{G} = -(dU/dr)\hat{\mathbf{r}}, \quad (9.32)$$

where $\hat{\mathbf{r}}$ is a unit vector directed radially outward. If we have an expression for U

in terms of the variables x, y, z in a Cartesian coordinate system, the generalization of (9.32) turns out to be

$$\mathscr{G} = -[\mathbf{i}(\partial U/\partial x) + \mathbf{j}(\partial U/\partial y) + \mathbf{k}(\partial U/\partial z)],*$$

where $\mathbf{i}$, $\mathbf{j}$, and $\mathbf{k}$ are unit vectors along the X, Y, and Z axes, respectively.

Example.   Use (9.32) or a related expression to find the value of $\mathscr{G}$ near the earth's surface and at points well outside the earth's surface.

Near the earth's surface $E_P = mgh$ and $U = E_P/m = gh$. The relation applicable is $\mathscr{G} = -(dU/dh)\hat{\mathbf{h}} = -g\hat{\mathbf{h}}$, where $\hat{\mathbf{h}}$ is a unit vector pointing vertically upward.

At points well outside the earth, we start with the value of U given in (9.31). We note that U is the sum of a constant GM_E/R_E and a term $-GM_E/r$ that depends on r. The derivative of the constant is zero, so application of (9.32) yields

$$\mathscr{G} = -\hat{\mathbf{r}} \, d/dr \, (-GM_E/r) = -(GM_E/r^2)\hat{\mathbf{r}},$$

where $\hat{\mathbf{r}}$ is a unit vector directed radially outward. Happily, this value of $\mathscr{G}$ agrees with our original expression in (9.28)!

QUESTIONS

1. The philosopher William of Occam (c. 1285–c. 1349) proposed the following test, known as "Occam's Razor" for physical theories: "If two theories account equally well for the same phenomena, the simpler theory is to be preferred." Apply Occam's Razor to the Ptolemaic geocentric theory and the Copernican heliocentric theory of planetary motion. What basis might one use for deciding which of two theories is the simpler?

2. Give two reasons for the fact that a 1-kg body weighs slightly more at the north and south poles than at the equator.

3. On the basis of (9.5′) the earth exerts a larger force on a 10-kg body than on a 5-kg body. Why does the 10-kg body not have a greater acceleration in free fall?

4. How does the gravitational force on an astronaut vary as a journey from the earth to the moon is made? How does the astronaut's weight as measured by a set of "spring scales" inside the space craft vary during the journey from the earth to the moon?

5. How can you determine the mass of the moon?

6. What is the zero-level of potential energy in the simple expression $E_P = mgh$? in the expression given in (9.20)?

7. Although the zero-level of potential energy assumed in (9.20) is convenient for use in describing the launching of rockets from the earth's surface, there are situations in astronomy where it is more convenient to set $E_P = 0$ at infinite distance from the earth. With

---

* The symbol $\partial U/\partial x$ represents a so-called partial derivative which is used to denote a derivative with respect to x in which y and z are treated as constant. The symbols $\partial U/\partial y$ and $\partial U/\partial z$ have similar meanings. This is discussed in the Appendix.

$E_P = 0$ at $R = \infty$, how would the computation of (9.19) be changed? Equation (9.20) is replaced by $E_P = -GM_Em/r$. (See Problem 23.) Discuss the meaning of the minus sign in this equation; what is the significance of negative potential energy?

8. Is it possible to place an earth satellite in a stable orbit in a plane that does not include the center of mass of the earth?

9. Although we think of the moon as moving in an orbit around the earth, the center of mass of the earth and the center of mass of the moon actually revolve around the center of mass C of the earth–moon system. How would you determine the distance of C from the center of the earth?

10. The gravitational force exerted on the moon by the sun is larger than the gravitational force exerted on the moon by the earth. Why does the moon not escape from the earth? Using your answer to Question 9, make a qualitative drawing of the moon's path around the sun.

11. The magnitude of the gravitational force exerted on the earth by the sun is much greater than the gravitational force exerted on the earth by the moon. Why are the tidal effects of the moon greater than those of the sun?

12. Tidal motion results in the dissipation of mechanical energy as a result of frictional processes. What is the effect of this mechanical energy dissipation on the total angular momentum of the earth–moon system? Discuss possible effects on the motions of the earth and moon.

13. The velocity of escape from the earth (19.22) is 11.2 km/s. If an object were fired with this muzzle velocity from the barrel of a giant cannon located at the earth's surface, would the object actually escape from the earth?

14. After they lose energy and descend to lower orbits, earth satellites usually burn up in the atmosphere before they reach the earth's surface. In view of this fact, why don't they burn up in the atmosphere when they are launched initially upward from the earth's surface?

15. Show that the gravitational field strength $\mathscr{G}$ can be expressed in m/s² as well as in N/kg. At what point on a line drawn radially outward from the center of the earth to infinite distance does $\mathscr{G}$ have its maximum value? Where along this line does $\mathscr{G}$ have its minimum value?

16. Show that the relation $\mathscr{G} = -(dU/dr)\hat{r}$ given in (9.32) holds regardless of the zero-level chosen in obtaining the expression for the gravitational potential U.

PROBLEMS

In solving these problems be sure to use inertial coordinate systems. Use the astronomical data given in the following table.

Object	Mass (kg)	Mean radius (10⁶ m)
Earth	5.976×10^{24}	6.371
Jupiter	1.90×10^{27}	69.9
Moon	7.350×10^{22}	1.738
Sun	1.989×10^{30}	696.0

1. The radius of the earth's orbit about the sun is approximately 150 million kilometers. Compute the value of the gravitational force exerted on the earth by the sun. What is the value of the earth's centripetal acceleration in its nearly circular orbit around the sun?

2. On the basis of the results of Problem 1, compute the orbital speed of the earth in its motion around the sun and the time required for a complete revolution of the earth around the sun.

3. The density of gold is 1.93×10^4 kg/m³. Compute the force of mutual attraction between two solid gold spheres each 10 cm in diameter when the surfaces of the two spheres are in contact.

4. Generalize the results of Problem 3 to show that the gravitational force of attraction between two uniform spheres of the same size in contact is directly proportional to the densities of the materials involved and to the fourth power of the common radius of the spheres. What is the expression for the force if the two spheres are not the same size?

5. At a time when the moon and the earth are 400,000 km apart, at what distance from the earth on a line between the earth and the moon would the net gravitational force on an object of mass m be zero? If a body were in this position, would it be in stable equilibrium? Explain your reasoning.

6. Repeat the preceding problem for a gravitational system consisting of the earth and the sun. Use the data given in Problem 1.

7. Some prophets of doom predict dire events on the earth supposedly to be produced by gravitational forces exerted by the other planets. The largest of the planets is Juipter with a mass of about 1.9×10^{27} kg; at closest approach the distance between Jupiter and the earth is about 6.6×10^8 km. What gravitational force is exerted on the earth by Jupiter at closest approach? Compare the gravitational force exerted on the earth by Jupiter with the gravitational forces exerted on the earth by the sun and by the moon.

8. On the basis of (9.12) and (9.13) along with a similar relation for Jupiter, obtain the ratios of the tidal forces exerted on the earth by these three bodies. Consider Jupiter at its distance of closest approach to the earth as given in Problem 7. Use the mean earth–moon distance of 3.84×10^8 m and the earth–sun distance given in Problem 1. What would be the configuration of the sun, earth, moon, and Jupiter for which the net tidal force would be greatest?

9. What is the gravitational acceleration of free fall at the surface of the moon? at the surface of Jupiter? What is the weight of an 80-kg man at the surface of the earth, at the surface of the moon, and at the surface of Jupiter?

10. What is the gravitational potential energy of a 2-kg body at a height of 10 m above the surface of the earth? above the surface of the moon? above the surface of Jupiter?

11. What is the value of the acceleration of a 2-kg object experiencing free fall at a height of 6370 km above the earth's surface? Relative to objects at ground level, what is the potential energy of the 2-kg object at this height?

12. If the 2-kg object in Problem 11 were moving in a circular orbit about the earth, what would be its orbital speed? What would be its kinetic energy?

13. What is the minimum work required to remove a 10-kg object from the earth's surface in such a way that it never returns? If this is done by rocket propulsion, what is the minimum speed the object must have as it leaves the earth's atmosphere?

14. Compute the velocity of escape of objects

from the moon, the sun, and the planet Jupiter.

15. A communications satellite moves in a circular orbit above the earth's equator in such a way as to remain permanently above a given spot on the earth's surface. Find the radius of the orbit and the orbital speed of the satellite.

16. One of the early earth satellites had a height of 175 km *above the earth's surface* at perigee and a speed of 8300 m/s at perigee. The height of the satellite *above the earth's surface* at apogee was 2570 km. What was the speed of this satellite at apogee? What was the eccentricity of the satellite's orbit? Write an expression for the ellipse describing the orbit. Show that the total mechanical energies at perigee and apogee were the same.

17. If we approximate the earth by a uniform sphere of constant density and with radius R_E, what is the value of the gravitational intensity $\mathscr{G}$ at the following distances from the center of the earth: 0, $0.2R_E$, $0.4R_E$, $0.6R_E$, $0.8R_E$, R_E, $1.4R_E$, $1.8R_E$, $4R_E$, and ∞? Plot a curve showing the magnitude of $\mathscr{G}$ as a function of radial distance from the center of the earth.

18. At what height *above the earth's surface* does the gravitational intensity $\mathscr{G}$ have the same magnitude as at a point $R_E/2$ *below the earth's surface?* Use the assumptions of Problem 17.

*19. On the basis of the assumptions stated in Problem 17 obtain an expression for the gravitational potential U of the earth as a function of the distance from the center of the earth r relative to $U = 0$ at R_E. The general expression $U_P = -\int_{Ref}^{P} \mathscr{G} \cdot d\mathbf{l}$ can be used. The value of $\mathscr{G}$ for r in the range $R_E \leq r < \infty$ is given in (9.28); in the range $0 < r \leq R_E$ the value of $\mathscr{G}$ is given by $-\frac{4}{3}G\pi\rho r\hat{r}$, where $\rho = M_E/\frac{4}{3}\pi R_E^3$. Two

separate integrals should therefore be used, one for $r < R_E$ and a second for $r > R_E$. The final expressions for U should involve G, M_E, and R_E in addition to r. Plot a curve showing U as a function of r. Plot a second curve showing U as a function of r relative to the reference level $U = 0$ at $r = \infty$.

20. To what height above the earth's surface could we raise an object by doing the same amount of work as is required to raise the object from a distance $R_E/2$ below the earth's surface to the earth's surface? Use the assumptions of Problem 17 and the results obtained in Problem 19.

21. In our discussion of the launching of rockets and spacecraft from the earth's surface we have employed an approximately inertial frame of reference with its origin at the center of the earth. As indicated in (9.22) the velocity of escape in such a system is 11.2 km/s. However, launching platforms are attached to the surface of the rotating earth and are therefore not at rest in the inertial frame employed. If the rocket is launched from the earth's surface at the equator, what is the escape velocity relative to the launching platform if the rocket is headed (a) due east and (b) due west? What is the escape velocity relative to the launching platform if the rocket is launched from the north pole? Neglect air resistance.

22. If the earth were a perfect sphere with a radius of 6400 km and mass 5.976×10^{24} kg, what would be the weight of an 80-kg man as measured by a carefully calibrated spring scale at sea level (a) at the equator and (b) at the north pole? What will be the percentage change in the man's weight as he moves along the earth's surface from one location to the other?

23. Because we were considering the launch of objects from the earth's surface, we selected the surface of the earth as the arbitrary reference level for measuring potential energies and therefore the point at which the

gravitational potential U in (9.31) is zero. In many situations, it is more desirable to set the potential at infinite distance equal to zero; i.e., $U_\infty = 0$. Show that in this case the expression for the gravitational potential of the earth becomes

$$U = -\frac{1}{r}\, GM_E, \text{ with } U_\infty = 0.$$

Show that the gravitational intensity $\mathscr{G}$ computed from this expression by use of (9.32) is the same as that obtained from (9.31). Show also that the total work done in removing an object from the earth's surface to infinite distance as obtained from this expression for U is the same as that obtained in (9.21).

24. The total energy E of a particle is the sum of its kinetic energy E_K and its potential energy E_P. Show on the basis of the expression for U given in Problem 23 that a particle having positive total energy E can escape from the earth and still have kinetic energy at infinite distance. Show that a particle with total energy $E = 0$ can escape from the earth and come to rest at infinite distance. Show that a particle with negative total energy E is trapped by the gravitational field of the earth and cannot escape.

25. Using the convention $U_\infty = 0$ as discussed in Problem 23, find an expression for U at the center of the earth. Make a drawing of U as a function of r from $r = 0$ at the center of the earth to $r = \infty$. Show graphically on the basis of this diagram that a particle for which the total energy $E = E_P + E_K$ is positive can escape from the earth and that a particle for which the total energy $E = E_P + E_K$ is negative is trapped permanently by the earth's gravitational field.

26. If one were to launch a projectile from a point for which the radial distance from

the center of the earth is $r = 4R_E$, where R_E is the earth's radius, what would be the minimum launch speed required for permanent escape from the earth?

27. Consider the tidal forces shown schematically in Fig. 9.11. Let $\mathscr{G}_M$ be the gravitational intensity of the moon's gravitational field as given by an equation analogous to (9.28). Show that in good approximation the difference $\mathscr{G}_{MA} - \mathscr{G}_{MB}$ in the gravitational intensities at points A and B is given by $\mathscr{G}_{MA} - \mathscr{G}_{MB} = (d\mathscr{G}/dr)_C\, 2\, R_E\hat{\mathbf{r}}$.

28. In order to gain further insight into the nature of tidal motion, consider a nonrotating, water-covered earth moving in a circular orbit of radius r around the sun and use an approximately inertial frame with its origin at the center of the sun. Show that the center C of the earth has an angular velocity $\omega = v/r$ in its motion around the sun, where v is the speed of the earth in its orbit; show that $v = \sqrt{a_C r} = \sqrt{GM_S/r}$, where a_C is the centripetal acceleration of the earth in its orbital motion and M_S is the mass of the sun. Now consider three independent particles A, B, and C in the figure; show that the velocities of these three particles in circular orbits around the sun would be different. Let C be a particle of mass M_E at the center of the earth and let A and B be particles in the water envelope covering the earth. What gravitational forces must the earth exert on particles A and B to keep them moving in circular orbits at the same orbital angular velocity as that of the solid portion of the earth?

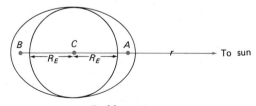

Problem 28

CHAPTER 10

Elasticity and Strength of Materials

Much of our attention in earlier chapters has been devoted to a study of rigid bodies, which undergo no change in size or shape when external forces are applied to them. Real bodies are, of course, not rigid bodies. Even "iron bars will bend and break" if we try to use them improperly when *London Bridge is Falling Down!* All bodies experience distortions of one kind or another when external forces are applied. However, if its distortion is not too great, a body may regain its original size and shape once the distorting forces cease to act; such a body is called an *elastic body.* The behavior of elastic bodies is described in good approximation by a very simple relation called *Hooke's Law,* which was formulated by Robert Hooke (1635–1703), a somewhat older contemporary of Newton. Hooke's Law can be generalized in such a way as to provide a description of the *elastic properties of materials* in terms of so-called *elastic constants;* once these properties are known, the elastic behavior of *bodies* can be computed.

If the distortion of a body becomes too great, the body never regains its original size and shape but acquires a "permanent set" or "permanent distortion." When work is done in producing the permanent distortion of a body, mechanical energy is dissipated; on the other hand, the work done in the *elastic* distortion of a body is stored in the form of elastic potential energy. If the distorting forces applied to a body are sufficiently large, the body will, of course, break. The onset of the permanent distortion of a material is determined by a property of the material known as its *elastic limit.* The actual rupture or breaking strength of a material is known as its *ultimate strength.*

We note that the elastic properties of a solid material are, in the final analysis, determined by the interatomic forces between the atoms of which the solid is composed. In principle, it should thus be possible to calculate the elastic constants of a material in terms of atomic properties; unfortunately, *solid-state physics* has attained this goal only for a few simple, pure materials. The elastic constants of materials tabulated in this chapter and those in the tables given in engineering handbooks are typical values based on numerous measurements. The elastic properties of a particular sample depend in an important way on the sample's history; for example, the properties of a sample of sheet steel depend on not only the steel's composition but also the heat treatment and the rolling processes involved in the fabrication of the sheet.

The subjects of elasticity and strength of materials are of special importance to mechanical, architectural, and metallurgical engineers. The values of the ultimate strengths of materials listed in most handbooks are typical values for materials at ordinary room temperatures. Increase in temperature usually reduces the ultimate strength of a metal. An engineer designing things like "pressure vessels" such as boilers for use at elevated temperatures usually consults the *insurance underwriter's handbooks* prepared by mechanical engineers; in these books empirical estimates of temperature effects are tabulated.

10.1 HOOKE'S LAW

We have all observed the bending of a diving board when a heavy man stands at the end before making his dive; after the dive has been completed the board regains its original shape. Similarly, a helical spring hanging vertically from a point of support at its upper end increases in length when a small load is attached to its lower end; when the load is removed, the spring regains its original length. These observed effects are those typical of *elastic bodies*. The alteration in the configuration of a body when forces are applied is called a *deformation* or *distortion*.

The recovery of the original configuration after distortion is nearly complete for bodies composed of many materials, which are regarded as *elastic materials,* provided the distorting forces are not too great. If the distorting forces *are* too great, the body fails to recover its original configuration and acquires a *permanent set* or *permanent deformation*. We can say in the case of permanent distortion that the body's *elastic limit* has been exceeded. For a body of a given shape and size, the elastic limit depends on the material; later we shall show how the elastic limit of a material is precisely defined. Materials for which the elastic limit is large are highly elastic materials; steel is a highly elastic material, because relatively enormous forces are required to produce permanent distortion of bodies composed of steel. Materials with extremely small elastic limits are called *inelastic materials;* dough, putty, and lead solder are examples of inelastic materials, because bodies composed of these materials can be permanently distorted by relatively small forces.

In 1678 the English physicist Robert Hooke reported an important empirical relationship:

HOOKE'S LAW: The deformation of an elastic body is directly proportional to the magnitude of the applied distorting force, provided the elastic limit is not closely approached or exceeded.

This law, which is based on direct experimental measurements, is valid for bodies composed of metals and many common structural materials. It is frequently not applicable to bodies composed of plastic materials. We refer to this relation as a

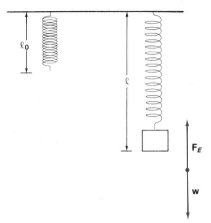

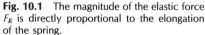

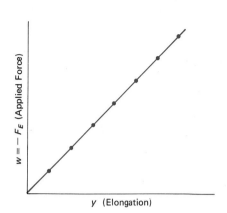

Fig. 10.1 The magnitude of the elastic force F_E is directly proportional to the elongation of the spring.

Fig. 10.2 Hooke's law for a spring.

law because of its limited range of application; however, in generalized form, Hooke's Law constitutes the basis of modern theories of elasticity.

The validity of Hooke's Law in a simple case can be verified by adding laboratory weights to a suspended helical spring constructed from an elastic material as suggested in Fig. 10.1. Before weights are added the spring has length l_0. After an object of weight w has been added, the length of the spring has increased to l, giving the lower end of the spring a downward displacement $y = l - l_0$; this downward displacement y is the *elongation* of the spring. Note that the spring exerts an upward force **F** on the suspended weight; the upward force **F** is called the *elastic force*. The elastic force **F** is equal in magnitude and opposite in direction to the weight **w** of the object attached to the spring: **F** = −**w**.

By adding weights and noting the resulting elongations of the spring, we find that over a considerable range the elongation of the spring is directly proportional to the applied force, as indicated in Fig. 10.2. This result confirms the validity of Hooke's Law as applied to the spring:

$$w = ky \quad \text{or} \quad F = -ky, \tag{10.1}$$

where the proportionality constant k is called the force constant of the spring.

The FORCE CONSTANT of a spring is the applied distorting force per unit elongation.

The force constant k is just the slope of the curve in Fig. 10.2; it is measured in newtons per meter: N/m. The minus sign in (10.1) indicates that a downward displacement of the end of the spring is associated with an upward elastic force exerted by the spring. Experiment shows that Eq. (10.1) also describes compression of the spring, for which y is negative, in a range where adjacent coils do not come into contact.

Hooke's Law can also be verified quite easily for the situation shown in Fig. 10.3, which involves the twist or torsional deformation of an elastic wire or rod. Figure

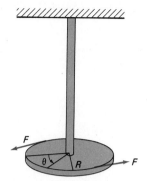

Fig. 10.3 The angular distortion is directly proportional to the applied torque.

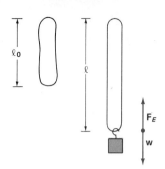

Fig. 10.4 Stretch of a rubber band.

10.3 shows a wire hanging vertically from a fixed point of support with a circular disk of radius R attached axially to the lower end of the wire. By applying equal but opposite external forces of magnitude F to the disk as shown in the figure, we can produce an applied torque $\tau_A = 2FR$ that tends to twist the wire. Experiment shows that the angular deformation θ is directly proportional to the applied torque. We can thus write

$$\tau_A = C\theta \quad \text{or} \quad \tau = -C\theta, \tag{10.2}$$

where τ is the elastic reaction torque exerted by the wire. The proportionality constant C in (2) is called *torsion constant* of the wire.

The TORSION CONSTANT of a wire or rod is the applied torque per radian of twist.

The torsion constant is measured in newton-meters per radian: $N \cdot m/rad$.

As an example of a case in which Hooke's Law does *not* apply, consider the stretch of a rubber band as suggested in Fig. 10.4. The rubber band is hooked over a nail that serves as a point of support; its initial length is l_0. If we attach laboratory weights to the lower end of the rubber band, the length of the rubber band increases to l. The elongation or deformation of the band thus has a magnitude $y = l - l_0$. However, experiment shows that the elongation of the band is *not* proportional to the applied force, which is equal to the weight w of the suspended object. Instead, we obtain a curve like that shown in Fig. 10.5. In the initial stage ① of deformation, the applied force produces little elongation of the rubber band. In stage ②, which represents most of the process of total elongation, little increase in the applied force is required to produce a large increase in elongation; thus, in stage ② "the band is easy to stretch." In the final stage ③, little additional stretch accompanies a large increase in distorting force; in stage ③, "the band is hard to stretch." We can easily verify qualitatively the existence of regions ② and ③ by merely stretching a rubber band using our hands.

The behavior of rubber is characteristic of one class of *plastic materials* to which Hooke's Law does not apply at all.

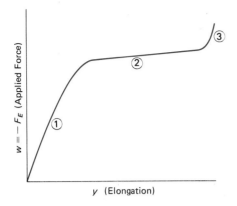

Fig. 10.5 Objects made of rubber do not obey Hooke's law.

10.2 ELASTIC POTENTIAL ENERGY

We are now in a position to compute the elastic potential energy associated with elastically distorted bodies. We recall that we can determine the potential energy of a body by finding the work required to give the body its position or configuration. In the case of gravitational potential energy, the work is done against gravitational forces as we raise the body from some arbitrary reference level to some other position in a gravitational field. In the case of elastic potential energy, we must do work against *elastic forces* in changing the body from one configuration to another. We shall set our arbitrary reference configuration as that of the undistorted body and shall set the potential energy of the undistorted body equal to zero.

In the case of the helical spring in Fig. 10.1 we must do work $dW = w\,dy$ in increasing the elongation by dy. But from (10.1) $w = ky$ so that $dW = ky\,dy$. The potential energy of the spring with some total elongation Y is then given by the integral

$$E_P = \int_0^Y ky\,dy = \tfrac{1}{2}\,kY^2; \quad \textit{(Stretched or Compressed Spring)} \qquad (10.3)$$

the limits of the integral are set at $y = 0$, where we have arbitrarily set $E_P = 0$, and at the total elongation Y. We see that the potential energy of the spring in Fig. 10.1 is proportional to the *square* of the spring's elongation. Because Y is squared, we see that we get the same value of E_P for a compression or negative elongation $-Y$; we could also store potential energy in the spring by compressing the spring instead of stretching it as suggested in Fig. 10.1. It is, therefore, better to summarize (10.3) by saying that the *potential energy of a spring is proportional to the square of its distortion*. We note that the potential energy (10.3) is also proportional to the force constant k of the spring.

By similar reasoning, it is easy to see that the elastic potential energy of a twisted wire or rod like the one in Fig. 10.3 is given by the integral

$$E_P = \int_0^\Theta \tau_A\,d\theta = \int_0^\Theta C\theta\,d\theta = \tfrac{1}{2}C\Theta^2, \quad \textit{(Twisted Wire or Rod)} \qquad (10.4)$$

where Θ is the magnitude of the wire's or rod's final angular distortion. Again we see that the elastic potential energy is proportional to the square of the distortion. In the case of the rod, we note that E_P is also directly proportional to the torsion constant C. Thus, for a given angular distortion, E_P would be greater for a thick rod than for a fine wire of the same material.

The relation between E_P and the square of the distortion given in (10.3) and (10.4) is generally characteristic of all bodies obeying Hooke's Law. However, in using energy relations like those given in (10.3) and (10.4) we must realize that distorted bodies not obeying Hooke's Law also possess potential energy. Every school child knows that a stretched rubber band like the one in Fig. 10.4 possesses potential energy that can be used in launching projectiles! To find the potential energy of a stretched rubber band we would have to determine the work done $W = \int_0^Y w\, dy$ in stretching the band by methods of numerical integration; this integral is just the area under the curve in Fig. 10.5.

10.3   GENERALIZATION OF HOOKE'S LAW

Hooke's Law in its original form would not be of much use in modern science or engineering. In Sec. 1 we have shown how to determine elastic force constants or torsion constants for *individual bodies*. With only Hooke's original law for guidance, a design engineer would have to make experimental tests on each and every structural member before using it in a proposed design. His task in designing a large structure would be very burdensome if not impossible in any practical situation.

Fortunately, it has proved possible to generalize Hooke's Law in such a way that it can be applied to *materials*. Once the elastic constants of a given material have been determined, the elastic force constants of any body made of this material can be calculated in a straightforward manner.

If we return to (10.1), we note that the force constant of an elastic body can be expressed as the ratio of the magnitude of an elastic force to the magnitude of an elastic distortion of the body:

$$\left| \frac{\text{Force}}{\text{Distortion}} \right| = \text{Force Constant of a Body.} \tag{10.1$'$}$$

In generalizing (10.1$'$) for a material, we replace the elastic force by a quantity called *stress S,* which is defined as the magnitude of the elastic force per unit area. The generalization of the distortion in (10.1$'$) is a dimensionless quantity called *strain* σ, which is defined as the ratio of the distortion of the body to the original dimension of the body. Just as in (10.1$'$) the ratio of elastic force to distortion gives us the force constant for a *body,* the ratio of stress to strain gives an elastic constant for a *material,* which is known as the *elastic modulus* of the material:

$$\left| \frac{\text{Stress}}{\text{Strain}} \right| = \text{Elastic Modulus of a Material.} \tag{10.5}$$

We note that because strain is dimensionless, the elastic modulus of a material has the same dimensions as stress and is measured in N/m².

The definitions that we have used in setting up (10.5) may seem rather vague at this point, but they will become clearer when we apply them in considering three important cases: the change in *length* of a slender rod when forces producing longitudinal stretch or compression are applied, the change in the *volume* of a body when normal forces are applied to its surface, and the change in the *shape* of a body when distorting forces are applied. Stress, strain, and the appropriate elastic modulus will be defined in each of these cases.

10.4 LONGITUDINAL STRESS AND STRAIN: YOUNG'S MODULUS

Perhaps the simplest type of distortion that we shall discuss is the elastic stretch or compression of a slender rod. In Fig. 10.6a we show a rod with cross-sectional area A and length l_0 attached at one end to a fixed mounting clamp. If we apply a force $\mathbf{F}$ to one end of the rod as in Fig. 10.6b, the fixed clamp provides an equal but oppositely directed force to the opposite end of the rod, under the assumption that the weight of the rod itself is negligible, and the rod experiences an elongation Δl. The longitudinal strain σ of the material in the rod is defined by the expression

$$\sigma = \Delta l / l_0. \quad \textit{(Longitudinal Strain)} \qquad (10.6)$$

The strain is accompanied by internal forces between various adjacent parts of the rod. An enlarged cross-sectional drawing of a typical portion of the rod is shown in Fig. 10.6c. The material to the right of the dividing plane at point P exerts a force $\mathbf{F}$ to the right on the material to the left of point P. Under the conditions of equilibrium being considered, the material to the left of point P exerts an equal but oppositely directed force $-\mathbf{F}$ on the material to the right of point P. The rod is said to be under uniform tension F. When internal forces of this type exist in a body, the body is said to be under stress. The stress S is defined by the expression

$$S = F/A. \quad \textit{(Longitudinal Stress)} \qquad (10.7)$$

We note that the internal forces are *perpendicular* or *normal* to the cross-sectional area. Because the cross-sectional area of the rod is uniform, the value of S is constant at all points along the rod, which we say is under uniform stress.

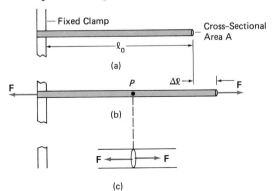

Fig. 10.6 Longitudinal stretch of a wire or slender rod.

Table 10.1.   Typical Values of Young's Modulus M_Y, Bulk Modulus M_B, and Shear Modulus M_S

Material	M_Y (10^{10} N/m²)	M_B (10^{10} N/m²)	M_S (10^{10} N/m²)
Aluminum	6.9	6.6	2.6
Brass	9.0	10	3.5
Copper	11	14	4.1
Steel	20	17	7.6
Glass	5.4	3.6	2.3
Ethyl Ether	—	0.06	—
Ethanol	—	0.11	—
Water	—	0.21	—
Mercury	—	2.8	—

According to (10.5) the ratio of stress to strain is equal to a constant called the elastic modulus of the material. In the case of longitudinal elongation, the elastic modulus is called Young's modulus* and is denoted by M_Y. Thus,

$$S/\sigma = M_Y. \quad \text{(Longitudinal Stretch or Compression)} \qquad (10.8)$$

Substituting the expressions for S and σ given by (10.6) and (10.7) into this equation, we obtain

$$(F/A)/(\Delta l/l_0) = Fl_0/\Delta l \cdot A = M_Y. \qquad (10.8')$$

Equation (10.8′) gives a valid prediction of the change in the length of a rod of initial length l_0 and cross-sectional area A when tensional forces are applied to the ends of the rod. Comparison with (10.1) shows that the force constant of the rod is given by $k = M_Y A/l_0$.

We note that all of the above discussion applies also to the compression of a slender rod. In the case of compression all the forces in Fig. 10.6 are reversed in direction and Δl represents a *decrease* in length.

Typical values of Young's modulus for a number of common materials are listed in Table 10.1.

10.5   VOLUME STRESS AND STRAIN: BULK MODULUS

Next we consider the problem of *volume elasticity*, which involves the change in the volume of a body when it is subject to compressional forces. Figure 10.7a shows a cubical body with initial volume V_0. If compressional forces of equal magnitude F are applied to all faces of the cube as in Fig. 10.7b, the volume of the cubical body is reduced to some smaller value V. In considering this figure, we must consider the normal forces applied to the faces of the body as being distributed uniformly

---

* Named for Thomas Young, English physician and experimental physicist (1773–1829).

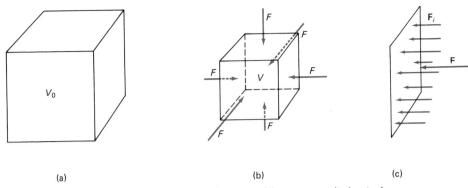

Fig. 10.7   The volume of a cube decreases when normal forces are applied to its faces.

across the faces as suggested in Fig. 10.7c so that the compression is uniform through-out the body.

   In dealing with volume elasticity, we define the stress as the ratio of the normal force F_N to the area A of the face on which it acts: $S = F_N/A$. We note that, for *uniform stress,* the stress on a noncubical body is the same when computed in terms of the normal force acting on each face: $F_1/A_1 = F_2/A_2 = F_3/A_3$, as suggested in Fig. 10.8. This idea is treated at length in Chapter 11, where the concept of pressure is developed. The volume strain σ of a body is defined as $\sigma = -\Delta V/V_0$. The minus sign is introduced because as the stress increases, the volume of the body decreases and the change in volume $\Delta V = V - V_0$ becomes more and more negative. By giving σ the above definition, we avoid negative values for the *volume* or *bulk modulus* of elasticity M_B. From (10.5) we have

$$S/\sigma = M_B. \quad \textit{(Volume Compression)} \tag{10.9}$$

Substitution of the expressions for stress S and strain σ given above into (10.9) gives

$$(F_N/A)/(-\Delta V/V_0) = M_B. \tag{10.9'}$$

Typical values of M_B for various common materials are listed in Table 10.1. Because no change in *shape* is involved in volume elastic compression, Eqs. (10.9) and (10.9') apply to liquids and gases as well as solids. We shall give detailed consideration to liquids in the following chapter and to gases in Chapter 15.

   We note that the volumetric elastic properties of a material are sometimes stated in terms of its *compressibility K.* The compressibility of a material is the reciprocal of the material's bulk modulus: $K = 1/M_B$.

10.6   SHAPE ELASTICITY: SHEAR MODULUS

   The third type of elastic distortion that we shall consider is one in which the *shape* of a body changes without any change in the *volume* of the body. The type

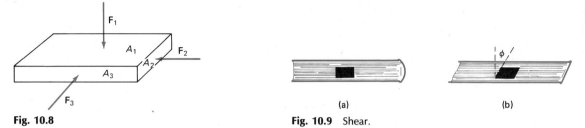

Fig. 10.8

Fig. 10.9   Shear.

of distortion involved is called a *shear* and is illustrated in Fig. 10.9. We note that the shape of the book in Fig. 10.9 has been altered without any change in the volume of the book. The rectangular element of surface area shaded in Fig. 10.9a becomes a parallelogram when shear occurs. The angle ϕ in the figure is called the *angle of shear*.

A book is an anisotropic body that is relatively inelastic to distortion of the type shown in Fig. 10.9. In order to see how a shear is produced in an isotropic elastic body, consider the unstressed rectangular body shown in Fig. 10.10a. If we apply *tangential forces* to faces ① and ② of the body as suggested in Fig. 10.10b, the body changes shape. The front face of the body changes from a rectangle to a parallelogram, but its area A_3 remains unchanged for small distortions. The shearing strain of the body is defined as the ratio x/h, where x and h are shown in the figure. Thus, the shear is given by $\tan \phi$. For a small angle of shear we have $\tan \phi \simeq \phi$ when ϕ is in radians. The angle of shear is always small in the distortion of elastic bodies, so we set the strain $\sigma = \phi$, where ϕ is measured in radians.

Shearing stress S is defined as the ratio of the *tangential force* F_T acting on a face to the area of the face: $S = F_T/A$. In order for the body in Fig. 10.10 to be in rotational equilibrium, it is necessary that $F_1/A_1 = F_2/A_2$, where F_1 and F_2 are the *tangential forces* acting on faces with areas A_1 and A_2, respectively. Therefore, we obtain the same value for S whichever of these faces we consider.

In accord with the general relation (10.5) we can write for shearing distortions

$$S/\sigma = (F_T/A)/\phi = M_S, \tag{10.10}$$

where M_S is called the *shear modulus* or the *modulus of rigidity*. Typical values of the shear modulus are listed in Table 10.1. Because liquids and gases will flow rather than undergoing shear distortion, the shear modulus is defined only for solids.

The drawings in Fig. 10.10 serve to introduce the ideas involved in shape elasticity, but they do not illustrate a good method for determining the shear modulus because there is no good way to distribute the tangential forces uniformly over the surfaces of the bodies shown. The bodies in Fig. 10.10 can, however, be regarded realistically as volume elements inside an extended body that is experiencing shearing stress.

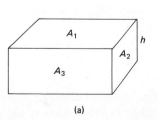

(a)

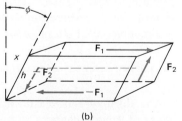

(b)   **Fig. 10.10**

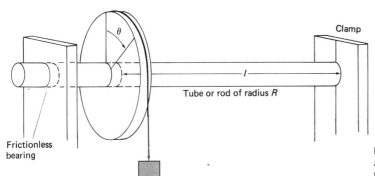

Fig. 10.11 The torsional distortion θ of a rod or thin-walled tube is directly proportional to the applied torque.

The shear modulus can be determined experimentally by use of a device also used to determine the torsion constant of a thin-walled tube or rod made of the material being investigated. A torque τ is applied to the tube or rod by attaching a known mass M to a metal belt wrapped around the rim of a wheel attached to the tube or rod as shown in Fig. 10.11. The torque applied in this way is easily determined from the familiar relation $\tau = MgR$, where R is the radius of the wheel. This torque produces an easily measured angular rotation θ of the end of the tube or rod to which the wheel is attached. The other end of the rod is held fixed. The torsion constant of the rod or tube is $C = \tau/\theta$ as defined in (10.2).

Now consider the enlarged schematic drawing of the tube of wall thickness t, length l, and radius R shown in Fig. 10.12. Part (a) of the figure shows the untwisted tube with a black rectangle painted along the outside surface of the tube. Figure 10.12b shows the tube after the torque τ has been applied to the upper end; because of the angular rotation of the upper end of the tube, the black rectangle is now a parallelogram like the one of the faces of the volume element in Fig. 10.10b. The known torque τ is transmitted along the tube across each section of the tube such as AA. Part (c) of Fig. 10.12 shows the twisted tube with the small shear angle ϕ indicated. The shearing strain is given by the relation

$$\sigma = \phi = a/l = R\theta/l, \quad (Shearing\ Strain) \qquad (10.11)$$

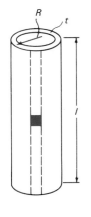

(a)

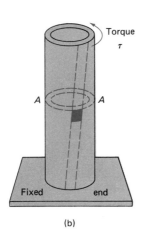

(b)

(c)

Fig. 10.12 Distortion of a thin-walled tube: $\phi = R\theta/l$.

where the displacement a is given in terms of the easily measured quantities R and θ by $a = R\theta$.

We can regard the torque τ transmitted across section AA as being due to tangential forces of magnitude $F = \tau/R$. The shearing stress S at section AA is given by the ratio of these forces F to the cross-sectional area $2\pi Rt$ of the wall. Thus,

$$S = F/2\pi Rt = \tau/2\pi R^2 t. \quad \textit{(Shearing Stress)} \qquad (10.12)$$

The ratio of stress S in (10.12) to strain σ in (10.11) gives the shear modulus M_S:

$$M_S = (\tau/2\pi R^2 t)/(R\theta/l) = \tau l/2\pi R^3 \theta t. \quad \textit{(Thin-Walled Tube)} \qquad (10.13)$$

The corresponding expression for a solid rod is given by the relation:

$$M_S = 2l\tau/\pi R^4 \theta. \quad \textit{(Solid Rod)} \qquad (10.13')$$

The derivation of the expression for a rod is left as a problem. In practice, it is usually more convenient experimentally to use a solid rod in measuring M_S for an elastic material. By use of the expression $C = \tau/\theta$ for the torsion constant, we can express (10.13) as $M_S = (l/2\pi R^3 t)C$ for the tube and (10.13') as $M_S = (2l/\pi R^4)C$ for the solid rod; thus, if we measure C for a tube or rod, we can obtain M_S in terms of our measured value of C together with the dimensions of the tube or rod.

Typical values of the shear modulus for various materials are listed in Table 10.1. We note that the shear modulus for a given material is usually smaller than the bulk modulus or Young's modulus for the same material. It is thus usually easier to change the shape of a body than to stretch or compress the body.

In this connection, we note that the force constant of a *helical spring* is determined by the torsion constant for a unit length of the wire of which it is made. Therefore, it is the shear modulus of the wire rather than its Young's modulus that is involved. As a spring elongates, the wire of which it is made does not stretch but merely *twists*. Any small section of the wire thus undergoes torsional distortion.

10.7   RELATIONSHIPS AMONG ELASTIC CONSTANTS

We have now defined three different elastic moduli in the manner summarized in Table 10.2. The processes involved in our definitions are not all independent of one another. For example, the stretching of a wire actually involves slight changes in the volume and shape of the wire as well as a change in length; therefore, volume elasticity and shape elasticity are both involved. As the length l of a wire increases, the diameter d of the wire decreases; this behavior is measured by means of a dimensionless quantity called *Poisson's ratio** ρ, which is defined as $\rho = (-\Delta d/d)/(\Delta l/l)$. Poisson's ratio is dimensionless and has a value the order of 0.3 for most metals.

Of all the elastic constants that can be defined for an isotropic elastic material, only two are independent. If two elastic constants can be accurately measured, all

---

* Named for the French physicist and mathematician Simèon Denis Poisson (1781–1840).

Table 10.2. **Summary of Definitions
of Elastic Moduli**

Young's Modulus	$M_Y = F l_0 / \Delta l \cdot A$
Bulk Modulus	$M_B = -F_N V_0 / \Delta V \cdot A$
Shear Modulus	$M_S = F_T / \phi \cdot A$
Poisson's Ratio	$\rho = (-\Delta d / d) / (\Delta l / l)$

others can be expressed in terms of these two. The direct determination of Young's modulus and the shear modulus is easy on the basis of the relatively simple laboratory measurements that we have described. Direct determinations of the bulk modulus M_B and Poisson's ratio ρ are considerably more difficult. However, on the basis of theoretical relationships among elastic constants, M_B and ρ can be obtained from the equations

$$M_B = \tfrac{1}{3}(M_S M_Y)/(3 M_S - M_Y)$$

and

$$\rho = (M_Y/2 M_S) - 1,$$

where M_Y and M_S are easily measured.

We need to emphasize that the relations above apply only to *isotropic* materials. They apply fairly well to ordinary polycrystalline metals and to amorphous materials like glass. They do *not* usually apply to single crystals or to anisotropic materials like wood, which has different elastic properties parallel to and perpendicular to the grain. In describing the elastic properties of anisotropic materials it is necessary to use more than two independent constants.

Hooke's Law in its generalized form (10.5) constitutes the basis for the theory of *linear elasticity* that has been found to be widely applicable. If stress is not directly proportional to strain as in (10.5), it is necessary to use a more general theory of *nonlinear elasticity,* which is considerably more complicated.

10.8 ELASTIC LIMIT AND ULTIMATE STRENGTH OF MATERIALS

The tensile properties of materials are usually determined by placing a test sample in a "materials testing machine" that is capable of applying enormous tensile forces to the ends of the sample. The original shape of a test sample is shown in Fig. 10.13a. The stress produced in the sample is $S = F/A$, where A is the cross-sectional area of the slender central portion of the sample. Hooke's Law is usually obeyed for all stresses up to the vicinity of the *elastic limit,* which marks the onset of permanent distortion. Samples of certain *brittle materials* like glass or phosphor bronze rupture as soon as the elastic limit is reached; brittle materials attain no "permanent set"; they simply break.

Other types of materials behave quite differently. When these materials are subject to stresses greater than the elastic limit, they acquire a permanent set from which

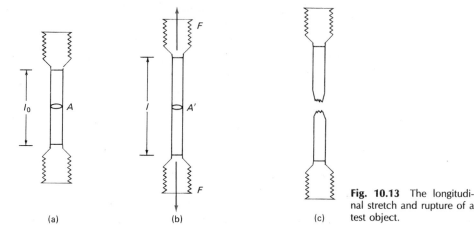

Fig. 10.13 The longitudinal stretch and rupture of a test object.

they do not recover their original configuration, as suggested in Fig. 10.13b. Such materials are said to be *ductile;* typical ductile materials include steel, copper, and gold. Ductile materials can be "worked" in various ways; steel can be cold-rolled, copper can be drawn through dies into wires, and gold, which is also termed *malleable,* can be hammered into thin sheets.

Permanent set or permanent distortion occurs for stresses greater than the elastic limit. For ductile materials, slightly above the elastic limit there is a characteristic stress S_{YP} known as the *yield point* beyond which the material in the sample appears to flow like a very viscous liquid. The length of the sample can be increased enormously with only small increases in the applied force F. Because the cross sectional area A' of the deformed sample decreases rapidly with increases in the applied force, it is customary to describe the behavior of the sample beyond the yield point in terms of a *nominal stress* defined as the ratio of the force actually applied to the *original* cross-sectional area A of the sample. As the applied tensional force F continues to increase, the sample eventually breaks or ruptures. The nominal stress value S_R at rupture is called the *rupture strength* or *ultimate strength* of the material.

The behavior of a material being tested in the manner just described can be represented by means of a stress–strain diagram like the one shown schematically in Fig. 10.14. The straight line between O and the point P represents the range to which Hooke's Law applies: $S \propto \sigma$. In the range on the curve between the straight line

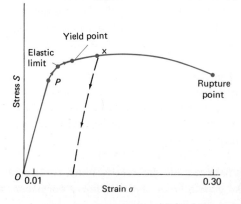

Fig. 10.14 Stress–strain curve for the material of which the test object in Fig. 10.13 is composed.

Table 10.3 Typical Values of the Elastic Limit and
Ultimate Strength for Various Materials
in Tension

Material	Elastic Limit (10^7 N/m^2)	Ultimate Strength (10^7 N/m^2)
Aluminum	13	14
Brass	38	46
Copper	15	34
Medium Steel	25	50
Spring Steel	41	69

and the elastic limit, the behavior of the material is still elastic in the sense that the material will recover its original state if the stress is reduced; however, in this small range stress is not directly proportional to strain. For the part of the curve between the elastic limit and the rupture point there is "permanent set" or distortion. If for stresses greater than the elastic limit we reduce the stress as indicated by the dotted line, we do not return to the origin.

In Table 10.3 we give typical values of tensile stress S_{EL} corresponding to the elastic limits and S_R corresponding to the rupture or ultimate strengths for several materials.

The ultimate strength of a material subject to shear is usually considerably smaller than the ultimate strength of the same material under tension. We make use of this comparative weakness to shear when we use a pair of shears or scissors to cut a copper wire or plate; we are using the sharp cutting edges of the blades to produce large shearing stresses in the metal. It is much easier to "snip" a copper wire with shears than to break it by tensional forces. In fabricating a metal object by means of a "punch and die" we also make use of the relative weakness of metals to shearing stress.

10.9 INELASTIC DEFORMATIONS: ENERGY CONSIDERATIONS

When we were discussing the motions of *rigid bodies,* we pointed out that the particles making up a rigid body always maintain the same positions relative to one another; this is what we mean by the term "rigid." No matter how large the forces we exert on an ideal rigid body, we can do nothing to change the relative positions of the particles making it up; the size and shape of the rigid body always remain the same.

In this chapter we have been discussing *elastic bodies,* the size and shape of which we can alter by the application of external forces. We have shown that the work done by the external forces is converted into *elastic potential energy,* as indicated by Eqs. (10.3) and (10.4). This potential energy can be used to do work as the distorted bodies regain their original configurations.

Like rigid bodies, elastic bodies are made up of particles—atoms and molecules—that have definite relative positions inside the undistorted body. However, when we use external forces to alter the configurations of the body, we alter the relative positions of the particles making up the body. When the body as a whole is distorted, each particle is subjected to a restoring force that tends to move the particle back to its original position relative to the other particles. When the external forces cease to act on the elastic body, the internal restoring forces return the particles to their original positions. The elastic potential energy of a distorted elastic body is simply the total potential energy of the particles making up the body; it is thus an *internal energy* that can be recovered as mechanical energy when the body does external work as it returns to its original undistorted configuration.

We can compute the total potential energy per unit volume of a material in terms of the stress S, the strain σ, and the elastic modulus M. We recall from (10.1') and (10.5) that we introduced stress as the generalization of a distorting force, strain as the generalization of a distortion, and the elastic modulus as a generalization of a force constant. In similar analogy with (10.3) and (10.4) we write for the elastic potential energy per unit volume of a stressed material that

$$E_P/V = \tfrac{1}{2}M\sigma^2 = \tfrac{1}{2}\sigma S = \tfrac{1}{2}S^2/M. \quad \textit{(Energy per Unit Volume)} \quad (10.14)$$

If the medium is not uniformly strained, this equation gives the local value $\delta E_P/\delta V$ at any point in the medium; σ and S are the stress and strain at the point in question and δV is a small volume element surrounding the point. That each of the expressions in (10.14) gives energy per unit volume can readily be seen by analysis of the units employed. Equation (10.14) can be derived quite easily in the case of the longitudinal stretch or compression of a slender rod. The derivation is left as a problem. Energy is stored in a strained elastic material and can be recovered when the stress is removed.

What happens to the work we do in distorting a body beyond its elastic limit? Because the body acquires a "permanent set," we know that the particles making up the body are moved away from their initial relative positions while the body is being distorted and once the elastic limit has been exceeded, the particles will not return to their initial positions when the stress is removed. Part of the work done to the body has resulted in a permanent alteration of the body, and this part of the work does not result in an increase of the potential energy of the body. We may have used mechanical energy to do the work in deforming the body, but we do not get the same amount of mechanical energy back out of the body when the stress is removed. The work we do in permanently altering the relative positions of the particles making up the body thus represents a *dissipation of mechanical energy*.

That mechanical energy is dissipated when a material is carried past its elastic limit can be illustrated on the stress–strain plot in Fig. 10.14. From (10.14) we note that the product $S\sigma$ has the dimensions of energy per unit volume. It can be shown that the area under the solid curve in Fig. 10.14 $\int S\,d\sigma$ is equal to the work done per unit volume as we distort the material. If we go up along the solid curve to Point X beyond the elastic limit, the area under the curve is equal to the work we have done per unit volume. If we stop at Point X and reduce the stress, we go back to $S = 0$ along the dotted curve. The area under the dotted curve represents the mechanical energy per unit volume that we can get out of the distorted material. The area between the solid curve and the dotted curve thus represents mechanical energy per unit volume that has been dissipated.

It is easy to recognize that the rigid body is an abstraction. Although the elastic

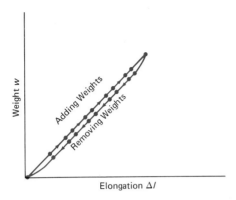

Fig. 10.15 Hysteresis represents the dissipation of mechanical energy.

body as we have described it in this chapter represents a closer approach to reality, a *perfectly* elastic body or material is also an idealization. No body or material is completely governed by Hooke's Law. Even a highly elastic material like steel shows departures from Hooke's Law. For example, if we gradually stretch a vertical steel wire by suspending weights one by one from its lower end, the wire becomes successively longer. If we make a plot of the suspended weight as a function of the wire's elongation as we *add* the weights, we get the upper curve in Fig. 10.15. If we then gradually *remove* the weights and measure the elongations, a plot of the results gives the lower curve in Fig. 10.15. We note that the mechanical energy added to the wire as we do work in adding the weights is given by the area $\int w\,dl$ under the upper curve. The mechanical energy removed from the wire as we removed the weights is given by the area under the lower curve. Because the mechanical energy removed from the wire is less than the mechanical energy added to the wire, some mechanical energy has been dissipated. The mechanical energy dissipated is given by the area between the curves in the plot. The effect shown in Fig. 10.15 represents what is called *hysteresis;* the region bounded by the two curves is called the *hysteresis loop;* the larger the area of the loop, the greater the energy dissipated. A more general type of plot of hysteresis gives stress S as a function of strain σ; the area of the loop gives energy dissipated per unit volume.

Even for the most highly elastic real materials, there are measurable hysteresis effects and thus mechanical energy dissipation as we distort the material and then allow it to return to its original state. Because of the mechanical energy dissipation, the process of elastic contraction is not *exactly* the reverse of the process of stretch, even though the material or body eventually returns to its original condition or state.

QUESTIONS

1. In earlier chapters we have dealt with "rigid bodies." If a rigid body actually existed, what would be the values of the elastic moduli of the material making it up? Which material listed in Table 10.1 most nearly approximates such a "rigid material"?

2. The average person regards rubber as a very elastic material. Discuss this view. What does the term *elastic* mean? What kinds of materials should be regarded as highly elastic?

3. Such materials as lead and putty are generally

regarded as being *inelastic*. Does this mean that their elastic moduli are zero? Which of their elastic properties are involved in their inelastic behavior?

4. Glass is generally regarded as being *brittle*. How would you expect this property to be reflected in the values of the elastic constants for glass?

5. What properties of gold make it *malleable?* What elastic properties of a material make

it *ductile;* i.e., capable of being drawn into the shape of wires?

6. Explain why the mechanical energy dissipated is given by the area of the hysteresis loop in Fig. 10.15.

7. As a scientific generalization, is Hooke's law comparable with the principle of universal gravitation? with the laws of friction?

8. What happens to mechanical energy when a distorted body acquires a permanent set?

PROBLEMS

1. When a 2-kg body is attached to the lower end of a suspended coil spring, the spring experiences an elongation of 3 cm. What is the force constant of this spring? How much elastic potential energy is stored in the stretched spring?

2. What will be the total elongation of the spring in Problem 1 if at equilibrium opposing forces of 30 N are applied to the ends of the spring? (One force has a magnitude of 30 N and is directed upward; the other force has a magnitude of 30 N and is directed downward.) How much work is done to provide the elastic potential energy of the distorted spring?

3. If we wish to use a coil spring in constructing a "weighing scale" like that shown in the figure, what should be the force constant of the spring if the spring is to have an elongation of 1 cm for each kilogram of mass suspended? What would be the separation between marks on the scale representing 10-N intervals?

4. What is the force constant of a spring if 1.5 J of work is done in giving the spring the elastic potential energy associated with an elastic elongation of 10 cm? What is the elastic potential energy of this spring when the spring has an elongation of 5 cm?

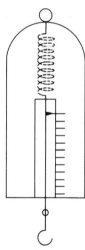

Problem 3

5. A 100-kg gun has an initial recoil velocity of 3 m/s when it is used to fire a projectile horizontally. We wish to use a large spring as a "recoil mechanism' to limit the distance of recoil to 120 cm. What should be the force constant of the spring? Recoil mechanisms are always equipped with damping devices that provide for the dissipation of mechanical energy. Why?

6. In constructing the spring scale of Problem 3 we made use of the *gravitational properties*

of matter. Consider how a spring scale might be based on the *inertial properties* of matter. Suppose that a 500-g body on a polished horizontal surface is set in motion by a horizontal force exerted by a coil spring. When the body is kept in motion at constant velocity, the spring's elongation is 2.4 cm; when giving the body an acceleration of 0.8 m/s², the spring has a total elongation of 3.4 cm. What is the force constant of the spring? What should be the spacing between marks representing 1-N intervals on the spring scale? What is the coefficient of kinetic friction between the 500-g body and the horizontal surface?

7. When two tangential forces each of 12 N magnitude are applied to a disk of radius 30 cm that is supported by a rod as in Fig. 10.3, the disk experiences an angular displacement of 30° from its equilibrium position. What is the torsion constant of the rod? What is the elastic potential energy of the rod when the angular displacement of the rod from its equilibrium position is 90°?

8. What torque is required to give the disk in Prob. 7 a rotation of 90° from its equilibrium position? Through what angle must the rod be twisted in order to store 1 J of energy in the rod?

9. A copper wire is 3 m in length and has a diameter of 2 mm. What is the elongation of this wire when opposing forces tending to stretch the wire, each of magnitude 90 N, are applied to its ends? What is the resulting strain? What is the stress?

10. Repeat Problem 9 for a steel wire of the same size.

11. A steel wire 2.2 m in length and 1 mm in diameter is attached to the ceiling of a laboratory room. What is the elongation of the wire when a 3-kg body is attached to its lower end? Calculate the stress and strain in the wire.

12. The wire in Problem 11 is attached to a 3-kg box at rest on a horizontal loading platform; the coefficient of kinetic friction between the box and the platform is 0.3 and the corresponding coefficient of static friction is 0.5. By pulling horizontally on the wire a woman sets the box in motion. Find the stress and the strain produced in the wire (a) in order to set the box in motion, (b) in order to keep the box moving at constant velocity, and (c) in order to give the moving box a horizontal acceleration of magnitude 3 m/s².

13. What is the change in the volume of two liters of water when it is subjected to a compressional stress of 10⁷ N/m²? What is the volume strain? What is the compressibility of water?

14. Repeat Problem 13 for a two-liter sample of ethyl ether.

15. In an arrangement like the one shown in Fig. 10.3 the disk is supported by a copper tube 1.5 m in length and 2.2 cm in diameter; the wall thickness of the tube is 1.3 mm. What is the torsion constant of this tube? What is the shearing stress in the copper when the disk has a rotation of 60° from its equilibrium position? What is the corresponding shearing strain?

16. Repeat Problem 15 for the case in which the disk is supported by a solid copper rod 1.5 m in length and having a diameter of 8 mm.

17. What is the maximum possible mass that can be supported by a copper wire 2 mm in diameter without snapping the wire?

18. A suspended brass wire 2 m in length and 3 mm in diameter is used to support a body attached to its lower end. What is the maximum mass that can be supported without producing a permanent distortion of the wire? What is the elongation of the wire when it is supporting this maximum load? What is the strain in the wire?

19. Mild steel has an ultimate strength of 3.5×10^8 N/m² for rupture by shear. What downward force would have to be applied to the blade shown in the figure in order to cut a piece of "strap steel" 2 mm thick and 4 cm wide? When an ordinary "pair of shears" is used to cut a wire, why is it usually desirable to place the wire as close to the hinge as possible?

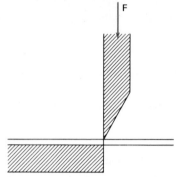

Problem 19

20. A hole can be punched into a sheet of metal by pushing a "punch" through the metal into a "die" consisting of a thick piece of metal in which there is a hole only slightly larger than the punch. What force would have to be exerted on the punch shown in the figure in order to produce a hole 2.3 cm in diameter in the mild-steel strap described in Problem 19?

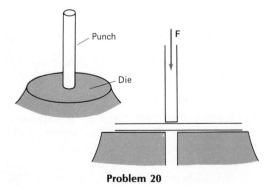

Problem 20

21. The drawing in Fig. 10.10 shows a body subject to uniform shearing stress S. By considerations of rotational equilibrium show that $F_1/A_1 = F_2/A_2$, so that we obtain the same value for the tangential stress regardless of our choice of face in computing $S = F_T/A$.

22. Show that for small volume changes Eq. (10.9′) can be rewritten as

$$F_N/A = +M_B \Delta\rho/\rho_0$$

in terms of density ρ rather than volume.

23. Hooke's original law applied to individual bodies such as a wire. Find an expression for the force constant of a wire in terms of the dimensions of the wire and the value of Young's modulus for the material of which the wire is composed. Explain your reasoning.

24. Derive (10.14) for the case of a wire under tensional stress. Note that the stored elastic potential energy is given by the work done *against the elastic restoring force* in stretching the wire.

25. On the basis of values of M_Y and M_S for metals listed in Table 10.1, determine Poisson's ratio for these metals. What is the average value of Poisson's ratio for all the metals listed in the table?

26. The figure shows a stick protruding over the edge of a table. By considering the conditions for translational equilibrium of the portion of the stick protruding over the edge, compute the tangential force exerted on the protruding portion along AA by the portion of the stick lying on the table top; express the result in terms of the weight

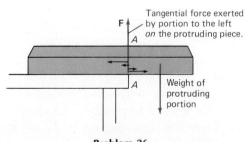

Problem 26

of the protruding portion. Show that for rotational equilibrium the upper portion of the stick at AA must be under tensional stress and the lower portion at AA must be under compressional stress. What is the shearing stress at surface AA?

27. A uniform 5-kg steel rod 2 m long is supported in a horizontal position by vertical wires attached to the ceiling and connected to the ends of the rod. The wire at end A is copper and has a cross-sectional area of 3 mm². The wire at end B is steel and has a cross-sectional area of 2 mm². Find the stresses and strains in the two wires.

28. At what position on the rod in Problem 27 would we have to suspend a 5-kg object (a) in order to produce equal stresses in the two wires and (b) in order to produce equal strains in the two wires?

29. A loaded elevator cage having a total mass of 2000 kg is supported by two stranded steel cables, each of which has an effective cross-sectional area of 1.6 cm². If the elastic limit of the steel in the cables is 2.5×10^8 N/m², what is the maximum upward acceleration that can be given to the loaded cage without producing a stress of more than one-half that corresponding to the elastic limit? Assume that each cable bears half the applied force.

30. A square steel rod measuring 4 cm on a side and 10 m in length stands upright. What is the maximum stress in this rod? Where is this maximum stress? If this rod were suspended from its upper end so that it hung in a vertical position, what would be the maximum stress in the rod? Where would this maximum stress be located? What would be the stresses in each case if we doubled the cross-sectional area of the rod?

*31. Equation (10.13) implies that the torque τ required to twist a thin-walled tube of radius R and wall thickness t through an angle θ is $\tau = (2\pi\theta M_S/l)R^3 t$. By considering a solid rod as made up of concentric cylindrical tubes of radius r and thickness dr, derive Eq. (10.13′).

32. A steel wire 1.5 m long with a diameter of 1 mm is butt-welded to a brass wire of the same diameter and length. One end of this composite wire is attached to the ceiling of a laboratory room, and a 3-kg body is attached to the other end of the wire. When the wire hangs vertically, what is its total elongation? What are the stresses in the two parts of the wire? What are the strains?

33. What is the maximum elastic potential energy that can be stored in a copper wire 2 m long and 2 mm in diameter if the elastic limit is not exceeded?

34. A 4-kg body is attached to one end of the flexible wire described in Problem 33 and the other end of the wire is attached to the ceiling. If the 4-kg body is raised to ceiling height at the point where the wire is attached and is then released, what happens when the wire becomes taut? Explain your reasoning.

35. When a flexible wire or cord is attached to a heavy object, the object can be set in motion by pulling steadily on the end of the wire. However, if the end of the wire or cord is suddenly jerked, the wire or cord snaps. Why? Give a quantitative explanation of this phenomenon.

36. A 40-kg body lies at rest on a horizontal surface. The coefficients of friction between the body and surface are $\mu_S = 0.5$ and $\mu_K = 0.3$. If a copper wire 1 mm in diameter is attached to one side of the body and is pulled horizontally, what is the maximum acceleration that can be imparted to the body?

37. The same wire as in Problem 36 is used to pull the same object along a plane inclined at an angle of 30° with the horizontal. If the frictional coefficients are the same

as those in Problem 36, what is the maximum acceleration of the object upward along the incline? Downward along the incline?

38. Compute the compressibilities K for the liquids listed in Table 10.1 and express them in proper SI units. Is it possible to infer any relationship between compressibility and the molecular structure of the materials involved?

39. The figure represents the cross section of a cubical block with sides of length l in shear. The area of each face of the cube is A. Show that a surface in the block perpendicular to the diagram and containing a line between ① and ①′ in the figure is under pure *tensile* stress S and obtain an expression for S in terms of F, l, and the shear angle ϕ. What is the limiting value of S for small ϕ?

40. Show that a surface in the block perpendicular to the diagram and containing a line between ② and ②′ in the figure is under pure compressive stress S and obtain an expression for S in terms of F, l, and the shear angle ϕ. What is the limiting value of S for small ϕ?

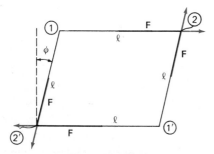

Problems 39 and 40

41. A cylindrical medium steel pipe 10 cm in outer diameter and 3 m in length is placed

vertically and is required to support a load of 20,000 kg. What is the minimum possible wall thickness of the pipe if the elastic limit is not to be exceeded? Discuss the possible practical advisability of filling the pipe with concrete even if the enclosed concrete column is slightly shorter than the pipe and thus bears no load.

42. What compressional stress is required to increase the density of each of the following materials by 0.1%: copper, glass, ethyl ether, water? See Problem 22.

43. What is the change in the cross section of the steel wire considered in Problem 11 when the 3-kg body is attached to its lower end? Is this change significant for the computation of the stress in the wire?

*44. A copper wire 2.8 m in length and 3 mm in diameter is fastened to the ceiling of a room. An object of mass 3.2 kg is attached to the lower end of the wire. What is the elongation of the wire? Devise a method for taking into account the mass of the wire itself in determining the elongation. What is the difference between the values of the elongation computed with and without taking into account the mass of the wire? Is this difference significant?

45. A 2-m length of 1.5-cm diameter steel rod attached to a 1-hp (0.7457 kW) motor shaft provides the connection between the shaft and the load. If the motor shaft has a rotational speed of 1800 rev/min, what torque is transmitted by the rod when the motor is running at full load? Through what angle does the rod twist under these conditions? What is the torsion constant of the rod? How much elastic potential energy is stored by the rod?

CHAPTER 11

Fluid Mechanics

The behavior of fluids has long been of interest to mankind. In fact, Thales of Miletus (ca. 600 B.C.), whom Aristotle regarded as the very first of the Greek natural philosophers, regarded a fluid, water, as "the basis of all things." Fluids—liquids and gases—behave quite differently from the solids that we have discussed in earlier chapters. Because fluids flow indefinitely when subjected to tangential stress, we conclude that fluids have no shear modulus. A liquid has a definite volume but always assumes the shape of the containing vessel; water poured into a bucket takes the shape of the bucket. A gas has neither a definite shape nor a definite volume; if we admit gas to a previously evacuated container, the gas will immediately fill the container and take the shape of the container. Although there are some *viscous* materials like gelatin, tar, or wax that constitute a borderline between liquids and solids, we shall in most of this chapter restrict our attention to liquids that flow freely without internal friction and to gases. We shall show how the Newtonian principles can be applied to fluids at rest and in motion.

Later in this chapter we shall discuss *viscosity* or fluid friction and show how it can be measured. Viscosity is always involved to some extent in fluid flow and is responsible for the dissipation of mechanical energy when solid objects move through a fluid. Such dissipation of mechanical energy is of great practical importance to systems of airborne and waterborne transportation.

It is perhaps surprising that, in spite of their very different appearances, gases and liquids have properties that are governed by the same set of physical laws. In this chapter we shall treat the mechanical properties that liquids and gases have in common and that are associated with their ability to flow. In some respects, liquids and gases *are* different; the phenomenon of liquid *surface tension,* which we treat briefly, is not encountered in gases, which have no free surfaces. In later chapters dealing with heat we shall find that the thermal properties of liquids and gases are indeed quite different.

11.1   FLUID PRESSURE

In our discussion of fluids we shall begin by considering the behavior of the liquid so dear to Thales: water. We are all familiar with this common liquid and can more easily visualize its behavior than that of air, which is our most common gas but is unfortunately invisible. Beginning with water has one other advantage; because of its large bulk modulus, we can treat it in good approximation as an *incompressible fluid*. Gases, on the other hand, are highly compressible. In spite of the differences in the compressibility of liquids and gases, many of the relations that we shall derive in our treatment of water and other liquids will also apply in good approximation to air and other gases.

First, consider water at rest in the rectangular swimming pool with length l and width x shown in Fig. 11.1. The flat bottom of the swimming pool is a distance h *below the surface* of the water in the pool. The total mass M of the water in the pool is $M = \rho lxh$, where ρ is the density of water. The earth exerts a downward gravitational force $\mathbf{w} = M\mathbf{g}$ on the water in the pool. Because the water has no downward acceleration, we know from Newton's Second Principle that the bottom of the pool is exerting an upward force $\mathbf{F}$ of equal magnitude on the water. Finally, we know from Newton's Third Principle that the water exerts a vertically downward force $\mathbf{F}' = \mathbf{w} = M\mathbf{g}$ on the horizontal bottom of the pool.

We now introduce a new physical quantity called *pressure* that we need to employ in our treatment of fluids.

> PRESSURE in a fluid is the magnitude of the normal force per unit area exerted by the fluid on any surface in the fluid.

In our definition we have specified the *magnitude* of the normal or perpendicular force per unit area. Therefore, *pressure is a scalar quantity;* it is measured in N/m². In the SI, the pressure unit is given a special name, the *pascal* with the abbreviation Pa, where 1 Pa = 1 N/m². The unit is named in honor of the French mathematician and philosopher Blaise Pascal (1623–1662).

The downward force on the bottom of the pool in Fig. 11.1 due to the weight of the water is $Mg = \rho ghlx$. Because this force is normal to the bottom of the pool,

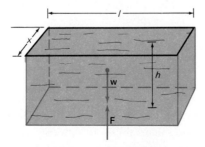

Fig. 11.1 The average hydrostatic pressure at the bottom of the pool is equal to the ratio of the weight of the water in the pool to the area of the bottom.

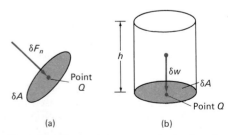

(a)   (b)

Fig. 11.2 The pressure at a *point* is given by the limit $\delta F_N / \delta A$ as $\delta A \to 0$ but always includes the point.

we can express the *average hydrostatic pressure* P_{AV} at the bottom of the pool, which is the normal force on the bottom divided by the area of the bottom as

$$P_{AV} = F_N/A = \rho ghlx/lx = \rho gh. \quad \text{(Average Hydrostatic Pressure)} \quad (11.1)$$

We use the term *hydrostatic pressure* because in arriving at F_N we have included only the weight of the *water* at rest in the pool and have for the time being ignored any effects that the atmosphere above the water may have on the pressure at the bottom of the pool.

It will be necessary for us to speak of the *pressure at a point* in a fluid, which can be defined by means of the diagram in Fig. 11.2a. In accord with (11.1), the average pressure P_{AV} on a small surface of area δA is given by the expression $P_{AV} = \delta F_N/\delta A$, where δF_N is the magnitude of the normal force acting on the surface. The pressure at point Q in the figure is given by the expression:

$$P = \lim_{\delta A \to 0} \frac{\delta F_N}{\delta A}, \quad \text{(Pressure at a Point)} \quad (11.2)$$

where $\delta A \to 0$ in such a way that point Q is always included. We note that δF_N in Fig. 11.2a is not vertically downward nor is δA a horizontal surface. As shown below the orientation in space is unimportant so long as δF_N is the force component normal to the surface.

In our discussion of hydrostatic pressure thus far we have talked about the normal force exerted by a fluid *on* the solid surface of the containing vessel, e.g., the swimming pool in Fig. 11.1. Note that on the basis of Newton's Third Principle the solid surface of the vessel exerts a force of *equal magnitude* and opposite direction on the fluid. Therefore, we could compute the pressure at a point as in Fig. 11.2 by considering the normal force exerted *by* the solid surface element *on* the fluid. Because only the *magnitude* of F_N is involved in (11.1) and in subsequent equations, we would get the same values of pressure as before.

In Fig. 11.2b we consider a small element of area δA at the bottom of the swimming pool shown in Fig. 11.1. The weight of a column of water with cross-sectional area δA rising vertically above area element δA at the bottom is $\delta w = \rho gh\delta A$, and this is just the value of the normal force δF_N acting on area δA. Therefore, the hydrostatic pressure at point Q is

$$P = \rho gh. \quad \left\{ \begin{array}{l} P \text{ in Pa} \\ h \text{ in m} \\ \rho \text{ in kg/m}^3 \\ g \text{ in m/s}^2 \end{array} \right\} \text{(Hydrostatic Pressure)} \quad (11.1')$$

We note that in the swimming pool shown in Fig. 11.1 the hydrostatic pressure is the same at all points on the bottom. The hydrostatic pressure at any point on the bottom thus depends only on the distance of the point below the surface.

Now we consider the pressures at points *inside* the body of a fluid and not on the surface of any wall of the containing vessel. We continue for the present to ignore any effects due to the atmosphere above the liquid. Consider a horizontal

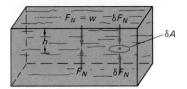

Fig. 11.3 The hydrostatic pressure at every point in a horizontal layer is equal to ρgh.

plane inside a liquid in Fig. 11.3 at a distance h below the surface. The liquid above the horizontal plane is in equilibrium and therefore the resultant force on it is zero. Because its weight ρghA is *downward,* the liquid below the horizontal surface must exert a force of equal magnitude upward on the liquid above the horizontal plane. The average pressure as determined by F_N/A for the downward force is the same as that as determined by F_N/A for the upward force. In either case, the average pressure for the entire horizontal plane and the pressure at any point in this plane is $P = \rho gh,$ where h is the vertical distance below the surface of the liquid.

We thus see the general necessity for forces acting across any "imaginary surface" inside a fluid as well as across the "real surfaces" of the walls of the containing vessel. A fluid flows freely when subjected to any tangential stress; therefore, a fluid at rest cannot exert any tangential forces across any surface—"real" or "imaginary." Furthermore, except in special and unusual circumstances, a fluid cannot withstand tensional strains and thus cannot exert a force involving a *pull* at any surface. A fluid in static equilibrium can experience only *compressive stresses;* thus, in general a fluid can apply *pushes* to surfaces but not *pulls.* This means that *pressure as we have defined it is a positive quantity.*

The pressure at any point in a fluid does not depend in any way on the orientation of the surface element on which the fluid forces act. In order to demonstrate this we must consider a volume element of fluid in which the faces of the volume element are not parallel. For example, consider the prism shown in Fig. 11.4, in which the Z axis is directed vertically upward. The fluid inside the prism is in equilibrium provided the resultant external force $\mathbf{F}_1 + \mathbf{F}_2 + \mathbf{F}_3 + \mathbf{w}$ acting on the prism is zero. Thus, the sum of the force components in the $+Y$ direction must be equal to the sum of the force components in the $-Y$ direction: $F_3 \sin \phi = F_2$; similarly, the sum of the upward force components must be equal to the sum of the downward force components: $F_1 = F_3 \cos \phi + w$, where w is the weight $w = \rho gV = \rho g\,(\tfrac{1}{2}\,l \sin \phi)(l \cos \phi)l$ of the fluid *inside* the prism. Now we can set $F_1 = P_{1AV}A_1 = P_{1AV}(l \cdot l\cos \phi)$, where P_{1AV} is the average pressure on the horizontal bottom

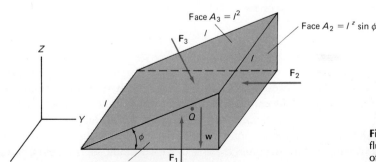

Fig. 11.4 The pressure at a point in a fluid does not depend on the orientation of the surface on which fluid forces act. (The Z axis is directed vertically upward.)

face of the prism having area $A_1 = l^2 \cos \phi$; similarly, $F_2 = P_{2AV}A_2 = P_{2AV}(l^2 \sin \phi)$; and $F_3 = P_{3AV}A_3 = P_{3AV}l^2$ for the slant face of the prism. Therefore, we can write for the horizontal Y force components

$$P_{3AV}l^2 \sin \phi = P_{2AV}l^2 \sin \phi \quad \text{or} \quad P_{3AV} = P_{2AV}$$

and for the vertical Z force components

$$P_{1AV}l^2 \cos \phi = P_{3AV}l^2 \cos \phi + \tfrac{1}{2}\rho g l^3 \sin \phi \cos \phi.$$

or
$$P_{1AV} = P_{3AV} + \tfrac{1}{2}\rho g l \sin \phi.$$

Now we let the size of the prism in Fig. 11.4 approach zero in such a way that Point Q is always included in the prism; as the prism dimension $l \to 0$, the term proportional to l also approaches zero and the average values P_{1AV}, P_{2AV}, and P_{3AV} become the pressures at Point Q. From the limits of the above equations, we see that $P_3 = P_2$ and $P_1 = P_3$ at Point Q so that we can conclude that $P_1 = P_2 = P_3$ at Point Q regardless of the orientations of the surfaces on which the fluid forces act. We note that the angle ϕ in Fig. 11.4, which determines the orientation of the slant face of the prism, can have *any* value because all functions of ϕ vanish from our final relations as $l \to 0$. Our conclusion that $P_1 = P_2 = P_3$ is valid for any orientation of the slant face of the prism in Fig. 11.4.

We can check our conclusion experimentally by means of the little pressure gauges shown in Fig. 11.5. The gauge in Fig. 11.5a consists of a flexible diaphragm supported at the center by a helical spring mounted inside an evacuated enclosure; the gauge in Fig. 11.5b consists of a thin corrugated sheet of elastic metal forming one wall of an evacuated enclosure. When the device is lowered into a liquid, the spring is compressed by liquid forces acting on the diaphragm. Motion of the center C of the diaphragm on the elastic metal wall can be registered by an attached pointer not shown in the figure. If we place the center of the diaphragm at some point in the liquid, we find that the position of C shows no change as we give the pressure gauge various orientations in the liquid.

At any point in a fluid the pressure does not depend on the orientation of the surface used in its measurement. *Pressure is a scalar quantity that has a definite value for each point in a fluid.*

11.2 LAWS OF FLUID STATICS

From Newton's principles, we shall now derive certain relations for fluids in static equilibrium that are known as the "Laws of Fluid Statics." In deriving these laws we shall not in general assume that the fluid is homogeneous. We shall, however, apply the laws to the particular case of an incompressible, homogeneous fluid. We note that some of the laws had been established on an empirical basis long before Newton's time.

Law I: The pressure is the same at every point in a continuous horizontal layer of a fluid at rest.

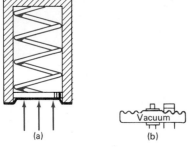

Fig. 11.5 Small pressure gauges.

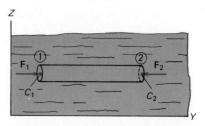

Fig. 11.6 The pressure is the same at every point in a continuous horizontal layer of fluid at rest.

Inside the fluid, we construct a thin cylinder with cross-sectional area $A = \pi r^2$ and its axis horizontal as shown in Fig. 11.6. Because the fluid inside the cylinder is at rest, the resultant force acting on the cylinder must be zero. The only forces acting in the Y direction are forces acting on the ends of the cylinder: $\mathbf{F}_1$ to the right and $\mathbf{F}_2$ to the left in the figure. We can set $F_1 = P_{1AV}A_1$ and $F_2 = P_{2AV}A_2$, where P_{1AV} is the average pressure at face ① and P_{2AV} is the average pressure at face ②. From Newton's Principles we know that $F_1 = F_2$ and can write

$$P_{1AV}A_1 = P_{2AV}A_2 \quad \text{or} \quad P_{1AV} = P_{2AV}$$

because $A_1 = A_2 = \pi r^2$. If we now let the cylinder's radius r approach zero, $P_{1AV} \to P_1$ and $P_{2AV} \to P_2$, where P_1 and P_2 are the pressures at points C at the centers of the ends of the cylinder; therefore, $P_1 = P_2$. Because the centers of the faces are at the same heights, they are two points in a horizontal plane; by choosing our cylinder of different lengths l with its axis in various horizontal orientations, we can verify that the pressure P at any point in the same horizontal layer is $P = P_1 = P_2$. Thus, we have derived Law I.

Our earlier result (11.1′) that $P = \rho gh$ for hydrostatic pressure is consistent with the more general relation given by Law I. The pressure is the same at all points the same distance h below the surface of a liquid.

Our second law deals with the fluid pressures at different heights:

Law II: The pressure at a lower level in a fluid is greater than the pressure at a higher level by an amount equal numerically to the weight of a fluid column of unit cross section connecting the two levels.

We derive this law by considering the fluid in Fig. 11.7, in which we measure heights as vertical distances upward from the XY plane. Consider fluid levels $z_2 - z_1$ apart. We connect these levels by a column of cross-sectional area A. Because the fluid inside the column is at rest under equilibrium conditions, we know from Newton's Principles that the resultant external force on the column must be zero. This means that the magnitude of the net upward force $F_1 - F_2$ exerted on the column by the surrounding fluid must be equal to the weight w of the fluid inside the column. Therefore, we can write $F_1 - F_2 = w$. Division of both sides of this equation by A

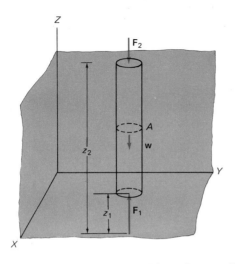

Fig. 11.7 The pressure at a lower level in a fluid is greater than the pressure at a higher level by an amount equal numerically to the weight of a column of liquid of unit cross section connecting the levels.

gives $F_1/A - F_2/A = w/A$ or $P_{1AV} - P_{2AV} = w/A$. In the limit where A becomes very small this gives

$$P_1 - P_2 = \text{Weight per unit cross-sectional area of column.} \qquad (11.3)$$

Because the weight per unit cross section of the column is numerically equal to the weight of a column of unit cross section, we have derived the above law.

For a *homogeneous* fluid, in which the density ρ is constant, (11.3) reduces to the expression

$$P_1 - P_2 = \rho g(z_2 - z_1). \qquad (11.3')$$

We note that (11.3') is in agreement with (11.1') provided we take cognizance of the fact that height h in Fig. 11.1 and z_1 and z_2 in Fig. 11.7 are measured from different reference levels.

Combination of the two laws allows us to compare the pressures at *any* two points in a continuous sample of a fluid. We simply join the points by a line consisting of straight horizontal and vertical segments and apply our two laws of fluid statics to each segment as we move from one point to the other. For example, we can show that the pressures are equal at two points at the same level in a *homogeneous* fluid such as two points D and E in the U-tube shown in Fig. 11.8a. Even though the points D and E cannot be connected by a horizontal line inside the fluid, $P_D = P_E$ because the two points are at the same height z. The pressures at points A and B are the same by Law I; the pressure increase in going from point E to point B has the same magnitude as the pressure decrease in going from point A to point D by Law II. We note, however, that if we have different immiscible fluids of *different* densities in the two arms of the U-tube as in Fig. 8.8b, $P_D = P_E$ but $P_{D'} \neq P_{E'}$. Why?

The third law that we shall derive gives the statement of a relation with important practical applications to problems involving ships, submarines, balloons, and other objects that are immersed in fluids. This relation is called Archimedes' Law and

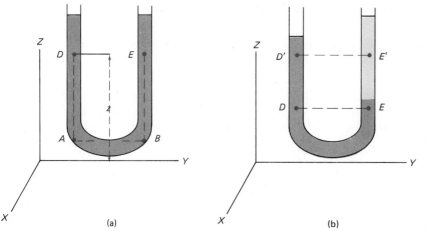

(a)   (b)   **Fig. 11.8**

was formulated by the Greek philosopher and mathematician Archimedes of Syracuse (287–212 B.C.), who is said to have determined the density, and hence the purity, of the "gold" in a crown by comparing the apparent weight of the crown when it was immersed in water with the weight of the crown in air. We can derive Archimedes' Law from the more general Newtonian Principles.

> ARCHIMEDES' LAW.   When a foreign body is immersed in a fluid, the fluid exerts a net upward force on the body that is equal in magnitude to the weight of the fluid displaced by the body. The upward force exerted by the fluid is called the BUOYANT FORCE.

If a body having the shape of the cylinder in Fig. 11.9 is completely immersed in a homogeneous fluid, we can immediately demonstrate by Law II that the difference in the magnitudes of the vertical forces $F_1 = P_1A$ and $F_2 = P_2A$ is equal to the weight of the displaced fluid:

$$F_1 - F_2 = (h_1 - h_2)\rho gA = \rho gV, \tag{11.4}$$

where ρ is the density of the fluid and $V = A(h_1 - h_2)$ is the volume of the fluid displaced by the cylinder. Similarly, (11.3) shows that for a nonhomogeneous liquid the difference $F_1 - F_2$ is equal to the weight of the fluid displaced by the cylinder.

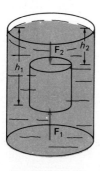

Fig. 11.9   Archimedes' Law: $F_B = F_1 - F_2 =$ weight of fluid displaced.

Thus, setting $F_1 - F_2 = F_B$, the buoyant force, we obtain

$$F_B = \text{Weight of the Fluid Displaced.} \quad \textit{(Archimedes' Law)} \qquad (11.5)$$

More generally, Archimedes' Law applies to the case of a body of irregular shape like the one shown in Fig. 11.10; the proof is straightforward. If the irregular foreign body were not present and were replaced by a body of the fluid having the same shape, the resultant of all the normal forces $\mathbf{F}_i$ exerted by the fluid *outside* the irregular body of fluid and acting on the fluid *inside* the irregular body of fluid would by Newton's Second Principle be equal in magnitude but opposite in direction to the weight $\mathbf{w}_F$ of the irregular body of fluid; i.e., the sum of the external forces exerted by the fluid outside would be equal to a force of magnitude w_F directed vertically upward. Now, when we place the irregularly shaped body in the fluid, the *external forces* are not changed. Therefore, once again, we obtain $F_B = w_F$, where w_F is the magnitude of the weight of the displaced fluid, just the result (11.5). This completes the derivation of Archimedes' Law.

What happens when we place a foreign body in a homogeneous fluid depends on the density of the foreign body relative to that of the homogeneous fluid. If the density of the foreign body is greater than that of the fluid, the foreign body sinks to the bottom. If the foreign body has a density less than that of the fluid, the body will float at the upper surface of the fluid; the body will sink through the surface until it has displaced a volume of the fluid having a weight equal to the weight of the body itself. If the density of the foreign body is exactly equal to that of the fluid, the foreign body will just float at any level inside the fluid. A list of the densities of a number of liquids and solids is given in Table 4.1. The density of a gas depends in a *major* way on pressure and temperature; this will be discussed in later chapters.

In our proof of Archimedes' Law, we showed that the fluid forces acting on a submerged object add vectorially to give an upward buoyant force $\mathbf{F}_B$ equal in magnitude to the weight of the displaced fluid. For the purpose of computing torques, this buoyant force can be considered to act at *the center of mass of the displaced fluid;* the corresponding point in the immersed object is called its *center of buoyancy.*

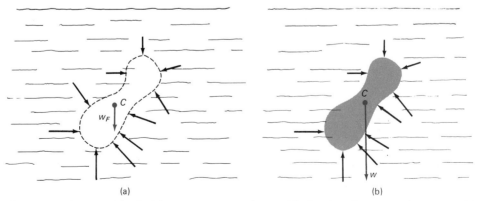

(a)   (b)

Fig. 11.10 The sum of the fluid forces acting on a submerged body of weight w is equal in magnitude to the weight w_F of the fluid displaced.

When a body is immersed totally or partially in a fluid, *the body is in a position of stable equilibrium when its own center of mass is below the center of buoyancy.* This fact is obviously of great practical importance in the proper design of ships!

We note that when two immiscible liquids are poured into the same vessel, the less dense liquid will always *float* on top of the liquid of greater density. For example, if we pour water, mercury, and carbon tetrachloride into a beaker, the water will float on the carbon tetrachloride which, in turn, floats on the mercury, which is at the very bottom of the beaker. Similarly, air floats on the water of the oceans.

Example.   If a 2-kg block of aluminum is submerged in water, what will be its "apparent weight" as registered by a spring sale supporting it as shown in Fig. 11.11?

The apparent weight of the body is equal to the magnitude of the force **F** exerted by the scale in supporting the body. From the figure we note that the sum of the upward forces **F** and $\mathbf{F}_B$ exerted on the block by the water must equal the downward gravitational force **w** acting on the block. The actual weight of the block is $w = Mg = (2 \text{ kg})(9.8 \text{ m/s}^2) = 19.6 \text{ N}$. The volume V of the fluid displaced by the block is $V = M_{Al}/\rho_{Al} = 2 \text{ kg}/(2700 \text{ kg/m}^3) = 7.4 \times 10^{-4} \text{ m}^3$. By Archimedes' Law, $F_B = \rho_w g V = (1000 \text{ kg/m}^3)(9.8 \text{ m/s}^2)(7.4 \times 10^{-4} \text{ m}^3) = 7.25 \text{ N}$. Therefore,

$$F = Mg - F_B = (19.6 - 7.25) \text{ N} = 12.4 \text{ N}.$$

Thus, the apparent weight of the block as registered by the spring sale is 12.4 N.

By comparing the actual measured weight in air and apparent weight when immersed in water of a "gold" crown, Archimedes was able to determine the density of the "gold" in the crown. Can you explain how this can be done?

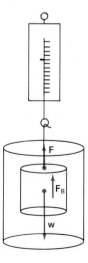

Fig. 11.11   The "apparent weight" of a submerged body is equal to the actual weight of the body minus the weight of the fluid displaced.

Example. Show that a *cylinder* of circular cross section composed of balsa wood can *never* float in a position of *stable* equilibrium at a sea water surface.

Because the density of balsa is only about one-eighth that of sea water, only about one-eighth of the volume of the balsa cylinder will be below the sea surface as the balsa floats. If we put one end of the cylinder down, the center of mass of the cylinder, which is at the geometrical center of the cylinder, will be well above the center of buoyancy at which the buoyant forces act. If the cylinder is tilted ever so slightly to one side, the torques exerted by the gravitational downward force at the center of mass and the buoyant force exerted at the center of buoyancy will cause the cylinder to fall until its axis of symmetry is horizontal. Even when the cylinder is horizontal, its center of mass is still above the center of buoyancy. Rotation of the cylinder about its axis of symmetry causes no further change in the locations of the center of mass and the center of buoyancy. However, because there is no restoring torque acting when we give the horizontal cylinder a slight rotational displacement, the position of the cylinder when its axis is horizontal can only be regarded as a position of *neutral equilibrium.*

11.3 ATMOSPHERIC PRESSURE: PRESSURE GAUGES

Although pure air is invisible and we usually become aware of it only when the wind blows or when we are moving through it at high speed, we live on the earth's surface at the bottom of a sea of air. Just as the water in a tank is responsible for the hydrostatic pressure at the bottom of the tank, the air above is responsible for a fluid pressure at the earth's surface. Because we are fully acclimated to the earth, we are largely unaware of this ever-present pressure. The fluid pressure at the earth's surface, which we call *atmospheric or barometric pressure,* is, however, an important aspect of meteorology; our daily weather reports include information about barometric pressure.

The Italian scientist Evangelista Torricelli (1608–1647) devised the first method of measuring atmospheric pressure. He became interested in the observation that a lift pump is unable to raise water to a height of more than about 10 m. A lift pump operates by creating a partial vacuum in a pipe, the lower end of which is immersed in water. The reason for its action had been "explained" on the Aristotelian principle that "nature abhors a vacuum"; water of its own accord was supposed to rush upward into the partial vacuum. Why nature suddenly ceased to abhor a vacuum when the water rose to a height of 10 m was, however, a mystery!

Torricelli's explanation was quite different. He believed that forces associated with atmospheric pressure at the surface of the water outside the pipe *pushed* the water upward into the evacuated pipe until the hydrostatic pressure due to the water column inside the pipe at the level of the water outside the pipe was equal to atmospheric pressure outside the pipe. Torricelli demonstrated the validity of his views by experiments dealing with mercury, a liquid of much higher density than water. His experi-

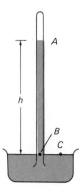

Fig. 11.12   A mercury barometer. The region of the tube above level A is called Torricelli's vacuum.

ments culminated in the invention of the *mercury barometer,* which has remained the standard device for determining atmospheric pressure.

To make a simple mercury barometer, take a straight glass tube about 1 m long and closed at one end. Fill the tube *completely* with mercury, close the open end with your finger, invert the tube, place the open end beneath the surface of mercury in an open dish, and then remove your finger. As soon as your finger is removed, the mercury in the tube will fall to a height h of about 76 cm above the level of the mercury in the dish, as shown in Fig. 11.12. The height h will be very close to 76 cm if the experiment is done at sea level; at laboratories at high altitudes above sea level h will be considerably smaller.

We can find the atmospheric pressure by applying Law I of the preceding section. The pressures at points C and B in Fig. 11.12 must be the same since points C and B are at the same horizontal level in a uniform fluid. The pressure at point C is atmospheric pressure P_{At} since the surface of the mercury in the dish is open to the atmosphere at the laboratory location. In a properly constructed barometer, the region above point A is essentially a vacuum—called "Torricelli's vacuum"—and contains only a small amount of mercury vapor at negligibly small pressure. Therefore, the pressure at point B is merely the pressure $\rho_{Hg}gh$ due to the column of mercury inside the tube. Because C and B are at the same pressure, $P_{At} = \rho_{Hg}gh$.

The pressure of the atmosphere at sea level is numerically equal to the weight of a column of air with a cross-sectional area of 1 m² and extending all the way to the top of the earth's atmosphere. Ninety-nine percent of the atmosphere lies within 30 km of the earth's surface. Atmospheric pressure decreases with altitude above the earth's surface because there is less air above the point at which measurements are made. The altimeter used in airplanes makes use of this variation of atmospheric pressure with altitude. At a given location on the earth's surface, there are day-to-day variations in atmospheric pressure that may amount to as much as 5%; these variations have important meterological significance.

Pressures are frequently specified in standard atmospheres (atm). When the actual atmospheric pressure has this standard value, the column in a mercury barometer has a height of exactly 76 cm at the temperature of melting ice at a location where $g = 9.80636$ m/s². The density of mercury at the temperature of melting ice has the carefully measured value 13,595.5 kg/m³. Under these conditions the atmospheric pressure is given by

$$P_{At} = \rho_{Hg}gh = (13{,}595.5 \text{ kg/m}^3)(9.80636 \text{ m/s}^2)(0.76 \text{ m}) = 101{,}325 \text{ Pa},$$

so

$$1 \text{ atm} = 101{,}325 \text{ Pa.} \quad \textit{(Standard Atmospheric Pressure)} \qquad (11.6)$$

In round numbers 1 atm $= 10^5$ Pa.

Example. To what maximum height can a lift pump raise water from an open well?

If a lift pump could create a perfect vacuum, the water would rise in the vertical pipe to a height h that would make the hydrostatic pressure inside the pipe at the level of the water in the well equal to atmospheric pressure. Thus, $\rho_w g h = P_{At}$ or $h = P_{At}/\rho_w g$. When atmospheric pressure has its standard value of 1.01×10^5 Pa, this height is $h = (1.01 \times 10^5 \text{ Pa})/(1000 \text{ kg/m}^3)(9.8 \text{ m/s}^2) = 10.3$ m.

In specifying fluid pressures, two different quantities are actually employed in practice:

ABSOLUTE PRESSURE gives the actual pressure at a point in a fluid.
GAUGE PRESSURE is the difference between the absolute pressure at a point in a fluid and atmospheric pressure. $P_g = P_{abs} - P_{atm}$

In calculating "hydrostatic pressures" in earlier sections, we have been stating gauge pressures because we have ignored the pressure of the atmosphere at the open surfaces of the liquids involved. The absolute pressure in a liquid with its surface open to the atmosphere is the sum of the hydrostatic pressure $\rho g h$ and the atmospheric pressure.

The mercury barometer is the standard instrument used for measuring atmospheric pressure. Less accurate measurements can be made by means of an *aneroid barometer,* which consists of a sealed evacuated metal box, rather flat and circular in shape with a corrugated front cover like the gauge shown in Fig. 11.5b. The front cover flexes elastically as the atmospheric pressure changes. Motion of the front surface is amplified mechanically and is transmitted to a pointer that moves along a printed scale. The scale readings indicated by the pointer must be calibrated against a mercury barometer. An aneroid barometer makes a handsome wall decoration but cannot be relied on in scientific work!

The normal density of air at the earth's surface at the temperature of melting ice is only 1.29 kg/m³ at standard atmospheric pressure. This density is so small that a change in elevation of 3 m changes the pressure by only 0.0004 atm. Thus, the reading of the barometer anywhere in a laboratory room applies in close approximation to all parts of the room.

A barometer like that in Fig. 11.12 measures absolute pressure at the level of the open dish in terms of the length of a mercury column. Liquid columns can also be used in pressure gauges that measure *gauge pressure*. One such gauge, shown schematically in Fig. 11.13, is called a *manometer*. The manometer is essentially a U-tube that is partially filled with a liquid: mercury for high pressures, water or oil for low pressures. One side of the U-tube is open to the fluid whose pressure is to be

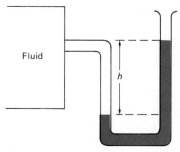

Fig. 11.13   A manometer.

Fig. 11.14   A Bourdon gauge.

measured, and the other side of the U-tube is open to the atmosphere. The difference between the fluid pressure and atmospheric pressure, which is the gauge pressure of the fluid, is measured by $\rho g h$, where ρ is the density of the liquid in the U-tube and h is the difference in the heights of the liquid surfaces in the two sides of the U-tube.

Example.   A U-tube with water in the lower part of the tube is usually employed in measuring the natural gas pressure in the pipe lines to homes where natural gas is used as a fuel. If the difference in the heights of such a manometer like the one in Fig. 11.13 is 40 cm, what is the gauge pressure of the natural gas in the line? What is its absolute pressure?

The observer reading the manometer would simply report the gauge pressure as "40 cm of water." In SI units the gauge pressure would be $P_G = \rho g h = (1000 \text{ kg/m}^3)(9.8 \text{ m/s}^2)(0.4 \text{ m}) = 3920$ Pa. The absolute pressure P would be atmospheric pressure plus the gauge pressure: $P = (101,000 + 3920)$ Pa $= 1.05 \times 10^5$ Pa, where we state only three significant figures.

Another type of pressure gauge is the Bourdon gauge, shown schematically in Fig. 11.14, that is employed in monitoring the pressure of compressed gases in the metal cylinders that are used in many commercial and industrial operations. The gauge consists of a flat spiral tube that is filled on the inside by the fluid whose pressure is to be measured while the outside of the tube is in contact with the atmosphere. When the pressure on the inside increases, the elastic properties of the metal allow the spiral tube to "unwind" and become straighter. The motion of the end of the spiral is imparted to a pointer. Careful calibration is necessary.

The hand gauge used to measure the pressure of the air in automobile tires involves the motion of a piston in a cylinder. Air emerging from the tire causes a displacement of the piston against opposing forces exerted by the atmospheric air and by friction. Such a gauge must be calibrated in terms of more reliable pressure-measuring devices.

11.4   FLUID DYNAMICS: BERNOULLI'S LAW

In treating fluids at rest we have derived the "laws of fluid statics" by direct application of Newtonian Principles. The behavior of moving fluids can be treated more effectively by the application of work–energy relations. We can derive a basic law describing fluid flow by applying these relations to the steady nonturbulent flow of a nonviscous incompressible fluid. By *steady flow* we mean that the velocity of the fluid at any point in space is constant and does not change with time; particles of fluid move along smooth, well-defined paths. In contrast, *turbulent flow* is highly erratic in character with rapid irregular fluctuations of velocity in both space and time. *Viscosity* is a measure of the frictional resistance of a fluid to the motion of one layer of fluid past another layer or past a solid surface; a nonviscous fluid is one for which such frictional forces are zero or negligibly small.

We shall apply work–energy relations to derive Bernoulli's Law, a relation that was formulated in 1739 by the Swiss mathematician and physicist Daniel Bernoulli (1700–1782). Although our derivation is based on an idealized situation, it turns out that Bernoulli's Law applies in good approximation not only to the steady flow of water but also the steady flow of air at speeds that are low as compared with the speed of sound. Bernoulli's Law constitutes the basis of the specialized subjects of *hydrodynamics* and *aerodynamics*. The detailed treatment of real-fluid flow is physically and mathematically complex. The simple form of Bernoulli's Law as we shall state it does not include effects of viscosity, finite compressibility, and turbulence, all of which must be considered in a general treatment of the flow of real fluids.

First, we shall consider the steady flow of an incompressible liquid through a pipe; the flow of water through a pipe constitutes a fair approximation that we can bear in mind as we consider Fig. 11.15. The figure shows a pipe with cross-sectional area gradually changing from A_1 in region ① to A_2 in region ②. For an incompressible fluid, we recognize that when a given volume ΔV enters the pipe at region ① an equal volume ΔV must leave the pipe at region ②. Let Δl_1 be the displacement of the fluid entering the pipe at ① in time Δt and Δl_2 be the displacement of the fluid leaving the pipe at ② in the same time Δt. Then we have

$$\Delta V = A_1 \Delta l_1 = A_2 \Delta l_2 \quad \text{or,} \quad \Delta V/\Delta t = A_1 \Delta l_1/\Delta t = A_2 \Delta l_2/\Delta t.$$

The flux Φ of the fluid through the pipe is defined as the volume of fluid entering or leaving the pipe per unit time, dV/dt. Thus, by taking the limit of the above equation as $\Delta t \to 0$ we can write

$$\Phi = dV/dt = A_1 \, dl_1/dt = A_2 \, dl_2/dt.$$

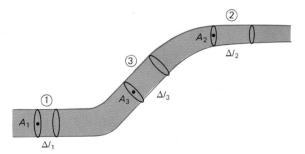

Fig. 11.15 The flow of an incompressible nonviscous fluid through a pipe. The flux Φ through the pipe is given by $\Phi = A_1 v_1 = A_2 v_2 = A_3 v_3$.

The fluid velocities at ① and ② have different magnitudes, $v_1 = dl_1/dt$ and $v_2 = dl_2/dt$; therefore we have

$$\Phi = A_1 v_1 = A_2 v_2, \quad \left\{ \begin{array}{l} \Phi \text{ in m}^3/\text{s} \\ A \text{ in m}^2 \\ v \ \text{ in m/s} \end{array} \right\} \quad \textit{(Volume Flux)} \qquad (11.7)$$

where the velocity $\mathbf{v}_1$ of the fluid at surface ① is parallel to the axis of the pipe and thus perpendicular to A_1 and there is a similar relationship between $\mathbf{v}_2$ and A_2. It is easy to see that a similar relation $\Phi = v_3 A_3$ also holds for any intermediate region of the pipe such as ③ in Fig. 11.15. If we wish to obtain the mass flux $\Phi_M = dM/dt$ of fluid through the pipe, we can simply multiply each term in (11.7) by the density ρ of the incompressible fluid.

In *nonviscous* flow, the walls cannot exert tangential forces on the stream nor can the fluid in any part of the stream exert tangential forces on the fluid in adjacent parts of the stream. The walls can only exert normal forces on the stream in the manner that we discussed when we were defining fluid pressure. In nonviscous flow the velocity $\mathbf{v}$ is constant across any cross section of the pipe in Fig. 11.15, as we have tacitly assumed in writing (11.7).

In order to derive Bernoulli's law for the steady flow of a nonviscous, incompressible fluid through a pipe like the one in Fig. 11.16, we first compute the work done to the material in the tube by external forces. Because there is no displacement of the fluid normal to the walls of the pipe, this work is done by fluid *outside* of the region between regions ① and ②. A force $F_1 = P_1 A_1$ in the direction of fluid displacement does work $W_1 = F_1 \Delta l_1$ on the fluid as it undergoes a small displacement Δl_1 in the vicinity of region ①. A force $F_2 = P_2 A_2$ acts in a direction opposite the small displacement Δl_2 in the vicinity of region ②; because F_2 tends to reduce the mechanical energy in the tube, $W_2 = -F_2 \Delta l_2$. The net work W done by external forces to the fluid experiencing the displacements shown in the figure is

$$W = W_1 + W_2 = F_1 \Delta l_1 - F_2 \Delta l_2 = P_1 A_1 \Delta l_1 - P_2 A_2 \Delta l_2.$$

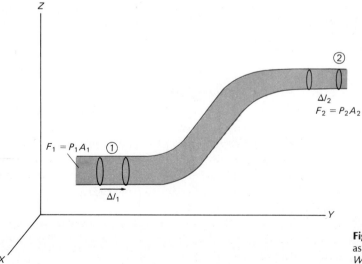

Fig. 11.16 Work done by external forces as a fluid moves through the pipe: $W = (P_1 - P_2) \Delta V$.

Because $A_1\Delta l_1 = A_2\Delta l_2 = \Delta V$, the volume of fluid displaced, we write

$$W = (P_1 - P_2)\Delta V.$$

If we now let the displacements Δl_1 and Δl_2 approach zero, we obtain

$$dW = (P_1 - P_2)dV. \quad \text{(Work Done)} \tag{11.8}$$

The net work dW in this equation serves to increase the mechanical energy of the fluid in the tube. The result of the displacement as this work is done is that the tube of fluid no longer occupies a volume dV at ① but has moved into a volume dV at ②. Therefore, the increase in the mechanical energy of the tube of fluid is equal to the difference in the mechanical energy of a sample of fluid of volume dV and mass ρdV at ② and the amount of energy that this same sample of fluid has at ①. Thus, the increase of energy is equal to

$$[(\tfrac{1}{2}\rho v_2^2 + \rho g z_2) - (\tfrac{1}{2}\rho v_1^2 + \rho g z_1)]dV. \quad \begin{array}{l}\text{(Increase in}\\ \text{Mechanical Energy)}\end{array} \tag{11.9}$$

Setting the work in (11.8) equal to the increase in mechanical energy in (11.9), we obtain

$$P_1 - P_2 = \tfrac{1}{2}\rho v_2^2 + \rho g z_2 - \tfrac{1}{2}\rho v_1^2 - \rho g z_1,$$

or

$$P_1 + \tfrac{1}{2}\rho v_1^2 + \rho g z_1 = P_2 + \tfrac{1}{2}\rho v_2^2 + \rho g z_2. \quad \text{(Bernoulli's Law)} \tag{11.10}$$

Bernoulli's Law (11.10) asserts that

In the steady flow of a nonviscous incompressible fluid through a pipe the sum of the pressure, the kinetic energy per unit volume, and the potential energy per unit volume is the same at all points in the pipe.

We note that in (11.10) P_1 and P_2 can be either absolute pressure or gauge pressure provided P_1 and P_2 are *both* clearly specified as either absolute or gauge pressure; this is easy to see because if P_1 and P_2 in (11.10) are initially given as absolute pressure, the change to gauge pressure merely involves subtracting the *same* quantity P_{At} from *both* sides of (11.10). We note also that the location of the arbitrary reference plane from which heights z_1 and z_2 are measured is unimportant provided both are measured from the *same* reference plane; it is the difference $z_2 - z_1$ that is the important consideration. The speeds v_1 and v_2 are measured relative to the stationary pipe walls, which are at rest in the XYZ reference frame in Fig. 11.16.

The derivation of Bernoulli's Law for fluid flow through a pipe makes use of an easily visualized special case. In the next section we discuss a more general situation and state Bernoulli's Law in a more general way.

Example. For a water conduit like the pipe shown in Fig. 11.16, the cross-sectional areas are $A_1 = 0.04$ m² and $A_2 = 0.01$ m², and the difference in levels is $(z_2 - z_1) = 2$ m. If the flux of water through the pipe is 0.02 m³/s, what are the speeds v_1 and v_2? What is the difference in the pressure between points ① and ②? If the water were at rest in the pipe, what would be the difference in pressure between points ① and ②?

From (11.7), we obtain $v_1 = \Phi/A_1$ and $v_2 = \Phi/A_2$: $v_1 = (0.02$ m³/s)/(0.04 m²) $= 0.5$ m/s and $v_2 = (0.02$ m³/s)/(0.01 m²) $= 2$ m/s. We can then find $P_1 - P_2$ from Bernoulli's Law: $P_1 - P_2 = \rho[g(z_2 - z_1) + \frac{1}{2}(v_2^2 - v_1^2)] = (1000$ kg/m³)[(9.8 m/s²)(2 m) $+ \frac{1}{2}(3.75$ m²/s²)] $= 21,500$ Pa.

If the water were at rest in the pipe, we could eploy (11.3') to write $P_1 - P_2 = \rho g(h_2 - h_1) = (1000$ kg/m³)(9.8 m/s²)(2 m) $= 19,600$ Pa. Thus, under static conditions the pressure difference is smaller than the pressure difference in the moving water for this particular pipe.

11.5   STEADY FLOW: STREAMLINES

Having discussed the flow of a fluid through a pipe, we now consider a more general case of steady flow such as the flow of air past a stationary airplane model in a wind tunnel or the flow of water past a stationary ship model in a naval model basin. This type of motion also includes the movement of "streamlined" vehicles through a stationary fluid such as air or water; in this case, the fluid is moving *relative* to the vehicle. In this section, we shall continue to restrict our attention to the steady flow of nonviscous, incompressible fluids.

As pointed out earlier, in the steady flow of a fluid, the fluid velocity at every point in space has a constant value; at every point, the fluid velocity has a definitie magnitude and direction, neither of which varies with time. We can represent the velocity directions by means of *streamlines* like those shown in Fig. 11.17. The stream-

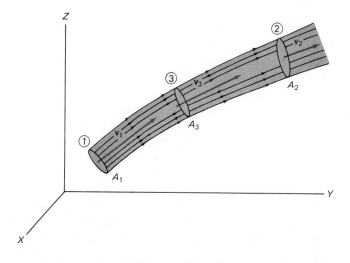

Fig. 11.17   Streamline flow.

lines are drawn in such a way that at every point in space the velocity vector is parallel to the streamline. A tubular region whose generators are streamlines is called a *streamtube*, which can be thought of as a "bundle" of adjacent streamlines. Because of the way in which streamlines are drawn, fluid inside the streamtube remains inside the tube and never crosses the lateral boundaries of the tube. Thus, fluid entering the end of a streamtube at Region ① in Fig. 11.17 remains inside the streamtube until it emerges at the other end of the tube at Region ②.

We see that a streamtube like the one in Fig. 11.17 is in certain ways similar to the pipe in Figs. 11.15 and 11.16. The same arguments used earlier for fluid flow through a pipe can be applied to fluid flow through a streamtube. Thus, for the flux of fluid through a streamtube we can write

$$\Phi = v_{1\text{AV}}A_1 = v_{2\text{AV}}A_2 = v_{3\text{AV}}A_3, \quad (Flux)$$

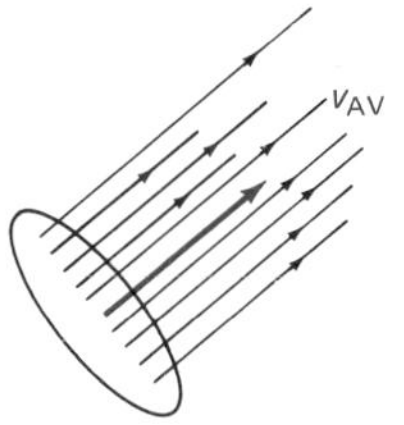

Fig. 11.18

where the average velocity in each case is perpendicular to the cross-sectional area of the tube, as suggested in Fig. 11.18. Similarly, we can derive an expression like (11.10) for a streamtube. However, there is one important difference between a streamtube and a pipe. Whereas a tapered pipe has cross-sectional areas that were fixed once and for all when the pipe was manufactured, we are free to change the cross-sectional areas of a streamtube by simply considering more slender tubes. In the limit where the cross-sectional areas approach zero so that the stream tube becomes a single streamline, Bernoulli's Law (11.10) continues to apply and we can give the law a more general statement for *points* along a single streamline:

$$P + \tfrac{1}{2}\rho v^2 + \rho gz = \text{constant.} \quad (Along\ a\ Streamline) \quad (11.11)$$

BERNOULLI'S LAW: At all points on the same streamline in a nonviscous, incompressible fluid in steady flow, the sum of the pressure, the kinetic energy per unit volume, and the potential energy per unit volume has the same value.

We can apply Bernoulli's Law to many practical problems. However, we must remember that (11.11) is at best a good approximation; it cannot be exact in cases involving real fluids.

A problem that was of great interest to Torricelli involves the speed of efflux from a "well-rounded orifice" in the wall of a large tank like the one shown schematically in Fig. 11.19. The problem involves the determination of the speed v_3 at which the water emerges from the orifice. In applying (11.11) to this problem, we find it convenient to employ gauge pressures and to measure potential energies from the level at which the water emerges from the orifice; this reference level is a distance h below the surface of the water in the tank. We assume that the tank is so large that the velocity of the bulk of the fluid inside the tank is negligibly small and that the surface level of water in the tank does not appreciably change; we could more realistically assume that the orifice in Fig. 11.19 is located in a dam confining a large body of water. By a "well-rounded orifice" we mean an opening with walls designed to ensure steady flow with streamlines perpendicular to the opening; a simple hole in the wall has sharp edges that tend to produce turbulence and that even in

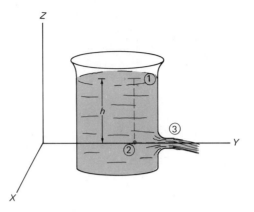

Fig. 11.19 Fluid emerging from a well-rounded orifice.

the most favorable case produce a narrowing of the emerging stream known as the *vena contracta*.

Consider the three points ①, ②, and ③ in Fig. 11.19. In finding the pressure at point ② consider a streamline connecting ① and ②. Because the velocity between these points is essentially zero, we can draw a "virtual streamline" joining ① and ② in any way that we wish. Under this condition Bernoulli's Law (11.11) becomes

$$P_2 + 0 + 0 = 0 + 0 + \rho gh \quad \text{or} \quad P_2 = \rho gh,$$

which is the same value that we would have obtained by using (11.1′) to calculate the hydrostatic pressure P_2.

We now join points ② and ③ by a streamline. In this case, Bernoulli's Law gives

$$0 + \tfrac{1}{2}\rho v_3^2 + 0 = P_2 + 0 + 0 \qquad \text{or} \qquad v_3 = \sqrt{2P_2/\rho}.$$

Substituting $P_2 = \rho gh$ gives the value of $v_3 = \sqrt{2\rho gh/\rho}$ or

$$v_3 = \sqrt{2gh}. \quad \textit{(Torricelli's Law)} \tag{11.12}$$

Equation (11.12) is a relation known as *Torricelli's Law,* which states that the speed of a liquid emerging through a well-rounded orifice in a tank wall at a distance h below the surface of the liquid in the tank is the same as the speed of an object after moving downward a vertical distance h in free fall. One interesting result of Torricelli's Law is that, if the orifice is rounded in such a way that the emerging water is directed vertically upward, the water will return to a height a distance h above the orifice.

Bernoulli's Law can provide an understanding of the operation of such devices as the Venturi flow meter, which is treated in a problem at the end of the chapter. By connecting points in a fluid at rest by virtual streamlines, it is easy to derive the first two laws of fluid statics from Bernoulli's Law; this also is left as a problem.

11.6 FLUID FLOW: GENERAL CONSIDERATIONS

In our discussion of the flow of fluid through a pipe or a streamtube we have been careful to select cross-sectional areas A to which the fluid velocities are normal. In order to compute the flux through some slanted surface S like the one shown in Fig. 11.20, we note that the velocity component normal to the surface S is $v \cos \theta$. Thus, we can write $\Phi = vS \cos \theta = vA$, where $A = S \cos \theta$ is an equivalent surface to which velocity $\mathbf{v}$ is perpendicular. If we represent the surface S by a vector $\mathbf{S}$ having the magnitude of S and a direction given by the normal to the surface, we can express the flux through the surface as $\Phi = \mathbf{v} \cdot \mathbf{S}$. If the surface S is curved, we must divide S into a very large number of small surface elements, each represented by a vector $d\mathbf{S}$, and compute the flux $d\Phi = \mathbf{v} \cdot d\mathbf{S}$ for each surface element and then integrate over the surface to determine the total flux. These ideas will prove useful later when we discuss *electric fields,* which are mathematically similar to the "fluid-flow fields" suggested in Fig. 11.17.

We have seen that the total flux through a streamtube like the one in Fig. 11.17 is constant. In fact, equations like (11.7) indicate that the total flux Φ through a pipe or a streamtube remains constant; all of the fluid entering a streamtube at one end must leave the streamtube at the other end. An equation like (11.7) that expresses the constancy of flux is called an *equation of continuity;* it simply states the fact that fluid in steady flow does not accumulate or "pile up" anywhere. Mathematically similar equations will prove to be of use to us in our later studies of *heat flow* as well as in our studies of electric and magnetic fields.

Before concluding our discussion of fluid flow we must consider the question regarding the origin and ultimate fate of the fluid in which we are interested. We have asserted that all the fluid entering one end of a streamtube eventually leaves the other end of the streamtube, but we are left with the questions: Where did the fluid come from and where did it go? In the case of the flux of water in a stream, the water may begin in a spring high in the mountains and end up in the ocean or in a sinkhole. In describing this we regard the spring as a *source* of the water and the ocean as a *sink*.

In the case of streamline flow of an incompressible fluid these ideas are illustrated symbolically in Fig. 11.21, which shows a streamtube between a single source and a single sink. Fluid enters the streamtube from the source and leaves the streamtube at the sink. The equation of continuity as applied to the streamtube in the figure

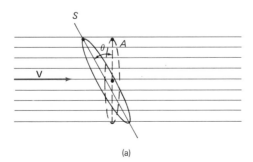

(a)

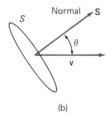

(b)

Fig. 11.20 The flux through surface S is given by $\Phi = vS \cos \theta = \mathbf{v} \cdot \mathbf{S}$.

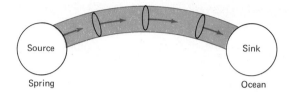

Fig. 11.21 The total flux from a *source* ends at one or more *sinks*.

states that the flux Φ_{source} leaving the source is equal to the flux Φ_{sink} reaching in the sink:

$$\Phi_{\text{source}} = \Phi_{\text{sink}}. \quad \textit{(Continuity Equation)} \tag{11.13}$$

The total flux leaving any source must ultimately arrive at one or more sinks.

11.7   FLUID FORCES

We are now able to analyze in some detail the ways in which moving fluids exert forces on solid objects with which they come into contact. In treating fluids, we shall make use of the form of Newton's Second Principle given in Eq. (4.15): $F_R = d\mathbf{p}/dt$, where $d\mathbf{p}/dt$ represents the time rate of change of the momentum of the particle or body on which the force $\mathbf{F}_R$ acts. When dealing with fluids we use a similar relation:

$$\mathbf{F}_R = \text{Time Rate of Change of Fluid Momentum.}$$

Consider the case of a stream of fluid striking a flat wall shown in Fig. 11.22a. The initial X component of the momentum of a "particle" of fluid of mass dm is vdm; its X component of momentum after it strikes the wall is zero. Thus, its change in momentum at the fixed wall is $-vdm$. It follows that the total time rate of change of momentum at the wall is $-(dM/dt)v$, where dM/dt represents the total mass of fluid striking the wall per second. As noted in Section 4, $(dM/dt) = \rho\Phi$, where ρ is the fluid density and Φ is the volume flux. Thus, the resultant force exerted *on* the stream *by* the wall is $F_x = -v(dM/dt)$. By Newton's Third Principle, the force exerted *on* the wall *by* the stream is

$$F_x = v(dM/dt). \quad \textit{(Force on Wall)} \tag{11.14}$$

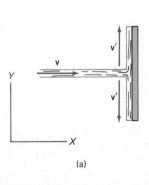

(a)

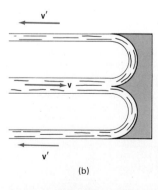

(b)

Fig. 11.22 Fluid force F_x on a stationary wall: $F_x = v(dM/dt)$ for the flat wall in (a); for the "dished" wall in (b) the force is doubled if $v' = v$.

If we equip the wall with "dishes" like those in Fig. 11.22b and assume that the magnitude of the fluid velocity is not changed in the collision, it is easily proved that the force on the wall can be doubled.

Equation (11.14) also gives the force exerted by a stream of fluid on the *stationary* blade of a rotary device like the one shown in Fig. 11.23. If we allow the device in Fig. 11.23 to rotate, we have a prime mover that utilizes the kinetic energy of mass motion of the fluid to provide rotational motion to the wheel that can be used in doing useful work. In a prime mover we wish to take as much energy as possible from the "working substance," which is the fluid in the present case. The force applied to the moving blade is less than the value given in (11.14), but energy is delivered to the rotating wheel because this force acts through a distance.

The wheel in Fig. 11.23 is of a type that mechanical engineers classify as *impulse turbines*, where all the energy transferred is supplied by the kinetic energy of the fluid. Another type of rotatory device is classified as a *reaction turbine,* a familiar example of which is the lawn sprinkler shown in Fig. 11.24. Fluid under pressure enters the device at the center, flows radially outward inside the hollow blades, and emerges with tangential velocity v_T. The maximum "reaction forces" on the blades are exerted when the speeds of the emerging streams are as large as possible. But this occurs for a fixed rotor, so in this case, no energy is delivered to the wheel. Application of Bernoulli's Law to the problem indicates that for a stationary rotor $\frac{1}{2}\rho v^2 = P$ or $v = \sqrt{2P/\rho}$, where v is the speed of the fluid emerging from the blades and P is the gauge pressure of the fluid in the pipe attached to the turbine. To get maximum efficiency from the turbine, the velocity of the fluid emerging from the moving rotor should be as much smaller than this as practically possible. As in the case of the impulse turbine, the greatest amount of energy is imparted to the wheel in Fig. 11.24, when the greatest amount of energy is removed from the fluid. It is not practically possible for the efficiency of either an impulse or a reaction turbine to be 100%. Why?

We note that the modern turbines actually used today as prime movers are complex devices representing cleverly designed combinations of the simple impulse and reaction turbines that we have described.

Streams of fluid provide the forces required to accelerate jet aircraft and rockets. Consider a stream of fluid that is ejected from a rocket with velocity **v** *relative to*

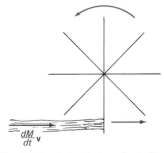

Fig. 11.23   A simple *impulse turbine.*

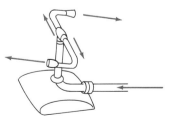

Fig. 11.24   A simple *reaction turbine.*

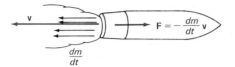

Fig. 11.25   The *thrust* exerted on a rocket.

the rocket, as suggested in Fig. 11.25. We use an inertial frame of reference with respect to which the rocket is initially at rest. Let $\mathbf{u}$ represent the velocity of the rocket with respect to this inertial frame of reference. The velocity of the fluid being ejected from the rocket with respect to this frame of reference is $\mathbf{v}_f = \mathbf{u} + \mathbf{v}$. Consider the situation at a time when the rocket has velocity $\mathbf{u}$ and the mass of the rocket and contents being accelerated is M. Suppose that in a small time interval dt a quantity of fluid of mass dm is ejected from the rocket. For simplicity let us assume that the rocket is in space far from any other object so that gravitational forces can be neglected.

After the mass dm of fluid is ejected, the velocity of the rocket is $\mathbf{u} + d\mathbf{u}$; the momentum change of the rocket is

$$d\mathbf{p}_R = (M - dm)(\mathbf{u} + d\mathbf{u}) - (M - dm)\mathbf{u} = M d\mathbf{u},$$

where we can drop the negligibly small quantity $dm\,d\mathbf{u}$. The momentum change of the ejected fluid is

$$d\mathbf{p}_f = dm(\mathbf{u} + \mathbf{v}) - dm\,\mathbf{u} = dm\,\mathbf{v}.$$

Since there are no external forces acting, the total momentum of the system must be constant, which requires that

$$0 = d\mathbf{p}_R + d\mathbf{p}_f = M d\mathbf{u} + dm\,\mathbf{v}.$$

Since the changes being considered occur in a time dt, we can conclude that

$$M(d\mathbf{u}/dt) = -(dm/dt)\mathbf{v}.$$

Then the final rocket velocity $\mathbf{u}_f$ at time t_f when a mass m of fuel plus oxidant has been ejected is given by

$$\mathbf{u}_f = \int_0^{\mathbf{u}_f} d\mathbf{u} = -\int_0^{t_f} (1/M)(dm/dt)\mathbf{v}\ dt = -\int_0^m (1/M)\mathbf{v}\ dm.$$

If we now assume that $\mathbf{v}$ is constant and that M can be replaced by the mass of the unfueled rocket M_R, we obtain

$$M_R \mathbf{u}_f = -m\mathbf{v}.$$

From this equation it is obvious that both m and v should be as large as possible if we wish the rocket speed u_f to be as large as possible; this is indeed correct.

However, something is seriously wrong with our equation. At ignition the mass being accelerated to the right in Fig. 11.25 is not M_R but is $M_R + m$; only as burnout occurs is the mass being accelerated really M_R. In expressing the rocket's final velocity we have obtained the *optimistic limit* that $u_f = (m/M_R)v$. A *pessimistic limit* $u_f = [m/(M_R + m)]v$ is obtained on the assumption that all the mass m of fuel and oxidant is being accelerated during the entire period of acceleration. A correct solution for the velocity of the rocket in the absence of gravitational forces and atmospheric drag under the assumption that mass is ejected at a constant rate is considered in Problem 31. This solution can be expressed as

$$u_f = v\left[\frac{m}{M_R + m} + \frac{1}{2}\left(\frac{m}{M_R + m}\right)^2 + \frac{1}{3}\left(\frac{m}{M_R + m}\right)^3 + \cdots\right].$$

The correct value of u_f lies between the optimistic and pessimistic limits.

The distinction between a rocket and a jet-propelled plane is that the rocket carries all of its own fuel and oxidant, whereas the jet plane carries only fuel and collects and compresses external air for use as an oxidant. The jet plane must therefore operate in the earth's atmosphere, whereas a rocket operates most efficiently in free outer space. Some of the effects involved in the launching of a rocket from the earth's surface are illustrated in the following example.

Example. A rocket with a *total* mass of 40,000 kg rises vertically from rest. It ejects gas at a speed of 1600 m/s at the rate of 450 kg/s for 40 s before the fuel is exhausted. Determine the initial upward acceleration of the rocket and its upward acceleration at the end of 20 s and 40 s. Neglect the variation of g with altitude.

We note that the upward force *on* the rocket exerted by the jet is constant: $F = (dm/dt)v = (450 \text{ kg/s})(1600 \text{ m/s}) = 720{,}000 \text{ N}$. Because of gravity, there is a downward force of $w = (40{,}000 \text{ kg})(9.8 \text{ m/s}^2) = 392{,}000 \text{ N}$ at $t = 0$; $w = \{[40{,}000 - 20(450)] \text{ kg}\}(9.8 \text{ m/s}^2) = (31{,}000 \text{ kg})(9.8 \text{ m/s}^2) = 304{,}000 \text{ N}$ at $t = 20$ s; and $w = \{[40{,}000 - 40(450)] \text{ kg}\}(9.8 \text{ m/s}^2) = (22{,}000 \text{ kg})(9.8 \text{ m/s}^2) = 216{,}000 \text{ N}$ at $t = 40$ s. Thus, the net upward forces at these times are: $F_N = 328{,}000 \text{ N}$ at $t = 0$; $F_N = 416{,}000 \text{ N}$ at $t = 20$ s; and $F_N = 504{,}000 \text{ N}$ at $t = 40$ s. Accelerations in rocketry are usually stated as the ratio of a to g: $a/g = F_N/w$. Thus, at $t = 0$, $a = (328{,}000 \text{ N}/392{,}000 \text{ N})g = 0.837g$; at $t = 20$ s, $a = (416{,}000 \text{ N}/304{,}000 \text{ N})g = 1.37g$; and at $t = 40$ s, $a = (504{,}000 \text{ N}/216{,}000 \text{ N})g = 2.33g$, where $g = 9.8 \text{ m/s}^2$ is the gravitational acceleration.

An airplane in flight is subject to an upward force called *lift* that is exerted by the surrounding air. Lift is somewhat different from the thrust forces that we have just described, but it can also be described in terms of the time rate of change of fluid momentum and Newton's Third Principle. Consider the streamlines around an airfoil as shown in Fig. 11.26; the frame of reference is that in which the airfoil is at rest. In order to achieve lift, the shape of the airfoil and the "angle of attack" θ must together be such that the stream of air is deflected downward. The downward force exerted by the airfoil on the air is given by the time rate of change of the momentum of the air as it passes the airfoil. By Newton's Third Principle there is

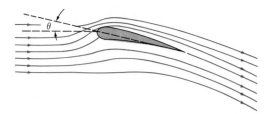

Fig. 11.26   Streamline flow past an airfoil.

an upward force of equal magnitude exerted on the airfoil by the air; this is the lift force.

We see in Fig. 11.26 that just above the airfoil the streamlines are closer together than far from the airfoil, while just below the airfoil they are farther apart than far from the airfoil. This represents increased air-velocity magnitudes just above the airfoil and decreased air-velocity magnitudes just below the airfoil compared to the air velocity far from the airfoil. From Bernoulli's Law, we conclude that the pressure below the airfoil is greater than the pressure above the airfoil; this pressure difference gives rise to the lift force described in the preceding paragraph. The lift on a section of wing is proportional to $\frac{1}{2}\rho(v_{\text{top}})^2 - \frac{1}{2}\rho(v_{\text{bottom}})^2$, where ρ is the air density and v is the magnitude of the air velocity.

Turbulence and viscosity are involved in a complete understanding of dynamical lift. The details are rather involved, but the general nature of the lift force is as we have described it.

11.8   VISCOSITY

Earlier in this chapter we stated that a fluid at rest is incapable of exerting tangential forces on solid surfaces. This statement is true for fluids at rest. However, we are all aware that work must be done to keep a ship moving at constant velocity through water or to keep an airplane moving at constant velocity through the air. A portion of this work can be attributed to the generation of turbulence, but even for keeping a well-streamlined ship or airplane in motion at constant velocity some work is required. This work is necessary because of the frictional resistance of a fluid to the motion of one layer of the fluid past other adjacent layers or past the surfaces of solid bodies; this fluid friction is known as *viscosity.* Viscosity also accounts for the slow flow of molasses or heavy motor oil when we attempt to pour these liquids out of a container on a cold morning. Viscosity effects become observable only when fluids flow or when we attempt to move an object through a fluid; viscous fluids in motion *are* able to exert tangential forces.

One way in which viscosity can be studied is by means of the arrangement shown schematically in Fig. 11.27, which shows an outer cylinder with radius R_2 mounted on a rotating platform and a coaxial inner cylinder of slightly smaller radius R_1 suspended by a thin wire. If we fill the thin annular space between the cylinders with a fluid and set the outer cylinder into rotation, we find that the inner cylinder is subject to a torque that tends to set it into rotation in the same sense. This torque is directly proportional to the rotational speed of the outer cylinder and depends on the nature of the fluid in the region between the cylinders; it is produced by

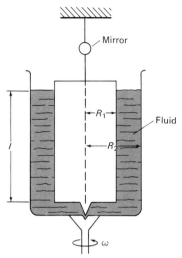

Fig. 11.27 A device used for the study of viscosity. The pointed projection at the bottom of the inner cylinder merely keeps the motion centered; it does not support the weight of the inner cylinder.

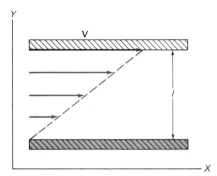

Fig. 11.28

tangential forces exerted on the inner cylinder by the surrounding fluid. At equilibrium the torque on the inner cylinder exerted by the fluid is balanced by the torque in the supporting wire, which can be determined if the angle of twist and the torsion constant of the wire are known.

The observed effects can be understood on the basis of the situation illustrated in Fig. 11.28, which shows in cross section two solid plates separated by a layer of fluid. The upper plate has a velocity $\mathbf{v}$ to the right relative to the lower plate. The region in the fluid between the plates is characterized by a set of horizontal streamlines. However, the velocity along the streamlines varies from $v_x = 0$ at the surface of the lower plate to $v_x = v$ at the surface of the upper plate. It is observed that the velocity of the fluid in immediate contact with a solid has the same velocity as the solid; *this contact layer of fluid is at rest relative to the solid surface. There is no slip between a fluid and the surface of an adjacent solid.*

The lower plate experiences a tangential force F_x directed toward the right in the figure. The magnitude of this tangential force is directly proportional to the area A of the facing plates and to the velocity v of the upper plate and is inversely proportional to the separation l between the plates; it also depends on the type of fluid separating the plates. These observations can be summarized by the equation

$$F_x/A = \eta\,(v_x/l), \quad \textit{(Viscosity)} \qquad (11.15)$$

where η is called the *coefficient of viscosity* of the fluid and is measured in $N \cdot s/m^2$ or $kg/m \cdot s$. The law expressed by this equation was first stated by Newton. The term F_x/A is a shearing stress. For an elastic solid we found in Chapter 10 that the shearing stress is directly proportional to the strain, the proportionality coefficient being the shear modulus. A fluid at rest cannot support a shearing stress. However, the term v_x/l in (11.15) can be interpreted as the time rate of change of

Table 11.1.   Typical Values of the Coefficient of Viscosity η and the Surface Tension σ for Various Fluids at 20°C

Material	η (10^{-5} kg/m·s)	σ (J/m² or N/m)
Gases		
Air	1.82	—
Carbon dioxide	1.47	—
Liquids		
Acetone	32.7	0.0237
Benzene	64.7	0.0289
Carbon tetrachloride	96.9	0.0270
Ethanol	120.0	0.0223
Mercury	155.4	0.465
Water	100.2	0.0728

the shearing strain of the fluid between the plates in Fig. 11.28. Thus, (11.15) says that the shearing stress is directly proportional to the rate of strain. The shearing stress is zero for a fluid at rest. For the situation of Fig. 11.28 the space rate of change, or gradient, of the fluid velocity taken in the direction normal to the plates is a constant equal to v_x/l. A more general version of (11.15) is

$$F_x/A = \eta(dv_x/dy), \tag{11.15'}$$

where the Y axis is perpendicular to the surface past which the fluid is flowing and F_x/A is the shearing stress on that surface. Values of the coefficient of viscosity η for several fluids at room temperature are listed in Table 11.1. The viscosity of many liquids decreases rapidly with increasing temperature. It is possibly surprising that the viscosity of gases is *nearly* independent of pressure.

When there is relative motion of a solid body and a fluid, the velocity of the

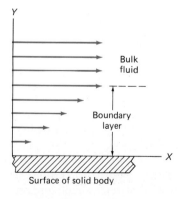

Fig. 11.29 Schematic representation of the boundary layer at the surface of a solid body.

fluid relative to the surface of the solid changes from zero at the surface of the solid to the stream velocity **v** characteristic of the mass motion of the bulk fluid relative to the surface of the solid. The layer in which the change from 0 to **v** occurs is called the *boundary layer* and is shown schematically in Fig. 11.29. In the case of the flow of air around an airplane wing, the boundary layer is very thin, characteristically of the order of millimeters. Viscous forces are effective only in the boundary layer, but, nevertheless, they can constitute a significant *viscous drag* on the solid surface.

Viscosity accounts for a force of fluid frictional drag on a solid body moving at velocity **v** through the fluid even when the solid body is well "streamlined" so that turbulence is kept to a minimum. For moderate speeds this drag force can be represented by $\mathscr{F}_F = -\mathscr{R}\mathbf{v}$, where $\mathscr{R}$ is a constant that depends on the viscosity of the liquid and on the size and shape of the moving body. Therefore, we must exert an applied force $\mathbf{F}_A = -\mathscr{F}_F = \mathscr{R}\mathbf{v}$ in the direction of motion to keep the body moving at constant velocity. The work that we must do in giving the body a displacement **D** is

$$W = \mathbf{F}_A \cdot \mathbf{D} = \mathscr{R}\mathbf{v} \cdot \mathbf{D}. \quad \textit{(Work Against Fluid Friction)} \quad (11.16)$$

Since **v** is constant and has the same direction as **D,** we can write

$$W = \mathscr{R}vD = \mathscr{R}v^2t = \mathscr{R}D^2/t. \quad (11.16')$$

Equations (11.16) and (11.16′) have some consequences of practical importance. Equation (11.16) states that we do very little work in moving an object from one place to another, provided we keep the velocity very low; however, (11.16′) reminds us that a great deal of time is required if the velocity is to be kept low. These facts have a bearing on the economics of transportation; in moving heavy cargoes, water transport—ocean freighters or river barges—wins out over air, rail, or highway transport in cases where long delivery times can be tolerated. Of course, it must be recognized that long delivery times run up the labor cost involved in the remuneration of the crew!

The above equations indicate that the energy required for a given trip goes up directly with increases in velocity. We note also that the output power of the engines propelling a vehicle goes up as the square of the speed: $P = \mathscr{R}v^2$. At higher speeds the drag is determined primarily by turbulence rather than viscosity; in many such situations the drag force is approximately proportional to the square of the speed. Speed boats gobble fuel at an alarming rate!

Example. Because motor-driven ships carry a finite quantity of fuel, they have a limited "cruising radius," which is the distance a ship can travel away from home port and still be able to return home without refueling. How does the cruising radius *r* depend on the ship's speed?

Recognizing that the fuel tank's capacity determines the amount of work W

that can be done in propelling the ship at constant speed, we can use (11.16')
with $D = 2r$ to write

$$r = W/2\mathcal{R}v \quad \text{or} \quad r = \sqrt{Wt/4\mathcal{R}}.$$

If the fuel begins to run low aboard a vessel, a wise captain will "slow down"
the ship!

11.9 SURFACE TENSION OF LIQUIDS

In our introductory statements we indicated that fluids cannot in general exert
tensional forces. Although this statement is generally true for the interior of fluids,
the *surfaces* of liquids represent an exception. The surface of a liquid acts as if it
were covered by a thin elastic film that exerts forces associated with a phenomenon
known as *surface tension*.

The reasons for the existence of surface tension can be understood in terms of
the simple diagram in Fig. 11.30. A molecule in the body of the liquid is subject to
forces of attraction exerted by surrounding molecules on all sides; these forces add
to zero because surrounding molecules exert forces of equal magnitude in all directions.
The forces of *attraction* on a molecule at the surface do not add to zero but tend
to pull the molecule back toward the body of the liquid. Once a molecule in the
surface layer becomes closer to adjacent molecules below it, forces of repulsion set
in that eventually become equal to the downward resultant of the forces of attraction
so that a molecule at the surface is in equilibrium.

As a molecule from the interior approaches the surface moving against downward
forces, it acquires potential energy relative to its initial position in the interior of
the liquid. The number of molecules having this potential energy is proportional to
the area of the surface. The ratio of the total potential energy of the surface to the
area of the surface is a characteristic constant called *surface tension* σ of the liquid;
$\sigma = E_P/A$. The total potential energy of this type is thus proportional to the surface
area:

$$E_P = \sigma A. \quad \begin{cases} E_P \text{ in J} \\ A \text{ in m}^2 \\ \sigma \text{ in J/m}^2 \end{cases} \tag{11.17}$$

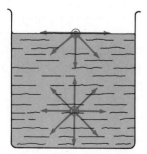

Fig. 11.30 A molecule at the surface of a liquid experiences a net force
directed toward the body of the liquid.

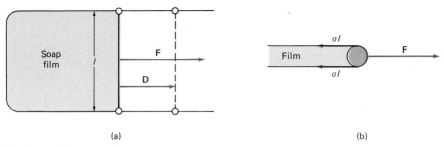

Fig. 11.31 Surface tension.

Surface tension can be visualized in a somewhat different way, as suggested in Fig. 11.31a, which shows a soap film being stretched over a rectangular frame. By exerting a force **F** to the right on a movable wire that forms one side of the frame, we do work FD against elastic forces in increasing the area of the film by an amount $A = 2Dl$; the 2 appears because the film has two surfaces, as illustrated in Fig. 11.31b. Setting $FD = \sigma A = \sigma \cdot 2Dl$, we obtain

$$F = 2\sigma l. \quad \left\{ \begin{array}{l} F \text{ in N} \\ l \ \text{ in m} \\ \sigma \text{ in N/m} \end{array} \right\} \tag{11.17'}$$

Because 1 N/m = 1 J/m², the dimensions of σ in (11.17) and (11.17') are actually the same. Values of the surface tension for several liquids are listed in Table 11.1; surface tension generally decreases with increasing temperature.

We can visualize σ by looking at Fig. 11.31b, which shows a cross section of the film in the vicinity of the movable wire. We can think of the force F on the wire as being opposed by one force σl exerted on the wire by the upper layer of the film and a second force σl exerted on the wire by the lower surface of the film. The work FD that we do to the film increases the total area of the film, thereby bringing more molecules to the surface layers where they have greater potential energy.

When we discussed the equilibrium of a dynamical system, we pointed out that a dynamical system is in stable equilibrium when the potential energy of the system is a minimum. If we consider a given small volume of a liquid as a dynamical system, we conclude from (11.17) that the surface potential energy of the liquid is a minimum when the surface of the fluid is a minimum. Because the ratio of surface area to total volume is a minimum for a sphere, small quantities of liquids tend to be spherical. For example, rain droplets in the air are usually spherical in shape. Because σ is large for mercury, mercury tends to collect into drops whenever it is splashed on a table top. For large volumes of liquid, the influence of gravitational forces becomes more important than the proportionately smaller forces due to surface tension, and the liquid assumes the shape of its container. What would be the shape of a sample of liquid in a "space probe" not subject to appreciable gravitational forces?

QUESTIONS

1. How do liquids and gases differ from solids? How do liquids and gases differ from each other?

2. A large building has a flat roof. Because of the large quantity of air above the roof, the atmosphere exerts an enormous downward force on the roof. Why doesn't the roof collapse?

3. Why is pressure regarded as a positive quantity? Can you imagine any situation where a negative pressure would be meaningful?

4. Water stands at the *same height* in three glass vases of different sizes and shapes but with bottoms of the same area. Does the pressure at the bottom of these vases depend on the size and shape of the vases? If the three vases were placed on a platform scale, would the registered weight depend on the size and shape of the vases? (Assume that the weight of glass is the same for all vases.)

5. If the arrangement shown in Fig. 11.11 were placed inside an elevator cage, how would the "apparent weight" of the block depend on the motion of the cage?

6. A block of wood floats half submerged in a bucket of water on the floor of a laboratory. What would happen to the block if the bucket were at rest on the surface of the moon? Would it rise, sink, or merely float in the same way?

7. Explain in detail why Torricelli found it impossible to raise water to a height of more than 10 m by means of a *lift pump*. Water can be raised to much greater heights by means of "force pumps." Design a simple force pump that would be suitable for this purpose.

8. A loaded barge barely remains afloat at the eastern entrance to the Gulf of St. Lawrence. What would happen to this barge if it were towed up the St. Lawrence River toward Lake Ontario? Explain your reasoning.

9. A rustic riddle: "Why is it that with a tubfull of water on a platform weighing scale the scale reading does not change when a *live* fish is placed in the water?" Beware of riddles that begin with *why!*

10. In a lecture demonstration a ping pong ball is balanced on a vertical air jet. Explain in detail how this can be done.

11. A tin can floats stably in a vertical position in a tub of water with three lead slugs in the bottom of the can. If one of the slugs is removed from the can and dropped into the water, what will be the effect on the water level in the tub?

12. When two fast-moving trucks pass each other while traveling in opposite directions on a two-lane highway, what fluid forces act on them? Apply Bernoulli's Law.

13. What is streamline motion? What is turbulence?

14. The force exerted on a stationary wall by a stream of fluid can be doubled by "dishing" devices like the one shown in Fig. 11.22. Discuss the forces exerted on a water wheel or turbine with flat blades and with dished blades. Are these forces the same as those exerted on a stationary wall?

15. It has been asserted that the first jet-propelled vehicles were the fire boats on Lake Erie, which take in lake water and pump it out in jets. Discuss this kind of propulsion system. Is such a fireboat really jet-propelled?

16. Why do rain drops attain a *terminal velocity* as they fall through the air? Is it true that the motions of heavy objects and light objects are the same as they fall through the air?

17. What would be the shape of 100 cm³ of water in a space module if the water were not in contact with the walls but were at rest with respect to the walls?

18. Why does a stream of falling water tend to break up into drops as the water moves downward?

19. How is it possible for an airplane to fly upside down?

PROBLEMS

*1. A swimming pool with a horizontal bottom is 20 m wide and 50 m long. If the pool is filled with water to a depth of 3 m, what is the total weight of the water in the pool? What is the average hydrostatic pressure at the bottom of the pool? What is the average hydrostatic pressure on the sides of the pool?

*2. A swimming pool with a flat slanting bottom is 20 m wide and 50 m long. If the depth of the water is 1 m at the shallow end of the pool and 3 m at the deep end, what is the total weight of the water in the pool? What is the average hydrostatic pressure on the bottom of the pool? on the wall of the deep end? on the wall at the shallow end? at the side walls?

3. What is the hydrostatic pressure at a point 20 m below the surface of a deep fresh water lake? What is the hydrostatic pressure at a point 20 m below the surface of the ocean?

4. A U-tube like the one shown in Fig. 11.8b has mercury in the arm at the left and water above the mercury in the arm at the right. The height of the mercury in the left-hand tube is 30 cm and the height of the mercury–water interface in the right-hand tube is 4 cm, where the heights are measured from a reference level at the bottom of the U-tube. What are the hydrostatic pressures at points D and E, which are 3 cm above the reference level? What are the hydrostatic pressures at points D' and E', which are 20 cm above the reference level? What is the total length of the water column above the mercury–water interface?

5. An aluminum casting with a volume of 0.2 m³ is dropped from the deck of a barge into a river having a depth of 4 m. What buoyant force acts on the casting as it reaches the bottom? How much work must be done in order to raise the casting to the surface of the river?

6. When a cylindrical oak log floats at the surface of a fresh-water lake, what fraction of the total volume of the log is below the surface? Locate the heights of the log's center of mass and center of buoyancy with respect to the surface of the water in terms of the log radius R.

7. When a block of ice floats in fresh water, what fraction of the volume of the block is above the surface of the water? A piece of ice having a total volume of 27 cm³ floats in a glass of water that is filled to the brim. How many cm³ of water will flow over the rim of the glass when the ice melts?

8. A balsa surfboard has a total mass of 2 kg. What downward force must be exerted on the surfboard in order to hold it below the surface of the sea? What is the potential energy of this board with respect to objects at the surface when the board's center of mass is 3 m below the surface? If the board were released from rest when it is 3 m below the surface and were not subject to friction, how high would the board rise above the surface following release?

9. A cylinder of balsa wood is 2 m long and has a radius of 20 cm. By attaching a thin lead plate to one end it is possible to make

the balsa cylinder float in stable equilibrium in an upright position. How much lead would be required to make the center of gravity 40 cm below the center of buoyancy?

10. The ice on a lake has a thickness of 40 cm. What is the minimum area that the upper surface of a block of this ice can have if it is to support a 1200-kg automobile? If the surface of the block is rectangular, where should the car be parked for maximum safety?

11. On a day when the barometer reads 751 mm of mercury, what is the atmospheric pressure in pascals? On this day to what height might it be possible to raise water by means of a lift pump? On this day what is the magnitude of the downward force exerted on the flat roof of a building 40 m long and 20 m wide? Will the roof collapse?

12. At normal atmospheric pressure (760 mm Hg) ground-level air at the temperature of melting ice has a density of 1.29 kg/m³. If all the air in the atmosphere had this density, what would be the thickness of the atmosphere? (Neglect the variation in g with altitude.)

13. On a day when the barometer reads 760 mm of mercury what is the gauge pressure at a point 30 m below the surface of a freshwater lake? What is the absolute pressure at this point? At what distance below the surface would the absolute pressure be 3 atm?

14. A water manometer like the one in Fig. 11.13 is used to measure the pressure in a tank of fuel gas. If the level of the water in the arm of the manometer connected to the tank is 40 cm below the level in the arm open to the atmosphere, what is the absolute pressure of the enclosed gas when the barometer reads 756 mm of mercury?

15. The end of a horizontal pipe 10 cm in diam-

eter is connected by a tapered section to a smaller pipe 2 cm in diameter. Water emerges from the open end of the small pipe at a rate of 5 liters per second. What is the speed of the water moving through the small pipe? through the large pipe? What is the difference in the fluid pressures between the large and small pipes? Discuss the advantages and disadvantages of equipping fire hoses with nozzles.

16. For a water conduit like the one shown in Fig. 11.16 the pipe cross-sectional areas are $A_1 = 0.05$ m² and $A_2 = 0.02$ m² and the difference in levels $(z_2 - z_1) = 3$ m. If the flux through the pipe is 0.03 m³/s, what are the speeds v_1 and v_2? What is the difference in pressure between points ① and ②?

17. A horizontal pipe with cross-sectional area $A_1 = 0.06$ m² has a tapered constriction with area $A_2 = 0.01$ m². Because water cannot normally withstand tensile stresses, water vapor begins to form in regions where the absolute pressure drops to zero; this process is known as *cavitation* and results in large energy losses. What is the maximum water flux that can be achieved in the pipe shown in the figure without the occurrence of cavitation if P_1 is 1.4 atm?

18. By connecting a mercury manometer between regions ① and ② in the figure it is possible to measure the pressure difference $(P_1 - P_2)$. The *Venturi flowmeter* employs such a device to determine the flux through a pipe like the one shown in the figure. Derive an expression for the flux Φ in terms of $(P_1 - P_2)$ and the cross-sectional areas of the pipe. If the difference in mercury levels is the "reading" of the flowmeter, what approximations are involved in the

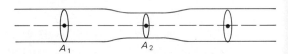

Problems 17 and 18

measurement of water flow and air flow through a pipe like the one in the figure?

19. The air speed of a plane is measured by means of a Pitot-static tube like the one shown in the figure. Such a device can be seen protruding from the wing or fuselage of an aircraft. Use Bernoulli's Law to show that the air speed v of the plane is given by the expression $v = \sqrt{2(P_1 - P)/\rho}$, where ρ is the density of air at the altitude of the plane. Note that v_1 is zero and the pressure and velocity outside the holes at ② have the freestream values.

of mass of the baseball and remember that the air in actual contact with the ball does not "slip" with respect to the surface of the ball. (It should be remembered that a baseball is not really a "streamlined" object and there is always some turbulence behind the moving ball; this turbulence accounts for the erratic behavior of "knuckle balls," which have little or no spin.)

23. Apply Bernoulli's Law to the siphon shown schematically in the figure. Once the siphon is filled with liquid, it will continue to flow. (a) Show that the speed of emergence is

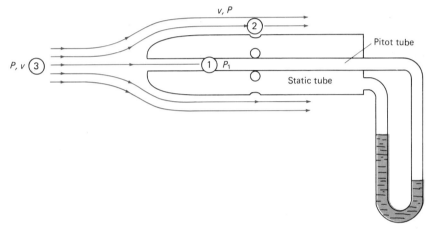

Problems 19 and 20

20. If a plane is flying at an air speed of 640 km/h at an altitude where the density of air is 0.9 kg/m³, determine the difference $(P_1 - P)$ as determined by its Pitot-static tube in mm of mercury. (See Problem 19.) What additional information would the pilot need in order to determine the ground speed of the plane?

21. By the use of virtual streamlines show how the first two laws of fluid statics can be derived from Bernoulli's Law.

22. By application of Bernoulli's Law and Newton's Principles explain how a baseball pitcher is able to throw a "curve" by making the ball spin. Suggestion: Use a coordinate system with its origin at the center

that given by Torricelli's Law and does not depend on the distance between the intake and the surface. (b) Find an expression for the maximum distance Z above the liquid surface that can be attained by a siphon.

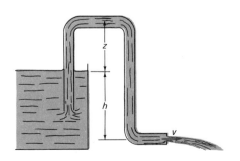

Problems 23 and 24

24. If water emerges from the siphon shown in the figure at a level 4.9 m below the water surface level, what is the speed of the emerging water? For $Z = 4.9$ m, what is the gauge pressure at ②? Assume that the siphon tube has the same cross-sectional area all along its length. What is the maximum value of Z that can be achieved by this siphon when the atmospheric pressure is 760 mm of mercury?

25. "Old Faithful" geyser periodically ejects a stream of water that attains a height of 36 m. What approximate gauge pressure inside the geyser is required to cause the stream to reach this height? What is the speed of the water as it emerges from the geyser?

26. The pumping unit of a fire engine operates at a gauge pressure of 1.10×10^6 Pa. What is the speed of the emerging water? What height can be attained by the emerging stream? If frictional losses were negligible, what would be the power rating of the pump if it is to deliver 1 m³ of water each minute?

27. A stream of water from a fire hose is directed against the flat, stationary wall of a building as suggested in Fig. 11.22a. If the speed of the water is 6 m/s and 3.6 m³ of water are delivered each minute, what is the magnitude of the force exerted on the wall? How much energy is delivered to the wall in one minute? Show that the force can be increased by the use of "dishes" like those shown in Fig. 11.22b.

28. If the gauge pressure inside the water pipe leading to the reaction turbine shown in Fig. 11.24 is 0.2 atm, what is the approximate tangential speed of the water emerging from the jets? Assume that the rotor is held stationary. If 0.04 m³ of water emerges each second from each opening, what tangential force acts on each arm of the rotor? Why are several firemen usually required to handle a fire hose?

29. A rocket with a total initial mass of 40,000 kg rises vertically from rest. It ejects hot gases at the rate of 400 kg/s with a speed of 2000 m/s relative to the rocket for 40 s before the fuel is exhausted. Determine the initial upward acceleration of the rocket and its acceleration at the end of 20 s and 40 s. Neglect the variation of g with altitude.

30. A rocket is in "free space" where gravitational effects are negligible. The mass of the unfueled rocket is 8000 kg and that of the fuel and oxidant is 4000 kg. If the jet speed is 2000 m/s relative to the rocket and burnout occurs in 40 s, what is the thrust on the rocket? Assume that the fuel is expended at a uniform rate. Calculate the total change in the velocity of the rocket in the *optimistic* and *pessimistic* limits mentioned in the text. What is the actual change in the rocket's velocity?

*31. A rocket of mass M in free space carries a load of fuel and oxidant of mass m and has initial velocity zero relative to an inertial frame of reference. As the fuel is burned, the rocket ejects hot gases at a speed v_r relative to the rocket at the *constant rate* μ kilograms per second. Thus, at time t the mass being accelerated is $(M + m) - \mu t$. Let u represent the rocket speed; use Newton's Second Principle to show that

$$\frac{du}{dt} = \frac{\mu v_r}{M + m - \mu t}$$

Integrate this expression and find u as a function of t. Show that the final rocket speed after burnout is

$$u_f = -v \ln[1 - m/(M + m)].$$

By use of the expansion $\ln(1 + x) = x - x^2/2 + x^3/3 - x^4/4 + \cdots$, $-1 < x \le 1$, obtain the result stated in the text.

32. On the basis of (11.16) and (11.16′) show that the power required to keep a streamlined ship in motion through still water is directly proportional to the square of the ship's speed. Some ocean vessels make a transatlantic crossing in five days; what fraction of the energy required might be saved if the crossing time were increased to ten days? Discuss the application of the ideas involved to highway speed limits.

*33. In 1654 Otto von Guericke, Burgomaster of Magdeburg and inventor of the air pump, gave a public demonstration in which two teams of eight horses each could barely pull apart two evacuated bronze hemispheres like those shown in the figure. Show that for a perfectly evacuated sphere of radius R the forces required would have had magnitudes $\pi R^2 P_0$, where P_0 is the atmospheric pressure. If the hemispheres were 60 cm in diameter and partially evacuated to 0.1 atm, what forces F would be required to pull them apart?

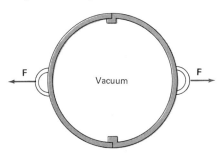

Problem 33

34. Show that the pressure P inside a water droplet of radius R is given by the expression $P = P_0 + 2\sigma/R$, where P_0 is the atmospheric pressure outside the drop and σ is the surface tension of water. (Suggestion: Write an expression for the static equilibrium of *one-half* of the drop as suggested in the figure.) Note that P becomes enormous as R becomes very small; actually a water droplet will not begin to form in air unless some dust particle or electric charge is present to serve as a "nucleus." In the

above expression $P \to \infty$ as $R \to 0$; how does our theory begin to fail long before $R \to 0$?

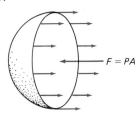

$F = PA$

Problem 34

35. (a) Two soap bubbles of different radii are connected by means of a glass tube as suggested in the figure. As soon as the connection has been established, what happens? (b) If the two bubbles had been initially of the same size, what would have eventually happened?

A B

Problem 35

36. A liquid droplet tends to assume the form of a sphere, which represents the configuration of minimum potential energy. What is the ratio of the surface energy of a hypothetical cubical droplet to that of a spherical droplet of equal volume? What is the ratio of the surface energy of a cylindrical droplet with a length equal to twice its diameter to the surface energy of a spherical droplet of equal volume?

37. A frictional drag force $\mathscr{F} = -\mathscr{R}\mathbf{v}$ acts on a body moving slowly through a viscous fluid; the constant $\mathscr{R}$ in this relation depends on the size and shape of the object and on the viscosity of the fluid. Show that although an object falling from a great height through the air has an initial downward acceleration g, it eventually attains a final constant downward velocity called the *terminal velocity* v_T. Obtain an expression for v_T in terms of m, g, and $\mathscr{R}$.

*38. If a block of aluminum supported beneath the surface of water in a still lake were released from rest, what would be the direction and magnitude of its initial acceleration? How would the acceleration change with time?

39. If a block of balsa wood held initially at rest below the surface of a fresh-water lake were released from rest, what would be the direction and magnitude of its initial acceleration?

40. Computation of the constant $\mathcal{R}$ in the expression for the frictional drag force $\mathcal{F}_F$ encountered by an object moving slowly through a viscous fluid is in general extremely difficult. The computation for a spherical body was carried out by the British mathematical physicist G. G. Stokes (1819–1903). His result for the terminal velocity v_T of a spherical body of density ρ and radius R falling slowly through a fluid of density ρ_F and viscosity η is

$$v_T = \frac{2gR^2(\rho - \rho_F)}{9\eta} \; \text{(Stokes' Law).}$$

Starting with this relation, find the expression for $\mathcal{R}$ that applies to a spherical body.

41. For the case of rain or fog droplets in air, use Stokes' law as given in Problem 40 to compute the terminal velocities of droplets with the following radii: 1 μm, 0.5, 1, and 2 mm. Because the density of air is only about 0.001 that of water, it can be neglected. Find the terminal velocities of hailstones with radii of 0.5 and 3 cm.

42. From what heights in *free fall* near the earth's surface would an object have to descend in order to attain the downward velocities obtained in Problem 41? Ignore the variation of g with altitude.

43. What is the ratio of the kinetic energy of a hailstone with a *diameter* of 6 cm to the kinetic energy of a hailstone with a diameter of 1 cm if each has attained its terminal velocity while falling through the air? See Problem 40.

44. A solid aluminum sphere and a solid sphere of balsa wood initially are held below the surface of a fresh water lake. If the spheres have equal diameters, what will be the ratio of the resistive forces due to viscous drag acting on the spheres when they are moving through the water with equal speeds? What will be the ratio of the resistive forces for equal speeds if the two spheres have equal masses? See Problem 40.

*45. The downward acceleration a of an object of mass m falling through the air can be obtained from Newton's Second Principle: $ma = mg - \mathcal{R}v$, where $\mathcal{R}v$ is the resistive drag due to viscosity. Recalling that $\mathbf{a} = d\mathbf{v}/dt$, show by integration that the downward velocity of a body falling from rest at $t = 0$ is given by the expression

$$v = \frac{mg}{\mathcal{R}}(1 - e^{-(\mathcal{R}/m)t}) = v_T(1 - e^{-(\mathcal{R}/m)t}),$$

where v_T is the terminal velocity of the body. Show that the quantity $m/\mathcal{R}$ has the dimensions of time. Make a plot of v as a function of t for $m/\mathcal{R} = 0.1$, 1, and 10 s. Show that $v \simeq 0.6321v_T$ when $t = m/\mathcal{R}$. Show that the expression for v reduces to the free-fall expression $v = gt$ for sufficiently small values of $\mathcal{R}$ and t.

46. A solid sphere of balsa wood of radius 3 cm is fastened to a string that is tied to the bottom of a large beaker. The beaker is filled with water so that the balsa sphere is totally submerged and is placed in an elevator. What is the tension in the string (a) when the elevator is moving with constant velocity, (b) when the elevator has an upward acceleration of 5.2 m/s^2, and (c) when the elevator has a downward acceleration of 3.6 m/s^2?

47. The bag of a balloon has a volume of 8200 m³ filled with helium of density 0.178 kg/m³. What total mass of fabric, gondola, and contents can be lifted by this balloon in air of density 1.29 kg/m³?

48. A beaker of water stands on the platform of a scale, which registers its weight as 9.0 N. An aluminum sphere of radius 2.5 cm that is attached to the end of a string is lowered into the water until the sphere is completely submerged. What is the tension in the string? By how much will the reading of the scale change?

49. In a perfume aspirator, air of density 1.25 kg/m³ is blown across the top of a glass tube that dips down into a bottle of perfume of density 0.9 times that of water. What is the minimum air speed if the perfume is to be lifted 10 cm in the tube?

*50. Reconsider the derivation of Torricelli's law (11.12) but now take into account the drop in water level inside the tank. Consider a cylindrical tank open to the atmosphere with uniform cross section of area A_1; let the area of the *small* orifice be A_2. Find an expression for the speed of efflux from the orifice in terms of h, A_1, and A_2. If the initial level of water in the tank is a height h_0 above the orifice, how much time is required for the water surface to drop to the level of the orifice?

CHAPTER 12

Vibrational Motion

In earlier chapters we have discussed *translational motion,* involving the motion of a body from one position in space to another, and *rotational* motion, involving changes in the spatial orientation of a body. Because any motion of a body can be treated as a combination of translation and rotation, it would appear that we have exhausted all possibilities. In a sense, we have! However, in this chapter we deal with a special type of motion known as *vibration;* a particle in vibrational motion has some position of equilibrium about which it oscillates. An extended body can have not only an equilibrium location in space about which it can perform translational oscillations but also an equilibrium orientation about which it can execute rotational oscillations.

Vibrational motion occurs when a body supported by a coil spring is pulled downward from its equilibrium position and then released. Other examples of this type of motion are the vibrations of bridges and buildings, the vibrations of the strings and air columns in musical instruments, and the oscillation of a pendulum or balance wheel of a clock. Later we shall find that the atoms in a solid execute vibratory motion about their mean positions; similarly, the separations of atoms in molecules can change periodically as a result of molecular vibrations.

Vibrational motion, like the motion of a particle in a circular path, is an example of *periodic motion.*

A PERIODIC MOTION is one in which the motion of a body or particle is repeated over and over in a succession of equal time intervals.

For example, a particle moving at constant speed in a circular path traverses the same path over and over again, attaining the same velocity and acceleration at any given point in each traversal of the path. Similarly, the pendulum of a clock repeats its to-and-fro motion again and again.

The complete "round trip" of a particle or a body executing periodic motion is called a *cycle*.

A CYCLE is one complete execution of a periodic motion.

The PERIOD of a periodic motion is the time T required for the completion of a cycle.

The FREQUENCY of a periodic motion is the number f of cycles completed per unit time.

From their definitions, we can readily see that the period and frequency of a periodic motion are related by the expressions

$$f = 1/T \quad \text{and} \quad T = 1/f. \tag{12.1}$$

In the SI, frequency is measured in a special unit called the *hertz* (Hz), named for the German physicist Heinrich Hertz (1857–1894), who first produced and experimented with radio waves. The hertz is defined in terms of the relation given in (12.1):

One hertz (Hz) is the frequency of a periodic motion that has a period of one second.

Thus, it follows that 1 Hz = 1 cycle per second.

The ideas regarding periodic motion presented in this chapter can be employed not only in mechanics but also in our later studies of sound, electromagnetism, and light. Sound waves, alternating electric currents, radio waves, and light waves all involve periodic phenomena. Any student of science or engineering will encounter vibrational phenomena repeatedly.

12.1 SIMPLE HARMONIC MOTION

Simple harmonic motion is a type of periodic motion executed by a particle when it is subject to a force proportional to its displacement from its equilibrium position and in a direction tending to restore it to its equilibrium position; such forces are exerted by elastic bodies obeying Hooke's Law. In Fig. 12.1 we show a block on a horizontal frictionless surface, which can be approximated by a laboratory "air track." The block is attached to two springs of negligible mass and can move in one dimension; we choose the X axis to lie along this direction of possible motion. In the position shown in the figure the horizontal forces exerted on the body by the springs are equal in magnitude and opposite in direction; the body is in equilibrium because no resultant force acts on it. If, however, we pull the block toward the right, forces to the left exerted by the springs tend to *restore* the body to its original position; if we pull the body to the left, forces exerted toward the right by the springs also tend to *restore* the body to its equilibrium position. The resultant force tending to restore the body to its equilibrium position is called the *restoring force*.

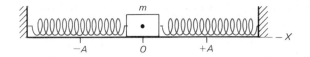

Fig. 12.1 A harmonic oscillator.

SIMPLE HARMONIC MOTION (SHM) is the motion of a particle about an equilibrium position when the restoring force is directly proportional to the particle's displacement from its equilibrium position.

We assume that the springs in Fig. 12.1 obey Hooke's Law; then the restoring force acting on the particle is of the type required for simple harmonic motion. We can express the restoring force F_x acting on the particle in Fig. 12.1 as

$$F_x = -kx, \quad \textit{(Simple Harmonic Motion)} \tag{12.2}$$

where k is the *effective force constant* for the springs. Note that when the body is displaced toward the right in the figure, the restoring force acts toward the left; similarly, if the body is displaced toward the left, the restoring force acts toward the right. The resultant force on the particle is zero when the particle is at its equilibrium position $x = 0$ in the figure.

Now suppose that we pull the body a distance A to the right from its equilibrium position in Fig. 12.1 and release it from rest. The restoring force acting on the body will accelerate the body toward its equilibrium position. When it reaches its equilibrium position, the body has momentum directed toward the left and will continue to move toward the left in the figure. It follows from the discussion in Section 10.2 that the initial potential energy of the body is $\frac{1}{2}kA^2$. Since there is no dissipation of energy, when the body passes through its equilibrium position it still has this same total energy, but in kinetic form. The motion continues to the left until all the energy is again potential. Thus, the restoring force brings the body to rest at a distance A to the left of its equilibrium position. The restoring force then accelerates the body toward the right until it reaches its equilibrium position, where the body will once again "overshoot" and move back a distance A to the right, to the position from which we originally released it. The motion then repeats itself over and over again between $x = A$ and $x = -A$ in Fig. 12.1. The magnitude of A in Fig. 12.1 is called the *amplitude* of the motion.

The AMPLITUDE of a simple harmonic motion is the magnitude of the maximum displacement of the vibrating body from its equilibrium position.

Observation of the simple harmonic motion of an object like the body in Fig. 12.1 shows that the period T and thus also the frequency f of the motion are independent of the amplitude as long as Hooke's Law (12.2) applies.

We now wish to find out how the frequency and the period of the motion depend on the effective force constant k and the mass m of the moving body, which we can regard as a particle located at the body's center of mass. In order to do this, we must apply Newton's Second Principle to the particle:

$$F_x = ma_x \quad \text{or} \quad F_x = m(d^2x/dt^2). \tag{12.3}$$

Combining the Newtonian-principle statement in (12.3) with the Hooke's Law statement in (12.2) leads to

$$m\left(\frac{d^2x}{dt^2}\right) = -kx \quad \text{or} \quad \frac{d^2x}{dt^2} = -\left(\frac{k}{m}\right)x. \tag{12.4}$$

Because k and m are constants, we note that x in the equation must be some function of time whose second derivative with respect to time is equal to a negative constant $-(k/m)$ times the function itself. In our search for such a function, we think immediately of functions like $\sin \omega t$ and $\cos \omega t$, where ω is some constant having the dimension s^{-1} as required to make the argument ωt a pure dimensionless number.

One satisfactory solution of (12.4) is a function having the form $x = A \cos 2\pi f t$, where A is the amplitude and f is the frequency of the motion. We note that with this solution the displacement x has its maximum positive value $x = A$ at time $t = 0$, because $\cos 0° = 1$. The displacement x has the value $+A$ again at time $t = T$, where T is the period of the motion, because $\cos 2\pi f T = \cos 2\pi = 1$. In the time interval $0 \leq t \leq T$ the displacement x goes through its entire range of values and returns to its initial value; the motion described by the expression $x = A \cos 2\pi f t$ goes through one complete cycle during one period T. The motion is repeated over and over again as time goes on.

The relation $x = A \cos 2\pi f t$ is satisfactory as a solution of (12.4) provided the particle has initial displacement $x = A$ at time $t = 0$. If the particle had some other initial displacement, we can still use the cosine solution by introducing an *initial phase angle* ϕ_0 so that $x = A \cos(2\pi f t + \phi_0)$. Then the initial displacement of the particle at $t = 0$ is given by $x = A \cos \phi_0$ and the initial velocity is given by $dx/dt = -2\pi f A \sin \phi_0$. The function $x = A \cos(2\pi f t + \phi_0)$ is periodic because at time $t = T$ the displacement is $x = A \cos(2\pi + \phi_0)$, which is exactly equal to its initial value at $t = 0$. The motion is repeated over and over again as time t increases, as is required for simple harmonic motion.

An equation of the form given in (12.4) is called a linear second-order differential equation: *second-order* because the second derivative d^2x/dt^2 is the highest derivative involved and *linear* because the variable x and its derivatives appear only in the first power. Mathematicians have shown that a general solution to such an equation must involve two constants that depend on the initial conditions. In our solution the amplitude A and initial phase angle ϕ_0 represent the two constants that are required.

By substituting our solution $x = A \cos(2\pi f t + \phi_0)$ in (12.4) we can determine the frequency f of the motion in terms of the force constant k and mass m. We note that $d^2x/dt^2 = -4\pi^2 f^2 A \cos(2\pi f t + \phi_0)$; upon substitution in (12.4) we obtain

$$-4\pi^2 f^2 A \cos(2\pi f t + \phi_0) = -(k/m)A \cos(2\pi f t + \phi_0).$$

In order that this relation hold for all times t we must require that the frequency f of the motion satisfy

$$f = \frac{1}{2\pi}\sqrt{\frac{k}{m}} \cdot \quad \left\{ \begin{array}{l} f \text{ in Hz} \\ k \text{ in N/m} \\ m \text{ in kg} \end{array} \right\} \quad \textit{(Frequency)}$$

Because $T = 1/f$, the period of the motion is

$$T = 2\pi\sqrt{m/k}. \quad \left\{ \begin{array}{l} T \text{ in s} \\ m \text{ in kg} \\ k \text{ in N/m} \end{array} \right\} \quad \textit{(Period)} \qquad (12.6)$$

We note that the frequency and period depend *only* on the force constant of the spring and the mass of the particle involved and not at all on the constants A and ϕ_0. The results given in (12.5) and (12.6) are thus applicable for all values of A and ϕ_0. The values of f and T would have been the same if we had selected the alternative function $x = A \sin(2\pi ft + \phi_0')$ as a solution to (12.4); this is demonstrated in the following example.

Example.   A particle executing simple harmonic motion of the type indicated in Fig. 12.1 has its maximum positive displacement $x = +A$ at time $t = 0$. What is the initial phase angle ϕ_0 for the motion if we choose $x = A \cos(2\pi ft + \phi_0)$ as a solution? What is the initial phase angle ϕ_0' if we choose $x = A \sin(2\pi ft + \phi_0')$ as a solution? Demonstrate that the second choice $x = A \sin(2\pi ft + \phi_0')$ is indeed a solution of (12.4).

In the case of the cosine solution, we note that the initial displacement x at time $t = 0$ is a maximum, which occurs when the cosine is unity. Therefore, $\cos \phi_0 = 1$; our solution must have the form $x = A \cos 2\pi ft$, and the initial phase angle is $\phi_0 = 0$.

In the case of the sine solution, we note that the initial displacement is a maximum, which occurs when the sine is unity. Therefore, $\sin \phi_0' = 1$; the initial phase angle must have the value $\phi_0' = \pi/2$. Our solution thus has the form $x = A \sin(2\pi ft + \pi/2)$.

We can see that the general expression $x = A \sin(2\pi ft + \phi_0')$ is indeed a solution of (12.4) by making the substitution $d^2x/dt^2 = -4\pi^2 f^2 A \sin(2\pi ft + \phi_0')$ in (12.4), with the result

$$-4\pi^2 f^2 A \sin(2\pi ft + \phi_0') = -(k/m)A \sin(2\pi ft + \phi_0').$$

This equality holds for all times t provided that the frequency f is given by (12.5). Then $x = A \sin(2\pi ft + \phi_0')$ is a solution of (12.4) for all amplitudes A and initial phase factors ϕ_0'.

We see that either $A \cos(2\pi ft + \phi_0)$ or $A \sin(2\pi ft + \phi_0')$ is a satisfactory solution of (12.4) provided we make the proper choices of A, ϕ_0, and ϕ_0' on the basis of the initial conditions. In order that the two relations describe the same motion we must have $\phi_0' = \phi_0 + \pi/2$.

Example.   If the mass of the body in Fig. 12.1 is 100 g and the effective force constant of the springs is 8 N/m, what is the frequency of oscillatory motion? What is the period? If in starting the oscillator we moved the body 10 cm to the right of its equilibrium position and released it from rest at $t = 0$, what is the amplitude of the motion and what is the initial phase angle ϕ_0?

From (12.5) we write $f = (1/2\pi)\sqrt{k/m} = (1/2\pi)\sqrt{(8 \text{ N/m})/(0.1 \text{ kg})}$ = 1.42 Hz. This gives a value for the period of $T = 1/f = 0.702$ s. The magnitude of the initial displacement gives the amplitude A of the motion for the situation as described, because at no later time will the body ever be farther from its equilibrium position. Because $x_0 = A$ at $t = 0$, we see from $x_0 = A \cos \phi_0$ that ϕ_0 is equal to zero. The equation $x = A \cos(2\pi ft + \phi_0)$ describing the motion of the body in the present case is therefore $x = (0.1 \text{ m})\cos(2\pi ft)$, where $f = 1.42$ Hz and t is in s so that the argument $2\pi ft$ is dimensionless.

We can find the velocity of the object executing SHM by taking the time derivative of $x = A \cos(2\pi ft + \phi_0)$ since $v_x = dx/dt$. Thus,

$$v_x = -2\pi fA \sin(2\pi ft + \phi_0). \quad \textit{(Velocity)} \tag{12.7}$$

Similarly, we obtain the acceleration by taking a second time derivative: $a_x = dv_x/dt = d^2x/dt^2$. Thus,

$$a_x = -4\pi^2 f^2 A \cos(2\pi ft + \phi_0). \quad \textit{(Acceleration)} \tag{12.8}$$

In Fig. 12.2 we use arrows to give a pictorial representation of the velocity and the acceleration of a particle at various points during its vibrational motion. We note that the greatest magnitude of the velocity occurs when the displacement of the particle from its equilibrium position is zero. We note also that, in accordance with (12.4), the magnitude of the acceleration is directly proportional to the magnitude of the particle's displacement from equilibrium and the direction of the acceleration is opposite to the direction of the displacement.

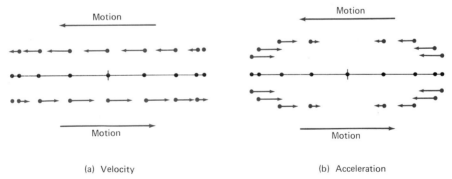

(a) Velocity   (b) Acceleration

Fig. 12.2 Velocity and acceleration of a particle executing SHM, shown at intervals of $\frac{1}{16}T$, where T is the period.

Example. What are the magnitudes of the maximum velocity and the maximum acceleration of the body described in the preceding example? Write equations giving the particle's velocity and acceleration as functions of time.

We found in the preceding example that $x = (0.1 \text{ m})\cos(2\pi ft)$ with $f = 1.42$ Hz. Thus, $v_x = -2\pi f(0.1 \text{ m})\sin(2\pi ft) = (-0.892 \text{ m/s})\sin(2\pi ft)$; the magnitude of the maximum velocity is therefore $v_{xM} = 0.892$ m/s. At what times is this maximum velocity magnitude attained? Similarly, $a_x = -4\pi^2 f^2(0.1 \text{ m})\cos(2\pi ft) = (-7.96 \text{ m/s}^2)\cos(2\pi ft)$. The maximum value of the magnitude of the acceleration is therefore $a_{xM} = 7.96$ m/s². At what times is this maximum acceleration magnitude attained?

In Fig. 12.3 we give plots of the displacement, the velocity, and the acceleration attained by a particle executing simple harmonic motion over a time interval equal to twice the period of the oscillator. The values plotted in the figure thus cover two complete cycles of the motion. The curves shown in Fig. 12.3 are for an initial phase factor $\phi_0 = \pi/6$ rad. Note this means that at time $t = 0$ the displacement, velocity, and acceleration are all nonzero. The plots in the figure merit careful study.

A simple experimental arrangement for demonstrating simple harmonic motion is illustrated in Fig. 12.4, which shows a steel ball of mass m suspended from a spring of negligible mass. When the ball is hung on the end of the spring and allowed to come to rest at its equilibrium position, the spring stretches an amount Y that according to Hooke's Law is given by $mg = kY$, where k is the force constant of the spring. In this equilibrium position the upward elastic force exerted on the ball by the spring is equal in magnitude to the downward gravitational force acting on the ball. If the ball is then displaced a distance y downward from the equilibrium position, the upward elastic force has magnitude $k(Y + y)$, which exceeds the down-

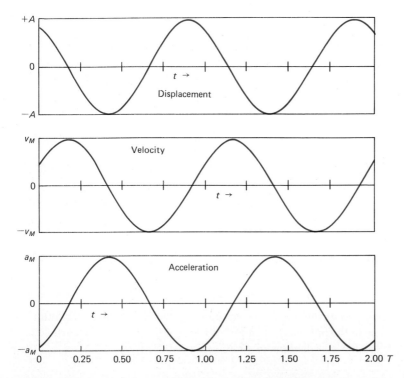

Fig. 12.3 The displacement, velocity, and acceleration of a particle executing SHM. The displacement x is given by the expression: $x = A\cos(2\pi ft + \phi_0)$, where the initial phase factor is $\phi_0 = \pi/6$ rad.

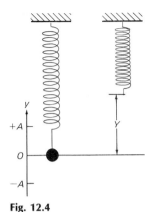

Fig. 12.4

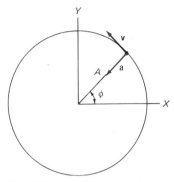

Fig. 12.5 The reference circle.

ward gravitational force by an amount equal to ky. There is thus a force of magnitude ky tending to restore the ball to its equilibrium position. If the ball is given an upward displacement of magnitude y from its equilibrium position, the upward elastic force is given by $k(Y - y)$, which is less than the downward gravitational force by an amount ky. Thus, again the ball is subject to a force of magnitude ky tending to restore equilibrium. If we let the displacement from equilibrium y be a quantity that is positive for upward displacements and negative for downward displacements, then both situations are described by writing for the restoring force $F = -ky$. But this is just the requirement for simple harmonic motion. If displaced from equilibrium and released, the ball will execute simple harmonic motion with a frequency $f = (1/2\pi)\sqrt{k/m}$.

Example. A light coil spring 2.5 m long hangs from the ceiling as in Fig. 12.4. When a 500-g body is attached to the lower end of the spring, the spring experiences an elongation of 20 cm. If the body is then pulled down an additional 10 cm and released, the body executes simple harmonic motion. What is the frequency of the motion? Write an equation describing the motion, assuming that upward displacements from equilibrium are positive.

The force constant k of the spring is $k = mg/Y$, where Y is the initial elongation of the spring; thus, $k = (0.5 \text{ kg})(9.8 \text{ m/s}^2)/(0.2 \text{ m}) = 24.5 \text{ N/m}$. The frequency of the oscillatory motion is given by $f = (1/2\pi)\sqrt{k/m} = (1/2\pi)\sqrt{(24.5 \text{ N/m})/(0.5 \text{ kg})} = 1.11$ Hz. We write the equation of motion in the form $y = A \cos(2\pi ft + \phi_0)$; the amplitude is $A = 0.1$ m and the frequency is $f = 1.11$ Hz. To find the initial phase angle ϕ_0, we note that $y_0 = -0.1$ m at $t = 0$. Therefore, from $y_0 = A \cos \phi_0$ we see that $\cos \phi_0 = -(0.1 \text{ m}/0.1 \text{ m}) = -1$. Therefore, $\phi_0 = \pi$ rad.

Example. Show that the motion of the projection on a diameter of the circle of the position of a particle in uniform motion on a circular path is identical to the motion of a particle undergoing simple harmonic motion.

Consider the particle in Fig. 12.5. The angular displacement of the particle from the X axis is given by $\phi = \omega t + \phi_0$, where ω is the angular velocity of the particle and ϕ_0 is the angular displacement of the particle at time $t = 0$. The X coordinate of the particle is given by the expression $x = A \cos \phi = A \cos(\omega t + \phi_0)$. Remembering that $\omega = 2\pi f$, we can write $x = A \cos(2\pi f t + \phi_0)$; this is just the equation for simple harmonic motion along the X axis, which corresponds in the figure to a diameter of the circle. We can obtain v_x and a_x by differentiating the expression for x as in (12.7) and (12.8). Note that the radius A of the "reference circle" in the figure is equal to the amplitude of the simple harmonic motion.

In the figure, the tangential velocity of the particle is $v_T = A\omega = 2\pi f A$ and the radial or centripetal acceleration is $a_R = v^2/A = A\omega^2 = 4\pi^2 f^2 A$. Show by geometric arguments that the projections of these quantities on the X axis are just v_x and a_x as obtained by differentiation.

What would have been the result if we had chosen to take the projection of the circular motion onto the Y axis in Fig. 12.5?

The so-called "Reference Circle" in Fig. 12.5 is helpful in providing a means of visualizing the meaning of the phase angle $\phi = 2\pi f t + \phi_0$. In some of our later work it will be important to compare several harmonic oscillations having the same frequency. We say that one harmonic motion leads another having the same frequency if the initial phase angle of the first is greater than that of the second, meaning that the particle representing the first motion moves around the reference circle *ahead* of the second. Similarly, we say that the first harmonic motion *lags* the second if the initial phase angle of the first is less than that of the second, meaning that the particle representing the first motion moves around the reference circle *behind* the second.

12.2   ENERGY RELATIONS IN SIMPLE HARMONIC MOTION

Now we consider the energy relations for a system undergoing simple harmonic motion such as that shown in Fig. 12.1. Suppose that we start the motion by giving the system a displacement A and releasing it from rest. To give the system its initial displacement A, we must do work $W = \frac{1}{2} kA^2$ against elastic forces. We recognize that $\frac{1}{2} kA^2$ represents the initial potential energy of the system: $E_{PO} = \frac{1}{2} kA^2$; the initial kinetic energy of the system is zero. We assume that there are no frictional effects in the system that dissipate energy; therefore, the total mechanical energy E of the system remains constant. Thus, once the motion has begun with $E = E_{PO}$, we can be assured that

$$E_K + E_P = E, \tag{12.9}$$

or

$$\frac{1}{2} mv_x^2 + \frac{1}{2} kx^2 = \frac{1}{2} kA^2. \tag{12.9'}$$

We can verify the validity of this relation by substituting the values of x and v_x from Sec. 12.1 into the energy equation. We obtain

$$E_K + E_P = \tfrac{1}{2}\,m[4\pi^2 f^2 A^2\,\sin^2(2\pi ft + \phi_0)] + \tfrac{1}{2}\,k[A^2\,\cos^2(2\pi ft + \phi_0)].$$

Replacing f^2 in the first term by $(1/4\pi^2)k/m$ from (12.5) gives

$$E_K + E_P = \tfrac{1}{2}\,kA^2[\sin^2(2\pi ft + \phi_0) + \cos^2(2\pi ft + \phi_0)].$$

Because $\sin^2\phi + \cos^2\phi = 1$ for all values of ϕ, the last equation reduces to $E_K + E_P = \tfrac{1}{2}kA^2$. Therefore, we have verified the validity of (12.9′); the value of the total energy E is at all times equal to $\tfrac{1}{2}kA^2$. Replacing k by its value $k = 4\pi^2 f^2 m$ from (12.5) gives the expression

$$E = \tfrac{1}{2}\,kA^2 = 2\pi^2 f^2 A^2 m. \tag{12.10}$$

This equation says that

The total energy of a particle of mass m executing simple harmonic motion is directly proportional to the square of the amplitude and to the square of the frequency of the motion.

Returning to (12.9′), we note that the energy relations for a simple harmonic oscillator can be presented graphically by the diagram given in Fig. 12.6. Here energy is plotted as the ordinate and displacement is plotted as the abscissa. The potential energy $E_P = \tfrac{1}{2}kx^2$ is represented by the parabola shown as the heavy curve in the figure. The total energy of the oscillator is represented by a horizontal line at the value $E = \tfrac{1}{2}kA^2$. At any displacement x in the range $-A \le x \le A$ the total energy is the sum of E_P and E_K; therefore, the kinetic energy E_K is represented by the vertical distance between the potential energy parabola and the horizontal line representing total energy.

We have derived (12.9) and (12.9′) on the basis of general energy considerations. If we wish to find the velocity v_x of the particle in Fig. 12.1 for a given value of its displacement x from the equilibrium position, we can make use of (12.9′) to write

$$v_x = \pm\sqrt{k/m}\,\sqrt{A^2 - x^2}. \tag{12.11}$$

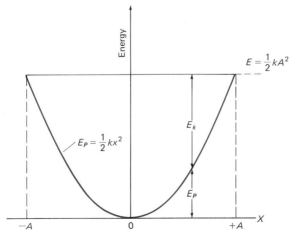

Fig. 12.6 The parabola $E_P = \tfrac{1}{2}kx^2$ gives the potential energy as a function of displacement. The total mechanical energy E is at all points equal to the sum of the potential and kinetic energies: $E = E_P + E_K$.

We can, in fact, use (12.11) to develop the result $x = A \cos(2\pi ft + \phi_0)$. We begin by noting that $v_x = dx/dt$; substitution of this value into (12.11) gives

$$\frac{dx}{dt} = \pm\sqrt{\frac{k}{m}(A^2 - x^2)} \quad \text{or} \quad \frac{dx}{\pm\sqrt{A^2 - x^2}} = \sqrt{\frac{k}{m}}\,dt.$$

Integration of this equation gives

$$\int \frac{dx}{\pm\sqrt{A^2 - x^2}} = \sqrt{\frac{k}{m}}\,t + C,$$

where C is a constant of integration. In order to evaluate the integral on the left-hand side of this expression, we make the change of variable $x = A \cos\theta$. This gives

$$\int \frac{dx}{\pm\sqrt{A^2 - x^2}} = \int \frac{-A \sin\theta\;d\theta}{\pm A\sqrt{1 - \cos^2\theta}} = \int \frac{-\sin\theta\;d\theta}{-\sin\theta} = \theta.$$

The choice of sign in the denominator is made by noting that (12.11) must be consistent with $dx/dt = -A \sin\theta\;(d\theta/dt)$. We now have $\theta = \sqrt{k/m}\;t + C$, which means that

$$A \cos\theta = x = A \cos(\sqrt{k/m}\;t + C).$$

We identify C as the initial phase angle ϕ_0, and we thereby recover $x = A \cos(2\pi ft + \phi_0)$ with f given by (12.5). We can proceed to determine v_x and a_x by differentiation of the expression for x as we did previously in obtaining (12.7) and (12.8).

12.3   ROTATIONAL SIMPLE HARMONIC MOTION

We have discussed linear simple harmonic motion where a particle or a rigid body has a to-and-fro motion along a straight line; this is a special type of rectilinear motion. As one might well expect, there is a rotational analogue of linear simple harmonic motion. Consider a body like the disk shown in Fig. 12.7; the disk is supported by a wire or slender rod that obeys Hooke's Law for torsional deformations. If we give the disk an angular displacement θ as suggested in the figure, the wire exerts a *restoring torque* $\tau = -C\theta$ on the disk, where C is the torsion constant of the wire as discussed in Chapter 10. If the body is given an angular displacement θ and is then released, by the rotational analogue of Newton's Second Principle this restoring torque gives the disk an angular acceleration α such that $\tau = I\alpha = I(d^2\theta/dt^2)$, where I is the rotational inertia of the disk. Combining these two relations, we obtain

$$I(d^2\theta/dt^2) = -C\theta,$$

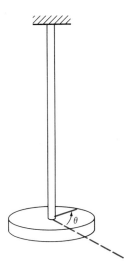

Fig. 12.7   The torsional oscillator executes rotational SHM.

or

$$\frac{d^2\theta}{dt^2} = -\frac{C}{I}\theta. \tag{12.12}$$

The mathematical form of (12.12) is exactly the same as the form of Eq. (12.4). Hence, we can immediately write down the solution to (12.12) by analogy with the solution $x = A \cos(2\pi ft + \phi_0)$ of (12.4). Thus, we have

$$\theta = \Theta \cos(2\pi ft + \phi_0), \tag{12.13}$$

where Θ is the rotational amplitude of the motion and ϕ_0 is the initial phase angle satisfying $\theta_0 = \Theta \cos \phi_0$. By analogy with (12.5), the frequency of the oscillatory motion of the body is

$$f = \frac{1}{2\pi}\sqrt{\frac{C}{I}}. \quad \begin{cases} f \text{ in Hz} \\ C \text{ in N·m/rad} \\ I \text{ in kg·m}^2 \end{cases} \tag{12.14}$$

By differentiation of (12.13) with respect to time, we can immediately obtain expressions for the angular velocity ω and the angular acceleration α of the body:

$$\omega = d\theta/dt = -2\pi f\Theta \sin(2\pi ft + \phi_0), \tag{12.15}$$

$$\alpha = d\omega/dt = -4\pi^2 f^2\Theta \cos(2\pi ft + \phi_0) = -4\pi^2 f^2\theta. \tag{12.16}$$

Equations (12.15) and (12.16) are the exact rotational analogues of Eqs. (12.7) and (12.8), respectively. Thus, we see that the motion of the body in Fig. 12.7 is the exact rotational analogue of the linear simple harmonic motion of the body in Fig. 12.1.

Motion like that of the body in Fig. 12.7 is called *rotational or angular simple harmonic motion*. The body suspended by the wire in Fig. 12.7 is sometimes called a *torsional pendulum* and is said to execute *torsional oscillations*.

We can immediately write down the energy relations for a body executing angular simple harmonic motion. If we start the oscillator in Fig. 12.7 by giving the body an initial angular displacement Θ and then releasing it from rest, we do work $W = \frac{1}{2} C \Theta^2$ to the system. This work gives the system a total mechanical energy $E = \frac{1}{2} C \Theta^2$; in the absence of energy dissipation by work against friction, this remains the total mechanical energy of the oscillator. For any angular displacement θ in the subsequent motion, the potential energy is $E_P = \frac{1}{2} C \theta^2$ and the kinetic energy is $E_K = \frac{1}{2} I \omega^2$. As long as mechanical energy is conserved we can write

$$E_P + E_K = E \quad \text{or} \quad \tfrac{1}{2} C \theta^2 + \tfrac{1}{2} I \omega^2 = \tfrac{1}{2} C \Theta^2, \tag{12.17}$$

which is consistent with (12.13), (12.14), and (12.15). From (12.17) we can immediately determine the angular velocity ω of the body at any angular displacement θ:

$$\omega = \pm \sqrt{\frac{C}{I}} \sqrt{\Theta^2 - \theta^2} \tag{12.18}$$

in exact analogy with (12.11).

12.4   THE MOTION OF A PENDULUM

A body that is suspended vertically and is able to "swing" about a horizontal axis through its point of support is called a pendulum. The properties of the pendulum were first studied intensively by Galileo Galilei. At the age of seventeen Galileo noted that the period of oscillation of a swinging lamp in the cathedral at Pisa, as timed by his own pulse, was constant as the amplitude of the oscillations died down. He found that the pendulum was very useful in measuring time intervals; pendulum motion is still used as a timing device in pendulum clocks or "grandfather clocks."

As our first example of pendulum motion, we shall consider the motion of the *simple pendulum* shown in Fig. 12.8. A simple pendulum consists of a small "bob" approximating a particle of mass m suspended from a point O by a light wire or thread of length l and negligible mass.

We can consider the motion of the simple pendulum in Fig. 12.8 as a rotational oscillation about a horizontal axis through O, the fixed point of support. Because l does not change during the motion, we can treat the pendulum as a "rigid body" with $I_0 = ml^2$. The equilibrium position of the pendulum is the position in which the center of mass of the bob is directly below the point of support. If we give the pendulum an angular displacement θ and then release it, the pendulum executes oscillations about its equilibrium position. For small values of θ, we shall show that the motion of the pendulum closely approximates angular simple harmonic motion.

If the pendulum has the angular displacement θ shown in Fig. 12.8, the force of gravity mg exerts a torque τ that tends to *restore* the pendulum to its equilibrium position. The magnitude of this restoring torque is $mgl \sin \theta$. The tension force $\mathbf{F}$

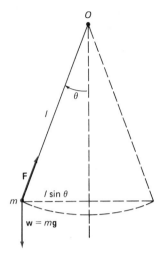

Fig. 12.8 A simple pendulum.

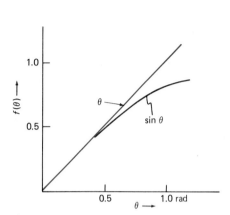

Fig. 12.9 Comparison of θ and $\sin\theta$ for $\theta < 1$ rad.

in the supporting wire or thread exerts no torque about O since it has zero lever arm. For small values of θ, the function $\sin\theta$ can, in excellent approximation, be replaced by θ itself measured in radians, as is illustrated in Fig. 12.9. Hence, *for small values of θ*, we can write

$$\tau \simeq -mgl\theta,$$

where the negative sign is used because the torque is counterclockwise when θ is clockwise, and vice versa. This torque gives the pendulum an angular acceleration α in accord with $\tau = I_0\alpha$, where I_0 is the rotational inertia of the pendulum about an axis through O. Noting that $\alpha = d^2\theta/dt^2$, we can write

$$\frac{d^2\theta}{dt^2} \simeq -\left(\frac{mgl}{I_0}\right)\theta.$$

This equation is exactly the same as (12.12) with $C = mgl$. The simple pendulum thus has angular simple harmonic motion when its amplitude is small.

Because $I_0 = ml^2$, the frequency of a simple pendulum is independent of the mass of the bob and is given by the expression

$$f = \frac{1}{2\pi}\sqrt{\frac{g}{l}}; \qquad T = 2\pi\sqrt{\frac{l}{g}}. \qquad \textit{(Simple Pendulum)} \qquad (12.19)$$

The frequency f or period T of a simple pendulum can be easily measured in the laboratory by counting the number of complete oscillations of the pendulum while a stopwatch ticks off a given time interval; similarly, the distance l from the center of mass of the bob to the point of support can be measured quite easily. Thus, (12.19) provides a very accurate method of determining the local value of the gravitational acceleration g.

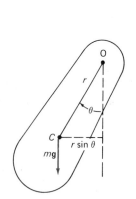

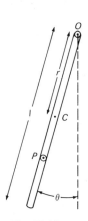

Fig. 12.10   A physical pendulum.

Fig. 12.11

Fig. 12.12   A damped harmonic oscillator.

We must remember that we obtained (12.19) on the assumption of *small angular displacements*. It is possible to show that the exact relation for the period of a simple pendulum can be expressed in the form

$$T = 2\pi\sqrt{l/g}\,[1 + \tfrac{1}{4}\sin^2(\Theta/2) + \tfrac{9}{64}\sin^4(\Theta/2) + \cdots], \qquad (12.19')$$

where Θ is the angular amplitude of the oscillations. For an angular amplitude of 20° the first correction term has the value $\tfrac{1}{4}\sin^2(\Theta/2) = 0.00754$. Thus, (12.19) gives an excellent approximation for the period of a simple pendulum with $\Theta < 20°$. We note that if the angular amplitude is not small, the period will depend significantly on Θ, a matter of importance when the pendulum is used as a timing device.

The simple pendulum is an idealization. Because its length l when it is in operation does not change, we have actually regarded it in our discussion as a rigid body with rotational inertia $I_0 = ml^2$ about the horizontal axis through its point of suspension. A rigid pendulum where the mass is not essentially all concentrated at one point, such as the pendulum used in grandfather clocks, is called a *physical pendulum*. A physical pendulum also executes angular simple harmonic motion when its amplitude is small, but there is not a single simple relation for the rotational inertia about the horizontal axis through the point of suspension.

Figure 12.10 represents a physical pendulum pivoted about a horizontal axis perpendicular to the diagram and passing through the point O located at a distance r from the center of mass C of the body. If the body has an angular displacement θ from its equilibrium position, the restoring torque has the value $\tau = -mgr\sin\theta$ or, for small displacements, $\tau \simeq -mgr\theta$. This restoring torque produces angular acceleration α in accord with $\tau = I_0\alpha = I_0(d^2\theta/dt^2)$. Thus, we are led to the relation

$$d^2\theta/dt^2 = -(mgr/I_0)\theta,$$

which is the relation for angular simple harmonic motion. In analogy with (12.5) and (12.6) we can express the frequency and period of the physical pendulum in the forms

$$f = \frac{1}{2\pi} \sqrt{\frac{mgr}{I_0}}, \quad T = 2\pi \sqrt{\frac{I_0}{mgr}}. \quad \textit{(Physical Pendulum)} \qquad (12.20)$$

Once again we must note that (12.20) applies only for small amplitudes of oscillation. The exact expression for the period for arbitrary amplitude has a form similar to the one given in (12.19').

Example. What is the frequency for small oscillation of a meter stick pivoted at one end as shown in Fig. 12.11? What is the length of a simple pendulum that has the same frequency?

With l as the total length of the stick, the distance r between O and the center of mass is $r = l/2$. From the value $I_C = \frac{1}{12}ml^2$ and the parallel-axis theorem, we obtain $I_0 = I_C + mr^2 = \frac{1}{3}ml^2$. Hence, the frequency as given by (12.20) is

$$f = \frac{1}{2\pi} \sqrt{\frac{mgl/2}{ml^2/3}} = \frac{1}{2\pi} \sqrt{\frac{3g}{2l}} = \frac{1}{2\pi} \sqrt{\frac{3(9.8 \text{ m/s}^2)}{2(1 \text{ m})}} = 0.610 \text{ Hz}.$$

From (12.19), we can find the length l' of an equivalent simple pendulum having the same frequency: $f = (1/2\pi) \sqrt{g/l'}$ so $l' = g/4\pi^2 f^2 = (9.8 \text{ m/s}^2)/4\pi^2(0.610 \text{ Hz})^2 = 0.667$ m. The position of the bob of the equivalent simple pendulum is shown as point P in Fig. 12.11.

12.5 DAMPED OSCILLATIONS

Thus far, we have treated harmonic oscillators, torsional oscillators, and pendulums as if they were completely free of energy dissipation due to friction. In many important cases this is a good approximation. However, we recognize that oscillating bodies sooner or later come to rest. A child in a swing usually waits for "the cat to die" before getting out of the swing!

When the amplitude of an oscillator gradually decreases, we say that the oscillator is *damped*. In many important cases, the most important damping force is proportional to the velocity. Such a force is the force of fluid friction $\mathscr{F} = -\mathscr{R}\mathbf{v}$ that we discussed in Chapter 11; we recall that this is the force on a body that moves at velocity $\mathbf{v}$ through a fluid and that the constant $\mathscr{R}$ depends on the geometry of the body and on the viscosity η of the fluid.

If we suspend a steel ball and an attached metal vane with combined mass m from the lower end of a coil spring having force constant k, the frequency f of the oscillation is $(1/2\pi)\sqrt{k/m}$ in accord with (12.5). However, if we place a beaker of oil or water below the oscillator so that the vane remains immersed in the fluid as in Fig. 12.12, we find that that the oscillations damp out rapidly. This can be understood by considering the forces acting on the suspended mass.

In accord with Newton's Second Principle, we can write $ma_y = -ky + \mathscr{F}$ where y is the vertical displacement from equilibrium. Here, $-ky$ is the elastic force and $\mathscr{F} = -\mathscr{R}v_y$ is the frictional force acting on the moving mass m. Recognizing that $v_y = dy/dt$ and $a_y = d^2y/dt^2$, we can write the equation of motion as

$$m\frac{d^2y}{dt^2} + \mathscr{R}\frac{dy}{dt} + ky = 0. \tag{12.21}$$

If the frictional force is not too large, the general solution of this differential equation has the form

$$y = A_0 e^{-\alpha t}\cos(2\pi f' t + \phi_0), \tag{12.22}$$

where A_0 is the initial amplitude of the oscillator, α is called the exponential *damping factor,* and f' is the modified frequency of the oscillator. Substitution of this solution in (12.21) shows that

$$\alpha = \frac{\mathscr{R}}{2m} \quad \text{and} \quad f' = \frac{1}{2\pi}\sqrt{\frac{k}{m} - \frac{\mathscr{R}^2}{4m^2}}.$$

We see that we must have $\mathscr{R}^2/4m^2 < k/m$ for a solution of the form of (12.22) to be valid. If $\mathscr{R} \ll 2m$, the modified frequency f' is very nearly the same as the frequency f of the undamped oscillator. The solution of Eq. (12.21) then reduces to

$$y \simeq A_0 e^{-\mathscr{R}t/2m}\cos(2\pi ft + \phi_0). \tag{12.22'}$$

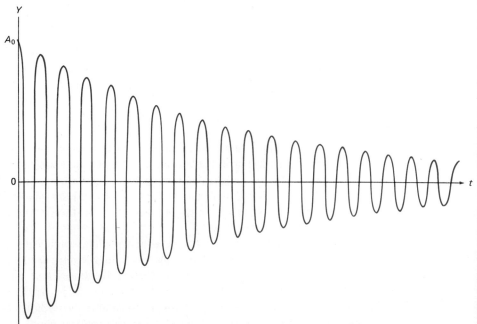

Fig. 12.13   The displacement y of a damped oscillator as a function of time: $y = A_0 e^{-\alpha t}\cos(2\pi f' t)$.

A small damping force has little effect on the frequency of the oscillator but causes the amplitude A to decrease exponentially with time: $A = A_0 e^{-\mathscr{R}t/2m}$. A plot of displacement as a function of time as given by (12.22) is shown in Fig. 12.13.

12.6 ENERGY DISSIPATION IN DAMPED OSCILLATORS

We recall that the mechanical energy of an undamped oscillator is proportional to the square of the amplitude of the motion. The initial energy E_0 of the damped oscillator discussed in the preceding section is given by the relation $E_0 = \frac{1}{2} k A_0^2$, where A_0 is the initial amplitude and k is the elastic force constant involved. Because by (12.22) the amplitude $A = A_0 e^{-\alpha t}$ decreases exponentially with time, the approximate energy of the oscillator $E = \frac{1}{2} k A^2$ also decreases exponentially in accord with the relation

$$E = E_0 e^{-\beta t}$$

where $\beta = 2\alpha$. The time rate at which this energy changes is given by the expression

$$dE/dt = -\beta E_0 e^{-\beta t}.$$

The negative sign indicates that the mechanical energy is decreasing. It is, in fact, being *dissipated* in work against frictional forces. See Problem 41.

If we wish to keep a damped oscillator in oscillation at its initial amplitude A_0, we must do work to the oscillator at the same time rate at which mechanical energy is being dissipated. In other words, we must supply power P to the oscillator; the power required is

$$P = (dE/dt)_{t=0} = \beta E_0 = (\mathscr{R}/m)E_0.$$

This power can be supplied most effectively by exerting a periodic *driving force* $F_D = F_M \cos(2\pi f' t)$ applied at the oscillator frequency f'; periodic driving forces at other frequencies are largely ineffective.

In this chapter we have considered only situations where a system is given an initial disturbance and then released to undergo its "natural" oscillations. The situation is different if the system is subjected to a periodic driving force having frequency f_D. We shall leave investigation of the quantitative details of this situation for later courses; however, we make several qualitative observations. The system will respond to the periodic driving force by oscillating with the driving frequency f_D. However, unless f_D is close to the natural frequency of oscillation of the system, the transfer of energy from the source of the driving force to the oscillating system is small, and the oscillations have relatively small amplitude. As the driving frequency approaches the natural frequency of the system, the transfer of energy to the system becomes large, and the amplitude of the oscillations can build to extremely large values. This phenomenon is known as *resonance*. Under resonance conditions the amplitude of the oscillations of a structure can become so large that the structure is destroyed.

There is a close analogy between mechanical and electrical oscillations. Electrical oscillations and electrical resonance phenomena will be considered in Chapter 31.

QUESTIONS

1. Make a list of naturally occurring periodic motions. Which of these might be used in the measurement of time intervals?

2. Exactly what is meant by the term *simple harmonic motion?* How is this different from periodic motion? Can *strictly* simple harmonic motion be produced in the laboratory?

3. In discussing the arrangement shown in Fig. 12.4, we completely ignored the mass of the spring. If the mass of the spring is not negligible, how is the frequency of the oscillation changed?

4. Describe the exchange of mechanical energy between the massive oscillating object and the light springs in Fig. 12.1.

5. If the springs in Figs. 12.1 or 12.4 were replaced by rubber bands, would the oscillating body execute simple harmonic motion? Explain your reasoning.

6. Can a truly *simple* pendulum be constructed?

7. If the period of a pendulum at sea level is 1 s, how would its period be altered by raising the pendulum to the top of Mr. Everest? What would be its period of the surface of the moon?

8. Why can't a pendulum clock be employed successfully on shipboard?

9. How would the motion of an oscillator like that in Fig. 12.1 be modified if it were immersed in water? How would the motion be modified if the oscillator were operated in vacuum?

10. What becomes of the mechanical energy lost by a damped oscillator?

11. How does the motion of a simple pendulum operating with a large amplitude of oscillation differ from its motion when it operates with a small amplitude?

12. A steel ball is attached to the lower end of a string that passes through a small hole in a horizontal steel plate. The resulting simple pendulum is set into oscillatory motion when the length of the string between the plate and the ball is approximately 2 m. If the string is pulled *very slowly* upward through the small hole, how does the motion change? Are there changes in the frequency or the amplitude of the pendulum? Does the total mechanical energy of the system remain constant?

PROBLEMS

1. When a 200-g object is attached to the lower end of a suspended coil spring, the spring experiences an elongation of 4 cm. If the object is raised 6 cm above its equilibrium position and then released, the object executes simple harmonic motion (SHM) about its equilibrium position. Find the amplitude, the frequency, and the period of this SHM.

2. The displacement y of the object in Problem 1 from its equilibrium position can be expressed in the form $y = A \cos(2\pi ft + \phi_0)$. What is the value of ϕ_0, the initial phase angle of the motion? Write the resulting expressions for the body's velocity and acceleration. What are the magnitudes of the maximum velocity and acceleration attained by the particle?

3. A 500-g body like the one shown in Fig. 12.1 oscillates in SHM about its equilibrium position with a period of 0.2 s and with an amplitude of 10 cm. What is the frequency of the motion? What is the effective force constant of the springs? What is the magnitude of the elastic restoring force exerted on the body when it is 5 cm from its equilibrium position?

4. What is the magnitude of the maximum velocity attained by the body in Problem 3 in the course of its motion? At what points of the motion is this maximum velocity attained? What is the magnitude of the maximum acceleration attained by the body? At what points of the motion does this maximum acceleration occur?

5. When a 1-kg body is attached to the lower end of a suspended coil spring, the spring experiences an elongation of 8 cm. If we wish to use this spring in making a simple harmonic oscillator with a period of exactly one second, what is the mass of the object that we should attach to the spring? What should we make the amplitude of the motion if we wish the total energy associated with the motion to be exactly 1 J?

6. In starting the oscillator in Problem 5 we raise the object 12.8 cm above its equilibrium position and then release it. Write an expression for the displacement y in the form $y = A \sin(2\pi ft + \phi_0)$. What is the value of ϕ_0 in this expression? Write expressions for the velocity v_y and the acceleration a_y of the object as a function of time. Show that the same values of y, v_y, and a_y at time t are obtained if the displacement is expressed in the form $y = A \cos(2\pi ft + \phi_0')$.

7. A 500-g body like the one in Fig. 12.1 is acted on by springs having an effective force constant of 1200 N/m. If the body is displaced 8 cm to the right of its equilibrium position and then released, the body executes SHM. What is the initial potential energy of the system? What is the speed of the body as it passes through its equilibrium position? What is the speed of the body when it is 4 cm away from its equilibrium position?

8. Write expressions for the displacement and for the velocity of the body in Problem 7 as a function of time. Show that the total mechanical energy $E_P + E_K$ of the oscillator is constant and is equal in magnitude to the initial potential energy of the system. How does the total energy of the system depend on the amplitude and the frequency of the motion?

9. Two oscillators employing moving "bobs" of exactly the same mass. Oscillator ① has a frequency of 4 Hz and oscillator ② has a frequency of 8 Hz. If the two oscillators have equal amplitudes A, what is the ratio of their total energies? What is the ratio of the maximum speeds involved in the motions of the two oscillators?

10. If we wish to make the total mechanical energies of the two oscillators in Problem 9 exactly the same and keep the same amplitude A for ①, what should we make the amplitude of oscillator ②? Could we make the mechanical energies of the two oscillators the same by keeping their amplitudes the same and changing the mass of oscillator ②?

*11. Consider a particle moving at constant speed around the reference circle shown in Fig. 12.5. Show that the value of the Y coordinate of the particle is given by $y = A \sin(2\pi ft + \phi_0)$, which is merely the projection of the particle's position vector on the Y axis. Obtain expressions for $v_y = dy/dt$ and $a_y = dv_y/dt$. Show that the maximum value of v_y is $2\pi fA = v_T$ and that the maximum value of a_y is $4\pi^2 f^2 A = v_T^2/A$. Show geometrically that the projections of the tangential velocity and the radial acceleration on the Y axis are the same as the values v_y and a_y obtained by differentiation. Note that the values of y, v_y, and a_y are the same as those of an oscillator having SHM with amplitude A parallel to the Y axis.

12. If we wished to construct an oscillator that would oscillate parallel to the Y axis of the coordinate system used in Problem 11 in exactly the same way as the projected uniform circular motion, what would be our possible choices of the mass m_{osc} and force constant k of the oscillator? What would be the amplitude of the motion? Show that the total mechanical energy of the oscillator would equal $\frac{1}{2} m_{osc} v_T^2$, where v_T is the tangential speed of the particle moving at constant speed around the reference circle.

13. A 1.2-kg solid disk ($I_C = MR^2/2$) with a radius of 30 cm is attached to the end of a vertical rod as suggested in Fig. 12.7. The rod has a torsion constant of 0.4 N · m/rad. If the disk is given an angular displacement of 90° from its equilibrium orientation and then released from rest, it executes angular SHM about its equilibrium position. What is the frequency of the motion? What is the period of the motion?

14. What is the total mechanical energy of the oscillator in Problem 13? What is the maximum angular speed attained by the disk in the course of its motion? When is this maximum angular speed attained? What is the magnitude of the maximum angular acceleration attained by the disk in the course of its motion? When is this maximum angular acceleration attained?

15. A 3-kg steel bar ($I_C = Ml^2/12$) of length 2 m is attached laterally to the end of a rod in place of the disk shown in Fig. 12.7. The bar is horizontal and is attached to the end of the rod at the center of the bar. The torsion constant of the rod is 1.2 N·m/rad. If the bar is given an angular displacement of 180° from its equilibrium orientation and released from rest, the bar executes angular SHM. What is the fre-

quency of the motion? What is the period of the motion? What is the total mechanical energy associated with the motion?

16. What is the maximum angular speed attained by the bar of Problem 15 and when does it occur? What is the angular speed of the bar when it has an angular displacement of 90° from its equilibrium orientation? What is the magnitude of the maximum angular acceleration of the bar and when is it attained?

17. What is the length of a simple pendulum having a period of exactly 1 s at a place where the acceleration of a freely falling body is 9.8066 m/s²? Thomas Jefferson once proposed that a standard time unit or a standard length unit could be *defined* in terms of the length of a simple pendulum; discuss this proposal, which involves in essentials a basic relationship between the *meter* and the *second*.

18. What are the period and frequency of a simple pendulum with a length of exactly one meter at a place where $g = 9.8066$ m/s²?

19. What would be the frequency of a simple pendulum exactly 1 m long if you measured the frequency on an elevator (1) with a constant velocity of 4.9 m/s, upward; (2) with a constant acceleration of 4.9 m/s², upward; and (3) with a constant acceleration of 4.9 m/s², downward? ($g = 9.8$ m/s²). Does the moving elevator provide an inertial frame of reference? Discuss.

20. What would be the frequency of a simple pendulum 1 m in length if it were operated on the surface of the moon? on the surface of Jupiter? (See Problem 9, Chapter 9.)

21. A small hole bored at the 60-cm mark of a meter stick is used to suspend the stick from a horizontal nail. If the meter stick is given a small displacement from its equilibrium position and then released, it oscillates as a pendulum. What is the frequency

of the motion? What is the length of a simple pendulum having the same period?

*22. If we wish to make a physical pendulum from a meter stick as in Problem 21 and wish to make the frequency of the pendulum a maximum, how far from the 50 cm mark should we place the axis of rotation? What is the frequency in question?

23. A brass ring of radius R is suspended from a nail as suggested in the figure. If the ring is given a small displacement to one side and released, it swings as a pendulum. What is the frequency of its motion? What is the length of a simple pendulum having the same frequency?

24. How would the frequency of the motion of the pendulum in Problem 23 be affected if we cut off the lower half of the ring? The lower third of the ring?

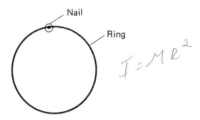

Problems 23 and 24

25. What would be the frequency of the pendulum motion of a solid disk if it were suspended from a nail by means of a small hook as suggested in the figure?

Problem 25

26. The pendulum of a "grandfather clock" has a period of 2 s. It consists of a 600-g brass disk with a radius of 12 cm attached at its rim to the lower end of a 200-g thin brass rod, the upper end of which is attached to the point of support of the pendulum. What is the length of the rod?

27. A 100-g ball attached to the lower end of a suspended coil spring oscillates at a frequency of 4 Hz when it is displaced from its equilibrium position and then released. What is the force constant of the spring? The amplitude A of oscillation of the ball after t seconds of motion is found to be given by the relation $A = A_0 e^{(-t/12\,s)}$, where A_0 is the initial amplitude. At what rate is energy being dissipated after 5 s if the initial amplitude of the oscillation is 10 cm?

28. What power would have to be supplied to the oscillator in Problem 27 to keep the ball in motion with a constant amplitude of 10 cm?

29. In most common methods of measuring mass, an unknown mass is determined in terms of a standard mass by comparing the gravitational forces exerted on the masses by the earth; in other words, the determination is based on the *gravitational properties* of mass. Masses can also be compared in terms of their *inertial properties* by what is called an "inertial balance." In such a device, bodies are subjected to horizontal restoring forces exerted by springs so that they execture SHM in the manner suggested in Fig. 12.1. If the frequency of oscillation of such a motion were *exactly* 1 Hz for a standard mass of 1 kg, what would be the frequencies observed for the following masses: 200 g, 400 g, 600 g, 2 kg, 4 kg, and 10 kg?

30. If a body of unknown mass causes the "inertial balance" described in Problem 29 to oscillate at a frequency of 1.72 Hz, what is the mass of the body?

31. As is discussed in Section 9.7, the gravitational force exerted on an object below the earth's surface is directly proportional to

the distance r of the object from the center of the earth provided the earth is homogeneous. If we ignore the earth's rotational motion and all frictional effects, show that if an object were dropped into a tunnel bored through the center of the earth as shown in the figure, the object would execute SHM about the earth's center. What would be the period of the motion and the frequency of the motion? What would be the maximum speed and the magnitude of the maximum acceleration attained by the object in the course of the SHM? ($R_E = 6370$ km)

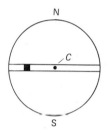

Problem 31

32. Suppose that a tunnel were drilled through the earth between two cities A and B, each at 60° N latitude, as shown in the figure. Show that an object dropped into the tunnel at A would execute SHM between A and B provided the conditions cited in Problem 31 were fulfilled. What would be the frequency of the motion? What would be the magnitudes of the maximum velocity and acceleration attained by the object in the course of its motion?

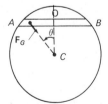

Problem 32

33. In our discussion of the simple pendulum we assumed that the rotational inertia of the pendulum about the point of support

is $I_0 = ml^2$. Actually, by the parallel-axis theorem the correct expression is $I_0 = ml^2 + I_C$, where I_C is the rotational inertia of the bob about an axis through its center of mass. Suppose that the "bob" consists of an iron sphere 10 cm in diameter and that the distance between the center of mass of the bob and the point of support of the pendulum is 1 m. What is the ratio of the correct value of I_0 to the approximate value $I_0 = ml^2$ that we employed in deriving (12.19)? What is the ratio of the correct value of the period T to the value given by (12.19)?

34. In our derivation of (12.19) we have used two different properties of mass: its *gravitational properties* in computing the torque $\tau = -mgl\theta$ and its *inertial properties* in computing $I_0 = ml^2$. If the gravitational mass m_G and the inertial mass m_I of a body were different, show that the expression for the period of a simple pendulum would be

$$T = 2\pi \sqrt{\frac{m_I l}{m_G g}} = \left(2\pi \sqrt{\frac{l}{g}}\right)\left(\sqrt{\frac{m_I}{m_G}}\right).$$

Numerous careful experiments with pendula employing many different materials have failed to reveal any detectable difference between m_I and m_G.

35. Suppose that a particle of mass m is constrained to move in the XY plane of a coordinate system in an inertial frame and is in equilibrium at the origin of the coordinate system. The particle is subject to a restoring force $\mathbf{F} = -k\mathbf{r}$, where $\mathbf{r}$ is the displacement of the particle from its equilibrium position. (a) Show that, if the particle is displaced from its equilibrium position to a position $x = A$, $y = 0$ and then released from rest, it will execute SHM described by the relation $x = A \cos 2\pi f t$, where $f = (1/2\pi)\sqrt{k/m}$. (b) Similarly, show that if the particle is displaced from its equilibrium position to a point $x = 0$, $y = A$ and then released from rest, it will execute SHM

described by the relation $y = A \cos 2\pi ft$ where $f = (1/2\pi)\sqrt{k/m}$.

36. Show that if the particle in Problem 35 is given an initial displacement to a point $x = A$, $y = A$ and released from rest, it will execute SHM described by the expression $r = R \cos 2\pi ft$, where as shown in the figure r is the displacement from the origin measured along a line making an angle of 45° with the X axis and $f = (1/2\pi) \sqrt{k/m}$. Show that the magnitude of the maximum displacement along this line is $R = \sqrt{2}A$. Show that the SHM in this case can be regarded as the combination of two SHM's: $x = A \cos 2\pi ft$ and $y = A \cos 2\pi ft$, which have the same phase. Show that the mechanical energy associated with the SHM of the particle along the line in the figure is equal to the sum of the mechanical energies of the two "in-phase" vibrations parallel to the X and Y axes.

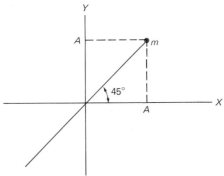

Problem 36

37. Suppose that the particle described in Problem 35 were given an initial displacement $x_0 = A$, $y_0 = 0$ and an initial velocity $v_{x0} = 0$, $v_{y0} = 2\pi fA$, where $f = (1/2\pi)\sqrt{k/m}$. Show that the displacement of the particle is given by the expressions $x = A \cos 2\pi ft$, $y = A \sin 2\pi ft$, and that the particle moves in a CCW sense in a circular path of radius A, similar to the motion of the particle in the reference circle in Fig. 12.5. Generalize these results to demonstrate that the motion of a particle at constant speed in a circular

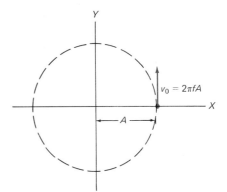

Problems 37 and 38

path can be regarded as the combination of two out-of-phase SHM's: $x = A \cos 2\pi ft$ and $y = A \sin 2\pi ft = A \cos(2\pi ft - \pi/2)$.

38. Continuing Problem 37, show that the mechanical energy associated with the motion in the circular path is equal to the sum of the mechanical energies of the two out-of-phase SHM's along the X and Y axes.

39. A 40-g particle moves CCW in a circular path of radius 14 cm and makes 3 revolutions per second. (a) Analyze this motion in terms of simple harmonic motions parallel to the axes of a Cartesian coordinate system. (b) What is the magnitude of the centripetal force acting on the particle? (c) What is the magnitude of the force constant k in the relation $\mathbf{F} = -k\mathbf{r}$, where $\mathbf{r}$ is the displacement of the particle from the center of its orbit?

40. A particle is subject to a restoring force $\mathbf{F} = -k\mathbf{r}$, where $\mathbf{r}$ is the displacement of the particle from its equilibrium position. Suggest procedures (a) for setting the particle into motion with constant speed in a CW sense in a circular path like that shown in the diagram for Problems 37 and 38 and (b) for setting the particle into SHM along a path perpendicular to the path shown in the diagram for Problem 36.

*41. Although (12.22) and Fig. 12.13 give a valid description of the behavior of a slightly damped oscillator, there are certain details of the motion that merit further consideration. At what stages of the oscillation is *no* energy actually being dissipated? At what stages of the oscillation is energy dissipation a maximum? Construct the quantity $\frac{1}{2}ky^2 + \frac{1}{2}m(dy/dt)^2$; why is $E = \frac{1}{2}kA^2$ only approximately the oscillator energy?

42. In a damped oscillator for which $\mathscr{R}^2/4m^2 = \frac{1}{2}k/m$, what is the ratio of the frequency f' to the frequency f of the same oscillator if there were no damping? What is the value of α for this oscillator in terms of $\mathscr{R}$ and m? Show that the amplitude A of the oscillations decreases to the value $(1/e)A_0$ in a time $t = 2m/\mathscr{R}$.

43. Verify by dimensional analysis that $\mathscr{R}/2m$ has the same dimensions as frequency f and thus that $1/\alpha$ in (12.22) has the dimensions of time. What are the SI units of $\mathscr{R}$?

44. For a damped oscillator with $\mathscr{R}^2/4m^2 = \frac{1}{2}k/m$ how long a time will be required for the energy E of the oscillations to decrease to $1/e$ times its initial value E_0? How much power must be supplied to the oscillator in order to maintain its energy at its initial level E_0? Express your results in terms of $\mathscr{R}$ and m.

45. How does the rate of decrease in the amplitude of a damped oscillator vary with the mass of the oscillator? How does the rate of decrease in the energy of a damped oscillator vary with the mass of the oscillator? Discuss these questions quantitatively for the case of a constant damping factor $\mathscr{R}$.

*46. Show that (12.22) is indeed a solution of (12.21) if α and f' have the appropriate values in terms of k, m, and $\mathscr{R}$.

47. Neglecting friction and the kinetic energy that is actually imparted to the water, show that a cylindrical log, weighted at one end so that it floats upright, if pushed down slightly and released will execute simple harmonic oscillations of frequency $f = (1/2\pi)\sqrt{\rho\ gA/m}$, where ρg is the specific weight of water, A is the cross-sectional area of the log, and m is the mass of the log.

48. How is the effective force constant in (12.2) related to the individual force constants of the two springs shown in Fig. 12.1? Explain your reasoning in detail. The two springs are *not* necessarily identical.

49. A small block rests on a horizontal platform that is itself vibrating horizontally with simply harmonic motion at a frequency of 2 Hz. If the coefficient of static friction between the bottom of the block and the surface of the platform is 0.6, what is the maximum amplitude that the platform's vibratory motion can have without the block slipping?

50. A small block is placed on top of a piston that is executing simple harmonic motion along a vertical line. If the frequency of this motion is 5 Hz, what is the maximum amplitude of the motion for which the block will remain continuously in contact with the piston?

PART 2

HEAT AND THERMODYNAMICS

CHAPTER 13

Temperature

The part of physics called *mechanics,* which we presented in earlier chapters, is based on only three fundamental physical quantities: *length, mass,* and *time.* All other mechanical quantities are derived quantities that are defined in terms of the three fundamental quantities.

With this chapter we begin a treatment of physical phenomena that *cannot* be interpreted completely by using quantities defined in terms of mass, length, and time. In addition to these three fundamental quantities, we shall need a fourth fundamental quantity: *temperature.* As in the case of the three fundamental quantities already defined, we must define temperature by specifying the operations involved in its measurement. In the case of temperature, the official SI definition is based on principles of *thermodynamics,* which we do not discuss fully until the final chapter of this part of the book! Therefore, we shall begin our treatment of temperature by discussing the way in which the ordinary Celsius scale was established and by pointing out some of the problems involved in constructing a thermometer. We then show how a gas thermometer can be used to establish an absolute temperature scale that is a very close approximation of the official SI thermodynamic scale of absolute temperature, which is known as the Kelvin scale.

13.1 THE CELSIUS TEMPERATURE SCALE

Temperature is usually determined by the measurement of some mechanical, electrical, or optical property of a material employed as a thermometer; this *thermometric property* of the material is presumed to have a one-to-one correlation with temperature. Thermometers employing the expansion of a liquid in a glass container were invented late in the 16th century. A mercury thermometer of this type is shown schematically in Fig. 13.1. Most of the mercury is contained in a thin-walled bulb at the lower

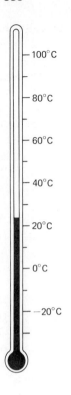

end of the thermometer; the bulb serves as the temperature-sensing element. A small amount of mercury extends upward from the bulb into a fine capillary tube in the thick-walled stem of the thermometer; the capillary tube above the mercury surface is evacuated. The cross-sectional area of the capillary tube is assumed to be constant. As the temperature of the thermometer bulb is raised, the volume of the mercury in the bulb increases and more mercury is pushed upward into the capillary so that the mercury surface inside the stem rises.

In establishing a temperature scale for everyday practical use we select two conveniently reproducible temperatures called *fixed points*. These are the ice point and the steam point.

The ICE POINT is the temperature of a mixture of pure ice and water exposed to the air at standard atmospheric pressure.
The STEAM POINT is the temperature of steam from pure water boiling at standard atmospheric pressure.

On the *Celsius scale,* which is employed in most scientific work and is in common use in most of the world, the ice point is taken as 0°C and the steam point as 100°C. This scale has been named the Celsius scale in honor of Anders Celsius (1701–1744), a Swedish astronomer who was one of the earliest proponents of a scale with 100 degrees between the ice point and the steam point.

Fig. 13.1 A liquid-in-glass thermometer.

In marking the scale on a thermometer like the one shown in Fig. 13.1, we carefully mark the positions of the end of the mercury column when the bulb is at the ice point and when the bulb is at the steam point. These two positions are then labeled 0°C and 100°C, respectively. We then divide the distance between these two marks on the stem into 100 equal parts that can be labeled at suitable intervals in the range between 0°C and 100°C as indicated in the figure. Once the *size* of the space between degree markings has been established, we can use it to provide markings above 100°C and below 0°C, as suggested in the figure. By this procedure we have produced a device that we can use for our own private purposes in estimating temperatures; in fact, many cheap thermometers supplied commercially are made in just the way that we have described. However, if we were to make a careful comparison of several mercury thermometers with scales constructed in the way just described, we would find that their scale readings always agree with one another at 0°C and at 100°C but rarely agree with one another at other temperatures. Careful comparison of the readings of a mercury-in-glass thermometer with those of a thermometer employing another liquid would probably show that the readings given by the two thermometers are *exactly* the same *only* at 0°C and 100°C.

There are two major sources of difficulty in attempting to use the procedure discussed above to establish a satisfactory scale of temperature. First, we have *assumed* that the capillary tube in the stem of the thermometer has uniform cross-sectional area. Second, we have *assumed* that exactly equal volumes ΔV of mercury move from the bulb into the capillary for equal increases in temperature ΔT. The expansion of the glass bulb as well as the expansion of mercury are both involved in this assumption. Clearly, we cannot establish a satisfactory temperature scale for general use on the basis of questionable assumptions regarding the construction of an artifact and the thermal expansion properties of particular materials like mercury and glass or other thermometric properties of particular materials.

The importance of the *thermodynamic scale* of temperature that is incorporated in the SI is that it is based on considerations that in no way depend on the thermal properties of any particular material or on any artifact. If we wish to use a thermometer like the one shown in Fig. 13.1 to give precise measurements of temperature, it must be calibrated in terms of "true readings" provided by measurements based on the thermodynamic scale. Carefully constructed mercury-in-glass thermometers intended for use in precise laboratory measurements have a scale of readings made in the way that we have described above; however, a manufacturer of such thermometers supplies a list of scale corrections based on comparisons of the thermometer readings with the corresponding readings of a device employing the thermodynamic temperature scale. After these calibration corrections have been applied, the user of the thermometer can determine Celsius temperatures with the assurance that his results will agree with those of workers in other laboratories in which properly calibrated thermometers are employed.

Even after a liquid-in-glass thermometer of the kind shown in Fig. 13.1 has been properly calibrated, it can be used only over a portion of the temperature range between the melting and boiling points of the liquid. Mercury freezes at −40°C; below this temperature alcohol thermometers can be employed. The upper limit of the range for which a thermometer should be used is well below the boiling point of the liquid and also well below the temperature at which glass begins to soften.

Although liquid-in-glass thermometers are the most common devices for the measurement of temperature, various other types of thermometer are important in scientific work. Many of these other devices can easily be used at temperatures below and above the limits attainable with liquid-in-glass thermometers. These devices depend on a wide variety of thermometric properties of materials. All devices making use of the thermometric properties of particular materials must be calibrated in terms of the thermodynamic scale before they can be used in precise temperature measurement.

13.2 THERMAL EQUILIBRIUM

When we make use of any type of thermometer for temperature measurements, our operations are based on the following principle that is based on general experience:

PRINCIPLE OF THERMAL EQUILIBRIUM: If objects with different initial temperatures are placed in a perfectly thermally insulated enclosure, all the objects eventually come to the same final temperature.

A perfectly thermally insulated enclosure is one equipped with walls that prevent the temperatures of objects inside from being influenced by bodies outside the enclosure. Perfect thermal insulation is, of course, an idealization, but it can be closely approximated.

In an insulated enclosure like the one provided by a "picnic hamper" of the familiar polystyrene-foam type, objects that were initially hot become cooler and objects that were originally cold become warmer. Eventually, the enclosed objects, the enclosed air, and the inner walls of the hamper reach the same final temperature. At this stage *thermal equilibrium* is said to be established. When this stage has been reached, no rearrangement of the objects inside the enclosure will cause any further changes in temperature of any of the objects.

A thermometer is a device that gives a reading of its *own* temperature. When we use a thermometer to determine the temperature of some other body, we make use of the principle of thermal equilibrium. We first allow the thermometer bulb to come into thermal equilibrium with the object of interest and then note the reading of the thermometer. In general, when a thermometer is placed in intimate contact with another body—a solid, liquid, or gas—it will come to the same temperature as that of the other body and hence give a reading of the temperature of the other body.

13.3   THERMAL EXPANSION OF SOLIDS

When the temperature of a solid body is raised, the body usually expands. Although the expansion is usually small as compared with the total volume of the body, it is large enough to be an important factor in many practical problems. Thermal expansion makes it necessary to provide for "expansion joints" in buildings, bridges, and pavements; it makes possible the shrink-fitting of collars on shafts and steel tires on locomotive wheels; it results in the breaking of glass objects when one part of the glass is heated more than another.

The increase in any linear dimension of a solid such as its length, width, height, radius, or the distance between two marks on the solid is known as *linear expansion.* If, as suggested in Fig. 13.2, we use l to denote the length of any dimension of a solid and Δl to denote the change in length that accompanies an increase in temperature ΔT, we find experimentally that for most materials to a good approximation Δl is directly proportional to l and to ΔT; i.e., $\Delta l \propto l \Delta T$. The value of Δl for a given value of l and ΔT also depends on the *material* of which the object is made, so we can write

$$\Delta l = \alpha l \Delta T \quad \text{or} \quad \alpha = (\Delta l/l)/\Delta T, \qquad (13.1)$$

where α is called the *coefficient of linear expansion* of the material.

The COEFFICIENT OF LINEAR EXPANSION of a solid is the change in length per unit length per degree change in temperature.

With this definition of α, relation (13.1) becomes exact as ΔT approaches zero; thus, $dl = \alpha l dT$ and $\alpha = (1/l) \; (dl/dT)$. We note that α can vary with temperature. The common units for α are Cdeg^{-1}.

Fig. 13.2   Linear expansion: $\Delta l = \alpha/\Delta T$.

Table 13–1. Typical Values of the Linear Expansion Coefficient for Various Materials Near Room Temperature

Material	α (10^{-6} Cdeg^{-1})	Material	α (10^{-6} Cdeg^{-1})
Aluminum	24	Brick	9
Brass and Bronze	19	Soft Glass	9
Copper	17	Pyrex Glass	3
Gold	14	Ice	51
Iron	11	Quartz (fused)	0.4
Lead	29	Wood	
Silver	19	Oak, across fiber	54
Steel	12	Oak, parallel to fiber	5
Tin	20	Pine, across fiber	34
Tungsten	4.3	Pine, parallel to fiber	5

Typical values of α for various materials are listed in Table 13.1. Although the values of α are different for different materials, it is easy to remember the order of magnitude of α: a 1 m length of solid increases by about 1 mm for a temperature rise of 100 Cdeg. For this case

$$\alpha = \Delta l/l\Delta T = 10^{-3}\,\text{m}/(1\,\text{m} \times 10^2\,\text{Cdeg}) = 10^{-5}\,\text{per Cdeg}.$$

Because α is so small, it makes no difference whether we use the initial or final value of l in (13.1); experimental values of α are usually valid to only two or three significant figures; i.e., values carefully obtained have an uncertainty of approximately 1%.

If we consider a solid with initial length l_0 at 0°C, the ΔT in (13.1) becomes merely T_C, the final temperature on the Celsius scale, and we can express $\Delta l = \alpha l_0 T_C$ as the increase or decrease in length of the object when the temperature is changed from 0°C to T_C. Thus, we can write

$$l = l_0 + \Delta l = l_0(1 + \alpha T_C). \tag{13.2}$$

Note that we are using the symbol T_C to represent *Celsius* temperatures.

Linear expansion is a thermometric property that can be employed in such devices as the bimetallic strip used in thermostats. Such a bimetallic strip consisting of brass and steel is shown in Fig. 13.3. If two thin strips of brass and steel are welded together at some initial temperature T_0, the resulting bimetallic strip is straight. Because $\alpha_{\text{steel}} < \alpha_{\text{brass}}$, a reduction in temperature will cause the composite strip to curve toward the left in the figure, whereas an increase in temperature will cause the composite strip to curve toward the right in the figure. With proper calibration, the displacement of the free end of the strip provides a measure of temperature. The displacement of the free end of the bimetallic strip in a thermostat can provide a means of opening and closing an electric switch.

Once the linear expansion coefficient has been determined for a material, changes in the surface area of a body composed of the material can easily be computed. Consider the face of the rectangular plate in Fig. 13.4, which has dimensions a_0

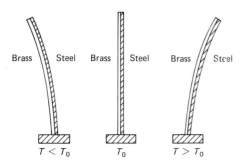

Fig. 13.3 A bimetallic strip.

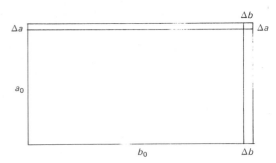

Fig. 13.4 Superficial or surface expansion. What part of this figure do we ignore when we drop the term $\alpha^2 T_c^2$ to obtain Eq. (13.3)?

and b_0 at 0°C; its area at 0°C is $A_0 = a_0 b_0$. At any other temperature T_C, its area can be expressed as

$$A = ab = a_0(1 + \alpha T_C)b_0(1 + \alpha T_C) = a_0 b_0 (1 + \alpha T_C)^2$$

or

$$A = A_0(1 + 2\alpha T_C + \alpha^2 T_C^2).$$

Because α is of the order of 10^{-5} per Cdeg, α^2 is of the order of 10^{-10} per Cdeg²; thus, the third term in this equation can be neglected in most practical cases. Thus, in excellent approximation the above equation becomes

$$A = A_0(1 + 2\alpha T_C) = A_0(1 + \sigma T_C), \qquad (13.3)$$

where $\sigma = 2\alpha$ is called the *coefficient of superficial or surface expansion.*

The same value for σ can be justified in another way by use of the calculus. In the limit that ΔT becomes very small we have from (13.1) that $dl/dT = \alpha l$. Consider a square surface measuring l on each side with area $A_0 = l_0^2$ at 0°C. Its area at any other temperature T_C is given by $A = l_0^2 (1 + \alpha T_C)^2 = l^2$, and the rate of change of A with respect to temperature is given by

$$dA/dT = 2l \, dl/dT = 2\alpha l^2 = 2\alpha A.$$

If in analogy with (13.1) we define the coefficient of surface expansion by $\sigma = (1/A)(dA/dT)$, we have $\sigma = 2\alpha$. For small finite temperature changes ΔT we can write

$$\Delta A = 2\alpha A \Delta T = \sigma A \Delta T. \qquad (13.3')$$

For small finite temperature changes $\sigma = 2\alpha$ is an excellent approximation.

Next let us consider the volume expansion of a cube measuring l_0 on each edge at $T_C = 0$°C and thus having a volume $V_0 = l_0^3$ at this temperature. The cube's volume at any other temperature T_C is given by

$$V = l^3 = l_0^3 (1 + \alpha T_C)^3 = V_0(1 + 3\alpha T_C + 3\alpha^2 T_C^2 + \alpha^3 T_C^3)$$

or $V = V_0(1 + 3\alpha T_C)$, where we neglect the terms involving α^2 and α^3. This relation is usually written

$$V = V_0(1 + \beta T_C), \tag{13.4}$$

where $\beta = 3\alpha$ is called the *coefficient of cubical or volume expansion*. In general for a small finite temperature change ΔT we have $\beta = \Delta V / V \Delta T$ or

$$\Delta V = \beta V \Delta T = 3\alpha V \Delta T. \tag{13.4'}$$

At a given temperature $\beta = (1/V)(dV/dT)$ provides a definition β.

In concluding our discussion of the thermal expansion of solids, we should note that, although the assumption that α is constant and the relations $\sigma = 2\alpha$ and $\beta = 3\alpha$ are satisfactory over the ranges of temperature normally encountered by the structural engineer and the experimental scientist, we must not make the mistake of assuming that α itself is constant over *all* temperature ranges. The values of α listed in Table 13.1 are actually average values for use over a fairly wide temperature range in the vicinity of ambient laboratory temperatures. The values of α for very low temperatures and for temperatures near the melting points of solids may be significantly different.

13.4 EXPANSION OF LIQUIDS

Because a liquid has no shape of its own but merely assumes the shape of its container, the concepts of linear or superficial thermal expansion are not applicable to liquids. The only kind of thermal expansion that can be exhibited by a liquid is volume expansion.

Experiment shows that to a good approximation the change ΔV in the volume of a given quantity of a liquid is directly proportional to the change ΔT in the temperature of the sample and to its total volume V; i.e., $\Delta V \propto V \Delta T$. The volume change otherwise depends only on the nature of the liquid. Thus, it is possible to define a *coefficient of volume expansion* β for a liquid by writing

$$\Delta V = \beta V \Delta T \quad \text{or} \quad \beta = \Delta V / V \Delta T, \tag{13.5}$$

where β is expressed in Cdeg^{-1}; at a given temperature T, we can write the exact relation $\beta = (1/V)(dV/dT)$. For most liquids the value of β is nearly independent of the temperature range at which the change ΔT occurs. Typical values of β for several liquids are listed in Table 13.2. It is to be noted from this table that β for liquids is typically about 10 times the volume coefficient $\beta = 3\alpha$ for solids. Mercury, a liquid metal at laboratory temperatures, is an exception.

Because solid containers of one kind or another are always required, the volume expansion coefficient of a liquid cannot be determined quite as easily as the coefficient

Table 13–2.   Typical Values of the Volume Expansion Coefficient for Various Liquids Near Room Temperature

Material	β (10⁻⁵ Cdeg⁻¹)	Material	β (10⁻⁵ Cdeg⁻¹)
Benzene	124	Glycerol	51
Carbon Tetrachloride	124	Mercury	18.2
Ethanol	112	Methanol	120
Ethyl Ether	166	Turpentine	97

of linear expansion of a solid. As we increase the temperature of a liquid, we also increase the temperature of its solid container. Because the container as well as the liquid increases in volume as the temperature is raised, we must usually measure $\Delta V_{\text{Liq}} - \Delta V_{\text{Solid}}$ in arriving at a value for β for the liquid. One method involves completely filling a glass flask of known volume V and then measuring the volume of the liquid that flows out of the flask as the temperature is raised by ΔT. At the initial temperature the flask and the liquid have the same volume V. After the temperature has been raised, the volume of the liquid is $V_L = V + \beta V \Delta T$ and the volume of the solid flask is $V_S = V + 3\alpha V \Delta T$, where α is the linear expansion coefficient of the glass. The measured volume of the liquid overflow is $V_L - V_S = (\beta - 3\alpha) V \Delta T$; thus, $\beta = 3\alpha + (V_L - V_S)/V \Delta T$. In order to determine β by this method, we must, of course, know the coefficient of linear expansion of the glass container.

Another method of measuring the volume expansion coefficient of a liquid involves a measurement of the liquid's density ρ as the temperature of the liquid is changed. The influence of temperature on density can be determined by the following considerations. The mass m of a given sample of liquid is given by the expression $\rho V = m$. Taking the derivative of both sides of this equation with respect to temperature, we obtain

$$\rho (dV/dT) + V(d\rho/dT) = 0 \quad \text{or} \quad (1/\rho)(d\rho/dT) = -(1/V)(dV/dT)$$

because the mass m of the sample is constant. Since $(1/V)(dV/dT) = \beta$, we can write $d\rho = -\beta\rho dT$; for a finite temperature change ΔT, we obtain

$$\Delta\rho = -\beta\rho\Delta T \quad \text{or} \quad \beta = -\Delta\rho/\rho\Delta T. \tag{13.5'}$$

If we measure the density of a liquid as a function of temperature, we can then determine β.

If we know the volume V_0 of a liquid sample at 0°C, we can make use of (13.5) to determine the volume V of the liquid at any Celsius temperature T_C from the relation

$$V = V_0(1 + \beta T_C). \tag{13.6}$$

Similarly, if we know the density ρ_0 of a liquid at 0°C, we can use (13.5') to determine its density ρ at any Celsius temperature T_C from the relation

$$\rho = \rho_0(1 - \beta T_C). \tag{13.6'}$$

Relations (13.6) and (13.6′) hold for liquids for which β is constant. For such liquids volume and density can be used as thermometric properties. We note that in using an ordinary liquid-in-glass thermometer like the one shown in Fig. 13.1 we make the assumption that both β for the liquid and α for the glass bulb are constant.

As an important example of a liquid that does *not* have a constant coefficient of volume expansion, consider the anomalous behavior of *water* as shown by the plot given in Fig. 13.5. If we start with 1 g of pure water at 0°C and gradually raise the temperature, the volume of the water *decreases* slightly as its temperature rises to 4°C. Above 4°C the volume of the water increases slowly at first and then more rapidly as the temperature is raised to 100°C. The actual *contraction* of water as its temperature is raised from 0°C to 4°C is a phenomenon that is extremely rare among liquids. This unusual behavior is important in explaining the way that water in a pail freezes from the top down when the pail is left out of doors on a cold night. Lakes and ponds also freeze from the top down, a phenomenon that is important to aquatic life forms.

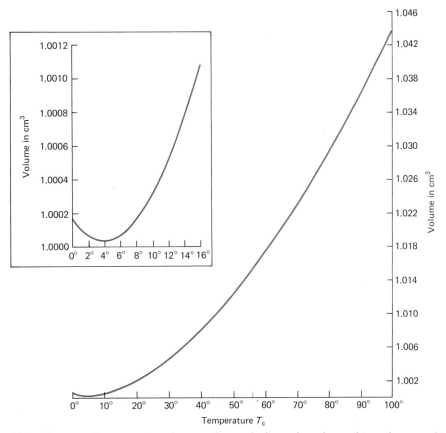

Fig. 13.5 The anomalous expansion of water. The graph shows the volume of 1 g of water, which actually decreases from 1.00016 cm³ at 0°C to 1.00003 cm³ at 4°C.

13.5   THE GAS LAWS

typical solids; thus, it would appear that gases would be excellent materials for use in thermometers. Although this conclusion is correct, the designer of a gas thermometer has to take account of the fact that the volume of a given quantity of gas in contrast to solids and liquids is *strongly* influenced by pressure as well as by temperature. The dependence of the volume of a gas sample on pressure and temperature is readily described in terms of a few very simple relations known as the *gas laws,* which have been determined directly from experiments.

The first of these laws was enunciated by Sir Robert Boyle (1627–1691), an early British scientist who helped establish rigorous experimental methods in many areas of physics and chemistry. Boyle found that *at a given temperature the volume of a gas sample is inversely proportional to its total absolute pressure.* Thus, at a given temperature we can write the relation

$$PV = \text{constant} \quad \text{(at constant temperature).} \quad \textit{(Boyle's Law)} \tag{13.7}$$

If a gas sample has a volume V_0 at 0°C and standard atmospheric pressure P_0, its volume V at any other pressure P is given by the relation

$$PV = P_0 V_0 \quad \text{or} \quad V = V_0(P_0/P) \tag{13.7'}$$

provided the temperature of the gas remains at 0°C. Boyle's Law (13.7) gives a valid description of gases over a wide range of pressure and temperature but begins to fail at extremely high pressures and at low temperatures.

The relation between the volume of a gas and its temperature under conditions of constant pressure was discovered in 1787 by the French physicist Jacques Charles (1746–1823). This discovery was widely publicized in 1802 by the French physical chemist Joseph Gay-Lussac (1778–1850), who considerably improved Charles's experimental procedures. These investigators found that for a sample of air having an initial volume V_0 at a pressure of 1 atm and a temperature of 0°C the change in volume ΔV was given by the relation

$$\Delta V = \beta V_0 T_C \quad \text{(at constant pressure)} \tag{13.8}$$

provided the pressure remained constant at 1 atm. Here T_C is the Celsius temperature of the gas and the volume expansion coefficient β has a value of approximately 3.66×10^{-3} per Cdeg. Experiment shows that this value of β applies to *all* gases provided the pressure is not too high or the temperature too low.

Because the numerical value of β is approximately 1/273°C, Eq. (13.8) can be written in a different way:

$$\Delta V = V_0(T_C/273°C) \quad \text{(at constant pressure).} \tag{13.8'}$$

Using this expression for ΔV, we can express the total volume V of a gas sample at Celsius temperature T_C in the forms

$$V = V_0 + \Delta V = V_0(1 + T_C/273°C),$$
$$V = V_0[(T_C + 273°C)/273°C],$$

or

$$V/(T_C + 273°C) = V_0/273°C. \quad \text{(at constant pressure)} \quad \textit{(Charles' Law)} \quad (13.9)$$

The expression (13.9) is known as Charles' Law.

13.6 THE ABSOLUTE TEMPERATURE SCALE

Consideration of the form of Charles' Law given in (13.9) suggests the possibility of writing the relation in a simpler form by using a different temperature scale. We note that a gas obeying Charles' Law would have zero volume at $-273°C$: $V = 0$ at $T_C = -273°C$. If we call this temperature *absolute zero*, it is possible to express temperatures on an *absolute scale*, called the Kelvin scale. The Kelvin scale has temperature scale *divisions* that are equal to those employed on the Celsius scale; i.e., 1 Kdeg = 1 Cdeg. Thus, on the Kelvin scale the ice point, which is 273 K degrees above absolute zero, becomes 273°K; the steam point, which is 373 K degrees above absolute zero, becomes 373°K. In general, if we know any Celsius temperature T_C, we obtain the corresponding Kelvin temperature T by adding 273° to this value;* i.e.,

$$T = T_C + 273°. \quad (13.10)$$

We shall use the symbol T to denote temperature on the Kelvin scale unless we specify otherwise.

By using absolute temperatures we can obtain a very simple expression for Charles' Law (13.9):

$$V/T = V_0/T_0 \quad \text{(at constant pressure)}. \quad \textit{(Charles' Law)} \quad (13.11)$$

Charles' Law can then be stated in words with corresponding simplicity. *At a given pressure, the volume of a gas sample is directly proportional to the absolute temperature of the gas.*

The expression for Charles' Law given in (13.11) supplies a convenient description of the dependence of the volume of a gas sample on temperature when the pressure of the gas does not change. The expression for Boyle's Law in (13.7) gives a valid description of the volume of a gas sample when the temperature of the gas does

---

* The best modern value of the temperature of the ice point is 273.1500°K. Thus, the numerical value in (13.10) should actually be 273.1500°. These matters are discussed further in Chapter 17.

not change. The behavior of a gas sample subject to changes in both pressure and temperature can be described by the relation

$$PV/T = P_0 V_0 / T_0. \quad \textit{(General Gas Law)} \tag{13.12}$$

This relation, known as the *general gas law,* is applicable to all gases at low pressures and at temperatures high above the boiling points of the liquids from which the gases are formed.

Although the behavior of all real gases departs from the behavior predicted by (13.12) if we go to extremely high pressures or extremely low temperatures, the general gas law provides an excellent guide to the behavior of real gases in many practical situations. Equation (13.12) also provides us with a useful concept known as an ideal gas. By definition, *an ideal gas is a gas that obeys the general gas law under all conditions of temperature and pressure.* Although no ideal gas actually exists, the concept proves to be a useful one. Boyle's Law, Charles' Law, and the general gas law are sometimes called the *ideal gas laws.* At temperatures and pressures at which real gases obey the ideal gas laws, they are behaving like ideal gases.

The general gas law in the simple form that we have given applies to any enclosed *sample* of a gas. In a later chapter, we shall restate the general gas law in a more general form. We shall find that the general gas law provides insight into the behavior of the molecules of gases.

13.7   THE IDEAL-GAS THERMOMETER

The general gas law (13.12) would seem to offer a solution to the problem of establishing a satisfactory temperature scale. For example, we might employ Charles' Law (13.11) to determine absolute temperature T in terms of the measured volume V of a gas sample having volume V_0 at temperature T_0, provided the pressure of the sample is kept constant. In practice it is more desirable to employ a constant-volume gas thermometer and to determine T in terms of T_0 and the measured values of sample pressure. Thus, we can solve (13.12) for T for a case in which the gas volume is kept constant with $V = V_0$:

$$T = T_0 (P/P_0). \quad \textit{(Constant-Volume Ideal Gas Thermometer)} \tag{13.13}$$

This relation permits us to determine Kelvin temperature T in terms of the ice point $T_0 = 273°K$ and a measured pressure ratio P/P_0. The measurements of pressures P and P_0 are based on quantities involving only length, mass, and time. Thus, Eq. (13.13) would seem to provide a satisfactory definition of Kelvin temperature in terms of the single fixed point, which we have chosen as the ice point and to which we have *assigned* the temperature $273°K$.

Although the use of (13.13) to define an absolute temperature scale is logically satisfactory, it is subject to one serious operational shortcoming: *We do not have an ideal gas to use as the thermometric substance.* At sufficiently low temperatures, all real gases actually condense to form liquids before we reach absolute zero. However,

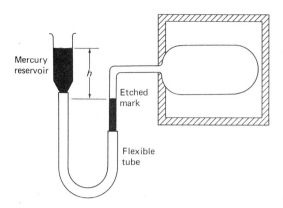

Fig. 13.6 Schematic diagram of a constant-volume gas thermometer.

as we have noted earlier, the behavior of all real gases closely approximates that of an ideal gas at sufficiently high temperatures and low pressures. Under these conditions we can employ any gas in a constant-volume thermometer to determine temperature from (13.13).

Various gases such as helium, hydrogen, and nitrogen have been used for thermometric purposes. Because hydrogen does not condense at atmospheric pressures until the temperature has been reduced to 20.4°K and has certain other desirable properties, the constant-volume hydrogen thermometer proves extremely useful in the work done at standardizing laboratories. It was actually used as an international standard prior to 1927. Helium thermometers can be used at temperatures as low as 4.2°K. A schematic diagram of a constant-volume gas thermometer is shown in Fig. 13.6. The gas is enclosed in a bulb of fused quartz in an insulated region the temperature T of which is to be measured; from the bulb a tube with small volume extends outside the enclosure. The volume of the gas is kept constant by raising or lowering the mercury reservoir at the left in the figure so that the mercury in the right-hand tube always stands at a clearly etched mark on the small tube. The pressure of the enclosed gas can then be determined in terms of the difference between the heights of the mercury levels in the reservoir and at the etched mark along with a knowledge of atmospheric pressure determined by an auxiliary barometer in the laboratory. Because in (13.13) only the *pressure ratio* P/P_0 is employed in determining T in terms of T_0, pressures can be conveniently specified in terms of cm or mm of mercury just as they are in an ordinary mercury barometer.

Although the constant-volume hydrogen thermometer is a reliable device for use in measuring absolute temperatures at temperatures well above the boiling point of liquid hydrogen, it is not entirely satisfactory as a basis for the establishment of the SI Kelvin scale of temperature. Fortunately, as we have suggested earlier, there are thermodynamic principles that can be employed to establish a satisfactory temperature scale without depending on the specific thermal properties of any particular material such as hydrogen. This thermodynamic scale is consistent with the scale that would be provided with a constant-volume ideal gas thermometer—if we had an ideal gas. For the present, we can define absolute zero as the temperature at which the pressure of an ideal gas would be zero. In subsequent chapters we shall present other more satisfactory definitions of absolute zero. In the chapter on thermodynamics we shall discuss certain refinements of the absolute temperature scale that are involved in the official Kelvin scale as adopted by the commission responsible for the *Système International.*

Until we treat thermodynamics we shall regard temperature as a fundamental quantity temporarily defined by (13.13). In expressing absolute temperatures we shall from now on follow the SI commission's recommendations of stating temperatures in *kelvins* (K) rather than in °K; for example, the ice point will be stated as 273 K rather than 273°K. The commission further recommends that temperature intervals ΔT also be expressed in *kelvins* rather than K-degrees. Because the size of the Celsius degree and the Kelvin degree are the same, we can express expansion coefficients in K^{-1} rather than in "per Cdeg" or in "Cdeg^{-1}."

QUESTIONS

1. Suggest several physical quantities that might be used as thermometric properties.

2. Why are fixed points defined in terms of the properties of water? As pointed out in connection with Fig. 13.5, some of the physical properties of water are relatively complex.

3. The original version of the Celsius temperature scale assigned the temperature 0°C to the steam point and the temperature 100°C to the ice point. Are there any inherent difficulties with such a scale, or is having the steam point at a higher temperature than the ice point simply a matter of taste?

4. A large container holding a mixture of liquid water and ice at 0°C is brought into thermal contact with a container of liquid water at 0°C and a container of ice at 0°C. Will the three systems be in thermal equilibrium? Will the three systems be in complete equilibrium, or will ice form in the container of liquid water and liquid water in the container of ice?

5. What are the dimensions of the coefficient of linear expansion α? Does the value of α depend on the particular unit used to measure length, e.g., meters or centimeters or feet? Does the value of α depend on the particular unit used to measure temperature, e.g., Celsius degrees or Fahrenheit degrees or kelvins?

6. Exactly what are the natures of the approximations involved in the statement that $\beta = 3\alpha$? What quantities must be small in comparison with what other quantities?

7. It is possible to compensate for the change with temperature of the period of a clock pendulum by fastening tubes of mercury to the bob of the pendulum. Explain the physical mechanism that is involved. Are the exact number, size, shape, and location of the tubes of mercury of crucial importance?

8. How is it possible that a solid sphere and a hollow sphere made of the same material and having the same radii at 0°C will expand by the same amounts when the temperature is raised? Will not the expansion of the material in the center of the solid sphere force it to expand more than the hollow sphere?

9. Why isn't it satisfactory to base the definition of an absolute temperature scale on the ideal gas equation? There may not be any real gases that obey this equation exactly, but the abstract concept of an ideal gas is certainly well defined.

10. Is it in any sense meaningful to assign a temperature to a vacuum?

11. Why are uninsulated water pipes in danger of bursting in a northern winter?

PROBLEMS

1. If steel railroad rails are laid when the temperature is 15°C, how much gap must be left between one standard 12-m rail and the next if the rails just touch when the ground temperature is 50°C? What will be the gap between adjacent rails when the ground temperature is −20°C?

2. A locomotive wheel is 96 cm in diameter at 20°C. A steel rim or "tire" with a diameter 0.8 mm "undersize" at 20°C is to be shrunk on the wheel. To what temperature should the *tire* be heated in order to make it 0.8 mm "oversize"?

3. A copper box is 40 cm high, 60 cm wide, and 120 cm long at the temperature of melting ice. What will be the increases in the height, width, and length of the box if its temperature is raised to the steam point? What are the corresponding increases in the outer surface area and in the volume of the box?

4. The radius of a copper sphere at −10°C is 25 cm. What will be the increases in the diameter, the surface area, and the volume of the sphere if its temperature is increased to 120°C?

5. A shop worker bends a 1-m copper rod so that it forms a nearly complete circle with only 2.4 mm between the ends of the bent rod. If the length of a rod is 1 m at 20°C, to what temperature must a straight rod be raised in order to cause its length to increase by 2.4 mm? At this temperature does the bent rod form a complete circle? Can the worker obtain a complete circle by cooling the bent rod? Discuss.

6. A shop worker mills a square hole into a brass plate 30 cm in diameter and 1.5 cm thick. If the square is exactly 2.54 cm on a side at 20°C, what will be the length of each side at 150°C?

7. A sample of mercury has a volume of 500 cm³ at 20°C. What will be the increase in the volume of the sample if its temperature is raised to the steam point? What will be the decrease in the volume of the sample if its temperature is lowered to −38°C?

8. A narrow-necked brass bottle is just filled with 700 cm³ of ethanol at 0°C. How much ethanol "spills over" if the temperature is raised to 40°C? If this bottle were filled with water at 0°C, how much water would spill over if the temperature were raised to 100°C?

9. If a 150-cm³ narrow-necked bottle of soft glass were filled with mercury at 20°C, how much mercury would spill over if the temperature were raised to the steam point?

10. A certain mercury thermometer is fabricated from Pyrex glass. At 0°C there are 0.6 cm³ of mercury in the bulb and capillary up to the 0° mark. What should be the cross-sectional area of the capillary tube in the stem of the thermometer if the degree marks on the Celsius scale engraved on the stem are to be 2 mm apart when the temperature of the glass is 20°C.

11. Show that when the temperature changes by a small amount ΔT, the pressure remaining constant, the height h of the mercury column of a barometer changes by $\Delta h = \beta h \Delta T$, where β is the coefficient of volume expansion of mercury.

12. By use of Fig. 13.5 obtain an average value for the volume expansion coefficient of water in the range 0°C to 4°C and in the range 4°C to 100°C.

13. Show that Boyle's Law (13.7) and Charles' Law (13.11) can be combined to give the general gas law. In order to do this, imagine a gas with an *initial state* P_0, V_0, and T_0. By considering first a change from the initial

state to an *intermediate state P, V', and T_0* and then a change from the intermediate state to a *final state P, V, T,* obtain (13.12).

14. Show that the general gas law (13.12) when stated in terms of densities has the form $\rho T/P = \rho_0 T_0/P_0$. Dry air has a density of 1.29 kg/m³ at 0°C and standard atmospheric pressure. What will be the density of an air sample initially at 0°C and 1 atm if it is heated to 100°C (a) at constant pressure and (b) at constant volume?

15. If a sample of dry nitrogen has a volume of 500 cm³ at a pressure of 76 cm of mercury at 0°C, at what Celsius temperature would its volume be 250 cm³ if the pressure remained unchanged? At what Celsius temperature would its pressure be 25 cm of mercury if its volume remained constant at 500 cm³?

16. If an ideal gas sample at 0°C and one standard atmosphere has a volume of 1 liter, at what Kelvin temperatures would its volume be 0.2 liter, 0.5 liter, 1.5 liters and 2 liters at a pressure of one standard atmosphere? If its volume were maintained at 1 liter, at what Kelvin temperatures would its pressure be 0.1, 0.3, 0.8, 1.2, and 2 atm?

17. If the bulb of the constant-volume hydrogen thermometer shown in Fig. 13.6 is made of fused quartz, what error is involved in our assumption that the volume of the hydrogen gas is constant? If the temperature of the quartz bulb of the thermometer in Fig. 13.6 were raised from the ice point to the steam point, what would be the ratio of the final hydrogen pressure based on the assumption of constant volume to its actual final pressure when the expansion of the quartz bulb is considered?

18. A carelessly made barometer has some air trapped above the mercury. The mercury in the tube stands at 72 cm when the air space in the tube above the mercury column is 10 cm long and the true atmospheric pressure is 76 cm of mercury. What is the atmospheric pressure when the faulty barometer reads 68 cm at the same temperature?

19. A faulty barometer like the one in Problem 18 reads 74.2 cm when the air space above the mercury is 8 cm long. When the barometer tube is pushed down into the mercury reservoir so that the air space is only 4 cm long, the barometer stands at 72.2 cm. What is the true atmospheric pressure?

20. Show that when its temperature changes by a small amount ΔT the rotational inertia of a solid object changes by $\Delta I = 2\alpha I \Delta T$.

21. Show that the period τ of a physical pendulum changes by $\frac{1}{2}\alpha\tau\Delta T$ when its temperature changes by a small amount ΔT. Use the result of Problem 20.

22. Two glass bulbs with volumes 300 cm³ and 100 cm³ are connected by a capillary tube. This container is filled with dry air at a temperature of 20°C and a pressure of 76 cm of mercury. The larger bulb is then immersed in steam at 100°C and the smaller bulb in ice water at 0°C. Neglecting thermal expansion of the glass, find the resulting pressure.

23. What is the pressure inside the container described in Problem 22 when the larger bulb is placed in ice water at 0°C and the smaller bulb in steam at 100°C?

Note: In the following problems use the elastic constants given in Chapter 10 and assume that they do not vary with temperature.

24. In modern practice railroad rails are sometimes butt-welded into a continuous length. If steel rails are laid and welded in summer when the ground surface temperature is

35°C, what is the tensile stress in winter when the ground surface temperature is −20°C? Will the rails acquire a permanent set?

25. A steel bar 4 cm in diameter and 50 cm in length is mounted with no clearance between two fixed vertical columns when the temperature is 10°C. When the temperature of the bar is raised to 35°C, what forces does the bar exert on each vertical support?

26. A closed steel tank is completely filled with water at 0°C. What is the pressure inside the tank at 100°C? Assume that the tank expands only because of the temperature rise and not because of the increased water pressure.

27. What pressure in standard atmospheres is required to keep mercury from expanding as its temperature is raised from 0°C to 100°C?

28. A hollow copper ball is partially filled with lead shot so that the ball just floats in water at 20°C. What happens if the temperature is raised to 90°C? What is the ratio of the buoyant force exerted on the ball by the water at 20°C to the corresponding buoyant force at 90°C?

29. A grandfather clock is equipped with a pendulum consisting of a slender brass rod with one end of a brass cylinder attached to its lower end. If the clock operates correctly at 20°C, what error in s/h is introduced if the temperature drops to 0°C? At the lower temperature does the clock run "fast" or "slow"?

30. A steel tape of the type used by surveyors is correctly calibrated at 0°C. With what tensile stress would it have to be stretched in order to read correctly at −30°C?

31. A steel tape of the type used by surveyors is correctly calibrated at 0°C. What *percent-*

age error is involved when this tape is used at 30°C? If the tape is used to measure the length of a copper rod at 30°C, is the true length of the rod larger or smaller than the value as measured by the tape?

32. The "bag" of a balloon is a sphere 25 m in diameter that is filled with hydrogen at 0°C and a pressure of 1 atm. Under these conditions the density of hydrogen is 0.090 kg/m³ and the density of the air is 1.29 kg/m³. What total mass of fabric, car, and contents can be lifted by the balloon under these conditions? If after the balloon has been launched the temperature drops to −15°C while the pressure remains constant, what happens to the balloon and its load?

33. We showed in (13.4) that the volume of a solid at temperature T_C is given by $V = V_0(1 + \beta T_C)$, where V_0 is its volume at 0°C and $\beta = 3\alpha$. Make a careful drawing of a cube of edge length l and show graphically what volume we are neglecting in using (13.4) instead of $[l_0(1 + \alpha T_0)]^3$ in obtaining V. The melting point of aluminum is 659°C; do we make an appreciable error in using (13.4) to determine the volume of an aluminum cube at this temperature?

34. A metal rod is initially placed between two rigid vertical stationary posts positioned horizontally in such a way that the rod fits snugly between the posts at 0°C. If the temperature of the rod is *raised by* ΔT, show that the resulting compression stress S in the rod is given by the expression $S = \alpha M_Y \Delta T$, where α is the coefficient of linear expansion and M_Y is Young's modulus for the metal. What happens if the temperature of the rod drops below 0°C?

35. A piece of copper wire is stretched between two fixed rigid supports when the temperature is 30°C; the diameter of the wire is 2 mm and the initial tension in the wire is

400 N. If the temperature of the wire is reduced sufficiently, the wire is permanently deformed. At what temperature is the elastic limit of the wire exceeded?

36. A circular steel band 2 cm in circumference and 1 mm thick fits snugly around an aluminum rod at 0°C. If the temperature is raised to 100°C, what is the tensional stress in the steel band?

CHAPTER 14

Heat and Thermal Energy

When hot bodies and cold bodies are placed inside a thermally insulated enclosure, the temperatures of the hot bodies decrease and the temperatures of the cold bodies increase until all the bodies come to a common final temperature. In the 18th century it was generally believed that this achievement of thermal equilibrium involved the flow of a *caloric fluid** from the hot bodies to the cold bodies; the caloric fluid was supposed to flow from regions of high temperature to regions of low temperature just as water tends to flow from high elevations to low elevations on the earth's surface. Although all attempts to gain direct evidence for the actual existence of a caloric fluid failed, some of the 18th-century terminology is still used in studies of what we now call *heat flow* or *heat transfer*.

In this chapter we first describe the ways in which quantities of heat can be measured in the laboratory. Then we shall discuss the effects produced when heat is added to or removed from bodies and the mechanisms involved in the transfer of heat from one place to another. The experiments of Rumford and Joule on the dissipation of mechanical energy provide insight into the nature of heat, which we now recognize as the transfer of *thermal energy* from hot bodies to cold bodies. The thermal energy of a body is a form of *internal energy*, which a body can possess without changes in its mechanical energy.

The recognition that bodies can possess internal energy, which not only can be transferred from one body to another but also under certain circumstances can be converted into mechanical energy, led to the formulation of one of the most important principles of physics: *The Conservation of Energy*. In this chapter we present some of the experimental evidence on which this principle is based.

14.1 QUANTITY OF HEAT: CALORIMETRY

Studies of the processes involved in the establishment of thermal equilibrium are made with a *thermometer* and a *calorimeter,* which is just a container that serves

---

* The Latin word for heat is *caior.*

to insulate the objects under study. The results of such studies show that the final common temperature attained by the bodies inside the calorimeter depends on the initial temperatures of the bodies, the masses of the bodies, and the materials of which the bodies are composed.

Early quantitative experiments on the establishment of thermal equilibrium showed that all observed results could be accounted for by introducing a physical quantity Q called "quantity of heat." The total quantity of heat inside a calorimeter appeared to be conserved. The net result of the heat transfers that take place while thermal equilibrium is being established inside the calorimeter is given by the *calorimetric relation:*

$$\text{Heat lost by hot bodies} = \text{Heat gained by cold bodies;}$$
$$Q_{\text{Lost}} = Q_{\text{Gained}}. \quad \textit{(Calorimetry Relation)} \qquad (14.1)$$

This relation is consistent with the *conservation* of the quantity of heat of the system of bodies inside the calorimeter.

Before we can use this relation we must define the unit in terms of which heat is to be measured. This unit is called the calorie (cal), originally defined as *the quantity of heat required to raise the temperature of one gram of water from 14.5° C to 15.5° C.* Because we have been using the kilogram as the mass unit in the SI system, we shall find it convenient to use the *kilocalorie* which is simply the quantity of heat required to raise the temperature of one kilogram of water from 14.5°C to 15.5°C.

14.2 HEAT CAPACITY; SPECIFIC HEAT CAPACITY

In the days when heat was regarded as a caloric fluid, it was believed that a body had a certain capacity for holding or storing the fluid. In the modern terminology of calorimetry, this general picture is in a sense retained when we speak of the *heat capacity* of a body:

The HEAT CAPACITY of a body is the quantity of heat required to raise the temperature of the body one degree.

The heat capacity of a body is measured in units such as cal/Cdeg, cal/K, or kcal/K.

The heat capacity of a body is directly proportional to the mass of the body and depends on the material of which the body is composed. The dependence on the material is described by a quantity called the *specific heat capacity* of the material:

The SPECIFIC HEAT CAPACITY of a material c is the quantity of heat required to increase the temperature of unit mass of the material by one degree.

The specific heat capacity c of a material is thus measured in cal/g·Cdeg or cal/g·K or in kcal/kg·Cdeg or kcal/kg·K. The numerical value of c is the same in any of these units. Why?

The heat capacity of a body is equal to $c \cdot m$, where m is the mass of the body

Table 14.1. Typical Values of the Specific Heat Capacity for Various Solids and Liquids Near Room Temperature

Metallic Solids	c (kcal/kg·K)	$(10^2\,\text{J/kg·K})$	Nonmetallic Solids	c (kcal/kg·K)	$(10^2\,\text{J/kg·K})$	Liquids	c (kcal/kg·K)	$(10^2\,\text{J/kg·K})$
Aluminum	0.212	8.87	Ice	0.48	20.1	Water	1.000	41.84
Brass	0.090	3.77	Clay	0.22	9.2	Ethanol	0.58	24.3
Copper	0.094	3.93	Concrete	0.16	6.7	Gasoline	0.5	21
Gold	0.031	1.30	Glass	0.12–0.20	5.0–8.4	Mercury	0.033	1.38
Iron, Steel	0.11	4.60	Limestone	0.22	9.2	Methanol	0.60	25.1
Lead	0.031	1.30	Paraffin	0.69	28.9	Petroleum	0.51	21.3
Platinum	0.032	1.34	Rubber	0.48	20.1	Sea Water	0.93	38.9
Silver	0.056	2.34	Wood	0.3–0.7	13–30	Turpentine	0.41	17.2

and c is the specific heat capacity of the material of which the body is composed.

Although the specific heat capacity of a material varies to some extent with the temperature range in which the temperature change takes place, it is sufficient for our present discussion and for many engineering purposes to regard the specific heat capacity of a material as a constant that is independent of temperature. Values of the specific heat capacity for various solids and liquids are listed in Table 14.1. It is to be noted that water has the highest specific heat capacity listed in the table. Approximate values of the specific heat capacities of materials in the neighborhood of room temperature can be determined calorimetrically by the so-called "method of mixtures" based on (14.1); this method is illustrated by the examples at the end of this section.

On the basis of our definitions of heat capacity, we can compute the heat Q that must be added to a body of mass m to raise its temperature by an amount ΔT as follows:

$$Q = cm\,\Delta T, \quad \left\{ \begin{matrix} Q & \text{in kcal} \\ c & \text{in kcal/kg·K} \\ m & \text{in kg} \\ \Delta T & \text{in K} \end{matrix} \right\} \quad \text{or} \quad \left\{ \begin{matrix} Q & \text{in cal} \\ c & \text{in cal/g·K} \\ m & \text{in g} \\ \Delta T & \text{in K} \end{matrix} \right\} \quad (14.2)$$

where c is the specific heat capacity of the material of which the body is composed.

Example.   The cup of a calorimeter like the one shown in Fig. 14.1 consists of copper and has a mass of 250 g. The cup has an initial temperature of 20°C as measured by the thermometer. When 50 g of water initially at 30°C are poured into the calorimeter cup, the final common temperature of the cup and the water is 26.8°C. What value does this experiment give for the specific heat capacity of copper? What is the heat capacity of the cup?

We use the calorimetry relation (14.1) to write $Q_{\text{Gained by Cup}} = Q_{\text{Lost by Water}}$;

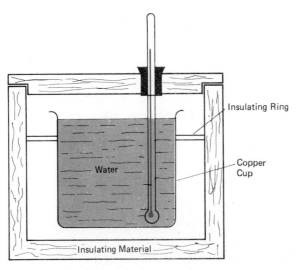

Insulating Ring

Copper Cup

Water

Insulating Material

Fig. 14.1   A calorimeter.

from the information given, we have $(250 \text{ g})c_{Cu}(26.8 - 20)K = (50 \text{ g})(1 \text{ cal/g} \cdot K)(30 - 26.8)K$, where c_{Cu} is the specific heat of copper and $1 \text{ cal/g} \cdot K$ is the specific heat of water, and we remember that $1 \text{ K} = 1 \text{ Cdeg}$. Solving this equation for c_{Cu}, we obtain

$$c_{Cu} = (1 \text{ cal/g} \cdot K)(50/250)(3.2/6.8) = 0.094 \text{ cal/g} \cdot K.$$

The heat capacity of the cup is given by the product of the cup's mass m and the specific heat capacity of copper; therefore, $mc_{Cu} = (250 \text{ g})(0.094 \text{ cal/g} \cdot K) = 23.5 \text{ cal/K}$.

Example. Now that we have determined the heat capacity of the copper cup of the calorimeter in the preceding example, we can use the calorimeter to determine the specific heat capacities of other materials. In such a determination a 300-g block of aluminum is raised to a temperature of 100°C by placing it in the steam above water boiling at atmospheric pressure. This block of aluminum is quickly placed into the calorimeter cup, which contains 400 g of water at an initial temperature of 20°C. The aluminum block, the copper cup, and the water come to a final common temperature of 30.4°C. What is the specific heat capacity of aluminum as given by this experiment?

Again we use the calorimetry relation (14.1) to state that the heat lost by the aluminum block is equal to the heat gained by the copper cup and the water:

$$m_{Al}c_{Al}(100 - 30.4)K = (m_{Cu}c_{Cu} + m_w c_w)(30.4 - 20)K.$$

We remember from the previous example that the heat capacity of the copper cup is $m_{Cu}c_{Cu} = 23.5 \text{ cal/K}$; we also note that the heat capacity of the water in the cup is $m_w c_w = 400 \text{ cal/K}$. Therefore, we can write

$$(300 \text{ g})c_{Al}(69.6 \text{ K}) = (423.5 \text{ cal/K})(10.4 \text{ K})$$

or

$$c_{Al} = (4404 \text{ cal})/(300 \text{ g})(69.6 \text{ K})$$
$$= 0.211 \text{ cal/g} \cdot K.$$

The general technique illustrated in the above examples is known in calorimetry as the method of mixtures because we mix materials having unknown specific heat capacities with other materials for which the specific heat capacities are known from previous measurements.

14.3 CHANGE OF PHASE: LATENT HEATS

When we add heat to a solid such as ice, the temperature of the solid rises by an amount that is directly proportional to the quantity of heat added until the melting point of the solid is reached. When the melting point is reached, there is no further increase in temperature as we continue to add heat until *all* the solid has melted.

For example, in the case of ice at its melting point we must add nearly 80 cal of heat for each gram of ice that melts to form water at 0°C. This value, 80 cal/g or 80 kcal/kg, is called the *latent heat of fusion* of ice.

> The LATENT HEAT OF FUSION of a material is the heat that must be added to unit mass of the solid to change it to a liquid at the same temperature and pressure.

The concept of latent heat and the name itself were first introduced by the Scottish physician and chemist Joseph Black (1728–1799).

If we have a solid of mass m at its melting point, we must add heat

$$Q = mL_F \quad \text{(Fusion)} \tag{14.3}$$

in order to change the solid to a liquid without change in temperature. We use the symbol L_F for the latent heat of fusion. If we have a liquid at its melting point, we must remove heat in accord with (14.3) in order to freeze *all* of the liquid to solid at the melting point.

If we start with a liquid at the melting point and add heat, the temperature of the liquid rises until the boiling point of the liquid is reached. At this temperature the further addition of heat causes no further rise in temperature but does cause the boiling liquid to *vaporize* or *evaporate*. Thus, if we heat water in a pan on the stove, the temperature of the water will rise to 100°C. When this temperature has been reached, the addition of heat produces no further increase in temperature but does convert the hot water into steam at 100°C. We have to add approximately 540 cal of heat to convert each gram of boiling water into steam at 100°C. The value 540 cal/g or 540 kcal/kg is called the *latent heat of vaporization* of water.

> The LATENT HEAT OF VAPORIZATION of a material is the heat that must be added to unit mass of the liquid to change it to vapor at the same temperature and pressure.

Thus, the addition of heat

$$Q = mL_V, \quad \text{(Vaporization)} \tag{14.3'}$$

where L_V is the latent heat of vaporization, is required to convert mass m of liquid to vapor at the same temperature. Similarly, heat Q must be removed from a hot vapor in order to produce a liquid at the same temperature and pressure.

Latent heats are always involved in ordinary *phase changes:* solid-to-liquid, liquid-to-vapor, and solid-to-vapor. The solid-to-vapor phase change is known as *sublimation.* It is familiar to those living in cold climates who have observed a newly washed sheet "freeze dry" on an out-of-doors clothes line; the sublimation of "dry ice" (solid CO_2) is another familiar phenomenon. The values of latent heats depend on both temperature and pressure. However, the latent heats of most practical importance are those for normal atmospheric pressure. The values of the latent heats of fusion of various substances at their melting points at a pressure of one standard atmosphere

Table 14.2.   Latent Heats of Fusion and Vaporization for Various Materials at a Pressure of One Atmosphere

Material	Melting Point(K)	Latent Heat of Fusion (kcal/kg)	Latent Heat of Fusion (10⁴ J/kg)	Boiling Point(K)	Latent Heat of Vaporization (kcal/kg)	Latent Heat of Vaporization (10⁶ J/kg)
Water	273	79.70	33.346	373	539.2	2.256
Ammonia	198	108.0	45.19	239	327.1	1.369
Ethanol	158	24.9	10.42	352	204.3	0.855
Helium	—	—	—	4	5.97	0.0250
Hydrogen	14	15.0	6.28	20	106.7	0.446
Methane	91	14.5	6.07	112	138	0.577
Methanol	175	22.0	9.20	338	262.8	1.100
Nitrogen	63	6.2	2.59	77	47.8	0.200
Oxygen	54	3.3	1.38	90	51	0.213
Aluminum	933	93.0	38.91	2329	2000	8.37
Copper	1356	50.6	21.17	2868	1760	7.36
Gold	1336	16.1	6.74	3239	446	1.87
Iron	1812	65	27.2	3013	1620	6.78
Lead	600	6.3	2.64	2017	222	0.93
Mercury	234	2.7	1.13	630	71	0.30
Platinum	2047	27.1	11.34	4680	640	2.68
Silver	1233	24.3	10.17	2485	552	2.31
Tin	505	14.4	6.02	2543	650	2.72
Tungsten	3673	44	18.4	6200	1180	4.94
Zinc	692	24.1	10.08	1180	362	1.51

are listed in Table 14.2 along with the corresponding heats of vaporization at their boiling points at a pressure of one standard atmosphere.

Latent heats are highly important; the amount of heat required to melt a block of ice is the same as that required to raise the temperature of the resulting ice water from 0°C to 80°C, just 20 Cdeg below the boiling point. Similarly, the heat required to convert water to steam at the boiling point is 5.4 times the heat required to raise the temperature of the water from the ice point to the boiling point. Latent heats can be determined approximately by the calorimetric "method of mixtures" that we have discussed earlier.

14.4   THE NATURE OF HEAT: JOULE'S EXPERIMENTS

Looking back at what we have said regarding heat, we can appreciate the 18th century views of heat as a "subtle fluid" that is transferred from regions of high temperature to regions of low temperature; the term "*subtle* fluid" was used because this invisible fluid had no observable mass or other properties to be expected of an ordinary fluid. We note that we have measured specific heat capacities and latent heats by comparing their thermal properties with those of water. In using the calorimetry relation $Q_{Lost} = Q_{Gained}$ we have implied that the total amount of heat inside an insulated enclosure is conserved. On the basis of our discussions thus far, we might be inclined to regard heat as a fundamental physical quantity. This was indeed the state of knowledge on the subject until the closing years of the 18th century.

However, in 1798 Count Rumford† reported certain observations that could not be interpreted in terms of the caloric-fluid theory. He observed that when cannon-boring machinery was operated with a very dull boring tool so that only "work against friction" was involved, the cooling water surrounding the boring tool became hot and boiled continuously away even though little useful drilling was accomplished. The amount of heat that could be generated by doing work against friction appeared to be limitless; the longer the machinery was operated, the more heat was generated and added to the water around the boring tool. Hence, Rumford concluded that the results of his experiments could not be explained in terms of the conservation of a caloric fluid. Rather, Rumford proposed that heat in a body must somehow be associated with the motion of the particles of which the body is composed. Such an idea had been proposed by Hooke, Newton, and other 17th century thinkers but had gone out of favor. Although Rumford's observation was acknowledged as cogent, the caloric theory was not abandoned until a satisfactory quantitative theory was available to replace it.

Nearly a half century later, the English physicist James Prescott Joule (1818–1889) established a *quantitative* relationship between the amount of heat generated and the amount of work done against frictional forces. As part of a long series of experiments on the nature of heat, in 1843 Joule devised an apparatus in which water in a calorimeter cup was stirred vigorously by a set of rotating paddles. The mechanical energy supplied to rotate the paddles could be accurately measured; the amount of heat produced could be accurately measured in terms of the rise in the temperature of the water and a knowledge of the combined heat capacities of the water, the paddles, and the calorimeter cup. Joule's experiments showed that the amount of heat generated was directly proportional to the amount of mechanical energy dissipated in stirring the water. Thus, the dissipation of mechanical energy in the water was found to be *equivalent* to adding heat to the water. The modern value for the equivalence is given by the experimental relation

$$1 \text{ cal} = 4.184 \text{ J} \quad \text{or} \quad 1 \text{ kcal} = 4184 \text{ J}. \tag{14.4}$$

This relation gives the so-called *mechanical equivalent of heat* and is now used as the SI *definition* of the calorie.

Because adding heat to a body and doing work to the body in such a way as to dissipate mechanical energy are equivalent in so far as thermal effects are concerned, we may ask what becomes of the mechanical energy being added. The answer is that when *mechanical* energy is dissipated, energy does not disappear but remains inside the body in the form of *random* kinetic and potential energy of the atoms making up the body. The word *random* must be emphasized. We use this word to distinguish the *thermal* motions of the atoms inside the body from the *ordered* motion

† Benjamin Thompson (1753–1814) was born in Woburn, Massachusetts, and was a Tory at the time of the American Revolution. Later he followed a career that combined brilliant scientific and technological research with political administration and intrigue, first in England and later in Bavaria. He was made a Count of the Holy Roman Empire by the Elector of Bavaria in 1791; the name Rumford was chosen in honor of Rumford, N.H., his first wife's birthplace.

of the atoms when the body moves as a whole. Mechanical energy of the body as a whole is associated with ordered motion of its atoms. Random thermal motion of its consituent atoms does not give the body a resultant motion or mechanical energy. The random thermal motion of the atoms in a body is superposed on any ordered motion that the body may have.

Because random motion of its atoms does not contribute to the *mechanical energy* of a body, the energy associated with this random atomic motion is called *thermal energy*.

THERMAL ENERGY is the potential and kinetic energies associated with the random motions of atoms or molecules.

Because the thermal energy of a body produces no detectable effects on the motion of the body as a whole relative to external objects, the thermal energy of a body is classified as a form of *internal energy*.

Although the term *heat* is sometimes used as a synonym for thermal energy, the term *heat* actually has a more restricted technical meaning:

HEAT is thermal energy in the process of being added to or removed from a body or in the process of being transferred from one place to another in the same body.

The relation between *heat* and *thermal energy* is analogous to the relation between *work* and *mechanical energy*. When a resultant external force does work to a body initially at rest, the mechanical energy of the body increases; when heat is added to a body, the thermal energy of the body increases.

Recognition that heat is actually thermal *energy* in the process of transfer makes it possible to measure heat in *joules* rather than *calories*. This greatly simplifies calorimetry measurements in the laboratory because heat can be added to the contents of a calorimeter cup by an easily calibrated electric immersion heater without opening the calorimeter and without the necessity of weighing the hot or cold objects to be added to the cup.

Because the joule is the SI unit for work and energy, it is frequently more desirable to employ the joule instead of the calorie for heat measurements. Therefore, in Table 14.1 we also list the values for specific heat capacities in the SI units joules/kilogram·kelvin. Similarly, in Table 14.2 we also list latent heats in joules/kilogram.

Recognition that heat is merely a form of energy that can be measured in the same units that we have used in our treatment of mechanics gives us further insight into the nature of temperature. The temperature of a body is *not* a measure of the thermal energy of the body. If we denote the thermal energy of a body at some arbitrary temperature by U_0, the addition of heat Q to the body causes an increase $\Delta U = Q$ in the thermal energy of the body. Thus, with $\Delta U = U - U_0$ we can write

$$Q = U - U_0 \quad \text{or} \quad U = U_0 + Q \qquad (14.5)$$

a relation that holds *provided no mechanical energy is delivered to or taken away from the body.* In order to see that temperature is *not* a measure of the body's thermal energy, we need only to consider 1 kg of ice at its melting point. We can call its thermal energy U_0. If we melt the ice without increase in temperature, we must add heat $Q = L_F m = (333,000 \text{ J/kg}) (1 \text{ kg}) = 333,000 \text{ J}$, where we have used the value of L_F given in Table 14.2. However, because water and ice at the melting point are at the same temperature, the water is unable to give up any heat to the ice even though water has more thermal energy.

Temperature is a measure of the body's ability to give up thermal energy to other bodies. Therefore,

> ABSOLUTE ZERO is the temperature of a body that is incapable of giving up thermal energy to other bodies.

This definition of absolute zero does not involve the properties of any hypothetical substance like the ideal gas that we used in our earlier discussion of the absolute temperature scale. Note that in the definition of absolute zero given above we have *not* stated that the thermal energy of a body at that temperature is zero. We have merely stated that such a body cannot give up thermal energy to other bodies.

We now consider the methods of heat transfer: *convection, conduction,* and *radiation.*

14.5   CONVECTION

Convection is a method of heat transfer in which hot *material* is actually moved from one place to another. By this definition, shooting a hot cannonball from one place to another would be a convective process. However, in all cases of practical importance convection involves the motion of *fluids.*

In one type of convection, called *forced convection,* the fluid is moved from one place to another by some type of pump or fan. This is the method employed in nearly all modern domestic heating systems. In a "hot-air" system air is heated in a chamber that is itself directly heated by the furnace and is then distributed through air ducts to various parts of the house by a large electric fan or "rotary blower."

In a "hot-water" heating system hot water from a boiler is pumped through pipes, which can be insulated in all regions except those where the heat is to be delivered. In delivery regions the bare pipe is usually equipped with a set of thin metal fins which by contact heat the air in their vicinity. The heated air can then be distributed to the room by forced-convection processes using a small blower or by free convection.

Free or *gravitational* convection occurs because fluids expand when they are heated. This expansion is accompanied by a decrease in density. If the heated fluid is surrounded by colder, more dense fluid, buoyant forces will act on the hot fluid in accord with Archimedes' Law and the hot fluid will be forced upward. The result is a circulation of fluid called a "convection cell," in which colder fluid at low levels approaches the source of heat and the heated fluid first rises vertically from the source of heat and then eventually cools and comes back down in remote regions and returns to the source. Figure 14.2a shows the convection cell in a room where the air is heated by an old-fashioned cast-iron stove close to one wall. Cold air at floor level moves toward the stove and rises after it has been heated by contact with the stove. Figure 14.2b shows the corresponding convection pattern in a beaker

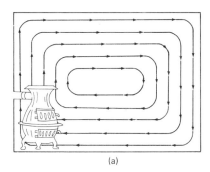
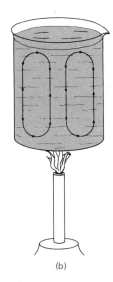

(a)   (b)   **Fig. 14.2** Convection cells.

of water that is being heated by a flame of a Bunsen burner; by dropping a few crystals of potassium permanganate or cupric sulfate in the water we can for a time observe the circulation paths in the beaker as the colored initially concentrated solution moves through the clear surrounding water.

Gravitational convection in the earth's atmosphere plays an extremely important role in establishing the climatic patterns of the earth and is responsible for the great planetary wind systems of the earth.

14.6   CONDUCTION

Conduction is a process of heat transfer in which random kinetic and potential energy is passed from molecule to molecule *through* a material. The thermal energy of the material is greater in regions of high temperature than in regions of low temperature. The transmission of heat is thus from atoms or molecules having greater random energy to atoms or molecules having less random energy. Although heat is transmitted through the material, there is no transfer of material in the process of conduction. Because the molecules of fluids are more or less free to move from one place to another and transport energy by convection, the transfer of heat by conduction through *solids* is more important than through fluids.

The general process of conduction depends on temperature differences, on the configuration of the bodies involved, and on time. We shall consider only the rather simple case of heat conduction under *steady-state conditions,* in which the temperatures of different parts of a body remain constant. This situation is illustrated in Fig. 14.3 in which one face of a large wall is in contact with a tank of hot water at high temperature T_H and the other face of the wall is in contact with a tank of water at low temperature T_L. These tanks of water can be regarded as *heat reservoirs;* by this term we mean that the tanks are so large that their temperatures are essentially unchanged when heat is removed from one tank and delivered to the other. Therefore, the temperatures T_H and T_L remain constant and a *steady-state* condition is established.

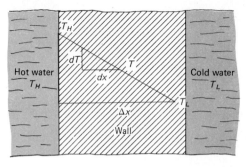

Fig. 14.3 Steady-state heat conduction through a wall. The heat conducted through unit area in unit time is proportional to the temperature gradient dT/dx and also depends on the conductivity of the wall material.

Under steady-state conditions it is found by experiment that to an excellent approximation the total quantity of heat Q conducted through the wall is *directly proportional* to the temperature difference $\Delta T = T_H - T_L$ between the faces of the wall, to the area A of the wall, and to the elapsed time t during which measurements are made; the quantity of heat transmitted through the wall is inversely proportional to the thickness Δx of the wall. The amount of heat transmitted also depends on the material of which the wall is composed. We can summarize these relations by the equation

$$Q = k(T_H - T_L)At/\Delta x, \tag{14.6}$$

where the proportionality constant k is called the *thermal conductivity* of the wall material. The conductivity k must be measured in units that make Eq. (14.6) balance dimensionally: kcal/s·m·K or J/s·m·K, depending on the units employed for measuring Q.

Although (14.6) is satisfactory for determining the heat conducted through a flat wall or slab, we must consider the situation further in order to solve more complex problems involving heat conduction. Accordingly, we shall rewrite (14.6) in the form

$$\frac{Q}{At} = k\frac{\Delta T}{\Delta x},$$

where the term on the left represents the heat conducted per second per unit area of the wall and the term $\Delta T/\Delta x$ on the right represents the average space-rate of change of termperature inside the wall material. In the limit that the thickness of the slab of material becomes very small we have

$$\frac{Q}{At} = k\frac{dT}{dx}. \tag{14.7}$$

The space-rate of change dT/dx is known as the *temperature gradient; Q/t* is the conduction of heat per unit time through a wall of area A when the temperature gradient in the wall is dT/dx; $(Q/t)/A$ is thus the heat flow per unit time per unit area. Because

$$k = (Q/At)/(dT/dx),$$

we can define the thermal conductivity of a material as follows:

The THERMAL CONDUCTIVITY of a material is the time rate of heat flow by conduction per unit area perpendicular to the flow direction per unit temperature gradient.

The units for k are those given above in our discussion of (14.6). Several of the problems at the end of this chapter illustrate how (14.7) can be applied when the geometry is other than the plane parallel slab of Fig. 14.3.

Table 14.3 lists typical values of thermal conductivity for various materials. We note that metals have much larger thermal conductivities than nonmetals, greater by a factor of 10^2 or more. The best thermal conductors are silver, copper, and gold. The thermal conductivities of fluids are so small that they are difficult to measure because the convective effects encountered are much greater than the conductive effects involved. The heat transferred by conduction in liquids and gases is usually negligible as compared with the heat transferred by convection. However, if air is confined in very small spaces so that it cannot circulate, convective processes are

Table 14.3. Typical Values of the Thermal Conductivity for Various Materials at 25°C

Material	k	
	$(10^{-4} \text{ kcal/s} \cdot \text{m} \cdot \text{K})$	$(\text{W/m} \cdot \text{K})$
Metals		
Aluminum	560	235
Brass	260	109
Copper	950	399
Gold	760	317
Iron	190	80
Mercury	22	9.0
Silver	1020	426
Steel	110	46
Nonmetallic Solids		
Brick	1.7	0.71
Concrete	4.1	1.7
Glass	1.4	0.58
Ice	5.3	2.2
Wood (across grain)	0.3	0.12
Porous Materials		
Corkboard	0.10	0.04
Glass Wool	0.10	0.04
Plastic Foam	0.07	0.03
Sawdust	0.14	0.06
Wool	0.10	0.04
Liquids		
Ethanol	0.38	0.16
Water	1.43	0.60
Gases		
Air	0.055	0.023
Hydrogen	0.41	0.17

inhibited; no convection cells can be formed. Because the conductivity of air is low, porous materials like those listed in Table 14.3 also have low thermal conductivities and are regarded as *heat insulators*. The "dead air" spaces in woolen fabrics make these materials good insulators suitable for use in blankets and winter clothing. Similarly, the dead air spaces in glass wool, corkboard, and plastic "foams" make these materials excellent insulators.

We add a word of caution regarding the practical use of (14.6) to compute the heat conducted through the wall of a house on through the pane of a window. In using (14.6) we cannot set the wall or glass temperatures equal to the temperatures of the indoor and outdoor air. Only a part of the temperature difference between inside and outside air occurs in the wall or in the glass; the rest of the temperature difference occurs in layers of air just inside and outside the surfaces of the wall or the glass. In using (14.6), we must set the temperature drop $T_H - T_L$ equal to the actual temperature differences between the inner and outer surfaces of the wall or the glass itself. Architectural engineers use semiempirical rules to predict the actual heat losses through the windows and walls of buildings.

14.7   RADIATION

Whereas convection involves the movement of matter from one place to another and conduction involves the transfer of random thermal energy from one place to another through a material, *no material* is necessarily involved in the transfer of heat by *radiation*. Radiation is a process responsible for the transfer of thermal energy from one place to another by electromagnetic waves; such a radiative process takes place most efficiently in vacuum. No material medium is required for the transmission of electromagnetic waves. For example, the transmission of heat from the sun to the earth involves *radiant power* associated with electromagnetic waves transmitted through the near vacuum of interplanetary space.

It is easy to believe that the earth receives energy from the sun. We can *see* the light from the sun with our eyes and *feel* "the warmth of the sun" by means of our cutaneous sense of hotness and coldness. Thus, solar radiation can be directly *perceived* by an observer. It is somewhat more difficult to believe that *all bodies at temperatures above absolute zero are continually radiating energy*.

A description in a textbook of an experiment done in 1864 by the English physicist John Tyndall (1820–1893) on the radiation of a platinum wire heated to incandescence by an electric current led the Austrian physicist Josef Stefan (1835–1893) in a paper published in 1879 to conclude that the total radiant power P radiated by an opaque solid body was directly proportional to T^4, the fourth power of the body's absolute temperature, and directly proportional to the surface area of the body, a result he found to be consistent with available experimental evidence. It was found that the total radiant power emitted from a body also depends in an important way on the condition of the body's surface; indeed, the body's ability to *emit* radiant power depends on the body's ability to *absorb* incident radiant power.

In order to understand the relationships between emission and absorption, consider the schematic drawing in Fig. 14.4, which shows in cross section a large solid body maintained at a constant temperature T throughout. Within the large body are two

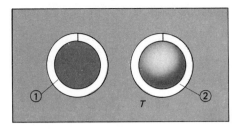

Fig. 14.4 The small bodies suspended in the evacuated cavities come into thermal equilibrium with the large body at temperature T.

evacuated spherical cavities; within each cavity a small body is suspended by a nonconducting thread. For the sake of simplicity, we assume that the small suspended bodies have the same size and shape. Body ① has a dark surface that absorbs a large fraction α_1 of any incident radiant power; body ② has a bright, shiny surface that absorbs only a small fraction α_2 of any incident radiant power. The quantity α is called the *absorptance* of the surface. As the cavities are evacuated and the small bodies are supported by nonconducting threads, the suspended bodies can exchange heat with the large solid body only by radiative processes. Experiment shows that bodies ① and ② come into thermal equilibrium with the large solid body at temperature T. Under equilibrium conditions there can be no *net* transfer of heat between the large body and the suspended bodies.

In order for thermal equilibrium to be maintained, the radiant power absorbed at the surfaces of the small bodies must at all times be equal to the radiant power emitted by the surfaces of the small bodies. This situation is shown schematically in Fig. 14.5, where P' represents the radiant power *incident* at the surface of the small bodies. This incident power must be either reflected or absorbed at the surfaces of the small bodies. The absorbed power is $\alpha P'$; we represent the reflected power by $\rho P'$, where ρ is called the *reflectance* of the surface and where $\rho + \alpha = 1$.

In order for thermal equilibrium to be maintained, the following relation must hold for each small body:

Radiant Power Emitted = Radiant Power Absorbed,

or

$$P_1 = \alpha_1 P' \quad \text{and} \quad P_2 = \alpha_2 P',$$

where P_1 and P_2 represent the radiant powers emitted by bodies ① and ②, respectively. Dividing the first equation by the second, we find that

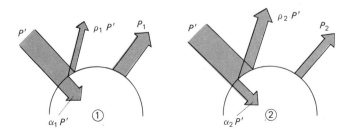

Fig. 14.5 In radiative thermal equilibrium a body must radiate as much radiant power as it absorbs. "Good absorbers are good radiators."

$$P_1/P_2 = \alpha_1/\alpha_2. \tag{14.8}$$

Thus, we see that the body with the larger absorptance α_1 emits more radiant power than does the body with smaller absorptance α_2. This leads to the qualitative conclusion that "good absorbers are good radiators."

Before drawing a more general conclusion, we introduce a new quantity R called the *radiant emittance* of a surface; this quantity is defined as the radiant power P emitted per unit area A of surface: $R = P/A$. In the discussion leading to (14.8) we have assumed for convenience that the small suspended bodies were of equal size and shape; therefore, we can set $P_1 = R_1A$ and $P_2 = R_2A$. Substitution of these values in (14.8) gives

$$R_1/R_2 = \alpha_1/\alpha_2. \tag{14.9}$$

This equation leads to a generalization formulated by the German physicist Gustav Robert Kirchhoff (1824–1887) in 1859:

KIRCHHOFF'S PRINCIPLE OF RADIATION: The ratio of the radiant emittances of any two surfaces at the same temperature is equal to the ratio of the absorptances of the two surfaces.

This conclusion about the total energy per unit area emitted or absorbed per unit time by a surface is strictly valid only for the situation of Fig. 14.4 where the incident radiant power on the surface has the character of radiation in a cavity within a solid body in thermal equilibrium at some temperature T.

There is an obvious maximum value that the absorptance α can attain. Because no surface can absorb *more* than *all* of the incident radiant power, the maximum value that α can have is unity: $\alpha_{\text{Max}} = 1$. In view of (14.9), we can assert that a surface that has the maximum radiant emittance is one that absorbs *all* of the radiant power incident upon it. Such a surface is *black* with $\alpha_{\text{Max}} = 1$ for all types of radiant power. Therefore, we may define a *perfect radiator* as follows:

A PERFECT RADIATOR is a body that absorbs *all* incident radiant power and is therefore called a BLACK BODY. A perfect radiator is a perfect absorber.

The black-body concept was introduced by Kirchhoff in 1862. To the human eye, such a body would appear black unless it was sufficiently hot to be self-luminous.

No material surface absorbs *all* of the radiant power incident upon it; even lamp black reflects about 1% of such incident power. However, a perfectly black surface can be closely approximated by a very small opening forming a hole in the wall of a large cavity like the one shown schematically in Fig. 14.6. Since only an extremely small part of the radiant power entering the hole ever escapes even when the inner walls of the cavity are good reflectors, the opening is an excellent approximation of a *perfect absorber* or *black body*.

The inside walls of the cavity are radiating as well as absorbing. If the inside walls of the cavity are at a uniform temperature T, the radiant power that escapes

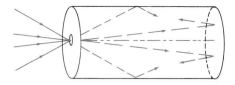

Fig. 14.6 When radiant power enters the large cavity through the small hole, little if any of the power entering escapes from the cavity as a result of reflection from the inner walls.

through the hole is almost identical with that to be expected from a perfect radiator at temperature T.

The total radiant power emitted from the "surface" of a cavity radiator like the one shown in Fig. 14.6 increases rapidly with increasing temperature. The radiant emittance R_{BB} from an ideal radiator or black body obeys Stefan's T^4 relation:

$$R_{BB} = \sigma T^4, \quad \text{(The Stefan–Boltzmann Law)} \tag{14.10}$$

where σ is a constant having the value 5.670×10^{-8} W/m²K⁴. This relation was derived from general thermodynamic considerations in 1883 by the Austrian physicist Ludwig Boltzmann (1844–1906). The total radiant power P emitted by a cavity radiator is given by the relation $P = R_{BB} \cdot A$, where A is the area of the opening in the cavity wall. We note that a cavity radiator at absolute zero would emit *no* radiant power at all; this is consistent with our earlier definition of absolute zero.

The radiant power emitted from many surfaces that are not black is also proportional to the fourth power of the absolute temperature, as was concluded by Stefan. This is true of bodies composed of platinum, iron, tungsten, carbon, and many other materials. The radiant emittance R of such a surface is given by the relation

$$R = \epsilon R_{BB} = \epsilon \sigma T^4, \tag{14.11}$$

where ϵ is called the *emissivity* of the surface. Radiators that obey (14.11) are called *gray bodies;* because the radiant emittance of a gray body is always less than the radiant emittance of a black body at the same temperature, ϵ is always less than unity. The emissivity of a surface not only depends on the particular material but also on its surface condition. In the wide variety of cases where (14.9) is valid for the incident radiant power characteristics of interest, we can write from (14.9) that $R = R_{BB}\alpha/\alpha_{BB} = \alpha R_{BB}$, where we set $\alpha_{BB} = 1$. Comparison with (14.11) then shows that $\epsilon = \alpha$.

14.8 THERMODYNAMICAL SYSTEMS

Now that we have shown how heat can be measured and have discussed the methods by which heat can be transferred, we shall proceed with a more general discussion of mechanical energy and thermal energy. In our earlier treatment of mechanical energy, we found that the total mechanical energy of an isolated *dynamical system* is conserved provided there are no forces of kinetic friction and provided there are no inelastic collisions between bodies within the dynamical system. We also found that the mechanical energy of a system is increased when work is done to the system by resultant external forces.

In our discussion of calorimetry earlier in this chapter we treated a system of bodies that was inside an insulated enclosure and *thermally isolated* from the rest of the universe. By analogy with a dynamical system, such a group of bodies can be considered as a *thermal system;* the "bodies" included can consist of liquids and gases as well as solids. When we use the calorimetry relation (14.1), we are asserting that the total thermal energy of the isolated thermal system under consideration is constant. If we add heat Q to a thermal system in a calorimeter, the thermal energy U of the system increases by an amount $\Delta U = Q$.

However, the work of Rumford and Joule implies that the thermal energy of a system can also be increased by work done against frictional forces. With the recognition that the dissipation of mechanical energy by frictional effects or inelastic collisions within a system produces thermal energy, we realize that in order to deal with more general considerations about energy we must deal with relations among the external work done to a system, the heat added to the system, and changes of both mechanical and thermal energy within the system. Any well-defined collection of matter considered in this way is called a *thermodynamical system.*

The energy relations involved are illustrated schematically in Fig. 14.7. When heat Q is added to the system from external sources and when work W is done to the system by external agents of any kind, the total energy of the system increases; we regard the energy of the system as consisting of the system's total thermal energy together with the total mechanical energy—kinetic and potential—of the bodies composing the system. Thus, we can write

Heat Added to System + Work Done to System
    = Increase in (Thermal Energy and Mechanical Energy of System);

$$Q + W = \Delta U + \Delta E_K + \Delta E_P. \qquad (14.12)$$

In this relation a negative value for Q means that the system actually *lost* heat to its surroundings. Similarly, a negative value for W means that the system actually did work to its surroundings.

If we add no heat Q to the system and do no external work to the system, we can write

$$\Delta U + \Delta E_K + \Delta E_P = 0$$

or

$$U + E_K + E_P = \text{constant.} \quad \textit{(Isolated Thermodynamical System)} \qquad (14.13)$$

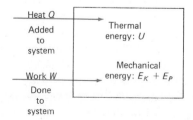

Fig. 14.7 Schematic diagram of a thermodynamical system. Heat added to the system and work done to the system cause increases in the total energy of the system: $Q + W \to$ Increase in the total energy $(U + E_K + E_P)$ of the system.

Equation (14.13) does not imply that U = constant or that $E_K + E_P$ = constant but merely that the *sum* of the thermal energy and the mechanical energy of the system remains unchanged. Within the isolated system, mechanical energy may be dissipated as a result of friction between the bodies included in the system or of inelastic collisions between these bodies. However, if mechanical energy is dissipated in this way, Eq. (14.13) assures us that an equal amount of thermal energy is produced. Similarly, Eq. (14.13) assures us that any decrease in the thermal energy of the isolated system will be accompanied by a corresponding increase in the mechanical energy of the system.

Our discussion of the thermodynamical system symbolized in Fig. 14.7 thus leads us to a relation known as the *First Principle of Thermodynamics,* which can be stated in the following form:

FIRST PRINCIPLE OF THERMODYNAMICS: The heat added to a system plus the work done to a system equals the net increase in thermal plus mechanical energy of the system. For an isolated system, when mechanical energy disappears, an equal quantity of thermal energy appears; and when thermal energy disappears, an equal quantity of mechanical energy appears.

This principle will prove extremely useful to us in subsequent developments of thermodynamics.

In a heat engine thermal energy is converted to mechanical energy that can be used in doing *external work.* By external work we mean work performed on bodies external to the system under consideration. In the performance of external work *by* the thermodynamical system shown in Fig. 14.7, the arrow representing the work done would be reversed, and W in (14.12) would be a negative quantity. Unless we added to the system a quantity of heat Q at least equal to the magnitude of W, the total energy $U + E_K + E_P$ of the thermodynamical system would *decrease.*

14.9 CHEMICAL ENERGY

In our discussion of thermodynamical systems we have considered only mechanical energy and thermal energy; the First Principle of Thermodynamics as we have stated it deals only with energy transformations involving these two forms of energy.

When we began our discussion of thermal energy, we pointed out that thermal energy was a form of *internal energy.* There are other forms of internal energy, the most familiar of which is *chemical energy.* A striking example of chemical energy is that associated with the explosive shell that we considered earlier (p. 101). Such a shell travels along a parabolic trajectory above the earth's surface; after the detonation of its explosive charge, the center of mass of the shell fragments continues to move along the parabolic path because only internal forces are involved in the explosion and internal forces have no effect on the motion of the center of mass of a dynamical system such as the shell. However, an enormous amount of additional mechanical energy is associated with the motions of the shell fragments after the explosion. The source of this additional mechanical energy is the *chemical energy* associated with the chemical bonding of the molecules of the explosive charge prior to the

Table 14.4. Typical Values of the Heat of Combustion for Various Materials

Material	Heat of Combustion	
	(kcal/kg)	(10^6 J/kg)
Solid Fuels		
Anthracite Coal	8000	33
Bituminous Coal	7500	31
Coke	6000	25
Pine Wood	4500	19
Liquid Fuels		
Diesel Oil	10 500	44
Ethanol	6 400	27
Gasoline	11 400	48
Kerosene	11 200	47
Foods		
Carbohydrates	4000	17
Fats	9500	40
Proteins	4000	17

explosion. Because the presence of this chemical energy prior to the explosion has no effect on the mechanical energy associated with the motion of the center of mass of the shell along its trajectory, the chemical energy associated with the explosive charge is a form of *internal energy*. When the charge is detonated, some of this chemical energy is transformed into mechanical energy of the shell fragments.

Whenever a chemical reaction occurs, the chemical energy of the final reaction products is different from the chemical energy of the initial reactants. From the engineering standpoint, among the most important types of chemical reaction are those involved in the combustion of fuels in air. The heats of chemical reaction involved are called *heats of combustion*. Table 14.4 lists the heats of combustion for some important solid and liquid fuels. In determining these heats of combustion, samples of the materials are burned in an excess supply of air or pure oxygen.

Also listed in Table 14.4 are the heats of combustion of major types of food stuffs. We list these in kcal/kg and J/kg as in the case of the fuels listed in the table. Physiologists and dieticians use the term *calorie* for what is really the *kilocalorie*. In specifying diets, their recommendations are thus actually stated in kilocalories.

14.10　CONSERVATION OF ENERGY

We have now discussed three types of energy: (1) *mechanical energy*, which is associated with macroscopic motions of bodies; (2) *thermal energy*, which is associated with the random motion of atoms and molecules making up macroscopic bodies; and (3) *chemical energy*, which is associated with the chemical composition of bodies.

We have shown how energy can be *transformed* from one of these types to other types.

When heat is transferred from a hot body to a colder body by radiation, thermal energy is given up at the surface of the hot body and delivered to the surface of the colder body. Through the space between the bodies, there is a flow of *radiant power;* because the radiant power represents the transmission of energy per unit time, *radiant energy* must for a brief time be associated with the space between the two bodies. This energy is actually transferred with the speed of light; both radiant energy and light involve the transmission of energy by electromagnetic waves.

In this century we have found that the nuclei of atoms can under certain conditions react in a way that is analogous to the way in which chemical reactions occur for atoms and molecules. Thus, we must include *nuclear energy,* analogous to the chemical energy of molecules, among the forms of energy to be recognized.

Recognition of the different forms in which energy can exist and the study of the processes by which energy can be transformed has led to one of the most important generalizations of modern science:

PRINCIPLE OF ENERGY CONSERVATION: Energy cannot be created or destroyed.

Although we recognize that energy can be transformed from one form to another, we have never discovered any case in which energy is created or destroyed. The total energy of an isolated system does not change. If the entire universe can be considered an isolated system, the total energy of the universe presumably never changes!

The conservation-of-energy principle is *not* self-evident nor can it be derived from any more basic principles. It represents a broad generalization of experience based on observation and experiment. Because energy can have a number of different forms, our belief in its conservation is based on a wide variety of experience. Thus, it is not surprising that the conservation principle was formulated by a wide variety of people. During the brief period 1842–1847, the conservation-of-energy principle was enunciated independently by Julius Robert Mayer (1814–1878), a German physician who emphasized philosophical and conceptual considerations; J. P. Joule, whose work we have previously mentioned and who was one of the most thorough and painstaking experimenters who ever lived; Ludwig August Colding (1815–1888), a Danish engineer; Sir William Grove (1811–1896), an English judge and physicist; and the great German scientist Hermann von Helmholtz (1821–1894), who was a physician and physiologist as well as a physicist and mathematician. It is generally recognized that the energy-conservation principle was most clearly expressed in the formulation given by Helmholtz. One serious difficulty involved in all the early formulations of the principle was the lack of a suitable vocabulary. The word *energy* itself was first systematically used as we have used it at a somewhat later time by W. M. J. Rankin and by William Thompson, Lord Kelvin.

Although new forms of energy have been recognized, in the period of more than a century since the conservation-of-energy principle was first formulated, *no violations of this principle have ever been discovered.*

QUESTIONS

1. Explain why the specific heat capacity of a material has the same numerical value in units of cal/g · Cdeg, kcal/kg · Cdeg, or kcal/kg · K.

2. Describe several phenomena of common experience that have as an essential feature the fact that the specific heat capacity of liquid water is relatively large as compared with the specific heat capacities of other materials.

3. In describing the method of mixtures, we neglected transfer of heat to or from the stand supporting the calorimeter cup, the insulating material, the air in the calorimeter, and the thermometer. Discuss how one might attempt to take all these heat transfers into account in a practical measurement.

4. Why must relatively large amounts of heat be supplied to accomplish phase changes of melting, vaporization, or sublimation when the temperature of the material doesn't change?

5. When we touch an object that has a temperature not too far from our body temperature, we say that the object feels hot or feels cold. Is there a connection between the sensation of hotness or coldness and the heat capacity of the object? Is there a connection between the sensation of hotness or coldness and the thermal conductivity of the material of which the object is made?

6. Distinguish clearly between the concepts of *heat* and *thermal energy*.

7. Describe a process in which there is a change in the temperature of a system without any transfer of energy to or from the system in the form of heat.

8. Describe a process in which there is a transfer of energy in the form of heat to or from a system without any change in the temperature of the system.

9. In a process of "heat conduction," exactly what is it that is conducted?

10. Explain the difference between a *dynamical system* and a *thermodynamical system*.

11. It is not hard to see that a small hole in the wall of a large cavity will act as a nearly perfect absorber. But how can the same hole be treated as a nearly "perfect" emitter? How can a hole in a wall act as an emitter of radiation?

12. Discuss the similarities and differences in the natures of the statements about our physical universe made by the Principle of Conservation of Energy, Newton's Second Principle of Motion, and Newton's Principle of Universal Gravitation.

13. Discuss the similarity of the equations describing heat conduction to the equations of continuity employed in describing the flux of an incompressible fluid.

PROBLEMS

1. The aluminum inner cup of a calorimeter like the one in Fig. 14.1 has a mass of 300 g. What is its heat capacity? If the initial temperature of the cup is 20°C and 150 g of water at 40°C are poured into the cup, what will be the final temperature of the cup and its contents after thermal equilibrium has been established?

2. The calorimeter cup in Problem 1 contains 150 g of water at an initial temperature of

20°C. When 400 g of lead shot heated in a steam bath to a temperature of 100°C are poured into the calorimeter cup, the final equilibrium temperature of the mixture is 24°C. What value does this experiment give for the specific heat of lead?

3. How much heat must be added to 2 kg of limestone to raise its temperature from 10°C to 40°C? If an equal quantity of heat were added to 2 kg of water initially at 10°C, what would be the final temperature of the water?

4. How much heat must be added to a 4-kg sample of sea water in order to raise its temperature by 20 Cdeg? If an equal quantity of heat were added to a 4-kg sample of clay, what would be the rise in the sample's temperature?

5. If the calorimeter cup in Problem 1 contains 150 g of water at an initial temperature of 30°C, what will be the final temperature of the mixture after a 10-g block of ice at 0°C is placed in the cup? What would have been the final temperature if an 85-g block of ice at 0°C had been placed in the cup?

6. The contents of a plant room in a greenhouse are thermally equivalent to 1000 kg of clay at 20°C. How much heat must be removed from the *contents* in order to reduce the temperature to −2°C? If tubs filled with one cubic meter of water at 20°C are placed in the plant room, how much additional heat must be removed before the temperature in the plant room falls to −2°C? This scheme is often used in greenhouses in severe weather.

7. The calorimeter cup in Problem 1 contains 150 g of water at an initial temperature of 20°C. If 20 g of steam at a temperature of 100°C are bubbled into the cup, what will be the final temperature of the mixture? How much steam would have to be condensed in the cup containing 150 g of water at 20°C in order to produce a final temperature of 100°C if all the steam is condensed?

8. In an industrial process it is desirable to produce water at 100°C by bubbling steam at 100°C into water at an initial temperature of 20°C. What is the minimum amount of steam that must be condensed in one cubic meter of water at 20°C in order to produce water at 100°C?

9. How much heat must be added to 4 kg of ice at −20°C in order to produce 4 kg of steam at 100°C? What fraction of the added heat goes into: (a) raising the temperature of the ice, (b) melting the ice, (c) raising the temperature of water, and (d) vaporizing the water?

10. A hot 500-g iron horseshoe at a temperature of 1200°C is dropped into an insulated chest filled with crushed ice at 0°C. How much ice melts?

11. A 500-kg crate slides from rest down an inclined plane. When the vertical displacement of the crate is 4.9 m, the speed of the crate is 2 m/s. How much mechanical energy has been dissipated? How much thermal energy in kcal has been produced?

12. A 50-g bullet moving at a speed of 300 m/s strikes a bale of cotton and comes to rest. How much thermal energy in kcal is produced?

13. An electric water heater is guaranteed to heat one liter of water from room temperature (20°C) to the boiling point in one minute. What is the minimum possible power rating of the heater?

14. How long will it take a 500-W electric water heater to heat two liters of water from the ice point to the steam point if no heat is lost?

15. The temperature of the air in contact with a stove like the one in Fig. 14.2a is 200°C; the temperature of the air in the lower part of the room in the figure is 20°C. The density of air at 0°C and normal atmospheric pressure is 1.29 kg/m³. Compute the buoyant force acting on one cubic meter of hot air

near the stove. What is the resultant force acting on this hot air sample?

16. If the temperature of the water just above the Bunsen flame in Fig. 14.2b is 60°C and that of the surrounding water is 20°C, what is the buoyant force per cubic meter acting on the hot water? What is the resultant force per cubic meter acting on the hot water?

17. The temperature of the inner surface of the concrete wall of a room is 20°C and the temperature of its outer surface is −10°C; the thickness of the wall is 30 cm and its area is 12 m². How much heat is conducted through the wall in one hour? What should be the power rating of an electric heater if it is to compensate for heat lost through the wall?

18. Repeat Problem 17 for a room with a wall of wood having a thickness of 20 cm and area 12 m² if the inside and outside temperatures remain 20°C and −10°C, respectively.

19. If the concrete wall in Problem 17 were faced on the inside with a 5-cm layer of glass-wool insulation and the other conditions were unchanged, what would be the temperature of the interface between the glass wool and the concrete? How much heat would be conducted through the wall during one hour? What should be the power rating of an electric heater if it is to compensate for heat losses through the wall?

20. Repeat Problem 19 for the case in which the wood wall of Problem 18 has an inner facing of 10 cm of glass wool.

21. Commercial suppliers of insulating materials market their products in terms of "R-values," where the value of R is inversely proportional to the thermal conductivity of the insulating material and directly proportional to its thickness. Discuss why it is reasonable to interpret R as measuring the "resistance" of the material to heat flow. What would be the thickness of a brick wall that has the same R value as 10 cm of glass wool?

22. What are the thicknesses of concrete and wood that have the same R value as 10 cm of glass wool?

Note: Thus far, we have considered only unidirectional heat conduction through extended plane parallel slabs. Frequently other geometries are of interest. It is then necessary to use the differential form (14.7), which says Q/t = kA dT/dx, and determine the heat flow by integration. The next few problems illustrate this idea for several simple cases.

23. The figure shows the cross section of a hollow sphere whose inner surface of radius R_1 is maintained at temperature T_1 and whose outer surface of radius R_2 is maintained at temperature T_2. (a) Show that the rate of steady-state heat flow Q/t through a spherical shell of radius r and thickness dr is $Q/t = -k \cdot 4\pi r^2 \cdot dT/dr$, where outward flow is taken as positive. (b) Explain why Q/t must be independent of r in steady-state flow; show that

$$Q/t = 4\pi k(T_1 - T_2)R_1 R_2/(R_2 - R_1).$$

24. A hollow steel sphere has an inner radius of 4 cm and outer radius of 8 cm. (a) The inside of the sphere is maintained at the steam point and the temperature of the outer surface of the sphere is 50°C. What is the steady-state rate at which heat is conducted through the sphere? At what radial distance from the center of the sphere is the temperature 75°C? (b) If a 60-W light bulb were placed inside the sphere and the outer surface of the sphere were maintained at 30°C, what

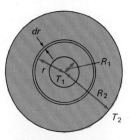

Problems 23 and 24

CHAPTER 15

Ideal Gases

The mathematical relationship between the volume, pressure, and temperature of a sample of a material is called the *equation of state* of the material. The equation of state of an ideal gas is very simple; it is given by the *general gas law*. The equations of state for solids and liquids are by no means so simple. The mathematical simplicity of the general gas law enables us to make calculations for gases that cannot easily be made for solids and liquids.

The simple form of the general gas law has provided valuable insights into the molecular nature of matter. In this chapter we shall introduce the *kinetic theory of gases,* which provides a *quantitative* treatment of the behavior of the molecules of a gas. In earlier studies of chemistry most readers have doubtless become familiar with many of the ideas that we shall employ such as the *mole* as a measure of what the SI terms "quantity of substance." Because we have used the kilogram rather than the gram as our mass unit, we shall generally use the *kilomole* in our equations in a manner analogous to our earlier use of the kilocalorie rather than the calorie.

15.1 ATOMIC MASSES

During the 19th century chemists made great progress in identifying the naturally occurring chemical elements and in determining their chemical properties and the relative masses of their atoms. The Russian chemist Dimitri Ivanovich Mendeléev (1834–1907) in 1869 found that, if he arranged the elements in order of increasing relative atomic mass, certain chemical properties *periodically* recurred; Mendeléev's discovery led to the development of the Periodic Table that now adorns the walls of most chemistry and physics lecture halls. The atomic masses (or "atomic weights") listed in the Periodic Table actually give the *relative masses* of the atoms of the elements; they are specified in such a way that no atom has a relative mass less than unity. In the present scheme, the unit on the mass scale employed is based on the lightest isotope of carbon:

The ATOMIC MASS UNIT (u) is $\frac{1}{12}$ the mass of the lightest naturally occurring isotope of carbon.

In studies of chemical reactions it is usually convenient to express the masses of atoms and molecules in terms of atomic mass units. However, when we use the masses of atoms or molecules in any of the equations of physics based on the SI, we must, of course, express them in kilograms. The relation between the atomic mass unit (u) and the kilogram is:

$$1\ \text{u} = (1.66057 \pm 0.00001) \times 10^{-27}\ \text{kg}. \tag{15.1}$$

The relation between these units of mass involves the definition of the kilomole, which we present formally in the following section.

15.2   AVOGADRO'S LAW; THE KILOMOLE; AVOGADRO'S NUMBER

In 1808 Gay-Lussac discovered that when gases react chemically there are simple, definite ratios between the volumes of the initial reactants and the volume of the reaction products, provided the volumes are measured under the same conditions of temperature and pressure. To explain this experimental result, Amadeo Avogadro (1776–1856) in 1811 advocated an hypothesis now called

AVOGADRO'S LAW: Equal volumes of any two gases under the same conditions of temperature and pressure contain equal numbers of molecules.

The validity of this law has been demonstrated for most gases at the temperatures and pressures encountered in the atmosphere near the earth's surface. On the basis of this law it is possible to determine the relative masses of the molecules of different gases by merely weighing equal volumes of the gas under the same conditions of temperature and pressure.

It is convenient to treat *amount of substance* as an auxiliary fundamental physical quantity and to define as a unit for its measurement the amount of the substance containing a specified number of particles. The SI unit is called the *mole* (mol) and is defined as follows:

One MOLE is an amount of substance containing the same number of particles as there are atoms in 12 g of the lightest naturally occurring isotope of carbon.

Because we have been using the kilogram rather than the gram as our mass unit, it will usually be desirable for us to use the kilomole (kmol), which is 1000 mol. From the definition of the atomic mass unit it follows that

One kilomole of an element of atomic mass M is M kilograms of the element;

similarly, one kilomole of a chemical compound of molecular mass M is M kilograms of the compound.

Thus, 1 kmol of hydrogen gas H_2 is 2.02 kg of the gas; 1 kmol of oxygen gas O_2 is 32.00 kg of the gas; 1 kmol of water H_2O is 18.02 kg, whether the H_2O is in the form of ice, liquid, or vapor; 1 kmol of CO_2 is 44.00 kg of this material; and 1 kmol of gold is 196.97 kg of this metal.

The actual number of particles N_A in a mol or kmol, called *Avogadro's Number,* is

$$N_A = 6.0220 \times 10^{23} \text{ particles/mol} = 6.0220 \times 10^{26} \text{ particles/kmol}. \quad (15.2)$$

Later in this chapter we shall describe one method of determining Avogadro's Number, and we shall introduce other methods in later chapters. Once N_A has been established, the value of the atomic mass unit in (15.1) can readily be computed. How? Once the value of N_A is known, the total number N of particles in n kmol of a substance is merely $N = nN_A$.

Now that we have introduced the kilomole, we can restate Avogadro's Law as follows:

The volume occupied by one kilomole of an ideal gas depends only on temperature and pressure and not on the nature of the gas.

We find by experiment that the volume of an ideal gas at 273.15 K and a pressure of 1 atm is given by

$$V/\text{kmol} = (22.414 \pm 0.001) \text{ m}^3/\text{kmol} \quad \text{(at 273.15 K and 1 atm).} \quad (15.3)$$

The conditions of pressure and temperature stated in (15.3) are sometimes called "normal" conditions of temperature and pressure (NTP) or "standard" conditions of temperature and pressure (STP).

15.3 THE GENERAL GAS LAW

In Chapter 13 we stated the general gas law for any sample of ideal gas in the form $PV/T = P_0V_0/T_0$. Now that we have introduced the kilomole, we can express the general gas law in a more general form. For any pressure P and temperature T the volume V of gas will be directly proportional to the number of kmoles n of gas in the sample. If V_0 refers to 1 kmol of gas, we can write

$$PV = n(P_0V_0/T_0)T. \quad (15.4)$$

We can once and for all evaluate P_0V_0/T_0 for 1 kmol of gas at STP by the use of (15.3). Thus, for 1 kmol of gas at STP

$$\frac{P_0V_0}{T_0} = \frac{(1.01325 \times 10^5 \text{ N/m}^2)(22.414 \text{ m}^3)}{273.15 \text{ K}} = (8314 \pm 1) \text{ J/K},$$

where we have set $1 \text{ N} \cdot \text{m} = 1 \text{ J}$. Use of this numerical result in (15.4) gives

$$PV = nRT, \quad \left\{ \begin{array}{l} P \text{ in N/m}^2 \\ V \text{ in m}^3 \\ n \text{ in kmol} \\ R \text{ in J/kmol} \cdot \text{K} \\ T \text{ in K} \end{array} \right\} \quad \textit{(General Gas Law)} \tag{15.5}$$

where $R = (8314 \pm 1) \text{ J/kmol} \cdot \text{K}$ is called the *universal gas constant.*

Equation (15.5) is the *equation of state* of an *ideal gas.* Any gas that obeys the general gas law is by definition an ideal gas. As we have pointed out earlier, all gases obey the general gas law at sufficiently high temperatures and low pressures.

The expression of the general gas law given in (15.5) is valuable for use when we are dealing with enclosed gas samples, the volume of which can be definitely specified. However, we often need to be able to apply the general gas law to unconfined gases. We can do this by stating the general gas law in terms of density $\rho = m/V$. If the molecular mass of the gas is M, 1 kmol of the gas has a mass of M kg. The volume V of 1 kmol of the gas can be determined from (15.5) with $n = 1$; thus, with $V = RT/P$, we obtain

$$\rho = \frac{(M \text{ kg})P}{RT}. \quad \textit{(General Gas Law)} \tag{15.5'}$$

We note that the density of a gas is directly proportional to the pressure P and inversely proportional to the absolute temperature. The density is also directly proportional to the molecular mass M of the gas, in accord with Avogadro's Law.

We now introduce a gas law developed in 1803 by John Dalton (1766–1844) that applies to mixtures of gases:

DALTON'S LAW OF PARTIAL PRESSURES: If several ideal gases are in the same container, the total pressure is the sum of the partial pressures that each gas would exert if it alone occupied the container.

For example, if n_A kilomoles of gas A alone occupied the container, the pressure would be

$$P_A = n_A RT/V$$

on the basis of (15.5). If n_B kilomoles of gas B alone occupied the container, the pressure would be

$$P_B = n_B RT/V.$$

According to Dalton's Law, if both gases occupied the container, the total pressure would be

$$P = P_A + P_B = (n_A + n_B)RT/V, \tag{15.6}$$

where P_A and P_B are known as *partial pressures*. The partial pressures P_A and P_B of the different types of gas are proportional to n_A and n_B, respectively; the total pressure P is proportional to the total number of molecules of the gases present. Equation (15.6) thus implies that the general gas law (15.5) applies to mixtures of ideal gases.

This is an important consideration when we are dealing with air. In dry air, 78.09% of the molecules are N_2, 20.95% are O_2, 0.93% are argon, and the other 0.03% include CO_2, He, Ne, Kr, and Xe along with traces of polyatomic gases. This composition gives an "average molecular mass" of 28.97. For nearly all practical purposes, air behaves like an ideal gas with a molecular mass of 29. Use of (15.5′) shows that at STP dry air has a density

$$\rho_0 = \frac{(M\,\text{kg})}{V_0} = \frac{29\text{ kg}}{22.4\text{ m}^3} = 1.29\text{ kg/m}^3. \quad \textit{(Dry Air at STP)} \quad (15.7)$$

We note that the density of air at STP is only about 1/1000 that of water, which has a density of 1000 kg/m³.

15.4 EXTERNAL WORK; THERMAL ENERGY

We can apply the First Principle of Thermodynamics to an enclosed gas sample like the one shown in Fig. 15.1a and consider the important case in which the gas does external work by expanding. If a gas expands by pushing back the walls of its container, the gas itself does work to the walls; for example, if the gas in Fig. 15.1 pushes the piston to the right against an opposing external force *F*, the gas does work. This work is called external work done *by* the gas; in setting up the energy-balance relations required by the First Principle of Thermodynamics, we shall from now on follow the most common convention and regard work done *by* the gas *to* its surroundings as a *positive* quantity. If the piston moves to the left in Fig. 15.1a, the external force does work *to* the gas; in this case, we shall regard the work done *by* the gas as *negative*.

With this convention, we can express the First Principle in the following form:

$$Q_{\text{Added to gas}} = \Delta U_{\text{Increase}} + W_{\text{Done by gas}}. \quad (15.8)$$

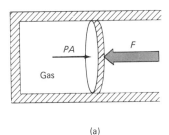

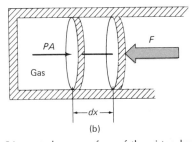

(a)   (b)

Fig. 15.1 Gas in a cylinder. In quasiequilibrium the force *PA* exerted on one face of the piston by the gas is equal to the total external force *F* exerted on the opposite face. Work is done as the gas expands.

Thus, the *addition* of heat to the gas can result in an *increase* in the thermal energy of the gas and in external work done by the gas. In using (15.8), we shall regard the *removal* of heat from the gas, *decrease* in thermal energy, and work done *to* the gas as negative quantities. This will be the "book-keeping system" to be used in requiring that the energy-balance required by the First Principle be maintained. Note that in writing (15.8) we are assuming that the enclosed gas does not acquire mechanical energy as a result of macroscopic mass motion.

If the system in Fig. 15.1b is always in "quasistatic equilibrium" or "quasiequilibrium" so that neither the gas nor the piston has appreciable acceleration and thus acquires mechanical energy, the magnitude of the force PA exerted on the piston by the gas will be equal to the magnitude of the opposing external force F exerted on the piston: $PA = F$. If the gas does external work dW in moving a distance dx to the right in the figure, we can write $dW = F\,dx = PA\,dx$. However, $A\,dx$ is merely the change dV in the volume of the gas; therefore, we can write the more general relation

$$dW = P\,dV \quad \text{or} \quad W = \int_{V_1}^{V_2} P\,dV \tag{15.9}$$

for the external work done by an expanding gas. This relationship in (15.9) is valid in general so long as quasiequilibrium is maintained, even if the expansion is more complicated than simply pushing back a piston. As we shall see later, *the amount of work done by a gas in expanding from a small initial volume V_1 to a larger final volume V_2 depends on the relation between pressure and volume during the expansion.* If the gas is compressed from a large initial volume V_2 to a smaller final volume V_1, the amount of work W required is also given by the integral in (15.9). However, because this work is done *to* the gas by external forces, we regard the external work as negative when we use it in (15.8). With somewhat more mathematical nicety, we can determine the amount of external work done *to* the gas by reversing the limits of the integral in (15.9) so that work done *to* the gas comes out automatically with a negative sign!

We now must consider the thermal energy U of a gas sample. The "state" of an ideal gas is given by the general gas law (15.5), which provides an expression for the *volume V* of n kmoles of gas in terms of the *pressure P* and the absolute *temperature T* of the gas. We need to know how the thermal energy of a gas sample depends on these "state variables." The simplest determination of the dependence of thermal energy on state variables is provided by Joule's *free-expansion experiment,* * which employed the apparatus shown schematically in Fig. 15.2. Two vessels or "tanks" are connected by a tube fitted with a valve or stopcock. Initially one of the vessels is filled with the gas sample at a moderately high pressure and the other vessel is evacuated. The two vessels are then immersed in water in a carefully insulated calorimeter cup and are allowed to come into thermal equilibrium with the water. After thermal equilibrium has been established, the valve is opened so that gas can rush from the filled vessel into the empty one. Although the volume of the gas sample

---

* This experiment actually was first performed by Gay-Lussac in 1807. It was repeated by Joule in 1845 with much higher precision.

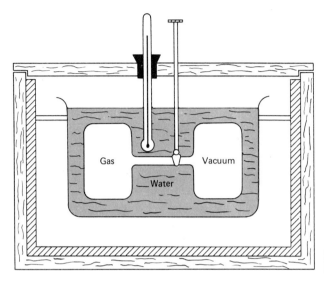

Fig. 15.2 Schematic diagram of Joule's free-expansion experiment.

has been greatly increased, the gas has done *no external work* because it has merely expanded into a vacuum; there has been no opposing force like *F* in Fig. 15.1. Because both pressure and volume have changed, the gas will either give heat up to the water in the calorimeter cup or take heat away from the water in accord with (15.8) if its thermal energy *U* depends on pressure or volume. Experimentally, Joule found *no change* in the temperature of the water; therefore, the gas sample neither gave heat up to the water nor took heat away from the water. This result indicates that the thermal energy *U* of the gas does not depend on either the volume or the pressure of the sample.† Because the only other state variable involved is *temperature*, we conclude that

> *The thermal energy of an ideal gas sample depends only on the temperature, the number of kilomoles involved, and the kind of gas; the thermal energy of an ideal gas sample is independent of pressure and volume.*

The dependence of the thermal energy of a gas on the type of gas will be discussed further in the following section. Our statement regarding the thermal energy of gases applies rigorously to an ideal gas and to real gases in the ranges of temperature and pressure in which the real gases obey the general gas law (15.5).

15.5 HEAT CAPACITY PER KILOMOLE AT CONSTANT VOLUME

In our earlier treatment of the heat capacities of solids and liquids we have introduced the term *specific heat capacity* to represent the heat added per kilogram per kelvin. In dealing with gases it turns out to be more convenient to specify an analogous term, *heat capacity per kilomole*. In view of the energy-conservation relation given

† If the experiment is performed with sufficient accuracy for a *real gas*, a very slight cooling effect is usually observed.

in (15.8), it is obvious that thermal effects of the addition of heat to a gas depend in a significant way on the amount of external work done by the gas as heat is added. There are two important cases for which we shall discuss the heat capacities per kilomole: *constant volume* and *constant pressure*.‡

If we place a sample of gas in a container of fixed volume and add heat to the gas, we can see from (15.8) that *all* the heat added goes into increasing the thermal energy of the gas because the gas does no external work. Thus, the increase in the thermal energy of a gas can be expressed in terms of the heat capacity per kilomole at constant volume.

The HEAT CAPACITY PER KILOMOLE AT CONSTANT VOLUME is the amount of heat that must be added to one kilomole of a gas to increase its temperature by one degree when the volume of the gas is held constant.

The heat capacity per kilomole at constant volume is denoted by C_V, where we use capital C to distinguish this quantity from specific heat capacity, which we denoted by lower case c in Chapter 14. The amount of heat Q that must be added to n kilomoles of gas to increase the temperature by ΔT is thus

$$Q = nC_V\Delta T. \quad \left\{\begin{matrix} Q \text{ in J} \\ n \text{ in kmol} \\ C_V \text{ in J/kmol·K} \\ \Delta T \text{ in K} \end{matrix}\right\} \quad \text{or} \quad \left\{\begin{matrix} Q \text{ in kcal} \\ n \text{ in kmol} \\ C_V \text{ in kcal/kmol·K} \\ \Delta T \text{ in K} \end{matrix}\right\} \quad (15.10)$$

Because all of the heat added goes into thermal energy, the increase ΔU in the thermal energy of the gas is given by

$$\Delta U = nC_V\Delta T. \quad (15.11)$$

This equation is of special importance because it gives the increase in thermal energy that is associated with a temperature rise ΔT for an ideal gas whether or not the volume of the gas changes while the temperature is rising. This statement follows from the conclusion that we have drawn from the results of Joule's free-expansion experiment: the thermal energy of an ideal gas depends only on temperature.

Experiment shows that over a large temperature range including room temperature C_V has a very simple form that depends only on the nature of the gas involved. For monatomic gases like He, Ne, Ar, Kr, Xe, and Hg-vapor, $C_V = \frac{3}{2}R$, where R is the universal gas constant in (15.5). For light diatomic gases like H_2, N_2, CO, and O_2, $C_V = \frac{5}{2}R$. These values apply in excellent approximation over a very wide range of temperatures. However, for diatomic molecules there are important deviations at very low and very high temperatures. For heavy diatomic gases like Cl_2 and Br_2 and for polyatomic gases at room temperature, $C_V > \frac{5}{2}R$ and increases with increasing temperature.

‡ These cases can also be distinguished for solids and liquids, but in general the difference is very small, and in any event the overwhelming practical concern is with processes occurring at a constant pressure equal to that of the atmosphere, as was implicitly assumed in Chapter 14.

The expression (15.11) gives a valid expression for *changes* in the thermal energy of any gas that obeys the general gas law. If we had an ideal gas that remained a gas even at absolute zero, we could find the thermal energy U of the gas at temperature T by taking the ΔT in (15.11) from absolute zero to temperature T. For an ideal gas with C_V independent of temperature we can write

$$U = nC_V T. \quad (Ideal\ Gas) \qquad (15.12)$$

On the basis of the values of C_V listed for monatomic and light diatomic gases, we can express the total thermal energy per kilomole of an ideal monatomic gas as $\frac{3}{2}RT$ and the total thermal energy per kilomole of an ideal diatomic gas as $\frac{5}{2}RT$. These expressions cannot be applied to real gases, which liquefy and solidify at sufficiently low temperatures. For real gases, (15.11) gives a good estimate of the *increase* in the total thermal energy of a gas as its temperature is raised by an amount ΔT above its boiling point.

15.6 HEAT CAPACITY PER KILOMOLE AT CONSTANT PRESSURE

We now consider the heat capacity per kilomole of a gas when the *pressure* of the gas remains constant:

The HEAT CAPACITY PER KILOMOLE AT CONSTANT PRESSURE is the amount of heat that must be added per kilomole per degree increase in temperature when a gas is heated and the pressure of the gas is kept constant.

We shall denote this quantity by C_P. From this definition we see that the heat Q required to raise the temperature of n kilomoles of gas by ΔT degrees is given by the relation

$$Q = nC_P\Delta T. \quad \left\{\begin{array}{l} Q \text{ in J} \\ n \text{ in kmol} \\ C_P \text{ in J/kmol·K} \\ \Delta T \text{ in K} \end{array}\right\} \text{ or } \left\{\begin{array}{l} Q \text{ in kcal} \\ n \text{ in kmol} \\ C_P \text{ in kcal/kmol·K} \\ \Delta T \text{ in K} \end{array}\right\} \qquad (15.13)$$

In order for the pressure of the gas to remain constant as its temperature is raised, the volume of the gas must increase in accord with the general gas law (15.5). Therefore, the addition of heat Q must by (15.8) result in the performance of external work W as well as an increase ΔU in the thermal energy of the gas. The external work done by a gas expanding at constant pressure can easily be evaluated from (15.9):

$$W = \int_{V_1}^{V_2} P\, dV = P \int_{V_1}^{V_2} dV = P(V_2 - V_1). \qquad (15.14)$$

Therefore, substitution in (15.8) leads to

$$Q = \Delta U + P(V_2 - V_1). \qquad (15.15)$$

However, by (15.11) $\Delta U = nC_V\Delta T$ for an ideal gas. By the general gas law $V_2 = nRT_2/P$ and $V_1 = nRT_1/P$; thus, $V_2 - V_1 = (nR/P)(T_2 - T_1) = (nR/P)\Delta T$. Substituting these values in (15.15), we obtain

$$Q = nC_V\Delta T + nR\Delta T.$$

Since by (15.13) $Q = nC_P\Delta T$, we obtain the relation

$$C_P = C_V + R. \qquad (15.16)$$

Thus, we note that because external work is involved, C_P for an ideal gas is always greater than C_V for an ideal gas by an amount R. Using the values of C_V given in the preceding section, we note that for monatomic gases $C_P = \frac{5}{2}R$ and for light diatomic gases $C_P = \frac{7}{2}R$; for other gases $C_P > \frac{7}{2}R$. A quantity of considerable importance to later discussions is the *ratio* C_P/C_V, which is denoted by γ. We note that $\gamma = 1.67$ for monatomic gases, $\gamma = 1.40$ for light diatomic gases, and that $\gamma < 1.40$ for other gases.

15.7   WORK DONE IN ISOTHERMAL PROCESSES

When we add heat to a gas sample at constant volume, *all* of the heat added results in an increase ΔU in the thermal energy of the gas: $Q = \Delta U$. When we add heat to a gas sample at constant pressure, only part of the heat added results in an increase in thermal energy, and the remainder goes into the performance of work W done by the gas: $Q = \Delta U + W$. Now we shall consider a process in which the addition of heat results *only* in the performance of external work; *all* the heat added in such a process goes into external work: $Q = W$.

In view of (15.8), we might expect the addition of heat to a gas to result in both an increase in thermal energy and in the performance of work whenever the volume of a gas increases. However, on the basis of (15.11) we note that any increase in the thermal energy of an ideal gas is accompanied by an increase ΔT in the temperature of the gas; if the temperature of an ideal gas remains constant, there is no increase in thermal energy and all the heat added goes into the performance of external work by the gas. Such a process is called an *isothermal expansion.*** *An isothermal process is one that occurs at a constant temperature.*

Such an expansion might conceivably be accomplished by the arrangement shown schematically in Fig. 15.3, which shows a gas enclosed in a cylinder equipped with a frictionless piston that is a perfect insulator. The cylinder walls are also perfect insulators—with the exception of the conducting wall at the left end of the cylinder. The conducting end wall of the cylinder is in thermal contact with a heat reservoir at temperature T. If the system is maintained in quasiequilibrium, the temperature of the gas inside the cylinder can differ only infinitesimally from T as its volume changes. In dynamical equilibrium the force PA exerted on the cylinder by the gas

---

** The word isothermal comes from the Greek words *isos* meaning *identical* and *therme* referring to temperature.

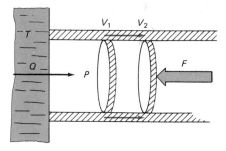

Fig. 15.3 In an isothermal expansion all the heat Q added to the gas is converted to external work as the gas expands.

is *exactly* equal to the opposing external force F; in quasiequilibrium the external force F can be reduced infinitesimally so that the gas can expand and thus do external work.

In view of (15.9), we can set the work dW done by the gas in a small expansion dV equal to $P\,dV$; in an expansion from an initial volume V_1 to a final volume V_2 the work done by the gas is $W = \int_{V_1}^{V_2} P\,dV$. In order to evaluate this integral, we must express P in terms of V. We can do this by making use of the general gas law:

$$P = nRT/V,$$

where T is the temperature of the gas in thermal quasiequilibrium with the heat reservoir in Fig. 15.3. The work done by the expanding gas is

$$W = nRT \int_{V_1}^{V_2} dV/V = nRT(\ln V_2 - \ln V_1) = nRT \ln(V_2/V_1),$$

where V_2/V_1 is called the *expansion ratio*. Because the temperature of the gas does not change during the isothermal expansion, *all* of the heat Q added to the ideal gas by the heat reservoir goes into external work, and from (15.8) we can write

$$Q = W = nRT \ln(V_2/V_1). \quad \textit{(Isothermal Expansion or Compression)} \quad (15.17)$$

We note that the work done by the gas sample is directly proportional to the number of kilomoles in the sample, to the absolute temperature of the gas, and to the natural logarithm of the expansion ratio V_2/V_1.

Under the conditions we have described, the isothermal expansion of a gas is an example of a *reversible process*. By this term we mean that by making an *infinitesimal* increase in the external force F we can *compress* the gas sample from its final volume V_2 back to its initial volume V_1. When we describe this process in terms of (15.8), the work W that we must do *to* the gas is negative. As the gas is compressed isothermally, it must give up heat Q to the heat reservoir so that the Q to be used in (15.8) is to be regarded as negative. With this sign convention, Eq. (15.17) also describes an isothermal compression.

We recognize that the reversible isothermal expansion and compression of an ideal gas are processes that can only be achieved experimentally in approximation; however, these ideal processes will prove to be extremely useful when we consider heat engines in a later chapter. It is instructive to give a graphical representation of (15.17) like the one given in Fig. 15.4, which shows the pressure of a gas at constant temperature T as a function of its volume. The curve plotted represents the equation $PV = nRT$. The area under the curve represents the work W done by the gas in an isothermal expansion; this work is done as a result of heat $Q = W$ *added to* the gas from the heat reservoir at temperature T. During an isothermal compression the external work is done *to* the gas and results in the *rejection* of heat Q to the reservoir; thus, for compression the direction of the arrow indicating the addition of heat should be reversed. The heat added to the gas during expansion is removed from the gas during compression.

15.8   WORK DONE IN ADIABATIC PROCESSES

There is another process that we must consider in our discussion of ideal gases. This type of process involves the reversible expansion or compression of a gas during which no heat is added to or removed from the gas. Such a process is called *adiabatic*.‖ *An adiabatic process is one that takes place without the addition or removal of heat.*

In applying our general energy-balance relation (15.8) to an adiabatic process we find that

$$0 = \Delta U_{\text{Increase}} + W_{\text{Done by Gas}} \quad \text{or} \quad W_{\text{Done by Gas}} = -\Delta U_{\text{Increase}}.$$

Noting that $-\Delta U_{\text{Increase}}$ is merely a decrease $\Delta U_{\text{Decrease}}$ in the thermal energy of the gas, we can write

$$W_{\text{Done by Gas}} = \Delta U_{\text{Decrease}}. \quad \textit{(Adiabatic Process)} \tag{15.18}$$

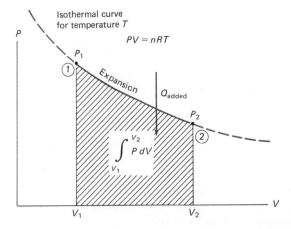

Fig. 15.4 In an isothermal expansion $Q_{\text{Added}} = \int_{V_1}^{V_2} P\, dV$, where P is the pressure at constant temperature T. Note that only a portion of the isotherm $PV = nRT$ is shown in the diagram.

‖ The word *adiabatic* comes from the Greek word *adiabatikos* meaning unable to go through; thus, perfectly insulated.

Thus, if a gas does external work in an adiabatic expansion process, its own thermal energy is decreased.

An adiabatic expansion can be visualized in terms of the schematic diagram in Fig. 15.5, which shows a gas sample enclosed in a cylinder with a frictionless piston. The piston and the walls of the cylinder are regarded as perfect thermal insulators, so that no heat Q can be added to or removed from the gas during expansion or compression. Again we assume that the expansion takes place under conditions of quasiequilibrium, with the force PA exerted on the piston by the gas at all times nearly equal to the external force F and with no appreciable temperature gradients in the gas itself.

Under these conditions, the work $W = \int_{V_1}^{V_2} P \, dV$ done by the gas in expanding from an initial volume V_1 to a final volume V_2 is exactly equal to the *decrease* $\Delta U_{\text{Decrease}}$ in the thermal energy of the gas. However, the decrease in the thermal energy of an ideal gas depends only on changes in its temperature; from (15.1) we can express the decrease in the thermal energy of the gas in the form $\Delta U_{\text{Decrease}} = nC_V(T_1 - T_2)$, where T_1 is the initial temperature of the gas at volume V_1 and T_2 is the low temperature of the gas after it has expanded to volume V_2. Thus,

$$W = nC_V(T_1 - T_2). \quad \text{(Adiabatic Expansion and Compression)} \quad (15.19)$$

The adiabatic expansion of an ideal gas always results in a reduction in the temperature of the gas. The external work done by a gas sample in an adiabatic expansion thus depends only on the number of kilomoles in the sample, C_V for the gas, and the temperature decrease accompanying the expansion.

When external work is employed to compress a gas adiabatically, the thermal energy of the gas increases and its temperature rises. All the external work done in compressing the gas goes into increasing the thermal energy of the gas. Thus, (15.19) can be used to describe the adiabatic compression of a gas from volume V_2 to volume V_1 with an accompanying increase in temperature from T_2 to T_1.

In order to give a plot of an adiabatic process corresponding to the one in Fig. 15.4 for an isothermal process, we need to develop a relationship between the pressure and volume of a gas undergoing an adiabatic process. In deriving such a relation, we can start with the statement of the First Principle (15.8) and with the general gas law (15.5). For a small adiabatic change in volume, we have from (15.8) by use of (15.9) and (15.11) that

$$nC_V \, dT = -P \, dV. \quad (15.20)$$

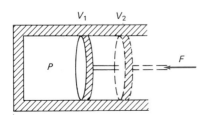

Fig. 15.5 In an adiabatic process no heat is added.

Differentiation of (15.5) gives

$$P\,dV + V\,dP = nR\,dT. \tag{15.21}$$

Elimination of dT between (15.20) and (15.21) and use of the relation $C_P - C_V = R$ leads to

$$\frac{dP}{P} + \gamma\frac{dV}{V} = 0,$$

where $\gamma = C_P/C_V$. Integration of this equation leads to

$$\ln P + \gamma\,\ln V = \text{constant},$$

and taking the antilog of both sides of this equation gives

$$PV^\gamma = \text{constant}. \quad \textit{(Adiabatic Process)} \tag{15.22}$$

Now we can make a plot of (15.22) as in Fig. 15.6. The work done by an ideal gas in an adiabatic expansion from volume V_1 to volume V_2 is given by the area under the curve. If the state of the gas at point ① is given by P_1, V_1, and T_1 and the state at point ② is given by P_2, V_2, and T_2, Eq. (15.22) states that

$$P_1 V_1^\gamma = P_2 V_2^\gamma. \quad \textit{(Adiabatic Process)} \tag{15.22'}$$

Combination of this equation with the general gas law (15.5) leads to other relations that are sometimes useful:

$$T_1 V_1^{\gamma-1} = T_2 V_2^{\gamma-1} \text{ and } T_1 P_1^{(1-\gamma)/\gamma} = T_2 P_2^{(1-\gamma)/\gamma}. \quad \textit{(Adiabatic Process)} \tag{15.22''}$$

These forms are useful because by (15.19) the area under the curve in Fig. 15.6 is equal to $nC_V(T_1 - T_2)$; if we know T_1 and T_2, it is easy to obtain the value of the area corresponding to the work done.

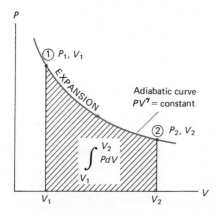

Fig. 15.6   In an adiabatic expansion the external work done by the gas is provided by the internal energy of the gas: $\int_{V_1}^{V_2} P\,dV = -\Delta U$. Note that only a portion of the adiabatic curve $PV^\gamma = $ constant is shown in the plot.

15.9   THE KINETIC THEORY OF GASES

The gas laws are rather simple relations between the *macroscopic* quantities pressure, volume, and temperature. During the latter part of the 19th century Maxwell, Boltzmann, and others realized that the simplicity of the gas laws implied that the gases themselves have a very simple structure on the *microscopic* scale that can be described in terms of the molecules of the gases. The molecular model developed to interpret the gas laws is the basis for the *kinetic theory of gases;* the name *kinetic* was employed to distinguish the presently accepted theory from the unsuccessful *static theory* proposed much earlier by John Dalton.

According to the kinetic picture, a gas consists of "free" molecules that move rapidly about and exert no forces on one another except during actual collisions. Collisions between these rapidly moving molecules and the walls of the containing vessel are responsible for the fluid pressure at the walls. Before beginning our detailed discussion, we give the following kinetic picture of a gas at STP. At STP one kilomole of gas has a volume V of 22.4 m³ and the number of molecules in one kilomole is given by Avogadro's Number $N_A = 6.02 \times 10^{26}$; thus, the number $\mathcal{N}$ of molecules per m³ is given by $N_A/V = 6.02 \times 10^{26}$ molecules/22.4 m³ $= 2.69 \times 10^{25}$ molecules/m³. The molecules of a monatomic gas behave as if they were hard spheres with diameters of the order of 0.2 nm, and the molecules of diatomic gases behave like rigid dumbbells of comparable size; of course, molecules are not really rigid objects, but the forces involved in molecular collisions are so small that they produce no appreciable changes in the structures of the molecules. The molecules are on the average about 15 diameters apart. Between collisions, they move about in straight lines at speeds of the order of 500 m/s and travel on the average about 1500 diameters between collisions. The molecular collisions are essentially elastic, no translational kinetic energy is transformed to molecular internal energy. The *molecular energies are themselves the thermal energy of the gas;* the kinetic theory gives an interpretation of this *microscopic* molecular energy in terms of the *macroscopic* quantities involved in the general gas law.

We begin our discussion by considering elastic collisons between the molecules of the gas and the walls of a container like the cubical box in Fig. 15.7. Consider a single molecule ① with velocity $\mathbf{v}_1$ having components v_{x1}, v_{y1}, and v_{z1}. We assume that on the average the wall exerts only a normal force on a colliding molecule. Therefore, when the molecule makes an elastic collision with a wall, its velocity component perpendicular to the wall will be reversed and its other velocity components will not be changed. Thus, if the molecule strikes wall A of the box, the X component v_{x1} of the particle's velocity will be reversed but v_{y1} and v_{z1} will be unchanged. The total change Δp in the particle's momentum during a collision with wall A is

$$\Delta p = p_{\text{final}} - p_{\text{initial}} = (-\mu v_{x1}) - (\mu v_{x1}) = -2\mu v_{x1},$$

where μ represents the mass of the molecule. Now suppose that after its collision with wall A the molecule travels to wall B and back without colliding with other molecules; the time interval Δt between the initial collision and the following collision with wall A will be $\Delta t = 2l/v_{x1}$. The time rate of change of momentum at wall A

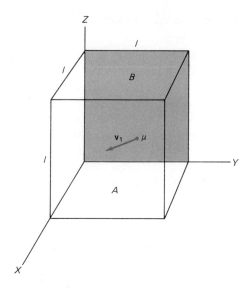

Fig. 15.7　Gas in a cubical box.

therefore is $\Delta p/\Delta t$ and the average force F_1' exerted by the wall on the single molecule will be**

$$F_1' = \frac{\Delta p}{\Delta t} = -\mu v_{x1}^2/l.$$

The total average force F' exerted by wall A on *all* the molecules actually in a box like the one in Fig. 15.7 will be

$$F' = -(\mu/l)(v_{x1}^2 + v_{x2}^2 + v_{x3}^2 + \cdots),$$

where the sum includes all the N molecules in the box. The force F exerted by the molecules on wall A is by Newton's Third Principle given by the relation $F = -F'$; the corresponding pressure at wall A is given by the relation $P = F/A = F/l^2$. Thus,

$$P = (\mu/l^3)(v_{x1}^2 + v_{x2}^2 + v_{x3}^2 + \cdots) = (\mu/V)(v_{x1}^2 + v_{x2}^2 + v_{x3}^2 + \cdots),$$

where $V = l^3$ is the volume of the container. We can introduce N into this equation as follows:

$$P = \mu\frac{N}{V}\left(\frac{v_{x1}^2 + v_{x2}^2 + v_{x3}^2 + \cdots}{N}\right).$$

The expression in parentheses is merely the average value $\overline{v_x^2}$ for all the molecules. For any molecule $v^2 = v_x^2 + v_y^2 + v_z^2$, and because the large number of molecules

---

** Note that the time interval Δt used in computing the average force is the total time between collisions and is not to be confused with the much shorter time interval during which a single collision is actually taking place.

are moving with random velocities in all directions, $\overline{v_x^2} = \overline{v_y^2} = \overline{v_z^2}$, so that $\overline{v_x^2} = \overline{v^2}/3$. Therefore,

$$P = \frac{1}{3}\frac{\mu N}{V}\overline{v^2} = \tfrac{1}{3}\rho\overline{v^2}, \tag{15.23}$$

where the density ρ of the gas is equal to the product of the number of molecules per unit volume $\mathcal{N} = N/V$ and the mass of a single molecule μ.

Although we have neglected collisions between molecules, the expression given in (15.23) turns out to be valid. Although the pressure P in (15.23) was obtained by considering only molecular collisions with face A of the box in Fig. 15.7, the laws of fluid statics (Chap. 11) assure that P is the same at all points inside the box provided the vertical height of the box is not so large that we need to consider the gravitational forces μg acting on the molecules.

We can verify that molecular collisions do not affect the result (15.23) by considering a thin layer of gas at one wall as suggested in Fig. 15.8. By making the thickness $\Delta l = v_x \Delta t$ of the layer so small that all molecules with velocity components $+v_x$ will strike the wall in time Δt before making collisions with other molecules, we can obtain a result that is identical with the one given in (15.23).

On the basis of (15.23), we can derive other interesting information by using the general gas law. Thus, by writing (15.23) in the form $PV = \tfrac{1}{3}N\mu\overline{v^2}$ and comparing it with (15.5), we note that

$$\tfrac{1}{3}N\mu\overline{v^2} = nRT \quad\text{or}\quad \overline{v^2} = 3nRT/N\mu. \tag{15.24}$$

The number of molecules in the gas sample N is equal to the number of kilomoles n times Avogadro's Number N_A: $N = nN_A$. Also, $N_A\mu$ is simply $(M\,\text{kg})$, where M is the molecular mass of the gas. Hence,

$$\overline{v^2} = 3RT/(M\,\text{kg}) \quad\text{or}\quad v_{\text{RMS}} = \sqrt{3RT/(M\,\text{kg})}, \tag{15.25}$$

where $v_{\text{RMS}} = \sqrt{\overline{v^2}}$, the square root of the average of the squares of the molecular speeds, is called the *root-mean-square* speed of the molecules. This equation gives the RMS speed of the molecules of any gas at absolute temperature T.

The simple model of a gas employed in kinetic theory gives an entirely satisfactory description of the gas pressure at a wall in terms of the bombardment of the wall

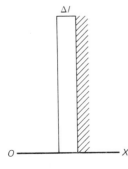

Fig. 15.8 All molecules moving to the right with velocity component v_x in a layer of gas of thickness $\Delta l = v_x \Delta t$ strike the wall in time Δt.

by rapidly moving molecules. We now show that kinetic theory also provides insight into the thermal properties of gases. Consider the first equation in (15.24); because the mean kinetic energy of a molecule is $\frac{1}{2}\mu\overline{v^2}$, we can rewrite the equation for a sample containing 1 kmol in the form

$$\tfrac{2}{3}N_A(\mu\overline{v^2}/2) = RT \quad \text{or} \quad N_A(\mu\overline{v^2}/2) = \tfrac{3}{2}\,RT.$$

The expression $N_A(\mu\overline{v^2}/2)$ is simply the total translational kinetic energy of the molecules in one kilomole of gas. In order to see how this quantity changes with temperature, we can take the derivative of both sides of the equation with respect to temperature:

$$\frac{d}{dT}\text{(Translational Kinetic Energy of Molecules in Kilomole)} = \tfrac{3}{2}\,R. \quad (15.26)$$

By comparing this result with our earlier discussion of (15.11), we can identify $\tfrac{3}{2}R$ with C_V; $C_V = dU/dT = \tfrac{3}{2}R$ for a monatomic ideal gas. This identification indicates that the *thermal energy U of a monatomic ideal gas is equal to the total translational kinetic energy of the molecules.*

Because molecules like the ones in the box in Fig. 15.7 can move in three directions, parallel to the *X, Y,* and *Z* axes in Fig. 15.7, we say that they have three translational *degrees of freedom.* Identifying *U* with the total translational energy of the gas and setting $U = nC_VT = n[\tfrac{3}{2}RT]$ in (15.12), we note that energy $\tfrac{1}{2}RT$ per kilomole can be associated with each of the translational degrees of freedom of monatomic gas molecules; this means that C_V consists of $R/2$ for each translational degree of freedom. Because an atom has negligible rotational inertia about any axis through its center of mass, rotational motion of monatomic molecules makes no contribution to their thermal energy.

However, we noted earlier that for light diatomic molecular gases $C_V = \tfrac{5}{2}R$. Of this we can attribute $R/2$ to each of the three translational degrees of freedom. For diatomic gases rotation about the internuclear axis makes no contribution to the molecular energy; as suggested in Fig. 15.9, such a rotation would have negligible rotational inertia and would be similar to the noncontributing rotation of monatomic molecules. However, a diatomic molecule does have energy associated with rotation about two axes perpendicular to the internuclear axis. If energy is partitioned equally among all degrees of freedom, we must attribute $R/2$ to each of the degrees of active rotational motion. Therefore, for a diatomic gas we predict

$$C_v = \underset{\text{(Translation)}}{\tfrac{3}{2}R} + \underset{\text{(Rotation)}}{\tfrac{2}{2}R} = \tfrac{5}{2}R,$$

in agreement with experiment for light diatomic gases in a wide temperature range around room temperature. Thus, by (15.12) the thermal energy *U* of an ideal light diatomic gas consists partly of translational motion and partly of rotational motion:

$$U = nC_VT = n[(3R/2)_{\text{Trans.}} + (2R/2)_{\text{Rot.}}]T.$$

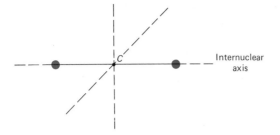

Fig. 15.9 Rotation of a diatomic molecule about its internuclear axis makes no contribution to the molecular energy; however, there is a contribution from rotation about other axes through center of mass C.

For heavy diatomic molecules, and for light diatomic molecules at sufficiently high temperature, the vibrational motion of the atoms in the molecules contributes to the energy. For most polyatomic molecules, three rotational degrees of freedom are involved and several vibrational degrees of freedom are also involved along with the three translational degrees of freedom. The simple kinetic theory that we have presented gives a valid description of the contribution of translational motion to the thermal energy of gases. In order to give a satisfactory description of the corresponding contributions of molecular rotational and vibrational motions, it is necessary to employ quantum mechanics.

15.10 BROWNIAN MOTION; BOLTZMANN'S CONSTANT

The kinetic theory presented thus far provides a satisfactory interpretation of the general gas law and provides insight into the thermal properties of gases; however, we are left with the question of whether there is any further independent evidence for the kinetic theory. Before discussing such independent evidence, we must give a further discussion of molecular kinetic energies of translation.

If we return again to the first equation in (15.24), we can write this equation in the form

$$\tfrac{1}{2}\,\mu\overline{v^2} = \frac{3}{2}\frac{nR}{N}\,T,$$

where $N = nN_A$ is the total number of molecules in a sample of gas. By substituting nN_A for N in the equation, we can express this equation in the simple form

$$\tfrac{1}{2}\mu\overline{v^2} = \tfrac{3}{2}kT, \quad \textit{(Single Molecule)} \qquad (15.27)$$

which states that the average translational kinetic energy of a single molecule is directly proportional to the absolute temperature. The constant k in the equation is the ratio of the gas constant R to Avogadro's number N_A: $k = R/N_A$. This constant k is called *Boltzmann's Constant* and has the value

$$k = R/N_A = 1.3807 \times 10^{-23}\ \text{J/K}. \quad \textit{(Boltzmann's Constant)} \qquad (15.28)$$

Boltzmann's Constant can be used to advantage in the treatment of the energies of single atoms or molecules. By substituting k for R/N_A in the general gas law we obtain the very interesting expression

$$P = \mathcal{N}kT, \quad \text{(General Gas Law)} \tag{15.29}$$

where $\mathcal{N}$ represents the number of molecules per unit volume. This equation asserts that *at a given temperature, the pressure of a gas depends only on the number of molecules per unit volume.*

An interesting application of (15.27) can be made to the problem of *Brownian motion.* In 1827 the English botanist Robert Brown (1773–1858) in using his microscope discovered that small particles of pollen, dust, or smoke suspended in a fluid continually execute random motion; as a biologist, Brown was at first inclined to believe that the motion of the pollen particles was in some way connected with *life processes,* but he was forced to abandon this hypothesis when he discovered that small particles of nonbiologic material executed similar motions. In 1905 Albert Einstein (1879–1955) presented a detailed theoretical explanation of Brownian motion. According to Einstein's theory, any particle—even one large enough to be seen by means of a microscope—has thermal motions of translation similar to those of a single molecule; the motion of the visible particle occurs because the particle is under constant bombardment by surrounding molecules, which are themselves much too small to be visible through even the most powerful optical microscope. Because the bombarding molecules *are* invisible, the visible particle seems to have a random motion "of its own," as noted by Brown.

If we consider a particle executing Brownian motion to be merely a "big molecule" of mass m, the mean kinetic energy $\frac{1}{2}m\overline{v^2}$ of the particle is equal to $\frac{3}{2}kT$ in accord with (15.27). In a brilliant series of experiments conducted around 1908, the French physicist Jean Perrin (1870–1942) and others made careful, quantitative studies of particles executing random Brownian motion and found that Einstein's predictions based on kinetic theory were valid in all details. *These detailed observations of Brownian motion provided direct and convincing evidence for the validity of kinetic theory* and marked the final establishment of the "real" existence of atoms and molecules.

In his theory of Brownian motion, Einstein obtained an expression giving the RMS *displacement* of a particle at the end of a definite observation time. This expression provided a relationship between Boltzmann's constant k, the RMS displacement of the particle, and other pertinent physical quantities that can be measured experimentally. By careful measurements of particle displacements under carefully controlled conditions, Perrin and others were able to determine Boltzmann's constant k.

Once k has been determined by studies of Brownian motion, it was possible to determine *Avogadro's Number*

$$N_A = R/k, \tag{15.30}$$

where R has a well-known value based on the general gas law (15.5).

15.11   THE BOLTZMANN FACTOR

The factor kT, which has dimensions of energy, turns out to be an important kind of "natural unit" in terms of which to measure the energies of atoms and molecules at temperature T in solids and liquids as well as gases. As an example of what is involved, let us consider the relationship between kT and the gravitational potential energy of molecules in an *isothermal atmosphere* at temperature T. The molecules move so rapidly that gravitational forces have negligible effects on the trajectories of the molecules in a box like the one in Fig. 15.7; because of their high velocities and the brief flight times between collisions, molecules move in essentially straight lines between collisions. Because of the small differences in the heights of molecules above any arbitrary reference level in the box in Fig. 15.7, we have ignored the gravitational potential energies of the molecules. However, we cannot ignore the gravitational potential energies of molecules in the unconfined gas in the earth's atmosphere, which extends to enormous heights above the earth's surface.

Let us for simplicity consider the atmosphere to be at constant temperature T and then let us apply the laws of fluid statics to a column of air extending vertically upward from the earth's surface. In order for the air between level h and level $h + dh$ to be in static equilibrium, the difference between the upward force PA on the lower surface of the volume element shown in Fig. 15.10 and the downward force $(P + dP)A$ on the upper surface of the volume element must be exactly equal to the weight of the air $\rho g\, dV = \rho gA\, dh$ in the volume element. Thus,

$$[P - (P + dP)]A = (\rho g\, dh)A \text{ or } dP = -\rho g\, dh,$$

which implies that the pressure decreases with altitude h above the earth's surface, as we might expect. In determining the pressure P from the equation above, we can express the gas density as a function of pressure by means of the general gas law (15.5′). Making this substitution and separating the variables, we obtain

$$\frac{dP}{P} = -\left(\frac{(M\,\text{kg})g}{RT}\right)dh\,,$$

whence

$$\int_{P_0}^{P} \frac{dP}{P} = -\left(\frac{(M\,\text{kg})g}{RT}\right)\int_0^h dh,$$

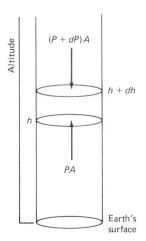

Altitude

$(P + dP)A$

$h + dh$

h

PA

Earth's surface

Fig. 15.10 In equilibrium $PA - (P + dP)A = \rho gA\, dh$.

where we assume that h is sufficiently small that we can ignore the variation of g with height above the earth's surface. Integration leads to the result

$$P = P_0 e^{-[(M\text{kg})g/RT]h}, \tag{15.31}$$

where P is the pressure at height h above the earth's surface and P_0 is the atmospheric pressure at the earth's surface.

We can make use of (15.29) to obtain pressures in terms of the number of molecules per unit volume; furthermore, we note that $N_A\mu = M$ kg and that $R = N_A k$ to obtain

$$\mathcal{N} = \mathcal{N}_0 e^{-\mu gh/kT}, \tag{15.32}$$

where $\mathcal{N}$ is the number of molecules per unit volume at height h, $\mathcal{N}_0$ is the number of molecules per unit volume at ground level, and μgh is the gravitational potential energy at height h. The factor $e^{-E/kT}$, where E is the energy of a single molecule, is known as the *Boltzmann factor* and appears in many relationships involving the thermal energy of molecules and atoms in equilibrium at a temperature T. A plot of the Boltzmann factor $e^{-E/kT}$ as a function of molecular energy E is a simple exponential curve decreasing from unity at $E = 0$ to zero at $E = \infty$. We note that with $E = kT$, the value of the Boltzmann factor is $1/e \cong 0.3679$. Applying this to (15.31) and (15.32) indicates that at a height h for which $\mu gh = kT$, $P = 0.3679P_0$ and $\mathcal{N} = 0.3679\mathcal{N}_0$.

The expression (15.32) has additional important interpretations. Going back to the column of gas of cross-sectional area A shown in Fig. 15.10, we note that the number of molecules per unit volume between heights h and $h + dh$ is just $\mathcal{N}$ as given by (15.32). The number of molecules in a volume element of cross-sectional area A and thickness dh located at height h is $\mathcal{N}A\,dh$. Division of $\mathcal{N}A\,dh$ by the total number N of the molecules in the column gives the *probability* of finding a molecule at height h above ground level. We can think of the probability $\mathcal{N}A\,dh/N$ as consisting of two factors: an *a priori* factor, which in the case of the gas column in Fig. 15.10 is the same for all values of h, and the *Boltzmann factor* $e^{-E/kT}$, which depends on the thermal energy required to raise the molecule to height h.

15.12   DISTRIBUTION OF MOLECULAR SPEEDS

Earlier in this chapter we determined the RMS speed of the molecules of a gas at a given temperature. However, the actual speeds of *individual* molecules vary over a wide range. In any gas sample there is a characteristic *speed distribution* that for an ideal gas depends only on the molecular mass of the molecules and on the absolute temperature of the gas. This speed distribution is known as a *Maxwellian distribution* because it was first determined in 1859 by the Scottish physicist James Clerk Maxwell (1831–1879), who introduced statistical techniques in kinetic theory. Maxwell determined the speed distribution from certain probability assumptions; later Ludwig Boltzmann provided a rigorous derivation for the speed distribution from a detailed consideration of the dynamics of molecular collisions.

We can develop the Maxwellian speed-distribution equation by consideration of two probability factors. The first is an *a priori* geometrical factor that represents the probability of a molecule having a speed in a given range v to $v + dv$ so far as geometrical effects are concerned. The average *velocity* of all the molecules in an enclosed gas sample must be zero, otherwise the center of mass of the whole gas would move away from its initial position to some other position in the container. The distribution of *velocities* in a gas can be visualized by means of the diagram in Fig. 15.11a; so far as geometrical effects are concerned, the *velocities* are assumed to be random in magnitude and random in direction with all velocities **v** having equal *a priori* probability. It follows that the *a priori* probability of molecular *speeds* in the range v to $v + dv$ is proportional to the "volume element" $4\pi v^2 dv$ in which the velocity vectors end in a velocity plot like the one in Fig. 15.11b. Because there are an increasingly greater number of ways in which velocity vectors can end in this volume element, the *a priori* probability $4\pi v^2 dv$ increases rapidly with increasing speed.

The other probability factor is the already familiar *Boltzmann factor* $e^{-E/kT}$, which represents the availability of molecular energy E for an individual molecule in a sample in equilibrium at temperature T. In considering a molecular speed distribution, the pertinent molecular energy is the translational kinetic energy $E = \mu v^2/2$. The appropriate Boltzmann factor is therefore $e^{-\mu v^2/2kT}$.

Using these two factors, we set the total probability $\mathscr{P}(v)dv$ for a molecule to have a *speed* in the range v to $v + dv$ equal to a constant A times their product:

$$\mathscr{P}(v)\,dv = \underset{\substack{\left(\text{Normalization}\right) \\ \text{Factor}}}{A} \cdot \underset{\substack{\left(a\ priori\right) \\ \text{Factor}}}{(4\pi v^2 dv)} \cdot \underset{\substack{\left(\text{Boltzmann}\right) \\ \text{Factor}}}{e^{-\mu v^2/2kT}} \cdot$$

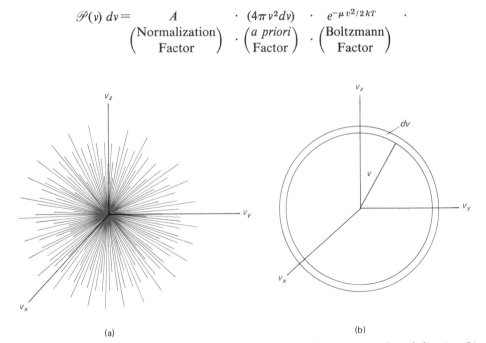

(a)   (b)

Fig. 15.11 (a) The velocities of the molecules of a gas are random in magnitude and direction. (b) The velocity vectors corresponding to speeds between v and $v + dv$ end in the spherical shell of volume $4\pi v^2\,dv$.

The value of A, which is called a "normalization factor," can be determined by noting that any molecule must have *some* speed so that $\int_0^\infty \mathscr{P}(v)\,dv = 1$. The appropriate value of A is $(\mu/2\pi kT)^{3/2}$. The expression of Maxwell's probability distribution $\mathscr{P}(v)\,dv$ is simply the product of the *a priori* probability factor, the Boltzmann factor, and the normalization factor.

If we have a gas sample consisting of N molecules, the number of molecules $N(v)\,dv$ with speeds in the range v to $v + dv$ will be given by the product $N\mathscr{P}(v)\,dv$. Thus, for the Maxwellian distribution of molecular speeds, we can write the expression

$$N(v) = N \cdot (\mu/2\pi kT)^{3/2} \cdot (4\pi v^2) \cdot e^{-\mu v^2/2kT}. \quad \textit{(Maxwellian Distribution)} \quad (15.33)$$

In this final expression, $N(v)\,dv$ is the number of molecules having speeds between v and $v + dv$ so that $\int_0^\infty N(v)\,dv = N$; thus, $N(v)$ is expressed as the number per unit speed interval: number/(m/s).

A generalized plot of the Maxwellian speed distribution for molecules is given in

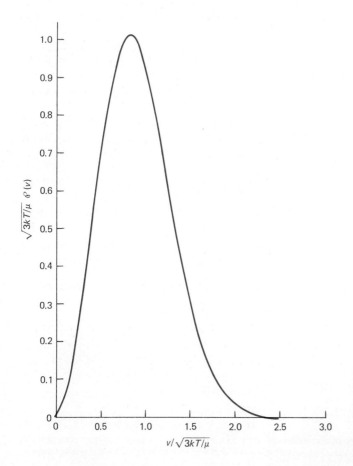

Fig. 15.12 Generalized Maxwellian distribution of molecular speeds. Unity on the abscissa scale corresponds to the RMS speed $= \sqrt{3kT/\mu}$. The most probable speed is $\sqrt{2kT/\mu}$ and appears at 0.816 on the abscissa scale. The average speed is $\sqrt{8kT/\pi\mu}$ and appears at 0.921 on the abscissa scale.

Fig. 15.12. In this plot, we show the dimensionless quantity $\sqrt{3kT/\mu}\ \mathscr{P}(v)$ as a function of speed divided by $\sqrt{3kT/\mu}$. Thus, unity on the horizontal scale represents the RMS speed. The average speed of all the molecules is $\sqrt{8/3\pi} = 0.921$ times the RMS speed. The most probable speed, at which the distribution curve is a maximum, is $\sqrt{2/3} = 0.816$ times the RMS speed.

At low temperatures the actual distribution curve for a gas such as H_2 or N_2 is sharply peaked. As the temperature increases, the distribution curve becomes broader. Note that appreciable numbers of molecules have speeds *much* greater than the RMS speed.

QUESTIONS

1. How is the value of one atomic mass unit in kilograms related to Avogadro's number?

2. Why is it necessary that the temperature in the ideal-gas equation of state be expressed on an absolute scale? Must the temperature necessarily be in K, or could some other absolute scale be used? Could the equation be rewritten in such a way that gauge pressures rather than absolute pressures could be used?

3. What is meant by a quasiequilibrium process? Why do we require that the processes we consider in this chapter, such as those represented by Figs. 15.4 and 15.6, be carried out under conditions of quasiequilibrium?

4. Why isn't the gravitational potential energy of the gas molecules included in (15.8)?

5. Why is it possible to substitute $\Delta U = nC_V\Delta T$ in (15.15)? The process being considered occurs at constant pressure, not constant volume.

6. What is the physical reason why C_P is always greater than C_V?

7. Explain why the work done by the gas is equal to the area under the curve in Fig. 15.4 and in Fig. 15.6.

8. Describe several examples of actual processes that are to a good approximation adiabatic.

9. Describe qualitatively how the discussion of Section 15.9 would have to be changed if one wall of the container were maintained at a temperature different from that of the other walls.

10. The quantity $\mathscr{P}(v)\ dv$ is the probability for a molecule to have a speed in the range v to $v + dv$. Explain the physical meaning of the "normalization" condition $\int_0^\infty \mathscr{P}(v)\ dv = 1$. Why does the integral have to be extended from zero to infinity? Surely no molecule can have infinite speed!

11. Explain the difference between the average speed and the RMS speed for a Maxwellian speed distribution. Why are both of these values greater than the speed for which the distribution curve is a maximum? What is the average *velocity* of the molecules?

12. Why do you believe in the existence of atoms? of molecules?

13. Explain how you can get an *estimate* of the size of molecules by considering the density of a liquid. For example, what is the volume of 1 kmole of water in the liquid state? How much volume must be assigned to each molecule if we assume that the liquid is closely packed and then assign a volume ΔV to each molecule?

PROBLEMS

1. The density of air at STP is 1.29 kg/m³. Regarding air as an ideal gas with $M = 29$, find the number of kmoles and the total number of molecules in one cubic meter of air at STP.

2. Find the densities of hydrogen H_2, carbon monoxide CO, and carbon dioxide CO_2 at STP. How many molecules would each cubic meter of these gases contain at STP? Find the densities of these gases at a pressure of one atmosphere when the gases are at the temperature of boiling water. If these gases were at 0°C at a pressure of two atmospheres, what would be their densities?

3. Two kilograms of hydrogen H_2 and two kilograms of nitrogen N_2 at 27°C are confined in a tank having a volume of 0.4 m³. What is the absolute pressure inside the tank? What is the gauge pressure?

4. Carbon dioxide CO_2 at 27°C is confined in a "gas cylinder" with a volume of 0.2 m³ at a gauge pressure of 11 atm. What is the total mass of the confined gas?

5. A sample of argon Ar gas has an initial volume of 0.4 m³ at a temperature of 27°C and a gauge pressure of two atmospheres. How much work is done by the gas in expanding at constant pressure to a volume of 1.087 m³? How much does the thermal energy of the gas change during this process?

6. If the temperature of a sample of argon gas is raised while the pressure of the gas remains constant, what fraction of heat added goes into increasing the thermal energy of the gas and what fraction of the heat added is converted to external work as the gas expands? Repeat the problem for a sample of nitrogen gas.

7. If the argon gas sample in Problem 5 had expanded at constant temperature, how much work would have been done by the

gas? How much would the thermal energy of the gas change during the process?

8. Repeat Problem 7 for a sample of nitrogen gas N_2 that expands isothermally.

9. A 2-kg sample of helium He gas is in a container of fixed volume. How much heat must be added to the helium to raise its temperature from 0°C to 100°C? What is the resulting increase in the thermal energy of the gas?

10. A 2-kg sample of hydrogen gas H_2 is in a container of fixed volume. What is the specific heat capacity of hydrogen at constant volume? How much heat is required to raise the temperature of the gas from 273 K to 373 K? What is the resulting increase in the thermal energy of the gas?

11. How much heat must be added to raise the temperature of 2 kg of helium gas He from 273 K to 373 K at constant pressure? What is the resulting increase in the thermal energy of the gas? How much external work is done by the gas as it expands?

12. How much heat must be added to two kilograms of hydrogen gas H_2 in order to raise its temperature from 0°C to 100°C at constant pressure? What is the specific heat capacity of hydrogen at constant pressure? What is the increase in the thermal energy of the gas? How much work is done by the gas as it expands?

13. How much heat must be added to 2 kg of nitrogen gas N_2 at 0°C in order to cause the gas to expand isothermally from an initial volume of 0.30 m³ to a final volume of 0.82 m³? How much work is done by the gas as it expands? What is the increase in the thermal energy of the gas?

14. How much heat must be added to 2 kg of helium gas He at 27°C to cause an isothermal expansion from an initial volume of 0.20 m³ to a final volume of 1.48 m³? How much

work is done by the gas during the expansion? What is the change in the thermal energy of the gas?

15. Two kilograms of hydrogen gas H_2 at an initial temperature of 800 K expand adiabatically until the temperature of the gas is 400 K. How much work is done by the expanding gas? What is the resulting *decrease* in the thermal energy of the gas?

16. How much work is required for the adiabatic compression of 0.2 kg of nitrogen gas N_2 if its temperature rises from 0°C to 300°C? What is the resulting increase in the thermal energy of the gas?

17. Air at 27°C and a pressure of 1 atm is introduced into the cylinder of a diesel engine. What is the temperature of the air after it has been compressed adiabatically to $\frac{1}{24}$th of its initial volume? What is the pressure of the compressed gas? (Treat air as a diatomic ideal gas.)

18. A sample of helium gas He has a volume of 1 liter at 0°C and a pressure of 1 atm. If the gas is compressed adiabatically until its final volume is 0.2 liter, what is the final pressure of the gas? What is its final temperature?

19. From Eq. (15.22′) and the general gas law (15.5) derive equations (15.22″).

20. A sample of a monatomic *ideal* gas expands adiabatically. If the initial temperature of the gas is 500 K and the final temperature of the gas is 300 K, what fraction of the initial kinetic energy of the molecules is converted to work during the expansion?

21. What is the mean translational kinetic energy of a nitrogen molecule N_2 at 300 K? What is the root-mean-square speed v_{RMS} of a nitrogen molecule at this temperature?

22. Find the RMS speeds predicted for hydrogen, nitrogen, and carbon dioxide molecules at the temperature of melting ice.

23. What is the ratio of v_{RMS} for carbon dioxide

molecules CO_2 in the atmosphere to v_{RMS} for nitrogen molecules N_2?

24. The temperature of the visible portion of the sun's surface is approximately 6000 K. What are the root-mean-square speeds of hydrogen *atoms* and helium atoms in this region of the sun? Repeat these calculations for the interior of a star where the temperature is 50,000,000 K.

25. An oil droplet with a diameter of 4 μm suspended in air at 27°C is observed by means of a microscope. If the density of the oil is 900 kg/m³, what is the RMS speed of the oil droplet?

26. To what temperature should hydrogen be raised in order to make it possible for molecules with speeds $v > 4v_{RMS}$ to escape from the earth? The speed of escape from the earth is 11.2 km/s.

27. Under normal or standard conditions of temperature and pressure (NTP or STP), how many "molecules of air" are there in one cubic meter? (See Problem 1.) If this number is doubled by compressing an air sample isothermally, what is the final pressure of the air sample?

28. In discussing the thickness of planetary atmospheres, astronomers use a term called the scale height, defined as the height H above the surface at which the pressure is $1/e$ times the pressure at the surface. Obtain an expression for the scale height H of a planet of radius R and mass m if it has an isothermal atmosphere at temperature T.

29. What would be the scale height H of the earth's atmosphere if the entire atmosphere were at 273 K? (See Problem 28.)

30. As air rises above the earth's surface, the air undergoes an approximately *adiabatic* expansion. On a day when the air at the earth's surface is at STP, what is the temperature of the air at a height where the pressure is one-half the pressure at the earth's surface?

Meterologists use a term called the "normal adiabatic lapse rate" to describe the rate dT/dh at which air temperature T decreases with altitude h above the earth's surface.

31. The ceiling of a room is 2.5 m above the floor; the length of the room is 5 m and its width is 4 m. At STP what is the total mass of the air in the room? How many molecules are in the room?

32. What is the total amount of translational kinetic energy associated with the molecules of the air in the room described in Problem 31?

33. A diving bell initially containing a total volume of 30 m³ of surface air is lowered into the sea. If the air at the surface is at STP, what will be the volume of the air in the bell 30 m below the surface if the temperature of the surrounding water is 7°C? The density of sea water is 1030 kg/m³.

34. How many additional kilograms of air from the surface must be pumped into the lowered diving bell in Problem 32 in order to fill it completely with air?

35. A well insulated, sealed box at the earth's surface contains 1 m³ of air at STP. What is the total translational kinetic energy of the air molecules in the box? If we raise the box to a height of 100 m above the earth's surface, how much work must we do in raising the enclosed air to this height? How much has the mechanical energy of the enclosed air increased? After the total energy of the air has been increased by this amount, what is the temperature of the enclosed air?

36. Although the molar heat capacity at constant volume C_V is a useful quantity to use in discussions of many properties of gases, we sometimes need to employ the specific heat capacity of gases at constant volume c_V in kcal/kg·K. Starting with the values of C_V, determine the values of c_V for the following gases: H_2, O_2, N_2, Ar, and Xe.

37. Discuss the results of Problem 36 on the basis of the kinetic theory of gases and show that c_V for any ideal gas is directly proportional to the number of molecules in 1 kg of the gas. Show that in fair approximation similar considerations apply to the values of c for the metallic solids listed in Table 14.1. Why was it unnecessary for us to list both c_V and c_P for the solids in this table?

38. Compute the RMS speeds at 0°C for the following gases: H_2, He, N_2, O_2, Ar, CO_2, Kr, and Xe.

39. Consider a planet of mass M and radius R with an isothermal atmosphere at temperature T. If the atmosphere of this planet at ground level consists of equal numbers of molecules of H_2, N_2, and O_2, discuss quantitatively the variation of the atmospheric composition with altitude h above the surface of the planet.

40. The best vacuum that can be routinely produced in the laboratory is of the order of 10^{-9} mm of mercury. How many molecules are there in each cm³ of such a vacuum at 20°C?

41. When a monatomic ideal gas expands at *constant pressure,* what fraction of the heat added goes (a) into increasing the thermal energy of the gas and (b) into performing the work done in the expansion? Answer the same questions for expansion of the gas at *constant temperature.*

42. Repeat Problem 41 for a diatomic gas. Generalize the results of this problem to apply to any ideal gas by writing them in terms of $\gamma = C_P/C_V$.

43. Two glass bulbs with volumes of 500 cm³ and 200 cm³ are connected by a capillary tube. This container is sealed when it contains dry air at 15°C and a pressure of 76 cm of mercury. The larger bulb is then immersed in steam at 100°C and the smaller in ice water at 0°C. Neglecting the

thermal expansion of the glass, find the resulting pressure.

44. The volume of an oxygen storage tank is 0.3 m^3. When the temperature is 22°C, the pressure gauge reads $13 \times 10^5 \text{ N/m}^2$. How many kilomoles of oxygen are in the tank? What is the density of the enclosed oxygen?

45. A compressed-gas tank is initially weighed on a platform weighing scale when the tank is "empty" and open to the atmosphere. The tank is next evacuated and then filled with hydrogen until the weight of the filled tank as measured on the scale is equal to the initial measured weight of the "empty" cylinder. What is the pressure of the hydrogen?

46. How much heat must be added to 3 kg of O_2 gas in order to raise its temperature from −100°C to 25°C at constant pressure? What is the increase in the thermal energy of the gas? How much work is done by the expanding gas? How much heat would be needed to accomplish the temperature increase at constant volume?

47. An argon sample at 20°C and 1 atm is placed in a closed steel tank. If the tank and its contents are heated to 100°C, what is the resulting increase in pressure inside the tank? If a similar tank were completely filled with mercury at 20°C and then sealed, what would be the increase in pressure inside the tank if the temperature of the tank and the enclosed mercury were raised to 100°C? As-

sume that the volume of the tank increases only because of thermal expansion.

48. A tank filled with dry air at 30°C and a pressure of 4 atm is connected by a thick-walled capillary tube to an identical tank that is initially evacuated and immersed in a dry-ice cooled bath at −79°C. If a stop cock is opened so that some of the air flows into the initially evacuated tank, what is the resulting pressure in the connected tanks? What fraction of the total mass of the enclosed gas is in the colder tank?

49. The kinetic theory of gases provides an interpretation of macroscopic quantities like pressure in terms of probability considerations of the behavior of large numbers of molecules. *Localized* fluctuations in pressure from the average predicted values can occur; for example, the pressure in a local region in a gas can fluctuate in accord with the general gas law $P = \mathcal{N}kT$ as the number $\mathcal{N}$ of molecules per unit volume fluctuates. That such fluctuations are small can be seen by considering N noninteracting molecules in a box of volume V. The probability of any particular molecule ⓐ being in a designated small volume ΔV inside the box is $\Delta V/V$; a similar probability holds for another molecule ⓑ. Thus, the probability for both ⓐ and ⓑ being in the small volume ΔV is $(\Delta V/V)^2$. What is the probability that all of the N molecules are in the small volume ΔV? What is the probability that all molecules are in the upper half of the box?

CHAPTER 16

Change of Phase

Matter as we know it on earth exists in three states or phases—gaseous, liquid, and solid. In this chapter we shall discuss the conditions involved in the transition or change of materials from one phase to another. Such changes are strongly influenced by pressure and temperature. We shall restrict our attention to pure materials that are crystalline in the solid phase; such materials are characterized by a sudden transition from solid to liquid at definite temperatures called their melting points.

The change of a material from one phase to another is usually accompanied by a *latent heat.* One part of the required latent heat goes into increasing the thermal energy of the material and another part goes into the external work done as the material increases in volume against external pressure.

Along with our discussion of the influence of such *macroscopic* variables as pressure and temperature on phase changes, we shall also give a qualitative *microscopic* picture of the processes in terms of molecules and atoms. In our earlier treatment of gases, we pointed out that the mean energy of the molecules of a gas at temperature T is of the same order of magnitude as kT, where k is Boltzmann's Constant. The same relationship is true for molecules in the solid and liquid phases; in these phases as well as in the gas phase, some individual molecules have energies *much* greater than the average energy and some have energies considerably lower. In a gas or vapor, the molecules are *free* of one another except during brief collision times; the mean time between collisions is relatively large. In a liquid the molecules are never really free from forces exerted by their neighbors and collisions are very frequent; in a liquid a given molecule has no fixed position but is able to move about among its neighbors. In crystalline solids molecules, atoms, or ions have definite equilibrium positions in a *crystal lattice;* although such particles can *vibrate* about their equilibrium positions, they are usually unable to move away to other equilibrium positions. The type of crystal structure involved varies from one material to another. For example, in sodium chloride positive sodium ions and negative chloride ions occupy the corners of cubes; the crystal form is therefore cubic, as we can see by looking at table salt through a simple microscope; each grain of salt is a little cube. On the other hand, the H_2O molecules in ice form hexagonal crystals.

16.1 VAPORIZATION; CONDENSATION

Thus far we have considered only the vaporization of a liquid at its normal boiling point at a pressure of one atmosphere and have listed latent heats of vaporization for such a situation. Actually, a liquid can vaporize at temperatures other than its normal boiling point. When we hang wet clothes on a clothesline, they become dry as a result of evaporation; in the drying process, liquid water has changed to water vapor at temperatures considerably below the normal boiling point of water.

In order to understand the process involved, consider the schematic drawing of the pressure vessel in Fig. 16.1, which contains *only* liquid water and water vapor. The walls of the vessel are equipped with heating and cooling coils so that the temperature of the vessel's contents can be varied at will. The vessel is equipped with a pressure gauge that enables us to determine the vapor pressure as a function of temperature. Because the water vapor is at all times in contact with the surface of the liquid, we call the measured pressure the *saturated vapor pressure.*

The saturated vapor pressure of any liquid as a function of temperature can in principle be determined by an arrangement similar to the one shown schematically in Fig. 16.1. The results for water are shown graphically in Fig. 16.2 and are listed in tabular form in Table 16.1. The curve in the figure gives the pressure of water vapor when it is in *equilibrium* with liquid water at various temperatures. The saturated vapor pressure increases slowly with increasing temperature from its value at the melting point of ice at 273 K to a value of 760 mm of Hg at 373 K.

We can get a microscopic interpretation of the results given in Fig. 16.2 by considering the molecules represented in Fig. 16.1. Any molecule in the interior of the liquid is subject to forces exerted by neighboring molecules, which average to zero because there are equal numbers of molecular neighbors on all sides. However, a molecule

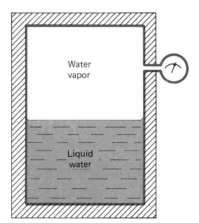

Fig. 16.1 In a closed vessel of constant volume containing *only* water and water vapor the pressure depends only on temperature.

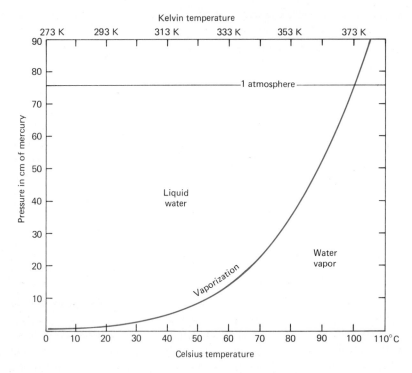

Fig. 16.2 The vaporization curve for water. The curve gives the conditions of temperature and pressure for which liquid water and water vapor can exist in equilibrium.

at the surface of the liquid has no close neighbors above it, and the resultant force acting on it is downward because of the forces of attraction exerted by molecules below it. As a result of these surface forces, most molecules approaching the surface are pulled back into the body of the liquid. We can think of a molecule approaching the surface as encountering a *barrier* when it gets to the surface of the liquid; because of the existence of the resultant force directed downward into the bulk of the liquid, the upward component of its velocity tends to decrease as the molecule gets to within a few molecular layers of the surface.

The average translational kinetic energy of a liquid molecule is of the order of kT, and this average energy is not sufficiently great to enable a molecule to get over the barrier. However, as we have pointed out earlier, some molecules have

Table 16.1.   Pressure of Saturated Water Vapor

Temperature (°C)	Pressure (mm of Hg)	Temperature (°C)	Pressure (mm of Hg)	Temperature (°C)	Pressure (mm of Hg)	Temperature (K)	Temperature (°C)	Pressure (atm)
−60	0.008	12	10.52	32	35.67	373	100	1.000
−40	0.097	14	11.99	34	39.90	383	110	1.414
−30	0.287	16	13.64	36	44.57	393	120	1.959
−20	0.779	18	15.48	38	49.70	403	130	2.666
−10	1.956	20	17.54	40	55.34	413	140	3.566
0.01	4.579	22	19.83	50	92.54	423	150	4.697
2	5.29	24	22.38	60	149.4	473	200	15.35
4	6.10	25	23.76	70	233.8	523	250	39.25
6	7.01	26	25.21	80	355.3	573	300	84.79
8	8.04	28	28.35	90	525.9	623	350	163.2
10	9.21	30	31.83	100	760.0	647.15	374.15	218.3

energies much greater than kT. When one of these fast-moving molecules headed in the upward direction strikes the surface barrier, it is able to pass through the surface and become a part of the vapor in the upper part of the container in Fig. 16.1. Thus, *some* fast-moving molecules of the liquid are able to escape from the liquid into the vapor. On the other hand, *all* molecules of the vapor that strike the surface will go into the liquid because they are subject to resultant downward forces in the surface layer. Under *equilibrium* conditions as many molecules of the liquid pass into the vapor as return from the vapor. If we increase the temperature of the liquid–vapor system in Fig. 16.1, we increase the average energy $\sim kT$ of the molecules so that more molecules are able to pass into the vapor; the number of molecules in the vapor phase increases until a new equilibrium is established. Similarly, if we decrease the temperature of the system, we decrease the number of molecules able to pass from the liquid into the vapor; the number of molecules in the vapor phase decreases until a new equilibrium is established. Because the pressure in the vapor is directly proportional to the number of molecules per unit volume, the saturated vapor pressure assumes a definite value at a given temperature. At higher temperatures the number of molecules per unit volume is greater; this accounts for the observed increase in saturated vapor pressure with increasing temperature.

Why does water in an open vessel evaporate? As we have noted *some* of the molecules of a liquid are able to pass over the surface barrier and become water-vapor molecules. In the open air many water-vapor molecules drift away and never make re-entry collisions with the surface of the liquid. Therefore, there is a net gradual flow of molecules from the liquid into the vapor state, and the water in an open vessel gradually "dries up."

We must note that the vapor-pressure curve in Fig. 16.2 is the *locus* of points on the *P-T* plot for which the liquid is in equilibrium with its own vapor. Other conditions of pressure and volume are also possible. We can place water in a closed cylinder equipped with a movable piston in the arrangement shown schematically in Fig. 16.3. If at a given temperature we exert a force **F** on the piston in such a way as to make the pressure inside the cylinder *greater* than the saturated vapor pressure at that temperature, *all* of the material inside the cylinder will be in the liquid state. If at this same temperature we reduce the force on the piston sufficiently to make the pressure inside the cylinder *less* than the saturated vapor pressure at the temperature in question, *all* of the material inside the cylinder goes into the vapor state. Because the density of the vapor is so much smaller than the density of the liquid, we would have to move the piston an enormous distance in accomplishing the change from all liquid to all vapor. This change from liquid to vapor is an *isothermal* change and corresponds to a vertical excursion in the downward direction on the *P-T* plot in Fig. 16.2.

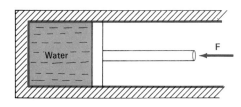

Fig. 16.3 Schematic drawing of a cylinder completely filled with water.

Let us now start with liquid in the cell in Fig. 16.3 at a pressure greater than that of the saturated vapor and exert a constant external force **F** on the piston in such a way as to keep the pressure constant. If we now add heat to the liquid, the temperature of the liquid will rise, but no vapor will be formed until we reach the temperature at which the saturated vapor pressure is equal to the constant pressure produced by the external force. If we continue to add heat beyond this point, more and more of the liquid will vaporize until *all* of the liquid has been converted to vapor; during this process the volume of the enclosed material will increase enormously. Still further addition of heat will cause the vapor to expand further in the same way that a real gas expands. The set of operations just described causes the material inside the cylinder to undergo an *isobaric* (constant-pressure) process and corresponds to a horizontal excursion to the right in the plot in Fig. 16.2.

From the above discussion, we can conclude that in all regions of the *P-T* plot of Fig. 16.2 that are above and to the left of the vaporization curve water can exist *only* in the liquid state; for these pressures and temperatures only liquid water would exist in the cylinder shown in Fig. 16.3. Points on the *P-T* plot in Fig. 16.2 that are below and to the right of the vaporization curve correspond to conditions of pressure and temperature at which *all* of the material in the cylinder in Fig. 16.3 is in the vapor state. Water vapor under conditions corresponding to pressures and temperatures to the right and below the vaporization curve is called *superheated vapor* or *superheated steam*.

In order to vaporize liquid water to form water vapor, we must supply the necessary *latent heat.* A part of this latent heat goes into an increase in the thermal energy of the material; this part of the latent heat represents work done in pulling the molecules of the liquid away from one another against intermolecular forces of attraction. The remainder of the latent heat goes into the external work done against external forces as the relatively small volume occupied by the liquid expands to the much larger volume occupied by the vapor.

We have discussed in considerable detail the vaporization curve for water. The same considerations are involved in the vaporization of other chemically pure materials. Many liquids such as ether, ethanol, and acetone, all are more *volatile* than water; i.e., they are characterized by saturated vapor pressures higher than the saturated vapor pressure for water at the same temperature.

16.2 THE CRITICAL POINT

A complete vaporization curve for water is shown in Fig. 16.4. Because of the large increases in the pressure of saturated water vapor at temperatures above 373 K, pressures in Fig. 16.4 are more conveniently expressed in atmospheres than in cm of mercury as used for Fig. 16.2. The vaporization curve for water actually *ends* at a point on the *P-T* plot where the densities of liquid water and saturated water vapor are the same. The point on a *P-T* plot at which its vaporization curve ends is called the *critical point* for a material; the corresponding values of temperature, pressure, specific volume, and density are called *critical constants* of the material. The critical temperature for water is 647.4 K; the critical pressure for water is 218.3 atm. The critical constants for several materials are listed in Table 16.2.

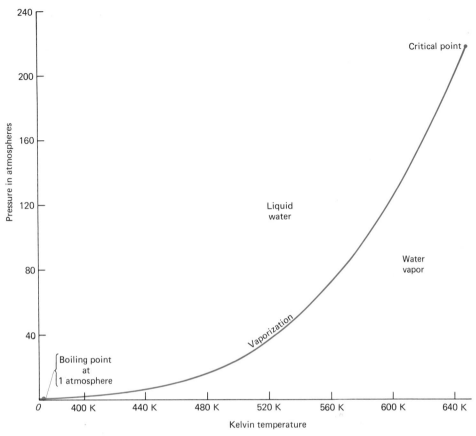

Fig. 16.4 The complete vaporization curve for water *ends* at the critical point. No liquid–vapor transition occurs at temperatures greater than the critical temperature or at pressures greater than the critical pressure.

Table 16.2. Critical Constants of Various Materials

Material	Critical Temperature (K)	Critical Pressure (atm)	Critical Density (kg/m³)
Ammonia	406	111	235
Argon	151	48.0	531
Carbon dioxide	304	72.8	468
Helium	5	2.3	69
Hydrogen	33	12.8	31
Nitrogen	126	33.5	311
Oxygen	155	50.1	410
Sulfur dioxide	431	77.8	525
Water	647.4	218.3	326

Above the critical temperature, no liquid–vapor transition occurs for any pressure; above the critical pressure, no liquid–vapor transition occurs for any temperature. If we have a sample of liquid and its saturated vapor enclosed in a transparent container such as a fused-quartz tube, at low temperatures the liquid and its vapor are clearly separated. As we raise the temperature, the liquid expands and the vapor is compressed. At the critical temperature the surface separating the liquid from the vapor disappears; we can no longer regard the material as either liquid or vapor; the material in the container is said to be in the *amorphous* or *fluid phase*. At pressures above its critical pressure a substance can exist in only two phases: *the solid phase* and *the fluid phase*. At pressures higher than the critical pressure, with increasing temperature the properties of a substance in the fluid phase gradually change from those similar to those of a liquid, which are encountered at low temperatures, to those of an ideal gas at temperatures much higher than the critical temperature; however, no phase change occurs and no latent heat is involved.

The fact that the vaporization curve *ends* at the critical point means that it is possible to change a liquid to a vapor without a phase change or the addition of *latent* heat. For example, we can convert liquid water at 373 K and 1 atm to steam at 373 K and 1 atm by the following process: (1) increase the pressure from 1 atm to a pressure higher than the critical pressure without change in temperature; (2) then increase the temperature from 373 K to a temperature higher than the critical temperature without change in pressure; (3) then decrease the pressure to 1 atm without change in temperature; and (4) finally decrease the temperature to 373 K without change in pressure. In these four processes, we have started with liquid water at 373 K and a pressure of 1 atm and have ended with water vapor (steam) at the same temperature and pressure without ever *crossing* the vaporization curve and thus having to add a latent heat of vaporization. By making such an "end run" around the vaporization curve we can always avoid the addition of latent heat. However, the final thermal energy of a kilogram of steam at 373 K and 1 atm is the same regardless of whether we have directly crossed the vaporization curve by adding the latent heat to water at 373 K and 1 atm or have made an "end run" of the kind that we have described. Going from one point to another on a *P-T* diagram like those in Figs. 16.2 and 16.4 involves the same change in *thermal energy* regardless of *how* the change is made. In contrast, the total heat flow to or from the system and the total work done to or by the system will depend on the particular process followed.

16.3   THE FUSION CURVE: MELTING AND FREEZING

Following our discussion of transitions between liquid and vapor phases, we shall now consider transitions between the solid and liquid phases of pure materials. In selecting one of the fixed points on the Celsius temperature scale we chose 0°C as the temperature of melting ice in air when the atmospheric pressure is exactly one standard atmosphere. If a sample of ice completely fills a closed cylinder like the one in Fig. 16.3 from which the air has been removed, we find that the melting point of ice has a slight dependence on pressure. On a *P-T* diagram like the one in Fig. 16.5, the melting points fall on what is known as the *fusion curve*.

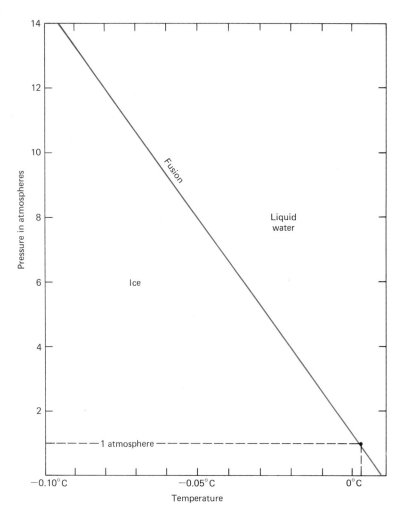

Fig. 16.5   The fusion curve for air-free pure water. The melting point of pure air-free water is not 0°C, but 0.0024°C, at 1 atm. It is the melting point of ice in contact with water saturated with air by being open to the atmosphere that is 0° on the Celsius scale at 1 atm pressure.

The melting point of water varies only slightly with pressure; it *decreases* by only 0.00750 K for each atmosphere increase in pressure. From the figure we see that we can make ice melt not only by increasing the temperature but also by increasing the pressure. The extremely low friction encountered in skating can be attributed to this tendency of ice to melt under increased pressure. The sharp blades of skates make contact with the ice over a very small area, where the pressure is enormous. In this small surface area the ice melts, and the skater actually glides on a thin layer of liquid water. As soon as the skate moves, the surface freezes once again, a process known as *regelation*.

Because a decrease in volume occurs when ice melts, it seems reasonable that increased pressure causes ice to melt because the increased pressure also tends to decrease the volume. Materials like water, bismuth, and gallium that shrink when they melt have fusion curves that slant upward and to the left in a *P-T* diagram like the one in Fig. 16.5. Most materials expand when they melt and have fusion curves that slant upward and to the right on *P-T* plots; increased pressure on the liquid phase of such materials tends to cause them to solidify.

When heat is added to a solid under conditions of pressure and temperature corresponding to a point on the fusion curve of the material, the solid melts. However, a clean, pure liquid can sometimes be cooled several degrees below its freezing point before solidification begins. Small droplets of pure water typically freeze at temperatures from 240 K to 232 K, depending on their radius. A liquid that has been cooled below its normal freezing point at a given pressure is said to be *supercooled*. Supercooled liquids correspond to points to the left of the fusion curve in a *P-T* diagram like Fig. 16.5; they are inherently unstable. Introduction of a small crystal into a supercooled liquid will cause the entire liquid to solidify rapidly.

The latent heat of fusion is the heat that must be supplied to change 1 kg of solid to 1 kg of liquid *with no change of temperature or pressure*. In contrast to the relatively large changes in the latent heat of vaporization observed with changes in temperature, the latent heat of fusion varies only slightly as we move from point to point along the fusion curve. Because melting causes a relatively small change in the volume of a material, nearly all the latent heat of fusion goes into increasing the thermal energy of the material; little external work is done by a material as it melts. Because ice shrinks in volume when it melts, we must regard the work done *by* the ice as *negative;* external forces do work to the ice as it melts.

Because of the addition of the latent heat of fusion, the average energy of molecules in the liquid state is greater than the average energy of molecules in the solid at the same temperature. In the solid the molecules seldom escape from their close neighbors but merely vibrate about their positions of equilibrium; in the liquid the molecules have sufficient energy to move about among their neighbors.

16.4 SUBLIMATION; THE TRIPLE POINT

Consider again the container shown in Fig. 16.1 that contains *only* liquid water and water vapor. If we reduce its temperature to a value below 273 K, the water freezes to form ice. However, the pressure gauge does not register zero. Under equilibrium conditions there is still water vapor in the region above the ice; the observed pressures are those indicated in Table 16.1 for the temperature range below 273 K. The pressures and temperatures at which the ice is in equilibrium with its saturated vapor are shown in Fig. 16.6 by the curve labeled "sublimation." If at a given temperature we reduce the pressure below its equilibrium value, all of the ice will be converted to water vapor. The change of phase of a substance from solid to vapor is known as *sublimation;* a definite latent heat of sublimation L_S, which varies slightly with temperature, is involved in the process. The saturated vapor pressure of ice at 268 K is 3 mm of mercury; the latent heat of sublimation at this point is about 688 kcal/kg.

In giving a molecular picture of sublimation, we note that some of the most energetic molecules in the surface layers of the solid have energies sufficiently great for them to escape from the crystalline lattice in which their vibrational motions occur and become free molecules of the vapor. Nearly all vapor molecules that strike the surface of the solid will join the other molecules in the lattice. Under equilibrium conditions

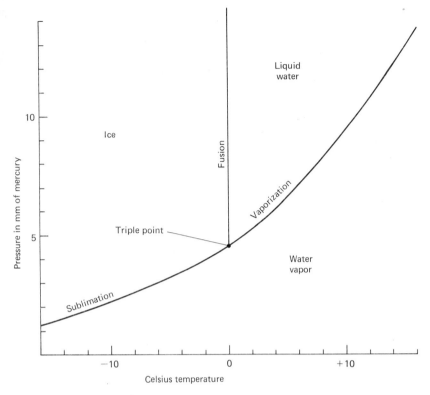

Fig. 16.6 The triple-point diagram for water. The temperature at the triple point has been *assigned* the exact value 273.16 K in *defining* the SI Kelvin scale of temperature.

the number of molecules leaving the lattice and the number returning to the lattice are exactly equal.

Careful consideration of the experimental data shown in Fig. 16.6 indicates that the vaporization curve is not a direct continuation of the sublimation curve; there is a slight difference in the slopes of the two curves at the point where they meet on the *P-T* plot. The point where the sublimation curve, the vaporization curve, and the fusion curve all meet is known as the *triple point*. For water the triple point occurs at

$$P = 4.579 \text{ mm of mercury and } T_C = 0.0100°\text{C}.$$

In the laboratory it is relatively easy to establish the triple point of water. If we place liquid water and ice in an insulated enclosure like the one shown schematically in Fig. 16.7 and use a pump to remove all the air from the region above the water surface, the mixture of liquid water, ice, and water vapor will come into thermal equilibrium *at the triple point. There is only one temperature and pressure at which liquid water, ice, and water vapor can exist in stable equilibrium.* Because of its ready reproducibility, the triple point has been selected as the single fixed point on which the modern SI Kelvin scale is based. The triple point of water has been *assigned* the *exact value*

$$T_{TP} \equiv 273.16 \text{ K.} \quad \textit{(Triple Point of Water)} \tag{16.1}$$

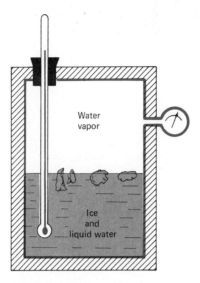

Fig. 16.7 At the triple point solid, liquid, and vapor are in equilibrium.

We recall that the ice point and the boiling point of water, which we used in our introductory discussion of the Celsius scale, both depend on atmospheric pressure. Because the triple point depends *only* on the properties of water and not on external pressure, it constitutes a much more satisfactory standard of temperature.

16.5 MIXTURES OF GASES AND VAPORS: HYGROMETRY

Let us now return to Fig. 16.1 and consider what happens when air as well as water vapor is present above the surface of the liquid. Air is only slightly soluble in water; very few molecules of air will enter the water. Unlike water vapor molecules, all of which enter the liquid when they collide with its surface, most of the air molecules that strike the water surface bound off just as they would in making collisions with a solid surface.

In accord with Dalton's law of partial pressures, the total pressure registered by the gauge in Fig. 16.1 will be the sum of the pressure due to the enclosed air and the saturated vapor pressure of water. The pressure of the enclosed air increases with increasing temperature in accord with the general gas law; the pressure of the saturated water vapor increases with increasing temperature in accord with the vaporization curve given in Fig. 16.2 just as if the air were not present. This relationship holds as long as the enclosed mixture of air and water vapor remains in contact with liquid water under equilibrium conditions.

Meteorologists use the term humidity to describe the water-vapor content of the atmosphere. They use the term *absolute humidity* to specify the mass of water vapor present per unit volume of air in units of kg/m³. A somewhat more useful term, and one more widely used in reporting weather conditions, is *relative humidity*:

The RELATIVE HUMIDITY is the ratio of the partial pressure of water vapor actually in the open air to the pressure of saturated water vapor at the same temperature.

The relative humidity is also, to a close approximation, the ratio of the actual density of the water vapor in the air to the density of saturated water vapor at the same temperature, because water vapor obeys the general gas law at the vapor pressures and temperatures encountered in the earth's atmosphere.

Relative humidity is based on measurements of the *dew point* of air samples. In determining the dew point of the air, we slowly cool a polished metal surface in still air and note the temperature at which dew first begins to cloud the surface of the metal. In this procedure, the air in immediate contact with the metal surface is in thermal equilibrium with the surface; the formation of dew indicates that the water vapor has reached its saturated vapor pressure at the surface temperature. The relative humidity of the air can then be expressed as the ratio of the actual vapor pressure of water in the air, which is equal to the saturated vapor pressure of air at the dew-point temperature, to the saturated vapor pressure at the temperature of the air sample.

QUESTIONS

1. In desert regions of the Southwest, water can be cooled by placing it in a *porous* ceramic bottle and suspending the bottle from a support in a place where there is free circulation of air. Why does the water inside the bottle become cool?

2. Why is it easier to dry damp laundry on an out-of-doors clothes line than on a clothes line inside a closed room?

3. Why is an "automatic clothes drier" operated at a temperature considerably above room temperature? Why should such a drier be vented to the out-of-doors?

4. What is the "critical point" of a material? Explain carefully.

5. What is the effect of increasing pressure on the melting point of glycerol? of glacial (anhydrous) acetic acid? of gallium?

6. Why does damp laundry "freeze dry" when placed on an out-door clothes line when the temperature is below $0°C$?

7. What is meant by the "triple point" of a substance?

8. Why is the triple point of water chosen instead of the ice point or the steam point as the single fixed point on the SI Kelvin scale of temperature?

9. Distinguish carefully between the terms *relative humidity* and *absolute humidity*.

10. How is the *dew point* of an air sample used in determining the relative humidity of the sample?

11. What is meant by the term *boiling point?* How does the boiling point of water on top of Pike's Peak compare with the boiling point of water at sea level?

12. Can the ideal gas law ever be applied to water vapor? If so, under what conditions would this be legitimate.

13. There is a persistent folk tale that a bucket of hot water left outdoors on a cold winter day will freeze faster than a similar bucket of cold water. Are there any circumstances when this might in fact be true? If so, explain how this could occur.

PROBLEMS

NOTE: *The saturated vapor pressure of mercury is extremely low at laboratory temperatures, being 0.0001 cm of mercury at 20° C and 0.028 cm of mercury at 100° C.*

1. In a carelessly made mercury barometer a small quantity of water is trapped above the mercury at the upper end of the barometer tube. What will be the height of the mercury column in this barometer at 273 K when the actual atmospheric pressure is 760 mm of mercury?

2. Repeat Problem 1 for cases in which the true atmospheric pressure is 760 mm of mercury and the temperature is 10°C, 20°C, and 30°C.

3. What will be the height registered by a water barometer when the temperature is 305 K, the pressure is 1 atm, and $g = 9.81$ m/s²?

4. On a day when the barometer reads 760 mm of mercury water is boiled vigorously in a narrow-necked flask until all the air above the water surface has been replaced by steam. A tightly fitting stopper is then inserted in the neck of the flask and the flask and its contents are allowed to cool. What is the pressure inside the flask when the temperature is 20°C? At what temperature would the pressure in the flask be twice this value?

5. A closed cylinder like the one in Fig. 16.3 contains only "live" or superheated steam at a temperature of 200°C. If the steam is slowly and isothermally compressed by means of the piston, the steam begins to condense; at what pressure will the cylinder contain a mixture of water and steam? What happens if the pressure is raised to 40 atm? How would you characterize the material in the cylinder when the pressure is 300 atm? Explain.

6. If the closed cylinder in Fig. 16.3 is at a temperature of 423 K and a pressure of 39.25 atm, all of the material in the cylinder is in the form of liquid water. If the pressure is kept constant and the temperature is gradually raised, at what temperature does steam begin to form? If the pressure were kept constant and the temperature were raised to 573 K, what would the cylinder contain? How could you use isothermal and isobaric processes to produce the final state of the material without crossing the vaporization curve?

7. What is the maximum temperature at which ice can melt? How could you obtain ice at this temperature?

8. A 120-kg man rests his entire weight on a single ice skate. If the cutting edge of the skate has a total area of 2 mm², what is the melting point of the ice immediately below the cutting edge? Would the friction between the skate and the ice be greater when the temperature of the ice is 273 K or 223 K?

9. A 4-liter vessel contains 4 g of water H_2O at 100°C. What fraction of the water is in the form of water vapor?

10. A boiler with a volume of 0.4 m³ contains 60 kg of water H_2O at 200°C. How many kilograms of steam are in the boiler?

11. At the triple point the specific volumes of liquid water, ice, and water vapor are 1.00×10^{-3}, 1.09×10^{-3}, and 206.3 m³/kg, respectively. The latent heat of fusion is 79.7 kcal/kg; the latent heat of vaporization is 597.4 kcal/kg. The pressure at the triple point is 4.58 mm of mercury. Compute the latent heat of sublimation of ice at the triple point. Find the difference between the thermal energies of 1 kg of liquid water and 1 kg of ice at the triple point; find the difference between the thermal energies of 1 kg of water vapor and 1 kg of liquid water at the triple point.

12. Referring to Problem 11, show that if heat is added to a vessel of constant volume containing ice, liquid water, and water vapor, almost all of the heat added goes into melting the ice to form liquid water and that very little of the heat added goes into the formation of more water vapor.

13. In a chemistry laboratory where the temperature is 16°C and the barometric pressure is 740 mm of mercury, a student collects 858 cm³ of hydrogen over water in an inverted bottle. The volume is measured with the water level the same inside and outside the bottle. What volume of dry hydrogen would the student have at 0°C and 1 atm? What is the total mass of the hydrogen collected?

14. A vessel containing only air and steam is sealed at 100°C with total pressure 760 mm of mercury, of which 210 mm is due to water vapor. If the sealed vessel is allowed to cool, what is the total pressure inside the vessel at 50°C and at 20°C?

15. A bottle is partly filled with warm water at 70°C. After the air in the bottle above the water surface has become saturated, the bottle is tightly corked. If the barometer reads 760 mm of mercury at the time the bottle is corked, what will be the pressure inside the bottle on the following day when the temperature is 20°C and the barometric pressure is 750 mm of mercury?

16. On a certain day the temperature of the air near the earth's surface is 25°C and the relative humidity is 50%. If the barometer reads 760 mm of mercury, what portion of the pressure is due to dry air?

17. On a certain day the temperature is 25°C and the dew point is 14°C. What is the relative humidity of the air? What is the absolute humidity on this day?

18. On a day when the ground is covered with snow and the temperature is −10°C, outside air is brought into a house and raised to a temperature of 20°C. If no moisture is added to the air, what is the relative humidity inside the house? If the total atmospheric pressure is 760 mm of mercury and the total volume of the house is 120 m³, how much water must be added to the inside air to raise the relative humidity to 50%?

19. In hot sultry weather sports announcers sometimes describe the air as being "heavy." What is the density of dry air at 30°C when the pressure is 760 mm of mercury? What is the density of air at 30°C at a pressure of 760 mm if the relative humidity is 80%?

20. The text states that the energy of a molecule in the liquid and solid states is of the order of kT. Show that this statement implies that the heat capacity per kilomole is of the order of R. Using the specific heat capacities c_P of the metallic solids listed in Table 14.1, compute the heat capacities per kilomole for these materials. Note that for these metals C_P is approximately equal to $3R$.

21. Using the data given in Table 16.1, prepare a table giving the *absolute humidity* of saturated air in the temperature range −20°C to 40°C.

22. A person enters a room where the temperature is 20°C from the out-of-doors where the temperature is 4°C. If his glasses "steam up," what can he conclude about the relative humidity in the room?

23. On a winter day the outdoor temperature is −10°C and the ground is covered with snow. If fresh outside air is brought into a house and heated without addition of moisture, what is the relative humidity inside the house if the inside air is at 20°C?

24. On a hot summer day the temperature is 32°C and the relative humidity is 80%. What is the dew point of the air?

25. One type of air-conditioning system works in summer by cooling the air below the desired temperature to condense out unwanted

water vapor and then reheating the air. If the outside air is at 32°C and has a relative humidity of 70%, to what temperature should the air be cooled if the reheated air is to be at 20°C with a relative humidity of 50%?

26. On a certain day the temperature is 30°C, the relative humidity is 60%, and the barometer reads 760 mm of mercury. What fraction of the total atmospheric pressure is due to dry air?

27. Show that the ratio of the density of saturated air at Celsius temperature T to the density of dry air at the same temperature is given by the expression

$$[P_S(18/29 - 1) + P_{At}]/P_{At},$$

where P_S is the pressure of saturated water vapor at the temperature in question and P_{At} is the barometer reading. Note that the ratio is always less than or at most equal to unity.

28. At a pressure of 1 atm and at −78.5°C, which is its sublimation temperature, solid CO_2 has a density of 1530 kg/m³. Using the vapor density as given by the general gas law, find the fraction of the latent heat of sublimation that goes into external work. The latent heat of sublimation of CO_2 at atmospheric pressure is 137.9 kcal/kg.

29. A dehumidifier reduces the humidity of summer air in a room by using a fan to blow air over cool refrigerator coils and allowing the condensed water to leave the room through a drain. If the air in a room is at 25°C, what should be the temperature of the coils if the air in the room is to be maintained at a relative humidity of 40%?

30. Two liters of water in a shallow pan are placed in a closed room where the air has a temperature of 25°C and an initial relative humidity of 40%. The room is 10 m long, 4 m wide, and 3 m high. How much of the water will evaporate?

31. A hollow sphere 40 cm in diameter with a wall thickness of 1 mm is constructed of steel that has an ultimate strength of 5×10^8 N/m². (a) What is the maximum pressure produced by an enclosed fluid that can be sustained by the sphere in air at 1 atm without bursting? (b) If the sphere were completely filled with air-free water at 2°C and the temperature were lowered, at what temperature would the water freeze and thus rupture the sphere? (See Fig. 16.5.) (c) If the temperature of the water were raised, at what temperature would the sphere burst? (See Fig. 13.5.) (d) If the sphere were filled with air at 2°C and atmospheric pressure along with an amount of water sufficiently large to keep the air saturated, at what temperature would the sphere burst? (See Table 16.1.)

32. Repeat Problem 31 for a long steel pipe plugged solidly at both ends if the diameter of the pipe is 12 cm and its wall thickness is 1 mm. Assume that the curved walls of the pipe burst before the ends give way.

CHAPTER 17

Thermodynamics

The first heat engines developed in the 18th century were truly *inventions* in the sense that there was no basic scientific understanding of the physical principles involved in their operation. However, from the very outset the practical importance of these devices was clearly recognized. Heat engines are the prime movers on which the industrial revolution is based. One of the major scientific activities of the 19th century was the development of an understanding of the physical phenomena involved in the operation of heat engines. Once the basic principles were understood, it became possible to improve the design of heat engines with a view to attaining greater efficiency.

In this chapter we give a brief introduction to the subject of *thermodynamics,* an important discipline developed in the 19th century. On the basis of the two general *principles of thermodynamics,* we can derive important theorems that have proved to be valid and have led to important engineering applications. Thermodynamics is a unique branch of modern science in the sense that its principles and the theorems derived from them are stated in terms of directly observable *macroscopic* quantities such as pressure, volume, temperature, work, and energy without reference to the atomic nature of matter.

As the name *thermodynamics* implies, the initial development of the subject was involved with the interconversion of thermal and mechanical energy. However, it was quickly recognized that the general discipline has much wider applications. In a very real sense, the thermodynamic work of J. Willard Gibbs (1839–1903) laid the foundation for modern physical chemistry.

17.1 THE SECOND PRINCIPLE OF THERMODYNAMICS

The First Principle of Thermodynamics, which we discussed in Chapter 14, is simply the application of the general conservation-of-energy principle to the interconversion of thermal energy and other forms of energy. In an isolated system, the

425

sum of all different kinds of energy present is constant. If there are no electric, magnetic, chemical, or nuclear processes that convert other forms of energy to thermal or mechanical energy within the system, then for an isolated system when mechanical energy disappears, an equal amount of thermal energy appears; when thermal energy disappears, an equal amount of mechanical energy appears:

$$\text{Mechanical Energy} \rightleftharpoons \text{Thermal Energy.} \quad \textit{(First Principle)} \qquad (17.1)$$

The First Principle imposes no restrictions on the conversion of mechanical energy to thermal energy or on the reverse process so long as the total energy remains constant. The oceans of the earth constitute a vast reservoir of thermal energy; nothing in the First Principle tells us that we cannot withdraw thermal energy from the oceans and convert it into mechanical energy that can be used in doing useful work. However, experience has shown that this is impossible.

Experience shows that it is easy to convert mechanical energy into thermal energy; this occurs whenever work is done against frictional forces of any kind, when inelastic collisions occur, and when a body is stretched beyond its elastic limit. There are, however, important restrictions on the conversion of thermal energy to mechanical energy. For example, a rotating wheel *always* slows down as its kinetic energy is converted into thermal energy in the bearings; the kinetic energy is dissipated and the bearings become warm. The reverse process in which the wheel speeds up and the bearings become cool is *never* observed. Mechanical energy can always be converted to thermal energy, but thermal energy can be converted to mechanical energy only under certain restrictions; the Second Principle of Thermodynamics specifies these restrictions.

There are several alternative statements of the Second Principle of Thermodynamics. The various statements can be shown to be logically equivalent in that each implies the others, but on the surface they appear rather different. The statement we shall employ refers to a *continuously acting* heat engine. This is any device where some material, called the *working substance,* is caused repeatedly to go through a *cycle* of processes such that at the completion of each cycle the state of the device is exactly what it was at the beginning of the cycle. The environment of the engine, by contrast, undergoes permanent change as the engine operates.

The only way in which we can operate a continuously acting heat engine to convert thermal energy into mechanical energy is to have at least *two* heat reservoirs at two *different* temperatures. If we have two such reservoirs and operate between them some suitable device, we can convert *some,* but *only some,* of the thermal energy from the hot reservoir into work. The Second Principle is an inference based on experience that summarizes these results.

SECOND PRINCIPLE OF THERMODYNAMICS: It is impossible to construct a continuously acting engine that will deliver mechanical work derived from heat extracted from a single thermal reservoir without rejecting some heat to a second reservoir at lower temperature.

This statement of the Second Principle is represented schematically in Fig. 17.1. Part 17.1a shows a heat engine extracting heat Q_H from a reservoir at some high

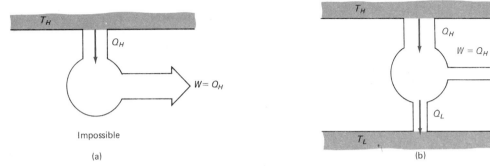

Fig. 17.1   The Second Principle of Thermodynamics.

temperature T_H and converting all of the heat into work W. So long as $W = Q_H$ such a process would not violate the First Principle. However, the Second Principle states that the process illustrated in Fig. 17.1a is *impossible* for a continuously acting engine. Processes that convert heat from a single reservoir into work are possible when the engine undergoes internal changes, but no engine operating *cyclically* that will perform this conversion can be constructed.

Figure 17.1b represents a situation that *is* possible on the basis of the Second Principle. In this part of the figure, a continuously acting heat engine accepts heat Q_H from a high-temperature reservoir at temperature T_H and rejects heat Q_L to a low-temperature reservoir at temperature T_L. Let us call any continuously acting engine that operates between only two thermal reservoirs a *simple* engine. A simple heat engine operating as shown in Fig. 17.1b would have a useful work output $W = Q_H - Q_L$ according to the First Principle, because the working substance is returned to its initial state. The important point is that any continuously acting heat engine operating between the two heat reservoirs must reject *some* heat to the low-temperature reservoir. The Second Principle assures us that an engine not rejecting some heat Q_L to a low-temperature reservoir cannot be devised.

Although practical heat engines do not act simply between two thermal reservoirs, it is nonetheless desirable for us to study the properties of a simple engine. The efficiency of any device is defined as the ratio of the useful work output W to the total energy supplied to the device. Thus, for the simple heat engine, the efficiency is given by the relation

$$\text{Efficiency} = \frac{W}{Q_H} = \frac{Q_H - Q_L}{Q_H} = 1 - \frac{Q_L}{Q_H}, \quad \textit{(Simple Heat Engine)} \quad (17.2)$$

where Q_H represents the thermal energy supplied to the heat engine and $W = Q_H - Q_L$ represents the work output of the engine; Q_H, Q_L, and W must, of course, be expressed in the same energy units. Examination of (17.2) indicates that the efficiency would be unity if $Q_L = 0$; however, the Second Principle asserts that no heat engine will operate with $Q_L = 0$; some heat must be rejected to the low-temperature reservoir. Thus, the Second Principle tells us that *we can never construct a heat engine with an efficiency of 100%.*

A simple engine that acts oppositely to the heat engine just considered can be devised, and we can produce the *simple refrigerator* shown in Fig. 17.2; note that all the arrows shown in Fig. 17.2 are opposite to those shown in Fig. 17.1b. By doing mechanical work W *to* the device in Fig. 17.2 we are able to extract heat Q_L from the low-temperature reservoir and deliver heat $Q_H = W + Q_L$ to the high-temperature reservoir. Refrigerators are usually rated in terms of what is called a performance coefficient representing the ratio of the heat extracted Q_L to the work W supplied to the refrigerator. For a simple refrigerator we have

$$\text{Performance Coefficient} = \frac{Q_L}{W} = \frac{Q_L}{Q_H - Q_L}. \quad \textit{(Simple Refrigerator)} \quad (17.3)$$

Work W must be done to any continuously acting refrigerator; otherwise it would be possible to violate the Second Principle by combining a "perfect" refrigerator requiring no work W with a simple heat engine acting between the same two reservoirs. We merely adjust things so that the magnitude of Q_L for our perfect refrigerator equals the magnitude of Q_L for the simple heat engine shown in Fig. 17.1b. The net effect of both continuously acting devices operating simultaneously between the two reservoirs would then be as shown in Fig. 17.1a, which is forbidden by the Second Principle.

In our discussion thus far we have used the First Principle of Thermodynamics to write expressions for the efficiency of a simple heat engine and the performance coefficient of a simple refrigerator in terms of the heat Q_H received from or transferred to a high-temperature reservoir and the heat Q_L rejected to or extracted from a reservoir at lower temperature. The Second Principle assures us that no simple heat engine can have an efficiency of 100% and no simple refrigerator can have an infinite performance coefficient. However, we are left with the question as to whether by clever schemes of engine design we can arbitrarily increase the efficiency of a simple engine operating between two reservoirs by increasing Q_H and decreasing Q_L. Although we have shown that, because Q_L can never be zero, even the most cleverly designed engine cannot be 100% efficient, we have not shown that there are any other limitations on its efficiency. In fact, the Second Principle implies that there are indeed *inherent limitations* on the efficiency of heat engines operating between any two reservoirs. Such limitations were first discussed by Sadi Carnot (1796–1832), a French military engineer, whose work we shall consider in the following section. Carnot's work, which was published in 1824, was a remarkable achievement in view of the fact that it was done long before the First and Second Principles were established and at a time when the caloric-fluid theory of heat was still widely accepted. As we have

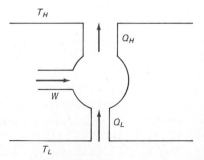

Fig. 17.2   A simple refrigerator.

noted in Chapter 14, the First Principle was developed between 1842 and 1847. The Second Principle was first enunciated by the German physicist Rudolf Clausius (1822–1888) in 1850. Clausius combined the insights of Carnot with the clarified picture of the nature of heat provided by the First Principle.

17.2 THE CARNOT CYCLE: CARNOT EFFICIENCY

Carnot considered an idealized simple engine that could be operated reversibly in a cycle known as the Carnot Cycle. A process is *reversible* if the system and its total environment can be returned to their initial states. In order for this to be possible the system must always be in quasiequilibrium, that is, infinitesimally close to a true equilibrium state. There can be no friction or other dissipative processes and no heat conduction associated with finite temperature differences. A reversible process is an idealization that in practice can be closely approximated but not actually attained. However, like other idealizations we have encountered such as the ideal gas, the idea of a reversible process is important in developing and clarifying theoretical concepts. In the Carnot Engine, a "working substance" enclosed in a leak-proof cylinder with perfectly insulating walls and piston goes through a cycle shown schematically in Fig. 17.3. Although, in principle, any material can be used as a working substance, we shall assume that the working substance is an ideal gas. We make this assumption merely because an ideal gas obeys very simple laws and has simple properties with which we are already familiar; as we shall show later, the use of an ideal gas in no way limits the conclusions that we shall draw regarding engine efficiency.

The first step in the Carnot Cycle, shown in Fig. 17.3a, is accomplished by placing the end of the cylinder in contact with the heat reservoir at the same temperature

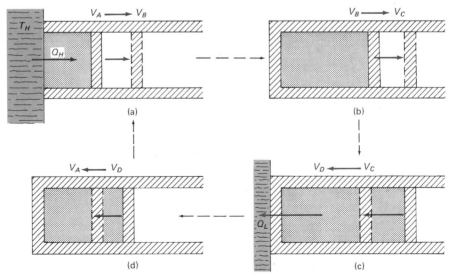

Fig. 17.3 In a Carnot Engine the working substance undergoes the following processes: (a) An isothermal expansion at temperature T_H from volume V_A to volume V_B; (b) an adiabatic expansion from V_B, T_H to V_C, T_L; (c) an isothermal compression at T_L from V_C to V_D; and (d) an adiabatic compression from V_D, T_L to V_A, T_H. In a Carnot Refrigerator the order and directions of the processes are reversed.

T_H as the gas and removing the insulation from the end of the cylinder. With the gas in contact with the reservoir, the gas undergoes a reversible isothermal expansion at temperature T_H from an initial volume V_A to some final volume V_B. Because there is no change in the temperature of the gas and hence no change in its thermal energy, all the heat Q_H added to the gas goes into the external work $W_{A \to B}$ done by the gas. Thus, by (15.17), we can write

$$Q_H = W_{A \to B} = nRT_H \ln(V_B/V_A), \quad \text{(Work done by Ideal Gas} \quad (17.4)$$
$$\text{in Isothermal Expansion)}$$

where n is the number of kmols of gas in the cylinder and R is the universal gas constant.

In the second step of the Carnot Cycle, shown schematically in Fig. 17.3b, we replace the insulation on the end of the cylinder and allow the gas to undergo a reversible adiabatic expansion from volume V_B to volume V_C. The external work $W_{B \to C}$ done *by* the gas in this expansion is accomplished as a result of a decrease in the thermal energy of the gas as its temperature drops from T_H to the lower temperature T_L. By (15.19), we can write

$$W_{B \to C} = nC_V(T_H - T_L), \quad \text{(Work done by Gas in} \quad (17.5)$$
$$\text{Adiabatic Expansion)}$$

where C_V is the molar heat capacity of the gas at constant volume.

In the third step of the cycle, shown in Fig. 17.3c, we place the end of the cylinder in contact with the low-temperature reservoir at temperature T_L and again remove the insulation from the end of the cylinder. Then by applying an external force to the cylinder we reversibly and isothermally compress the gas from volume V_C to volume V_D. Because the thermal energy of the gas is unchanged, all the work $W_{C \to D}$ done *to* the gas goes into rejecting heat Q_L to the low-temperature reservoir. Thus, by the same arguments used in (17.4), we can write

$$Q_L = W_{C \to D} = nRT_L \ln(V_C/V_D). \quad \text{(Work done to Ideal Gas} \quad (17.6)$$
$$\text{in Isothermal Compression)}$$

The final step of the Carnot Cycle, shown in Fig. 17.3d, is a reversible adiabatic compression of the gas from volume V_D back to its initial volume V_A. Because no heat is given up by the gas during this adiabatic process, all the work $W_{D \to A}$ that we do in compressing the gas goes into increasing the thermal energy of the gas in accord with the relation $\Delta U = nC_V(T_H - T_L)$. Thus, we can write

$$W_{D \to A} = nC_V(T_H - T_L). \quad \text{(Work done to gas} \quad (17.7)$$
$$\text{in Adiabatic Compression)}$$

This step completes the Carnot Cycle. We started out with an ideal gas with initial volume V_A and temperature T_H and have now completed the cycle with the gas restored to its initial state.

We can now summarize the processes just described by means of the *PV* diagram

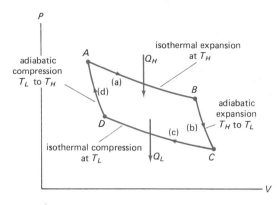

Fig. 17.4 Schematic diagram showing the changes in the state of the working substance in a Carnot Engine. Heat Q_H is added in step (a) and Q_L is removed in step (c).

shown in Fig. 17.4. In the isothermal expansion from A to B we have added heat Q_H from a heat reservoir at temperature T_H; in the isothermal compression from C to D, we have rejected heat Q_L to a heat reservoir at temperature T_L. The work done in each of the steps corresponds to the area $\int P\,dV$ under the curve representing that step. Comparison of (17.5) and (17.7) shows that the work done *by* the gas in adiabatic expansion from V_B to V_C is exactly equal to the work done *to* the gas in adiabatic compression from V_D to V_A. Therefore, the *net* amount of work W done *by* the gas during the complete cycle is merely the difference between the work $W_{A \to B}$ done by the gas in isothermal expansion from V_A to V_B and the work done *to* the gas as we isothermally compress it from V_C to V_D; i.e., from (17.4) and (17.6), $W = Q_H - Q_L$, as is required by the First Principle. The efficiency W/Q_H of a Carnot Engine is given by (17.2):

$$\text{Efficiency} = \frac{Q_H - Q_L}{Q_H} = 1 - \frac{Q_L}{Q_H}. \quad \textit{(Carnot Engine)} \qquad (17.8)$$

Because the Carnot Engine is reversible, it can be operated as a Carnot Refrigerator. Its operation as a refrigerator can be accomplished by a reversal of each of the steps shown in Fig. 17.3; for a refrigerator each of the processes shown in the *PV* plot of Fig. 17.4 would be reversed.

Now let us give further consideration to Eqs. (17.4) and (17.6). From these equations we can obtain the ratio of Q_L to Q_H in the form

$$\frac{Q_L}{Q_H} = \frac{nRT_L \ln(V_C/V_D)}{nRT_H \ln(V_B/V_A)} = \frac{T_L \ln(V_C/V_D)}{T_H \ln(V_B/V_A)}. \qquad (17.9)$$

However, we note that points B and C are on the same adiabatic curve and the volumes V_C and V_B are therefore related by Eq. (15.22″) for an adiabatic process:

$$T_L V_C^{\gamma-1} = T_H V_B^{\gamma-1}. \qquad (17.10)$$

Similarly, points A and D are on the same adiabatic curve, and we can write

$$T_L V_D^{\gamma-1} = T_H V_A^{\gamma-1}. \qquad (17.11)$$

Division of (17.10) by (17.11) then demonstrates that

$$V_C/V_D = V_B/V_A. \tag{17.12}$$

Substitution of this result in (17.9) leads to the very important result

$$Q_L/Q_H = T_L/T_H. \tag{17.13}$$

The result given in (17.13) allows us to rewrite expression (17.8) for the efficiency of a Carnot Engine using an ideal gas as a working substance in the form

$$\text{Efficiency} = 1 - \frac{T_L}{T_H} = \frac{T_H - T_L}{T_H} . \quad \textit{(Carnot Efficiency)} \tag{17.14}$$

We shall see that (17.14) holds for a Carnot Engine regardless of the particular working substance used. As we shall prove in the next section, the Carnot Efficiency given in (17.14) is the maximum efficiency that can be expected of any simple engine operating between reservoirs at temperatures T_H and T_L. All real engines operating between these two reservoirs have lower efficiencies. The Carnot Efficiency thus represents the ultimate goal that can be approached by clever inventors of heat engines.

17.3   CARNOT'S THEOREMS

Although the Carnot Engine is a highly idealized device, it provides extremely useful criteria for the anticipated performance of real heat engines. We shall use the Principles of Thermodynamics to prove several theorems that are useful in providing a guide to the results to be expected from real engines. Although these theorems are proved rigorously from thermodynamical principles established long after Carnot's time, they are usually referred to as Carnot's Theorems.

THEOREM I: All reversible engines have the same efficiency when they operate between reservoirs at the same two temperatures.

This theorem can be proved by assuming that the opposite is true and then showing that our assumption leads to a contradiction of the Second Principle. Thus, consider Fig. 17.5, which shows a Carnot Engine that uses an ideal gas as the working substance along with a second simple reversible engine which we shall for convenience call the "Eiselstein Engine." Let us assume that the Eiselstein Engine has a greater efficiency than the Carnot Engine, as suggested in Fig. 17.5a. We choose the sizes of the engines such that each of the engines rejects the same amount of heat Q_L to the low-temperature reservoir. Since the Eiselstein Engine is assumed to be more efficient, it will have a larger useful output $W_E = Q_{HE} - Q_L$ than the output $W_C = Q_{HC} - Q_L$ of the Carnot Engine for equal heat rejections Q_L. Because the Carnot Engine is reversible, we can let the more efficient Eiselstein Engine "run the Carnot Engine backwards" as a Carnot Refrigerator, as suggested in Fig. 17.5b. As indicated in the figure, the work W_C required to remove heat Q_L from the low-temperature

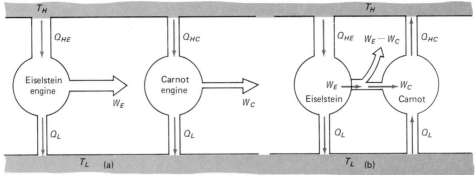

Fig. 17.5 The reversible Eiselstein Engine is *assumed* to be more efficient than a Carnot Engine operating between the same two heat reservoirs.

reservoir is less than the work output W_E of the Eiselstein Engine; therefore, the Eiselstein Engine can operate the Carnot Refrigerator and still have an output $W_E - W_C$ left over for other uses.

However, this result is a contradiction of the Second Principle. This can be seen from Fig. 17.6 in which the combined Eiselstein–Carnot devices are regarded as a single unit. In Fig. 17.6a we show the Eiselstein Engine delivering heat Q_L directly to the Carnot Refrigerator rather than to the low-temperature reservoir, which actually has no role in the Eiselstein–Carnot combination. As shown in Fig. 17.6b, the net effect of the combined Eiselstein–Carnot device is to take heat $Q_{HE} - Q_{HC}$ from the high-temperature reservoir and convert all of this heat into work. This result is a contradiction of the Second Principle. What is wrong with our argument is our assumption that the efficiency of the reversible Eiselstein Engine is greater than that of the Carnot Engine.

By the same kind of reasoning we arrive at the same contradiction of the Second Principle if we assume that the efficiency of the Carnot Engine is greater than the efficiency of the Eiselstein Engine.

The only tenable conclusion that we can reach is that the reversible Eiselstein

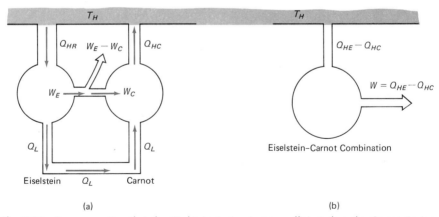

Fig. 17.6 Our assumption that the Eiselstein Engine is more efficient than the Carnot Engine leads to a violation of the Second Principle of Thermodynamics. All *reversible* engines operating between the same heat reservoirs have the same efficiency.

Engine and the reversible Carnot Engine have exactly the same efficiency. This concludes the proof of the above theorem.

Note that the Eiselstein Engine in the argument might well have been a Carnot Engine that used some working substance other than the ideal gas that we considered in Sec. 17.2. In fact, any *reversible* simple engine must follow the Carnot Cycle. Our theorem thus says a Carnot Engine using any working substance has the efficiency given in (17.14). *All* simple reversible engines have the efficiency stated in (17.14) when they are working between two reservoirs at temperature T_H and T_L.

> THEOREM II: No real simple engine can have an efficiency greater than that of a reversible engine working between the same two temperatures.

In view of our earlier discussions, this theorem seems obvious. A real engine is not a reversible device. It always has frictional losses that cause nonreversible transformations of mechanical energy into thermal energy, departures from thermal equilibrium that cause nonreversible transfers of heat, loss of thermal energy to other bodies, etc. The work output of a real engine is always less than $Q_H - Q_L$ for a reversible engine; $W < (Q_H - Q_L)$ implies an efficiency less than the Carnot Efficiency.

A rigorous proof of the theorem can be provided by the same reasoning used in the first part of our proof of Theorem I. By exactly the same steps we can prove that a "real Eiselstein Engine" cannot be more efficient than a reversible Carnot Engine. However, because real engines are not reversible devices, we cannot turn the argument around and show that a Carnot Engine cannot be more efficient than a real Eiselstein Engine. Real engines usually have much smaller efficiencies than Carnot Engines operating between the same temperatures. The best that we can possibly expect of a real engine is an efficiency approaching that of the Carnot Efficiency (17.14); a real engine can *never* have greater efficiency.

> THEOREM III: The performance coefficient Q_L/W of any simple refrigerator acting between two reservoirs cannot be greater than the performance coefficient of a Carnot Refrigerator acting between the same two reservoirs.

The formal proof of this theorem is similar to that used in connection with Theorems I and II. We assume the opposite and show that it leads to a contradiction of the Second Principle.

We have seen how Carnot's Theorems can be proved from the First and Second Principles of Thermodynamics. They are important for numerous reasons. From them we can conclude that the efficiencies of all Carnot Engines are given by (17.14) regardless of the working substance; the working substance could be a real gas, a liquid, or even a solid instead of the ideal gas that we used in our derivation of (17.14). Carnot's Theorems show that the efficiency of the Carnot Engine is one that can be approached but never surpassed by a real heat engine, no matter how clever the designer is and no matter what gadgetry he may devise!

17.4 THE THERMODYNAMIC TEMPERATURE SCALE

In Chapter 13 we pointed out the impossibility of setting up a satisfactory standard temperature scale on the basis of the thermal properties of any particular materials such as those of the mercury and glass in an ordinary laboratory thermometer. In the same chapter we pointed out that an absolute temperature scale could be defined in terms of the properties of an ideal gas and in subsequent chapters we have employed temperatures that have been based on an ideal-gas scale. This scale still depends on a particular equation of state in addition to the serious operational shortcoming that there is really no such thing as an ideal gas!

As early as 1848 the Scottish physicist William Thomson (Lord Kelvin) (1824–1907) pointed out that it is possible to define an *absolute thermodynamic temperature scale* based on Carnot's Theorems that *does not depend on the thermal properties of any substance or on any equation of state.*

We have shown in our derivation of (17.13) that for a Carnot Engine involving an ideal gas the ratio of the heat Q_H received from the high-temperature reservoir to the heat Q_L rejected to the low-temperature reservoir is equal to the ratio of the absolute temperatures of the two reservoirs; thus we can write

$$T_H/T_L = Q_H/Q_L. \tag{17.15}$$

However, when we proved Carnot's First Theorem from the Second Principle of Thermodynamics, we showed that all reversible engines acting between two reservoirs at the same two temperatures have the same efficiency. This means that a Carnot Engine employing a real substance has the same efficiency as a Carnot Engine employing an ideal gas. Thus, Eq. (17.15) holds for *any* material used as a working substance in a Carnot Cycle.

The fact that the ratio Q_H/Q_L for a reversible engine is a universal property independent of the working substance makes it possible to use (17.15) to *define* a temperature scale that is independent of the particular properties of any substance. Since only temperature *ratios* are defined by (17.15), we must assign the numerical value of the temperature of one fixed point in order to establish an absolute temperature scale. Because of its ready reproducibility, the triple point of water has been selected as the single fixed point on the present SI Kelvin Scale; the triple point of water is *assigned* the exact value

$$T_{TP} = 273.16 \text{ K}. \tag{17.16}$$

This particular value was chosen so that the SI Kelvin Scale would agree as closely as possible with older Kelvin Scales based on other fixed points. On the basis of (17.15) we can determine all other temperatures from the relation

$$T = (Q/Q_{TP})T_{TP}, \tag{17.17}$$

where Q and Q_{TP} are the heats extracted from or rejected to thermal reservoirs at the temperatures T and T_{TP}, respectively, by a reversible engine acting between those reservoirs. The heat ratio Q/Q_{TP} is a ratio of two energies and energies can, in principle, be measured in terms of the fundamental quantities mass, length, and time. Thus, relation (17.17) can be regarded as a valid definition of temperature in terms of an arbitrary but universally accepted fixed point.

In establishing the Kelvin scale, it is not necessary to construct a real Carnot engine; the scale is based on the isothermal and adiabatic curves determined from studies of a real substance. Suppose that we have an arbitrary quantity of a substance

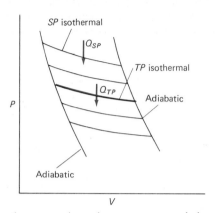

Fig. 17.7 The Kelvin temperature of the steam point is given by $T_{SP} = (Q_{SP}/Q_{TP})T_{TP}$ for *any* working substance.

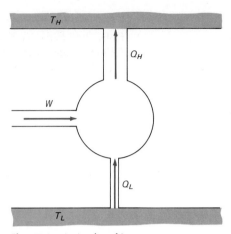

Fig. 17.8   A simple refrigerator.

such as a real gas and carry it through a set of isothermal and adiabatic processes like those shown schematically in the PV diagram of Fig. 17.7. Let us further suppose that we have studied the thermal properties of the substance in great detail, employing some arbitrary temperature scale such as one based on a mercury thermometer. In particular, we know the pressure P and volume V of the real substance as a function of temperature as measured by our mercury thermometer; and we know C_P and C_V in J/kmole · arbitrary degree, where "arbitrary degrees" are measured on our mercury thermometer. This information permits us to compute the heat Q that would have to be added to the substance in an isothermal expansion or removed from the substance in an isothermal compression at any temperature on the mercury-thermometer scale that we are using.

Now consider the Carnot Cycle defined by the triple-point temperature and some other temperature such as the steam point. On the basis of measurements involving our arbitrary mercury-thermometer scale, we can determine the values of Q_{TP} and Q_{SP}. Once these are known, we can determine the Kelvin temperature T_{SP} of the steam point from (17.17):

$$T_{SP} = (Q_{SP}/Q_{TP})T_{TP}.$$

The Second Principle of Thermodynamics assures that we shall obtain the *same* value for T_{SP} regardless of the working substance that we have employed in the Carnot Cycle and regardless of the arbitrary temperature scale that we have used in determining the thermal properties of the working substance. The value of any temperature T on the thermodynamic scale can be similarly determined by appropriate experimental measurements and the use of (17.17) with data on Q provided by an arbitrary thermometer scale.

The values of the temperatures of the steam point and the ice point are determined on the SI Kelvin Scale are

$$T_{SP} = (373.146 \pm 0.004) \text{ K and } T_{IP} = (273.1500 \pm 0.0002) \text{ K}.$$

These two temperatures differ by 100 K within the limits of experimental uncertainty; thus, the official SI Kelvin Scale gives a degree of size in agreement with the common Celsius Scale, originally defined in terms of the ice point and steam point. In addition, the SI Kelvin Scale is in agreement with the ideal-gas scale as we have used it in earlier chapters; it also provides for valid temperature measurements in the low-temperature range where real gases do not behave even approximately as an ideal gas.

17.5 REFRIGERATORS

As we have pointed out earlier, a reversed Carnot Engine acts as a Carnot Refrigerator. It extracts heat Q_L from a reservoir at low temperature T_L and rejects the heat to a reservoir at high temperature T_H. To accomplish this transfer requires work W so that the heat Q_H delivered to the hot reservoir is $Q_H = Q_L + W$, as suggested in Fig. 17.8. We recall from (17.3) that the performance coefficient of a simple refrigerator is defined as the ratio of the heat extracted Q_L to the work W required. In view of the relation (17.13) for a Carnot Engine, we can express the performance coefficient of a Carnot Refrigerator as

$$\text{Carnot Performance Coefficient} = Q_L/W = \frac{1}{(T_H/T_L) - 1} = \frac{T_L}{T_H - T_L}. \quad (17.18)$$

Thus, the performance coefficient of a Carnot Refrigerator depends only on the temperatures of the reservoirs involved. The relation (17.18) gives the performance coefficient of any reversible refrigerator operating between reservoirs at temperatures T_L and T_H. The third Carnot Theorem assures us that no real refrigerator can have a higher performance coefficient.

We can rearrange (17.18) to give the work W required to remove a given amount of heat Q_L from the low-temperature reservoir. The result is

$$W = Q_L \left(\frac{T_H - T_L}{T_L} \right). \quad (17.19)$$

This represents the *minimum* amount of work that would be required to operate *any* refrigerator between the two temperatures; more work would be required by any real refrigerator. We note that the work required increases as the temperature difference $T_H - T_L$ between the two reservoirs increases and also increases as T_L decreases. We note that the work required to remove a finite amount of heat Q_L from a low-temperature reservoir increases rapidly as T_L approaches absolute zero; in the limit as $T_L \to 0$ K we see that $W \to \infty$. This result is in agreement with the definition of absolute zero as the temperature of a body or reservoir that is incapable of giving up heat. We note also that the fact that $W \to \infty$ as $T_L \to 0$ suggests the impossibility of ever attaining absolute zero.

The refrigeration cycle typically used in commercially available refrigerators employs a vapor that is easily condensed by increased pressure. Ammonia NH_3, sulfur dioxide SO_2, and "Freon" CCl_2F_2 are in common use as the working substance. As suggested schematically in Fig. 17.9, the system consists of a condenser at temperature

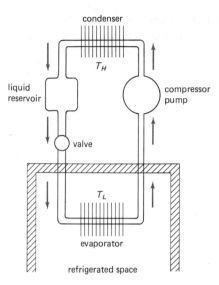

Fig. 17.9 Schematic diagram of a refrigeration system. Heat is extracted at low temperature T_L and given up at high temperature T_H.

T_H and an evaporator at temperature T_L. The compressor pump regulates the high pressure in the condenser; the low pressure in the evaporator is regulated by an expansion valve. The working substance evaporates at low temperature T_L; the latent heat required is furnished by the material inside the refrigerated space. The working substance condenses at high temperature T_H; the latent heat is released to the outside air. The conventional home air conditioner also employs this system; cooled air is delivered inside the house by a fan blowing air past the coils of the evaporator; in the condenser, heat is transferred to the outside air by a fan blowing air past the condenser coils. Both evaporating and condensing coils are usually equipped with a set of "fins" to improve the transfer of heat between the working substance and the air.

When a refrigerator is used to remove heat from cold bodies—the ground, underground water, or air—outside a house or building and deliver the heat to the air inside a warm building, the refrigerator is call a *heat pump*. The removal of heat from the out-of-doors and delivery to the interior of a house requires work; the work required by a Carnot Refrigerator is that given in (17.19); more work to transfer the same heat is required by real heat pumps. Provided the temperature difference between the inside and the outside air is not too great, the amount of work required is considerably less than the amount of heat transferred. The amount of heat transferred is usually several times the work required to operate the compressor pump in a commercial system. The performance coefficient of a heat pump gives the ratio of the heat transferred to the equivalent electrical energy that would be delivered to the house by an electrical resistive heater operating in place of the electric motor required to operate the compressor pump. The performance coefficient of a heat pump being greater than one thus represents an economic advantage in using electricity to run a heat pump rather than for direct resistance heating. Economic comparison of heat pumps with fossil-fuel furnaces requires consideration of how the electricity is generated and how the fossil fuels are obtained as well as consideration of the combustion properties of the fuels. Heat pumps are coming into wide use in regions of our country where mild winters are encountered and the usual temperature difference $T_H - T_L$ is not too large. In colder regions, where conventional furnaces are required, heat pumps can serve as a source of auxiliary heating.

17.6 PRACTICAL HEAT ENGINES

Although the refrigerators we have described have some relationship to the Carnot Engine in that high-temperature and low-temperature heat reservoirs are involved, this is rarely the case in practical heat engines. No real heat engine is reversible and few of them can be regarded as working between heat reservoirs.

Therefore, there are difficulties in arriving at values for their efficiencies. The maximum possible efficiency is usually stated as an equivalent Carnot Efficiency

$$\text{Carnot Efficiency} = (T_H - T_L)/T_H,$$

where T_H is the highest temperature of the working substance encountered in the operation of the device and T_L is the corresponding lowest temperature.

The thermal efficiency of an engine is defined as the ratio of the work W done by the engine to the heat Q_H added to the working substance in an external combustion engine or to the reaction products inside an internal combustion engine or in the combustion chamber of a jet engine:

$$\text{Thermal Efficiency} = \frac{\text{Work Done}}{\text{Heat Added}}.$$

The thermal efficiency of any real engine is always less than its equivalent Carnot Efficiency.

Another type of efficiency sometimes stated is the "overall efficiency," which is defined as the ratio of the work done by the engine to the chemical energy of the fuel supplied to it:

$$\text{Overall Efficiency} = \frac{\text{Work Done}}{\text{Chemical Energy of the Fuel Used}}.$$

The overall efficiency of any real engine is always even lower than the thermal efficiency of the engine, because combustion of the fuel may not be complete and some of the heat produced by the burning fuel may never be added to the working substance.

17.7 ENTROPY

Looking back at our statements of the First and Second Principle, we note that the First Principle is merely an assertion that the total energy of a system is conserved but that the Second Principle deals with certain *limitations* on the conversion of thermal energy to mechanical energy, limitations that involve the temperatures of heat reservoirs between which an engine is used to perform work. In other words, the Second Principle deals with the *availability* of thermal energy for use in doing work. Experience indicates that in any real system thermal energy becomes increasingly unavailable for use in doing work. The physical quantity that gives a *measure of the unavailability of thermal energy* for doing work is called *entropy.*

We first define the change dS in the entropy of a working substance when heat dQ is added to the substance at temperature T:

$$dS = dQ/T. \quad \begin{cases} dS \text{ in J/K} \\ dQ \text{ in J} \\ T \text{ in K} \end{cases} \qquad (17.20)$$

We note that entropy dS is *not* an energy but represents the ratio of the heat dQ added to the temperature T at which the process occurs; it is thus measured in J/K. We can obtain the entropy difference $\Delta S = S_B - S_A$ of a substance between two states A and B by means of the integral

$$S_B - S_A = \int_A^B \frac{dQ}{T} \qquad (17.21)$$

taken along any path on a *PV* diagram between A and B that represents a *reversible* process. This is in contrast to the net heat transferred Q and the net work done W, which depend on the particular path followed as well as the initial and final states.

Experience indicates that *all naturally occurring processes are accompanied by an increase in entropy.* Because all naturally occurring processes are irreversible, this means that in *all* naturally occurring processes there is a decrease in the availability of energy for doing useful work. It is possible to state the Second Principle in terms of entropy; the entropy of an isolated system never decreases and usually tends to increase. For all naturally occurring process the entropy of the system always increases:

SECOND PRINCIPLE OF THERMODYNAMICS: The entropy of an isolated system can increase but can never decrease.

The entropy form of the Second Principle was first enunciated by Clausius in 1865. We leave it for more advanced texts to develop the reasoning showing the logical equivalence of this statement with our earlier statement of the Second Principle. Considering the whole universe as an isolated system, we can expect the entropy of the universe to increase until all parts of the universe are at the same temperature. When this happens, the unavailability of energy will be complete. When and if this condition is reached, all physical, chemical, and biological processes will cease. This condition is called "the heat death of the universe"—and presents a gloomy prospect indeed!

QUESTIONS

1. Can the principles of thermodynamics be derived from Newton's Principles?

2. Give examples of physical processes that can occur on the basis of the first principle of thermodynamics but are not permitted according to the second principle of thermodynamics.

3. Why can't we operate the factories of our country by using heat extracted from the waters of the oceans?

4. According to the caloric theory of heat, heat tends to flow from a region of high temperature to a region of low temperature just as water tends to flow from high elevations to low elevations. Is this idea at variance with the ideas presented by Sadi Carnot in his treatment of heat engines?

5. If the nature of the working substance in a Carnot engine is of no importance, why are we interested in obtaining petroleum?

6. If you are free to raise the high temperature T_H of the high-temperature reservoir by an amount ΔT or to reduce the temperature T_L of the low temperature reservoir by an equal amount ΔT, which choice should you make in order to produce the greater increase in the efficiency of a Carnot engine?

7. If your kitchen were equipped with a refrigerator with an "automatic ice cube maker" and you absent-mindedly left the refrigerator door open when you departed for a trip, what would you find when you returned a week later? Explain your conclusions.

8. How is it possible to establish a temperature scale by selecting only *one* "fixed point?" For example, are not values required for both the freezing point and the boiling point of water?

9. What factors make real heat engines and real refrigerators less than ideal?

10. Discuss the practical advantages of using a heat pump for domestic heating instead of resistive electric heating.

11. Discuss why it is necessary for a system to be always in quasiequilibrium if the processes it undergoes are to be reversible.

PROBLEMS

1. A 2000-kg automobile moving at an initial speed of 90 m/s is braked to rest on a level road. How much thermal energy is produced? If all of this thermal energy were added to 2 kg of water at an initial temperature of 20°C, what would be the effect on the water?

2. Two kilograms of steam at 100°C and atmospheric pressure are condensed, and the resulting water is cooled to 20°C. How much has the thermal energy of the steam been reduced? If all of the resulting heat could be used in accelerating a 2000-kg automobile, what would be the speed of the automobile?

3. If 2 kcal of heat from a high-temperature heat reservoir are supplied to a heat engine and 0.85 kcal are rejected by the engine to a low temperature reservoir, what is the maximum efficiency to be expected from this heat engine? What is the maximum useful work output to be expected from this engine?

4. If heat is supplied to a heat engine at the rate of 1 kcal/s and is rejected at a rate of 0.6 kcal/s, what is the maximum power output to be expected of this engine? If the actual power output is 1.5 kW, at what rate is mechanical energy being dissipated in the engine?

5. If 0.4 kg of water at 20°C is placed in the ice compartment of a refrigerator, how much heat must be removed in order to produce ice at 0°C? If this is accomplished by furnishing 42,000 J of mechanical energy to the refrigerator, what is the performance coefficient of the refrigerator? Could we freeze 0.4 kg of water in an old-fashioned "ice box" if we put 5 kg of ice into its ice compartment? Explain your answer.

6. A refrigerator is operated by an electric motor with an effective power output of 150 W. If we put 500 g of water at 20°C in the freezing compartment of the refrigerator, we find that it takes 10 min to produce ice at 0°C. What is the performance coefficient of the refrigerator?

7. What is the efficiency of a Carnot Engine operating between a heat reservoir at 100°C and a heat reservoir at 0°C? If this engine had a useful power output of 100 W, (1) at what rate would heat be removed from the hotter reservoir? (2) at what rate would heat be rejected to the colder reservoir?

8. If a Carnot Engine operated from a heat reservoir at 200°C, what should be the temperature of the low-temperature heat reservoir in order to give the engine the following efficiencies: 0.25, 0.50, 0.75, 0.95?

9. If a Carnot Engine employs a low-temperature heat reservoir at 0°C, what should be the temperature of the high-temperature heat reservoir in order to give the engine the following efficiencies: 0.25, 0.50, 0.75, 0.95?

10. What would be the efficiency of a Carnot Engine operating between one reservoir at the boiling point of hydrogen and a second reservoir at the boiling point of helium? (See Table 14.2.)

11. Suppose that we have heat reservoirs at the following temperatures: 600 K, 400 K, and 200 K. If we remove 1000 J of heat from the 600 K reservoir, how much work can be done if we operate a Carnot Engine between the 600 K reservoir and the 200 K reservoir? If we remove 1000 J of heat from the 600 K reservoir, how much work can be done if we use this heat to operate one Carnot Engine between the 600 K reservoir and the 400 K reservoir and then a second Carnot Engine between the 400 K reservoir and the 200 K reservoir? Discuss the implications of these results in the design of real heat engines.

12. What is the performance coefficient of a Carnot Refrigerator operating between a low-temperature heat reservoir at 0°C and a second heat reservoir at 100°C? How much work would have to be done in removing 1 kcal of heat from the 0°C reservoir and rejecting it to the 100°C reservoir?

13. What is the minimum amount of work that would be required to remove 1 kcal of heat from a reservoir at 4 K and deliver it to a reservoir at room temperature (300 K)?

14. If we had heat reservoirs at 100 K, 200 K, and 300 K, what would be the amount of work required to remove 1 kcal of heat from the 100 K reservoir and deliver it to the 300 K reservoir (a) if we used a single Carnot Refrigerator and (b) if we used two Carnot Refrigerators, one operating between 100 K and 200 K and the second operating between 200 K and 300 K? The energy of the 200 K reservoir is to be the same at the end as at the start of the process.

15. A steam engine is operated from a boiler in which the pressure is 4.70 atm and exhausts into a condenser at 50°C. The engine consumes 1 kg of bituminous coal for each kilowatt-hour of work done by the engine. What is the Carnot Efficiency of this engine? What is its overall efficiency?

16. The temperature of the combustion products in a diesel engine as combustion occurs is 1200 K and their temperature during the exhaust stroke is 400 K. The engine requires 0.25 kg of diesel oil for each kilowatt-hour

of work done by the engine. What is the Carnot Efficiency of the engine? What is its overall efficiency?

17. What is the minimum energy that must be supplied to an air conditioner that removes 1 kcal of heat from the interior of a house that is to be maintained at a temperature of 24°C on days when the outside temperature is 25°C, 30°C, and 35°C?

18. What is the Carnot performance coefficient of a heat pump required to maintain the interior of a house at a temperature of 20°C on days when the outside temperature is 15°C, 10°C, 0°C, −10°C, and −20°C?

19. What is the change in entropy when a 2 kg sample of steam at 100°C and a pressure of 1 atm condenses to form water at this temperature?

20. Show for a *real* simple heat engine that the total work potentially available, including the work actually done by the engine, becomes less as the engine operates between reservoirs having temperatures T_H and T_L. Assume that the lowest temperature reservoir that is available has a temperature $T_0 \leq T_L$.

21. One mole of an ideal gas is used as the working substance in a Carnot engine operating between reservoirs at 400 and 300 K. If 100 cal of heat are added to the gas during its isothermal expansion at 400 K, how much work can be obtained from the engine during each complete cycle? If the cycle is repeated 8 times per second, what is the useful power output of the engine? If the heat delivered to the low temperature reservoir by the engine were used to melt ice, how much ice could be melted in 1 h?

22. Energy from the sun reaches the top of the earth's atmosphere at a rate of 1.35 kW/m². If 40% of this radiant energy is absorbed in the clear atmosphere, at what rate would radiant energy reach the 10 m by 8 m flat roof of a building in Quito, Ecuador (located

on the equator) at noon on 21 March when the sun is at the zenith? Assume that the air is clear. What is the minimum power required to operate an air conditioner in order to keep the inside air at a temperature 10 Cdeg below that of the outside air at 38°C if *all* of the radiant energy striking the roof actually enters the building?

23. If a Carnot engine following the cycle shown in Fig. 17.4 contains 0.172 kmol of diatomic ideal gas for which $\gamma = 1.4$, and if $P_A = 10$ atm, $P_B = 5$ atm, $T_H = 273°C$, and $T_L = 0°C$, determine (a) the heat added to the gas, (b) the work done by the gas, and (c) the increase in thermal energy, in each of the four steps of the cycle and for the whole cycle.

24. Repeat Problem 23 for a case where the Carnot engine contains 0.25 kmol of monatomic ideal gas with $\gamma = 1.67$, $P_A = 12$ atm, $P_B = 8$ atm, $T_H = 400°C$, and $T_L = 20°C$. How do your answers change if the engine is operated in reverse, as a refrigerator?

25. In Problem 23 what is the change in entropy in each of the four steps of the cycle and in the whole cycle?

26. In Problem 24 what is the change in entropy in each of the four steps of the cycle and in the whole cycle?

27. What is the increase in entropy of 1 kg of ice at 0°C that is melted to water at 0°C? Take the latent heat of fusion as 80 kcal/kg. To compute the entropy change we must assume the heat is added reversibly; discuss in principle how the heat might be added (almost) reversibly.

28. Show that the increase in entropy of a mass m of water that is heated from absolute temperature T_1 to T_2 is given by

$$\Delta S = c\, m \ln(T_2/T_1).$$

Assume that no phase change occurs in the temperature range from T_1 to T_2. To compute the entropy change, we must assume the heat to be added reversibly; discuss in principle how the heat might be added (almost) reversibly.

29. An electric motor is used to operate a Carnot heat pump. Compare the cost of operating the heat pump with the cost of operating an electric resistive heater, in which all the electrical energy is converted directly into thermal energy. To do this, compute the power that must be used in delivering heat from the outside of a house to the inside of the house at the rate of 1 kW for the following outside temperatures: 10°C, 0°C, −10°C, and −20°C when the inside temperature is to be maintained at 20°C. The ratio of the electric power delivered to the heat pump to 1 kW delivered to the electric heater gives the ratio of costs. (It should be remembered that the initial cost of a heat pump is considerably greater than that of an electric heater.)

30. A Carnot refrigerator is used to extract 1 kcal of heat from a body at −73°C and to give it to a body at 127°C. How much mechanical energy must be supplied to the refrigerator? How many kcal must actually be delivered to the hotter body?

31. It is proposed that an ideal gas be used as the working substance in an engine that operates in a cycle consisting of two processes occurring at constant pressure and two processes occurring at constant volume. Consider a gas with initial volume $V_A = 1$ m³, temperature $T_A = 400$ K and pressure of $P_A = 2$ atm that expands at constant pressure to a volume $V_B = 2$ m³. The gas is then cooled in such a way that its pressure decreases to 1 atm at constant volume so that $V_C = V_B = 2$ m³. The gas is then compressed at constant pressure to volume $V_D = 1$ m³. Finally, the gas is heated so that its pressure rises to 2 atm without change in volume. Make a plot of these four processes on a PV diagram. How much work is done by

the gas as it expands from V_A to V_B? How much work is done to the gas as it is compressed from volume V_C to volume V_D? How much net work is done by the gas during the cycle? What is the highest temperature attained by the gas during the cycle? What is the lowest temperature? At what stages in the cycle is it necessary to add heat to the gas? At what stages must heat be removed from the gas?

32. A monatomic ideal gas is carried through a three-step cycle. The gas with an initial state P_A, V_A, T_A is allowed to expand adiabatically to a state P_B, V_B, T_B; the gas is then compressed to state P_C, $V_C = V_A$, T_C without change in pressure; and finally is returned to its initial state without change in volume. Make a plot showing these three steps on a PV diagram. Discuss the energy changes in each step in the cycle.

33. If 1 kmole of argon is carried through the cycle described in Problem 32 with $V_A = 2$ m³ and $T_A = 600$ K, how much work is done by the gas in its expansion if $T_B = 400$ K? What is the net external work done during the cycle?

34. An ideal gas is carried around a three-step cycle: (1) expansion at constant temperature from V_A, P_A, T_A to V_B, P_B; (2) compression at constant pressure from V_B, P_B to a smaller volume $V_C = V_A$; and finally (3) heating at constant volume from V_C, P_C back to V_A, P_A, T_A. Draw a diagram of this cycle on a PV diagram. Discuss the energy changes in each of the three steps.

35. If 1 kmole of argon is carried through the cycle described in Problem 34 for which $V_A = 3$ m³, $T_A = 500$ K and $V_B = 8.15$ m³, what is the net work done by the gas in one complete cycle?

36. Energy from the sun reaches the top of the earth's atmosphere at a rate of 1.35 kW/m². Treating the earth as a sphere with a radius of 6400 km, calculate the total rate at which

the earth receives energy from the sun. If there were no losses in transmission through the earth's atmosphere, at what maximum rate would solar energy reach a large concave mirror with a radius of 2 m. Discuss ways in which such a mirror might be used in supplying energy to a heat engine.

37. By determining their slopes dP/dV on a PV diagram, show that the adiabatic curve for an ideal gas at a given point P, V is steeper than the isothermal curve for the ideal gas at that point.

PART 3

WAVE MOTION AND SOUND

CHAPTER 18

Mechanical Waves

Mechanical energy can be transferred from one place to another by two different methods. The first method involves the transfer of matter, while the second method involves mechanical wave motion, which we shall consider in this chapter. In wave motion there is no transfer of matter from one place to another, but instead there is the transmission of a mechanical disturbance through some elastic medium.

As an example of mechanical energy transport, let us consider the work involved in demolishing some kind of wall. We might do this work by shooting cannonballs against the wall or by directing a stream of water from a fire hose against the wall. In these cases the energy required is delivered by the actual displacement of matter— cannonballs or water—from one place to another. On the other hand, we might demolish the wall by means of the *shock wave* produced by an explosion in the air at some distance from the wall. In the case of the shock wave, there is no transfer of matter from the point of the explosion to the wall; instead there is the transmission of a mechanical disturbance through the air between the explosion and the wall.

The sudden release of chemical energy in the detonation of an explosive such as dynamite in air raises the pressure of the air in the immediate vicinity. This large pressure increase near the explosion is transmitted to air further away as a result of molecular collisions. The region of increased pressure spreads outward from the explosion as an advancing *wave front*. Although the magnitude of the pressure increase becomes smaller as the wave front travels outward through the air, the increased pressure associated with the advancing wave front can be sufficiently large to demolish the wall. A shock wave transports mechanical energy capable of breaking windows or rattling dishes kilometers away from the explosion. No matter travels these kilometers; the actual displacement of air by a shock wave is relatively small; the same air molecules are in the vicinity of the initial explosion long after the shock wave has passed. After the wave has passed, the air quickly recovers its initial state; the air has merely served as an *elastic medium* through which the disturbance has been transmitted.

Familiar to all of us are the surface waves that move across a body of water. By dropping a pebble into still water we can produce a *wave pulse* that travels outward in ever increasing circles from the point where the pebble "broke the surface." Although the wave disturbance travels outward, the individual water particles undergo only a momentary localized motion and never move far from their initial positions. If we disturb the water surface in some periodic manner, we can produce a series of disturbances that travel outward; a set of disturbances of this kind is called a *wave train* or *continuous wave*. Sounds like those produced by a musical instrument consist of wave trains produced by periodic vibrations of the instrument that are transmitted through the air as fluctuations in pressure.

In this chapter we shall examine some general characteristics of *mechanical waves*. A mechanical wave has three important aspects: a *source* that initiates the disturbance and supplies the energy that is carried by the wave; the *disturbance* itself, which will be a local motion of particles of matter about their equilibrium positions; and an *elastic medium* in which the disturbance exists and propagates. We use the word "elastic" to describe the medium in which the disturbance exists because the medium recovers its original state after the wave passes.

The water waves, shock waves, and sound waves mentioned above are all examples of mechanical waves. Although water waves and shock waves are a part of common experience, detailed discussion of their properties is complex. In order to emphasize basic ideas, we shall consider simpler systems that are more easily analyzed. In particular, we shall examine simple waves transmitted along a stretched string and waves transmitted through a tube filled with a fluid; the string and the fluid constitute the required elastic media. Many ideas that we shall develop are applicable to more complex waves.

We shall also describe some properties of waves that are within broad limits independent of the particular kind of wave being considered. Of especial importance are the superposition principle and interference effects that arise from it. Many of the things we learn about mechanical waves can also be applied to the electromagnetic waves that we shall discuss in later chapters.

18.1   ONE-DIMENSIONAL MECHANICAL WAVES

Waves in an extended medium like air tend to spread radially outward from the source. Thus, the energy supplied by the source travels outward in three dimensions *X*, *Y*, and *Z*. We begin our discussion by considering a simpler situation in which energy from the source is transmitted by waves that propagate in a single direction, which we take as the *X* axis of the coordinate system. We first describe two cases in which wave pulses are transmitted in a single direction; in later sections we analyze the phenomena in terms of Newton's Principles.

In Fig. 18.1 we show one end of a long flexible string being held by a physics teacher; the far end of the string is attached to a rigid support. By giving the end of the string an impulsive down–up motion, the teacher generates a wave disturbance that is transmitted in the $+X$ direction along the string, which constitutes the elastic medium. The lower panels of the figure show the configuration of the string at successively later times t_1, t_2, and t_3. Although the wave disturbance is propagated in the

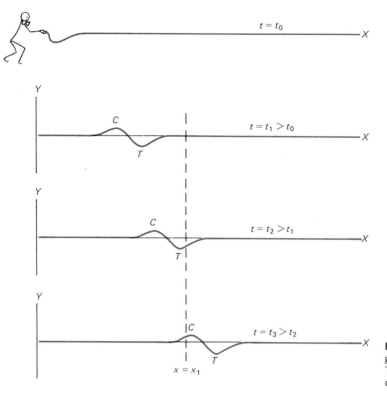

Fig. 18.1 A transverse wave propagating along a stretched elastic string. The letter *C* denotes a wave crest; *T* denotes a wave trough.

$+X$ direction, the particles of the string move back and forth parallel to the *Y* axis. A wave of this type in which the particles of the elastic medium move in a direction *perpendicular* to the direction of wave propagation is called a *transverse wave*.

In equilibrium the displacement *Y* of any particle of the string is zero. If a particle is displaced from its equilibrium position, forces exerted by neighboring particles of the elastic string tend to restore the particle to its equilibrium position. As we shall show in Sec. 18.5, the displaced particles do work to particles to their right in Fig. 18.1 in such a way that mechanical energy is transmitted to the right along the $+X$ axis. A local maximum positive displacement of the particles in the string is called a *crest* and is denoted by *C* in Fig. 18.1. A local maximum negative displacement of the particles in the string is called a *trough* and is denoted by *T* in the figure.

In order to describe the wave, we must know the displacement *Y* of particles of the string as a function of the location *x* along the string and as a function of the time *t*. We can consider the configuration of the string at various locations in space for some particular time. This information can be displayed in a graph of *Y* vs. *x* for fixed *t*, which is equivalent to a photograph of the string taken at the time *t*. Figure 18.1 thus shows several such "snapshot" representations of the wave at progressively later times. Alternatively, we can consider the motion of the string at a particular location *x* as a function of time *t*. This information can be displayed on a graph of *Y* vs. *t* for fixed *x;* for example, Fig. 18.2 shows the displacement of the string at the location x_1 of Fig. 18.1 as a function of time. Note that time increases

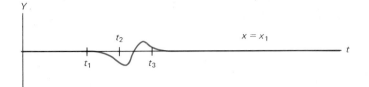

Fig. 18.2 The displacement from equilibrium of the string particle at location x_1 of Fig. 18.1 as a function of time.

from top to bottom in Fig. 18.1 and from left to right in Fig. 18.2. The two viewpoints described here are complementary; both kinds of information, Y vs. x and Y vs. t, are required to describe the wave. The velocity v_y of a particle at point x in the string is simply $v_y = \partial Y/\partial t$ and can be obtained from the plot of Y vs t in Fig. 18.2. As is discussed in the Appendix, the symbols $\partial/\partial t$ and $\partial^2/\partial t^2$ denote differentiation with respect to t when x is held constant; similarly $\partial/\partial x$ and $\partial^2/\partial x^2$ denote differentiation with respect to x at a constant value of t. Thus, $\partial Y/\partial t$ and $\partial^2 Y/\partial t^2$ are the velocity and acceleration of the particle of the string at x in its up and down motion; $\partial Y/\partial x$ and $\partial^2 Y/\partial x^2$ are the slope and second derivative of the curve contained in a snapshot of the string at instant t.

An important characteristic of a wave is the speed with which the disturbance propagates. In order to determine this speed, we fix our attention on some feature of the wave such as the crest C or trough T shown in Fig. 18.1. The speed of propagation of the wave is the distance Δx traveled by the feature divided by the elapsed time interval Δt in the limit of small time intervals. Note that this is the speed with which the *disturbance* moves along the string; the speed of any particle of the string as it moves about its equilibrium position is a different quantity.

The wave speed depends on the nature of the coupling by which a displaced particle of the string exerts forces on neighboring particles and sets them into motion and on an inertia factor characteristic of the string. We shall show later that for a transverse wave on a stretched string the wave speed is $v = \sqrt{F/\mu}$, where F is the tensional force in the string and μ is the mass per unit length, both measured when the string has its equilibrium configuration. This is a particular case of the following general result that applies to the transmission of a mechanical wave through any elastic medium:

$$\text{Wave Speed} = \sqrt{\frac{\text{Elastic Factor}}{\text{Inertia Factor}}}. \tag{18.1}$$

In the case of the string, the tension F is the elastic factor and the mass per unit length μ is the inertia factor. A relation of this type holds generally for any mechanical wave provided the disturbance is small and if the "elastic factor" and the "inertia factor" are suitably defined in each case.

Another important type of wave, called a *longitudinal wave,* occurs when the motion of the particles of the medium is *parallel* to the direction of wave propagation. A one-dimensional wave of this type can be produced in a long helical spring resting on a frictionless surface as suggested in Fig. 18.3, which shows a longitudinal pulse being transmitted to the right. The agent serving as the source of this wave provides energy to the spring by giving one end an impulsive push to the right followed by

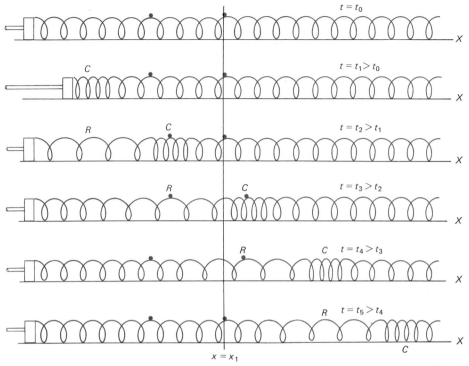

Fig. 18.3 A longitudinal wave on a helical spring. Condensations and rarefactions are denoted by the letters *C* and *R*, respectively. Two dots mark definite points on the spring to aid the reader in visualizing the motion of a spring "particle" as the wave passes.

a pull back to the original position of the end, as indicated in the top panel of the figure; these forces compress one portion of the spring and stretch another portion near one end. The remote end of the spring, not shown in the figure, is free. After the distorting forces act, a wave disturbance is transmitted to the right in the diagram along the $+X$ axis. This wave is shown in the lower panels of Fig. 18.3 at successively later times t_1, t_2, and t_3. The wave disturbance is associated with the displacement of particles of the spring from their equilibrium positions; these displacements are parallel to the X axis. Let us represent the displacement of a particle from its equilibrium position by ξ. Positive ξ represents displacement of a particle in the $+X$ direction from its equilibrium position; negative ξ represents displacement of a particle in the $-X$ direction from its equilibrium position. When the longitudinal wave disturbance in the coil in Fig. 18.3 passes a location x_1 in the figure, the particle at this location is first displaced to the right and then returns to its equilibrium position as a result of restoring forces exerted by neighboring particles.

A plot of ξ as a function of time t is given in Fig. 18.4a for a particle having equilibrium position x_1 in Fig. 18.3. The particle's velocity $v_x = \partial \xi / \partial t$ can be evaluated from the plot in Fig. 18.4a; v_x is positive until the particle has achieved its maximum displacement and then becomes negative as the particle returns to its equilibrium position. A plot of ξ as a function of x at time t_3 is given in Fig. 18.4b. These plots indicate that ξ for points in the coil is never negative for the longitudinal

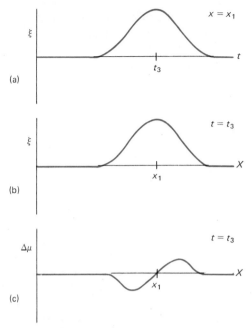

Fig. 18.4 A plot of displacement of spring particles from their equilibrium location versus equilibrium location for the situation shown in Fig. 18.3 at time $t = t_3$.

pulse traveling in the $+X$ direction shown in Fig. 18.3. How can you produce a wave pulse traveling to the right in the coil in Fig. 18.3 in which ξ is always negative?

Although a longitudinal wave can properly be described in terms of the *displacement* ξ of particles from their equilibrium positions, an alternative description of a longitudinal wave can be given in terms of variations in the density of the elastic medium through which the wave travels. In the case of the longitudinal wave in a helical coil as shown in Fig. 18.3, this variation in density can be measured in terms of the change in the number of turns per unit length. A region where the turns of the spring are closer together than at equilibrium is called a *condensation;* a region where the turns of the spring are farther apart than at equilibrium is called a *rarefaction.* The condensation and rarefaction associated with the wave pulse in Fig. 18.3 are denoted by C and R, respectively. In Fig. 18.4c, the positions of the condensation and rarefaction are given in a plot that shows the variation $\Delta\mu$ in mass per unit length of spring as a function of x at time t_3. Here $\Delta\mu = \mu - \mu_0$, where μ is the actual mass per unit length of the spring and μ_0 is the corresponding quantity for the equilibrium configuration of the spring. It is easily seen that μ and μ_0 are proportional to the number of turns per unit length; therefore, $\Delta\mu \propto \Delta\eta = \eta - \eta_0$, where η is the number of turns per unit length at any time and η_0 is the corresponding coil spacing in the undistorted spring. The speed of propagation of a longitudinal wave is the speed at which a condensation or rarefaction moves along the spring. A detailed analysis confirms the relation illustrated in Figs. 18.4b and 18.4c that the change in mass per unit length at a given time is proportional to the negative of the slope of the ξ vs. x curve for the particular time, provided that this slope is small.

For a longitudinal wave on a helical spring the wave speed is $v = \sqrt{kl/\mu_0}$, where k is the force constant for a length l of the spring measured along the helix axis and μ_0 is the mass per unit length at equilibrium. We recall that the force constant is the applied force divided by the resultant elongation of the spring. If the length of spring considered is halved and the same force is applied, the elongation is halved. Thus, the product kl is a constant for a given type of spring independent of the particular length of the spring; this is necessary since the wave speed must be determined by the local conditions and not by where the ends of the spring happen to be located.

18.2 SINUSOIDAL ONE-DIMENSIONAL WAVES

Waves like those shown in Figs. 18.1 and 18.3 where the disturbance is nonzero over only a localized region of space at any time and requires only a short time to pass any location are called *pulses*. In contrast, we are often concerned with waves where the disturbance has a repetitive pattern that extends over a large region of space at any time; such waves we call *periodic waves* or *wave trains*. We shall see that waves of this type can be represented in terms of linear combinations of sinusoidal functions of space and time. Therefore, we shall consider in detail the important special case of sinusoidal waves.

We can think of a sinusoidal transverse wave on a stretched string as being generated by some source that causes one end of the string to execute simple harmonic motion, as suggested in Fig. 18.5. The distance at any particular time between adjacent crests or adjacent troughs in such a wave is called the *wavelength* λ. An observer at a fixed location x will see the particle of string at that location executing simple harmonic motion, that is, sinusoidal oscillations as a function of time; the time required for one complete oscillation is the *period T*. The *frequency f* of the wave is the number of oscillations per second at any fixed location; this is just the reciprocal of the period: $f = 1/T$.

Since the end of the string must move with the oscillating source at $x = 0$, and each successive particle of the string must move up and down in concert with the preceding particle in order to maintain the continuity of the string, the frequency of the wave must equal the oscillation frequency of the source of the disturbance. On the other hand, as we have noted the speed of the wave is determined by the properties of the string: $v = \sqrt{F/\mu}$. Clearly a wave crest must move a distance λ in the time required for one oscillation of the source. Therefore, we have

$$v = \lambda/T \quad \text{or} \quad v = f\lambda. \tag{18.2}$$

In general, the frequency f of a sinusoidal wave is that of its source and its speed of propagation v is determined by the elastic properties of the medium; its wavelength $\lambda = v/f$ thus depends on both the source and the medium.

In considering a situation like that shown in Fig. 18.5 we must remember that the wave transports energy away from the source. The source must be *driven* by some agent that supplies this energy and keeps the source oscillating with constant amplitude. The *amplitude of the wave* is the magnitude of the maximum displacement of particles of the medium from their equilibrium positions.

Let us now develop a mathematical description of the sinusoidal wave shown in

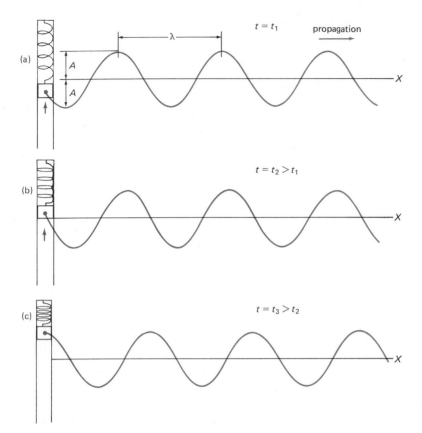

Fig. 18.5 A device that causes one end of a stretched string to execute simple harmonic motion generates a sinusoidal transverse wave on the string.

Fig. 18.5. At $x = 0$ the displacement of the string from equilibrium Y follows the simple harmonic oscillations of the source. Thus, from our description of simple harmonic motion in Chapter 12 we know that Y at $x = 0$ equals $A \sin(2\pi ft + \phi)$, where ϕ is a phase constant chosen to give the motion of the particle at $x = 0$ at the time $t = 0$. We shall take the time $t = 0$ to occur after the wave is well established. Then in the region to the right of the origin in Fig. 18.5 the shape of the string at time t must be a sine function that goes through one complete oscillation as the value of x increases by an amount λ and that reduces to the correct value $A \sin \phi$ at $t = 0$ and $x = 0$. Two functions meeting these conditions are $Y(x,t) = A \sin(2\pi ft \pm 2\pi x/\lambda + \phi)$. We can make the correct choice of sign by considering a crest that is at the origin at some particular time. After a time interval Δt this crest has moved a distance $\Delta x = v\Delta t = f\lambda\Delta t$ to the right along the X axis, where we have made use of (18.2). The location of the crest corresponds to the maximum displacement $Y = A$. Thus, when the time term in the argument of the sine function *increases* by $2\pi f\Delta t$, the space term $\pm 2\pi \Delta x/\lambda$ must *decrease* by an equal amount so that the argument as a whole does not change. Because Δt and Δx are both positive, this requires that we choose the minus sign to represent a wave traveling in the positive X direction:

$$Y(x,t) = A \sin(2\pi ft - 2\pi x/\lambda + \phi). \quad \textit{(Propagation in} \qquad (18.3)$$
$$\textit{Positive X Direction)}$$

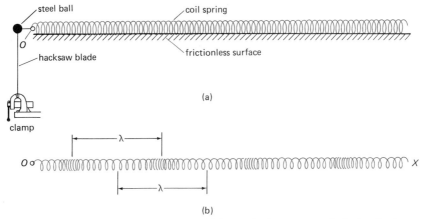

Fig. 18.6 A device that generates sinusoidal longitudinal waves on a helical spring by causing one end of the spring to execute simple harmonic motion.

Similar considerations show that the positive sign choice describes a situation like that of Fig. 18.5 but with the wave traveling in the negative X direction:

$$Y(x,t) = A \sin(2\pi ft + 2\pi x/\lambda + \phi). \quad \textit{(Propagation in} \qquad (18.3')$$
$$\textit{Negative X Direction)}$$

By the use of (18.2) and (18.3) the transverse displacement of the particle of string at any location x can be calculated at any time t if we know the frequency f of the source, the propagation speed v characteristic of the stretched elastic string, and the amplitude A and phase constant ϕ associated with the particular disturbance.

Similar relations can be used to describe a one-dimensional longitudinal sinusoidal wave such as could be generated in a helical spring by the arrangement suggested in Fig. 18.6. In this case the wavelength λ is the distance between adjacent condensations or adjacent rarefactions. The disturbance is displacement ξ of particles of the spring from their equilibrium locations. For a sinusoidal wave the spring particles undergo simple harmonic oscillations about their equilibrium positions that can be described by relations analogous to (18.3): $\xi(x,t) = A \sin(2\pi ft - 2\pi x/\lambda + \phi)$ for propagation in the positive X direction and $\xi(x,t) = A \sin(2\pi ft + 2\pi x/\lambda + \phi)$ for propagation in the negative X direction.

Example. The oscillating "piston" at the end of the string in Fig. 18.5 moves up and down through a total vertical distance of 4 cm at a frequency of 9 Hz. At time $t = 0$ the piston is at the origin and is moving upward. The tension in the string is 7.5 N, and the string has a mass of 8 g per meter of length. What is the wavelength of the transverse wave generated on the string? What is the equation that represents this wave as a function of position and time?

The propagation speed for transverse waves on the stretched string is given by $v = \sqrt{F/\mu} = \sqrt{7.5 \, N/(0.008 \, kg/m)} = 30.6$ m/s. The wavelength can then be determined from (18.2): $\lambda = v/f = (30.6 \text{ m/s})/9 \text{ Hz} = 3.40$ m. The amplitude of the wave is just half the total vertical distance transversed by the piston: $A = 2 \text{ cm} = 2 \times 10^{-2}$ m. Since the arrangement of Fig. 18.5 gives wave propagation in the positive X direction, we use (18.3) to describe the wave. It remains only to determine the phase constant ϕ.

The wave disturbance at the origin is $Y_0(t) = A \sin(2\pi ft + \phi)$. We are told that at time $t = 0$ this disturbance is zero and that the piston is moving upward, which means $dY_0/dt = 2\pi fA \cos(2\pi ft + \phi)$ is positive when $t = 0$. Thus, $Y_0 (t = 0) = A \sin \phi = 0$, which means that $\phi = 0$ or π, and $(dY_0/dt)_{t=0} = 2\pi fA \cos \phi > 0$, which is true for $\phi = 0$ but not for $\phi = \pi$. Therefore, $\phi = 0$.

With $\phi = 0$ we have from (18.3) that the equation representing the wave is $Y(x,t) = A \sin[2\pi ft - 2\pi x/\lambda] = (2 \times 10^{-2} \text{ m}) \sin[2\pi(9 \text{ Hz})t - 2\pi x/(3.4 \text{ m})]$. Since the argument of the sine function must be dimensionless, values of the time t must be inserted in this expression in seconds and values of the distance x must be expressed in meters.

We can use (18.3) to deduce a differential equation governing many different kinds of waves. By taking derivatives of $Y(x,t)$ first with respect to t while holding x fixed and then with respect to x while holding t fixed we obtain the following:

$$\partial Y/\partial t = 2\pi fA \cos(2\pi ft - 2\pi x/\lambda + \phi),$$

$$\partial Y^2/\partial t^2 = -4\pi^2 f^2 A \sin(2\pi ft - 2\pi x/\lambda + \phi) = -4\pi^2 f^2 Y,$$

$$\partial Y/\partial x = -(2\pi/\lambda)A \cos(2\pi ft - 2\pi x/\lambda + \phi),$$

and

$$\frac{\partial^2 Y}{\partial x^2} = -(2\pi/\lambda)^2 A \sin(2\pi ft - 2\pi x/\lambda + \phi) = -(2\pi/\lambda)^2 Y.$$

We see that $\partial^2 Y/\partial x^2 = -(4\pi^2/\lambda^2)Y = (4\pi^2/\lambda^2)(1/4\pi^2 f^2) \partial^2 Y/\partial t^2$, and by use of (18.2) we can reduce this relation to

$$\frac{\partial^2 Y}{\partial x^2} = \frac{1}{v^2}\frac{\partial^2 Y}{\partial t^2}. \quad \textit{(Wave Equation)} \qquad (18.4)$$

This relation is known as the one-dimensional wave equation. Exactly the same result is obtained from an analysis of (18.3'). Although we have deduced (18.4) by considering a transverse sinusoidal wave, it is found to apply generally to all one-dimensional waves, provided the amplitude is not too large. The wave equation is one of the most important equations in physics and merits careful study. Its solutions include not only sinusoidal waves similar to (18.3) but also expressions of the form $Y = f(x \pm vt)$, where f is *any* function of the quantity $(x \pm vt)$; thus, both pulses and continuous waves are solutions of the same wave equation (18.4).

18.3   ANALYSIS OF TRANSVERSE WAVES ON AN ELASTIC STRING

We shall now consider how (18.4) can be derived for a transverse wave on a stretched elastic string from a careful analysis in terms of Newton's Second Principle. In Fig. 18.7 we show a small segment of the string at a particular time t. The displace-

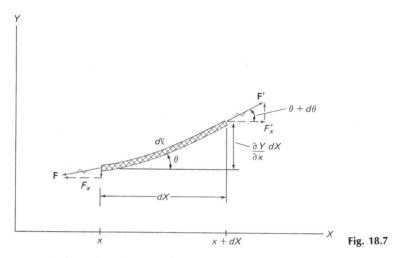

Fig. 18.7

ment of the string from equilibrium at position x and time t is given by the function $Y(x,t)$. The mass of string per unit length at equilibrium is μ, and the mass of the segment shown in Fig. 18.7 is μdX. The segment is slightly stretched from its equilibrium length dX to length dl in the configuration shown, but it has the same mass as in the equilibrium configuration before it was so stretched. We assume that the amplitude of oscillation and the angle θ are very small. As more detailed analysis shows, we can then assume to a good approximation that there is no horizontal motion of any part of the string. Because the segment of string has no acceleration in the X direction, the horizontal components of the forces **F** and **F′** exerted on the segment in Fig. 18.7 must be equal in magnitude and opposite in direction, and each component in magnitude equals the horizontal forces F_x exerted by the supports at the ends of the string. We assume that the string is "perfectly flexible" so that the pieces adjoining the segment in Fig. 18.7 exert forces **F** and **F′** on it directed along the string. We then have

$$F' \cos(\theta + d\theta) = F \cos \theta = F_x. \qquad (18.5)$$

The change in angle θ between the ends of the segment of string is associated with a net vertical force on the segment. The resultant vertical force on the segment of string is given by $F' \sin(\theta + d\theta) - F \sin \theta$. By substituting for F and F' from (18.5) we obtain for the resultant vertical force on the segment of string the value $F_x \tan(\theta + d\theta) - F_x \tan \theta$, and by Newton's Second Principle this must equal the mass of the segment of string times its acceleration:

$$F_x \tan(\theta + d\theta) - F_x \tan \theta = (\mu dX)\partial^2 Y/\partial t^2. \qquad (18.6)$$

We now note that $\tan \theta$ is just the slope of the string at the location x: $\tan \theta = \partial Y/\partial x$. Also, $\tan(\theta + d\theta)$ is the slope of the string at the location $x + dX$; because dX is small, we can express this in the form

$$\tan(\theta + d\theta) = \frac{\partial Y}{\partial x} + \frac{\partial}{\partial x}\left(\frac{\partial Y}{\partial x}\right) dX = \frac{\partial Y}{\partial x} + \frac{\partial^2 Y}{\partial x^2} dX,$$

where all the derivatives are evaluated at the location x. Substitution in (18.6) of these relations for $\tan \theta$ and $\tan(\theta + d\theta)$ yields

$$\frac{\partial^2 Y}{\partial x^2} = \frac{\mu}{F_x} \frac{\partial^2 Y}{\partial t^2}. \tag{18.7}$$

Comparison of (18.7) with (18.4) shows that we have deduced the wave equation without the assumption of a specific functional form $Y(x,t)$ describing the wave and that the speed of propagation of a transverse wave on a stretched elastic string is given by

$$v = \sqrt{F_x/\mu}, \tag{18.8}$$

a result already stated in Sec. 18.1. The speed given by (18.8) applies to all transverse waves in a string provided the amplitude is small.

Analyses similar to the above can be used to deduce the appropriate wave equation for other kinds of mechanical waves. These derivations are somewhat above the general mathematical level of this text, and we shall omit them. However, in the next section we illustrate another type of argument that can be used to deduce the propagation speed of a mechanical wave.

18.4   SPEED OF A ONE-DIMENSIONAL LONGITUDINAL WAVE IN A FLUID

Consider a nonviscous fluid confined in a tube of constant cross section A with rigid walls as shown in Fig. 18.8a. The tube has a piston at one end; initially the fluid and piston are in equilibrium at rest. The equilibrium pressure in the tube is P_0; the equilibrium density of the fluid is ρ_0.

At time $t = 0$ the force applied to the piston is increased corresponding to a small increase ΔP in pressure so that $P = P_0 + \Delta P$, and the piston is moved to the

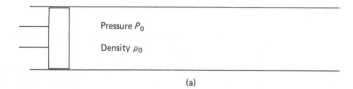

Pressure P_0

Density ρ_0

(a)

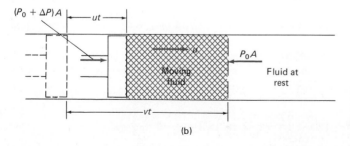

$(P_0 + \Delta P)A$

ut

u

$P_0 A$

Moving fluid

Fluid at rest

vt

(b)

Fig. 18.8   A longitudinal wave can be generated in a fluid confined in a tube of cross section A with rigid walls by motion of a piston located at one end of the tube.

right with a speed u that is much less than the speed v of propagation of a longitudinal compressional wave in the fluid. The compressional disturbance in the fluid moves to the right with the characteristic wave speed v. At some later time t the situation is as shown in Fig. 18.8b. The cross-hatched part of the fluid with volume $Avt - Aut$ is moving to the right with speed u; the pressure in this portion of the fluid is $P_0 + \Delta P$. This portion of the fluid originally occupied a volume Avt, so its change in volume is $\Delta V = -Aut$. By the definition of the bulk modulus given in Chapter 10 we have

$$M_B = -\Delta P / (\Delta V/V) = \Delta P / (Aut/Avt) = (\Delta P)v/u.$$

The resultant force on this part of the fluid is $(\Delta P)A$, and the impulse of this resultant force acting for a time t is $(\Delta P)At = uM_BAt/v$. The mass of the moving fluid is $\rho_0 Avt$ and its momentum is $\rho_0 Avtu$. By the impulse–momentum relation deduced from Newton's Second Principle in Sec. 4.11 we have

$$uM_BAt/v = \rho_0 Avtu,$$

from which it follows that the propagation speed of a longitudinal compressional wave in a fluid confined in a tube of constant cross section is

$$v = \sqrt{M_B/\rho_0}. \tag{18.9}$$

We note that this expression is of the general form given in (18.1) with the bulk modulus M_B as the elastic factor and the density ρ_0 as the inertia factor.

In our derivation of (18.9) we have neglected viscosity effects. In this respect our result is an approximation even for small ΔP.

18.5 ENERGY TRANSPORT BY A ONE-DIMENSIONAL SINUSOIDAL WAVE

We noted at the beginning of this chapter that an essential characteristic of waves is the transport of energy without any resultant displacement of matter. Both kinetic energy and elastic potential energy are associated with the motion of the medium when it is traversed by a wave. Suppose we have a wave of the form (18.3) propagating in the X direction in an elastic medium. If the wave disturbance Y represents displacement of particles of the medium from equilibrium and μ is the mass per unit length along the X axis of the elastic medium, then the kinetic energy associated with a segment of length dX corresponds to that of a particle of mass μdX and can be expressed as

$$E_K = \tfrac{1}{2}\mu (\partial Y/\partial t)^2 \, dX.$$

For the sinusoidal wave (18.3) this becomes

$$E_K = 2\pi^2 f^2 \mu A^2 \cos^2(2\pi ft - 2\pi x/\lambda + \phi)dX. \tag{18.10}$$

Calculation of the potential energy of the medium when the wave is present is a more delicate matter. Consider the case of a stretched elastic string. At any given time t the potential energy of a segment of the string will equal the work required to take the segment from its equilibrium configuration along the X axis to its final configuration $Y(x,t)$. This work is required to stretch the string since it is slightly longer when the wave is present than at equilibrium. The force acting to produce the stretching is approximately the tension F_x. By consideration of the increase in length when a wave is present it is possible to show that, for small amplitudes, the potential energy associated with a segment of string of equilibrium length dX is

$$E_P = \tfrac{1}{2}F_x(\partial Y/\partial x)^2\,dX.$$

For the sinusoidal wave (18.3) this becomes

$$E_P = \tfrac{1}{2}F_x(2\pi/\lambda)^2 A^2 \cos^2(2\pi ft - 2\pi x/\lambda + \phi)dX.$$

By using (18.8) and (18.2) we can write this in the form

$$E_P = 2\pi^2 f^2\mu\, A^2 \cos^2(2\pi ft - 2\pi x/\lambda + \phi)dX. \tag{18.11}$$

From (18.10) and (18.11) the total energy of the segment of string of length dX is

$$E_{\text{tot}} = E_K + E_P = 4\pi^2 f^2\mu A^2 \cos^2(2\pi ft - 2\pi x/\lambda + \phi)dX. \tag{18.12}$$

The energy associated with the wave is transmitted to the right with the wave speed v. Each segment of the string is continuously doing work to the segment to its right. In order to verify this statement, consider Fig. 18.9, which shows a sinusoidal wave traveling to the right in five successive positions 1–1, 2–2, 3–3, 4–4, and 5–5 during one half-cycle of the motion. During this half-cycle the string particle at AA is moving down, while the string particle at BB is moving up. We show in Fig. 18.9 the forces that the string segments to the left of AA and BB exert on the segments to the right. While the string is changing from configuration 1–1 to configuration 5–5, the force at AA has a downward component; it acts on a body moving down, so the string segment to the left does work to the segment to the right. During the following half-cycle conditions at AA would be exactly like those shown in Fig. 18.9

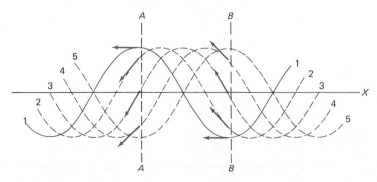

Fig. 18.9

at *BB;* the force then has an upward component exerted on a body moving up, so again the string segment to the left does work to the segment to the right. Thus, when a sinusoidal wave is traveling from left to right, energy is transmitted from left to right all along the length of the string.

We can compute the *time rate* at which energy is transmitted by the wave in the following way. Consider the segment of string shown in Fig. 18.7. The *upward* force exerted by the string to the left on the segment of string shown is $-F_x \tan \theta = -F_x(\partial Y/\partial x)$. In time dt this force exerted at point x acts through a distance $dY = (\partial Y/\partial t)dt$ since $\partial Y/\partial t$ is the upward velocity of a particle of the string. The total work done on the segment of string in a finite time interval from t_0 to t_1 is

$$W = \int_{t=t_0}^{t=t_1} -F_x \tan \theta \ dY = \int_{t_0}^{t_1} -F_x \frac{\partial Y}{\partial x} \frac{\partial Y}{\partial t} \ dt.$$

The derivatives $\partial Y/\partial x$ and $\partial Y/\partial t$ for a sinusoidal wave were computed in the development leading to (18.4). Substituting these expressions in the above integral, we obtain

$$W = F_x 4\pi^2 (f/\lambda)A^2 \int_{t_0}^{t_1} \cos^2(2\pi ft - 2\pi x/\lambda + \phi)dt.$$

If the time interval $t_1 - t_0$ contains a whole number of cycles of the wave, then the integral, which is to be evaluated for fixed x, has the value $\frac{1}{2}(t_1 - t_0)$ independent of the value of x. Also by using (18.8) and (18.2) we obtain $F_x(f/\lambda) = \mu v^2 f^2/v = \mu vf^2$. Thus, the work done on the segment of string in the time interval from t_0 to t_1 is

$$W = (2\pi^2 f^2 A^2 \mu)v(t_1 - t_0),$$

and the average power transmitted across any plane perpendicular to the X axis is the work divided by the time interval in which it is done:

$$P_{av} = (2\pi^2 f^2 A^2 \mu)v. \tag{18.13}$$

Since the time average of the function $\cos^2(2\pi ft - 2\pi x/\lambda + \phi)$ over an interval containing a whole number of cycles is $\frac{1}{2}$, we recognize the quantity in parenthesis in (18.13) as the average total energy per unit length as computed from (18.12). We can interpret (18.13) as saying that the energy passing any point x in a time t is just that contained in a length vt of the wave; the total kinetic and potential energy of the wave disturbance moves along the string with the wave speed v.

The general ideas of this discussion apply to any type of sinusoidal mechanical traveling wave. *The energy associated with the disturbance of the elastic medium is transmitted with the speed of the wave itself. The power carried by a sinusoidal mechanical wave is directly proportional to the square of the amplitude and the square of the frequency and to the speed of propagation of wave.*

The relations we have deduced for wave speed, energy, and power are strictly true only for waves of amplitude small compared with the wavelength: $A \ll \lambda$. Small amplitudes are usually involved for example in ordinary sound, and we shall use these results in our discussion of sound in the next chapter. For the sake of clarity Fig. 18.9 was not drawn for small amplitude; the figure would be satisfactory if the vertical dimension were decreased by a factor of about 10.

18.6   THE SUPERPOSITION PRINCIPLE AND WAVE INTERFERENCE

It is a matter of experience that several wave disturbances can propagate through a given medium at the same time. For example, in the case of sound a conversation can be carried on with a radio or television playing in the background; the sounds of particular instruments can be recognized in the playing of an orchestra. These phenomena for mechanical waves of small amplitude are governed by the following general principle:

SUPERPOSITION PRINCIPLE: When two or more waves move simultaneously through a region of space, each wave propagates independently as if the other waves were not present. The resultant disturbance at any location at a given time is the sum of the disturbances associated with the individual waves. If the wave disturbance is a vector quantity, this is a vector sum.

This principle holds for mechanical waves provided the disturbances are small; it holds rigorously for electromagnetic waves in free space.

We can demonstrate the superposition principle mathematically by noting that the equations governing small-amplitude mechanical waves, such as (18.4), are *linear*. That is, if the disturbances Y_1 and Y_2 are solutions of the equation, then the superposition $Y_{tot} = Y_1 + Y_2$ is also a solution of the equation. For mechanical waves of large amplitude the governing partial differential equations are not linear, and the solutions when multiple disturbances are present are not simply related to the individual disturbances. For electromagnetic waves in free space the governing equations are linear for all amplitudes, and the superposition principle is rigorously true.

Note carefully that it is the *disturbances* that add according to the superposition principle. Generally detectors of waves have responses proportional to the power transmitted by the wave, and therefore we shall want to determine the power carried by the composite wave. In order to do this, we must first find the resultant total disturbance by use of the superposition principle and then calculate the power; an attempt to add directly the powers transmitted by the individual waves will in general lead to incorrect results.

An important feature of the superposition principle is that it allows us to analyze a complex wave in terms of a sum of simpler components. Of particular importance in this regard is a mathematical result obtained by J. B. J. Fourier (1768–1830), French mathematician and political administrator, and brought to final form in a publication of 1822. Fourier's theorem states in essence that any periodic disturbance can be represented mathematically as a sum of sinusoidal functions of various frequencies. In general a sum with an infinite number of terms is required, but in many practical cases a good approximate representation is obtained with only a few terms. An illustration of this result is shown in Fig. 18.10. An important extension of Fourier's theorem says that an aperiodic disturbance such as a wave pulse can be represented

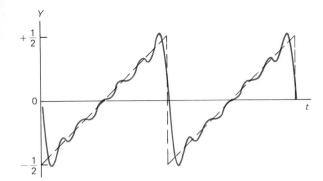

Fig. 18.10 The solid curve is the result of adding the first six terms of the Fourier series representation of the dashed "sawtooth" wave for the location $x = 0$. The sawtooth curve has period T and frequency f. The first six terms of the Fourier series are

$$-\sin(2\pi ft) - \tfrac{1}{2}\sin(4\pi ft) - \tfrac{1}{3}\sin(6\pi ft)$$

$$-\tfrac{1}{4}\sin(8\pi ft) - \tfrac{1}{5}\sin(10\pi ft) - \tfrac{1}{6}\sin(12\pi ft).$$

mathematically by an integral with respect to frequency over an integrand that is a sinusoidal function with frequency-dependent amplitude. According to the superposition principle we can consider separately the propagation of each component wave. Because of this result, we can restrict our attention to sinusoidal waves.

The physical phenomena resulting from the simultaneous presence in the same region of space of several waves are called *interference* phenomena. As an example, consider the superposition of two one-dimensional sinusoidal waves of the same frequency and amplitude traveling in the $+X$ direction, $Y_1 = A\sin(2\pi ft - 2\pi x/\lambda + \phi_1)$ and $Y_2 = A\sin(2\pi ft - 2\pi x/\lambda + \phi_2)$. According to the superposition principle, the resultant disturbance is

$$Y = Y_1 + Y_2 = A\sin(2\pi ft - 2\pi x/\lambda + \phi_1) + A\sin(2\pi ft - 2\pi x/\lambda + \phi_2).$$

By using the trigonometric identity $\sin\alpha + \sin\beta = 2\cos[(\beta - \alpha)/2]\sin[(\beta + \alpha)/2]$ we can express this in the form

$$Y = 2A\cos[(\phi_2 - \phi_1)/2]\sin[2\pi ft - 2\pi x/\lambda + (\phi_2 + \phi_1)/2]. \qquad (18.14)$$

This corresponds to a new sinusoidal wave of the same frequency as the waves that were superimposed but with amplitude $2A\cos[(\phi_2 - \phi_1)/2]$. If ϕ_2 and ϕ_1 are nearly equal so that the waves are practically *in phase*, the resultant amplitude is close to $2A$, as is illustrated in Fig. 18.11a. In this case we say that we have *constructive interference*. If $\phi_2 - \phi_1$ is close to π or $-\pi$ radians so that the waves are almost *out of phase*, the resultant amplitude is close to zero, as is illustrated in Fig. 18.11b. In this case we say that we have *destructive interference*. What is the form of (18.14) when the waves are exactly in phase with $\phi_1 = \phi_2$? What is the form of the resultant curve in Fig. 18.11 when the waves are *exactly* in phase or exactly out of phase with $\phi_2 - \phi_1 = \pi$ or $-\pi$?

18.7 REFLECTION OF WAVES

Up to now we have considered waves that propagate in a homogeneous medium that extends indefinitely in the X direction. In any real situation there will be junctions or boundaries where the nature of the medium changes. This can produce reflection

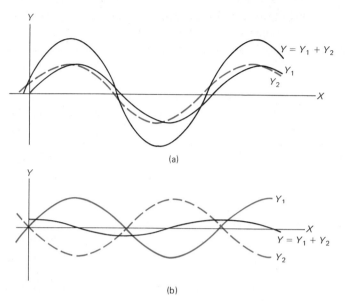

(a)

(b)

Fig. 18.11   (a) The superposition of two sinusoidal waves of the same frequency and amplitude that are almost in phase. (b) The superposition of two sinusoidal waves of the same frequency and amplitude that are almost out of phase.

of some of the energy carried by the wave. The presence of both incident and reflected waves in the same region of space leads to interference effects. The nature of the reflection depends on the specific conditions at the boundary where the character of the medium changes. We shall consider a situation where there is an abrupt change in the properties of the medium. In particular, we consider a junction between two stretched strings having different values of mass per unit length.

The situation at equilibrium is shown in Fig. 18.12. It is convenient to put the origin at the junction between the two strings. By Newton's Second Principle the tensions in the two strings must have the same magnitude F. Suppose that at the remote end of string ① there is an apparatus like that of Fig. 18.5 that generates a sinusoidal wave $Y_I = A_I \sin(2\pi f_I t - 2\pi x/\lambda_I)$ traveling to the right on string ①, where f_I is the frequency of the source as pointed out in Sec. 18.2. We use the subscript I because we shall want to think of this as the wave *incident* on the junction. Given this situation, we want to determine (a) the nature of the wave on string ② and (b) whether there is a reflected wave traveling to the left on string ①.

There are two conditions that must be satisfied at the junction at any time t.

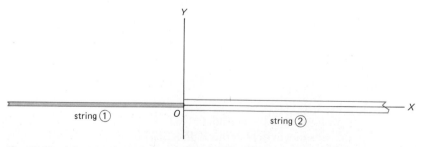

Fig. 18.12   A junction between two strings having different values of mass per unit length.

First, the displacement of string ① at $x = 0$ must equal the displacement of string ② at $x = 0$ since the strings are joined together. Second, the slope $\partial Y_1/\partial x$ of string ① at $x = 0$ must equal the slope $\partial Y_2/\partial x$ of string ② at $x = 0$. If this were not true, an analysis like that of Sec. 18.3 would lead to the conclusion that the particle of string at the junction has infinite acceleration.

Let us assume that the *transmitted* wave on string ② has the form $Y_T = A_T \sin(2\pi f_T t - 2\pi x/\lambda_T)$. We shall discover that in order to fit both conditions at the junction it may be necessary for the reflected wave to have a shifted phase angle; therefore, to represent the *reflected* wave traveling to the left on string ① we use $Y_R = A_R \sin(2\pi f_R t + 2\pi x/\lambda_R + \phi_R)$. By the superposition principle, the total wave on string ① is $Y_1 = Y_I + Y_R$. The requirement that the displacements of the two strings be equal at $x = 0$ gives us the condition

$$A_I \sin(2\pi f_I t) + A_R \sin(2\pi f_R t + \phi_R) = A_T \sin(2\pi f_T t), \qquad (18.15)$$

which must be true for all times t. In particular, at time $t = 0$ we have $A_R \sin \phi_R = 0$, which requires that either $\phi_R = 0$ or $\phi_R = \pi$. A proof that a third possibility $A_R = 0$ is not acceptable is considered in one of the problems. With these two possibilities for ϕ_R, relation (18.15) reduces to

$$A_I \sin(2\pi f_I t) \pm A_R \sin(2\pi f_R t) = A_T \sin(2\pi f_T t),$$

the plus sign being for $\phi_R = 0$ and the minus sign for $\phi_R = \pi$. In order that this equation hold true for *all* times t we must have

$$f_I = f_R = f_T.$$

Otherwise, the sine functions would oscillate at different rates, and while the equation might be valid at some particular time it would not remain valid as time progressed. Therefore, all three waves have the frequency f of the source. Also we must have

$$A_I \pm A_R = A_T. \qquad (18.16)$$

The requirement that the slopes of the two strings be equal at $x = 0$ gives us the condition

$$-(2\pi/\lambda_I)A_I \cos(2\pi f t) + (2\pi/\lambda_R)A_R \cos(2\pi f t + \phi_R) = -(2\pi/\lambda_T)A_T \cos(2\pi f t),$$

where we have set $f_I = f_R = f_T = f$ and ϕ_R has the value 0 or π. Considering these two values for ϕ_R leads to the condition

$$-A_I/\lambda_I \pm A_R/\lambda_R = -A_T/\lambda_T, \qquad (18.17)$$

where the plus sign is for $\phi_R = 0$ and the minus sign is for $\phi_R = \pi$. A simultaneous solution of (18.16) and (18.17) and use of the relations $v_1 = f\lambda_I = f\lambda_R$ and $v_2 = f\lambda_T$, where $v_1 = \sqrt{F/\mu_1}$ and $v_2 = \sqrt{F/\mu_2}$, produces the results

$$\frac{A_T}{A_I} = \frac{2v_2}{(v_2 + v_1)} \quad \text{and} \quad \frac{A_R}{A_I} = \pm \frac{(v_2 - v_1)}{(v_2 + v_1)}. \qquad (18.18)$$

Now the amplitude ratio A_R/A_I must be positive since by our definition wave amplitude is an inherently positive quantity. Therefore, the plus sign above, meaning $\phi_R = 0$, must correspond to $v_2 > v_1$ and the negative sign, meaning $\phi_R = \pi$, must correspond to $v_2 < v_1$.

Given the values of the mass per unit length for the two strings and the tension in the strings, these results allow us to determine the forms of the reflected and transmitted waves for a given incident wave. We note that if the strings are the same so that $v_1 = v_2$, our relations correctly predict that there is no reflected wave and that $Y_T = Y_I$. Of particular interest are the limiting cases of a *fixed end* of string ①, which corresponds to $\mu_2 \to \infty$, and of a *free end* of string ①, which corresponds to $\mu_2 \to 0$. For a fixed end we have $v_2 \to 0$, whence $A_T/A_I \to 0$ and $A_R/A_I \to 1$ with $\phi_R = \pi$. There is a phase reversal on reflection; a crest is reflected as a trough. For a free end we have $v_2 \to \infty$, whence $A_T/A_I \to 2$ and $A_R/A_I \to 1$ with $\phi_R = 0$. In this case a crest is reflected as a crest. These results are illustrated in Fig. 18.13. Examination of (18.13) shows that in both the free-end and the fixed-end limits the power carried by the transmitted wave approaches zero.

18.8 STANDING WAVES

We shall now consider oscillations of an elastic medium of finite extent. The oscillations must satisfy definite conditions at the edges or boundaries of the medium; these conditions restrict the possible modes of sustained oscillation compared with the variety of waves that could propagate in the medium if it were of infinite extent. In particular, we shall examine the possible oscillations of a stretched elastic string with fixed ends; some other physical systems will be considered in the next chapter.

Suppose that we have a string of mass per unit length μ stretched with a tension F between two supports a distance L apart. We take the orign of coordinates to be at one end of the string and choose the X axis to coincide with the equilibrium configuration of the string. We assume that the points where the string is attached to the supports are *fixed* in location; this requires that when the string oscillates its

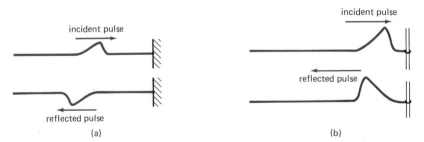

Fig. 18.13 (a) The reflection of a pulse at a fixed end of a string; a crest is reflected as a trough. (b) The reflection of a pulse at a free end of a string; a crest is reflected as a crest. In order to represent a free end we show the string attached to a ring that slides without friction on a vertical rod.

displacements at $x = 0$ and $x = L$ must always be zero. This is consistent with the result of the previous section for reflection at a fixed end. The reflected wave has the same amplitude as the incident wave and a phase shift of π radians; the superposition of the incident and reflected waves gives zero total displacement at the fixed end of the string.

Suppose that a vibration of frequency f is given to the string, say by the arrangement suggested in Fig. 18.14 located somewhere near the central portion of the string. Waves of frequency f and wavelength $\lambda = v/f = (1/f)\sqrt{F/\mu}$ will travel along the string in both directions. When they reach the ends of the string they will be reflected with unchanged amplitude but reversed phase. After a short time the string will reach a steady state of oscillation that can be described as a resultant wave $Y_1 = A\sin(2\pi ft - 2\pi x/\lambda)$ traveling to the right and a resultant wave of the same amplitude but a phase difference of π radians, $Y_2 = A\sin(2\pi ft + 2\pi x/\lambda + \pi)$, traveling to the left. By using the same trigonometric identity that was used in the derivation of (18.14), we find that the total disturbance on the string can be expressed as

$$Y = Y_1 + Y_2 = 2A\cos(2\pi x/\lambda + \pi/2)\sin(2\pi ft + \pi/2)$$
$$= -2A\sin(2\pi x/\lambda)\cos(2\pi ft). \tag{18.19}$$

However, it is possible to generate such oscillations with non-negligible amplitude only for certain characteristic frequencies. The displacement Y of the string must be zero at the fixed ends located at $x = 0$ and at $x = L$. From (18.19) we see this requires that $\sin(2\pi L/\lambda) = 0$, which will be true if λ has a value such that

$$2\pi L/\lambda = \pi, 2\pi, 3\pi, \ldots,$$

or

$$\lambda = 2L/n, \text{ where } n = 1,2,3 \ldots.$$

In terms of frequency, this condition says that for a string of mass per unit length μ stretched with tension F between fixed supports a distance L apart the allowed frequencies of oscillation are

$$f_n = \frac{n}{2L}\sqrt{\frac{F}{\mu}}, \qquad n = 1,2,3,\ldots. \quad \textit{(Stretched String)} \tag{18.20}$$

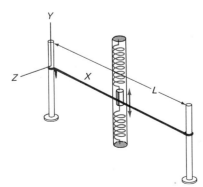

Fig. 18.14 A string stretched between two fixed supports a distance L apart is caused to oscillate by a harmonic driving force of frequency f.

By taking the time derivative of (18.19) and then setting $t = 0$ we see that the cosine time function in (18.19) is appropriate for representing an oscillation where all elements of the string are at rest at time $t = 0$.

The oscillations (18.19) of the stretched string with frequencies given by (18.20) are called *normal modes* of vibration of the string. The lowest frequency f_1 is called the *fundamental frequency;* the other allowed frequencies are called *overtones: f_2* is the first overtone, f_3 is the second overtone, etc. Oscillations of more complex systems can also be described in terms of a fundamental frequency and overtones, but in general the overtones are not integral multiples of the fundamental frequency. In the simple case where the overtone frequencies are integral multiples of the fundamental, as in (18.20), the allowed frequencies are called *harmonics: f_1* is the first harmonic, f_2 is the second harmonic, etc.

The normal modes of vibration (18.19) of a stretched string of length L with fixed ends for the fundamental and the first four overtone frequencies are shown in Fig. 18.15. We note that there are certain locations on the string, called *nodes*, where the amplitude of the disturbance is always zero. These locations are determined by the condition that $\sin(2\pi x/\lambda_n) = 0$. The boundary conditions guarantee that all normal modes have nodes at $x = 0$ and at $x = L$; the number of other nodes increases with n, as is shown in the following table:

n	λ_n	Node Locations—Values of x for which $Y(x,t) = 0$
1	$2L$	$0, L$
2	$2L/2$	$0, L/2, L$
3	$2L/3$	$0, L/3, 2L/3, L$
4	$2L/4$	$0, L/4, L/2, 3L/4, L$
.	.	.
.	.	.
.	.	.
n	$2L/n$	$0, L/n, 2L/n, 3L/n, \ldots, nL/n = L$

We see that *the distance between adjacent nodes is always $\lambda_n/2$.*

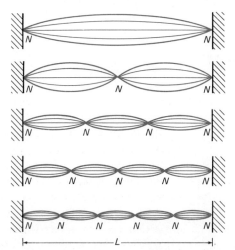

Fig. 18.15 The normal modes of vibration of a stretched string of length L with fixed ends for the fundamental and the first four overtone frequencies.

A particle of string located at position x between nodes executes simple harmonic oscillations with frequency f_n and maximum displacement $2A \sin(2\pi x/\lambda_n)$. This motion has greatest amplitude at points exactly midway between the nodes, which are called *antinodes*. Because the patterns of oscillation represented by (18.19) and illustrated in Fig. 18.15 are stationary in space, such oscillations are called *standing waves*.

The superposition principle applies to standing waves as well as to traveling waves. The most general oscillation of the string in Fig. 18.14 will be a superposition of normal modes. We can express this idea in the form of an equation by writing

$$Y(x,t) = C_1 \sin(2\pi x/\lambda_1) \cos(2\pi f_1 t) + C_2 \sin(2\pi x/\lambda_2) \cos(2\pi f_2 t)$$
$$+ C_3 \sin(2\pi x/\lambda_3) \cos(2\pi f_3 t) + \cdots, \tag{18.21}$$

where we have assumed that the oscillation is excited by giving the string a certain distortion and releasing it from rest. The coefficients C_n will depend on the initial shape of the string $Y(x,0)$; they can be determined by applying the rules of Fourier's theorem so that the right-hand side of (18.21) correctly represents $Y(x,0)$ when $t = 0$.

If the string is set in oscillation and left to itself, the vibrations will gradually die out. The motion is damped by dissipation of energy through the supports at the ends of the string, by the resistance of the air to the motion, and by internal friction. The damping increases with frequency, so the higher-frequency components die out first. We can pump energy into the system by applying a driving force. If the driving frequency is near some allowed frequency, the string will oscillate at that frequency with large amplitude at the antinodes. We say that the driving force is in *resonance* with the oscillating system. The oscillations build to the point where the rate of energy input from the driving force matches the rate of energy loss due to the various damping mechanisms. Because the string has a large number of allowed frequencies, resonance can occur at many different frequencies.

If the frequency of the driving force is much different from an allowed frequency of the system, the oscillations are erratic and of small maximum amplitude. The oscillating system does work *to* the driving system as well as receiving energy from it.

18.9 WAVES IN THREE DIMENSIONS

Many interesting wave phenomena are not evident for one-dimensional situations but are displayed by two-dimensional waves such as ripples on the surface of a pond and by three-dimensional waves such as the sound waves spreading out from a factory whistle. Let us use the symbol ξ to represent the disturbance of a particle in an elastic medium that is transmitting whatever wave we want to discuss. In general the wave disturbance depends on all three space coordinates and the time: $\xi = \xi(x,y,z,t)$. Imagine a surface in space drawn at a particular time through all contiguous points where the disturbance has the same state of motion. Such a surface is called a *wave front*. For example, we might consider all contiguous points where the disturbance has its local maximum value. For a periodic wave we could in this way define a

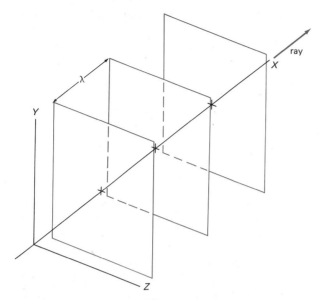

Fig. 18.16   For a plane wave the wave fronts are parallel planes oriented perpendicular to the direction of propagation.

whole family of wave fronts, each one wavelength from its nearest neighbors. For a homogeneous, isotropic medium the direction of energy propagation is always normal to the wave fronts. A line normal to the wave fronts indicating the direction of energy propagation is called a *ray*.

Let us consider further two kinds of wave fronts that are both common and geometrically simple: planes and spheres. For a *plane wave* the wave fronts are parallel planes as indicated in Fig. 18.16. It is convenient to choose the coordinates so that one of the axes, say the X axis, is perpendicular to the wave fronts; the ray direction is then parallel to this axis. Although the wave exists in three dimensions, the description of a simple plane wave requires reference only to the X coordinate. A sinusoidal plane wave is described mathematically by an expression of the form already written in (18.3):

$$\xi(x,y,z,t) = A \sin(2\pi ft - 2\pi x/\lambda + \phi). \quad \textit{(Plane Wave)} \qquad (18.22)$$

A source of relatively small dimensions in a homogeneous, isotropic medium will generate waves having wave fronts that are spheres centered on the source, as illustrated in Fig. 18.17. The rays in this case are radially outward from the source. The mathematical representation of a sinusoidal spherical wave will involve a factor of the form $\sin(2\pi ft - 2\pi r/\lambda + \phi)$. However, in this case the wave amplitude cannot be the same for locations that are different distances from the source. We can see why this is so by considering the energy transported by the wave.

For a wave in three dimensions it is convenient to describe the energy transported by the wave in terms of a quantity called the *intensity:*

The INTENSITY I of a wave in three dimensions is the time rate at which energy is transported per unit area of wave front.

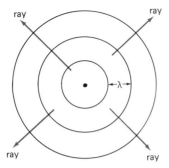

Fig. 18.17 For a spherical wave the wave fronts are concentric spheres centered on the source.

In the SI the dimensions of intensity are $J/(s \cdot m^2)$ or W/m^2. Suppose that the source supplies an average power P to the wave and the wave propagates uniformly in all directions. Consider two imaginary spheres centered on the source with radii r_1 and r_2, where $r_1 < r_2$. Since there is no net accumulation or depletion of energy in any region of space, the average rate at which energy is carried through the surface of sphere 2 must equal the average rate at which energy is carried through the surface of sphere 1, and both these rates must equal P. By the definition of intensity given above, the rate at which energy is carried through the surface of a sphere of radius r is $4\pi r^2 I$. Furthermore, by arguments such as those in Sec. 18.5 we can show in general that the average intensity is proportional to the square of the amplitude of the wave. If we let K represent the constant of proportionality with appropriate dimensions, we have $I_{av} = KA^2$. Then for our spherical wave we have $P = 4\pi r_1^2 K A_1^2 = 4\pi r_2^2 K A_2^2$. If we define a new constant $C = \sqrt{P/4\pi K}$, we have in general for a spherical wave that $A = C/r$. Thus, a sinusoidal spherical wave will have the form

$$\xi(r,t) = (C/r)\sin(2\pi ft - 2\pi r/\lambda + \phi), \quad (Spherical\ Wave) \qquad (18.23)$$

where C/r is the amplitude of the disturbance at a distance r from the source.

In a more general situation the source might supply energy preferentially in certain directions. The amplitude function would then depend on the particular radial direction out from the source that is considered as well as on the distance from the source.

18.10 TWO-SOURCE INTERFERENCE IN THREE DIMENSIONS

In Secs. 18.6 and 18.8 we introduced the idea of interference of two one-dimensional waves that are simultaneously traveling in the same or in opposite directions. We shall now consider an example of a common type of interference where the waves propagate in three dimensions and the phase difference arises at least in part because they travel over different path lengths from their source to the detector. In particular, consider sound waves of frequency f emanating from two identical loudspeakers S_1 and S_2 separated by a distance $2d$ that are driven *in phase* by an electric oscillator E as shown in Fig. 18.18. The loudspeakers each emit waves that for simplicity we shall assume are of the form of (18.23). The solid lines in Fig. 18.18 denote the

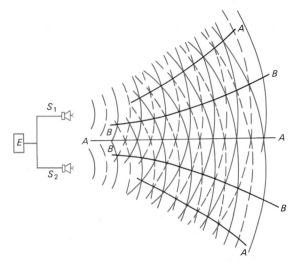

Fig. 18.18 Sound waves of frequency f are emitted by two identical loudspeakers S_1 and S_2 separated by a distance $2d$ that are driven in phase by the electric oscillator E. The solid lines denote condensations and the dashed lines denote rarefactions for a particular time t.

locations of condensations and the dashed lines denote the locations of rarefactions in the XY plane for a particular time t.

Along curves AA in the figure are points where condensations of the two waves coincide and points where rarefactions of the two waves coincide; these curves locate points of *constructive interference*. Along curves BB are points where condensations of one wave coincide with rarefactions of the other wave; these curves locate points of *destructive interference*. Constructive interference occurs when the difference in the lengths of the paths traveled by the two waves from their respective sources to the particular location is a whole number of wavelengths: $|R_2 - R_1| = n\lambda$, where $n = 0, 1, 2, 3, \ldots$. This is illustrated for point P_A in Fig. 18.19. Destructive interference occurs when the difference in the lengths of the paths traveled by the two waves from their respective sources to the particular location is a half-integral number of wavelengths: $|R_2 - R_1| = (n + \frac{1}{2})\lambda$, $n = 0, 1, 2, 3, \ldots$. This situation is illustrated for point P_B in Fig. 18.19.

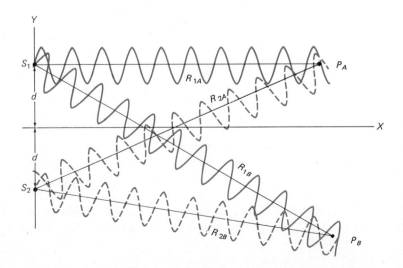

Fig. 18.19 Constructive interference occurs when the path difference is a whole number of wavelengths, as shown for point P_A. Destructive interference occurs when the path difference is a half-integral number of wavelengths, as shown for point P_B.

Example.   A sound detector is mounted on a track running perpendicular to the X axis in the XY plane at a distance $x = 12$ m from the speakers of Fig. 18.18, as indicated in Fig. 18.20. The frequency of the sound emitted by the speakers is 4000 Hz; the speed of sound in air under the prevailing conditions is 340 m/s; the distance between the loudspeakers is $2d = 120$ cm. As the detector is moved in the positive Y direction from the X axis, at what points P are the first two intensity minima encountered?

From the geometry shown in Fig. 18.20 we see that $R_2 = \sqrt{x^2 + (y+d)^2}$ and $R_1 = \sqrt{x^2 + (y-d)^2}$. Thus, the condition for destructive interference is

$$|R_2 - R_1| = \sqrt{x^2 + (y+d)^2} - \sqrt{x^2 + (y-d)^2} = (n+\tfrac{1}{2})\lambda, \ n = 0, 1, 2, \ldots ,$$

and we are interested in the cases $n = 0$ and $n = 1$ since these points will lie closest to the X axis. We rearrange this equation to read $\sqrt{x^2 + (y+d)^2} = (n+\tfrac{1}{2})\lambda + \sqrt{x^2 + (y-d)^2}$. Squaring both sides gives

$$x^2 + y^2 + 2yd + d^2 = (n+\tfrac{1}{2})^2\lambda^2 + 2(n+\tfrac{1}{2})\lambda\sqrt{x^2 + (y-d)^2} + x^2 + y^2$$
$$- 2yd + d^2$$

or

$$4yd - (n+\tfrac{1}{2})^2\lambda^2 = 2(n+\tfrac{1}{2})\lambda\sqrt{x^2 + (y-d)^2}.$$

By squaring again we obtain

$$16y^2d^2 - 8yd(n+\tfrac{1}{2})^2\lambda^2 + (n+\tfrac{1}{2})^4\lambda^4 = 4(n+\tfrac{1}{2})^2\lambda^2(x^2 + y^2 - 2yd + d^2).$$

Finally, solving this equation for y^2 yields

$$y^2 = \frac{4(n+\tfrac{1}{2})^2\lambda^2(x^2 + d^2) - (n+\tfrac{1}{2})^4\lambda^4}{16d^2 - 4(n+\tfrac{1}{2})^2\lambda^2}. \tag{18.24}$$

Note that n must be small enough that the denominator is positive; this is just the condition that the greatest possible path difference is $2d$.

In order to calculate a numerical value for y, we must determine λ. From (18.2) we have $\lambda = v/f = (340 \text{ m/s})/(4000 \text{ Hz}) = 8.5 \times 10^{-2}$ m. Thus, for $n = 0$ we have

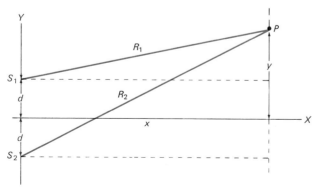

Fig. 18.20

$$y_0 = \left\{ \frac{(8.5 \times 10^{-2}\ \text{m})^2[(12\ \text{m})^2 + (0.6\ \text{m})^2] - (\tfrac{1}{16})(8.5 \times 10^{-2}\ \text{m})^4}{16(0.6\ \text{m})^2 - (8.50 \times 10^{-2}\ \text{m})^2} \right\}^{1/2} = 0.426\ \text{m}.$$

Similarly, for $n = 1$ we obtain $y_1 = 1.28$ m.

An important feature of the physical situation just considered is that the locations in space of points of constructive and of destructive interference do not change in time; the interference pattern is *stationary,* even though the waves giving rise to the pattern are traveling waves. The stationary nature of the interference pattern exists because the two sources produce waves of the *same frequency* and *constant phase difference;* such sources are said to be *coherent.* For loudspeakers producing sound waves these conditions can easily be met with relatively simple electronic devices. For sources of light waves the situation is considerably more complex, as we shall see in later chapters on light.

In cases for which $x \gg d \gg \lambda$ *and n is not too large,* (18.24) assumes the simple form

$$y \simeq (n + \tfrac{1}{2})\lambda x / 2d. \tag{18.25}$$

We shall have occasion to use this form in later chapters dealing with light waves.

QUESTIONS

1. Are there any methods other than mass transport or mechanical waves by which mechanical energy can be transferred from one place to another?

2. Is it possible for the frequency of transverse wave motion in a string like the one shown in Fig. 18.5 to be different from the frequency of the source? If so, give an example; if not, explain why not.

3. In what ways is wave motion different from the vibrational motions that we discussed in Chapter 12?

4. Why is it impossible to transmit transverse waves through a fluid?

5. Transverse waves are transmitted along a stretched string that shows a gradual increase in mass per unit length as we move away from the source. How do the wavelength and the wave speed change as the waves move away from the source?

6. How does the amplitude of the wave motion in a string like the one described in Question 5 vary as the wave disturbance moves away from the source? Is mechanical energy conserved?

7. What are the effects of viscosity on longitudinal wave motion through a fluid?

8. What is the *superposition principle?* Does it hold for waves having different frequencies?

9. Can Fourier's theorem be applied to a very short unrepeated wave pulse? If so, what is the result? Can Fourier's theorem be applied to a sinusoidal wave train of infinite length? If so, what is the result?

10. Is mechanical energy conserved when waves strike a boundary between two elastic media?

11. Is energy transported from one place to another by a standing wave? Is mechanical energy associated with a node in a standing wave?

12. What is meant by the term *wave intensity?* How is it related to wave amplitude and frequency?

13. Is mechanical energy conserved in situations where wave *interference* is observed?

14. What is meant by the term *coherence* when it is applied to the sources of waves? If two sources are coherent, will the resulting wave trains be coherent?

PROBLEMS

1. A piece of flexible steel wire of diameter 1 mm is stretched with a tension of 125 N. (a) What is the speed of propagation of transverse waves along the wire? (b) If the diameter of the wire were doubled, what would be the propagation speed of transverse waves?

2. A certain flexible rope of length 4 m has a mass of 0.150 kg. (a) What is the speed of propagation of transverse waves along the rope if it is stretched with a tension of 480 N? (b) A sudden rainstorm causes the rope to absorb water. Assume that there is no change in the length of the rope and that the tension is adjusted to maintain the value of 480 N. How much water would the rope have to absorb to change the propagation speed for transverse waves by 6%? Will the speed increase or decrease? (c) To what value should the tension be changed to restore the wave speed to its original value if the length remains 4 m?

3. A certain helical spring has a mass of 95 g per meter of length measured along its axis. If a tensile force of 17 N is applied to a 130 cm length of the spring, the resulting elongation is 27 cm. What is the speed of propagation of a longitudinal wave along the spring?

4. It is observed that a longitudinal wave on a certain helical spring propagates with a speed of 12 m/s. The spring is 30 m long and has a total mass of 3.5 kg. (a) If a section 180 cm long were cut from the spring, what would be the force constant of the cut-out segment of the spring? (b) Explain why the force constant depends on the length of the cut-out segment.

5. A flexible steel wire of diameter 2.5 mm is stretched between two fixed supports with a tension of 175 N when the temperature is 10°C. (a) If the ambient temperature rises to 22°C but the distance between the supports does not change, will the speed of propagation of transverse waves along the wire be increased, decreased, or stay the same? Explain your reasoning. (b) Compute the wave speeds for the two temperatures.

6. A flexible uniform rope of length L and mass M is suspended from the ceiling. Find a formula for the speed of a transverse wave on the rope as a function of the distance from the ceiling. Show that the time required for a disturbance initiated at the ceiling to propagate the length of the rope is $2\sqrt{L/g}$. Explain in words why this result does not depend on the mass of the rope.

7. A camper standing on a dock sees a beaver in the middle of a small lake slap the water with his tail. Twenty seconds later a train of waves generated by this disturbance reaches the shore. The camper observes that six crests pass the end of the dock in 5 seconds; by comparing the distance between crests with the known dimensions of the dock he deduces that the wavelength is 2 m. What is the wave speed? How far was the beaver from the end of the dock?

8. As we shall discuss in the next chapter, sound is a longitudinal mechanical wave. Assume that under the conditions of Problem

7 the speed of sound in air is 330 m/s. In a later chapter we shall see that the speed of light in air is approximately 3×10^8 m/s. How long does it take a light signal to travel from the beaver to the camper? How long after the beaver slaps the water will the camper on the dock hear the sound of the slap? A swimmer is in the water at the end of the dock with both ears submerged; how long after the beaver slaps the water does the swimmer hear the sound propagated through the water? How far away would the beaver have to be to give a one-second difference in the arrival times of the two sound waves? How long would it take the water surface waves to travel this distance? Use (18.9) to obtain the speed of sound in water.

9. A transverse wave on a string is represented by the equation $Y = 0.0020 \sin(60t - 0.02x + \pi/4)$, where Y and x are in meters and t is in seconds. (a) What are the amplitude, frequency, wavelength, and speed of the wave? (b) In what direction is the wave propagating? Explain your reasoning. (c) Deduce an expression for the speed of a *string particle*. How does the maximum particle speed compare with the wave propagation speed?

10. Write an equation representing a sinusoidal transverse wave traveling in the negative direction along the X axis if the wave has an amplitude of 0.010 m, a frequency of 17 Hz, and a speed of 37 m/s. At time $t = 0$ the displacement at the origin is 0.003 m and the particle at the origin is moving upward.

11. A sinusoidal transverse wave propagates in the positive X direction along a string that is stretched with a tension of 49 N. The time required for the string particle at a particular location to move from maximum positive displacement to maximum negative displacement is observed to be 0.40 s. The mass per unit length of the string is 5×10^{-3} kg/m. At time $t = 0$ the string particle at the origin has zero displacement and is moving upward.

(a) What are the period, frequency, propagation speed, and wavelength of the wave? (b) Write an equation representing the wave as a function of position and time if the maximum positive displacement of any string particle is 8 mm. (c) How would the result of (b) be changed if at time $t = 0$ the string particle at the origin had its maximum negative displacement?

12. A flexible steel wire of diameter 1.4 mm is stretched with a tension of 120 N. A transverse traveling wave on this wire is generated by an electrically driven vibrator that oscillates with a frequency of 220 Hz; the wave has an amplitude of 0.0021 m. (a) What is the average energy per unit length associated with this wave? What is the power carried by this wave? Assume that energy losses as the wave propagates are negligible. (b) If the diameter of the wire is doubled but the power delivered to the wire by the vibrator remains constant and the same tension is applied to the wire, what is the new wave amplitude?

13. The vibrator of Problem 12 is used to generate a transverse traveling wave on a flexible aluminum wire of diameter 1.4 mm stretched with a tension of 120 N. What should be the amplitude of the wave if the power transmitted is to be the same as for the steel wire of Problem 12a? It is proposed to increase the power transmitted by doubling the tension of the wire. What difficulty attends this proposal?

14. A flexible steel wire and a flexible aluminum wire, both of diameter 1.5 mm, are connected end to end. The composite wire is stretched with a tension of 75 N. A transverse wave of amplitude 1.0 cm and frequency 88 Hz approaches the junction from the aluminum side. What are the amplitudes of the transmitted and reflected waves? What are the phases of these waves relative to the incident wave?

15. For the situation of Problem 14, what are

the average powers transmitted by the incident, transmitted, and reflected waves? Is the result consistent with energy conservation? Discuss qualitatively why it is legitimate to consider the powers carried by the incident and reflected waves separately when the superposition principle says we should superpose the *displacements* and then consider energy and power relations for the composite wave.

16. Show that the choice $A_R = 0$ in (18.15), which then requires that $A_I = A_T$ and $f_I = f_T$, is not compatible with the condition that the slopes of the two strings be equal at $x = 0$.

17. A steel piano wire of length 0.50 m and mass 5 g is stretched with a tension of 400 N. (a) What is the frequency of its fundamental mode of vibration? (b) How many of the normal modes of vibration of the wire have frequencies less than 10^4 Hz?

18. A string is stretched in a north–south direction between two fixed supports that are 4 m apart. The tension is 75 N; the mass of string between the supports is 0.140 kg. It is desired to have the string vibrate in such a way that there is a node 1.5 m from the south end. There may also be other nodes; we do not care where they occur so long as the node we want is present. What are two oscillation frequencies that are consistent with the presence of the desired node?

19. A flexible steel wire of diameter 1.6 mm and length 50 cm is stretched with a tension of 120 N. (a) What is the fundamental frequency of the wire? By what factor must the tension be changed in order to increase the fundamental frequency by 10%? Will this change alter the overtone frequencies by the same factor? (b) What is the fundamental frequency of a flexible aluminum wire of the same diameter and length subjected to the same tension? Is it possible to adjust the tension so that the aluminum wire has the same fundamental frequency as the steel wire? If

so, what is the required tension? (c) Can the aluminum wire be given the same fundamental frequency as the steel wire by changing its diameter while keeping the tension at 120 N? if so, what is the required diameter?

20. A segment of the helical spring considered in Problem 3 is placed in a horizontal frictionless trough. The ends of the spring are fastened to vertical plates that are then fixed with a separation equal to the equilibrium length of the spring segment, which is 125 cm. (a) What are the fundamental and the first three overtone frequencies for longitudinal standing waves on this spring? (b) Use words and diagrams to describe the fundamental mode of oscillation in terms of displacement of "particles" of the spring. (c) Repeat (b), but describe the oscillation in terms of the number of turns of the spring per unit length.

21. A string 4 m long with a mass of 0.160 kg is stretched with a tension of 110 N. The string is oscillating in its second harmonic mode ($n = 2$) with a maximum amplitude of 2 cm. Write an equation representing the standing wave as a function of position and time.

22. A certain string is oscillating in a standing-wave mode described by the equation $Y = -(0.01 \text{ m}) \sin(5\pi x) \cos(880\pi t)$, where x is in meters and t is in seconds. (a) What are the amplitudes and propagation speeds of the two traveling waves that are superposed to produce this standing wave? (b) If this oscillation is the second overtone, how long is the string?

23. Discuss the significance, if any, of the minus sign in (18.19). Consider oscillations at the fundamental and the first overtone frequencies. How would these standing waves be changed if we changed the minus sign to a plus sign? *Hint:* consider the locations and velocities of string particles at time $t = 0$.

24. Do two transverse traveling waves on a string having the same amplitude and frequency

but opposite propagation directions always produce standing waves regardless of their phase difference? If so, why did we require that the phase difference be π radians in the derivation of (18.19)?

25. A string fixed at both ends oscillates simultaneously in the modes corresponding to its fundamental frequency ($n=1$) and its second overtone ($n=3$). Both modes of oscillation have the same amplitude. Sketch the resulting standing wave disturbance for several instants of time. Is the result unique? Explain your answer.

26. Suppose that standing waves are initiated on a stretched string by striking the string sharply rather than by giving it a displacement and releasing it from rest. This means that at time $t=0$ each string particle has a certain velocity, but has zero displacement. Is an equation of the form of (18.19) capable of describing this situation? If not, how should the equation be modified? How will this affect the two traveling waves Y_1 and Y_2 that were superposed to produce (18.19)?

27. (a) Show that the time average total energy per unit length, kinetic plus potential, associated with the standing wave (18.19) is given by $4\pi^2\mu A^2 f^2$. (b) What is the energy of a piano string of mass 10 g and length 1.0 m oscillating in its fundamental mode of frequency 440 Hz with a maximum amplitude of 1.0 cm? (c) What should be the maximum amplitude of oscillation in the first overtone mode if the total energy is to be the same as in part (b)?

28. Two identical sources S_1 and S_2 each generate spherical waves of wavelength λ. Each source emits an average power P. The distance between the sources is $3\lambda/2$, as shown in the diagram. Assume that $R \gg 3\lambda/2$. Find expressions for the average intensity at points A and B in the diagram for the following situations: (a) Only one source is operating. (b) Both sources are operating and they are in phase. (c) Both sources are oper-

ating, but they are oscillating 180° out of phase. Note that for $R \gg 3\lambda/2$, rays from S_1 and S_2 to point B are *nearly* parallel.

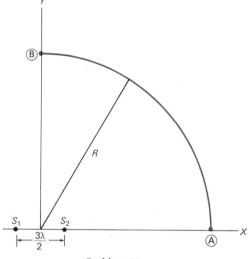

Problem 28

29. For the example of Sec. 10 find the values of y for the first two intensity maxima encountered by the detector off of the X axis.

30. (a) How is the situation of Problem 29 changed if the sources are operated π radians out of phase instead of being run in phase? (b) Repeat part (a) for the case where the sources are run so that the phase angle of S_1 is $\pi/2$ radians but the phase angle of S_2 is 0.

31. Use the trigonometric identities $\sin^2 \theta = \frac{1}{2} - \frac{1}{2} \cos 2\theta$ and $\cos^2 \theta = \frac{1}{2} + \frac{1}{2} \cos 2\theta$ and the oscillatory behavior of the cosine function to show that the average values of $\sin^2 \theta$ and of $\cos^2 \theta$ over an interval $\theta = 0$ to $\theta = 2\pi$ are both $\frac{1}{2}$.

32. The diagram shows a slightly redrawn version of Fig. 18.20. The diagram is drawn with $S_1P = BP = R_1$ so that the distance S_2B is the difference in path lengths $R_2 - R_1$. If $x \gg d \gg \lambda$ and θ is small, derive the condition (18.25) for destructive interference at P *directly* from the geometry of the diagram.

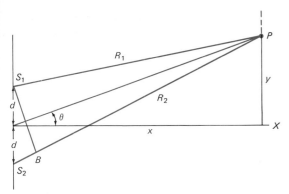

Problem 32

33. Apply (18.25) to the example of Sec. 18.10. Are the approximate values of y_0 and y_1 significantly different from the values calculated in the example? Repeat for $n = 10$.

34. Derive (18.18) from (18.16) and (18.17).

35. Prove that any function of the form $Y = f(x \pm vt)$ is a solution of (18.4).

36. Show that (18.3) and (18.3') are functions of the form $Y = f(x \pm vt)$.

37. Prove that if $Y(x,t)$ is a solution of (18.4)

and C is an arbitrary constant then the function $CY(x,t)$ is also a solution of (18.4).

38. Prove that if $Y_1(x,t)$ and $Y_2(x,t)$ are both solutions of (18.4) then the superposition $Y_{tot} = Y_1 + Y_2$ is also a solution of (18.4).

39. Suppose that $Y_1(x,t)$ and $Y_2(x,t)$ are both solutions of (18.4). Is the product function $Y_{prod} = Y_1 Y_2$ necessarily a solution of (18.4)? If not, can it ever be a solution of (18.4)? Explain your reasoning in detail.

40. By comparing the distance along the X-axis occupied by N turns of a helical spring like that in Fig. 18.3 at equilibrium with the distance occupied by N turns when a longitudinal wave involving displacements from equilibrium given by $\xi(x,t)$ is present, prove that the change in mass per unit length along the spring when the longitudinal wave is present is proportional to the negative of the slope of the ξ versus x curve for the particular time being considered provided that this slope is small.

CHAPTER 19

Sound

The sense of sound provides one of the most important ways in which human beings and animals obtain knowledge of their environment. Thunder, the noise of wind blowing past trees, the sound of running or dripping water, the noise of traffic, the siren of an emergency vehicle, or the barking of a dog can convey to us information about our surroundings. Sound furnishes our most important means of direct communication with other people. In music sound provides some of our most profound aesthetic experiences.

In order to discuss sound in physics and engineering we must distinguish between the physiological sensation of sound and the physical phenomena that give rise to this sensation; we shall give almost all our attention to the latter. For our discussion of the physics of sound we shall use the following definition:

SOUND is any longitudinal mechanical wave in a solid, liquid, or gas.

As a mechanical wave, a sound disturbance must exist in an elastic medium. A sound wave will not propagate through a vacuum, as can be demonstrated by suspending an electric doorbell by fine wires inside a glass bell jar from which the air can be pumped. If the bell is set ringing with air in the jar, the sound can be heard. When the air is pumped from the jar, the sound can no longer be heard, although the clapper can still be seen to be striking the bell.

For speech and hearing the most important elastic medium is air. We shall consider the physics of sound waves in air, and we shall also consider sound waves in liquid and in solid materials.

Generally the range of *audible* sound frequencies, for which human beings have the sensation of hearing, extends from approximately 20 Hz to approximately 20,000 Hz. Sound waves having frequencies outside this range have important technical applications. Frequencies below 20 Hz are called *infrasonic;* frequencies above 20,000 Hz are called *ultrasonic.*

19.1 THE NATURE OF SOUND WAVES IN A FLUID

A longitudinal wave in a fluid can be generated by an oscillating solid object in contact with the fluid, as when the cone of a loudspeaker moves in air. The motion of the solid object is imparted to adjacent fluid particles, which in turn cause neighboring fluid particles to be displaced. The restoring force responsible for limiting the displacement of a fluid particle is provided by the opposition of the fluid to being compressed.

Let us consider a longitudinal plane wave. Suppose that we choose the X axis to be in the direction of propagation of the wave and let ξ represent the displacement of a fluid particle from its equilibrium location. Then we can describe the wave by specifying ξ as a function of position x and time t. An alternative description that is also useful can be given in terms of the pressure change relative to the equilibrium pressure; we shall represent the change in pressure from the equilibrium value by $\mathscr{P}$. We shall now develop the relation between these two descriptions of the wave.

From the definition of the bulk modulus M_B given in Chapter 10 we have

$$\mathscr{P} = -M_B \Delta V/V,$$

where ΔV is the change in volume of a sample of fluid having equilibrium volume V. Consider the fluid inside a cylinder of cross section a oriented with its axis parallel to the X axis; assume that at equilibrium this fluid occupies the region between coordinates x and $x + \Delta x$. At a time t when the wave is present this sample of fluid occupies the region between coordinates $x + \xi(x,t)$ and $x + \Delta x + \xi(x + \Delta x, t)$ $= x + \Delta x + \xi(x,t) + \Delta \xi$, as shown in Fig. 19.1. The equilibrium volume of this sample of fluid is $a\Delta x$, and the volume when the wave is present is $a(\Delta x + \Delta \xi)$, so $\Delta V = a\Delta \xi$. Thus, we have

$$\mathscr{P}_{av} = -M_B a\Delta \xi / a\Delta x,$$

and in the limit as Δx becomes very small this reduces to

$$\mathscr{P} = -M_B \frac{\partial \xi}{\partial x}. \qquad (19.1)$$

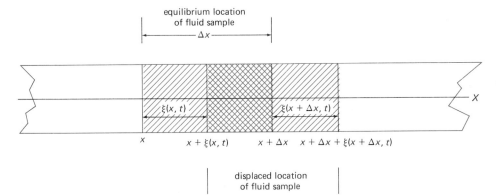

Fig. 19.1 Displacement of a small sample of fluid when a sound wave is present.

Equation (19.1) provides a relation between the description of the wave in terms of fluid particle displacements and the description in terms of pressure changes.

For a sinusoidal plane wave propagating in the $+X$ direction

$$\xi = A \sin(2\pi ft - 2\pi x/\lambda + \phi). \tag{19.2}$$

By (19.1) the pressure change $\mathscr{P}$ as a function of position and time for this wave is

$$\begin{aligned} \mathscr{P} &= (2\pi M_B A/\lambda) \cos(2\pi ft - 2\pi x/\lambda + \phi) \\ &= (2\pi M_B A/\lambda) \sin(2\pi ft - 2\pi x/\lambda + \phi + \pi/2). \end{aligned} \tag{19.3}$$

We see that the pressure and displacement oscillations differ in phase by $\pi/2$ radians. This means that *pressure changes are zero where the fluid particle displacements are maximum and vice versa.*

In Chapter 18 we showed that the wave speed for a longitudinal wave in a fluid is

$$v = \sqrt{M_B/\rho}, \quad \textit{(Longitudinal Wave in a Fluid)} \tag{19.4}$$

where ρ is the equilibrium mass density of the fluid. Also we know that $v = f\lambda$. Therefore, with $\lambda = v/f$ and $M_B = v^2\rho$ (19.3) can be written in the form

$$\mathscr{P} = (2\pi A \rho vf) \cos(2\pi ft - 2\pi x/\lambda + \phi). \tag{19.5}$$

The displacements described by (19.2) are superimposed on the incessant random thermal motions of fluid molecules. The important feature of the displacements that constitute a sound wave is not that they are larger than the random thermal displacements, but rather that they represent an *ordered motion* where essentially all the fluid molecules in a neighborhood move in the same way.

19.2   THE SPEED OF SOUND IN A GAS

The speed of sound in a fluid as given by (19.4) is sufficiently large that for sonic frequencies the distance from a condensation to a rarefaction, $\lambda/2 = vf/2$, is much greater than the distance over which significant amounts of heat can be conducted in a time equal to half the wave period. Thus, heat conduction is not effective in reducing any temperature differences between regions of condensation and regions of rarefaction. This means that the bulk modulus to be used in (19.4) should be measured under *adiabatic* conditions. This is important for gases, where there is a significant difference between the adiabatic bulk modulus and the isothermal bulk modulus.

For an ideal gas we can derive a simple expression for the adiabatic bulk modulus. From the definition of the bulk modulus we have

$$M_B = dP/(-dV/V) = -VdP/dV,$$

where dP and dV represent small changes in the pressure and volume. In Chapter

15 we showed for an ideal gas under adiabatic conditions that $PV^\gamma = \text{constant}$, where γ is the ratio of the specific heat at constant pressure to the specific heat at constant volume. By taking derivatives we find that under adiabatic conditions $dPV^\gamma + P\gamma V^{\gamma-1}dV = 0$, whence $dP/dV = -\gamma P/V$. Thus, we have

$$M_B(\text{adiabatic}) = -V(-\gamma P/V) = \gamma P,$$

so that (19.4) becomes

$$v = \sqrt{\gamma P/\rho}. \tag{19.6}$$

We recall that for an ideal gas $PV = NkT$, where N is the number of molecules, k is Boltzmann's constant, and T is the absolute temperature. If we let μ represent the mass of a single molecule, we have

$$\rho = \mu N/V = \mu P/kT.$$

Upon inserting this in (19.6) we obtain

$$v = \sqrt{\gamma kT/\mu}. \quad \text{(Ideal Gas)} \tag{19.7}$$

Example.   We noted in Chapter 15 that air can to a good approximation be treated as a diatomic ideal gas with a mass per molecule of 29 u. What is the speed of sound in air at 0°C? at 50°C? at 100°C? What is the speed of sound in hydrogen, in helium, and in oxygen at 0°C?

We recall that helium is monatomic while hydrogen and oxygen form diatomic molecules. For monatomic ideal gases $\gamma = \tfrac{5}{3}$ and for diatomic ideal gases $\gamma = \tfrac{7}{5}$. Also, $k = 1.38 \times 10^{-23}$ J/K and 1 u = 1.66×10^{-27} kg. Thus, we have the following results for the speed of sound in air:

T		$v = \sqrt{\dfrac{\gamma kT}{\mu}} = \sqrt{\dfrac{(\tfrac{7}{5})(1.38 \times 10^{-23}\text{ J/K})T}{(1.66 \times 10^{-27}\text{ kg/u})(29\text{ u})}}$
°C	K	
0	273	331 m/s
50	323	360 m/s
100	373	387 m/s

Similarly, the speed of sound in the various other gases at 0°C is as follows:

Gas	M (u)	γ	$v = \sqrt{\dfrac{\gamma kT}{\mu}} = \sqrt{\dfrac{(1.38 \times 10^{-23}\text{ J/K})(273\text{ K})\gamma}{(1.66 \times 10^{-27}\text{ kg/u})M}}$
Helium	4.00	$\tfrac{5}{3}$	972 m/s
Hydrogen	2.016	$\tfrac{7}{5}$	1255 m/s
Oxygen	32.00	$\tfrac{7}{5}$	315 m/s

Here M is the molecular mass of the gas in atomic mass units.

From the discussion in Sec. 15.9 we have that the root-mean-square speed of a molecule of an ideal gas is $v_{RMS} = \sqrt{3kT/\mu}$. Thus, from (19.7) the ratio of the speed of sound in an ideal gas to the root-mean-square molecular speed is $v_{sound}/v_{RMS} = \sqrt{\gamma/3}$. For monatomic gases this is 0.745 and for diatomic gases it is 0.683. It is not accidental that this ratio is close to unity. Since the molecules of an ideal gas exert forces on one another only when they collide, it is not possible for a disturbance in an ideal gas to be propagated faster than the typical speed of a molecule.

19.3   THE SPEED OF SOUND IN A SOLID

A description of the motion of an elastic solid that has been disturbed from equilibrium is more involved than a similar discussion for a fluid because the solid has both shear and volume elasticity. We shall simply note several of the main results for *isotropic* solids, which have properties that are the same for all directions. Both transverse and longitudinal mechanical waves can propagate in such a solid. In the bulk material the speed of longitudinal waves is

$$v_L = \sqrt{\frac{M_B + \tfrac{4}{3}M_S}{\rho}}, \quad \text{(Longitudinal Wave in a Solid)} \tag{19.8}$$

where ρ is the equilibrium mass density, M_B is the bulk modulus, and M_S is the shear modulus. Similarly, the speed of transverse waves is

$$v_T = \sqrt{M_S/\rho}. \quad \text{(Transverse Wave in a Solid)} \tag{19.9}$$

We note that $v_L > v_T$ for all solids. Computation of the magnitude of the difference in these speeds for several solid materials is the subject of one of the problems.

Since a fluid cannot sustain a shear, a transverse wave will not be transmitted by a fluid. The speed of longitudinal waves in a fluid, given by (19.4), is obtained from (19.8) if we set $M_S = 0$.

If the distance from the region where a wave is propagating to a surface of a solid is of the order of the wavelength or less, the surface can have a strong effect on the nature and propagation speed of the wave. The speed of a longitudinal wave in a wire or rod having diameter much less than a wavelength is

$$v_L = \sqrt{M_Y/\rho}, \quad \text{(Longitudinal Wave in a Rod)} \tag{19.10}$$

where ρ is the equilibrium mass density and M_Y is Young's modulus for the rod material.

Earthquakes generate both longitudinal and transverse waves that propagate through the earth. The differences in arrival times for transverse and longitudinal surface waves and for transverse and longitudinal waves that have propagated through the interior of the earth are used in seismology to estimate the distance of an earthquake from the observing station. Study of these "seismic waves" also aids in the deduction of the physical properties of the interior of the earth. Seismic waves produced by explosive charges at the earth's surface can be used in "prospecting" for petroleum and natural gas far below the surface.

19.4   PRODUCTION OF SOUND BY VIBRATING SOLIDS

One of the primary sources of sound waves in air is the motion of solid objects that set into motion the neighboring air. In order to produce a sustained sound, the solid object must undergo oscillatory motion. Of particular importance are objects that oscillate in a standing-wave mode. As in the case of the mechanical waves considered in Chapter 18, *the frequency of the sound wave is the same as the oscillation frequency of the object that acts as the source.*

Oscillating strings are used as the source of sound waves by many different musical instruments. We saw in Chapter 18 that the allowed oscillation frequencies for transverse standing waves on a string of length L having mass per unit length μ and stretched with a tension F between fixed supports are

$$f_n = \frac{n}{2L}\sqrt{\frac{F}{\mu}}, \qquad n = 1, 2, 3, \ldots . \tag{19.11}$$

The most general oscillation of such a string will be a superposition of normal modes having frequencies given by (19.11).

Because of its relatively small surface area, a string is not very effective in producing sound waves in the surrounding air. In order to enhance the generation of sound waves, a vibrating string can be mechanically coupled to an object having large surface area that more effectively transfers energy to the surrounding air. Examples are the sounding board of a piano and the body of a violin.

We see from (19.11) that an oscillating string can be "tuned" by adjusting the tension τ, the length L, or the mass per unit length μ. All three quantities are varied in musical instruments. Strings designed to produce the lower frequencies attained by an instrument are thicker, longer, and heavier than those producing the higher frequencies. The tension applied to the strings of an instrument is adjusted when the instrument is tuned before a performance. A violinist varies the effective lengths of the strings of the instrument by pressing the strings against the fingerboard at particular points.

Stretched membranes of various shapes will undergo standing-wave oscillations and generate sound waves in air. Analysis of the oscillations of a stretched membrane is more complex than for a string because waves on the membrane propagate in two dimensions rather than one. As for a string, there is a set of allowed normal modes of oscillation and corresponding characteristic frequencies. However, for a stretched membrane the overtone frequencies are not integral multiples of the fundamental frequency and do not form a harmonic series.

The nodes where the oscillation of a membrane has zero amplitude are lines on the two-dimensional oscillating surface. The locations of nodal lines for various allowed frequencies can be determined experimentally by subjecting the membrane to vibrations of known frequency from a loudspeaker placed close to the membrane. The membrane will oscillate with large maximum amplitude when the loudspeaker frequency matches one of the characteristic frequencies of the membrane. If the membrane is covered with a thin layer of fine powder, the powder will accumulate along the nodal lines. The portions of the membrane on opposite sides of a nodal line undergo oscillations that are π radians out of phase.

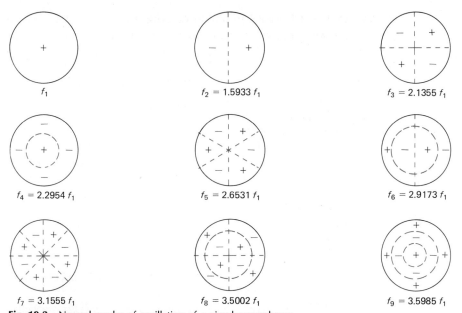

f_1

$f_2 = 1.5933 \, f_1$

$f_3 = 2.1355 \, f_1$

$f_4 = 2.2954 \, f_1$

$f_5 = 2.6531 \, f_1$

$f_6 = 2.9173 \, f_1$

$f_7 = 3.1555 \, f_1$

$f_8 = 3.5002 \, f_1$

$f_9 = 3.5985 \, f_1$

Fig. 19.2   Normal modes of oscillation of a circular membrane.

The first few normal modes of oscillation for a circular membrane under uniform tension around its rim and the corresponding characteristic frequencies are shown in Fig. 19.2. The membrane is assumed to be fixed around its rim, which therefore is a nodal line. Other nodal lines are indicated in Fig. 19.2 by dashed lines. The regions of the membrane marked with a plus sign move upward while the regions marked with a minus sign move downward, and vice versa. The fundamental frequency is

$$f_1 = \frac{0.38724}{R} \sqrt{\frac{\mathscr{T}}{\sigma}}, \quad \textit{(Circular Membrane)}$$

where R is the radius of the membrane, σ is the mass per unit area, and $\mathscr{T}$ is the force per unit length applied around the rim of the membrane. The first few overtone frequencies are given in Fig. 19.2 in terms of f_1.

19.5   PRODUCTION OF SOUND BY VIBRATING COLUMNS OF AIR

A column of air can undergo longitudinal standing-wave oscillations. Although the nature of the wave is different, the origin of the standing waves and the characteristic frequencies of the normal modes can be considered by reasoning very similar to that used for transverse standing waves on a stretched string. We shall consider the case of a cylindrical tube of length L. If a disturbance is initiated in the air column, the disturbance propagates along the tube and is reflected at the ends. We soon have two waves of the same frequency and amplitude propagating along the tube in opposite directions; the superposition of these waves produces standing waves as discussed in Chapter 18. If one or both ends of the tube are open, some of the standing-wave energy is imparted to the surrounding air, thus producing a sound wave.

The standing-wave oscillations must satisfy definite boundary conditions at the ends of the tube. We shall consider two kinds of condition. At a *closed end* there is a rigid barrier that does not move as the air column oscillates. Therefore, a closed end is a displacement node. From the discussion of Sec. 19.1 we know that this corresponds to a pressure antinode. At an *open end* the tube is open to the surrounding air. Specification of the boundary condition at an open end is more complicated. If the diameter of the tube is small compared to the wavelength, theory predicts and experiment confirms that the appropriate condition is a displacement antinode somewhere near but outside the open end. This corresponds to a pressure node; the pressure just outside the open end has a constant value equal to the external atmospheric pressure. This boundary condition can be expressed in terms of an "end correction" to the tube length that makes the effective length somewhat longer than the actual length L. The end correction is negligible if the radius of the tube is much less than the length of the tube. We shall ignore the end correction in our discussion.

By exactly the same reasoning as used in Chapter 18 for standing waves on a string, we can conclude that the distance between adjacent nodes is $\lambda/2$, where λ is the wavelength of the two traveling waves that are superposed to give the standing wave. Therefore, we can find the characteristic oscillation frequencies by simply determining what wavelengths "fit" in the tube to give the required conditions at the tube ends.

Consider first a tube of length L with both ends open, which is called an *open tube*. Each end of the tube must be a displacement antinode and a pressure node. This requires that the length of the tube be an integral number of half wavelengths:

$$L = n\lambda_n/2, \qquad n = 1, 2, 3, \ldots . \quad (Open\ Tube)$$

Since $v = f_n\lambda_n$, we have for the characteristic frequencies

$$f_n = nv/2L, \qquad n = 1, 2, 3, \ldots , \quad (Open\ Tube) \qquad (19.12)$$

where v is given by (19.4) or in the ideal-gas approximation by (19.7). We note that the overtone frequencies are integral multiples of the fundamental frequency and thus form a harmonic series. A representation of the air-particle displacements for the first few normal modes is shown in Fig. 19.3.

Another type of tube that can be used to produce sound waves in air has one end open and the other end closed; this is called a *closed tube*. The closed end of the tube must be a displacement node and a pressure antinode; the open end of the tube must be a displacement antinode and a pressure node. As is illustrated by the representations of the air-particle displacements shown in Fig. 19.4, the boundary conditions are met if the length of the tube is an odd integral number of quarter wavelengths:

$$L = m\lambda_m/4, \qquad m = 1, 3, 5, 7, \ldots . \quad (Closed\ Tube)$$

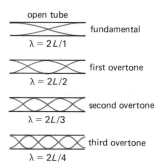

Fig. 19.3 Normal modes of oscillation of an open tube. The distance from the center line of the tube to the light lines drawn inside the tube gives the displacement amplitude at that position.

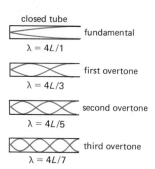

Fig. 19.4 The same as Fig. 3 except for a closed tube.

By using $v = f_m \lambda_m$ we obtain for the characteristic frequencies

$$f_m = mv/4L, \qquad m = 1, 3, 5, 7, \ldots, \quad \textit{(Closed Tube)} \qquad (19.13)$$

where v is given by (19.4) or (19.7). Again we see that the overtones form a harmonic series, but for the closed tube the even harmonics are absent. The fundamental frequency of a closed tube is half the fundamental frequency of an open tube of the same length.

Organs, flutes, and the various orchestral reed and brass instruments depend on vibrating air columns for the production of sound. They differ in the mechanisms by which the oscillations of the air column are initiated and sustained. In order to maintain the standing-wave oscillations of an air column, energy must be supplied continuously. The mechanism for initiating oscillations in a flute or a flue organ pipe is suggested in Fig. 19.5. A jet of air blown through a small orifice into relatively still air has turbulent motion with "eddies" or "vortices" formed along the edges of the jet. Vortices enter the tube with a frequency that depends on the jet speed and the distance from the orifice to the wedge that bisects the jet of air. The vortices entering the tube set the air column into oscillation. Air then rushes in and out of the opening between the wedge and the orifice with a frequency determined by the standing-wave mode. Vortices enter the tube when the air is rushing in; thus, energy is provided at the normal-mode frequency and the oscillation is stabilized. The opening acts as an open end of the tube.

The mouthpiece and reed of a single-reed instrument such as a clarinet are shown schematically in Fig. 19.6. With the reed in its normal position, there is an opening between the free end of the reed and the mouthpiece through which air can pass. When the air pressure in the player's mouth is greater than that in the tube, air rushes through this opening. The pressure of this moving air is less than the pressure on the bottom of the reed, and the reed is forced against the mouthpiece shutting off the flow of air. With the flow stopped, the pressures on the two sides of the reed again become nearly equal, and the elastic properties of the reed cause it to return to its initial position; the cycle is then repeated. This gives a series of pulses of air entering the tube that set the air column into oscillation. The reed and mouthpiece behave essentially like a closed end on the tube so far as the standing-wave boundary

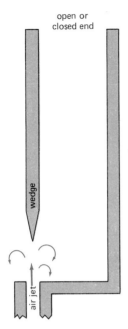

open or
closed end

wedge

air jet

Fig. 19.5 The oscillations of a flue organ pipe are initiated and sustained by a jet of air blown against a wedge.

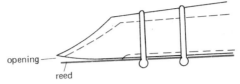

opening

reed

Fig. 19.6 The mouthpiece and reed of a single-reed instrument such as a clarinet.

conditions are concerned. Therefore, the standing wave has a pressure antinode at the mouthpiece, and the pressure fluctuations of the standing wave control the vibrations of the reed so that the pulses of air enter the tube at the normal-mode frequency and the oscillation is stabilized. With a brass instrument such as a trumpet the player's lips perform the function of the reed.

19.6   INTERFERENCE OF SOUND WAVES; BEATS

The superposition principle introduced in Chapter 18 applies to sound waves. Superposition of sound waves in various circumstances gives rise to many interesting interference phenomena. In Sec. 18.10 we considered the superposition of waves having the same frequency and amplitude generated by two loudspeakers operated with a constant phase difference. Another way to investigate interference of sound waves is to send sound from a *single source* along two different paths that eventually converge. An arrangement for doing this is the *acoustic interferometer* shown in Fig. 19.7. A vibrating diaphragm at S sends sound waves of a definite frequency f along the two paths A and B to the detector at O. The path lengths can be varied by adjusting the sliding tubes.

Suppose we start with the two paths having equal lengths. Then the two waves are *in phase* at O, and a loud sound resulting from constructive interference will be heard by the observer. If the length of path A is held constant and the length of path B is slowly increased, the intensity of the sound at O decreases, reaching a minimum resulting from destructive interference when the length of path B is one-half wavelength greater than the length of path A so that the waves are π *radians out of phase* at O. If the length of path B is further increased, the sound intensity

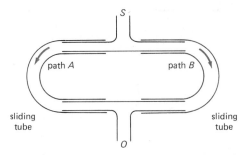

Fig. 19.7   An acoustic interferometer.

at O increases, reaching a second maximum again when the length of path B is one whole wavelength greater than the length of path A.

More generally, intensity maxima occur when the difference between the two path lengths is a whole number of wavelengths and intensity minima occur when the difference between the two path lengths is an odd number of half wavelengths. If we think of these two conditions in a slightly different way, we can formulate rules that apply even when the two sides of the interferometer contain different gases so that the sound velocities and wavelengths are different along the two paths. What we do is express the length of a path in terms of the number of wave oscillations that exist along the path at any time, which is just the geometrical path length divided by the wavelength. If l_A and l_B are the geometrical lengths of the two paths and λ_A and λ_B are the wavelengths of sound waves of frequency f along the respective paths, we can state the conditions for constructive and for destructive interference at O as follows:

Constructive Interference: $|l_A/\lambda_A - l_B/\lambda_B| = n,$ $n = 0, 1, 2, \ldots$;
Destructive Interference: $|l_A/\lambda_A - l_B/\lambda_B| = (n + \frac{1}{2}),$ $n = 0, 1, 2, \ldots .$

We shall next consider a phenomenon that arises from the superposition of two waves that differ slightly in frequency. For simplicity we shall assume that the two waves have the same amplitude.

Suppose that we have two longitudinal plane waves of amplitude A traveling in the X direction. The displacement of the first wave at some *fixed location* is $\xi_1 = A \sin(2\pi f_1 t + \phi_1)$ and the displacement of the second wave at the same location is $\xi_2 = A \sin(2\pi f_2 t + \phi_2)$. Since we are considering a particular location, the position terms in the arguments of the sine functions have been incorporated in the phase constants ϕ_1 and ϕ_2. By the superposition principle the total displacement is

$$\xi = \xi_1 + \xi_2 = A \sin(2\pi f_1 t + \phi_1) + A \sin(2\pi f_2 t + \phi_2).$$

By using the trigonometric identity $\sin \alpha + \sin \beta = 2 \sin \frac{1}{2}(\beta + \alpha) \cos \frac{1}{2}(\beta - \alpha)$ we can write this in the form

$$\xi = 2A \cos\left[2\pi \left\{\frac{f_2 - f_1}{2}\right\} t + \left\{\frac{\phi_2 - \phi_1}{2}\right\}\right] \sin\left[2\pi \left\{\frac{f_2 + f_1}{2}\right\} t + \left\{\frac{\phi_2 + \phi_1}{2}\right\}\right]. \quad (19.14)$$

When f_2 is close to f_1 we can conveniently think of (19.14) as a sinusoidal oscillation

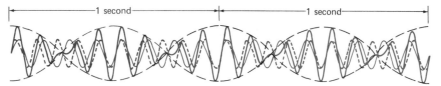

Fig. 19.8 Beats resulting from the superposition of wave ① having a frequency $f_1 = 8$ Hz, shown by the light solid curve, and wave ② having a frequency $f_2 = 10$ Hz, shown by the light dashed curve. The heavy solid curve is the resultant wave. The heavy dashed curves indicate how the amplitude changes with time.

of frequency $\frac{1}{2}(f_2 + f_1)$ with its amplitude modulated by the relatively slowly varying cosine function having frequency $\frac{1}{2}(f_2 - f_1)$. This is illustrated in Fig. 19.8 for a case where $f_2 = 10$ Hz and $f_1 = 8$ Hz. We see that the amplitude of the resultant disturbance attains a maximum $f_2 - f_1$ times each second; a listener will hear $f_2 - f_1$ pulsations in intensity called *beats* each second.

A musician tuning an instrument to agree with a "standard" tone often provided by a tuning fork will adjust for the absence of beats. Similarly, a precise small frequency difference can be attained by adjusting for a certain number of beats per second. If the difference between the two frequencies is greater than 10–15 Hz, the beats are so close together that they cannot be distinguished. However, the resultant tone of frequency $\frac{1}{2}(f_2 + f_1)$ will be perceived as having a distinct harshness or roughness that persists even when the frequency difference becomes sufficiently large that two tones are heard. The frequency difference required for perception of two tones varies from tens to several hundreds of Hertz, increasing with increasing mean frequency.

19.7 THE DOPPLER EFFECT

If the source or the observer of a sound wave is moving relative to the elastic medium through which the wave propagates, the observed frequency will differ from the frequency with which the source generates the waves. This frequency shift is known as the *Doppler Effect* in honor of the Austrian physicist Johann Christian Doppler (1803–1853), who gave the first discussion of the phenomenon in 1842. A common example of the Doppler Effect for sound is the change in pitch of an automobile horn as the vehicle sounding its horn passes the observer.

We shall limit our consideration of the Doppler Effect to cases where any motion of the source or the observer is along the line joining them, and we shall think principally of sound waves in still air, or more generally we shall use a frame of reference at rest with respect to the medium in which the waves propagate. We assume that both the source and the observer move with speeds less than the speed of sound in air v.

First consider a source S producing sound waves with a frequency f_S that is moving with a speed v_S *toward* an observer O who is at rest. Each wave condensation emitted by the source travels in all directions with speed v. However, because of the motion of the source each successive condensation is emitted from a location closer to the observer. The situation is shown in Fig. 19.9, where a number of wave fronts representing adjacent condensations are represented at a particular time t. The wave fronts are not concentric circles, but are circles with the center of each successively smaller

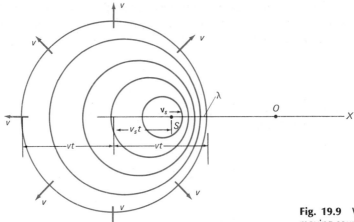

Fig. 19.9 Wave fronts emitted by a moving source.

circle a distance v_S/f_S closer to the observer, where $1/f_S$ is the time between emission of condensations by the source. The wavelength noted by the observer, which is the distance between the condensations along the X axis in Fig. 19.9, is $\lambda = \lambda_S - v_S/f_S$, where λ_S is the wavelength for a source of frequency f_S at rest. Since $\lambda_S = v/f_S$, this becomes $\lambda = (v - v_S)/f_S$. The frequency determined by the observer is $f_O = v/\lambda$, so we have finally that

$$f_O = vf_S/(v - v_S). \quad \text{(Source Approaching} \quad\quad (19.15)$$
$$\text{Stationary Observer)}$$

If the source is moving with a speed v_S *away* from an observer who is at rest, the distance between successive condensations reaching the observer is $\lambda = \lambda_S + v_S/f_S$. The same reasoning as used above then leads to

$$f_O = vf_S/(v + v_S). \quad \text{(Source Leaving} \quad\quad (19.16)$$
$$\text{Stationary Observer)}$$

We see from (19.15) and (19.16) that the observed frequency is raised when the source is approaching an observer at rest and is lowered when the source is leaving such an observer.

Next let us consider a situation where the source and the observer are *both moving toward one another*; the speed of the source is v_S and the speed of the observer is v_O. The wave fronts emitted by the source are again as shown in Fig. 19.9; the distance between these wave fronts along the X axis is again $\lambda = (v - v_S)/f_S$. However, now the observer does not stay in one place and collect these waves. Because of the motion toward the source the observer receives more waves per second than when at rest. The number of waves received per second is the number v/λ that would be received by an observer at rest plus the additional number v_O/λ that are received because of the forward motion of the observer. Thus,

$$f_O = \frac{v}{\lambda} + \frac{v_O}{\lambda} = \frac{(v + v_O)}{(v - v_S)} f_S. \quad \begin{array}{l}\text{(Source and Observer} \\ \text{Moving toward One Another)}\end{array} \quad (19.17)$$

If the source is moving in a direction away from the observer, but the observer is moving toward the source, the same reasoning applies except the distance between the condensations along the X axis is

$$\lambda = (v + v_S)/f_S, \qquad \text{leading to } f_O = f_S(v + v_O)/(v + v_S).$$

The situation where the source and the observer are both moving away from one another is also easily treated. As indicated above, the distance between the condensations produced by the source is $\lambda = (v + v_S)/f_S$. Because of the motion away from the source, the observer receives fewer waves per second than when he or she is at rest. The number of waves received by the observer per second is $f_O = (v - v_O)/\lambda$, where $(v - v_O)$ is the wave speed relative to the observer. Thus, we have

$$f_O = \frac{(v - v_O)}{(v + v_S)} f_S. \qquad \begin{array}{l}\textit{(Source and Observer Moving} \\ \textit{Away from One Another)}\end{array} \qquad (19.18)$$

Consideration of these results shows that all cases considered can be covered by a single equation if we introduce a sign convention for v_S and v_O. If we agree that v_S and v_O are each positive for motion directed toward the other object and negative for motion directed away from the other object, all cases are represented by the relation

$$f_O = \frac{(v + v_O)}{(v - v_S)} f_S. \qquad \begin{array}{l}\textit{(All Cases, with Proper Sign} \\ \textit{Convention for } v_O \textit{ and } v_S)\end{array} \qquad (19.19)$$

If either the source or the observer is at rest, (19.19) applies with the appropriate speed, v_S or v_O, set equal to zero.

The above considerations can be extended to treat sound waves reflected by a moving object. This is considered in the following example.

Example.   A car traveling east at 80 km/h is approaching a van traveling east at 60 km/h. The car sounds a horn having a frequency of 300 Hz. (a) What frequency is perceived by the van driver? (b) What frequency does an observer in the car perceive for the sound wave reflected from the back of the van? Assume that the speed of sound in air is 335 m/s and that there is no wind.

(a) The car is the source and is moving toward the van. Therefore, $v_S = +(80 \text{ km/h})(10^3 \text{ m/km})/(3600 \text{ s/h}) = +22.2$ m/s. The observer moves with the van in a direction away from the source. Therefore,

$$v_O = -(60 \text{ km/h})(10^3 \text{ m/km})/(3600 \text{ s/h}) = -16.7 \text{ m/s}.$$

Thus, by using (19.19) we obtain

$$f_O = \frac{(335 \text{ m/s} - 16.7 \text{ m/s})}{(335 \text{ m/s} - 22.2 \text{ m/s})} (300 \text{ Hz}) = 305 \text{ Hz}.$$

(b) For the reflected wave the van acts as a source moving in a direction away from the observer. Thus, for this part of the problem $v_S = -16.7$ m/s. The frequency with which reflected waves leave the van is just the observer frequency found in part (a); thus, $f_S = 305$ Hz. The observer for part (b) is moving with the car in a direction toward the source of the reflected wave, so $v_O = +22.2$ m/s. Thus, (19.19) applied to part (b) of the problem gives for the frequency of the reflected waves perceived by an observer in the car

$$f_O = \frac{(335 \text{ m/s} + 22.2 \text{ m/s})}{(335 \text{ m/s} + 16.7 \text{ m/s})} (305 \text{ Hz}) = 310 \text{ Hz}.$$

This is sufficiently close to the source frequency that the observer will not *hear* two tones; however, beats are possible.

19.8   INTENSITY OF SOUND WAVES

In Chapter 18 we defined the intensity of a wave to be the power transmitted through unit area normal to the direction of propagation. It is not difficult to express the average intensity of a sound wave in a fluid in terms of the pressure amplitude or the displacement amplitude and other wave parameters. Consider a sinusoidal plane wave where the particle displacements are given by (19.2):

$$\xi = A \sin(2\pi ft - 2\pi x/\lambda + \phi).$$

The particle velocities are given by

$$v_p = \frac{\partial \xi}{\partial t} = 2\pi fA \cos(2\pi ft - 2\pi x/\lambda + \phi). \tag{19.20}$$

Consider a cylinder of fluid of cross section a oriented with its axis in the direction of wave propagation as shown in Fig. 19.1. The resultant force on particles to the right of location x is $\mathscr{P}a$. Since these particles have velocity v_p, the rate at which energy is delivered across the cross section a at the location x and time t is $\mathscr{P}av_p$. By use of (19.3) and (19.20) we obtain

$$I = (4\pi^2 A^2 M_B f/\lambda) \cos^2(2\pi ft - 2\pi x/\lambda + \phi).$$

Since the time average over a whole number of cycles of the cosine squared function is ½ (see Problem 18.31) the average intensity of the wave is

$$I_{av} = 2\pi^2 fA^2 M_B/\lambda. \tag{19.21}$$

By using $\lambda = v/f$ and (19.4) we can write this in the form

$$I_{av} = 2\pi^2 f^2 A^2 v\rho. \tag{19.21'}$$

The displacement amplitude of the ordered motion associated with a sound wave is very small, as is illustrated by the following computation.

Example. Sound becomes painful at an average intensity of about 1 W/m². What is the displacement amplitude of a sound wave in air of this intensity and frequency 3000 Hz under conditions where the speed of sound in air is 331 m/s and the density of air is 1.29 kg/m³?

Upon solving (19.21') for A we obtain $A = (1/\pi f)\sqrt{I_{av}/2v\rho}$. Thus,

$$A = [1/\pi(3000 \text{ Hz})]\sqrt{(1 \text{ W/m}^2)/2(331 \text{ m/s})(1.29 \text{ kg/m}^3)}$$
$$= 3.63 \times 10^{-6} \text{ m}.$$

The range of sound intensities that is important in acoustics is enormous. Because of the size of this range, it has been found convenient to introduce a logarithmic scale for the comparison of sound intensities. The following definition is used:

The SOUND INTENSITY LEVEL IL in *decibels* is ten times the logarithm to the base 10 of the ratio of the sound intensity to a reference intensity I_0:

$$IL = 10 \log_{10}(I/I_0) \quad \text{(decibels)}. \tag{19.22}$$

By international agreement the reference intensity is $I_0 = 10^{-12}$ W/m². The abbreviation of decibel is dB; this unit is named in honor of Alexander Graham Bell (1847–1922), the inventor of the telephone.

Example. What is the ratio of the intensities of two sounds that differ in intensity level by 10 dB?

We have 10 dB $= IL_2 - IL_1 = 10 \log_{10}(I_2/I_0) - 10 \log_{10}(I_1/I_0) = 10 \log_{10}\{(I_2/I_0)/(I_1/I_0)\} = 10 \log_{10}(I_2/I_1)$. Thus, $\log_{10}(I_2/I_1) = 1$, so $I_2/I_1 = 10$.

19.9 RESPONSE OF THE HUMAN EAR TO SOUND WAVES

The physiology and psychology of hearing are complex and involve many unanswered questions. We shall merely give a brief description of the human ear and introduce some commonly used terminology.

The human ear consists of three major portions called the outer ear, the middle ear, and the inner ear, as shown in Fig. 19.10. Sound waves enter the outer ear, travel down the ear canal, and strike a thin membrane called the eardrum, which forms the boundary between the outer ear and an airspace called the middle ear. In the middle ear, a mechanism consisting of three small bones called the hammer, the anvil, and the stirrup transmit vibrations from the eardrum to the oval window. The oval window is a membrane that transmits vibrations to the inner ear, which is filled with a liquid. In the cochlear spiral, which is a tube about 3.5 cm long and 1 or 2 mm in diameter, are the terminals of the auditory nerve. There are approximately 30,000 nerve terminals in the cochlea, and different frequencies have their greatest

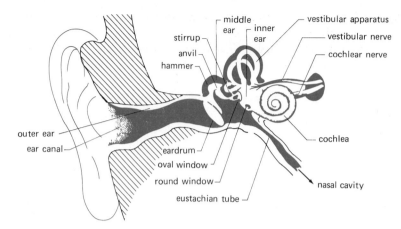

Fig. 19.10 The human ear.

effects on nerve terminals located at different positions along the spiral. Sound signals are "received" by these terminals, and are transmitted electrochemically to the brain. The vestibular apparatus shown in Fig. 19.10 is not associated with hearing. It consists of three fluid-filled semicircular canals in three orthogonal planes, and controls the sense of balance or equilibrium.

For a pure tone of a given frequency the perceived *loudness* increases with increasing intensity, but the general relation between loudness and intensity is complex. Like other perceptions of the senses, loudness cannot be measured in objective physical terms since it depends on the ear and the judgment of the particular observer. Two observers can usually agree that two sounds are equally loud, but different observers generally will not agree as to when one sound is "twice as loud" as another. The perception of loudness depends on frequency. Sounds at the high- and low-frequency ends of the range of human hearing must have greater intensity to be perceived as having loudness equal to sound with a frequency in the middle of this range. This is illustrated in Fig. 19.11, which shows curves representing intensities that will be

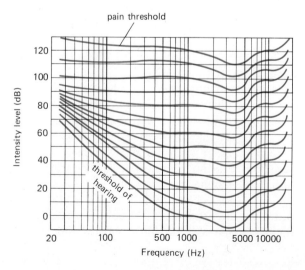

Fig. 19.11 Equal loudness curves. [From H. Fletcher and W. A. Munson, *J. Acous. Soc. Am.* **5,** 82 (1933).]

perceived as equally loud as a function of frequency for determinations averaged for a large number of observers.

The *pitch* of a sound is closely related to frequency, but the exact relation between pitch and frequency for complex sounds is not completely understood. For simple sounds, the greater the frequency the higher the pitch. In going up the scale one octave we double the frequency. However, for complex sounds pitch assignment is an involved psychological process. The interested student should consult specialized books on musical acoustics.

The *quality* or *timbre* of a sound is the property that allows us to distinguish among various musical instruments all sounding the same note. This same property allows us to distinguish different vowel sounds even when they are spoken with very different pitch and loudness. Detailed elucidation of the concept of quality is again a complicated psychological question. We can assert that the quality of a musical sound is determined by the intensities of the different overtones of the instrument relative to the intensity of the fundamental. In sounding a certain note, different instruments will produce the same fundamental frequency, but the overall *waveforms* resulting from the superposition of all the overtones and the fundamental will be very different. A musically "interesting" sound generally involves many overtones that are to a good approximation harmonically related.

QUESTIONS

1. If an electric door bell is suspended inside a bell jar, how does the intensity of the sound waves that are set up change as the pressure inside the jar is gradually reduced from atmospheric pressure to vacuum?

2. Why does the quantity γ appear in (19.7)?

3. How does the speed of transverse waves in a violin string compare with the speed of longitudinal waves in the string when the violin is properly tuned?

4. Why is the quality or timbre of a drum membrane different from that of a piano string having the same fundamental frequency?

5. Show that pressure antinodes in an organ pipe coincide with displacement nodes.

6. Are stationary interference patterns observed when two violins sound the same note? Explain your reasoning.

7. How are beats produced?

8. If a source is approaching an observer with the speed of sound, what observed frequency is predicted by (19.19)? What actually occurs? What is a "sonic boom?"

9. How could you produce a standard acoustical frequency in a laboratory by the use of a "siren disk," which consists of a circular metal disk having a set of evenly spaced holes near its perimeter that is mounted on the shaft of a motor?

10. What sort of frequency standard does a piano tuner carry? Is a separate standard needed for each key on the piano?

11. The pitch of the wind instruments rises and that of the string instruments falls as an orchestra warms up. Explain the reasons for these changes.

12. Discuss how the pitch of the voice will be affected if the speaker is breathing a mixture of helium and oxygen instead of nitrogen and oxygen. Repeat for a mixture of argon and oxygen.

PROBLEMS

1. Air at standard temperature and pressure ($T = 273$ K, $P = 1$ atm $= 1.01 \times 10^5$ Pa, $\rho = 1.29$ kg/m³) is disturbed by a sound wave of frequency 1800 Hz and pressure amplitude 8.5 Pa. (a) What are the wavelength, velocity, and displacement amplitude of the wave? (b) What is the maximum fractional change in pressure relative to the equilibrium value? (c) Write equations describing the wave in terms of pressure oscillations and in terms of displacement oscillations. (d) What is the maximum particle speed associated with this wave?

2. The pressure change from equilibrium for a certain sound wave in air is given by the equation

$$\mathcal{P} = (1.25 \text{ Pa}) \sin[(5600 \text{ s}^{-1})\pi t - (17.0 \text{ m}^{-1})\pi x + \pi/6].$$

   The equilibrium pressure is 1.008×10^5 Pa. (a) What are the frequency, wavelength, velocity, and pressure amplitude of the wave? (b) Write an equation describing the wave in terms of displacement oscillations. (c) What is the maximum particle speed associated with this wave?

3. Show that a longitudinal wave in a fluid can be described in terms of density oscillations as well as in terms of displacement and pressure oscillations. Derive a quantitative relation between the density and the pressure descriptions.

4. A timer for a footrace is instructed to start his stopwatch when he sees the flash of the starter's gun. Unfortunately, he loses sight of the starter and starts his stopwatch when he hears the sound of the starter's gun. If the starter is 100 m from the timer's location at the finish line, what will be the error in the time recorded for the race due to the timer's blunder? The temperature is 26°C; the speed of light in air is approximately 3.0×10^8 m/s.

5. A ship is in a dense fog in the Norwegian fjord. The charts indicate that the fjord is 1.25 km wide; the temperature is 5°C. In order to find the ship's location in the channel, the captain fires a gun and hears the first echo after 3.1 s as timed by a stopwatch. (a) How far is the ship from the center of the fjord? (b) How long after the gun was fired did the second echo arrive?

6. A stone is dropped from rest into a well. The sound of the splash when the stone hits the water is heard 4 s after the stone is dropped. How deep is the well? The temperature of the air in the well is 12°C.

7. What experimental evidence can you cite from your experience to support the proposition that the speed of sound in air is the same for all frequencies?

8. What is the wavelength of a sound wave of frequency 925 Hz (a) in air at STP and (b) in water?

9. What relations for the speed of sound in an ideal gas would replace (19.6) and (19.7) if the propagation of a sound wave were an isothermal process rather than being adiabatic? What percentage change would this make in the calculated speed of sound in air?

10. Compute the speed v_L of longitudinal waves, the speed v_T of transverse waves, and the difference $v_L - v_T$ for the solid materials listed in Table 10.1.

11. A long steel rod is rapped sharply on one end with a hammer. An auditor at the other end of the rod hears two sounds, one from the wave that has traveled through the rod and the other from the wave that has traveled through the air. Which sound arrives first? If the time between arrival of the two sounds is $\Delta t = 1.2$ s, how long is the rod? If the rod were a pipe filled with water, at what point in the interval Δt would the sound wave

traveling through the water reach the auditor? The air temperature is 25°C.

12. A flexible steel wire of diameter 1.4 mm is stretched with a tension of 52 N between two fixed supports that are 5 m apart. (a) What is the ratio of the speeds of longitudinal and transverse waves in this wire? (b) What are the fundamental and first overtone frequencies for these two kinds of oscillation? (c) Is it possible to adjust the tension so that the fundamental frequencies for the two kinds of oscillation are the same? If not, explain why not; if so, what is the required tension?

13. A cylindrical organ pipe operated as an open tube is 6 m long and has a radius of 3 cm. What are its fundamental and first three overtone frequencies if the air temperature is 10°C? By what percent does the fundamental frequency change if the temperature rises to 35°C? Does the same percentage change apply to the overtone frequencies? Explain your reasoning.

14. Repeat Problem 13 for the case where the organ pipe is a closed tube.

15. (a) What is the maximum length an open organ pipe can have if its fundamental frequency is to be in the audible range? (b) Repeat for a closed organ pipe. Take the speed of sound in air to be 330 m/s.

16. For a cylindrical tube of length L and radius R where $R \ll L$ the end correction at an open end is approximately $0.6R$. (a) What are the corrected frequencies of the fundamental and the first three overtones for the closed organ pipe of Problem 14? What are the percentage changes from the values computed by ignoring the end correction? (b) Repeat for the open organ pipe of Problem 13.

17. A certain open organ pipe is 8 cm long. (a) What is its fundamental frequency? (b) How many of the harmonics of this pipe are within the audible range? (c) Repeat for a closed

pipe 8 cm long. Take the speed of sound in air to be 330 m/s.

18. Under conditions such that the speed of sound in air is 333 m/s an organ pipe is found to have successive resonances at 315 Hz, 525 Hz, and 735 Hz. (a) How long is the pipe? (b) What is the fundamental frequency? (c) Is the pipe open or closed? (d) If three equally spaced frequencies are chosen *at random*, is it possible to design an open or closed organ pipe that will have the three frequencies as resonances? Explain your reasoning.

19. A simple apparatus for determining the speed of sound in air is shown in the diagram. Oscillations of the air in the tube are excited at a given frequency f by a tuning fork or by a small loudspeaker driven by an audio oscillator. The air column behaves like a closed tube; as the water level is lowered, a resonance, which will be indicated by a maximum in the intensity of the sound from the tube, will first be detected when the length of the air column is one-quarter wavelength. When an exciting frequency of 780 Hz is used in an experiment, it is found that subsequent resonances after the first occur when the water level is lowered by an integral multiple of 21.4 cm. What value does this experiment give for the speed of sound in air?

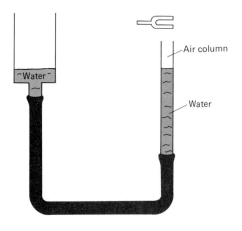

Problem 19

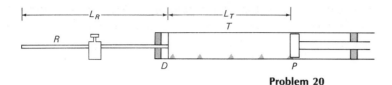

Problem 20

20. Another simple apparatus often used in student laboratories for speed of sound measurements is Kundt's apparatus shown in the diagram. The rod R of length L_R is clamped at its center; when it is stroked with a chamois, the rod is set into longitudinal oscillation with a node at its center and an antinode at each end. These oscillations are communicated to the gas in the glass tube T by the disk D. The length of the tube L_T is adjusted by moving the piston P. A fine dust or powder is spread along the bottom of the tube. For a tube length L_T that gives a resonance condition where standing waves are excited in the tube, the powder quickly collects at the nodes, as indicated in the diagram. The distance between nodes can be determined by measuring the distances between the piles of powder. (a) As is shown in the diagram, there is a node of the gas oscillations close to the disk D. How is this possible when D is at an antinode of the rod oscillations? (b) Suppose that the speed of sound in air is known to be 334 m/s from an experiment like that of Problem 19. The node spacing in Kundt's apparatus is found to be 8.5 cm when the length L_T is 85.0 cm. The length of the rod is $L_R = 1.30$ m. What is Young's modulus for the material of which the rod is made? The mass of the rod is 510 g and its diameter is 8 mm.

21. The Kundt's apparatus of Problem 20 is used under exactly the same conditions except that the tube is filled with helium. What node spacing is obtained? If the piston P is moved the minimum possible distance from the setting of Problem 20, what is the length L_T in the helium experiment? How many piles of powder are there in the tube besides the ones at D and at P?

22. Two identical piano wires are stretched with tensions such that their nominal fundamental frequencies are each 523 Hz. However, the tensions are slightly different, so that an auditor discerns five beats per second. (a) What is the percentage difference in the two tensions? (b) The tensions are adjusted until the auditor hears beats at a rate slower than one beat per 5 s. What is the maximum percentage difference in the two tensions?

23. An open organ pipe at the front of a church is tuned to 256 Hz at 20°C, and an open organ pipe in the echo organ at the rear of the church is tuned to 512 Hz at 20°C. On Sunday the front of the church is at 20°C, but the rear is at 25°C. How many beats per second occur between the fundamental of the pipe in the rear and the second harmonic of the pipe in the front when they are sounded together?

24. In the acoustic interferometer shown in Fig. 19.7 the path length l_A is set at 125 cm and the path length l_B is set at 150 cm. The frequency of the source S is set at 1000 Hz and is then slowly increased until an intensity maximum is heard at O. (a) What is the frequency that gives this intensity maximum? (b) With the source frequency fixed at the value found in part (a), the length of path B is slowly increased until it reaches 285 cm. For what lengths of path B are intensity maxima heard at O? (c) For what lengths of path B are intensity minima heard at O? Both arms of the interferometer contain air at 20°C.

25. In an acoustic interferometer similar to that shown in Fig. 19.7 path A is filled with air at 0°C and path B is filled with hydrogen at 0°C. If both path lengths are 2 m, what

is the lowest frequency of the source S that will produce an intensity maximum at O? What is the lowest frequency that will produce an intensity minimum at O?

26. On a day when there is no wind and the temperature is 26°C an ambulance traveling at 82 km/h and sounding a siren having a frequency of 1500 Hz passes close by a pedestrian standing beside the road. What are the maximum and the minimum frequencies heard by the pedestrian?

27. Locomotive A is traveling east at 40 km/h; locomotive B is traveling west on a parallel track at 35 km/h. A whistle on locomotive A is continuously sounding its fundamental frequency of 210 Hz as the locomotives pass one another. There is no wind; the speed of sound in air is 333 m/s. (a) What are the maximum and the minimum wavelengths of the sound waves produced by the whistle? (b) What are the maximum and the minimum frequencies heard by the engineer on locomotive B?

28. (a) How would the computation of the frequencies in part (b) of Problem 27 be changed if there were a wind blowing from the east at 20 km/h? (b) What is the minimum wind speed from the east that will change the observed frequency by at least 1 Hz when the locomotives are approaching one another?

29. An observer is sitting on a park bench looking at a cliff in the distance. Between the observer and the cliff an emergency vehicle begins to sound its siren, which has a fundamental frequency of 1100 Hz. The vehicle is traveling away from the cliff toward the observer at 75 km/h. There is no wind; the speed of sound in air is 335 m/s. (a) What is the frequency of the sound the observer hears directly from the siren? (b) What is the frequency of the sound the observer hears reflected from the cliff? (c) Will the observer hear beats between these two sound waves?

30. Bats obtain information about their environment by bouncing high-frequency sounds off of objects and analyzing the echos. Chirps that are primarily a single frequency can be used to determine the relative velocity of an object toward or away from the bat by means of Doppler shifts. Bats typically fly at speeds of 1 to 10 m/s. A certain bat emits chirps having a frequency of 83 kHz. (a) What echo frequency does the bat receive when flying toward a cave wall at 5 m/s? (b) What frequency difference must the bat be able to discern in order to know its velocity toward a cave wall to within 0.1 m/s? The temperature of the cave is 10°C.

31. Porpoises also obtain information about their environment by analyzing high-frequency sound echos. A porpoise swimming north at 3 m/s in still water is following a whale that is swimming north at 10 m/s. If the porpoise emits chirps having a frequency of 50 kHz, what will be the frequency of the echo received from the whale?

32. Analysis of the Doppler effect can be extended to take into consideration arbitrary directions of motion of the source and the observer. For example, the diagram shows a case where the observer is at rest with respect to the medium and the source is moving past the observer with a velocity v_S. Consider the waves emitted by the source between the time t_0 when it is at position S_0 and the time $t_1 = t_0 + \delta t$ when it is at position S_1, where $v_S \delta t$ is very small compared with r_0. The number of waves emitted in this interval is $f_S \delta t$. The first of these waves reaches the observer O at time $t_0 + r_0/v$. The last of these waves reaches the observer at time $t_0 + \delta t + r_1/v$. (a) Show that $r_1 \simeq r_0 - v_S \cos \theta \, \delta t$. (b) Show that the frequency perceived by the observer, given by the number of waves received divided by the reception time interval, is $f_0 = f_S v/(v - v_S \cos \theta)$. (c) Show that this result is consistent with (19.19).

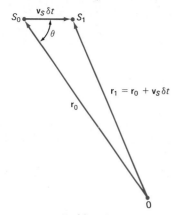

Problem 32

33. (a) Show a third version of Eqs. (19.21) and (19.21') is $I_{av} = \mathscr{P}_{max}^2/2\rho v$. (b) Consider two sound waves of the same frequency, one propagating in water and the other propagating in air at 30°C. If the waves have equal intensities, what is the ratio of their pressure amplitudes? (c) If the waves have equal pressure amplitudes, what is the ratio of their intensities? (d) of their displacement amplitudes?

34. According to Fig. 19.11 the threshold of hearing at a frequency of 90 Hz corresponds to an intensity of approximately 10^{-8} W/m². (a) What are the pressure and displacement amplitudes for a sound wave of this intensity in air at 30°C and 1 atm pressure? (b) Repeat for a sound wave in hydrogen at 30°C and 1 atm pressure.

35. Sound B has three times the displacement amplitude and three times the frequency of

sound A. What is the difference in intensity level of the two sounds?

36. The total intensity due to a collection of *independent, noncoherent* sources is the sum of the individual intensities. What is the rise in intensity level if there are five cocktail-party conversations going on in a small room compared with one, the same number of people being in the room in both cases? How many additional conversations are required to raise the intensity level again by this same amount?

37. A certain source of sound in air emits uniformly in all directions at a frequency of 3000 Hz. (a) At a distance of 10 m from the source the intensity level is 36 dB. What is the average power of the source? (b) What are the pressure and displacement amplitudes 10 m from the source? (c) At what distance from the source will the intensity level be 18 dB? The speed of sound in air is 331 m/s and the air density is 1.29 kg/m³.

38. Equation (19.14) describes beats at a particular location in terms of particle displacements. What is the corresponding description of the beats at this location in terms of pressure changes?

39. Derive an expression for the average intensity of the wave represented by (19.14). How is this related to the individual average intensities of the two waves that are superposed to produce (19.14)?

PART 4

ELECTROMAGNETISM

CHAPTER 20

Electric Charge: Coulomb's Principle

With this chapter we begin our study of electromagnetism. For a thousand years electricity and magnetism were regarded as entirely different subjects. However, late in the 18th century methods of producing electric currents were developed and it was discovered shortly thereafter that magnetic effects are associated with electric currents, that is, with moving electric charges. This discovery provided a connection between electricity and magnetism that has been of utmost importance to various scientific and technological developments of the 20th century. With the development of the generator, the transformer, and the electric motor, we now have systems of power distribution that provide for the clean efficient delivery of energy to locations where it is needed. Our modern systems of communication including long-distance telephone, radio, and television are based on electromagnetic waves associated with changing electric and magnetic fields that transport energy through space. Light consists of electromagnetic waves; radiant energy reaching the earth from the sun is transmitted by electromagnetic waves.

In later chapters we shall deal with all of these subjects, but in the present chapter we shall deal with *electrostatic phenomena* that can be interpreted in terms of *electric charges at rest*. Because we cannot at this point describe electric charge in terms of any simpler physical quantities, we shall tentatively treat it as a fundamental quantity; in later chapters we shall show how charge is related to current, which has actually been chosen as the SI fundamental electromagnetic quantity.

20.1 ELECTROSTATIC PHENOMENA

The word electricity is derived from the Greek work for amber, $\epsilon\lambda\epsilon\kappa\tau\rho o\nu$ *(electron)*. The early Greek natural philosophers observed that when a piece of amber is rubbed with a dry cloth, the amber temporarily acquires the ability to attract small objects such as lint, straw, bits of paper, and thin pieces of metal foil. The amber is said to be "electrified." Not only amber, but also many other materials become electrified when they are rubbed with other properly selected materials. Electrification by friction is a phenomenon familiar to all of us who live in cold, dry climates. After a few strokes through one's dry hair, a comb acquires the troublesome property of attracting the hair. The act of walking across a rug in a dry, heated room can produce electrification of the walker, who can experience a mild electric shock—and even a spark—when he touches a metal pipe or door frame.

Although electrification of amber was known to the Greeks, no extensive systematic investigations of the phenomenon were undertaken until the 18th century. By the late 17th century it was recognized that repulsion effects are also associated with electrified objects. It was found that a glass rod becomes electrified when rubbed with silk, and in addition to being able to attract light objects, it will repel a nearby similarly electrified glass rod, as suggested in Fig. 20.1a. It was found that a hard-rubber rod becomes electrified when rubbed with wool or cat's fur, and in addition to being able to attract light objects, it will repel a nearby similarly electrified rubber rod, as suggested in Fig. 20.1b. However, a hard-rubber rod rubbed with cat's fur will attract a nearby glass rod that has been rubbed with silk, as suggested in Fig. 20.1c.

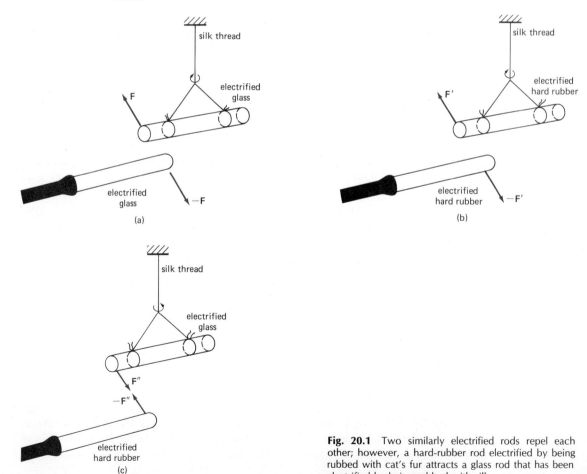

Fig. 20.1 Two similarly electrified rods repel each other; however, a hard-rubber rod electrified by being rubbed with cat's fur attracts a glass rod that has been electrified by being rubbed with silk.

A qualitative understanding of these phenomena was provided in 1733 by the French scientist Charles Francois de Cisternay du Fay (1698–1739), who concluded on the basis of numerous experimental studies that there are two different types of electric charge. Here we introduce the term "charge" to denote whatever property a material has acquired when it is electrified. The type of charge on the electrified glass rod rubbed with silk du Fay termed *vitreous charge;* the type of charge on the electrified hard-rubber rod rubbed with cat's fur he termed *resinous charge.* These names referred to attributes of certain materials displaying one or the other of the two types of electrification. After exhaustive experiments on the electrification of numerous materials, du Fay was unable to find any other type of charge. On the basis of experiments like those suggested in Fig. 20.1, du Fay concluded that:

Like charges repel each other.   *Unlike charges attract each other.*

In 1747 the two types of electric charge were named *positive* (vitreous) and *negative* (resinous) by Benjamin Franklin (1706–1790), who was at the time unaware of the earlier work of du Fay. Franklin's choice of the names *positive* and *negative* has been generally adopted because their algebraic connotations have proved useful in the mathematical formulation of electromagnetic theory.

POSITIVE ELECTRIC CHARGE is the kind of charge on glass that has been electrified by rubbing it with silk.

NEGATIVE ELECTRIC CHARGE is the kind of charge on hard rubber that has been electrified by rubbing it with cat's fur.

Among the devices employed in the 18th-century studies of electrostatics were small, metal-coated "pith balls" suspended vertically by dry silk threads.* When pith balls of this type are brought into contact with electrified glass or rubber rods, the pith balls themselves become electrified, as suggested in Fig. 20.2. The electrified pith balls supported by dry silk threads maintain their charges for considerable lengths of time; the silk threads are an example of a class of materials called *insulators* or *dielectrics* or *nonconductors* of electricity. Glass and indeed most dry, nonmetallic materials are insulators. When the separation of two electrified pith balls is decreased, the forces of mutual repulsion or attraction rapidly increase; in view of Newton's success with his inverse-square relation for gravitational attraction, it was assumed by the early investigators that some similar relation applied to electric charges.

In contrast to dry nonmetals, most metals are good conductors of electricity. Although extremely pure water is a fairly good insulator, water as it is usually encountered has materials dissolved in it that make it conducting.

The earth itself is an enormous *reservoir* of positive and negative charge. Charges can be taken away from the earth or given up to the earth without measurable effects on the earth itself. Therefore, we can discharge electrified objects by connecting them to the earth, as suggested in Fig. 20.3. Starting with a positively charged metal sphere in Fig. 20.3a, we connect the sphere to the earth in Fig. 20.3b by a wire connected to "ground," for example by attaching the wire to a water pipe, and find that the sphere is no longer charged; the sphere remains uncharged after the connection to

---

* A pith ball is a small sphere of some very light material. In reports of early research in electrostatics, spheres made of the pith of elder wood are frequently mentioned. Pith balls are often coated with some conductor to provide a conducting sphere of much smaller mass than a solid metal sphere.

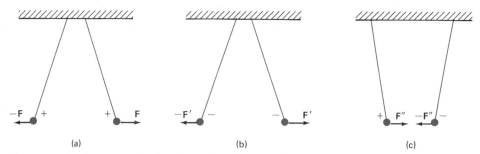

Fig. 20.2   Like charges repel each other; unlike charges attract each other.

ground has been broken as in Fig. 20.3c. Similar discharge of a negatively charged sphere is indicated in parts d, e, and f of Fig. 20.3.

Because the human body is composed largely of aqueous solutions, the body is a fairly good conductor. If a person touches an electrified object like the spheres in Figs. 20.3a and d with one hand while touching a water pipe with the other hand, the object quickly loses its charge; the charges initially on the object reach the ground through the person's body. A metal rod that is held in the hand cannot be electrified by rubbing; the charge will leak off through the holder's body. However, the rod can be electrified if it is supplied with a handle made of an insulating material.

The modern model of electrification is based on the atomic model of matter with which the reader is familiar from earlier courses in chemistry. An atom has a small, dense, positively charged nucleus surrounded by a cloud of negative electrons. In the normal, uncharged situation the total positive and total negative charges on a body are of equal magnitude. For many pairs of materials, it is possible through intimate contact to transfer electrons from one material to the other, giving the latter material a net negative charge and leaving the first material with an equal positive charge. The number of electrons actually transferred in such a process compared to the number available is very small.

In terms of this model, conductors are materials that have some of their electrons free to move and offer little opposition to the motion of these electrons; insulators are materials that offer a great deal of opposition to the motion of electrons.

20.2   FORCES EXERTED BY CHARGED BODIES

We can now give a qualitative treatment of the way in which electrified bodies attract small nearby uncharged objects. Consider the situation in Fig. 20.4a in which an electrified glass rod is held near an uncharged metal-coated pith ball. The electrons of the conductor are attracted by the positively charged rod, and some of the free electrons will move to the part of the sphere closest to the rod, giving that part of the sphere a negative charge. The opposite side of the sphere is then deficient in electrons and therefore has a net positive charge, as indicated in Fig. 20.4a. The negative part of the sphere, being closer to the rod, is attracted with a force of magnitude greater than that of the repulsive force on the positive part of the sphere. Thus, the net result is attraction of the sphere toward the rod. Similarly, a negatively charged rubber rod will exert a net force of attraction on an uncharged metal-coated pith ball, as indicated in Fig. 20.4b.

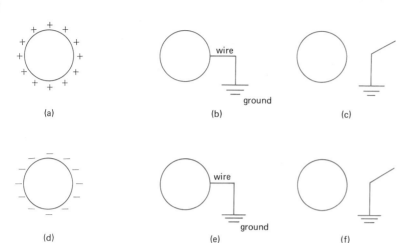

(a)

(b)

(c)

(d)

(e)

(f)

Fig. 20.3 An insulated charged metal sphere can be discharged by connecting it to "ground" with a metal wire.

The earliest observations of electrostatic attraction involved the forces exerted by an electrified body on light bodies like dry paper and lint, which are nonconducting materials in which there are no charges free to move about, in contrast to the case of metals. The interpretation of this situation is given schematically in Fig. 20.5, in which we show a greatly enlarged representation of the individual molecules of the dielectric material. Each molecule is electrically neutral, but because of the electric forces exerted by the charges on the electrified rod, the charges on each molecule are displaced from their equilibrium positions. Thus, as indicated in Fig. 20.5a, the center of negative charge in each molecule is closer to the positively charged glass rod than the center of positive charge in each molecule, because the negative charges are attracted by the charged glass rod and the positive charges are repelled by the charged glass rod. The material is said to be *polarized*. Because the negative charges in each molecule tend to be closer to the glass rod than the corresponding positive charges in each molecule, there is a net force of attraction exerted on the dielectric material by the rod. In Fig. 20.5b we show the corresponding situation for the case of a negatively charged hard rubber rod near a neutral, nonconducting material. In

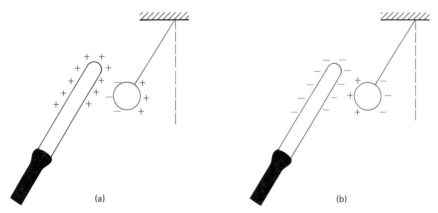

(a)

(b)

Fig. 20.4 A charged rod exerts a net attractive force on an uncharged metal-coated pith ball because it produces displacement of conduction electrons in the metal.

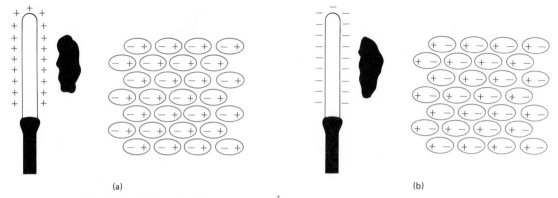

(a)   (b)

Fig. 20.5   A charged rod exerts a net attractive force on a small piece of dielectric material because it "polarizes" the material. At the right is an enormously enlarged representation of the molecules of the material.

this case the positive charges in each molecule tend to be closer to the charged rod than the negative charges in each molecule. There is, therefore, a net force of attraction between the uncharged dielectric material and the negatively charged rubber rod.

Some molecules, for example those of water, have a nonsymmetric charge distribution in their normal state, as suggested in Fig. 20.6. The presence of an external charged object such as the electrified glass and rubber rods considered above may increase their polarization as just described. It will also cause them to tend to be aligned with their ends of the same sign as the external charge farthest away; this effect is of great importance for fluids, in which the molecules are free to rotate. The qualitative net result of attraction of the material by the external charge is as already described. The molecular alignment will not be so uniform as indicated in Fig. 20.5 because of the thermal agitation of the molecules.

20.3   CHARGING BY ELECTROSTATIC INDUCTION; THE ELECTROSCOPE

We have indicated that insulated metal objects can be charged by actual contact with an electrified glass or rubber rod. This method of charging is rather crude; a metal body can be charged in a much more controllable manner by the process of *electrostatic induction*.

The scheme involved is demonstrated in Fig. 20.7. In part a we show two metal spheres in contact. If a negatively charged rubber rod is brought close to the left-hand sphere, as shown in part b of the figure, the sphere farther from the rod becomes negatively charged because electrons are repelled by the negatively charged rod; the sphere nearer the rod becomes deficient in electrons and thus is positively charged. The next step in the process, shown in Fig. 20.7c, is to separate the spheres *with the rubber rod still in position*. The final step, shown in part d of the figure, is to

Fig. 20.6   A water molecule has a nonspherically symmetric distribution of charge.

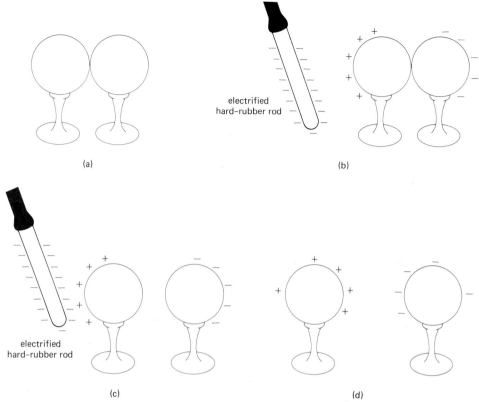

Fig. 20.7 Two metal spheres on insulating stands can be given charges of equal magnitude and opposite sign by the process of electrostatic induction.

remove the rubber rod; the final result is that we have two charged spheres, one with a positive charge and the other with a negative charge of equal magnitude. We could have obtained the same final result if we had used a positively charged glass rod.

As frequently employed, the process of electrostatic induction involves a single conductor that can be "grounded" in the manner shown in Fig. 20.8. In Fig. 20.8a

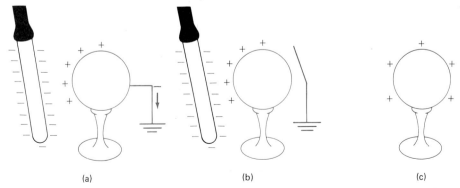

Fig. 20.8 A metal sphere on an insulating stand with a conducting connection to "ground" can be charged by the process of electrostatic induction.

we show a negatively charged rubber rod near a grounded metal sphere. The negative electrons in the metal sphere are repelled by the negatively charged rod, and some of the free electrons move off to the earth through the wire connecting the sphere to ground. The sphere is then deficient in electrons and is, therefore, positively charged. *With the rubber rod still in position,* the connection to ground is removed, as indicated in Fig. 20.8b. This leaves the sphere with a net positive charge. Finally, as shown in Fig. 20.8c, the rubber rod is removed; the sphere retains its net positive charge. If we had used a positively charged glass rod in the process, we would have ended with a final negative charge on the sphere.

The 18th century investigators recognized the need for quantitative information about amounts of charge. Eventually a simple device for detecting and giving semiquantitative measurements of electric charges was developed. This device is known as the *electroscope.*

A modern version of a simple electroscope is shown in Fig. 20.9. The device consists of a conducting rod *AD* to which is attached a metal foil leaf *F*. The lower portion of the rod is inside a grounded conducting case *C,* which shields the rod and foil leaf from air currents and from external electrical effects. Glass windows in the case allow observation of the angle of divergence of the leaf from the rod. At point *B* where the rod enters the case there is an insulating collar that electrically isolates the rod from the case.

Suppose that the electroscope is uncharged and a positively charged object is brought near the knob at *A*. Electrons will be attracted to the knob, leaving the lower part of the rod and the foil leaf positively charged. The repulsion between the charges on the leaf and those on the lower end of the rod will cause the leaf to diverge from the rod. The angle of divergence of the leaf is a quantitative, though not necessarily linear, measure of the amount of charge on the leaf and lower rod, which for a given separation between the charged body and the knob is a measure of the amount of charge on the external object. The leaves of an uncharged electroscope will diverge in a similar fashion when a negatively charged object is brought close to the knob. Provided that the charges brought near the knob are on small objects placed at a

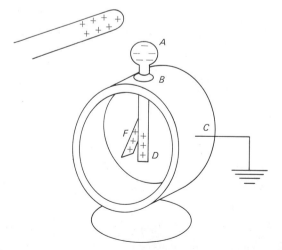

Fig. 20.9   An electroscope.

clearly established distance from the knob, an electroscope can be calibrated so that ratios of the magnitudes of charges can be measured quantitatively.

If we charge an electroscope by electrostatic induction until its leaf has a moderate angle of divergence from the lower rod, we can identify the kind of charge being brought close to the knob. For example, if the electroscope is charged positively, the divergence angle between the leaf and the lower rod will increase when a positive charge is brought close to the knob, but the divergence angle will decrease when a negative charge is brought close to the knob.

20.4 COULOMB'S PRINCIPLE

The results described in the preceding sections do not provide a basis for making quantitative predictions regarding the forces between charged bodies. We expect that some electrical concept analogous to the *particle* is needed in order to establish a basic principle for electrostatics. This entity is called the *point charge*. By point charge we mean a charged object with dimensions that are very much smaller than the distance between the charged object and any other charged objects with which interactions occur. Thus, in treating the forces between two charged spheres we can consider them as point charges if the radii of the spheres are much smaller than the distance between the centers of the spheres.

The magnitudes of the forces of attraction or repulsion between charged bodies increase rapidly as the distance between the charged bodies decreases. Because of the success of Newton's inverse-square relation for gravitation, scientists were disposed to look for a similar precise formula for the electric forces between point charges.

The first verification of the inverse-square law by systematic direct measurements of the forces between two charged objects approximating point charges was made in 1785 by Charles Augustin Coulomb (1736–1806). Coulomb used a torsion balance that he had invented†; a diagram of this device is shown in Fig. 20.10. Coulomb's "point charges" were two gold-coated pith balls, each having a radius of approximately

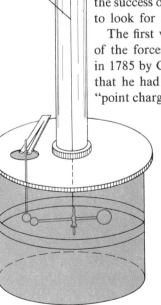

suspension head

fiber

Fig. 20.10 Coulomb's torsion balance.

---

† A similar torsion balance was later used by Cavendish to determine the gravitational constant G (see Chapter 9).

2 mm. By turning the suspension head, he could adjust the system for equilibrium for various distances between the charged pith balls. Thus, for a given rotation θ of the head he could measure the torque $\tau = C\theta$ in terms of the previously carefully determined torsion constant C of the supporting fiber. This torque exerted by the fiber is equal in magnitude and opposite in sense to the torque associated with the electric force **F** exerted on the charged particle attached to the lower end of the suspension. With this device Coulomb concluded that for a given pair of charges on the pith balls the magnitude of the electric force is inversely proportional to the separation d between the pith balls:

$$F \propto 1/d^2.$$

Coulomb did not have a way to experiment with arbitrarily chosen charges in any absolute sense. In determining the dependence of the force on the magnitudes of the charges Q_1 and Q_2 on the pith balls, Coulomb made use of the procedure suggested in Fig. 20.11. By starting with arbitrary charges Q_1 and Q_2 on the pith balls, he could divide these charges in such a manner as to measure the forces for a set of charges $Q_1, Q_1/2, Q_1/4, Q_1/8, \ldots$, and $Q_2, Q_2/2, Q_2/4, Q_2/8, \ldots$. By this procedure Coulomb was able to show that for a given separation d, the magnitude of the force between the pith balls is directly proportional to the product of the charges: $F \propto Q_1Q_2$.

The results of Coulomb's studies provide a principle on which a theory of electrostatics can be based:

COULOMB'S PRINCIPLE OF ELECTROSTATICS: The magnitude of the mutual force between two point charges is directly proportional to the product of the charges and inversely proportional to the square of the distance between the charges; like charges repel each other, unlike charges attract each other.

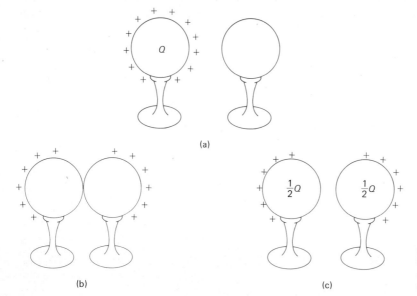

(a)

(b)

(c)

Fig. 20.11 Two identical metal spheres on insulating stands when brought into contact will each acquire half of the net total charge originally on the two spheres.

Stated mathematically, Coulomb's Principle asserts that

$$F \propto Q_1 Q_2/d^2 \quad \text{or} \quad F = \text{constant} \cdot (Q_1 Q_2/d^2). \tag{20.1}$$

The value of the proportionality constant depends on our choice of units for the measurement of the charges.

We note in Fig. 20.12 that the forces on the point charges are oppositely directed and act along the line joining the charges. In accordance with Newton's Third Principle,

$$\mathbf{F}_{12} = -\mathbf{F}_{21},$$

where $\mathbf{F}_{12}$ is the force exerted *on* charge Q_1 *by* charge Q_2 and $\mathbf{F}_{21}$ is the force exerted *on* charge Q_2 *by* charge Q_1; the magnitude of each force is given by (20.1).

In order to make use of the mathematical expression of Coulomb's Principle as given in (20.1), we must make a choice of the charge units to be used in measuring Q_1 and Q_2; once this choice has been made, the value of the proportionality constant is dictated. In the SI we must introduce one more fundamental physical quantity in addition to mass, length, time, and temperature. Tentatively we take this quantity to be electric charge; in a later chapter we shall see that for technical reasons current is a better choice.

The SI charge unit is called the *coulomb* (C). We define the coulomb by writing (20.1) in the form

$$F = (1/4\pi\epsilon_0)(Q_1 Q_2/d^2). \qquad \begin{cases} F \text{ in N} \\ Q_1, Q_2 \text{ in C} \\ d \text{ in m} \end{cases} \tag{20.2}$$

We write the proportionality constant in the form $(1/4\pi\epsilon_0)$ for reasons of convenience; if we insert the factor 4π explicitly in (20.2), such factors will not appear in certain other equations that are used more frequently than (20.2). The value of the proportionality constant is

$$1/4\pi\epsilon_0 = 8.98755178 \times 10^9 \text{ N} \cdot \text{m}^2/\text{C}^2.$$

For most of our computations it will be sufficiently accurate to use

$$1/4\pi\epsilon_0 \approx 9.0 \times 10^9 \text{ N} \cdot \text{m}^2/\text{C}^2.$$

We note that the proportionality constant in (20.2) is a *dimensional constant,* with its dimensions assigned to make (20.2) balance dimensionally. If the left-hand side

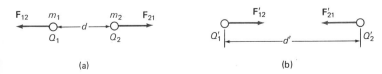

Fig. 20.12 The electrostatic forces between two point charges are directed along the line joining the charges. Part (a) shows charges of like sign that repel one another; part (b) shows charges of opposite sign that attract one another.

of (20.2) is expressed in N, the expression on the right-hand side of the equation must also be expressed in N. We accomplish this by expressing $1/4\pi\epsilon_0$ in $N \cdot m^2/C^2$. The numerical value of the proportionality constant is so unwieldy because, as we shall see later, the unit that actually is given an arbitrary operational definition is not the coulomb but the ampere, a unit of current. The size of the coulomb is then derived from the size of the ampere, and the proportionality constant must have the value given above in order that the coulomb fit with the already established sizes of the newton and the meter.

The quantity ϵ_0 appearing in the proportionality constant is called the *permittivity of free space;* for our present purposes this is merely a name. The value of ϵ_0 is

$$\epsilon_0 = 8.85418782 \times 10^{-12} \, C^2/N \cdot m^2 \approx 8.85 \times 10^{-12} \, C^2/N \cdot m^2.$$

Although we shall find that the coulomb is of a convenient size for use in current electricity, it is enormous for use in most electrostatic studies. The static charges encountered in laboratory studies of electrostatics are very much smaller and are more conveniently expressed in terms of picocoulombs ($1 \, pC = 10^{-12} \, C$), nanocoulombs ($1 \, nC = 10^{-9} \, C$), or microcoulombs ($1 \, \mu C = 10^{-6} \, C$).

We should also point out that, although Coulomb's experimental work was performed in air, the expression of Coulomb's Principle given in (20.2) applies strictly to charges in vacuum. Equation (20.2) holds in good approximation for the forces between point charges in air. However, the force relation in (20.2) must be modified if we are considering forces between point charges immersed in some material medium such as oil because the effects of the charges within the medium itself become important; the principle itself applies to *all* pairs of charges. The electrostatic properties of materials are discussed in Chapter 24.

Example.   An aluminum-coated pith ball with a mass of 1 g and carrying a charge $Q_1 = -10 \, nC$ is attached to the end of a silk thread of negligible mass. When undisturbed, the ball hangs vertically downward. A small aluminum ball carrying a charge $Q_2 = 200 \, nC$ is held as shown in Fig. 20.13a; the distance d shown in Fig. 20.13a is 10 cm. What is the magnitude of the angle θ when the pith ball is in this new equilibrium position?

In its equilibrium position the pith ball is acted upon by three forces: (a) A horizontal electric force $\mathbf{F}$ to the left, (b) a gravitational force $\mathbf{w} = m\mathbf{g}$ downward, and (c) an elastic force $\mathbf{T}$ equal to the tension in the string. The resultant of these forces must be zero. Using the diagram in Fig. 20.13b, we see that the horizontal force $\mathbf{F}$ to the left must be equal in magnitude to the horizontal force component $T \sin \theta$ to the right; thus, $F = T \sin \theta$. Similarly, the upward force component $T \cos \theta$ must be equal to the magnitude of the downward force, $w = mg$; thus $mg = T \cos \theta$. Division of the first of these relations by the second gives

$$\frac{F}{mg} = \frac{T \sin \theta}{T \cos \theta} = \tan \theta.$$

From Coulomb's Principle as expressed in (20.2), we obtain

$$F = (9 \times 10^9 \text{ N·m}^2/\text{C}^2) \{(10 \times 10^{-9} \text{ C})(200 \times 10^{-9} \text{ C})/(0.1 \text{ m})^2\} = 1.8 \times 10^{-3} \text{ N}.$$

For mg, we obtain $(10^{-3} \text{ kg}) (9.8 \text{ m/s}^2) = 9.8 \times 10^{-3} \text{ N}$. Thus we have $\tan \theta = F/mg = (1.8 \times 10^{-3} \text{ N})/(9.8 \times 10^{-3} \text{ N}) = 0.184$, from which we obtain $\theta = \arctan 0.184 = 10.4°$. Note that we have used an electric force, a gravitational force, and an elastic force in the same equations. *Regardless of the nature of the forces involved, Newton's Principles still apply!*

20.5 QUANTIZATION OF CHARGES; CHARGE CONSERVATION

We are defining charge by means of Coulomb's Principle. However, some questions that we might ask about the nature of charge can be answered experimentally. Is electric charge merely a "subtle fluid" that can be subdivided without limit? Or are there some final small "atoms" of charge that cannot be subdivided? In the case of a chemical element, we know that there are ultimate units of the element called atoms. The element can be said to be *quantized* in the sense that there can be no samples smaller than the atom that still have the characteristic properties of the element.

The answer to our question regarding the nature of charge is that charge is quantized. In 1897 the British physicist J. J. Thomson (1856–1940) showed that the basic carrier of negative charge can be characterized as a particle with a definite ratio of charge to mass. This most common entity having the negative quantum or "atom" of electric charge is called the *electron*. Its charge was first accurately determined in the years around 1910 in a series of classic experiments by the American physicist Robert Andrews Millikan (1868–1953). There is a corresponding quantum or atom of positive charge, as was shown by J. J. Thomson in a series of experiments begun in 1906. The most common simple entity having the positive quantum of electric charge is called the proton. The magnitudes of the charges of the proton and the electron are identical and have the value

$$e = 1.6021892 \times 10^{-19} \text{ C, or approximately } 1.60 \times 10^{-19} \text{ C}.$$

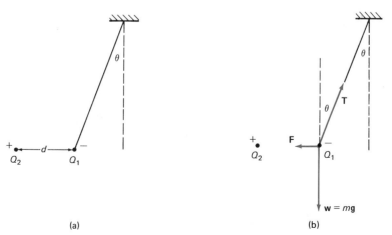

(a)   (b)   Fig. 20.13

The charge of the electron is thus $-e$; that of the proton is $+e$. Recent experiment has shown that the magnitudes of the charges of the proton and the electron differ at most by one part in 10^{20}.

All presently known particles or systems of particles have charges that are positive or negative integral multiples of the basic quantum of charge e. There have been theoretical speculations concerning the existence of microscopic objects having charges that are fractions of e, but there is at present no convincing direct experimental evidence for the existence of such objects.

Protons and electrons are material particles, the masses of which have been accurately determined (see Appendix); the mass of the proton is approximately 1837 times that of the electron. These two particles along with the neutron, an electrically neutral particle with a mass slightly greater than that of the proton, are the basic building blocks of atoms. The atom of an element is electrically neutral; it consists of a "cloud" of Z electrons clustered about a much smaller positively charged nucleus composed of neutrons and Z protons, where Z is the atomic number of the element in the Periodic Table of the Elements.

When correctly inserted into the structure of quantum physics, the Coulomb interaction accurately describes the dominant term in the binding of electrons in atoms, the binding of atoms in molecules, and the binding of molecules in solids and liquids. Higher-order terms involve magnetic interactions that depend on the motions of charged particles. Most forces of our daily experience are ultimately of either gravitational or electromagnetic origin. We have considered the importance of gravitational forces in astronomy and in being responsible for the weight of an object near the earth's surface. The elastic forces that we have discussed earlier are ultimately primarily electrostatic in nature. Electrostatic forces keep the atoms in solids from being pulled apart or pushed together; electrostatic forces between molecules cause liquids to resist compression. Frictional forces also have their ultimate origin primarily in electrostatic interactions.

Example.   The electrostatic forces we have discussed in the present chapter are seemingly very small; we have observed them by noting their effects on small objects like pith balls. Compare the electric force between the electron and the proton in a hydrogen atom with the corresponding gravitational force between these particles. The average electron–proton separation in a hydrogen atom is approximately 5.3×10^{-11} m; the masses of the proton and electron are given in the Appendix.

The magnitudes of the electrostatic and gravitational forces are

$$F(\text{electrostatic}) = \frac{1}{4\pi\epsilon_0}\frac{Q_1 Q_2}{d^2} = \frac{(9.0 \times 10^9 \text{ N}\cdot\text{m}^2/\text{C}^2)(1.6 \times 10^{-19} \text{ C})^2}{(5.3 \times 10^{-11} \text{ m})^2}$$

$$= 8.1 \times 10^{-8} \text{ N}$$

and

$$F(\text{gravitational}) = G\frac{m_1 m_2}{d^2}$$

$$= \frac{(6.7 \times 10^{-11} \text{ N} \cdot \text{m}^2/\text{kg}^2)(9.1 \times 10^{-31} \text{ kg})(1.7 \times 10^{-27} \text{ kg})}{(5.3 \times 10^{-11} \text{ m})^2}$$

$$= 3.7 \times 10^{-47} \text{ N}.$$

The gravitational force is completely negligible. *In atoms and molecules the electrostatic forces are the really important forces.*

When we electrify a hard-rubber rod by rubbing it with cat's fur, we transfer electrons from the cat's fur to the rubber rod; the resulting net positive charge on the cat's fur is exactly equal to the resulting negative charge on the rubber rod. We do not *create* any electric charge by frictional work; we merely transfer charge from one body to the other. Regarding the cat's fur and the hard-rubber rod as a *closed system,* we can say that the *net* charge of the system does not change; we merely rearrange the charges within the system. Initially each body in this two-body system is neutral with no net charge; after electrification, the cat's fur has a net charge $+Q$ and the rubber rod has a net charge $-Q$. Because the magnitudes of the positive and negative charges are equal, the net charge of the system remains zero.

On the basis of this idea, which is supported by a vast amount of experience, we can state a general principle:

PRINCIPLE OF CHARGE CONSERVATION: The net electric charge of any closed system is constant in time and is not changed by interaction between bodies inside the system.

We know of no violations of this principle. We cannot "create" a positive charge without also creating a negative charge of equal magnitude.

20.6   VECTOR FORMULATION OF COULOMB'S PRINCIPLE

Coulomb's Principle as stated in (20.2) gives the magnitude F of the mutual force of attraction or repulsion between two charges Q_1 and Q_2; we have separately state i the directions of the forces as along the line joining Q_1 and Q_2. Separate use of these two relations is reasonably convenient when only two charges are being considered. However, when we are considering a system consisting of more than two charges, we can simplify matters by stating Coulomb's Principle in vector form.

Consider some arbitrarily chosen system of coordinates with origin O. Assume that Q_1 is located by the position vector $\mathbf{r}_1 = x_1\mathbf{i} + y_1\mathbf{j} + z_1\mathbf{k}$ and Q_2 is located by the position vector $\mathbf{r}_2 = x_2\mathbf{i} + y_2\mathbf{j} + z_2\mathbf{k}$, as indicated in Fig. 20.14. Then the force on charge Q_2 due to the presence of charge Q_1 is

$$\mathbf{F}_{21} = \frac{1}{4\pi\epsilon_0} \frac{Q_1 Q_2}{r_{21}^2} \hat{\mathbf{r}}_{21}, \qquad (20.3)$$

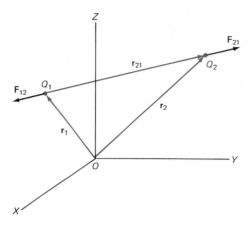

Fig. 20.14 Position vectors and force vectors involved in the vector statement of Coulomb's Principle; the figure is drawn for the case where charges Q_1 and Q_2 have the same sign.

where

$$\mathbf{r}_{21} \equiv \mathbf{r}_2 - \mathbf{r}_1 = (x_2 - x_1)\mathbf{i} + (y_2 - y_1)\mathbf{j} + (z_2 - z_1)\mathbf{k},$$

$$r_{21} \equiv |\mathbf{r}_{21}| = \sqrt{(x_2 - x_1)^2 + (y_2 - y_1)^2 + (z_2 - z_1)^2},$$

and $\hat{\mathbf{r}}_{21}$ is the unit vector, $\hat{\mathbf{r}}_{21} = \mathbf{r}_{21}/r_{21}$.

The quantities Q_1 and Q_2 in (20.3) must have algebraic signs according to the type of charge they represent, plus for a positive charge and minus for a negative charge. In accord with Newton's Third Principle, the force on charge Q_1 due to charge Q_2 is $\mathbf{F}_{12} = -\mathbf{F}_{21}$. The vectors involved in these relations are shown in Fig. 20.14, which has been drawn for the case where Q_1 and Q_2 have the same sign. If Q_1 and Q_2 have opposite signs, they attract each other, and the directions of $\mathbf{F}_{12}$ and $\mathbf{F}_{21}$ are the reverse of those shown in the figure.

If there are more than two charges, the interaction between each pair of charges is described by Coulomb's Principle (20.3). The total force on any single charge, say the ith one, is the *vector sum* of the individual contributions from all the other charges, each computed using (20.3). This is illustrated in Fig. 20.15, where it is assumed that all the charges have the same sign. A relation expressing this idea is

$$\mathbf{F}_i(\text{total}) = \mathbf{F}_{i1} + \mathbf{F}_{i2} + \mathbf{F}_{i3} + \cdots, \tag{20.4}$$

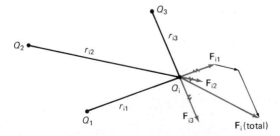

Fig. 20.15 The total Coulomb force on charge Q_i is the vector sum of the forces due to each of the other charges.

where $\mathbf{F}_i(\text{total})$ is the resultant force on the ith charge and, for example,

$$\mathbf{F}_{i1} = \frac{1}{4\pi\epsilon_0} \frac{Q_i Q_1}{r_{i1}^2} \hat{\mathbf{r}}_{i1}, \text{ etc.}$$

Example.   As an illustration of the use of this relation, consider three point charges Q_1, Q_2, and Q_3 fixed at the verticies of a right triangle as shown in Fig. 20.16. What is the resultant force on Q_3 exerted by Q_1 and Q_2?

It will be convenient to choose the origin of coordinates at the location of Q_1 with the X axis directed toward Q_2 and all three charges lying in the XY plane. Then $\mathbf{r}_1 = 0$, $\mathbf{r}_2 = (4 \times 10^{-3} \text{ m})\mathbf{i}$, and $\mathbf{r}_3 = (4 \times 10^{-3} \text{ m})\mathbf{i} + (3 \times 10^{-3} \text{ m})\mathbf{j}$, from which it follows that $\hat{\mathbf{r}}_{32} = \mathbf{j}$ and $\hat{\mathbf{r}}_{31} = \tfrac{4}{5}\mathbf{i} + \tfrac{3}{5}\mathbf{j}$. From (20.3) and (20.4) we have

$$\mathbf{F}_{32} = \frac{1}{4\pi\epsilon_0} \frac{Q_3 Q_2}{r_{32}^2} \mathbf{j}, \qquad \mathbf{F}_{31} = \frac{1}{4\pi\epsilon_0} \frac{Q_3 Q_1}{r_{31}^2} (\tfrac{4}{5}\mathbf{i} + \tfrac{3}{5}\mathbf{j}),$$

and

$$\mathbf{F}_3(\text{total}) = \mathbf{F}_{31} + \mathbf{F}_{32} = \frac{1}{4\pi\epsilon_0} Q_3 \left\{ \frac{Q_1}{r_{31}^2} \frac{4}{5}\mathbf{i} + \left(\frac{Q_1}{r_{31}^2} \frac{3}{5} + \frac{Q_2}{r_{32}^2} \right)\mathbf{j} \right\}$$

$$= (9 \times 10^9 \text{ N} \cdot \text{m}^2/\text{C}^2)(2 \times 10^{-9} \text{ C}) \left\{ \frac{(-5 \times 10^{-9} \text{ C})}{(5 \times 10^{-3} \text{ m})^2} \frac{4}{5}\mathbf{i} \right.$$

$$\left. + \left(\frac{(-5 \times 10^{-9} \text{ C})}{(5 \times 10^{-3} \text{ m})^2} \frac{3}{5} + \frac{(3 \times 10^{-9} \text{ C})}{(3 \times 10^{-3} \text{ m})^2} \right)\mathbf{j} \right\}$$

$$= (-2.88 \times 10^{-3} \text{ N})\mathbf{i} + (3.84 \times 10^{-3} \text{ N})\mathbf{j}.$$

In polar notation this is

$$\mathbf{F}_3(\text{total}) = \sqrt{(-2.88 \times 10^{-3})^2 + (3.84 \times 10^{-3})^2} \text{ N} = 4.80 \times 10^{-3} \text{ N}$$

and

$$\phi = \text{arc cos}(-2.88 \times 10^{-3} \text{ N}/4.80 \times 10^{-3} \text{ N})$$
$$= \text{arc tan}[(3.84 \times 10^{-3})/(-2.88 \times 10^{-3})] = 127°.$$

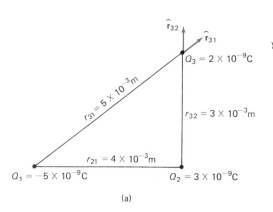

(a)

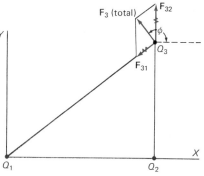

(b)

Fig. 20.16

QUESTIONS

1. Why is *rubbing* necessary to produce electrification of a pair of objects like a hard-rubber rod and a piece of cat's fur? In order to increase the amount of charge separation in a given time, should one press the surfaces together with greater force, or rub more rapidly, or both?

2. Someone proposes that a third kind of electric charge, different from the positive and negative charges defined in Section 20.1, is produced when a dry rod made of a certain kind of plastic is rubbed with a wool cloth. Describe a series of experiments that you might use to verify or refute this claim.

3. Electrification of a glass rod and a silk cloth or a hard-rubber rod and a piece of cat's fur can be produced by rubbing the objects together while holding them in one's hands. However, a hand-held copper rod will not become electrified when rubbed with any other material. Explain the difference in the two situations.

4. Why is it difficult to perform experiments in electrostatics when the humidity is high?

5. What will be the result if the metal-coated pith ball in Fig. 20.4 is allowed to touch the charged rod? Will the two objects cling together?

6. What limits the amount of charge that can be given to a metal sphere by an induction process like that shown in Fig. 20.8?

7. Explain how Coulomb could utilize procedures like that illustrated in Fig. 20.11 to reach the conclusion that the mutual force between two point charges is directly proportional to the *product* of the charges.

8. In discussing planetary motion in Chapter 9, we made no mention of electric forces. Why are electric forces unimportant in the dynamics of the solar system?

9. What does it mean to say that electric charge is *quantized?* Are there other basic physical quantities that are quantized?

10. It is asserted that a certain object on an insulating stand is charged. Describe experiments by which you could verify this assertion and determine the sign of the charge without touching the object. Be sure that your procedure is not susceptible to error because of induction or polarization effects.

11. You have a negatively charged hard-rubber rod, two identical uncharged conducting spheres on insulating stands, and several lengths of metal wire that can be used to connect the spheres to ground. Describe a procedure by which the spheres can be given equal negative charges.

12. At one time, most gasoline trucks dragged metal chains long enough to make contact with the ground. Can you imagine why this was done? Do you think the procedure was effective?

PROBLEMS

1. Two point charges each experience an electrostatic force of attraction of 1.25×10^{-3} N when they are separated by a distance of 25 cm. What will be their mutual force of attraction when they are (a) 100 cm apart? (b) 10 m apart? (c) 2 km apart? (d) 1.25 cm apart?

2. What is the magnitude of the mutual force between two point charges of equal magnitude when the charges are 10 cm apart for cases where the sizes of the charges are (a) 1 C, (b) 1 mC, (c) 1 μC, (d) 1 nC, and (e) 1 pC? In each case find the mass of a body that near the earth's surface where $w = mg$

would have a weight equal in magnitude to this electrostatic force.

3. A positive point charge and a negative point charge experience a mutual electrostatic force of attraction of 4.0×10^{-3} N when they are separated by a distance of 12 cm. Suppose that the positive charge is doubled and the negative charge is reduced in magnitude to one-quarter of its original size. The new charges are separated by a distance of 36 cm. What is the force on the positive charge? What is the force on the negative charge? What should be the separation of the charges if their mutual force of attraction is to have its original value of 4.0×10^{-3} N?

4. Suppose there were a 200 C point charge at the center of the earth. How large a charge would have to be placed on a 3-kg object at the earth's surface in order for the Coulomb force on it to be equal in magnitude to its weight? Assume that the force can be computed as if the charges were in a vacuum. The mass of the earth is 5.98×10^{24} kg. If the object were made of aluminum, how many electrons would it have to lose to acquire a positive charge of this magnitude? Is this possible?

5. Two point charges $Q_1 = 30$ nC and $Q_2 = 40$ nC are at the locations (0, 3 cm, 0) and (4 cm, 0, 0), respectively. What is the electrostatic force on Q_1?

6. What is the electrostatic force on Q_1 in Problem 5 if Q_2 is doubled? Repeat if Q_1 is doubled instead of Q_2.

7. The charges described in Problem 5 are moved so that Q_1 is located at (0, 6 cm, 0) and Q_2 is located at (8 cm, 0, 0). What is then the electrostatic force on Q_1?

8. For the situation considered in Problem 7, to what value should the charge Q_1 be changed in order to restore the force between Q_1 and Q_2 to the original value found in Problem 5?

9. Point charges Q_1 and Q_2 are located as in Problem 5. A third point charge $Q_3 = 20$ nC is placed at the origin. What is then the electrostatic force on Q_1? Repeat if the charge at the origin is -20 nC.

10. Consider a model of a hydrogen atom in which an electron of mass m_e moves uniformly in a circular orbit about a fixed proton of mass $m_p = 1836m_e$. Derive an expression for the kinetic energy of the electron in terms of the charge on the electron and the radius of the orbit.

11. The radius of a helium nucleus is approximately 1.5×10^{-15} m. The helium nucleus contains two protons and two neutrons. Calculate the magnitude of the electrostatic force between two protons separated by a distance of 3.0×10^{-15} m. What magnitude of acceleration would a resultant force of this magnitude give to a proton? The electrostatic force on the proton is enormous, but larger nonelectric forces of attraction act within the nucleus to make the nucleus stable.

12. Two very small equally charged spheres would each require the addition of 10^{12} electrons to become neutral. What is the electrostatic force between these spheres when their centers are 40 cm apart? Assume that the radii of the spheres are much smaller than their separation so they can be treated as point charges.

13. A small conducting bead of mass m can slide on a vertical silk thread near the surface of the earth. A second small, insulated conductor is fixed at the lower end of the thread. If each of the conductors has a positive charge Q, what is the equilibrium height h of the bead above the lower end of the thread? Ignore frictional effects. Find the value of h when $Q = 4.5$ μC and $m = 5.5$ g.

14. Three small conductors each of mass m and having a negative charge $-Q$ are fastened at the vertices of an equilateral triangle of side b to a horizontal insulating surface with

an insulating glue. This surface is near the surface of the earth. What is the force exerted on a particular one of the conductors by the insulating surface? Use a Cartesian coordinate system with Y axis through the chosen conductor and X axis through the other two conductors.

15. Two small conductors with masses and charges m_1, Q_1 and m_2, Q_2, respectively, are fastened at opposite ends of a helical spring of spring constant k. The spring itself is nonconducting. The system rests on a horizontal, frictionless, insulating surface. Describe in detail how one could obtain the elongation of the spring if its unstressed length, the spring constant, and the charges and masses of the conductors were given. How would the problem be complicated if the spring were conducting?

16. Two point charges that have equal magnitudes Q but opposite sign and are separated by a distance d are said to form an electric dipole. The orientation of the dipole is given by the direction of the displacement vector $\mathbf{d}$ from the negative charge to the positive charge. Two identical dipoles of fixed length d have their centers at $z = ad$ and $z = -ad$, respectively, on the Z axis, where $a > \frac{1}{2}$. The dipoles are both oriented parallel to the Z axis. What is the electrostatic force on the dipole at $z = +ad$ due to the other dipole?

17. Repeat Problem 16 if both dipoles are oriented parallel to the X axis.

18. Repeat Problem 16 if the dipole at $z = +ad$ is oriented parallel to the X axis and the dipole at $z = -ad$ is oriented antiparallel to the X axis.

19. Repeat Problem 16 if the dipole at $z = +ad$ is oriented parallel to the X axis and the dipole at $z = -ad$ is oriented parallel to the Y axis.

20. Repeat Problem 16 if the dipole at $z = +ad$ is oriented parallel to the Z axis and the dipole at $z = -ad$ is oriented parallel to the Y axis.

21. Consider three point charges Q_1, Q_2, and Q_3. When separated by a distance of 75 cm, charges Q_1 and Q_2 have a mutual force of electrostatic repulsion of 2.4×10^{-2} N. Charges Q_2 and Q_3 have a mutual force of electrostatic attraction of this same magnitude when separated by a distance of 47 cm. When brought to exactly the same position relative to the knob of an uncharged electroscope, charges Q_2 and Q_3 cause the same divergence of the electroscope leaf. Charge Q_3 is attracted by an electrified hard-rubber rod that has been rubbed with cat's fur. Determine Q_1, Q_2, and Q_3.

22. What should be the magnitude of equal point charges placed at the locations of the center of the sun and the center of the earth if they are to yield a Coulomb force equal in magnitude to the gravitational force between the earth and the sun? How many electrons would be required to give a charge of this magnitude? If each atom provides one electron, how large a sphere of copper would be required to furnish this many electrons? The mass of the earth is 5.98×10^{24} kg; the mass of the sun is 1.99×10^{30} kg.

23. A given charge Q is to be divided into two parts, q and $Q - q$, and these two charges are to be placed on the ends of a stick of fixed length l. What value of q will give the maximum force of repulsion between the two charges?

24. Two small, metal-coated pith balls, each initially uncharged, are charged by induction as shown in Fig. 20.7. When they are separated by a distance of 50 cm, their mutual force of attraction is 1.75×10^{-4} N. How many electrons have been transferred from the positive pith ball to the negative pith ball?

25. Two solid copper spheres, each of radius 1.0 cm, are mounted on insulating stands. The spheres are each charged by induction using the technique illustrated in Fig. 20.8. Sphere one is given a charge of $+2 \times 10^{-8}$ C and sphere two is given a

charge of -4.5×10^{-8} C. (a) If the spheres were initially neutral, how many electrons have been gained or lost by each sphere? (b) What fractions are these values of the total number of conduction electrons present for the neutral spheres? (c) If the spheres are separated by a distance of 1.75 m, what is their mutual electrostatic force of attraction? (d) The spheres are brought into contact and left until equilibrium is attained. They are then again separated by a distance of 1.75 m. What is the new mutual electrostatic force? Assume that each copper atom contributes one valence electron as a conduction electron.

26. You are given four identical metal spheres on insulating stands. Describe two different ways in which you could use charging by induction to obtain *equal* charges on three of the spheres with the fourth sphere uncharged. Is it possible to obtain three spheres with charges of equal magnitude, two positive and the third negative? If so, describe how.

27. A hard-rubber rod that has been rubbed with cat's fur is used to charge a small metal sphere by induction as shown in Fig. 20.8. The sphere is then brought into contact with an identical but uncharged sphere. The spheres are separated and placed 463 cm apart. The force between them then has a magnitude of 1.7×10^{-3} N. Is this a force of attraction or repulsion? How many electrons were transferred to or from ground in the original charging of the first sphere?

28. The density of table salt NaCl is 2165 kg/m³. The lattice structure is a cubic array with alternate positions occupied by positive and by negative ions. Each ion has six nearest neighbors of the opposite sign. Show that the spacing between adjacent sodium and chlorine ions is approximately 2.82×10^{-10} m. What is the magnitude of the Coulomb force of attraction between a sodium ion and a nearest neighbor chlorine ion?

29. (a) Two bodies attract each other electrically. Are they necessarily both charged? (b) Two bodies repel each other electrically. Are they necessarily both charged? Explain the reasons for your answers.

30. Two small, metal-coated pith balls, each having a mass of 12 g, are held at the ends of silk threads each 110 cm long. The other ends of the threads are fastened to the ceiling at a common point. Positive charges are given to each pith ball, and they come to equilibrium at a separation of 23 cm along a horizontal line. If the charge on one of the pith balls is $q_1 = 7.3 \times 10^{-8}$ C, what is the charge q_2 on the other pith ball?

31. Two fixed charges of $Q = -6 \times 10^{-6}$ C each are 21 cm apart. What resultant force do they exert on a third charge $Q_3 = +4.5 \times 10^{-6}$ C that is 28 cm from each of the two charges?

32. Two fixed charges of $Q_1 = +6.5 \times 10^{-6}$ C and $Q_2 = +3.25 \times 10^{-6}$ C are 12 cm apart. What resultant force do they exert on a third charge $Q_3 = +8.0 \times 10^{-6}$ C that is 10 cm from each of the two charges?

33. Four point charges, each having $Q = +2.34 \times 10^{-6}$ C, are fixed on four corners of a regular pentagon having sides of length a. What is the resultant electrostatic force they exert on a charge $q = -1.98 \times 10^{-6}$ C placed on the fifth corner of the pentagon if $a = 15$ cm?

34. Three point charges, $Q_1 = +2.0 \times 10^{-7}$ C, $Q_2 = +4.0 \times 10^{-7}$ C, and $Q_3 = +6.0 \times 10^{-7}$ C, are fixed at the vertices of an equilateral triangle having sides 8 cm in length. Find the resultant electrostatic force on each of the charges. If this system of charges is attached to a flat plate of mass 3.5 g that is resting on a horizontal frictionless surface, in what direction and with what magnitude will the plate be accelerated?

35. Two fixed charges of $Q_1 = +12 \times 10^{-6}$ C and $Q_2 = -7 \times 10^{-6}$ C are 11 cm apart. Where can a third charge Q_3 be placed so

that the resultant electrostatic force acting on it is zero?

36. For the situation of Problem 35, is the charge Q_3 in a position of stable, unstable, or neutral equilibrium? Explain your reasoning in detail. Does the sign of Q_3 make any difference in your conclusion?

37. How far apart must two electrons be if their mutual force of electrostatic repulsion is to be equal in magnitude to the weight of an electron close to the surface of the earth?

38. Two positive point charges each of magnitude 3.4×10^{-6} C are located, respectively, at the north and south poles of an insulating sphere of radius 87 cm. What are the magnitude and direction of the Coulomb force on a positive point charge of magnitude 0.84×10^{-6} C located on the equator of the sphere? If the sphere is rotating at 300 revolutions per minute, what is the tension in a string that ties the charge on the equator to the surface of the sphere if this charge is on a particle of mass 0.03 g? Ignore gravita-

tional effects and any force arising from electrical polarization of the material of the sphere.

39. Three point charges, each having $Q = +3.0 \times 10^{-7}$ C, are fixed at the vertices of an equilateral triangle having sides 2 cm in length. The triangle is in a horizontal plane, which we take as the XY plane, close to the surface of the earth. The Z axis is vertical and passes through the geometrical center of the triangle. What will be the initial acceleration of a small pith ball of mass 0.5 g carrying a charge $q = +3.0 \times 10^{-8}$ C if the pith ball is placed on the Z axis at 10 cm above the XY plane?

40. Three positive point charges of magnitudes 4×10^{-6} C, 5×10^{-6} C, and 6×10^{-6} C are located at coordinates $(a,0,0)$, $(0,a,0)$, and $(0,0,a)$, respectively, where $a = 12$ cm. What are the magnitude and direction of the Coulomb force on a charge $q = +2 \times 10^{-6}$ C located at the point (a,a,a)?

CHAPTER 21

The Electric Field

In our treatment of gravitational forces in Chapter 9 we noted that the gravitational force on a body can be interpreted as an interaction of the mass of the body with a gravitational field existing throughout space. This gravitational field can be determined by exploring a region of space with a small test particle of mass m_0 and assigning to each point in space a field-strength vector $\mathscr{G} = \mathbf{F}/m_0$, where $\mathbf{F}$ is the gravitational force on the test particle.

Field concepts were introduced into the study of electricity and magnetism during the 19th century by Michael Faraday (1791–1867) and were organized and extended in beautiful mathematical form by James Clerk Maxwell (1831–1879). From the modern viewpoint, the electromagnetic-field concept is the principal idea of electromagnetic theory. The electromagnetic field accounts not only for the forces involved in electromagnetic interactions between bodies but also for the transmission of energy through space in the form of electromagnetic radiation. For approximately 8 min between the time of its departure from the sun and the time of its arrival at the earth, the radiant energy reaching us from the sun is divorced from matter and is associated with an electromagnetic field in "empty" space.

The electromagnetic-field theory developed by Maxwell represents one of the greatest intellectual achievements of the 19th century. Practical applications of this theory have been essential in such major engineering developments of the 20th century as radio, radar, television, lasers, and the electric power industry. In this chapter we shall define the electric-field strength and then investigate how this quantity can be calculated for various electrostatic situations.

21.1 ELECTRIC-FIELD STRENGTH

We shall begin our study of electromagnetic fields by directing our attention to the electric-field strength. In order to give a precise, quantitative definition of this quantity, we need the concept of a *test charge,* which is a point charge that is so small in magnitude that its presence does not cause any measurable changes in the positions of other charges. Such a test charge can be used to determine the electric-field strength at various locations in space. Although the sign of a test charge is not of fundamental importance, it will be convenient to consider a *positive* test charge in establishing our definition. We define the electric-field strength as follows:

If the electric force on a positive test charge q_0 at rest at a given point in space is $\mathbf{F}_0$, then the ELECTRIC-FIELD STRENGTH $\mathscr{E}$ at the point is given by the ratio $\mathbf{F}_0/q_0$.

Thus, the electric-field strength gives a measure of the electric force per unit charge at any point in space:

$$\mathscr{E} = \mathbf{F}_0/q_0. \qquad \left\{ \begin{array}{l} \mathscr{E} \text{ in N/C} \\ F_0 \text{ in N} \\ q_0 \text{ in C} \end{array} \right\} \qquad (21.1)$$

Because $\mathbf{F}_0$ is a vector and q_0 is a scalar, the electric-field strength $\mathscr{E}$ is a vector; $\mathscr{E}$ has the same direction as the force $\mathbf{F}_0$ on a positive test charge.

The electric force $\mathbf{F}_0$ experienced by a test charge must be produced by other electric charges; therefore, the electric field at any point must be produced by other charges somewhere in space. These other charges that are responsible for the electric field are called *source charges.* As we show in detail below, the electric-field strength is independent of the particular test charge used. If a charge Q is sufficiently small that it does not cause shifts of the source charges and by its presence alter the field with which it interacts, we can express the electric force on the charge at some given point P in space by

$$\mathbf{F}(P) = Q\mathscr{E}(P), \qquad (21.2)$$

where $\mathscr{E}(P)$ is the electric-field strength at the point P. The quantity Q in (21.2) has an algebraic sign, plus for a positive charge and minus for a negative charge. If we place a positive charge at a given point, the direction of the electric force on the positive charge will be the same as the direction of the electric-field strength $\mathscr{E}$ at the point; if we place a negative charge at the point, the direction of the electric force on the negative charge will be opposite to the direction of $\mathscr{E}$ at the point. These relations are illustrated in Fig. 21.1.

The electric-field strength $\mathscr{E}$ determined from (21.1) is a characteristic of the source-charge distribution and the point in space; *there is an electric field at the point even when there is no test charge present.* If we try to employ (21.2) for increasingly larger charges Q, we eventually find that the measured force $\mathbf{F}$ is no longer proportional to Q. This is because the positions of the source charges have been changed as a result of their Coulomb interactions with Q. Because of the altered source-charge distribution, the modified field $\mathscr{E}'$ at the point where Q is located then depends on Q and does not equal the original field $\mathscr{E}$ given by (21.1). However, *if the source*

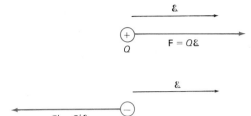

Fig. 21.1   The electric force on a positive charge is in the same direction as $\mathscr{E}$; the electric force on a negative charge is opposite to the direction of $\mathscr{E}$.

charges remain in fixed positions, the ratio $\mathbf{F}(P)/Q_0 = \mathscr{E}(P)$ for "test charges" Q_0 of any size; in such a hypothetical case, any charge Q_0 can be used to establish $\mathscr{E}(P)$.

21.2   ELECTRIC FIELD OF POINT SOURCE CHARGES

The simplest kind of source of an electric field is a single, fixed point charge. Let us consider a positive point source charge Q in vacuum with the origin of a coordinate system at the location of the point charge, as shown in Fig. 21.2a. If we place a positive test charge q_0 at the point P a distance r from the origin, the electric force $\mathbf{F}_0$ on the test charge given by Coulomb's Principle is $\mathbf{F}_0 = (1/4\pi\epsilon_0)(q_0 Q/r^2)\hat{\mathbf{r}}$, where $\hat{\mathbf{r}}$ is a unit vector directed radially away from Q; thus, by (21.1) we have the following expression for the electric-field strength $\mathscr{E}$ due to a fixed point charge Q in vacuum at the origin:

$$\mathscr{E} = \frac{1}{4\pi\epsilon_0}\frac{Q}{r^2}\hat{\mathbf{r}}. \quad \textit{(Point Source)} \tag{21.3}$$

Since Coulomb's Principle says that $\mathbf{F}_0$ is proportional to q_0, the electric-field strength given by (21.3) is independent of the test charge q_0 and depends only on the source charge, in agreement with the discussion of the preceding section.

The electric-field strength $\mathscr{E}$ arising from a negative fixed point source charge is also given by (21.3) if the proper algebraic sign is used for Q. In the case of a

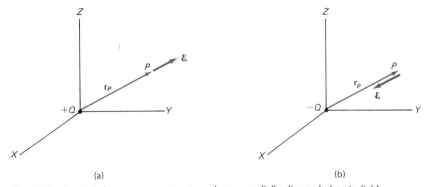

(a)   (b)

Fig. 21.2   A point-charge source at rest produces a radially directed electric field.

negative point source, the direction of $\mathscr{E}$ is radially inward toward the source charge, as indicated in Fig. 21.2b.

In the preceding chapter we learned that the resultant electric force on a charge due to a collection of other charges is the vector sum of the individual electric forces associated with each other charge computed as if that were the only other charge present. Thus, the resultant electric force $\mathbf{F}_{0R}$ on a test charge q_0 due to several point source charges Q_1, Q_2, Q_3 ..., is the vector sum of the forces due to each source considered separately: $\mathbf{F}_{0R} = \mathbf{F}_{01} + \mathbf{F}_{02} + \mathbf{F}_{03} + \cdots$. When we divide this force relation by q_0 and use (21.1), we obtain a linear-superposition relation for electric-field strength:

$$\mathscr{E}_R = \mathscr{E}_1 + \mathscr{E}_2 + \mathscr{E}_3 + \cdots. \tag{21.4}$$

Here $\mathscr{E}_R$ is the resultant electric-field strength at the location of the test charge and $\mathscr{E}_1$, $\mathscr{E}_2$, $\mathscr{E}_3$, etc., are the field strengths that the source charges Q_1, Q_2, Q_3, etc., would produce if each in turn were the only source charge present.

Suppose we want to know the resultant electric-field strength $\mathscr{E}_R(P)$ at a point P that is located by the position vector $\mathbf{r}_P$ when the sources of the electric field are point charges Q_1, Q_2, Q_3, . . . , that are located by position vectors $\mathbf{r}_1$, $\mathbf{r}_2$, $\mathbf{r}_3$, ... The displacement vector from the location of the jth source charge Q_j to the point P is given by $\mathbf{r}_{Pj} \equiv \mathbf{r}_P - \mathbf{r}_j$; the distance from Q_j to P is $|\mathbf{r}_P - \mathbf{r}_j| = r_{Pj}$. This situation is illustrated in Fig. 21.3a for a case having three source charges. The electric-field strength for a single point source charge is given by (21.3) except now we do not have the origin at the location of the point charge; this tells us how to write the individual terms on the right-hand side of (21.4). For N source charges we have that

$$\mathscr{E}_R(P) = \sum_{j=i}^{N} \mathscr{E}_j(P) = \sum_{j=i}^{N} \frac{1}{4\pi\epsilon_0} \frac{Q_j}{r_{Pj}^2} \hat{\mathbf{r}}_{Pj}. \tag{21.5}$$

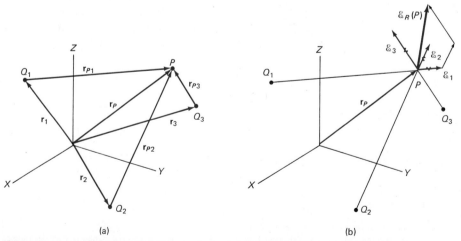

Fig. 21.3 The resultant electric-field strength at a point P is the vector superposition of the contributions from each of the source charges.

The superposition represented by (21.5) is illustrated in Fig. 21.3b for a case having three positive source charges.

Example. Consider the collection of fixed point charges in vacuum that is shown in Fig. 21.4a. What is the electric-field strength $\mathscr{E}(P)$ at the point P indicated in Fig. 21.4a, which has the position vector $\mathbf{r}_P = (3 \times 10^{-3}\,\text{m})\mathbf{j}$?

As indicated in Fig. 21.4a, the origin of coordinates is at the location of charge Q_1. From the diagram we see that the position vectors of the source charges are $\mathbf{r}_1 = 0$, $\mathbf{r}_2 = (4 \times 10^{-3}\,\text{m})\mathbf{i}$, and $\mathbf{r}_3 = (4 \times 10^{-3}\,\text{m})\mathbf{i} + (3 \times 10^{-3}\,\text{m})\mathbf{j}$. The unit vectors we need are $\hat{\mathbf{r}}_{P1} = \mathbf{j}$, $\hat{\mathbf{r}}_{P2} = -\tfrac{4}{5}\mathbf{i} + \tfrac{3}{5}\mathbf{j}$, and $\hat{\mathbf{r}}_{P3} = -\mathbf{i}$. Then from (21.5) we have

$$\mathscr{E}_R(P) = \mathscr{E}_1(P) + \mathscr{E}_2(P) + \mathscr{E}_3(P) = \frac{1}{4\pi\epsilon_0}\left\{ \frac{Q_1}{r_{P1}^2}\mathbf{j} + \frac{Q_2}{r_{P2}^2}\left(-\tfrac{4}{5}\mathbf{i} + \tfrac{3}{5}\mathbf{j}\right) + \frac{Q_3}{r_{P3}^2}(-\mathbf{i}) \right\}$$

$$= (9 \times 10^9\,\text{N}\cdot\text{m}^2/\text{C}^2)\left\{ \frac{(-5 \times 10^{-9}\,\text{C})}{(3 \times 10^{-3}\,\text{m})^2}\mathbf{j} + \frac{(3 \times 10^{-9}\,\text{C})}{(5 \times 10^{-3}\,\text{m})^2}\left(-\tfrac{4}{5}\mathbf{i} + \tfrac{3}{5}\mathbf{j}\right) \right.$$

$$\left. + \frac{(2 \times 10^{-9}\,\text{C})}{(4 \times 10^{-3}\,\text{m})^2}(-\mathbf{i}) \right\}$$

$$= (-1.99 \times 10^6\,\text{N/C})\mathbf{i} + (-4.35 \times 10^6\,\text{N/C})\mathbf{j}.$$

This vector superposition is shown graphically in Fig. 21.4b.

21.3 ELECTRIC LINES

A convenient method of visualizing an electric field involves the use of *electric lines,* which were introduced by Faraday. An electric line is a continuous, directed line drawn in such a way that at every point in space the line is tangent to the electric-field strength $\mathscr{E}$ at the point. The electric field in the vicinity of a positive or a negative point source charge as represented by electric lines is shown in Fig. 21.5. For a single positive source charge the electric lines go radially outward from

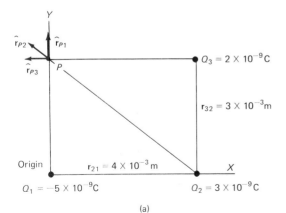

(a)

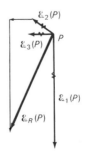

(b)　　**Fig. 21.4**

(a)

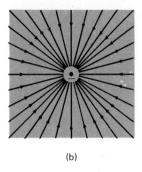

(b)

Fig. 21.5   (a) Electric lines go radially outward from a positive point charge. (b) Electric lines go radially inward toward a negative point charge.

the charge for an infinite distance; for a single negative source charge the electric lines come radially inward from infinite distance and end on the charge. Figure 21.5 shows those lines that lie in a plane passing through the source charge.

It is possible to use electric lines to represent the magnitude as well as the direction of the electric-field strength. To do this, the lines are drawn so that the number of lines per unit area through a small area element oriented perpendicular to the local electric-field strength direction is proportional to $\mathscr{E}$. In regions where $\mathscr{E}$ is large, the electric lines are close together; in regions where $\mathscr{E}$ is small, the electric lines are far apart. It is not obvious that it is possible to draw a continuous set of lines that meets these requirements. It turns out that this possibility depends on the inverse-square nature of Coulomb's Principle. We shall discuss this further in Chapter 23, where we shall see that electric lines defined in this way must begin on positive charges and end on negative charges, or extend to infinity, where $\mathscr{E}$ is zero.

Since a nonvanishing electric-field-strength vector at any point in space must have a unique direction, two electric lines cannot meet or intersect in space except at points where the magnitude of the electric-field strength is zero.

Since the pattern of electric lines for any system of source charges exists in three dimensions, the array of lines is not readily represented in a two-dimensional diagram. For a distribution of source charges possessing a plane of symmetry, a diagram showing the electric lines lying in that symmetry plane is often useful. If the source charge distribution possesses an axis of symmetry, the electric lines lying in any plane containing the symmetry axis can be drawn and the three-dimensional system of lines imagined by thinking of the two-dimensional drawing as being rotated about the symmetry axis.

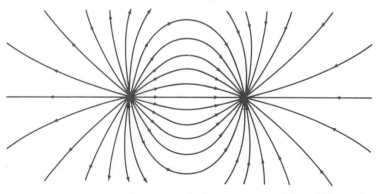

Fig. 21.6   Electric lines produced by two point charges of equal magnitudes but opposite signs.

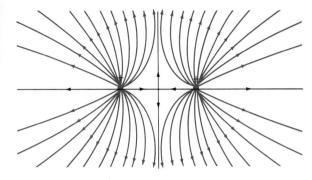

Fig. 21.7 Electric lines produced by two equal positive point charges.

The electric lines in the vicinity of several simple configurations of point source charges are shown in Figs. 21.6, 21.7, and 21.8. In each of these cases the source distribution possesses an axis of symmetry, and the figures represent the electric lines lying in a plane containing the symmetry axis. These figures illustrate the assertions that electric lines begin on positive charges and end on negative charges, or extend to infinity, and can meet only at points where $\mathscr{E} = 0$.

21.4   CONTINUOUS CHARGE DISTRIBUTIONS

Although electric charge is discrete at the atomic level, at the macroscopic level when very many atoms or molecules must be considered it is often convenient and

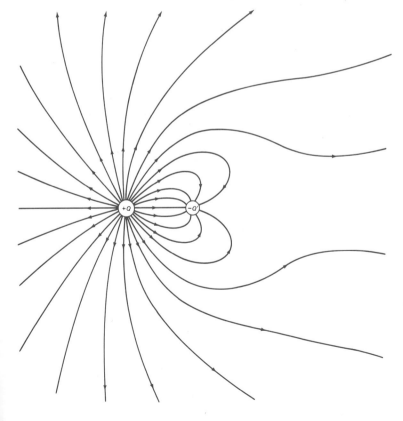

Fig. 21.8 Electric lines produced by two point charges of unequal magnitudes and opposite signs; $|Q|/|Q'| = 3$.

accurate to introduce the approximation of a continuous distribution of charge. To do this requires reasoning similar to that used when we defined mass density in Chapter 4. The approximation is possible if the smallest volume element that we need to consider in order to characterize the charge distribution is very large compared with the volume of an atom or molecule.

Let $\Delta\mathscr{V}$ be a volume element containing some point P; if we are using Cartesian coordinates, $\Delta\mathscr{V}$ might be a rectangular box of sides Δx, Δy, and Δz, as suggested in Fig. 21.9. Suppose that the total charge within this volume element is ΔQ. Then the average charge density in the volume element $\Delta\mathscr{V}$ is defined to be $\rho_{av} = \Delta Q/\Delta\mathscr{V}$. In general ρ_{av} will depend on the size of the particular volume element considered. However, in many cases if we consider smaller and smaller volume elements all containing the point P we find that ρ_{av} ceases to change with the size of the volume element while this size is still *very* large compared with the volume of an atom or molecule. In such a case we can do the following: Let $\delta\mathscr{V}$ be a volume element containing P that is macroscopically small so that it is a good mathematical approximation to treat it as a differential volume and use calculus, yet is microscopically large so that it contains very many atoms. We define the *volume charge density* $\rho(P)$ by the relation

$$\rho(P) = \lim_{\Delta\mathscr{V}\to\delta\mathscr{V}} \frac{\Delta Q}{\Delta\mathscr{V}} = \frac{dQ}{d\mathscr{V}}. \qquad \left\{\begin{array}{l} \rho \quad \text{in C/m}^3 \\ Q \quad \text{in C} \\ \mathscr{V} \text{ in m}^3 \end{array}\right\} \qquad (21.6)$$

We can treat $dQ = \rho\,d\mathscr{V}$ as a point charge located at the point P without introducing appreciable error provided the other distances involved in the problem are very large compared with the dimensions of atoms and molecules. This allows us to apply the relations we have previously developed for point charges while describing the charge distribution by a single, mathematically convenient function of position, the charge density, rather than by the coordinates of the myriad of microscopic charges that actually compose the distribution.

We shall encounter situations where charge is distributed over a surface rather than throughout a volume. In such a case we apply the ideas introduced above to a sequence of area elements lying in the surface and all containing some point P in the surface. We use the symbol ΔS to represent an element of surface area containing the point P. Following the same reasoning as used above we are led to define a *surface charge density* $\sigma(P)$ by the relation

$$\sigma(P) = \lim_{\Delta S\to\delta S} \frac{\Delta Q}{\Delta S} = \frac{dQ}{dS}. \qquad \left\{\begin{array}{l} \sigma \text{ in C/m}^2 \\ Q \text{ in C} \\ S \text{ in m}^2 \end{array}\right\} \qquad (21.7)$$

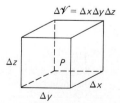

$\Delta\mathscr{V} = \Delta x\Delta y\Delta z$

Fig. 21.9   A rectangular volume element surrounding the point P.

We can treat $dQ = \sigma\,dS$ as a point charge located at the point P without introducing appreciable error provided the other distances involved in the problem are very large compared with the dimensions of atoms and molecules. The same reasoning can be applied when charge is distributed along some curve; this produces a linear charge density describing the charge per unit length along the curve.

21.5 THE ELECTRIC FIELDS OF CONTINUOUS CHARGE DISTRIBUTIONS

Suppose that we have a fixed source charge distribution that is described by a charge density. We shall write our general equations for the case of a volume charge distribution; the modifications required in order to treat a surface charge distribution or a linear charge distribution are straightforward.

In order to find the electric-field strength produced by a continuous distribution of charge such as that shown in Fig. 21.10, we treat the charge dQ associated with the volume element $d\mathscr{V}$ as a point charge: $dQ = \rho(\mathbf{r})d\mathscr{V}$, where the notation $\rho(\mathbf{r})$ indicates that the charge density ρ is a function of position. The contribution of this point charge to the electric-field strength at a point P is given by (21.3) modified to account for the charge not being at the origin. In terms of the position vectors shown in Fig. 21.10, we can express this contribution to the electric-field strength by the following relation:

$$d\mathscr{E}(P) = \frac{1}{4\pi\epsilon_0}\frac{dQ}{|\mathbf{r}_P - \mathbf{r}|^2}\frac{(\mathbf{r}_P - \mathbf{r})}{|\mathbf{r}_P - \mathbf{r}|} = \frac{1}{4\pi\epsilon_0}\frac{\rho(\mathbf{r})d\mathscr{V}}{|\mathbf{r}_P - \mathbf{r}|^3}(\mathbf{r}_P - \mathbf{r}).$$

The resultant electric-field strength at P is obtained by vector superposition of the contributions from all the volume elements of the charge distribution. Instead of the sum over discrete point charges that appears in (21.5), this superposition is now represented mathematically by an integration over the source volume elements $d\mathscr{V}$. For a volume distribution of charge three integration operations are required to cover the variations in the three spatial coordinates and include contributions from all the volume elements in the summation. Thus, we have

$$\mathscr{E}(P) = \iiint d\mathscr{E}(P) = \frac{1}{4\pi\epsilon_0}\iiint\frac{\rho(\mathbf{r})(\mathbf{r}_P - \mathbf{r})}{|\mathbf{r}_P - \mathbf{r}|^3}\,d\mathscr{V} \qquad (21.8)$$

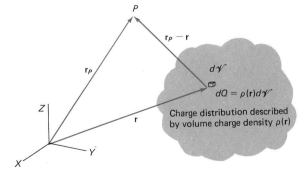

Fig. 21.10 Quantities involved in the expression for the electric-field strength produced by a continuous distribution of charge.

It can be shown that the integral in (21.8) converges and can be used to compute the electric-field strength even when the point P is inside the volume occupied by the charge distribution.

If we use Cartesian coordinates we have $d\mathscr{V} = dxdydz$. In terms of the Cartesian coordinates of the points that each locates, the position vectors in (21.8) have the forms $\mathbf{r} = x\mathbf{i} + y\mathbf{j} + z\mathbf{k}$ and $\mathbf{r}_P = x_P\mathbf{i} + y_P\mathbf{j} + z_P\mathbf{k}$. There is no difficulty in writing the expression (21.8) or in expressing it in terms of a particular system of coordinates. However, it is possible actually to evaluate the integral analytically only for charge distributions where the charge density is a relatively simple function of position. Often the integral can be evaluated analytically only for special points P that are in some way symmetrically located relative to the distribution of charge. In other cases, we must have recourse to numerical evaluation.

Example. What is the electric-field strength at an arbitrary point on the perpendicular bisector of a line of charge of length L having a linear charge density of λ coulombs per meter and a total charge $Q = \lambda L$?

Choose coordinates so that the origin is at the center of the line of charge and the line coincides with the X axis, as shown in Fig. 21.11. Let the perpendicular bisector of interest be the Z axis. We note that since the source charge distribution has cylindrical symmetry about the X axis, all directions perpendicular to the X axis are equivalent. If we derive an expression for the electric-field strength at an arbitrary point on the positive Z axis, we can immediately write down the electric-field strength for any point in the YZ plane.

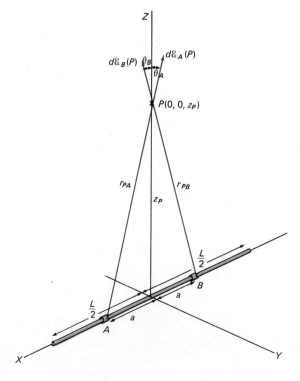

Fig. 21.11

We can reach a conclusion about the direction of $\mathscr{E}(P)$ from symmetry arguments. Consider two length elements A and B along the line of charge that are symmetrically located with respect to the origin, as shown in Fig. 21.11. We have $r_{PA} = r_{PB}$ and $\theta_A = \theta_B$, so when we superpose the contributions to the electric-field strength from the charges on the length elements A and B we obtain $d\mathscr{E}_A + d\mathscr{E}_B = 2d\mathscr{E}_A \cos\theta_A\,\mathbf{k}$. Since the whole line of charge can be considered in terms of pairs of length elements of this sort, we can conclude that $\mathscr{E}(P)$ has only a Z component.

In order to derive an expression for $\mathscr{E}(P)$ we now take the Z component of (21.8), suitably modified to treat a linear charge distribution. Our point P has coordinates $(0, 0, z_P)$; our source charges all lie along the X axis where $y = 0$ and $z = 0$. Thus we have the relation

$$\mathscr{E}(P) = \frac{1}{4\pi\epsilon_0} \int_{-L/2}^{+L/2} \frac{\lambda(z_P - 0)\mathbf{k}}{[(0 - x)^2 + (z_P - 0)^2]^{3/2}}\,dx = \frac{\lambda z_P \mathbf{k}}{4\pi\epsilon_0} \int_{-L/2}^{+L/2} \frac{dx}{(x^2 + z_P^2)^{3/2}}$$

$$= \frac{\lambda z_P \mathbf{k}}{4\pi\epsilon_0} \left[\frac{x}{z_P^2(x^2 + z_P^2)^{1/2}} \right]_{-L/2}^{+L/2} = \frac{\lambda \mathbf{k}}{4\pi\epsilon_0 z_P} \frac{L}{[(L/2)^2 + z_P^2]^{1/2}}.$$

In the limit $z_P \gg L$ this reduces to $Q\mathbf{k}/4\pi\epsilon_0 z_P^2$, the expression for the electric-field strength produced by a point charge Q. This is reasonable; if we are far enough away, the finite line of charge looks like a point charge. Another interesting limit is when the length of the line of charge becomes arbitrarily large, $L \to \infty$. In this limit we have

$$\mathscr{E}(P) \underset{L \to \infty}{\to} \frac{\lambda}{2\pi\epsilon_0 z_P}\,\mathbf{k}\,.$$

We shall return to this result in Chapter 23.

QUESTIONS

1. Explain the role of a *test charge* in the definition of electric-field strength.

2. How would the discussion in Section 21.1 be changed if a negative test charge were used to define the electric-field strength?

3. The electric-field strength is a *vector field* that assigns a vector to each point in space. Name several other physical quantities that have associated vector fields.

4. How can it be meaningful to assign a value of electric-field strength to a point in empty space? How can empty space have physical properties?

5. How must (21.3) be modified if the point charge Q is not located at the origin?

6. The magnitude of the electric-field strength given by (21.3) becomes arbitrarily large as r tends to zero. What is the significance of this behavior? Can a physically meaningful quantity become infinitely large?

7. Under what conditions, if any, do electric lines correspond to the trajectories of charged particles?

8. Why is it not possible for electric lines to meet or intersect except at points where the magnitude of the electric-field strength is

zero? What is special about such points that allows electric lines to meet there as in the center of Fig. 21.7? Shouldn't it be possible to violate this requirement if we can place arbitrary source charges, each with its own array of electric lines, at arbitrary locations?

9. The theorems of calculus are true in the limit that the small differences represented by differentials approach zero. However, in the limit in (21.6) the volume element does not approach zero. Why not? In view of this restriction on the limiting process, how can it be legitimate to use calculus in expressions like (21.8)?

10. How must (21.8) be changed if the source charge is distributed over some specified surface rather than throughout a volume?

PROBLEMS

1. The electric-field strength in a certain region of space is given as $\mathscr{E} = (6.4 \times 10^3 \text{ N/C})\mathbf{i}$. What is the force on a point charge $Q = 25$ nC that is placed in this region?

2. A small charged particle of mass 0.0032 g is held stationary in space by placing it in a downward directed electric field of magnitude 24×10^4 N/C. What is the charge on the particle?

3. (a) What are the magnitude and the direction of the electric-field strength at a point 26 cm from a point charge of $Q = +4.8 \times 10^{-7}$ C? (b) What are the magnitude and the direction of the electric-field strength at a point 26 cm from a point charge of $Q = -4.8 \times 10^{-7}$ C?

4. A point charge $Q_1 = +20$ nC is located at $x = 5$ cm, $y = 0$, $z = 0$ and a point charge $Q_2 = -20$ nC is located at $x = -5$ cm, $y = 0$, $z = 0$. What is the electric-field strength $\mathscr{E}$ at a point midway between the charges? What is the electric-field strength at points (15 cm, 0, 0) and (−15 cm, 0, 0)? Show that $\mathscr{E}$ is in the $+X$ direction at all points on the X axis except for points on the axis between the two charges.

5. For the two point charges in the preceding problem, what is the electric-field strength $\mathscr{E}$ at points (0, 15 cm, 0) and (0, −15 cm, 0)? Show that the electric-field strength $\mathscr{E}$ is in the $-X$ direction at all points on the Y axis.

6. Two point charges of equal magnitudes Q but opposite signs are located on the X axis at $x = +d/2$ and at $x = -d/2$. Show that at all points on the X axis for which $|x| \gg d$ the magnitude of the electric-field strength $\mathscr{E}$ is directly proportional to $Qd/|x|^3$. The quantity Qd is called the electric dipole moment of the charges.

7. For the situation of Problem 6, show that at all points on the Y axis for which $|y| \gg d$ the magnitude of the electric-field strength is directly proportional to $Qd/|y|^3$.

8. A point charge $Q_1 = +20$ nC is located at (−5 cm, 0, 0) and an equal point charge $Q_2 = +20$ nC is located at (+5 cm, 0, 0). What is the magnitude of the electric-field strength $\mathscr{E}$ midway between the charges? At what points on the X axis is $\mathscr{E}$ directed in the $+X$ direction? At what points on the X axis is $\mathscr{E}$ directed in the $-X$ direction?

9. For the charges described in Problem 8, what is the value of $\mathscr{E}$ at (0, 15 cm, 0)? at (0, −15 cm, 0)? At what points on the Y axis is $\mathscr{E}$ directed in the $+Y$ direction? At what points on the Y axis is $\mathscr{E}$ directed in the $-Y$ direction?

10. Two positive point charges of equal magnitudes Q are located on the X axis at $x = +d/2$ and at $x = -d/2$. Show that for all points on the X axis for which $|x| \gg d$ the electric-field strength $\mathscr{E}$ is nearly equal to

that of a point charge $+2Q$ located at the origin.

11. For the situation of the preceding problem, show that for all points on the Y axis for which $|y| \gg d$ the electric-field strength $\mathscr{E}$ is nearly equal to that of a point charge $+2Q$ located at the origin. The same result holds for all points in the XY-plane for which the radial distance r from the origin is very much greater than d. Explain why this is true.

12. Suppose that we have two positive point charges $Q_1 = 2.0 \times 10^{-6}$ C and $Q_2 = 8.0 \times 10^{-6}$ C on the X axis of a coordinate system. Is it possible to find an arrangement of these charges such that the resultant electric-field strength at the origin is zero? If not, explain why not; if so, give a specific example.

13. Suppose that we have two point charges $Q_1 = -2.0 \times 10^{-6}$ C and $Q_2 = +4.0 \times 10^{-6}$ C on the X axis of a coordinate system. Is it possible to find an arrangement of these charges such that the resultant electric-field strength at the origin is zero? If not, explain why not; if so, give a specific example.

14. Two equal point charges $Q_1 = Q_2 = 2.0 \times 10^{-6}$ C are fixed at opposite ends of a diagonal of a square of side $a = 1.0$ m. What is the resultant electric-field strength at the other two corners of the square?

15. Two point charges $Q_1 = +4.5 \times 10^{-7}$ C and $Q_2 = -8.5 \times 10^{-7}$ C are located at coordinates (5 cm, 0, 0) and (−9 cm, 0, 0), respectively. What is the electric-field strength at the point (0, 7.5 cm, 0)? Make a qualitative sketch of the pattern of electric lines lying in the XY plane.

16. Two point charges of equal magnitude $Q = 4.0 \times 10^{-6}$ C but opposite sign are fixed at the locations shown in the diagram; $a = 1.0$ m. (a) What is the electric-field strength at the point P? (b) Suppose we have an additional charge $Q_3 = +2.0 \times 10^{-6}$ C. Where should this charge be placed in order that

the electric-field strength at P be exactly half the result found in part (a)?

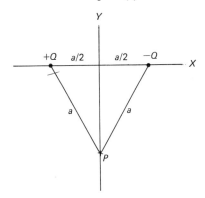

Problem 16

17. Two equal point charges $Q_1 = Q_2 = +2.0 \times 10^{-6}$ C are fixed on the X axis at $x = +3$ m and at $x = -3$ m. What charge Q must be placed at the origin in order to make the electric-field strength zero at the point $y = -3$ m on the Y axis?

18. Three point charges are fixed along the X axis, $Q_1 = +9.0 \times 10^{-7}$ C at the origin and $Q_2 = Q_3 = -1.3 \times 10^{-7}$ C at $x = +6$ cm and at $x = -6$ cm, respectively. Find the electric-field strength vectors at the points (10 cm, 0, 0), (0, 10 cm, 0), and (0, 0, 10 cm). Make a qualitative sketch of the pattern of electric lines for this system of source charges.

19. Consider the arrangement of point charges shown in the diagram; $Q_1 = Q_2 = +3 \times 10^{-6}$ C, $Q_3 = +6 \times 10^{-6}$ C, and $a = 2.0$ m. What is the electric-field strength at the point P, which is exactly in the center of the triangle? Make a qualitative sketch

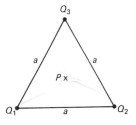

showing the pattern of the electric lines lying in the plane of the triangle.

20. Choose point charges Q_1, Q_2, and Q_3 to be placed at the points ①, ②, and ③ shown in the diagram such that the electric-field strength at the point P will be zero.

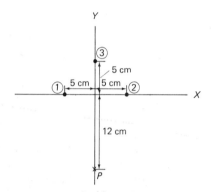

Problem 20

21. Four point charges are fixed at the corners of a plane rectangle as shown in the diagram; $Q_1 = Q_2 = -3 \times 10^{-6}$ C and $Q_3 = 2Q_4 = +4 \times 10^{-6}$ C. What is the resultant electric-field strength at the point P?

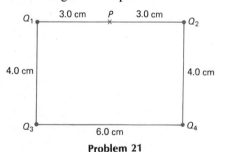

Problem 21

22. A spherical water droplet of radius 20 μm located in the atmosphere near the surface of the earth carries 270 excess electrons. What uniform vertical electric-field strength would be required to balance the gravitational force on the droplet and cause it to "float"? Ignore the buoyant effect of the air.

23. Two point charges that have equal magnitudes Q but opposite signs and are separated by a distance d are said to form an electric dipole. The orientation of the dipole is given by the direction of the displacement vector **d** from the negative charge to the positive charge. What are the force and the torque about the Z axis for a dipole having $Q = 25$ nC and $d = 20$ μm that is oriented parallel to the X axis in a region where the electric field is $\mathscr{E} = (6.4 \times 10^3$ N/C)**i**?

24. Repeat Problem 23 if the dipole is oriented parallel to the Y axis.

25. Repeat Problem 23 if the dipole is oriented parallel to the X axis in a region where $\mathscr{E} = (6.4 \times 10^3$ N/C)**i** $+ (4.6 \times 10^3$ N/C)**j**.

26. The dipole described in Problem 23 has its center at the origin. Write a representation of the electric-field strength due to this dipole at an arbitrary point away from the dipole. Use this representation of $\mathscr{E}$ to determine the electrostatic force on an identical dipole also oriented parallel to the X axis with its center on the Z axis at $z = 100$ μm.

27. A 2-mg pith ball carrying a charge $Q = +2.0 \times 10^{-6}$ C is projected horizontally close to the surface of the earth with an initial speed of 6 cm/s. Assume that air resistance can be neglected. What uniform electric-field strength (magnitude and direction) is required if the pith ball is to have a downward acceleration half of what it would be in the absence of the electric field?

28. Consider a region close to the surface of the earth where there exists a uniform, upward-directed electric field of strength $\mathscr{E} = 10^5$ N/C. A 1-g gold sphere carrying a charge of -2×10^{-9} C is projected upward with an initial velocity of magnitude 5 m/s. How high will the ball rise? How long will it take for the ball to return to its initial position? Assume that air resistance can be neglected.

29. A small sphere of mass 10 g carrying a charge $Q = 2.4 \times 10^{-6}$ C is in a vacuum chamber near to the surface of the earth where a uniform vertically upward electric field of strength 5.0×10^4 N/C has been established. The sphere is tied to the floor of the chamber

by two silk cords each of length $L = 25$ cm; the points where the cords are attached to the floor are 5 cm apart, as shown in the diagram. What is the tension in each of the cords?

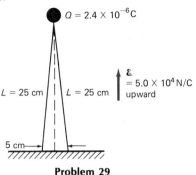

$Q = 2.4 \times 10^{-6}$ C

$L = 25$ cm $L = 25$ cm

$\mathcal{E} = 5.0 \times 10^4$ N/C upward

5 cm

Problem 29

30. A small sphere of mass 2.5 g carrying a charge $Q = 1.5 \times 10^{-8}$ C is released from rest at a point near the surface of the earth in a region where a constant electric field $\mathcal{E} = (6.5 \times 10^5 \text{ N/C})\mathbf{i} + (1.2 \times 10^6 \text{ N/C})\mathbf{j}$ has been established. The origin is at the initial location of the sphere; the Y axis is directed vertically upward, the X axis is horizontal and points east. Assume that the sphere does not strike any other objects and that air resistance can be neglected. What are the coordinates of the center of the sphere at a time 3 s after it is released?

31. A uniform downward electric field of magnitude $\mathcal{E} = 8.0 \times 10^3$ N/C is established between two horizontal plates in vacuum. The vertical distance between the plates is $d = 5.0$ cm. A proton is injected into the region between the plates from the position O indicated in the diagram with an initial velocity $v_0 = 8.0 \times 10^5$ m/s at an angle ϕ above the horizontal and to the east. If the length

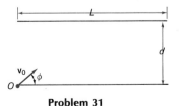

L

d

v_0

ϕ

O

Problem 31

of the plates in the eastwest direction is $L = 0.5$ m, for what angles ϕ does the proton *not* strike one of the plates?

32. An electron traveling horizontally along the X axis with a kinetic energy of 1.5×10^{-17} J is injected exactly midway between a pair of horizontal parallel plates having an 8 cm separation. Between the plates there is a uniform downward electric field of magnitude 4.8×10^4 N/C. The Y axis is perpendicular to the plates; the origin is at the point where the electron enters the region between the plates. What is the maximum length L parallel to the X axis that the plates can have if the electron is not to hit either plate? If L has *half* this length, what are the coordinates of the point where the electron strikes a screen oriented perpendicular to the X axis and placed 50 cm from the plane where the electron leaves the region between the plates? What is the length of time that the electron spends between the plates? Assume that the system is in vacuum and that there are no electric or magnetic fields except as described in the region between the plates. Deflecting plates of this sort are used to control the trajectories of electron beams in oscilloscopes and television tubes.

33. Two point charges of equal magnitudes 0.85×10^{-9} C but opposite sign are attached one on each end of a rod of length 1.05 cm. The rod is oriented parallel to the X axis with the positive charge at the larger X value. In this region there is a uniform electric field $\mathcal{E} = (5.4 \times 10^3 \text{ N/C})\mathbf{i} + (6.8 \times 10^3 \text{ N/C})\mathbf{j}$. What is the resultant force on the rod? What is the resultant torque on the rod about the Z axis? Ignore gravitational effects.

34. Show that the electric-field strength at a point P on the axis of a uniform ring of charge of radius R and total charge Q is given by $\mathcal{E} = (1/4\pi\epsilon_0)(Qz_P)/(R^2 + z_P^2)^{3/2}$, where the Z axis has been chosen to coincide

with the symmetry axis of the ring. What is the direction of $\mathscr{E}$? For what value of z does $\mathscr{E}$ have its maximum value? Make a qualitative sketch of the electric lines for this source distribution.

35. Consider a uniform circular disk of charge of radius a and negligible thickness. Take the origin of coordinates to be at the center of the disk and the Z axis to coincide with the axis of the disk, as shown in the diagram. The disk then lies in the XY plane. Let the total charge of the disk be Q; the distribution of charge is then described by a surface charge density $\sigma = Q/\pi a^2$. For an arbitrary point P we cannot analytically evaluate the integral for $\mathscr{E}(P)$; however, for the special case where P is on the axis of the disk it is possible to deduce a simple expression for $\mathscr{E}(P)$. Show that the expression for $\mathscr{E}$ at a point P on the positive Z axis in terms of Q, a, and the distance z_P of the point P from the origin is

$$\mathscr{E} = \{\hat{\mathbf{k}}Q/2\epsilon_0\pi a^2\}\{1 - (1 + a^2/z_P^2)^{-1/2}\}.$$

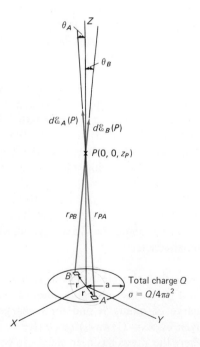

Hint: Set up the surface integral in Cartesian coordinates, then make a change of variables to polar coordinates in the XY plane. Make a qualitative sketch of the electric lines for this source distribution.

36. Consider a large, circular, uniformly distributed sheet of charge of negligible thickness lying in the XY plane with the origin at its center. The charge distribution is described by a constant surface charge density σ. Starting from the result obtained in Problem 35 for a disk of charge of radius a, deduce an expression for the electric-field strength at a point P on the positive Z axis in the approximation that the radius of the charge sheet is so large compared with z_P that the sheet can be considered as extending to infinity in all directions in the XY plane.

37. Consider a total charge Q that is uniformly distributed over a spherical surface of radius R. Take the origin of coordinates at the center of the sphere. Use spherical polar coordinates (R,θ,ϕ) to locate points on the surface of the sphere. Then an element of area on the surface of the sphere is given by $dA = R^2 \sin\theta\, d\theta\, d\phi$. Since the charge per unit area is $Q/4\pi R^2$, the charge associated with the element of area dA is $dq = (Q/4\pi R^2)(R^2 \sin\theta\, d\theta\, d\phi)$. (a) Give a symmetry argument leading to the conclusion that the electric-field strength $\mathscr{E}$ at any point outside the spherical surface is directed radially outward from or inward toward the origin. (b) Use a modified version of (21.8) to derive an expression for the magnitude of $\mathscr{E}$ at an arbitrary point on the Z axis outside the spherical surface. (c) Explain why knowing $\mathscr{E}$ at any point on the Z axis outside the spherical surface allows us to write down immediately the value of $\mathscr{E}$ at *any* point outside the spherical surface.

38. Consider a total charge Q that is uniformly distributed throughout a spherical volume of radius R. Divide the volume into concen-

tric spherical shells; let the radius of such a shell be represented by r and its thickness by dr. Using the result of the preceding problem for such a spherical shell of charge, apply the law of superposition to find the resultant electric-field strength at an arbitrary point outside the spherical volume.

39. Repeat Problem 37 for a point P that is inside the spherical surface.

40. Repeat Problem 38 for a point P that is inside the spherical distribution of charge; i.e., $r_P < R$.

CHAPTER 22

Electrical Potential

We have now studied the properties of two types of force fields, gravitational and electrical. These fields give, respectively, measures of gravitational force per unit mass and electrical force per unit charge at every point in space; they are characterized by the vectors $\mathscr{G}$ and $\mathscr{E}$ at all points in space and are called *vector fields*.

In addition to vector fields, there are also *scalar fields*, in which every point in space is characterized by a scalar quantity. For example, in considering heat conduction it is useful to characterize each point in a given region of space by its *temperature*. In the present chapter we shall introduce a very useful scalar quantity called electrical *potential*, which is defined as electrostatic potential energy per unit charge, and show how it is possible to assign a value of potential to each point in space.

Once the electrical potential in a given region of space is determined, it is possible to derive values of $\mathscr{E}$ throughout the region from the known values of the potential. Determination of $\mathscr{E}$ from the electrical potential usually proves to be mathematically easier than the determination of $\mathscr{E}$ by direct application of Coulomb's Principle to the distribution of source charges. The electrical potential thus proves to be a very useful quantity in dealing with electrostatic phenomena.

22.1 POTENTIAL DIFFERENCE

We have previously encountered the concept of potential energy in such forms as the gravitational potential energy of a raised body or the elastic potential energy of a compressed spring. In each case the *potential energy of an object represents the amount of external work required in the absence of friction to put the object into its particular position or configuration.* If the body is dropped or the spring is released, potential energy is converted to kinetic energy of motion.

There is also potential energy associated with the position of a charge in an electro-

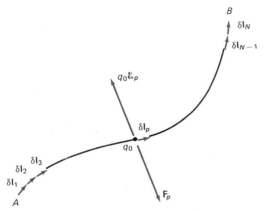

Fig. 22.1 The motion of a test charge q_0 from point Ⓐ to point Ⓑ can be considered as a sequence of infinitesimal displacements.

static field, representing the external work against electrical forces required to put the charge into its particular position. It has turned out to be convenient in the development of electromagnetic theory to focus attention on the electrostatic potential energy per unit charge. We call this the *electrical potential,* or often just the potential.

Consider two points A and B in a region of space where there exists an electrostatic field $\mathscr{E}$ produced by some distribution of source charges. We make the following definition:

The DIFFERENCE IN POTENTIAL V_{BA} between points B and A is the work done by some external agent against electric forces in moving a positive test charge *from* point A *to* point B, always keeping it in equilibrium, divided by the quantity of charge moved. In symbols,

$$V_{BA} = W_{A \to B}/q_0. \tag{22.1}$$

Recall that a test charge is a point charge that is small enough in magnitude that it does not disturb the sources producing the electric field.

If this definition is to be useful for quantitative work, we must know how to calculate $W_{A \to B}$. Suppose that the path taken from A to B is approximated by N successive infinitesimal displacements $\delta l_1, \delta l_2, \ldots, \delta l_N$, as shown in Fig. 22.1. Let the electric-field strength at the location of the pth displacement vector be $\mathscr{E}_p$. At this position the external agent moving the test charge must exert a force $\mathbf{F}_P = -q_0 \mathscr{E}_p$ in order that the test charge q_0 be in equilibrium. Thus, the work done by the external agent in the pth displacement is

$$\delta W_P = \mathbf{F}_p \cdot \delta l_p = -q_0 \mathscr{E}_p \cdot \delta l_p,$$

and the total work done for the whole path is the sum of such terms for all the small displacements. To obtain the work per unit charge we simply divide by q_0. In the limit where the magnitude of the largest displacement approaches zero and the number of displacements increases without bound, this sum defines an integral called the *line integral* of the electric field along the path followed from A to B. According to the above definition, this integral gives the difference in potential between points B and A. Thus, we can write the mathematical relation

$$V_{BA} = \frac{W_{A \to B}}{q_0} = \lim_{\substack{N \to \infty \\ \delta l_{max} \to 0}} \frac{1}{q_0} \sum_{p=1}^{N} (-q_0 \mathscr{E}_p \cdot \delta \mathbf{l}_p) = -\int_{A}^{B} \mathscr{E} \cdot d\mathbf{l}. \qquad (22.2)$$

Although it appears that the potential difference V_{BA} might depend on the particular path, we shall show shortly that the potential difference is independent of the path taken from A to B; it depends only on the locations of the end points A and B. It is easily seen from the definition that $V_{AB} = -V_{BA}$.

Since potential is work per unit charge, the SI unit of potential is the joule per coulomb. This unit is given the special name of *volt* (V),

$$1 \text{ volt} = 1 \text{ J/C},$$

in honor of Alessandro Volta (1745–1827), an Italian scientist whose contributions to electricity we shall consider in a later chapter. The name "potential" was coined by the English mathematician and physicist George Green (1793–1841), who discussed the use of the potential concept in electrostatics in a publication of 1828. Unfortunately, this work was not well known until after 1850.

22.2   THE RELATION BETWEEN POTENTIAL AND POTENTIAL ENERGY

The increase in electrostatic potential energy when we move a test charge from A to B is just the external work required to move the test charge without developing any kinetic energy. From (22.2) this is $W_{A \to B} = -\int_{A}^{B} q_0 \mathscr{E} \cdot d\mathbf{l}$; this quantity depends on the size of the particular test charge that is moved. The potential difference V_{BA}, being the potential energy difference per unit charge, does not depend on the test charge; it is a property solely of the electrostatic field.

Electrical potential and electostatic potential energy are more involved than gravitational potential energy because there are two types of charge, positive and negative. If positive work must be done by an external agent to move a positive test charge from A to B, then $V_{BA} > 0$. We say that B is at a higher potential than A. In this case a positive charge has greater potential energy at B than at A. This situation is analogous to a man lifting a rock to the top of a wall against gravitational forces.

If negative work must be done by an external agent to move a positive test charge from A to B, which means that a component of the charge's displacement is in the direction of the electric force so that the external agent must hold the charge back to keep it in equilibrium, then $V_{BA} < 0$. We say that B is at a lower potential than A. In this case a positive charge has less potential energy at B than at A. This situation is analoguous to a man lowering a rock over a cliff; the external agent in the analogy is the man controlling the rock's speed. Note that the electrostatic situation under discussion is not analogous to just throwing the rock off the cliff. Why?

If we are moving a negative test charge, (22.2) is unchanged; the potential difference between two points depends only on $\mathscr{E}$ and hence on the source charges, not on the magnitude or the sign of the test charge that is moved. However, the direction of the electrostatic force is reversed for a negative test charge, and the sign of $W_{A \to B}$ is the opposite of what it would be for a positive test charge. This means that the sign of the potential energy difference is also the opposite. If the potential at B is higher than at A, a negative charge has less potential energy at B than at A. If the potential at B is lower than at A, a negative charge has greater potential energy at B than at A. *The electrostatic force tends to move a positive charge from high to low potential and a negative charge from low to high potential.* In both cases the electrostatic force tends to move charge from regions of high potential energy to regions of low potential energy.

Example. Consider a raindrop of radius $R = 2$ mm and mass density $\rho_m = 10^3$ kg/m³ that carries a charge $Q = -1.7 \times 10^{-10}$ C. The drop falls 500 m through a thundercloud. Suppose that the thundercloud has a uniform electric-field strength of 1.08×10^5 N/C directed vertically downward. What is the electrical potential difference between the final and initial locations of the drop? Compare the electrostatic potential energy change of the drop with its gravitational potential energy change.

Choose the Z axis to be vertically downward along the line of fall of the raindrop, as indicated in Fig. 22.2. We then have $\mathscr{E} = (1.08 \times 10^5$ N/C$)\mathbf{k}$ and $d\mathbf{l} = dz\,\mathbf{k}$, so that (22.2) for this case becomes

$$V_{fi} = -\int_{z_i}^{z_f} \mathscr{E} \cdot d\mathbf{l} = -\int_{z_i}^{z_f} \mathscr{E}_z dz = -\mathscr{E}_z \int_{z_i}^{z_f} dz = -\mathscr{E}_z(z_f - z_i)$$
$$= -(1.08 \times 10^5 \text{ N/C})(500 \text{ m}) = -5.40 \times 10^7 \text{ V}.$$

The charge on the raindrop is sufficiently small that we can treat it as a test charge. Therefore, we have for the electrostatic potential energy change

$$\Delta(E_P) = W_{i \to f} = QV_{fi} = (-1.7 \times 10^{-10} \text{ C})(-5.4 \times 10^7 \text{ V}) = 9.18 \times 10^{-3} \text{ J}.$$

At thunderstorm altitudes it is a reasonable approximation to take $g = 9.8$ m/s² = constant. Then the gravitational potential energy change is

$$-mgh = -\tfrac{4}{3}\pi R^3 \rho_m g(z_f - z_i) = -\tfrac{4}{3}\pi(2 \times 10^{-3} \text{ m})^3(10^3 \text{ kg/m}^3)(9.8 \text{ m/s}^2)(500 \text{ m})$$
$$= -0.164 \text{ J}.$$

Are these results reasonable from the viewpoint of the principle of conservation of energy?

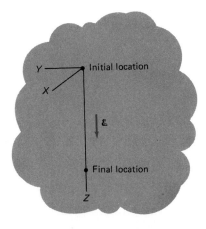

Fig. 22.2

22.3   POTENTIAL DIFFERENCE FOR A SINGLE POINT SOURCE CHARGE

Often it is desirable to calculate potential differences directly from the source distribution rather than first computing the electric-field strength and then using (22.2). Suppose that the source of the electric field is a single point charge Q in vacuum. For simplicity we put the origin of coordinates at the location of Q. We shall determine the potential difference between two points A and B located by position vectors $\mathbf{r}_A$ and $\mathbf{r}_B$, as shown in Fig. 22.3. Let the position vector $\mathbf{r}$ locate an arbitrary infinitesimal step $d\mathbf{l}$ at a point P on some path from A to B. The electric-field strength at this step is .

$$\mathscr{E} = \frac{1}{4\pi\epsilon_0} \frac{Q}{r^2} \hat{\mathbf{r}}.$$

Before using (22.2) to determine the potential difference, we resolve $d\mathbf{l}$ into two component vectors, one parallel to $\hat{\mathbf{r}}$ and the other perpendicular to $\hat{\mathbf{r}}$. This is shown in Fig. 22.4, where for the sake of clarity we have exaggerated the size of $d\mathbf{l}$ compared with r. We use the symbol dr to represent the change in the magnitude of the position vector. From Fig. 22.4 we see that

$$d\mathbf{l} = d\mathbf{l}_{\parallel} + d\mathbf{l}_{\perp} \quad \text{or} \quad d\mathbf{l} = dr\hat{\mathbf{r}} + d\mathbf{l}_{\perp},$$

so we have

$$\mathscr{E} \cdot d\mathbf{l} = \frac{1}{4\pi\epsilon_0} \frac{Q}{r^2} \hat{\mathbf{r}} \cdot (dr\hat{\mathbf{r}} + d\mathbf{l}_{\perp}) = \frac{1}{4\pi\epsilon_0} \frac{Q}{r^2} dr + 0.$$

Thus, from (22.2) we have

$$V_{BA} = -\int_A^B \mathscr{E} \cdot d\mathbf{l} = -\int_{r=r_A}^{r=r_B} \frac{1}{4\pi\epsilon_0} \frac{Q}{r^2} dr = \frac{Q}{4\pi\epsilon_0} \left(\frac{1}{r_B} - \frac{1}{r_A} \right). \qquad (22.3)$$

This result does not depend on the particular path taken from A to B; it depends only on the end points A and B of the path.

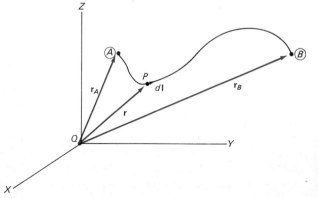

Fig. 22.3   The potential difference between points Ⓑ and Ⓐ can be determined by computing the line integral of the electric-field strength along a path joining the points.

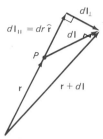

Fig. 22.4

Equation (22.3) implies an important property of the line integral of an electrostatic field. The potential difference V_{BA} is just the difference between two scalar functions depending on the locations of points B and A, respectively. This means that if the initial and final points of the path are the same, so the path forms a closed loop, then the line integral of the electrostatic-field strength taken around the closed path vanishes:

$$\oint \mathscr{E} \cdot d\mathbf{l} = 0. \qquad (22.4)$$

Here the symbol $\oint$ denotes that the path is closed and that the initial and final points of the line integral are one and the same. Although we have as yet considered only the field produced by a single point source, we shall see shortly that this result is a general property of electrostatic fields regardless of the distribution of source charges.

22.4 AN ABSOLUTE SCALE FOR POTENTIAL

So far we have considered only the *difference* in potential V_{BA} between two points. The symbols V_A or V_B referring to a single point do not yet have any meaning. It is usually convenient to assign a unique value of potential to each point in space, thus generating a scalar field. This can be done as follows: We choose a reference point, assign it some chosen potential V_{ref}, and assign to any other point P a potential V_P equal to the potential of the reference point plus the potential difference between the point P and the reference point. We can calculate V_P by evaluating the line integral of $\mathscr{E}$ from the reference point to P along any convenient path and using (22.2):

$$V_P = -\int_{ref}^{P} \mathscr{E} \cdot d\mathbf{l} + V_{ref}. \qquad (22.5)$$

Once we have established a potential field according to this procedure, the difference in potential between two points P_1 and P_2 can be obtained by taking the difference in the absolute potentials assigned to the two points.

The reference point can be chosen as is most convenient for any given situation. If the source charges are all contained within a finite region of space, it is possible and convenient to take the reference point to be a point at infinite distance, that is, extremely far from any of the source charges, and to set $V_{ref} = V_\infty = 0$. If we make this choice of reference, then for the case where the source is a single point charge Q in vacuum we obtain by use of (22.3) and (22.5) that

$$V_P = \frac{Q}{4\pi\epsilon_0}\left(\frac{1}{r_p} - \frac{1}{\infty}\right) = \frac{Q}{4\pi\epsilon_0 r_P}, \qquad (V_\infty = 0) \tag{22.6}$$

where r_P is the distance from the charge Q to the point P. This result depends only on the magnitude of the displacement from Q to P, not on the direction P is from Q. All points on the surface of a sphere with Q at its center have the same potential.

Example.   Suppose that a point charge $Q = 100$ C were placed at the location of the sun. What would be the potential at the earth? At Jupiter? (Assume that each planetary orbit is circular with radius equal to the actual mean sun–planet distance.) What would be the potential difference between the earth and Jupiter?

From the Appendix the mean distances of the earth and of Jupiter from the sun are $r(\text{Earth}) = 149.5 \times 10^6$ km and $r(\text{Jupiter}) = 777.8 \times 10^6$ km. Thus, we have from (22.6) that

$$V(\text{Earth}) = \frac{1}{4\pi\epsilon_0}\frac{Q}{r_E} = \frac{(9.0 \times 10^9 \text{ N}\cdot\text{m}^2/\text{C}^2)(100 \text{ C})}{(1.495 \times 10^{11} \text{ m})} = 6.02 \text{ V}$$

and

$$V(\text{Jupiter}) = \frac{1}{4\pi\epsilon_0}\frac{Q}{r_J} = \frac{(9.0 \times 10^9 \text{ N}\cdot\text{m}^2/\text{C}^2)(100 \text{ C})}{(7.778 \times 10^{11} \text{ m})} = 1.16 \text{ V}.$$

Then the potential difference V_{EJ} between the earth and Jupiter would be

$$V_{EJ} = V(\text{Earth}) - V(\text{Jupiter}) = 6.02 \text{ V} - 1.16 \text{ V} = 4.86 \text{ V}.$$

22.5   POTENTIAL DUE TO MULTIPLE SOURCES

If the source distribution is a collection of N point charges, as shown in Fig. 22.5 for $N = 3$, the resultant electrostatic-field strength at a point P is the vector sum of the fields produced by each source charge acting independently:

$$\mathscr{E}_R(P) = \mathscr{E}_1(P) + \mathscr{E}_2(P) + \mathscr{E}_3(P) + \cdots = \sum_{j=1}^{N} \mathscr{E}_j(P),$$

where

$$\mathscr{E}_j(P) = \frac{1}{4\pi\epsilon_0}\frac{Q_j}{r_{Pj}^2}\hat{\mathbf{r}}_{Pj}, \qquad j = 1, 2, 3, \ldots, N.$$

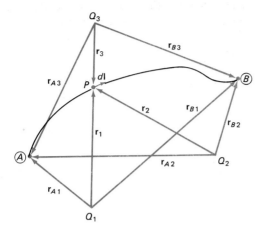

Fig. 22.5 The potential difference between points Ⓑ and Ⓐ produced by the source charges Q_1, Q_2, and Q_3 can be determined by computing the line integral of the electric-field strength due to these charges along a path joining the points.

This means that (22.2) has the form

$$V_{BA} = -\int_A^B \mathscr{E} \cdot d\mathbf{l} = -\int_A^B \mathscr{E}_1 \cdot d\mathbf{l} - \int_A^B \mathscr{E}_2 \cdot d\mathbf{l} - \int_A^B \mathscr{E}_3 \cdot d\mathbf{l} - \cdots.$$

Each of these integrals has the form of the integral in (22.3), so the difference in potential between points B and A is given by

$$V_{BA} = \frac{Q_1}{4\pi\epsilon_0}\left(\frac{1}{r_{B1}} - \frac{1}{r_{A1}}\right) + \frac{Q_2}{4\pi\epsilon_0}\left(\frac{1}{r_{B2}} - \frac{1}{r_{A2}}\right) + \cdots.$$

Here, for example, r_{B1} is the distance from charge Q_1 to point B.

This result is independent of the path taken from A to B; it depends only on the end points and the locations of the source charges. Since any source distribution can be considered as a collection of point charges, our earlier assertion about path independence is now verified in general.

If we again choose the reference point to be at infinity and set $V_{\text{ref}} = V_\infty = 0$, we have by the same reasoning as used for (22.6) that the potential at a point P is given by

$$V_P = \frac{Q_1}{4\pi\epsilon_0}\frac{1}{r_1} + \frac{Q_2}{4\pi\epsilon_0}\frac{1}{r_2} + \cdots = \sum_{j=1}^{N} \frac{Q_j}{4\pi\epsilon_0 r_j}, \quad (V_\infty = 0) \qquad (22.7)$$

where r_j is the distance from charge Q_j to the point P.

If the sources are described macroscopically by a continuous distribution of charge, as suggested in Fig. 22.6, we can conceptually divide the source distribution into infinitesimal point charges $dQ = \rho(\mathbf{r})d\mathscr{V}$, where $\rho(\mathbf{r})$ is the volume charge density at the point located by the position vector $\mathbf{r}$ and $d\mathscr{V}$ is an element of volume; in Cartesian coordinates, $d\mathscr{V} = dxdydz$. Each point charge dQ gives a contribution to the potential V_P like one of the terms on the right-hand side of (22.7); the sum in (22.7) is replaced by integration over the source volume elements. Three integration

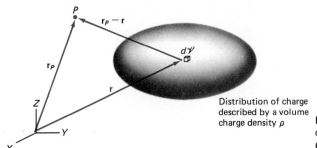

Distribution of charge
described by a volume
charge density ρ

Fig. 22.6   The potential at P arises from a distribution of charge that is described by a volume charge density ρ.

operations are required to cover the variations in the three spatial coordinates and include contributions from all the volume elements. Thus, we write

$$V_P = \frac{1}{4\pi\epsilon_0} \int\!\!\int\!\!\int \frac{\rho(\mathbf{r})}{|\mathbf{r}_P - \mathbf{r}|}\, d\mathscr{V}, \tag{22.8}$$

where $\mathbf{r}_P$ is the position vector locating the point P.

If the source charges are distributed over a surface, the volume charge density ρ is replaced by a surface charge density σ, and the integral in (22.8) is a double integral over the surface rather than a triple integral over a volume.

Example.   What is the potential at an arbitrary point P due to a positive charge q and a negative charge $-q$ separated by a distance a? Such an arrangement is called an *electric dipole*. The quantity $p = qa$ is called the *electric dipole moment* of the dipole.

Choose coordinates as indicated in Fig. 22.7. The physical situation has cylindrical symmetry about the Z axis; this means the final result should depend only on θ and r. From (22.7) we have

$$V_P = \frac{q}{4\pi\epsilon_0}\frac{1}{r_1} - \frac{q}{4\pi\epsilon_0}\frac{1}{r_2} = \frac{q}{4\pi\epsilon_0}\left[\frac{r_2 - r_1}{r_1 r_2}\right].$$

If $r \gg a$, then $r_2 - r_1 \approx a\cos\theta$ and $r_1 r_2 \approx r^2$. Thus, if the distance from the dipole to P is large compared with a, we have

$$V_P \approx \frac{q}{4\pi\epsilon_0}\frac{a\cos\theta}{r^2} = \frac{p\cos\theta}{4\pi\epsilon_0 r^2}. \tag{22.9}$$

The particular arrangement in Fig. 22.7 is the simplest of an unlimited variety of charge distributions that have a potential of the form of (22.9) for points sufficiently far from the charges. Any charge distribution that has total charge zero but has the centers of positive and of negative charge at different locations will have a dipole-type potential at distances very large compared with the largest linear dimension of the distribution. Polar molecules like HCl and H_2O have characteristic dipole moments.

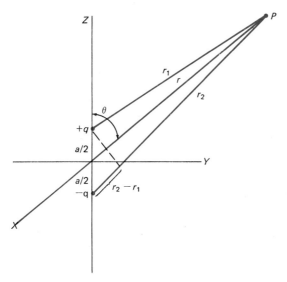

Fig. 22.7

22.6 POTENTIAL ENERGY OF A COLLECTION OF POINT CHARGES

Up to now we have been concerned with the work required to move a test charge in the electric field generated by a distribution of fixed source charges. A related question is often of interest. How much work is required to assemble a collection of charges in some specified configuration starting from a situation where all the charges are at rest and separated so far from one another that the Coulomb force between any pair of the charges is negligible? We call this work the *potential energy of the collection of charges.*

To be specific, let us assume that we have three charges Q_1, Q_2, and Q_3 whose final positions are located by position vectors $\mathbf{r}_1$, $\mathbf{r}_2$, and $\mathbf{r}_3$, respectively. We can calculate the work required to assemble these charges in a stepwise fashion; the steps are illustrated in Fig. 22.8. First move charge Q_1 to position $\mathbf{r}_1$. Since there are no other charges present to exert any force on Q_1 during this process, the work required

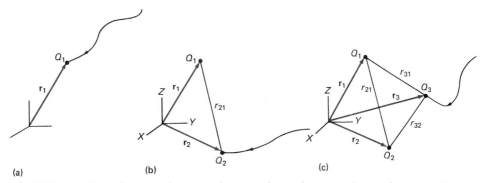

(a)   (b)   (c)

Fig. 22.8 In order to determine the potential energy of a configuration of point charges, we imagine that the charges are assembled one at a time and compute the work required to bring each successive charge to is final location.

is zero: $W_1 = 0$. Next, with Q_1 fixed in position, move charge Q_2 to position $\mathbf{r}_2$. By the definition of potential, the work required is $W_2 = Q_2 V_1(\mathbf{r}_2)$, where $V_1(\mathbf{r}_2)$ is the potential at $\mathbf{r}_2$ due to charge Q_1. By (22.6) this is just

$$W_2 = Q_2 V_1(\mathbf{r}_2) = \frac{Q_2 Q_1}{4\pi\epsilon_0 r_{21}}.$$

Finally, with Q_1 and Q_2 fixed in position, move charge Q_3 to point $\mathbf{r}_3$. By the definition of potential the work required is $W_3 = Q_3 V_{1\&2}(\mathbf{r}_3)$, where $V_{1\&2}(\mathbf{r}_3)$ is the potential at $\mathbf{r}_3$ due to charges Q_1 and Q_2. By (22.7) we have

$$W_3 = Q_3 V_{1\&2}(\mathbf{r}_3) = \frac{Q_3 Q_1}{4\pi\epsilon_0 r_{31}} + \frac{Q_3 Q_2}{4\pi\epsilon_0 r_{32}}.$$

Thus, the total work required to assemble all three charges is

$$W_{(\text{total})} = W_1 + W_2 + W_3 = \frac{Q_2 Q_1}{4\pi\epsilon_0 r_{21}} + \frac{Q_3 Q_1}{4\pi\epsilon_0 r_{31}} + \frac{Q_3 Q_2}{4\pi\epsilon_0 r_{32}}. \tag{22.10}$$

This result is independent of the order in which we consider the charges.

In (22.10) we have one term for each different pair of charges that we can form from the charges in the collection being considered. The generalization to an arbitrary number of charges is immediate. If r_{ij} denotes the distance between charges Q_i and Q_j, we have

$$W_{(\text{total})} = \sum_{\text{pairs}} \frac{Q_i Q_j}{4\pi\epsilon_0 r_{ij}}, \tag{22.11}$$

where the summation extends over all the different pairs of charges that we can form.

22.7 CALCULATION OF THE ELECTRIC FIELD FROM THE POTENTIAL

We have seen how to compute the electric potential at any point if we are given the electric-field strength. We would also like to be able to proceed in the opposite direction. Given the potential field, can we calculate the electric-field strength $\mathscr{E}$? Since the potential is obtained from $\mathscr{E}$ by an integration process, as represented by (22.5), we might expect that $\mathscr{E}$ can be obtained from the potential by some process of differentiation.

Let A and B be two points that are very close together; let $\Delta \mathbf{l}$ be the displacement from A to B. If A and B are sufficiently close, the electric-field strength $\mathscr{E}$ is essentially constant over the entire region between A and B. The situation is illustrated in Fig. 22.9. From (22.2) we have

$$\Delta V = V_{BA} = \frac{W_{A \to B}}{q_0} \approx -\frac{q_0 \mathscr{E} \cdot \Delta \mathbf{l}}{q_0} = -\mathscr{E} \cos\theta \, \Delta l.$$

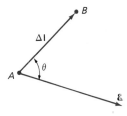

Fig. 22.9 If points Ⓐ and Ⓑ are sufficiently close to one another, the electric-field strength will be essentially constant over the region between the points.

Here $\Delta l \equiv |\Delta \mathbf{l}|$, and $\mathscr{E}\cos\theta \equiv \mathscr{E}_l$ is the component of $\mathscr{E}$ in the direction of $\Delta \mathbf{l}$. By rearrangement of this equation we obtain $\mathscr{E}_l \approx \Delta V/\Delta l$, and in the limit that Δl becomes macroscopically infinitesimal this becomes

$$\mathscr{E}_l = -\frac{dV}{dl}. \tag{22.12}$$

This result says that the component of the electric-field strength in any direction is the negative of the space rate of change of the potential in that direction. We say that the electric-field strength is the negative *gradient* of the potential.

In a direction in which the potential changes rapidly with position, the electric-field strength component is relatively large; in a direction in which the potential does not change with position, the electric-field strength component is zero. The minus sign in (22.12) means that $\mathscr{E}$ points in the direction of greatest rate of *decrease* of V. Why?

We can see by inspection of (22.12) that the electric-field strength must have dimensions of potential divided by distance. This means that an alternative unit for the electric-field strength $\mathscr{E}$ is the volt per meter:

$$1 \text{ V/m} = 1 \text{ N/C}.$$

We can readily express the gradient relation for the electric field in terms of Cartesian coordinates. To do this requires the concept of the total differential of a function expressed in terms of partial derivatives.

Introduce a Cartesian coordinate system so that each point in space is labeled by coordinates (x,y,z). Then the potential is a function of these three coordinates: $V_P = V(x,y,z)$. We learn in calculus that the total differential of such a function is given by

$$dV = \frac{\partial V}{\partial x}\,dx + \frac{\partial V}{\partial y}\,dy + \frac{\partial V}{\partial z}\,dz.$$

We can think of this as the scalar product of a vector $(\partial V/\partial x)\,\mathbf{i} + (\partial V/\partial y)\,\mathbf{j} + (\partial V/\partial z)\,\mathbf{k}$, which is denoted by the special symbol ∇V, and the infinitesimal displacement $d\mathbf{l} = \mathbf{i}\,dx + \mathbf{j}\,dy + \mathbf{k}\,dz$. Thus, mathematics says that

$$dV = \nabla V \cdot d\mathbf{l}.$$

But from (22.12) we have

$$dV = -\mathscr{E} \cdot d\mathbf{l}.$$

These relations must be true simultaneously. This implies that $(\mathscr{E} + \nabla V) \cdot d\mathbf{l} = 0$. Since $d\mathbf{l}$ is arbitrary (the displacement could be in any direction), we can conclude that $(\mathscr{E} + \nabla V) = 0$, or

$$\mathscr{E} = -\nabla V = -\frac{\partial V}{\partial x}\mathbf{i} - \frac{\partial V}{\partial y}\mathbf{j} - \frac{\partial V}{\partial z}\mathbf{k}. \qquad (22.13)$$

The electric-field strength can be obtained from the potential field if we can evaluate the three space partial derivatives of $V(x,y,z)$. Since V is a scalar field rather than a vector field, evaluation of $\mathscr{E}$ by this technique is frequently simpler than a direct calculation of $\mathscr{E}$ from the source-charge distribution.

22.8   EQUIPOTENTIAL SURFACES

In Section 22.4 we found that, if the source is a single point charge Q, all points on the surface of a sphere with Q at its center have the same potential. A surface of contiguous points having the same potential is called an *equipotential surface*. For a single point source charge Q, the equipotential surfaces are concentric spheres with Q at their common center.

Since V is constant on an equipotential surface, the space derivative of V taken in any direction lying in the surface is zero. By (22.12), this means that the component of $\mathscr{E}$ in any direction tangent to the equipotential surface is zero. We conclude that $\mathscr{E}$ *is perpendicular to the equipotential surfaces and points in the direction of decreasing potential.*

The combination of equipotential surfaces and electric lines provides a convenient pictorial way to visualize an electrostatic field. We do have the difficulty, mentioned in connection with electric lines, of representing a three-dimensional structure in a two-dimensional figure. Most such diagrams show lines representing the intersections of selected equipotential surfaces with the plane of the diagram. This is particularly effective in cases where the system of source charges has an axis of symmetry. If the equipotential surfaces are chosen so that each differs from the next by the same number of volts, then regions where the surfaces are close together in space represent regions where the gradient of the potential, and hence the magnitude of the electric-field strength, is large. The diagrams in Fig. 22.10 show the electric lines lying in a plane containing the charges and the intersections of equipotential surfaces with that plane for several simple arrangements of point source charges.

22.9   THE ELECTRON VOLT: AN ENERGY UNIT

For many situations, particularly in atomic physics, the joule is much too large to be a convenient unit of energy. Consider for example the electrostatic potential energy of the proton and electron that form a hydrogen atom. Their mean separation is 5.3×10^{-11} m, and their potential energy is, by (22.11),

$$\frac{Q_e Q_p}{4\pi\epsilon_0 r} = \frac{(9.0 \times 10^9 \text{ N} \cdot \text{m}^2/\text{C}^2)(1.602 \times 10^{-19} \text{ C})(-1.602 \times 10^{-19} \text{ C})}{(5.3 \times 10^{-11} \text{ m})}$$
$$= -4.36 \times 10^{-18} \text{ J}.$$

This amount of energy is an exceedingly small part of 1 joule!

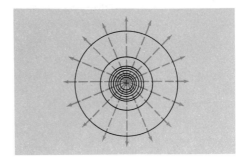

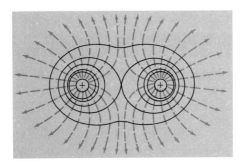 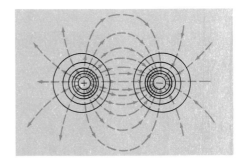

Fig. 22.10 Equipotential surfaces and electric lines for several point-charge configurations. Intersections of the equipotential surfaces with the plane of the figure are shown by solid lines; electric lines lying in the plane of the figure are shown by dashed lines.

When an electron, which has a charge $q = -1e$, is moved through a potential difference of 1 volt, the magnitude of the change in its potential energy is

$$(1e) \times (1 \ V) \approx (1.602 \times 10^{-19} \ \text{C}) \times (1 \ \text{V}) = 1.602 \times 10^{-19} \ \text{J}.$$

The amount of energy associated with an electron or proton moving through a potential difference of 1 volt has come to be widely used as a unit of energy. It is called the *electron volt,* or eV for short:

$$1 \ \text{eV} = 1.6021892 \times 10^{-19} \ \text{J}.$$

This unit can be used for any type of energy; it is not restricted to problems in electrostatics.

Example. How much energy in electron volts must be supplied to a hydrogen atom to produce an electron and a proton both at rest and separated by an "infinite" distance?

From the result determined above for the potential energy of the electron and proton that form a hydrogen atom, we have

$$\frac{Q_e Q_p}{4\pi\epsilon_0 r} = (-4.36 \times 10^{-18} \ \text{J}) \left[\frac{1 \ \text{eV}}{1.602 \times 10^{-19} \ \text{J}} \right] = -27.2 \ \text{eV}.$$

The electron and proton of a hydrogen atom also possess kinetic energy; the amount of kinetic energy turns out to be just half the magnitude of the potential energy. If we assume a simple model where the proton is fixed and the electron, with mass m_e, moves around it at constant speed v on a circular orbit whose radius is the mean electron–proton separation r, this result can be easily deduced using the ideas of Chapter 4. The centripetal force required for steady circular motion is provided by the Coulomb attraction of the electron and the proton. Thus,

$$\frac{m_e v^2}{r} = \frac{|Q_e| Q_p}{4\pi\epsilon_0 r^2},$$

from which it follows immediately that the kinetic energy is

$$E_K = \tfrac{1}{2} m_e v^2 = \frac{1}{2}\left(\frac{|Q_e| Q_p}{4\pi\epsilon_0 r}\right) = \tfrac{1}{2}|E_P| .$$

Thus, the initial energy of the hydrogen atom is

$$E_{tot} = E_K + E_P = -\tfrac{1}{2} E_P + E_P = \tfrac{1}{2} E_P = -13.6 \text{ eV}.$$

The energy of the final situation under consideration is zero, so the energy that must be supplied is $E_{(final)} - E_{(initial)} = 0 \text{ eV} - (-13.6 \text{ eV}) = 13.6 \text{ eV}.$

QUESTIONS

1. Name several physical quantities besides electric potential and temperature that are represented by scalar fields.

2. Why is it important to use a *test charge* in the definition of potential difference? Does it make any difference in the definition whether a positive or a negative test charge is used?

3. Why is it important that the potential difference between two points be independent of the path taken between the points?

4. Will an electron tend to move toward high or toward low potential under the influence of electric forces? In which sense will a proton tend to move?

5. Discuss the similarities between electrical potential energy and potential and gravitational potential energy and potential as were discussed in Chapter 9. Explain how the existence of two kinds of electric charge makes the electrical case more complicated than the gravitational case.

6. Why does it make physical sense to choose the reference point for potential at "infinity" when infinity represents a mathematical limit and not a point to which a test charge can be carried along some path?

7. How must (22.8) be changed if the source charge is distributed over some specified surface rather than throughout a volume?

8. Explain the physical distinction between the electric potential at a point produced by a collection of point charges and the electric potential energy of the collection of point charges.

9. Explain why the electric-field strength $\mathscr{E}$ is in the direction of the *greatest* rate of *decrease* of V.

10. Explain why knowledge of $\mathscr{E}$ at a point is not sufficient to determine V at the point or vice versa.

11. If V is constant throughout a certain region, what is the value of $\mathscr{E}$ in that region?

12. If $\mathcal{E}$ is constant throughout a certain region, what is the value of V in that region?

13. Can equipotential surfaces ever intersect? If so, explain the conditions under which an intersection is possible and give an example; if not, explain why not.

14. "High voltage" is supposedly dangerous, yet birds perch on high voltage power lines without apparent harm. Is it biologically dangerous for a living creature to be at a high electrical potential? If so, what is the nature of the danger?

PROBLEMS

1. (a) What is the difference in potential between two points A and B at distances 30 cm and 60 cm, respectively, from a fixed point charge of $Q = -5.0 \times 10^{-5}$ C? (b) Which point is at the higher potential? (c) How much work must be done to move a point charge $q = 2 \times 10^{-6}$ C from B to A? (d) How much work must be done to move a point charge $q' = -2 \times 10^{-6}$ C from B to A?

2. A point charge $Q = 8 \times 10^{-6}$ C is fixed at the origin. (a) What is the potential difference between two points A and B having coordinates (20 cm, 0, 0) and (−40 cm, 0, 0), respectively? (b) Find the potential differences between each of these points and a point C having coordinates (0, 40 cm, 0). (c) How much work must be done to move a point charge $q = 2 \times 10^{-8}$ C from point A to point C and then to point B?

3. A point A is 1.05 m from a fixed point charge $Q = 6.3 \times 10^{-6}$ C. (a) Where is a point B that has a potential 2550 V higher than point A? (b) Where is a point C that has a potential 7670 V lower than point A? (c) How much work must be done to move a point charge of $q = 8.2 \times 10^{-7}$ C from C to B? (d) How much work must be done to move a point charge $q' = -4.1 \times 10^{-7}$ C from C to B?

4. What is the potential difference between a point A having Cartesian coordinates (−3.5 m, 0, 0) and a point B having Cartesian coordinates (+4.0 m, 0, 0) if in the region of space where these points are located the electric-field strength is given by $\mathcal{E} =$ (300 V/m)$\mathbf{i}$ + (300 V/m)$\mathbf{j}$? Which point has the higher potential?

5. What is the potential difference between the origin and a point P on the positive Y axis 3.7 cm from the origin if in the region of space where these points are located the electric-field strength is given by $\mathcal{E} =$ (100 V/m³)$xy\mathbf{i}$ + (50V/m³)$(x^2 - y^2)\mathbf{j}$? Is V_P higher or lower than the potential at the origin?

6. What is the potential difference between a point A having Cartesian coordinates (0.50 m, 4.3 m, 0) and a point B having Cartesian coordinates (−2.0 m, 0, 5.6 m) if in the region of space where these points are located the electric-field strength is given by $\mathcal{E} =$ (100 V/m)$\mathbf{i}$ + (200 V/m)$\mathbf{k}$? Which point has the lower potential?

7. Suppose that at every point on the YZ plane we have $V = 10$ V, and everywhere between the YZ plane and the plane defined by $x = 10$ m we have $\mathcal{E} = \mathbf{i}(168$ V/m). Deduce a formula for the potential V as a function of position that is valid in the region $0 \leq x \leq 10$ m. Describe the equipotential surfaces for this situation.

8. A point charge $Q_1 = 4 \times 10^{-6}$ C is located at the origin. A second point charge $Q_2 = -8 \times 10^{-6}$ C is located on the X axis at $x = 12$ cm. For what locations on the X axis is the potential zero? For what locations on the X axis is the magnitude of the electric-field strength zero? Explain why the two answers are different. Describe the nature of the potential near locations where $\mathcal{E} = 0$.

9. A point charge $Q_1 = +20$ nC is located at (5 cm, 0, 0) and a second point charge $Q_2 = -20$ nC is located at (−5 cm, 0, 0). (a) What is the electric potential V midway between the charges; (b) at (15 cm, 0, 0); (c) at (−15 cm, 0, 0); (d) at (0, +15 cm, 0); (e) at (0, −15 cm, 0)?

10. For the situation of Problem 9, at what points on the X axis is the potential V positive? At what points on the X axis is the potential V negative? What is the potential at points on the Y axis?

11. Two point charges of equal magnitudes Q but opposite signs are located on the X axis at $x = +d/2$ and at $x = -d/2$. Show that the magnitude of the potential at points on the X axis for which $|x| >> d$ is directly proportional to Qd/x^2. The quantity Qd is the magnitude of the dipole moment of the two charges.

12. For the situation of Problem 11, use the relations $\mathscr{E}_x = -\partial V/\partial x$, $\mathscr{E}_y = -\partial V/\partial y$, and $\mathscr{E}_z = -\partial V/\partial z$ to deduce an expression for $\mathscr{E}$ from the expression for V. Show that your result agrees with that written directly from (21.5).

13. A point charge $Q_1 = +20$ nC is located at (5 cm, 0, 0) and a second point charge $Q_2 = +20$ nC is located at (−5 cm, 0, 0). (a) What is the potential at (15 cm, 0, 0); (b) at (−15 cm, 0, 0); (c) at (0, 15 cm, 0); (d) at (0, −15 cm, 0)?

14. Two positive point charges of equal magnitudes Q are located on the X axis at $x = +d/2$ and at $x = -d/2$. Show that the potential at points on the X axis for which $|x| >> d$ is nearly equal to the potential of a charge $2Q$ located at the origin. Similarly, show that for points on the Y axis for which $|y| >> d$ the potential is nearly equal to that of a charge $2Q$ located at the origin.

15. A fixed point charge $Q_1 = +200$ nC is 10 cm away from a point charge $Q_2 = +400$ nC.

(a) Regarding Q_1 as a source charge, find the value of the electric potential V at the location of Q_2. (b) From the definition of potential find the work W required to bring Q_2 from infinite distance to its location 10 cm away from Q_1. (c) Verify the result in (b) by the integration

$$W = -Q_2 \int_{\infty}^{P_2} \mathscr{E}_1 \cdot d\mathbf{r},$$

where $\mathscr{E}_1$ is the electric-field strength due to charge Q_1.

16. Repeat the preceding problem regarding Q_2 as the source of the electric field. (a) What is the potential due to Q_2 at the location of Q_1? (b) How much work W is required to bring Q_1 from infinite distance to its location 10 cm away from Q_2? (c) Verify the result by the integration

$$W = -Q_1 \int_{\infty}^{P_1} \mathscr{E}_2 \cdot d\mathbf{r},$$

where $\mathscr{E}_2$ is the electric-field strength produced by Q_2.

17. Two point charges $Q_1 = +25 \times 10^{-9}$ C and $Q_2 = -25 \times 10^{-9}$ C are located on two vertices of a triangle, as shown in the figure. (a) What is the potential at point A? (b) How much work must be done on a point charge $q = -8 \times 10^{-9}$ C in order to move it without acceleration from point A to point B if charges Q_1 and Q_2 remain fixed in position?

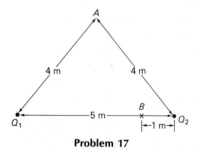

Problem 17

18. A positive and a negative point charge, each of magnitude Q, are located at the positions shown in the diagram. Derive a formula for

the electrostatic potential at an arbitrary point P on the X axis in terms of Q, a, and x_P. At what points on the X axis (other than $x \to \pm\infty$) will this potential be zero?

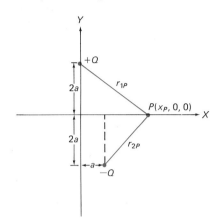

Problem 18

19. Three positive charges each of magnitude $Q = 2.0 \times 10^{-9}$ C are fixed on three corners of a square having sides of length 0.2 m. (a) What is the potential at the vacant corner of the square P? (b) An external agent must do 1.38×10^{-6} J of work in order to bring a charge q from P to the center of the square. What are the magnitude and sign of q?

20. Three charges Q_1, Q_2, and Q_3 are fixed in position in the XY plane at the vertices of an equilateral triangle; $Q_1 = Q_2 = 1.4 \times 10^{-9}$ C and $Q_3 = -0.6 \times 10^{-9}$ C. The Z axis passes through the exact center of the triangle; each side of the triangle has length 2.0 m. Charge Q_3 is on the positive X axis. (a) What is the potential at a point P on the Z axis 2.0 m above the XY plane? (b) How much work in eV is required to move a charge $q = 0.5 \times 10^{-10}$ C from point P to the origin?

21. Four positive charges, each of magnitude 3.2×10^{-19} C, are located at four of the corners of a three-dimensional cube as shown in the figure. The length of the cube edge is 1.8×10^{-10} m. What is the potential at the center of the cube? What is the potential energy in eV of an electron placed at the center of the cube?

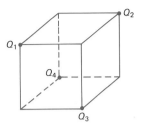

Problem 21

22. (a) Two positive charges each of magnitude Q are fixed in position on the X axis at $x = +a$ and at $x = -a$, respectively. Draw a qualitative graph of electrostatic potential energy versus position for a charge $Q' = Q/2$ that is carried along the Y axis from $y = +\infty$ to $y = -\infty$. (b) Repeat for the case where one of the fixed charges is $+Q$ and the other is $-Q$.

23. (a) Show that the potential on the positive Z axis far from the origin ($z \gg d$) for the configuration of point charges shown in the diagram is given by $(1/4\pi\epsilon_0)(q/z + 2qd/z^2)$. (b) What is the corresponding expression on the negative Z axis? (c) What would be the expression for the potential on the positive Z axis far from the origin if the upper charge were $-q$ and the center charge were $+2q$?

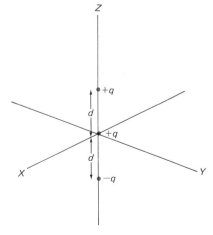

Problem 23

24. Consider a uniform distribution of charge along the Z axis from $z=-L/2$ to $z=+L/2$ having λ Coulombs per meter. Find an expression for the potential V_P at a point P having coordinates (x_P, y_P, z_P).

25. Show that the potential at a point P on the axis of a uniform circular disk of charge of negligible thickness, radius a, and total charge Q is

$$V_P = (\sigma z_P/2\epsilon_0)\,[(1+a^2/z_P^2)^{1/2} - 1],$$

where $\sigma = Q/\pi a^2$. The coordinates are chosen so that the disk lies in the XY plane with the origin at its center and the Z axis coincides with its symmetry axis, as shown in the diagram. *Hint:* Set up the integral in Cartesian coordinates, then make a change of variables to polar coordinates in the XY plane.

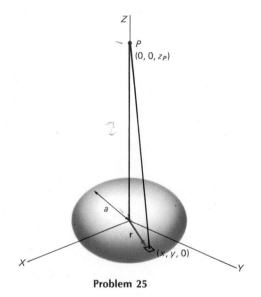

Problem 25

26. (a) Find the potential at a point P on the Z axis outside a uniform spherical shell of charge of radius R and total charge Q. Take the origin of coordinates at the center of the sphere. Use spherical polar coordinates (R, θ, ϕ) to locate points on the surface of the sphere. Then an element of area on the surface of the sphere is given by $dA =$

$R^2 \sin\theta\; d\theta d\phi$. Since the charge per unit area is $Q/4\pi R^2$, the charge associated with the element of area dA is $dq = (Q/4\pi R^2)(R^2 \sin\theta\; d\theta\; d\phi)$. (b) Use the spherical symmetry of the source charge distribution to generalize your result to give the potential at an arbitrary point outside the sphere.

27. Repeat Problem 26 for a point P *inside* the uniformly charged spherical shell.

28. Find the potential at arbitrary points P outside and inside a uniform sphere of charge of radius R and total charge Q. By "uniform sphere of charge" we mean that the volume charge density has the value $Q/(4\pi R^3/3)$ throughout the region $r < R$, where r is the distance from the origin, which we take at the center of the sphere. Divide the volume into concentric spherical shells; let the radius of such a shell be represented by r and its thickness by dr. Use the results of Problems 26 and 27 to find the contribution to the potential from each spherical shell, then sum all these contributions.

29. What is the electrostatic potential energy of the configuration of point charges considered in Problem 18 if $Q = 3 \times 10^{-6}$ C and $a = 4.5$ cm?

30. What is the electrostatic potential energy of the configuration of point charges considered in Problem 19?

31. Calculate the electrostatic potential energy of a system of three charges each having $Q = 3 \times 10^{-6}$ C placed one on each vertex of an equilateral triangle of side $a = 2$ m.

32. An electric dipole is formed of a positive and a negative point charge each of magnitude $q = 4 \times 10^{-8}$ C fixed at the ends of a thin rod that is 1 cm long. The center of the rod is fixed at the origin, but the rod can rotate in the YZ plane. Assume that there is in this region an electric field $\mathscr{E} = (120 \text{ V/m})\mathbf{k}$. (a) What is the torque on the dipole when the positive charge is on the

positive Y-axis? (b) How much work is required to rotate the dipole from an orientation with the positive charge on the positive Z axis (dipole aligned with the external field) to an orientation where the dipole makes an angle θ with the external field? The direction of the dipole is from the negative charge to the positive charge. Write a formula for this work in terms of the dipole moment of the dipole. We can think of this work as representing the potential energy of orientation of the dipole in the uniform external field.

33. Can the potential of a positively charged insulated conductor ever have a negative value? Explain your reasoning. If the answer is yes, give an example of how such a situation could occur.

34. (a) If V is zero throughout a region of space, does this necessarily mean that $\mathscr{E}$ is zero there? (b) If $\mathscr{E}$ is zero throughout a region of space, does this necessarily mean that V is zero there? Explain your reasoning.

35. Give a qualitative description of the equipotential surfaces for the system of point charges considered in Problem 8.

36. In a certain region of space the potential is given by $V = (4x^2 + 8x - 10)$ volts, where x is the X coordinate in meters. What is the electric-field strength in this region of space?

37. It is possible to give a symmetry argument showing that the electric field at points on the axis of a uniform circular disk of charge is parallel to the axis. Starting from this knowledge and the result given in Problem 25 for the potential on the axis of the disk, show that the electric-field strength at points on the axis of the disk is given by

$$\mathscr{E} = (\sigma/2\epsilon_0)[1 - (1 + a^2/z^2)^{-1/2}]\mathbf{k}.$$

38. Two large parallel conducting plates are located perpendicular to the vertical Z axis; the lower plate is in the XY plane; the upper plate is at $Z = 1.5$ cm. The upper plate is held at potential V_0; the lower plate is held at potential zero. As we shall show in the next chapter, except near the plate edges the potential of the region between the plates is given by $V(z) = (z/d)V_0$. (a) What is the electric-field strength at an arbitrary point between the plates? (b) Suppose that a drop of oil of mass density $\rho_m = 0.92$ g/cm³ and radius 2.8×10^{-4} cm is in the region between the plates and carries a charge due to two excess electrons. What should be the value of V_0 so that the electric force on the drop just balances its weight? Neglect the bouyant effect of the air.

39. Chemists commonly express reaction energies in units of cal/mole or kcal/kmole. What is the equivalent of a reaction energy of 1 kcal/kmole in terms of eV/molecule?

40. A point charge $q = 10e$ of mass 3.32×10^{-26} kg is released from rest at a distance 10^{-8} cm from a fixed point charge $Q = 98e$. What is the kinetic energy of charge q in electron volts when it is 1 mm from charge Q? What is the speed of charge q at this time? Discuss qualitatively how the situation would be changed if the charge Q were not fixed in position.

41. Using the relations $\cos\theta = z/r$ and $r = (x^2 + y^2 + z^2)^{1/2}$, apply (22.13) to the potential given by (22.9) and show that the electric-field strength far from the electric dipole shown in Fig. 22.7 is

$$\frac{1}{4\pi\epsilon_0} \left\{ \frac{3p\cos\theta}{r^4}\mathbf{r} - \frac{\mathbf{p}}{r^3} \right\},$$

where $\mathbf{p}$ is a vector of magnitude $p = qa$ directed from the negative to the positive charge of the dipole.

CHAPTER 23

Electric Flux: Gauss's Relation

We have described two ways of determining electric-field strengths, first by directly applying Coulomb's Principle to the source charges and second by computing the electric potential and then taking appropriate derivatives. In this chapter we introduce a consequence of Coulomb's Principle known as Gauss's Relation that allows easy determination of $\mathscr{E}$ for situations having sufficient spatial symmetry. We begin by extending the concept of flux to an electric field. Gauss's Relation makes a statement about the flux of an electric field. We shall show how Gauss's Relation follows as a consequence of Coulomb's Principle. This relation is then used to determine the electric-field strength arising from a number of different distributions of source charge having spherical, cylindrical, or planar symmetry. We shall also discuss some important macroscopic electrostatic properties of conductors that can be deduced with the aid of Gauss's Relation.

23.1 FLUX OF AN ELECTRIC FIELD

In order to have appropriate language for stating Gauss's Relation, we must extend the concept of *flux* that was introduced in Chapter 11. In Chapter 11 the flux through a surface element $d\mathbf{S}$ of an incompressible fluid flowing with velocity $\mathbf{v}$ was defined to be $d\Phi = \mathbf{v} \cdot d\mathbf{S}$. This quantity gives the volume rate of fluid flow through the surface element. The electric-field strength $\mathscr{E}$ does not describe the flow of a material, but a quantity that is defined mathematically like fluid flux proves to be very useful. Flux is always computed with respect to some surface S. This may be a closed surface that surrounds some volume of space, or it may be an open surface having an "edge." In order to compute the flux of the electric field through the surface S, we divide S into a very large number of approximately flat surface elements; we represent each surface element by a vector $d\mathbf{S}$ having a magnitude equal to its area and a direction

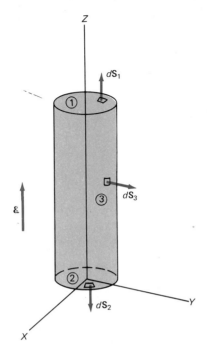

Fig. 23.1

that is normal to the element and away from its positive side. For a closed surface we shall always take the outer side as the positive side. We then form the scalar product of each surface-element vector $d\mathbf{S}$ with the local value of the electric-field strength $\mathscr{E}$ and sum the result over all the surface elements. In the limit where dS_{max} becomes infinitesimal this defines an integral called the flux $\Phi_{\mathscr{E}}$ of the electric field through the surface S. Two integration operations are required to cover variation of the two coordinates needed to locate points on the surface and include contributions from all surface elements. Thus, we write symbolically

$$\Phi_{\mathscr{E}} = \iint_S \mathscr{E} \cdot d\mathbf{S}. \qquad (23.1)$$

Example. Suppose that in some region of space we have a uniform electric field $\mathscr{E} = \mathscr{E}\mathbf{k}$, where $\mathscr{E}$ is a constant. What is the flux of this field through the surface of a right circular cylinder having a cross section of radius R and length L if the axis of the cylinder is parallel to the Z axis?

The situation is illustrated in Fig. 23.1, where we have taken the origin of coordinates at the center of the bottom face of the cylinder. We wish to compute $\Phi_{\mathscr{E}} = \oiint_S \mathscr{E} \cdot d\mathbf{S}$; the small circle on the integral signs is used to indicate that the particular surface under consideration is a closed surface. We shall consider this integral in three parts, the contributions from each of the two cylinder ends and the contribution from the side of the cylinder; representative surface-element vectors are shown in Fig. 23.1, where we have labeled the three pieces of the cylinder surface as ①, ②, and ③. Everywhere on the cylinder side ③ we have $\mathscr{E}$ perpendicular to $d\mathbf{S}_3$, which means $\mathscr{E} \cdot d\mathbf{S}_3 = 0$ so $\int\int_{③} \mathscr{E} \cdot d\mathbf{S}_3 = 0$. On end

① we have $\mathscr{E}$ parallel to $d\mathbf{S}_1$, so $\iint_① \mathscr{E} \cdot d\mathbf{S}_1 = \iint_① \mathscr{E} dS_1 = \mathscr{E} \iint_① dS_1 = \mathscr{E} \pi R^2$. On end ② we have $\mathscr{E}$ antiparallel to $d\mathbf{S}_2$, so $\int\int_② \mathscr{E} \cdot d\mathbf{S}_2 = \iint_② (-1) \mathscr{E} dS_2 = -\mathscr{E} \iint_② dS_2 = -\mathscr{E} \pi R^2$. Thus, the total flux is $\Phi_{\mathscr{E}} = \oiint_S \mathscr{E} \cdot d\mathbf{S} = \iint_① \mathscr{E} \cdot d\mathbf{S}_1 + \iint_② \mathscr{E} \cdot d\mathbf{S}_2 + \iint_③ \mathscr{E} \cdot d\mathbf{S}_3 = \mathscr{E} \pi R^2 - \mathscr{E} \pi R^2 + 0 = 0$.

23.2 GAUSS'S RELATION

We can now state a general and frequently useful result concerning electric fields*:

GAUSS'S RELATION: The flux of the electric field through any closed surface equals $1/\epsilon_0$ times the total charge inside the closed surface.

As an equation, we have for an arbitrary closed surface S that

$$\Phi_{\mathscr{E}} = \oiint_S \mathscr{E} \cdot d\mathbf{S} = Q_S/\epsilon_0, \tag{23.2}$$

where Q_S is the total charge inside S. In computing Q_S we must give each charge its proper algebraic sign, plus for a positive charge and minus for a negative charge.

Before deriving this relation, let us check that it is valid for the simple case of a single point charge Q. We take the origin at the location of the point charge and for the surface S consider a sphere of radius R with its center at the origin. The situation is shown in Fig. 23.2. At any position on the surface S the electric-field strength due to the point charge is given by $\mathscr{E} = (1/4\pi\epsilon_0)(Q/R^2)\hat{\mathbf{r}}$. The vector represen-

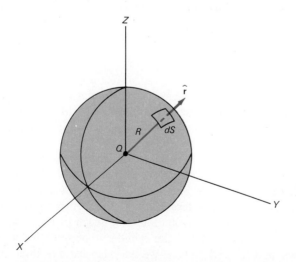

Fig. 23.2 A spherical Gaussian surface surrounding a point charge source.

* The German savant Carl Friedrich Gauss (1777–1855) was one of the greatest mathematicians who ever lived; he also made important contributions in physics and astronomy. The theorem we discuss in this chapter was formulated by Gauss in 1839.

tation of any surface element of S is $d\mathbf{S} = dS\hat{\mathbf{r}}$. Thus, for the flux through the closed surface S we have

$$\Phi_{\mathscr{E}} = \oiint_S \mathscr{E} \cdot d\mathbf{S} = \oiint_S (1/4\pi\epsilon_0)(Q/R^2)\hat{\mathbf{r}} \cdot \hat{\mathbf{r}} \, dS$$

$$= (Q/4\pi\epsilon_0 R^2) \oiint_S dS = (Q/4\pi\epsilon_0 R^2)4\pi R^2 = Q/\epsilon_0.$$

This is just the result that Gauss's Relation says we should obtain.

In deriving Gauss's Relation, we first consider an arbitrary convex surface S about a single point charge Q, as suggested in Fig. 23.3a. We take the origin at the location of the point charge. The electric-field strength at a point located by the position vector $\mathbf{r}$ is $\mathscr{E} = (1/4\pi\epsilon_0)(Q/r^2) \, \hat{\mathbf{r}}$. We imagine a sphere of radius R inscribed about Q, where R is small enough that the sphere is entirely within the surface S; such a sphere is shown in Fig. 23.3b. An element of surface on this sphere is $dS' = R^2 \sin \theta \, d\theta \, d\phi$, where θ and ϕ are the usual spherical polar coordinates. Consider the cone defined by drawing lines from the corners of dS' to the origin; this cone represents the *element of solid angle* subtended by the surface element dS' relative to the origin, which we shall represent by $d\Omega$. We establish a quantitative measure of $d\Omega$ by the following definition:

The SOLID ANGLE $d\Omega$ subtended by any surface element $d\mathbf{S}$ relative to the origin is the magnitude of the projection of $d\mathbf{S}$ taken normal to the position vector locating the center of $d\mathbf{S}$ divided by the square of the magnitude of that position vector.

Thus,

$$d\Omega = \frac{d\mathbf{S} \cdot \hat{\mathbf{r}}}{r^2}. \tag{23.3}$$

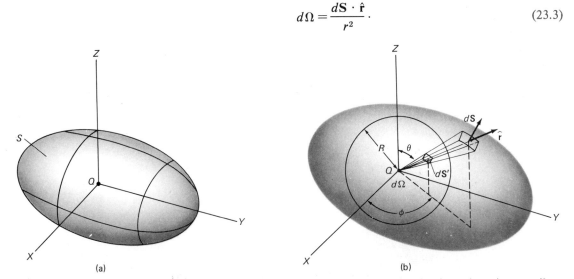

Fig. 23.3 (a) An arbitrary convex Gaussian surface surrounding a point charge source. (b) The surface elements $d\mathbf{S}$ and $d\mathbf{S}'$ subtend the same solid angle $d\Omega$ relative to the point charge Q.

A solid angle defined in this way is said to be measured in terms of a dimensionless unit called a *steradian*. Applying this general definition to the solid angle subtended by the surface element dS' on our sphere of radius R, we see that

$$d\Omega = \frac{dS'}{R^2} = \frac{R^2 \sin\theta \, d\theta \, d\phi}{R^2} = \sin\theta \, d\theta \, d\phi.$$

We now extend the cone representing $d\Omega$ until it intersects the surface S as in Fig. 23.3b; the "cap" of the cone where it intersects this surface we take as a surface element represented by the vector $d\mathbf{S}$. By this construction the solid angle subtended by $d\mathbf{S}$ is the same as the solid angle $d\Omega = \sin\theta \, d\theta d\phi$ subtended by dS'.

These geometrical concepts are now used in the computation of the flux of the electric field through the closed surface S. We have

$$\Phi_{\mathscr{E}} = \oiint_S \mathscr{E} \cdot d\mathbf{S} = \frac{Q}{4\pi\epsilon_0} \oiint_S \frac{\hat{\mathbf{r}}}{r^2} \cdot d\mathbf{S} = \frac{Q}{4\pi\epsilon_0} \oiint_S d\Omega. \tag{23.4}$$

The computation of $\oiint_S d\Omega$ involves summing the elements of solid angle subtended by all the surface elements of S. Since, as we have seen, these are the same as the elements of solid angle subtended by the corresponding elements of the sphere S', we can make the computation in terms of the spherical surface:

$$\oiint_S d\Omega = \oiint_{S'} d\Omega = \int_{\theta=0}^{\pi} \int_{\phi=0}^{2\pi} \sin\theta \, d\phi \, d\theta = 2\pi \int_{\theta=0}^{\pi} \sin\theta \, d\theta = 2\pi[-\cos\theta]_{\theta=0}^{\pi} = 4\pi.$$

This means that (23.4) for the flux of the electric field through the closed surface S becomes

$$\Phi_{\mathscr{E}} = \oiint_S \mathscr{E} \cdot d\mathbf{S} = \frac{Q}{4\pi\epsilon_0} 4\pi = \frac{Q}{\epsilon_0},$$

just the result prescribed by Gauss's Relation.

If the surface S is convoluted, as suggested in Fig. 23.4, some solid-angle elements $d\Omega$ will intersect the surface several times. Each outward piercing of the surface contributes $+d\Omega$ to $\oiint_S d\Omega$; each inward piercing contributes $-d\Omega$ to the integral. The minus sign in the latter case arises because the angle between $d\mathbf{S}$ and $\hat{\mathbf{r}}$ is greater than 90°, so $d\mathbf{S} \cdot \hat{\mathbf{r}}$ is negative. For a charge Q that is inside the surface S there will be one more outward intersection than there are inward intersections, so the net contribution to the integral for any given direction looking outward from the origin is $+d\Omega$. The overall result of the integration is therefore the same as for a simple convex surface.

If we have a point charge source that is outside the surface S, the situation is as suggested in Fig. 23.5. For any direction outward from the origin in which the solid-angle element intersects the surface S, there are equal numbers of outward and inward

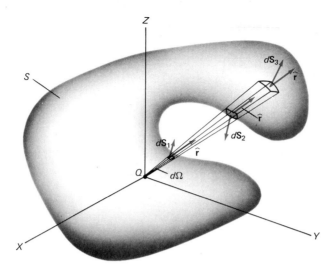

Fig. 23.4 A convoluted Gaussian surface surrounding a point charge source.

intersections. Therefore, the net contribution to $\oiint_S \, d\Omega$ for any direction is zero, and we have from (23.4) that

$$\Phi_{\mathscr{E}} = \oiint_S \mathscr{E} \cdot d\mathbf{S} = 0,$$

which is the result required by Gauss's Relation.

Finally, consider the situation where we have a number of source changes, some inside and some outside the surface S. We saw in Chapter 21 that the resultant electric-field strength at any point is obtained by a linear superposition of the field strengths arising from each source considered independently: $\mathscr{E}_R = \mathscr{E}_1 + \mathscr{E}_2 + \mathscr{E}_3 + \cdots$. Thus, for the flux of the resultant electric field through any closed surface

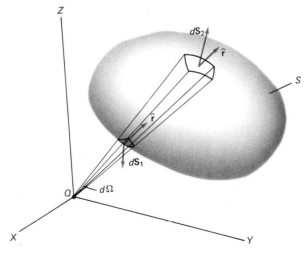

Fig. 23.5 A point charge source Q lying outside the Gaussian surface S.

S we have

$$\Phi_{\mathscr{E}} = \oiint_S \mathscr{E}_R \cdot d\mathbf{S} = \oiint_S \{\mathscr{E}_1 + \mathscr{E}_2 + \mathscr{E}_3 + \cdots\} \cdot d\mathbf{S}$$

$$= \oiint_S \mathscr{E}_1 \cdot d\mathbf{S} + \oiint_S \mathscr{E}_2 \cdot d\mathbf{S} + \oiint_S \mathscr{E}_3 \cdot d\mathbf{S} + \cdots . \qquad (23.5)$$

Each term on the right-hand side of (23.5) is of the form we have considered in the above discussion; thus, we have that

$$\oiint_S \mathscr{E}_j \cdot d\mathbf{S} = \begin{cases} Q_j/\epsilon_0 \text{ if the point source } Q_j \text{ is inside } S \\ 0 \text{ if the point source } Q_j \text{ is outside } S \end{cases} .$$

Therefore, the sum of terms on the right-hand side of (23.5) gives the result

$$\Phi_{\mathscr{E}} = \oiint_S \mathscr{E}_R \cdot d\mathbf{S} = Q_S/\epsilon_0,$$

where Q_S is the total charge inside S. We have now considered all possibilities, and Gauss's Relation is established in every case.

23.3   GENERAL PROPERTIES OF GAUSS'S RELATION

Gauss's Relation is true for any closed surface S that we want to imagine; a surface to which Gauss's Relation is applied is frequently called a *Gaussian surface*. The derivation of Gauss's Relation depends only on Coulomb's Principle and the superposition rule for field strengths due to different sources. In fact, the result turns out to be more general than Coulomb's Principle, being valid even in time-dependent situations.

Although it is generally true, Gauss's Relation is helpful for relating field strengths and source charge distributions only when the situation has a high degree of spatial symmetry that allows conclusions to be drawn about the geometrical nature of the electric field. For example, suppose that the source charge distribution is spherically symmetric. Then all directions outward from the center of the distribution are equivalent, and the magnitude of the electric-field strength can depend at most on the distance from the center of the source distribution, not on the particular direction out from this center. In terms of a system of spherical polar coordinates with origin at the center of the spherical source charge distribution we have $\mathscr{E} = \mathscr{E}(r)$, independent of the angles θ and ϕ. The spherical symmetry of the source charge distribution also requires that the direction of the electric-field strength be either radially outward or radially inward; any other direction for $\mathscr{E}$ would imply a favoring of some direction or sense of rotation in space, which is inconsistent with the spherical symmetry of the source charge distribution. Thus, for the situation of a spherically symmetric source charge distribution we can write

$$\mathscr{E} = \mathscr{E}(r)\,\hat{\mathbf{r}}. \quad (Spherical\ Source\ Symmetry) \qquad (23.6)$$

With this much known about the nature of the electric field from symmetry, we can complete the determination of $\mathscr{E}$ by application of Gauss's Relation to a spherical Gaussian surface S with its center at the center of the source charge distribution. Let R be the radius of S. We first suppose that R is so large that all the charge is inside S. An element of surface on S has the vector representation $d\mathbf{S} = dS\hat{\mathbf{r}}$. Thus,

$$\Phi_{\mathscr{E}} = \oiint_S \mathscr{E} \cdot d\mathbf{S} = \oiint_S \mathscr{E}(r = R)\hat{\mathbf{r}} \cdot dS\hat{\mathbf{r}} = \oiint_S \mathscr{E}(R)dS$$

$$= \mathscr{E}(R) \oiint_S dS = \mathscr{E}(R)4\pi R^2,$$

and so Gauss's Relation becomes

$$\Phi_{\mathscr{E}} = \mathscr{E}(R)4\pi R^2 = Q_S/\epsilon_0,$$

which implies that

$$\mathscr{E}(R) = Q_{\text{total}}/4\pi\epsilon_0 R^2.$$

The electric-field strength outside a spherically symmetric charge distribution is the same as if all the charge were collected on a point at the center of the distribution.

This same technique can be used to determine $\mathscr{E}$ within the charge distribution; we simply choose the radius R of the spherical Gaussian surface S to be less than the radius of the charge distribution. In this case Q_S is not the total charge of the charge distribution, but is only that fraction of the total charge that is within the surface S.

Example. What is the electric-field strength at an arbitrary point inside a uniformly distributed sphere of charge of radius a and total charge Q?

We choose the spherical Gaussian surface S exactly as above except we now take $R < a$. As before, we obtain for the flux through the surface S that $\Phi_{\mathscr{E}} = \mathscr{E}(R)4\pi R^2 = Q_S/\epsilon_0$. In order to find Q_S we note that for a uniformly distributed sphere of charge of total charge Q and radius a the volume charge density is $\rho = Q/(4\pi a^3/3)$. Thus, the charge inside the spherical surface S of radius R is

$$Q_S = \rho(4/3)\pi R^3 = \frac{Q}{(4/3)\pi a^3}(4/3)\pi R^3 = QR^3/a^3.$$

Substituting this result into the flux expression deduced from Gauss's Relation we obtain

$$\Phi_{\mathscr{E}} = \mathscr{E}(R)4\pi R^2 = QR^3/\epsilon_0 a^3,$$

whence we have for the field strength within the sphere of charge that

$$\mathscr{E}(R) = (Q/4\pi\epsilon_0 a^3)R.$$

The above treatment of a spherical charge distribution illustrates a common situation that occurs in applying Gauss's Relation to charge distributions having a high degree of spatial symmetry. In the above case we could choose a Gaussian surface S such that $\mathscr{E}$ was everywhere normal to the surface. In this event $\mathscr{E}$ and $d\mathbf{S}$ are parallel vectors, and the scalar product in (23.1) becomes $\mathscr{E} \cdot d\mathbf{S} = \mathscr{E}\, dS \cos 0 = \mathscr{E}\, dS$. In addition, we were able to argue that the magnitude of the electric-field strength was constant everywhere on the Gaussian surface S and therefore could be taken outside the integral. The integral for the flux through the Gaussian surface thus simplified in the following way:

$$\Phi_{\mathscr{E}} = \oiint_S \mathscr{E} \cdot d\mathbf{S} = \oiint_S \mathscr{E}\, dS = \mathscr{E} \oiint_S dS,$$

and $\oiint_S dS$ is just the area of the surface S.

We emphasize that this simplification depends on two conditions being true: $\mathscr{E}$ and $d\mathbf{S}$ are parallel vectors and $\mathscr{E}$ is constant over the Gaussian surface. Situations will be encountered where $\mathscr{E}$ is constant in magnitude and parallel to $d\mathbf{S}$ over only part of the Gaussian surface; in such a case the flux integral reduces in this way only over that particular part of the surface.

Another condition that allows simplification of the flux integral occurs when $\mathscr{E}$ and $d\mathbf{S}$ are perpendicular over a portion of the Gaussian surface. In this case we have $\mathscr{E} \cdot d\mathbf{S} = \mathscr{E}\, dS \cos(\pi/2) = 0$, so for that part of the surface where this condition holds we have $\iint \mathscr{E} \cdot d\mathbf{S} = 0$.

23.4 APPLICATION OF GAUSS'S RELATION TO SYMMETRICAL CHARGE DISTRIBUTIONS

We have noted that Gauss's Relation can be used to compute $\mathscr{E}$ if the source charge distribution has a sufficiently high degree of spatial symmetry. We found in the preceding section that for any spherically symmetric charge distribution

$$\mathscr{E} = (Q/4\pi\epsilon_0 r^2)\hat{\mathbf{r}}, \quad \textit{(outside spherically symmetric source)} \qquad (23.7)$$

where Q is the total charge, r is the distance from the origin at the center of the charge distribution, and $\hat{\mathbf{r}}$ is a unit vector that at any point is directed radially outward from the origin. This field is the same as that which would be produced by a point charge Q at the location of the center of the charge distribution. For a uniformly distributed sphere of charge of radius a we found that $\mathscr{E}_{\text{inside}} = (Qr/4\pi\epsilon_0 a^3)\hat{\mathbf{r}}$.

Another interesting case is a hollow spherical shell of charge of inner radius b, as shown in Fig. 23.6. The electric-field strength outside the shell is given by (23.7). For a Gaussian surface of radius $R < b$ we have $\Phi_{\mathscr{E}} = \mathscr{E}(R)4\pi R^2 = Q_S/\epsilon_0$. But in this case for $R < b$ we have $Q_S = 0$; there is no charge inside the Gaussian surface. We conclude that the electric-field strength vanishes inside an empty hollow spherical shell of charge. We have previously noted in Sec. 9.7 the analogous result for gravitation; the gravitational-field strength inside a hollow shell of matter vanishes. Determination of the electric-field strength for the region $b < r < a$ is the subject of one of the problems.

Now that we have an expression for the field strength produced by a spherically symmetric charge distribution, it is worthwhile to pause in our treatment of Gauss's Relation and compute the electrical potential due to such a distribution. We take the reference location at infinity and set $V_{\text{ref}} = 0$. Since the electric-field strength

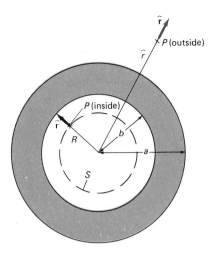

Fig. 23.6 A hollow spherical shell of charge of inner radius b and outer radius a.

outside the charge distribution has the same form as for a point charge source, the potential at a point P in the outside region has the same form as obtained in Chapter 22 for a point charge. We have

$$V_P = -\int_\infty^P \mathscr{E} \cdot d\mathbf{l} = -\int_\infty^{r=r_P} \frac{1}{4\pi\epsilon_0} \frac{Q}{r^2} \hat{\mathbf{r}} \cdot dr\hat{\mathbf{r}} = -\frac{Q}{4\pi\epsilon_0} \int_\infty^{r_P} \frac{1}{r^2} dr$$

$$= \frac{Q}{4\pi\epsilon_0} \frac{1}{r}\Big|_\infty^{r_P} = \frac{Q}{4\pi\epsilon_0 r_P}.$$

The situation is different for a point P within the spherical charge distribution. The expression for the electric-field strength in the integrand of the potential computation changes at the surface of the sphere. We illustrate this for the example of a uniformly distributed sphere of charge.

Example. What is the potential at an arbitrary point within a uniformly distributed sphere of charge having total charge Q and radius a?

The situation is illustrated in Fig. 23.7. We have seen that $\mathscr{E}_{\text{outside}} = (Q/4\pi\epsilon_0 r^2)\hat{\mathbf{r}}$ and $\mathscr{E}_{\text{inside}} = (Qr/4\pi\epsilon_0 a^3)\hat{\mathbf{r}}$. Thus we have for a point P where $r_P < a$ that

$$V_P = -\int_\infty^P \mathscr{E} \cdot d\mathbf{l} = -\int_\infty^{r=a} \frac{1}{4\pi\epsilon_0} \frac{Q}{r^2} \hat{\mathbf{r}} \cdot dr\hat{\mathbf{r}} - \int_{r=a}^{r=r_P} \frac{1}{4\pi\epsilon_0} \frac{Qr}{a^3} \hat{\mathbf{r}} \cdot dr\hat{\mathbf{r}}$$

$$= \frac{Q}{4\pi\epsilon_0 a} - \frac{Q}{4\pi\epsilon_0 a^3} \frac{r^2}{2}\Big|_{r=a}^{r=r_P} = \frac{Q}{4\pi\epsilon_0 a} - \frac{Qr_P^2}{8\pi\epsilon_0 a^3} + \frac{Q}{8\pi\epsilon_0 a}$$

$$= \frac{3Q}{8\pi\epsilon_0 a} - \frac{Qr_P^2}{8\pi\epsilon_0 a^3}.$$

The results for the magnitude of the electric-field strength and the potential as functions of the distance from the center of the spherical charge distribution are shown graphically in Fig. 23.8.

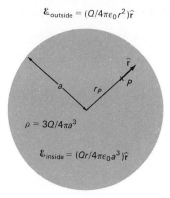

$$\mathscr{E}_{outside} = (Q/4\pi\epsilon_0 r^2)\hat{r}$$

$$\rho = 3Q/4\pi a^3$$

$$\mathscr{E}_{inside} = (Qr/4\pi\epsilon_0 a^3)\hat{r}$$

Fig. 23.7 A uniformly distributed sphere of charge having total charge Q and radius a.

Another type of charge distribution for which $\mathscr{E}$ can be determined by use of Gauss's Relation is that of an "infinite" cylinder of charge. We imagine a charge distribution that is cylindrically symmetric about the Z axis and that does not depend on the coordinate z over a distance that is *very* large compared to the perpendicular distance of the observation point from the Z axis. For an observer at such a point near the center of the distribution, the ends of the charge distribution are so far away that the details of the distribution there have no influence on the electric-field strength at his location. It is then a legitimate mathematical approximation to assume that the charge distribution extends without change to infinity in the $\pm Z$ directions. There is then invariance with respect to translations parallel to the Z axis; the observer can see nothing that changes with z or distinguishes up from down; therefore $\mathscr{E}$ must be independent of z and have a direction parallel to the XY plane. Also, all directions outward from the Z axis are equivalent; the observer can see nothing that changes with the angle of rotation ϕ about the Z axis or distinguishes clockwise from counterclockwise rotations. We can conclude that $\mathscr{E}$ is at any point directed

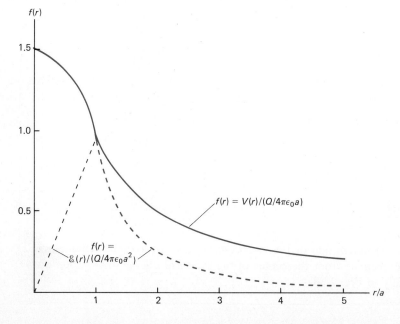

$f(r) = V(r)/(Q/4\pi\epsilon_0 a)$

$f(r) = \mathscr{E}(r)/(Q/4\pi\epsilon_0 a^2)$

Fig. 23.8 Magnitude of the electric-field strength and the electrical potential due to a uniformly distributed sphere of charge of total charge Q and radius a.

radially outward from or inward toward the Z axis and that its magnitude can depend only on the distance from the Z axis.

As an example of a charge distribution having this symmetry we shall consider an infinite line of charge. Some other cylindrical charge distributions are considered in the problems.

Example.   What is the electric-field strength in the vicinity of an "infinite" line of charge along the Z axis where the linear charge density in coulombs per meter is λ?

Let $\rho = \sqrt{x^2 + y^2}$ be the perpendicular distance of a point (x, y, z) from the Z axis and let $\hat{\rho}$ be a unit vector at this point directed radially outward from the Z axis; these quantities are shown in Fig. 23.9. From the reasoning described above we can conclude that $\mathscr{E} = \mathscr{E}(\rho)\hat{\rho}$. We can complete the determination of $\mathscr{E}$ by applying Gauss's Relation to a cylindrical Gaussian surface about the Z axis of radius R and length L. The situation is shown in Fig. 23.10. We consider the Gaussian surface S in three pieces: ① top, where $d\mathbf{S} = dS\mathbf{k}$; ② bottom, where $d\mathbf{S} = -dS\mathbf{k}$; and ③ side, where $d\mathbf{S} = dS\hat{\rho}$. Thus we have

$$\Phi_{\mathscr{E}} = \oiint_S \mathscr{E} \cdot d\mathbf{S} = \underset{①}{\iint \mathscr{E}(\rho)\hat{\rho} \cdot dS\mathbf{k}} - \underset{②}{\iint \mathscr{E}(\rho)\hat{\rho} \cdot dS\mathbf{k}} + \underset{③}{\iint \mathscr{E}(\rho)\hat{\rho} \cdot dS\hat{\rho}}.$$

Since $\hat{\rho}$ is perpendicular to $\mathbf{k}$, we have $\hat{\rho} \cdot \mathbf{k} = 0$. Therefore,

$$\Phi_{\mathscr{E}} = 0 - 0 + \underset{③}{\iint \mathscr{E}(\rho = R)dS} = \mathscr{E}(R) \underset{③}{\iint dS} = \mathscr{E}(R)2\pi RL.$$

Thus, Gauss's Relation becomes

$$\Phi_{\mathscr{E}} = \mathscr{E}(R)2\pi RL = Q_S/\epsilon_0 = \lambda L/\epsilon_0,$$

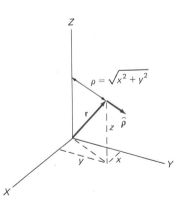

Fig. 23.9 Coordinates used to describe the electric-field strength produced by an "infinite" line of charge along the Z axis.

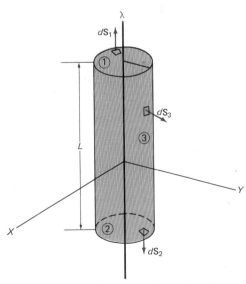

Fig. 23.10 Cylindrical Gaussian surface about an "infinite" line of charge along the Z axis.

from which we have that

$$\mathcal{E}(R) = \lambda L/2\pi\epsilon_0 RL = \lambda/2\pi\epsilon_0 R.$$

An equivalent result was obtained by direct integration in Sec. 21.5.

We emphasize that in making this computation we are not neglecting the charge that is outside the Gaussian surface. It is the presence of this charge that allows us to make the symmetry arguments leading to the conclusion $\mathcal{E} = \mathcal{E}(\rho)\hat{\rho}$. If the line of charge were of finite length, the symmetry argument would not be valid, and we would not be able to use Gauss's Relation in determining $\mathcal{E}$.

We can use the result we have obtained for $\mathcal{E}$ to compute potential differences in the vicinity of a line of charge:

$$V_B - V_A = -\int_A^B \mathcal{E} \cdot d\mathbf{l} = -\int_A^B \mathcal{E}(\rho)\hat{\rho} \cdot (d\rho\hat{\rho} + d\mathbf{l}_\perp)$$

$$= -\int_{\rho=\rho_A}^{\rho=\rho_B} \frac{\lambda}{2\pi\epsilon_0\rho}\,d\rho = \frac{-\lambda}{2\pi\epsilon_0}\ln\rho \Big|_{\rho_A}^{\rho_B} = \frac{\lambda}{2\pi\epsilon_0}\ln(\rho_A/\rho_B).$$

In writing $d\mathbf{l} = d\rho\hat{\rho} + d\mathbf{l}_\perp$ we have used reasoning analogous to that in Sec. 22.3. We note from this relation for potential difference that if we try to take the reference point at $\rho \to \infty$ and to set $V_{\text{ref}} = 0$, we reach a contradiction. The magnitude of the potential difference increases without bound as ρ_A becomes arbitrarily large. This sort of difficulty will always arise when we use the mathematical approximation that the charge distribution extends with nonzero charge density for an infinite distance in any direction.

As a final example of the determination of $\mathcal{E}$ by use of Gauss's Relation, we shall consider an infinite sheet of charge.

Example.   What is the electric-field strength at an arbitrary point P above or below a sheet of charge of negligible thickness coinciding with the XY plane and extending to infinity in all directions in that plane if the surface charge density in coulombs per square meter is σ?

From the symmetry, there can be nothing by which an observer can distinguish any dependence on the coordinates x or y or any direction parallel to the XY plane. Therefore, $\mathcal{E}$ must have the form $\mathcal{E} = \mathcal{E}(z)\mathbf{k}$. Furthermore, there should be nothing that allows a fundamental distinction of one side of the sheet of charge from the other. If σ is positive, $\mathcal{E}$ should be directed away from the sheet on both sides; if σ is negative, $\mathcal{E}$ should be directed toward the sheet on both sides. This requires that $\mathcal{E}(-z) = -\mathcal{E}(z)$.

We choose for a Gaussian surface a cylinder about the Z axis of radius R and length $2z_p$ oriented perpendicular to the charge sheet as shown in Fig. 23.11. We then have

$$\Phi_{\mathscr{E}} = \oiint_S \mathscr{E} \cdot d\mathbf{S} = \iint_{top} \mathscr{E}(z_P)\mathbf{k} \cdot dS\mathbf{k} + \iint_{bottom} -\mathscr{E}(z_P)\mathbf{k} \cdot dS(-\mathbf{k}) + \iint_{side} \mathscr{E}(z)\mathbf{k} \cdot dS\hat{\boldsymbol{\rho}}$$

$$= \mathscr{E}(z_P) \iint_{top} dS + \mathscr{E}(z_P) \iint_{bottom} dS + 0 = \mathscr{E}(z_P) 2\pi R^2.$$

Gauss's Relation then becomes

$$\Phi_{\mathscr{E}} = \mathscr{E}(z_P)2\pi R^2 = Q_S/\epsilon_0 = \sigma\pi R^2/\epsilon_0,$$

from which it follows that $\mathscr{E}(z_P) = \sigma/2\epsilon_0$.

23.5 PROPERTIES OF IDEAL CONDUCTORS

There are several important conclusions about the electric-field strength and charge distributions associated with ideal conductors that can be reached with the aid of Gauss's Relation. In the absence of any external source charges, every macroscopic volume element of an "uncharged" piece of conductor will be electrically neutral. Although the conduction electrons are not bound to any particular ion of the lattice, the distribution of conduction electrons throughout the material is uniform so that in any macroscopic volume element the numbers of positive and negative charges are equal. If a conductor is suddenly subjected to an external electrostatic field, the conduction electrons begin to migrate under the influence of the electric force $\mathbf{F} = Q\mathscr{E}$. This migration causes macroscopic volume elements into which electrons are moved to become negatively charged and the macroscopic volume elements from which they are moved to become positively charged. The redistribution of the charge of the conductor gives rise to an electric field within the conductor that tends to oppose further migration of conduction electrons. The charge distribution of the conductor *very rapidly* adjusts to a new equilibrium situation where a conduction electron

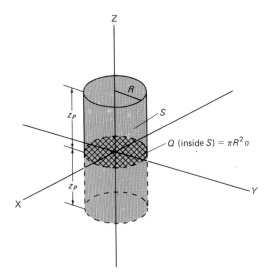

Fig. 23.11 Cylindrical Gaussian surface used to deduce the electric-field strength due to an "infinite" sheet of charge lying in the XY plane.

at any point in the material experiences no resultant macroscopic electric force. Thus, *in a static equilibrium situation the distribution of conduction electrons within a conductor is such that the resultant macroscopic electric-field strength at any point inside the conductor is zero.*

We emphasize two points: (1) It is the macroscopic electric-field strength that vanishes; that is, the field strength averaged over a volume element large enough to contain very many atoms or molecules is zero. At the microscopic level, within an individual atom, there are field strengths of large magnitude. (2) If the distribution of external source charges is suddenly changed, the relaxation of the conducting material to the new static situation occurs extremely rapidly.

Since the macroscopic electric-field strength vanishes at any point inside a conductor in a static situation, we can conclude immediately that the potential difference between any two points within the conductor must be zero; *the interior of a conductor must be an equipotential volume in a static situation.*

The vanishing of $\mathscr{E}$ within a conductor leads to another important conclusion. Consider *any* Gaussian surface lying wholly within the conductor. Gauss's Relation says that $\Phi_{\mathscr{E}} = \oiint_S \mathscr{E} \cdot d\mathbf{S} = Q_S/\epsilon_0$; putting $\mathscr{E} = 0$ in this relation immediately gives that $Q_S = 0$. Since this is true for *any* Gaussian surface S within the conductor, we conclude that *the net charge within any macroscopic volume inside a conducting material in a static situation is zero. If the conductor carries any excess charge, the surplus or deficiency of electrons must occur in the surface layer of the material.* Thus, any charged conductor in electrostatics will have its charge distribution described by a surface charge density σ; the volume charge density in the interior of the conductor will be zero.

We have argued that $\mathscr{E}$ inside a conductor is zero in a static situation. We can also reach a quantitative conclusion concerning the electric-field strength just outside the surface of the conductor. First we note that *the direction of $\mathscr{E}$ in a static situation must be normal to the surface at any point on the surface of a conductor.* If this were not true, there would be a component of $\mathscr{E}$ parallel to the surface; the free electrons in the surface layer of the conductor would migrate under the influence of the electric force parallel to the surface, and the situation would not be static.

To reach a conclusion about the magnitude of $\mathscr{E}$ at the surface of a conductor, we consider a coin-shaped Gaussian surface with one flat face just outside and the other just inside the surface of the conductor, as shown in Fig. 23.12. We take the area of a flat face of the Gaussian surface to be so small that the element of conductor surface ΔA within the Gaussian surface can be treated as being plane and the magnitude of $\mathscr{E}$ over this region can be taken as constant. We represent by $\hat{\mathbf{n}}$ a unit vector normal to this surface. We take the thickness t_0 of the Gaussian surface that protrudes outside the conductor to be vanishingly small. Applying Gauss's Relation and remembering that $\mathscr{E} = 0$ inside the conductor and $\mathscr{E}$ outside the conductor is normal to the conductor surface, we obtain

$$\Phi_{\mathscr{E}} = \oiint_S \mathscr{E} \cdot d\mathbf{S} = \iint_{\substack{\text{outside} \\ \text{face}}} \mathscr{E}_{\text{out}} \cdot d\mathbf{S} + \iint_{\substack{\text{rest} \\ \text{of } S}} \mathscr{E}_{\text{in}} \cdot d\mathbf{S} = \iint_{\substack{\text{outside} \\ \text{face}}} \mathscr{E}_{\text{out}}\, \hat{\mathbf{n}} \cdot d S \hat{\mathbf{n}} + 0$$

$$= \mathscr{E}_{\text{out}} \iint_{\substack{\text{outside} \\ \text{face}}} dS = \mathscr{E}_{\text{out}} \Delta A = Q_S/\epsilon_0 = \sigma \Delta A/\epsilon_0,$$

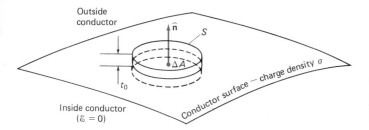

Fig. 23.12 Coin-shaped Gaussian surface used to deduce the electric-field strength at the surface of a conductor carrying a surface charge density σ.

from which we conclude that just outside the surface

$$\mathscr{E} = \sigma/\epsilon_0. \quad (at\ conductor\ surface) \tag{23.8}$$

Another conclusion we can reach about conductors is the following:

In a static situation the electric-field strength within an empty volume that is surrounded by a conductor vanishes, regardless of the distribution of source charges outside the conductor. The potential throughout the volume is equal to the potential of the conductor.

This result is the basis of *electrostatic shielding.* A region that is enclosed by a grounded conductor is shielded from the effects of external static distributions of charge. Any electric field that exists in the region must arise from source charges that are within the region. This result is not trivial; development of a proof is the subject of one of the problems.

23.6 THE FARADAY ICE-PAIL EXPERIMENT

We noted in Chapter 20 that the most sensitive experimental tests of Coulomb's Principle are concerned with the absence of electric force on a test charge within a hollow conductor. Experiments testing the absence of any electric-field strength inside a hollow conductor are testing a conclusion that follows from Gauss's Relation. But if the force relation were not exactly inverse square, Gauss's Relation would not be valid, so these experiments provide an indirect but ultimately extremely sensitive test of the form of Coulomb's Principle. Experiments of this sort were carried out with increasing sophistication by Franklin, Priestley, Cavendish, Maxwell, and others on to the present time.

An important experiment of this type was performed by Faraday in 1843. The sequence of operations is shown in Fig. 23.13. (a) An uncharged metal container is placed on an insulating stand. The container that Faraday used happened to be his laboratory ice pail, hence the name by which the experiment is known. The outer surface of the container is connected to an electroscope; the divergence of the electroscope leaves gives a measure of the amount of charge on the outside of the container.

(b) A metal ball mounted on an insulating handle is given a positive charge and is lowered into the interior of the container without touching the walls of the container. The leaves of the electroscope immediately diverge and maintain the same divergence

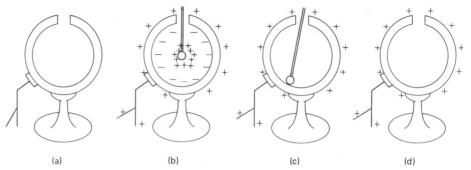

Fig. 23.13 The Faraday ice-pail experiment.

angle regardless of the location of the metal ball within the container. A test made at this time shows that the charge on the electroscope leaves is positive. We assume that the opening in the container through which the metal ball is inserted is small enough to have a negligible effect on the electrical situation. Then we can interpret the result of step (b) by use of Gauss's Relation. Consider a Gaussian surface S within the metal of the container. On this surface $\mathscr{E} = 0$; therefore, Gauss's Relation says that $Q_S = 0$. Thus, the negative charge induced on the inner surface of the container must be equal in magnitude to the positive charge on the metal ball. By charge conservation, the positive charge on the outer surface of the container and the electroscope must also have this magnitude since the container was initially uncharged.

(c) The metal ball is touched to the wall of the container. There is no change in the divergence of the electroscope leaves, but the excess electrons on the inner surface of the container flow to the metal ball and neutralize its charge. This is verified in (d), where the metal ball is withdrawn and a test with another electroscope shows it to be uncharged. The electroscope connected to the outside of the container maintains its same divergence.

Faraday had several years earlier performed a more spectacular but qualitative experiment of this kind in which he constructed a large box covered with metal foil and mounted on insulators. He conducted various simple electrostatics experiments while sitting inside this box with the outside of the box raised to a high electrical potential. All the results were the same as if the experiments had been performed in an ordinary laboratory.

QUESTIONS

1. Are the charges making up Q_S in (23.2) to be considered among the sources of $\mathscr{E}$, or is the electric-field strength being considered just that produced by charges outside the gaussian surface?

2. Draw a diagram showing a sphere of radius R with its center at the origin. Introduce a spherical polar coordinate system as in Fig. 1.8, and consider a point P with coordinates R, θ, ϕ. Show that if the angle ϕ increases to $\phi + d\phi$ while θ and R remain constant, the corresponding arc on the sphere has length $R \sin\theta \, d\phi$. Show that if the angle θ increases to $\theta + d\theta$ while ϕ and R remain constant, the corresponding arc on the

sphere has length $R\ d\theta$. Indicate on your diagram the surface element on the sphere having these two arcs as sides and having area $dS = R^2 \sin\theta\ d\theta\ d\phi$.

3. The flux of an electric field was discussed for either open or closed surfaces. Does Gauss's Relation apply equally well to open and to closed surfaces?

4. What are the dimensions of solid angle in terms of mass, length, and time?

5. Could Gauss's Relation be used to determine the form of the electric-field strength produced by an electric dipole? If so, explain how the relation could be used; if not, explain why not.

6. Why is it necessary to consider an *infinite* cylinder of charge in order that the electric-field strength can be determined from Gauss's Relation? No real charge distribution will be infinitely long; under what condi-

tions do the results for an "infinite" cylinder of charge correspond to a physically realistic situation?

7. Why is there difficulty in using the convention $V_\infty = 0$ when the source charge distribution extends to infinity? Does this difficulty mean that the concept of electric potential is not useful in such a situation?

8. It is asserted in the text that under static conditions the electric-field strength inside a conductor is zero. How is this possible? If we are very close to the nucleus of an atom, for example, the magnitude of the electric-field strength must be very large.

9. Under static conditions the excess charge on a conductor must reside on its surface. Does this mean that all the conduction electrons are in the surface layer of the material?

10. How is Gauss's relation related to Coulomb's Principle?

PROBLEMS

1. Suppose that a Gaussian surface encloses zero net charge. Does Gauss's Relation require that $\mathscr{E}$ equal zero for all points on the surface? Explain your answer; give an example.

2. A positive point charge Q is located within a cavity surrounded by a conductor. For a Gaussian surface S that is everywhere within the conducting material but encloses the cavity we have $\oiint_S \mathscr{E} \cdot d\mathbf{S} = 0$ since $\mathscr{E} = 0$ inside a conductor. How is this possible without violating Gauss's Relation since the charge Q is inside the Gaussian surface?

3. Show that a point charge located outside an uncharged, hollow conductor experiences a force if another point charge is placed within the hollow space, but a point charge located within the hollow space experiences no force if another point charge is placed outside the

conductor. Does this violate Newton's Third Principle? Explain your answer.

4. In a certain region of space around the origin there is no charge, but the electric-field strength is $\mathscr{E} = \mathscr{E}\mathbf{k}$, where $\mathscr{E}$ is a constant. By evaluating the surface integral, compute the electrical flux $\Phi_\mathscr{E}$ through a surface S consisting of a circular disk of radius R lying in the XY plane with its center at the origin plus a hemisphere of radius R with its center at the origin. The hemisphere is symmetric about the Z axis. Show that your result is in agreement with Gauss's Relation.

5. Consider a metal sphere of radius R carrying total charge Q. Show that Eq. (23.7) for the electric-field strength outside a spherically symmetric charge distribution is consistent with Eq. (23.8) for the electric-field strength just outside the surface of a conductor.

6. A certain conducting sphere of radius 4.25 cm carries a charge of -3.5×10^{-7} C. (a) What is the electric-field strength at the surface of the sphere? At 4.25 cm from the surface of the sphere? At 8.50 cm from the surface of the sphere? (b) What is the electrical flux through spherical Gaussian surfaces of radii 4.25 cm, 8.50 cm, and 12.75 cm if the surfaces are all concentric with the conducting sphere? (c) How many excess electrons are there per unit area on the surface of the sphere?

7. The maximum electric-field strength that can be sustained by air at standard atmospheric pressure without insulation breakdown is about 3×10^6 V/m. Use Gauss's Relation to find the total charge on an isolated metal sphere of diameter 4 cm when the field strength at its surface has this value. Suppose that the charge is negative; how many excess electrons are on the sphere? If the sphere is solid copper having one conduction electron per atom, what is the ratio of the number of excess electrons to the number of conduction electrons present when the sphere is neutral?

8. The electric-field strength in the atmosphere at the surface of the earth averaged over the earth's surface is about 130 V/m, downward. (a) What total charge does this imply there is on the earth? Treat the earth as a sphere of radius 6.37×10^6 m. (b) Express this total charge as a surplus or deficiency of electrons per unit area. (c) The result found in (a) is not a small charge. Why are Coulomb forces not significant in determining the orbits of the planets?

9. Find an expression for the electric-field strength for all $r > 0$ if the source charge distribution consists of a point charge $+Q$ at the origin plus a total charge $-Q$ that is distributed with spherical symmetry around the point charge with a volume charge density that is a constant for $r < a$ and is zero for $r > a$.

10. Repeat Problem 9 for a case where the charge $-Q$ is distributed with a volume charge density that is proportional to the inverse of the distance from the origin for $r < a$ and is zero for $r > a$.

11. A certain hollow spherical charge distribution has a uniform charge density $\rho = 1.25 \times 10^{-6}$ C/m^3. The inner sphere of radius $b = 10$ cm is empty of charge. The outer radius of the charge distribution is $a = 30$ cm. What is the electric-field strength at a point P located a distance $r = 20$ cm from the center of the charge distribution?

12. Consider a spherical shell of charge of inner radius b, outer radius a, and uniform charge density ρ. Find expressions for the potential for all distances from the origin, which is at the common center of the spheres; take the reference point for potential at infinity and set $V_{ref} = 0$. If the parameters a, b, and ρ have the values given in the preceding problem, what is the potential at the origin?

13. Within a certain sphere of radius R the electric-field strength is everywhere directed radially outward from the center of the sphere and of constant magnitude: $\mathscr{E} = \mathscr{E}\hat{r}$, where $\mathscr{E}$ is a positive constant. Use Gauss's Relation to determine the dependence of the volume charge density ρ on position for the region inside the sphere.

14. Two thin, concentric, conducting spherical shells of radii A and B $(A < B)$ carry charges Q_A and Q_B, respectively. Find expressions for the electric-field strength as a function of radius for (a) the region outside of both shells, (b) the region between the shells, and (c) the region inside of both shells. Suppose that $A = 2$ cm, $B = 8$ cm, $Q_A = -4 \times 10^{-8}$ C, and $Q_B = + 6 \times 10^{-8}$ C. Draw a graph showing the electric-field strength as a function of radius.

15. For the situation of the preceding problem, find general expressions for the potential as a function of radius for (a) the region outside

of both shells, (b) the region between the shells, and (c) the region inside of both shells. For the particular case where $A = 2$ cm, $B = 8$ cm, $Q_A = -4 \times 10^{-8}$ C, and $Q_B = +6 \times 10^{-8}$ C, draw a graph showing the potential as a function of radius. Take the reference point for potential at infinity and set $V_{ref} = 0$.

16. A point charge $Q = 8 \times 10^{-8}$ C is located at the center of an isolated, uncharged, conducting, spherical shell of inner radius $b = 10$ cm and outer radius $a = 15$ cm. (a) Use Gauss's Relation to deduce expressions for the electric-field strength for the region inside the shell and for the region outside the shell. (b) What are the surface charge densities that are induced on the inner and outer surfaces of the shell?

17. For the situation of the preceding problem, what is the potential of the conducting spherical shell? What is the potential of a point 0.05 m from the point charge Q? Take the reference point for potential at infinity and set $V_{ref} = 0$.

18. How are the results of the two preceding problems changed if the conducting spherical shell is grounded instead of being isolated?

19. In one early model proposed to represent the hydrogen atom, the electron was imagined as a point charge inside a uniformly distributed sphere of positive charge of radius R, the total positive charge of the spherical distribution having the same magnitude as the charge of the electron. Use Gauss's Relation to show that the electron would be in equilibrium at the center of the sphere and would be subjected to a force $\mathbf{F} = -k\mathbf{r}$ when at a position $\mathbf{r}$ relative to the center of the sphere, provided $r < R$. Deduce an expression for the constant k. Show that if disturbed from its equilibrium position and then released, the electron would undergo simple harmonic oscillations; find an expression for the frequency of these oscillations.

Evaluate this frequency for the case where $R = 5.3 \times 10^{-11}$ m.

20. Everywhere inside a sphere of radius R with center at the origin there is a uniform distribution of charge described by a constant volume charge density ρ except inside a sphere of radius b with center located by the position vector $\mathbf{a}$, where the charge density is zero. Assume that $R - a < b$ so the smaller, empty sphere is totally inside the larger sphere. Show that the electric-field strength inside the smaller sphere is given by $(\rho/3\epsilon_0)\mathbf{a}$. Determine expressions for $\mathscr{E}$ at locations outside the smaller sphere. To do this, note that the electric field due to a sphere of uniformly distributed charge of radius R can be considered as the field due to the charge inside a sphere of radius b at location $\mathbf{r} = \mathbf{a}$ plus the field due to all the other charge. Therefore, the electric field due to just the latter charge can be obtained from the difference between the field due to a uniformly distributed sphere of charge of radius R with its center at the origin and the field due to a small sphere of charge of radius b with its center at $\mathbf{r} = \mathbf{a}$.

21. Show that the mutual force between two spherically symmetric, nonoverlapping charge distributions having total charges Q_1 and Q_2, respectively, is the same as that between two point charges located at the positions of the centers of the charge distributions. To do this, first show that the force charge distribution one exerts on charge distribution two is the same as the force that a point charge Q_1 would exert on charge distribution two, next consider the same result with the roles of one and two interchanged, and finally invoke Newton's Third Principle.

22. The gravitational field strength $\mathscr{G}$ represents force per unit mass on a "test" particle and thus bears an analogy to the electric-field strength. Exploit this analogy to determine the form of Gauss's Relation for the gravitational case. Use this result to show that the

gravitational attraction of a spherically symmetric body for a particle in its vicinity is the same as if all the mass of the body were concentrated at its center.

23. Use the result of the preceding problem to show that the gravitational force between two spherically symmetric bodies of total masses M_1 and M_2, respectively, is the same as if all the mass of each body were concentrated at its center. (Compare with Problem 21.)

24. Charge is uniformly distributed throughout an "infinitely" long cylinder of radius a that is symmetric about the Z axis. Show that the electric-field strength outside the cylinder is the same as if all the charge were uniformly distributed as a line charge along the Z axis. What is the electric-field strength in the region inside the cylinder?

25. Two concentric conducting cylinders of "infinite" length are symmetric about the Z axis. The inner cylinder has outside radius b; the outer cylinder has inside radius a. The cylinders carry charges per unit length that are equal in magnitude but opposite in sign, the inner cylinder carrying the positive charge. Let the magnitude of the charge per unit length on either cylinder be λ. Show that all the charge on the inner cylinder is on its outer surface and all the charge on the outer cylinder is on its inner surface. Find an expression for the electric-field strength in the region between the cylinders. If $b = 1$ mm, $a = 5$ mm, and the potential difference between the cylinders is 750 V, what is λ?

26. Two plane parallel metal sheets are oriented perpendicular to the Z axis and extend to "infinity" in all directions parallel to the XY plane. The bottom surface of the upper sheet is at $z = d/2$ and carries a uniform surface charge density $+\sigma$; the top surface of the lower sheet is at $z = -d/2$ and carries a uniform surface charge density $-\sigma$. What is the electric-field strength in the region between the plates? If the separation of the

plates is 3 mm, what surface charge density σ is required to produce an electric-field strength of 5.0×10^5 V/m?

27. A negative charge of 1 C is spread uniformly over the XY plane out to a distance $R = 10{,}000$ m in all directions from the origin. What is the electric-field strength above the XY plane and below the XY plane for $|z| << R$ and $(x^2 + y^2) << R^2$?

28. There has been speculation as to whether the charges of the electron and proton are exactly equal. In one experiment to test this point, a large quantity of hydrogen gas at high pressure was placed into a well-insulated metal tank; the tank was first grounded, then with the ground connection removed the gas was allowed to escape. The potential of the "empty" tank was then measured. Compare this experiment with the Faraday ice-pail experiment; discuss the similarities and the differences. Suppose that 1 kmole of hydrogen gas were initially in the grounded tank. If all the gas were then removed with the tank insulated, what charge would remain on the tank if the ratio of the magnitude of the proton charge to the magnitude of the electron charge were greater than unity by one part in 10^{10}? (Recall that hydrogen forms diatomic molecules.) How many electrons gained or lost by the tank would this represent? (Experiments of this type have shown that the magnitudes of the proton and electron charges are equal to within one part in 10^{20}.)

29. Prove the assertion that in a static situation the electric-field strength vanishes within an empty volume that is surrounded by a conducting material. This can be done by the following sequence of arguments: (a) Use Gauss's Relation to prove that if electric lines are drawn so that the number of lines per unit area intersecting a surface element oriented normal to the lines is proportional to the magnitude of the electric-field strength, then electric lines can begin only on positive

charges and end only on negative charges. (b) Show that the line integral $\int \mathscr{E} \cdot d\mathbf{l}$ taken along an electric line is nonnegative and vanishes only if $\mathscr{E} = 0$ everywhere along the line. (c) Use (b) to show that a single electric line cannot intersect the same conductor surface twice. (d) Use (b) to show that in electrostatics electric lines cannot form closed loops. (e) Show as a consequence of (a), (c), and (d) that within a region empty of charge that is surrounded by a conductor, in a static situation, we must have $\mathscr{E} = 0$.

30. Use Gauss's Relation to prove that there cannot exist any location where a point charge would be in stable equilibrium under the action of electrostatic forces alone. To do this, consider what form the electric-field strength must have in the neighborhood of a point of stable equilibrium. From this, show that the electrical flux through a small Gaussian surface surrounding a point of stable equilibrium would have to be nonzero even when there is no charge at the point. Conclude that the existence of a point of stable electrostatic equilibrium is not consistent with Gauss's Relation.

CHAPTER 24

Capacitance and Dielectric Materials

Capacitors provide places where electrical charge and electrical potential energy can be stored. Capacitance is a measure of the ability of a pair of conductors, which together constitute a capacitor, to store electrical potential energy when a potential difference is established between them. As elements that help control the flow of charge, capacitors play a crucial role in many electrical circuits and electronic devices. At the same time, unwanted "stray" capacitance can have a deleterious effect on the operation of an electric instrument.

In this chapter we shall establish a quantitative definition of capacitance and see how it can be computed for simple geometries. We shall consider the work required to charge a capacitor and the electrical potential energy that is thereby stored. We shall also examine some properties of networks of capacitors; the behavior of a capacitor as an element in an electric circuit is a topic to which we shall return in later chapters.

Up to this point in our discussion of electrostatics we have considered only charges in vacuum or on ideal conductors. As an outgrowth of our treatment of capacitance we shall discuss some simple aspects of the electrostatic behavior of insulating materials. This will provide insight into how the relations of electrostatics can be generalized so they apply in the presence of arbitrary distributions of matter.

24.1 CAPACITORS AND CAPACITANCE

Suppose we have a number of charged conductors in the vicinity of one another, in vacuum; the potential of any conductor will in general depend upon the charge, location, and geometrical shape of each of the other conductors. In general, the quantitative expression relating charges, geometries, and potential differences will be complex. We shall focus our attention on the simple case of great practical impor-

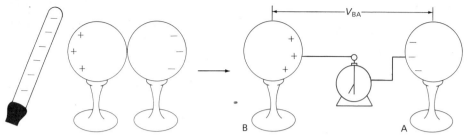

Fig. 24.1 A potential difference is established between two insulated conductors by removing electrons from one conductor and depositing an equal number of electrons on the other conductor. The electroscope indicates the potential difference.

tance where a single pair of conductors, because of their geometric proximity, strongly influence one another, but the effects of other charged conductors can be neglected. We call such a pair of conductors a *capacitor*. The two conductors are frequently called the "plates" of the capacitor whatever their geometric shape.

The important physical attribute of a capacitor is its ability to store electrical potential energy when a potential difference is established between its plates. A quantitative measure of this ability is provided by a property called capacitance.

Consider two conductors A and B forming a capacitor that are both initially uncharged and at the same potential. Suppose that we establish a potential difference V_{BA} between the conductors by pulling electrons off one of the conductors and depositing an equal number of electrons on the other conductor by electrostatic induction or by means of a battery, as suggested in Fig. 24.1. The conductor that loses electrons has its potential increased relative to the initial value; we call this conductor the positive plate. The conductor that gains electrons has its potential decreased relative to the initial value; we call this conductor the negative plate. Some external agent must do work to pull electrons off the positive plate and more work to push electrons onto the negative plate.

As this process proceeds and the potential difference between the plates V_{BA} increases from zero toward its final value, it requires more work to transfer each increment of charge. Let Q represent the magnitude of the positive charge on the positive plate and the equal magnitude of the negative charge on the negative plate; we shall refer to Q as the amount of charge "stored" by the capacitor. For simplicity in notation we shall drop the subscripts and simply write the potential difference between the plates as V so long as no confusion seems likely. From our previous treatment of electrical potential, we know that to change Q by an amount dQ requires an increment of work against electrostatic forces of amount

$$dW = dQ \ V. \qquad (24.1)$$

This work represents an amount of energy stored as electrical potential energy of the charged capacitor.

Since Q and V both change as the charging process proceeds, we cannot integrate (24.1) to find the total stored energy when the potential difference reaches its final value until we know how V changes with Q. This information is provided by the capacitance of the capacitor:

The CAPACITANCE C between two conductors is the ratio of the magnitude of the charge on either conductor to the potential difference between the conductors when the conductors have charges of equal magnitude but opposite sign.

We can express this definition by the equation

$$C = Q/V. \quad \left\{ \begin{array}{c} C \text{ in F} \\ Q \text{ in C} \\ V \text{ in V} \end{array} \right\} \quad (Capacitance) \qquad (24.2)$$

When the charge is in coulombs and the potential difference is in volts, the unit of capacitance is coulomb per volt (C/V). This unit is given the special name *farad* (F), in honor of Michael Faraday: 1 F = 1 C/V. Just as the coulomb is a very large unit of charge for electrostatic applications, the farad is much too large a unit for most ordinary situations. Capacitances in the range picofarads (1 pF = 10^{-12} F) to microfarads (1 μF = 10^{-6} F) are generally encountered in most actual applications.

A particularly important property of capacitance is that *the capacitance of a pair of conductors in vacuum depends only on their relative geometry.* For a given pair of conductors, C is a constant independent of both the potential difference and the amount of charge stored. We shall not give a general proof of this assertion, but we shall see that it holds true in several particular cases.

The property that C is independent of both Q and V allows us to complete our treatment of the energy stored by a capacitor. By using (24.2) to express V in (24.1), we have that the increment of work done against electrostatic forces to transfer charge dQ at a step of the charging process when the stored charge is Q is given by

$$dW = (Q/C) \, dQ.$$

This means that the total electrical potential energy stored by the capacitor when the stored charge is brought from zero to the final value Q_f is given by

$$W = \int_{Q=0}^{Q=Q_f} \frac{Q}{C} dQ = \frac{1}{C} \int_0^{Q_f} Q \, dQ = \frac{1}{2} \frac{Q_f^2}{C}.$$

We can use the relation $C = Q/V$ to write the result for the energy stored by a capacitor when the stored charge is Q and the potential difference between the plates is V in three alternative forms:

$$W = \frac{1}{2} \frac{Q^2}{C} = \tfrac{1}{2} QV = \tfrac{1}{2} CV^2. \qquad (24.3)$$

We have assumed that the pair of conductors forming our capacitor is in vacuum. The presence of air between the conductors at ordinary laboratory pressure does not make the situation significantly different from vacuum for most practical purposes. However, the presence of a solid or liquid insulating material between the conductors has a profound effect on the capacitance. We shall consider this situation shortly.

24.2 PARALLEL-PLATE CAPACITOR

In general, computation of the capacitance of a pair of conductors is a difficult problem. However, for certain situations of high geometrical symmetry—concentric spheres, coaxial cylinders, and plane parallel plates—the value of C can be readily calculated. Fortunately, these situations are important both in the further development of electrostatic theory and in the design of practical capacitors.

As our primary example we shall consider a geometry that is often used to exemplify all capacitors, the "ideal" parallel-plate capacitor. Consider a pair of flat conducting plates, parallel to one another and separated by a distance d that is very small compared to the characteristic lateral dimension of the plates. We shall use a convenient coordinate system having Z axis perpendicular to the plates and origin between the plates and far from any edge, as suggested in Fig. 24.2. Locations near the origin are so far from the plate edges compared to the perpendicular distance to either plate that for observations in this vicinity we can to a good approximation assume that the details of the edge geometry of the plates can be ignored. There should be no observation by which we can distinguish any dependence on the coordinates x and y or any particular direction parallel to the XY plane.

Suppose that we start with both plates uncharged and by some external means transfer charge so that one plate has a charge $+Q$ and the other a charge $-Q$. These excess charges must reside on the surfaces of the plates. Because of the symmetry just described, they must be uniformly distributed with respect to the x and y coordinates except near the plate edges; we describe this distribution by an appropriate surface charge density σ for each surface. At this point it might appear that we need to allow for a surface charge density on each of the four surfaces shown in Fig. 24.3. We have $\sigma_a + \sigma_b = Q/A$ and $-\sigma_c - \sigma_d = -Q/A$, where A is the lateral area of either plate.

We learned in Chapter 23 that the electric-field strength due to a plane sheet of charge of surface density σ has the form $\mathscr{E} = \sigma/2\epsilon_0$ and is directed away from a positive sheet and toward a negative sheet. If we apply this relation to the four sheets of charge shown in Fig. 24.3, we obtain for the resultant electric-field strength in region ① above the upper plate that

$$\mathscr{E}_R(\text{I}) = \mathbf{k}(\sigma_a + \sigma_b)/2\epsilon_0 - \mathbf{k}(\sigma_c + \sigma_d)/2\epsilon_0 = 0.$$

Similarly in region ③ below the lower plate we have $\mathscr{E}_R(\text{III}) = 0$. But we also learned in Chapter 23 that the electric-field strength just outside the surface of a conductor is equal in magnitude to the surface charge density on that surface divided by ϵ_0. Therefore, $\mathscr{E}_R(\text{I}) = 0$ implies that $\sigma_a = 0$ and $\mathscr{E}_R(\text{III}) = 0$ implies that $\sigma_d = 0$; the total excess charge on either plate resides on the inner surface of the plate and is distributed with a surface density $\sigma = Q/A$.

Therefore, the situation is as shown in Fig. 24.4. If we apply our result for the field due to a sheet of charge to the positive and negative charge sheets and superimpose the results, we find that the resultant electric-field strength between the plates has uniform magnitude $\mathscr{E}_R = \sigma/\epsilon_0$ and is directed away from the positive plate toward the negative plate. A representation of this field in terms of electric lines is given in

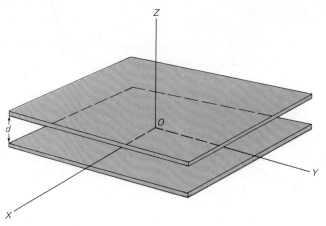

Fig. 24.2 A parallel-plate capacitor.

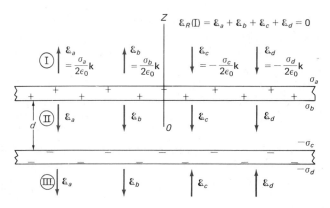

Fig. 24.3

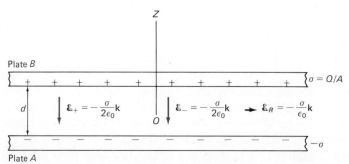

Fig. 24.4

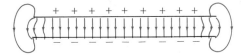

Fig. 24.5 The electric lines for a parallel-plate capacitor are perpendicular to both plates and directed from the positive plate to the negative plate except for fringing effects near the plate edges.

Fig. 24.5, in which we also show the so-called fringing effect near the plate edges where our results are not valid.

Having obtained the electric-field strength, we are in a position to compute the capacitance of our parallel-plate capacitor. In order to use (24.2), we must determine the potential difference between the two plates. Call the negative plate A and the positive plate B. Choose a path from A to B that is parallel to the Z-axis in Fig. 24.4. From Chapter 22 we have $V_{BA} = -\int_A^B \mathscr{E} \cdot d\mathbf{l}$; inserting our result for $\mathscr{E}$ and noting that $d\mathbf{l}$ is a displacement parallel to the Z axis we obtain

$$V_{BA} = -\int_A^B \mathscr{E} \cdot d\mathbf{l} = -\int_A^B \mathscr{E}_z \, dz = \frac{\sigma}{\epsilon_0} \int_A^B dz = \frac{\sigma d}{\epsilon_0}. \tag{24.4}$$

By using this result and $\sigma = Q/A$ in (24.2) we obtain

$$C = \frac{Q}{Qd/A\epsilon_0} = \frac{\epsilon_0 A}{d}. \quad \textit{(Parallel-Plate Capacitor)} \tag{24.5}$$

We see that this result depends solely on the geometry of the capacitor, not on the particular values of Q or V. Consideration of the dimensions of the quantities involved shows (24.5) implies that alternative units for ϵ_0 are farad/meter (F/m); ϵ_0 is often stated in these units. Can you show that this is consistent with the units $C^2/N\,m^2$ introduced for ϵ_0 in Chapter 20?

24.3 CYLINDRICAL CAPACITOR

A second case for which the capacitance is readily determined is that of two coaxial cylindrical conductors A and B as shown in Fig. 24.6. This geometry will be recognized as that of the "coaxial cable" widely used in interconnecting electronic instruments. Let the outer radius of the inner conductor be b and the inner radius of the outer conductor be a; choose the Z axis coincident with the common symmetry axis of the cylinders; let $\rho = \sqrt{x^2 + y^2}$ be the perpendicular distance of a point (x, y, z) from

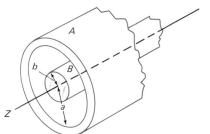

Fig. 24.6 A capacitor formed by two coaxial cylindrical conductors.

the Z axis; let $\hat{\rho}$ be a unit vector at this point directed radially outward from the Z axis. (See Fig. 1.9 and Fig. 23.12.) We assume that the conductors are very long compared with their separation $(a - b)$. Then, as argued in detail in Section 23.4, the electric-field strength must have the form $\mathscr{E} = \mathscr{E}(\rho)\hat{\rho}$, being directed radially away from the positive cylinder.

Suppose that we start with both conductors uncharged and by some external means transfer charge so that one conductor has a charge $+Q$ and the other has a charge $-Q$; to be concrete let us assume that the inner conductor B carries the positive charge. The excess charges must reside on the surface of the conductors and be uniformly distributed except near the cylinder ends. If the length of the conductors is L, the magnitude of the charge per unit length on either conductor is $\lambda = Q/L$.

Determination of the electric-field strength between the conducting cylinders was the subject of Problem 25 in Chapter 23. By use of Gauss's relation one can show that all the charge on the inner cylinder is on its outer surface, all the charge on the outer cylinder is on its inner surface, and the electric-field strength between the cylinders is $\mathscr{E} = (\lambda/2\pi\epsilon_0\rho)\hat{\rho}$. With this result we can determine the potential difference V between the two conductors. Since we have assumed that the inner cylinder is positive, it will be at the higher potential. Therefore, for the computation of V we choose a radial path from the outer cylinder to the inner cylinder. Then we have

$$V = -\int_{\rho=a}^{\rho=b} \mathscr{E} \cdot d\mathbf{l} = -\int_{a}^{b} \left(\frac{\lambda}{2\pi\epsilon_0\rho}\right) \hat{\rho} \cdot \hat{\rho}\, d\rho$$

$$= -\frac{\lambda}{2\pi\epsilon_0} \int_{a}^{b} \frac{d\rho}{\rho} = \frac{\lambda}{2\pi\epsilon_0} \ln\left(\frac{a}{b}\right).$$

Thus, for a pair of concentric conducting cylinders of length L we have, neglecting end effects,

$$C = \frac{Q}{V} = \frac{\lambda L}{(\lambda/2\pi\epsilon_0)\ln(a/b)} = \frac{2\pi\epsilon_0 L}{\ln(a/b)}. \quad \textit{(Cylindrical Capacitor)} \quad (24.6)$$

Again we see that the capacitance depends only on the geometry of the conductors.

24.4 DIELECTRIC CONSTANT

Up to this point we have assumed that the conductors forming a capacitor are in vacuum. In fact, in most of our development of electrostatics we have considered charges situated in vacuum or on the surface of an ideal conductor, though we have noted that our relationships remain true to good approximation in the presence of air at ordinary atmospheric pressure. We are now in a position to consider further the electrostatic behavior of simple materials.

In a series of experiments begun around 1835, Michael Faraday investigated the effect on properties of a capacitor if the region between the conductors is filled with a *dielectric* or electrically insulating material. If the potential difference applied between the plates is maintained constant—for example, by keeping the capacitor connected to the terminals of a battery—the amount of stored charge increases when a dielectric is inserted between the plates. If the amount of stored charge is maintained constant by keeping the plates of the capacitor electrically isolated, the potential difference between the plates decreases when a dielectric is inserted between them. From (24.2) we see these results mean that *the capacitance of a capacitor increases if a dielectric is inserted between its plates.*

For simple isotropic materials, experiment shows that it is possible to describe this behavior quantitatively by assigning to the dielectric material a single dimensionless parameter known as the dielectric constant, which can be defined as follows:

The DIELECTRIC CONSTANT κ of a dielectric material is the ratio of the capacitance of a capacitor in which the dielectric material completely fills the space between the plates to the capacitance of the same capacitor with vacuum between the plates.

Note that this definition does not refer to any special type of capacitor. The dielectric constant is a property of the particular material; it does not depend on the capacitor used for its measurement.

For a parallel-plate capacitor with the space between its plates filled with a dielectric material, we have from this definition and (24.4) that

$$C = \kappa \epsilon_0 A/d. \quad (Parallel\text{-}Plate\ Capacitor\ with\ Dielectric) \quad (24.7)$$

Similarly, for a cylindrical capacitor with a dielectric between its plates we have from (24.5) that

$$C = 2\pi\kappa\epsilon_0 L/\ln(a/b). \quad (Cylindrical\ Capacitor\ with\ Dielectric) \quad (24.8)$$

Typical values of the dielectric constant for various common materials under laboratory conditions of temperature and pressure are given in Table 24.1. Vacuum can be treated as a dielectric material having $\kappa = 1$. The value of κ for air is very close to 1; this is consistent with our earlier assertions that for most purposes the presence of air does not require alteration of our electrostatic relations.

Many materials have interesting dielectric properties that are too complex to be described by a single parameter. For example, nonisotropic crystalline materials can have different values of κ depending on how the applied electric field is oriented relative to the crystal axes. Some materials display a significant dependence of κ on the applied electric-field strength for sufficiently large values of $\mathscr{E}$. If the applied electric fields are time-varying rather than static, the value of κ can depend on the frequency of oscillation of the applied electric-field strength. We shall not become involved with these complications, but they are important in many applications.

We can gain important insight into the nature of the dielectric constant through the simple ideas about the electric polarization of matter that were introduced in Section 20.2. Consider a dielectric material between the plates of a charged parallel-plate capacitor. Because of the electric field generated by the charges on the capacitor plates, the molecules of the material are polarized, as suggested in Fig. 24.7. The

Table 24.1   Typical Values of Static Dielectric Constant and Dielectric Strength[a]

Material	Dielectric Constant κ	Dielectric Strength (kV/cm)
Dry air (1 atm, 0°C)	1.0006	30
(100 atm, 19°C)	1.055	
CO_2 (1 atm, 0°C)	1.0010	28
HCl (gas, 1 atm, 0°C)	1.0046	
(gas, 1 atm, 100°C)	1.0026	
Castor oil	4.3	130–190
Ethyl alcohol	25	
Transformer oil	2.2	50–150
Turpentine	2.2	110–160
Water (liq., 0°C)	88	
(liq., 25°C)	78	
(liq., 100°C)	56	
Mica	4.5–7.5	250–2000
Polyethylene	2.3	150–500
Porcelain	6.0–8.0	50–200
Pyrex glass	4.0–6.0	130–400
Rubber (vulcanized)	3.0	160–500

[a] Unless otherwise noted, the values given are for a temperature of 20°C–25°C and pressure of 1 atm. The exact value of κ will depend on the history of the sample and the external conditions under which the measurement is made. The dielectric strength depends strongly on the particular sample; precise values cannot be tabulated.

center of positive charge of each molecule is shifted toward the negative plate; the center of negative charge of each molecule is shifted toward the positive plate. Note that the charges remain bound to a particular molecule; there is no net transport of charge over macroscopic distances.

In the bulk of the material, the net charge in any macroscopic volume element remains zero. Remember that we very greatly exaggerate the size of a molecule in Fig. 24.7. However, the layer of the dielectric surface next to the positive capacitor plate carries a negative surface charge due to the polarization of the dielectric molecules; the molecules have their negative ends presented at the material surface. Similarly, the layer of the dielectric surface next to the negative capacitor plate carries

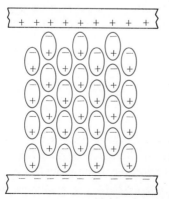

Fig. 24.7   A schematic representation of the polarization of molecules of a dielectric material between the plates of a capacitor. The figure represents the situation at a particular time; the molecules are in continual thermal agitation.

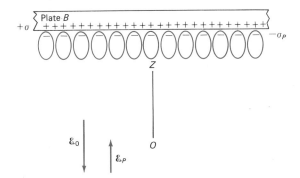

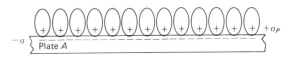

Fig. 24.8   A schematic representation of conduction surface charges on a pair of capacitor plates and polarization surface charges on a dielectric material between the plates.

a positive surface charge. These surface charges are bound to the molecules of the material, in contrast to the mobile surface charges on conductors that arise from an excess or deficiency of conduction electrons. They are called *polarization surface charges,* and are represented by a polarization surface charge density σ_P.

Like any distribution of charge, polarization surface charges act as sources of an electric field. Let $\mathscr{E}_0$ be the field strength generated by the surface charge densities $+\sigma$ and $-\sigma$ on the capacitor plates, as shown in Fig. 24.8. This would be the resultant field strength if the dielectric were not present. Let $\mathscr{E}_P$ be the field strength generated by polarization surface charges on the dielectric. The field due to the polarization charge will be opposite in direction to the field generated by the charge on the capacitor plates, as indicated in Fig. 24.8.

In thinking of the electric-field strength inside a dielectric material we are concerned with the average value over a volume element large enough to contain very large numbers of molecules, as was the case for the field strength inside a conductor. Although the basic idea is simple, the details of this averaging process are complex, and we shall not consider them in this text.

In the discussion of Section 24.2. we considered how the electric-field strength for the parallel-plate geometry depends on the surface charge density. If we choose the Z axis as indicated in Fig. 24.8, we have for the resultant electric-field strength between the capacitor plates that

$$\mathscr{E}_R = \mathscr{E}_0 + \mathscr{E}_P = \frac{-\sigma}{\epsilon_0}\,\mathbf{k} + \frac{\sigma_P}{\epsilon_0}\,\mathbf{k} = \frac{-(\sigma - \sigma_P)}{\epsilon_0}\,\mathbf{k}.$$

It follows as in (24.4) that the potential difference between the capacitor plates is given by

$$V = (\sigma - \sigma_P)d/\epsilon_0,$$

so the capacitance of the capacitor is

$$C = \frac{Q}{V} = \frac{\sigma A}{(\sigma - \sigma_P)d/\epsilon_0} = \frac{\epsilon_0 A}{(1 - \sigma_P/\sigma)d}. \tag{24.9}$$

Note that it is the mobile charge stored on the capacitor plates that is used to define the capacitance; the bound polarization charge of the dielectric is not included in Q.

According to our definition of the dielectric constant, the capacitance is also given by (24.7): $C = \kappa\epsilon_0 A/d$. Comparison of (24.7) and (24.9) shows that we must have $(1 - \sigma_P/\sigma) = 1/\kappa$; therefore, $\sigma_P = \sigma(1 - 1/\kappa) = \epsilon_0 \mathscr{E}_0(1 - 1/\kappa)$. We see that the dielectric constant is a measure of the effectiveness of a given charge on the capacitor plates in producing polarization of the dielectric. The closer κ is to unity, the smaller σ_P is for a given σ. We can now see that the small deviation of κ from unity for gases is due to their low density and consequent relatively small polarization surface charge density. In fact, the quantity $\kappa - 1$ for gases varies approximately directly with the pressure.

Note that throughout our discussion we have assumed that the dielectric completely fills the space between the capacitor plates. Situations where the dielectric only partially fills the space between the plates can also be treated. In such a case the ratio of the capacitance to the capacitance without the dielectric is not given simply by the dielectric constant. Several specific examples are suggested in the problems.

24.5   DIELECTRIC STRENGTH

As the potential difference applied across a vacuum capacitor is increased, the magnitude of the electric-field strength eventually becomes large enough that electrons are pulled from the surface of the negative plate and a flow of charge exists between the capacitor plates. The amount of charge per unit area per unit time pulled from the negative plate depends on the absolute temperature of the plate, the material of which the plate is constructed, and the electric-field strength at the surface of the plate. Measurable charge flow at room temperature can be obtained for $\mathscr{E}$ of the order of 10^8 V/m.

If there is a dielectric material between the capacitor plates, electrical breakdown generally will occur at a lower potential difference than that required to pull electrons from the negative plate in vacuum. When the magnitude of the electric-field strength reaches a certain value that depends on the particular dielectric material, electrons are pulled away from the molecules to which they belong. These electrons are accelerated by the electric field and collide with molecules of the dielectric. Consequent cumulative ionization of the molecules of the material can result in sudden and destructive discharge of the capacitor through the dielectric. The electric-field strength at which breakdown of a dielectric occurs is called the dielectric strength.

The DIELECTRIC STRENGTH of a material is the magnitude of the maximum electric-field strength that the material can withstand without electrical breakdown.

Representative values of dielectric strength for various materials are given in Table 24.1. The value of the dielectric strength depends on sample history, on sample impurities, and on the particular experimental conditions; precise values cannot be tabulated. Note that for most solid or liquid insulators the dielectric strength is greater than that of air. In a practical device the presence of a solid or liquid dielectric between the capacitor plates may be desirable not only because the capacitance is thereby increased, but also because it provides mechanical support and because it allows a greater potential difference to be applied without electrical breakdown than would the presence of air between the plates. Note also from Table 24.1 that the dielectric strength and the dielectric constant are essentially unrelated.

Example. An ideal circular parallel-plate capacitor of radius 3 cm and plate separation 1 mm has the space between its plates filled with glass of dielectric constant $\kappa = 5.5$ and dielectric strength 150 kV/cm. What is the maximum potential difference between its plates that the capacitor can withstand without breakdown? What is the maximum potential difference if the dielectric is dry air at 1 atm, for which κ is 1.0006 and the dielectric strength is 30 kV/cm? What are the charges on the capacitor plates when breakdown occurs for these two dielectrics?

For the parallel-plate geometry we have from (24.4) that the relationship between the magnitude of the resultant electric-field strength and the potential difference is $\mathscr{E}_R = V/d$. Thus, for the glass dielectric we have

$$V_{\text{max}} = \mathscr{E}_{R,\text{max}}\, d = (1.50 \times 10^7 \text{ V/m})(10^{-3}\text{m}) = 1.5 \times 10^4 \text{ V},$$

and for the air dielectric we have

$$V_{\text{max}} = \mathscr{E}_{R,\text{max}}\, d = (3.0 \times 10^6 \text{ V/m})(10^{-3} \text{ m}) = 3.0 \times 10^3 \text{ V}.$$

To determine the stored charge at breakdown we use (24.2) and (24.5):

$$Q = VC = V\kappa\epsilon_0 A/d.$$

Thus, for the glass dielectric we have

$$Q = (1.5 \times 10^4 \text{ V})(5.5)(8.854 \times 10^{-12} \text{ F/m})\pi(3 \times 10^{-2}\text{m})^2/10^{-3} \text{ m} = 2.1 \times 10^{-6} \text{ C},$$

and for the air dielectric we have

$$Q = (3.0 \times 10^3 \text{ V})(1.0006)(8.854 \times 10^{-12} \text{ F/m})\pi(3 \times 10^{-2} \text{ m})^2/10^{-3} \text{ m}$$
$$= 7.5 \times 10^{-8} \text{ C}.$$

24.6 COMBINATIONS OF CAPACITORS

It is often necessary to consider how capacitors behave when connected together in various ways. There are two major ideas to be used when considering such problems. First, the potential difference between any two points does not depend on the particular path followed from one point to the other. Second, charge must be conserved.

Example. A capacitor of capacitance $C_1 = 6 \ \mu F$ is charged to a potential difference of 12 V and then connected across an uncharged capacitor having capacitance $C_2 = 4 \ \mu F$. What are the final potential differences and stored charges of the capacitors? What are the initial and final total stored energies? What happened to the apparently lost energy?

The initial and final situations are illustrated in Fig. 24.9. We introduce the symbol $\dashv \vdash$ to represent a capacitor in schematic diagrams. Metal wires providing conducting paths connecting various devices are indicated in schematic diagrams by single lines. Under steady-state electrostatic conditions the potential is essentially constant along the lengths of the wires.

The charge stored by capacitor C_1 in the initial situation is $Q_1 = C_1 V_1 = (6 \times 10^{-6} \ F)(12 \ V) = 72 \times 10^{-6} \ C$. The stored energies for the two capacitors in the initial situation are $W_1 = \frac{1}{2} C_1 V_1^2 = \frac{1}{2}(6 \times 10^{-6} \ F)(12 \ V)^2 = 4.3 \times 10^{-4} \ J$ and $W_2 = 0$.

We see that in the final situation the *same* potential difference V' exists across both capacitors. Conservation of charge requires that the net charge on the connected plates of the two capacitors in the final situation be equal to the net charge on the same plates in the initial situation. Thus, $Q_1' + Q_2' = Q_1 + Q_2 = 72 \times 10^{-6} \ C + 0$. We obtain two additional relations by applying (24.2) to the capacitors in the final situation:

$$Q_1' = C_1 V' \quad \text{and} \quad Q_2' = C_2 V'.$$

Thus, we have

$$72 \times 10^{-6} \ C = Q_1' + Q_2' = C_1 V' + C_2 V' = (C_1 + C_2)V',$$

so

$$V' = (Q_1' + Q_2')/(C_1 + C_2) = (72 \times 10^{-6} \ C)/(6 \times 10^{-6} \ F + 4 \times 10^{-6} \ F) = 7.2 \ V.$$

It then follows that the stored charges in the final situation are

$$Q_1' = C_1 V' = (6 \times 10^{-6} \ F)(7.2 \ V) = 43 \times 10^{-6} \ C$$

and

$$Q_2' = C_2 V' = (4 \times 10^{-6} \ F)(7.2 \ V) = 29 \times 10^{-6} \ C.$$

For the stored energies in the final situation we have

$$W_1' = \frac{1}{2} C_1 (V')^2 = \frac{1}{2}(6 \times 10^{-6} \ F)(7.2 \ V)^2 = 1.6 \times 10^{-4} \ J$$

and

$$W_2' = \frac{1}{2} C_2 (V')^2 = \frac{1}{2}(4 \times 10^{-6} \ F)(7.2 \ V)^2 = 1.0 \times 10^{-4} \ J.$$

Thus the stored energy in the final situation is $W_1' + W_2' = 2.6 \times 10^{-4} \ J$; this is $1.7 \times 10^{-4} \ J$ less than the inital stored energy.

The Principle of Energy Conservation tells us that energy does not simply disappear; losses or gains in any type of energy in any process must be accounted for by conversions to or from other kinds of energy. For the present situation there are two primary mechanisms of energy conversion. First, as soon as the connection

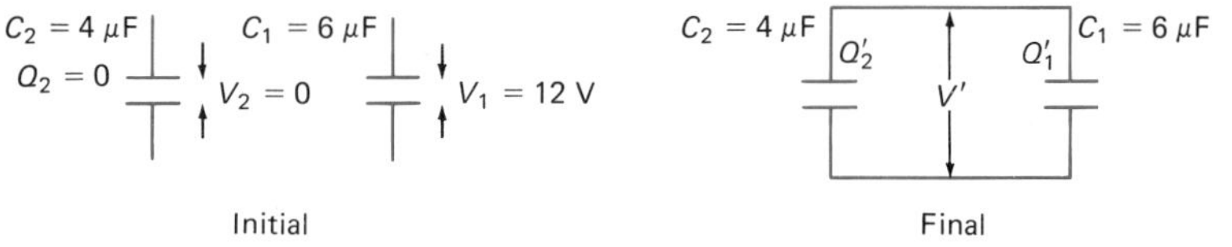

Fig. 24.9

is established, electric charge is transferred from the plates of the charged capacitor to the plates of the uncharged capacitor, and in this process electrical energy will be converted to heat in the wires as a result of inelastic collisions of electrons with the lattice of the conducting material. Second, there may be radiation of electromagnetic waves, which will be discussed in Chapter 32.

In analyzing the behavior of a combination of capacitors, it is sometimes convenient to introduce the single "equivalent" capacitor that could replace the combination so far as external connections are concerned. Two common types of connection for which there are simple formulas for the equivalent capacitance are series and parallel combinations.

We say that electrical devices are connected in *parallel* if the same potential difference exists across each device. Three capacitors connected in parallel are shown in Fig. 24.10. What is the single equivalent capacitor C that would have the same effect as the parallel combination so far as external connections between points A and B are concerned?

We immediately suspect that adding capacitors in parallel will increase the amount of charge stored for a given potential difference, so the equivalent capacitance should be larger than that of any of the individual capacitors. We establish this quantitatively as follows: Let Q be the total charge stored by the combination. We have $Q = Q_1 + Q_2 + Q_3$, where Q_1 is the charge stored by capacitor C_1, Q_2 is the charge stored by capacitor C_2, and Q_3 is the charge stored by capacitor C_3. The equivalent capacitance then is given by

$$C = Q/V_{BA} = (Q_1 + Q_2 + Q_3)/V_{BA}.$$

But $Q_1/V_{BA} = C_1$, $Q_2/V_{BA} = C_2$, and $Q_3/V_{BA} = C_3$. Therefore,

$$C = C_1 + C_2 + C_3. \quad (Capacitors\ in\ Parallel) \qquad (24.10)$$

This result is easily extended to an arbitrary number of capacitors connected in parallel.

If electrical devices are connected in sequence one after the other along a single conducting path, we say that they are connected in *series*. Three capacitors connected in series are shown in Fig. 24.11. What is the single equivalent capacitor C that

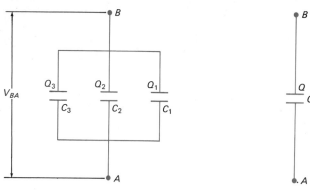

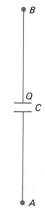

Fig. 24.10   A parallel combination of three capacitors.

would have the same effect as the series combination so far as external connections between points A and B are concerned?

Assume that the capacitors are all initially uncharged. If the series combination is then charged, say by connecting a battery between A and B, a charge $+Q$ is generated on the upper plate of C_1 and a charge $-Q$ is generated on the lower plate of C_3. Since there is no conducting path by which electrons can enter or leave the region enclosed by the dashed curve in Fig. 24.11, the net charge in this region must always be equal to its initial value, which is zero. Thus, the charge on the lower plate of C_1 must be equal in magnitude and opposite in sign to the charge on the upper plate of C_2. The same conclusion follows for the lower plate of C_2 and the upper plate of C_3. Moreover, the charges on the upper and lower plates of C_1 will both have magnitude Q. It follows directly that the magnitude of the charge on every plate in the series connection is Q.

The total potential difference V_{BA} is just the sum of the potential differences across the three capacitors: $V_{BA} = V_1 + V_2 + V_3$. By applying (24.2) to each of the capacitors we can express this as

$$\frac{Q}{C} = \frac{Q}{C_1} + \frac{Q}{C_2} + \frac{Q}{C_3}.$$

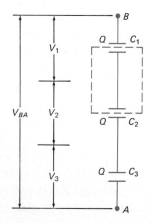

Fig. 24.11   A series combination of three capacitors.

Thus we have

$$\frac{1}{C} = \frac{1}{C_1} + \frac{1}{C_2} + \frac{1}{C_3}. \quad (\textit{Capacitors in Series}) \qquad (24.11)$$

This result is easily extended to an arbitrary number of capacitors connected in series. We see that the equivalent capacitance of a series combination is always less than the capacitance of any one of the individual capacitors.

QUESTIONS

1. Throughout this chapter we have considered capacitors having charges of the same magnitude on the positive and on the negative plate. Why don't we have to worry about cases where the magnitudes of these charges are not equal?

2. Why is it not correct simply to integrate (24.1) and conclude that the energy stored by a charged capacitor is $W = QV$?

3. In the derivation of (24.5) we required that the plate separation d be very small compared to the characteristic lateral dimension of the plates. Why is this restriction necessary?

4. Equation (24.5) depends only on the area and the separation of the capacitor plates. Why doesn't the capacitance of an ideal parallel-plate capacitor depend on the *shape* of the plates?

5. Describe in detail the physical behavior of a dielectric material that allows a capacitor to store more charge for a given potential difference with the dielectric between its plates than with vacuum between the plates.

6. What is the physical difference between inserting a dielectric slab between the plates of a charged capacitor and inserting a conducting slab of the same size and shape at the same location?

7. A dielectric slab is to be inserted between the plates of a parallel-plate capacitor. The plates are maintained at a constant potential difference by a battery. Will the slab be attracted into the region between the plates, or will it be repelled so that it must be pushed into position? Explain your reasoning.

8. Repeat Question 7 if the capacitor is initially charged and is isolated so that its stored charge remains constant as the dielectric slab is inserted between its plates.

9. In Table 24–1, water and ethyl alcohol have considerably larger dielectric constants than any of the other materials listed. Why is this so? Why are water and alcohol not used in commercial capacitors?

10. Why does the dielectric constant of water decrease with increasing temperature as indicated in Table 24–1?

11. For a certain parallel-plate capacitor, it is found that the dielectric strength of the dielectric is exceeded when the maximum desired potential difference is applied. Is it possible to change the parameters of the capacitor so that it has the same capacitance with the same dielectric between the plates but will not break down when the desired potential difference is applied?

12. Show that as the potential of a conductor is increased, the dielectric strength of the material surrounding the conductor is first exceeded where the curvature of the conductor surface is greatest. To do this, consider the shapes of equipotential surfaces near the conductor and also very far from the conductor.

PROBLEMS

1. (a) What is the capacitance of an ideal parallel-plate capacitor having plates that are copper squares 3 cm by 3 cm if the plates are in vacuum and the plate separation is 1.4 mm? (b) What potential difference must be applied to this capacitor in order to store an energy of 8.7 mJ? (c) What is the magnitude of the surface charge density on each plate when the stored energy has this value?

2. (a) What is the capacitance of an ideal parallel-plate capacitor having plates that are equilateral triangles of side length 5 cm if the capacitor stores 1.24 μJ of energy when a potential difference of 980 V is applied between its plates? Assume that the plates are in vacuum. (b) What is the plate separation? (c) How much charge is stored by the capacitor under the conditions of part (a)? (d) What is the magnitude of the electric-field strength between the plates under the conditions of part (a)?

3. (a) What is the capacitance per unit length of an ideal cylindrical capacitor like that shown in Fig. 24.6 with air between its plates if $b = 0.5$ mm and $a = 5.0$ mm? (b) How much charge is stored per unit length of this capacitor if the potential difference between the inner and outer conductors is 1260 V? (c) How much energy is stored per unit length? (d) What energy would be stored by an ideal parallel-plate capacitor with air between its plates when a potential difference of 1260 V is applied to it if the area of the plates is equal to the area of the inner surface of the outer conductor of a 1-m length of the cylindrical capacitor and the plate separation is equal to $(a - b)$?

4. Design an ideal cylindrical capacitor with air between its plates if the spacing between the conducting cylinders is to be 3 mm and the capacitor is to store 8×10^{-5} J per meter of length when a potential difference of 900 V is applied between the cylinders.

5. A variable air capacitor of the sort used to tune radios is constructed as shown in the diagram. The stack consists of n parallel plates; the diagram shows the particular case when $n = 9$. One set of plates is pivoted so that by turning a knob the area of overlap of the two sets of plates can be varied from a maximum value A to near zero. The separation of each plate from its nearest neighbors on either side is d. Show that, if edge effects can be neglected, the maximum capacitance of such a device is $(n - 1)\epsilon_0 A/d$, where we have used $\kappa_{air} \simeq 1.0$.

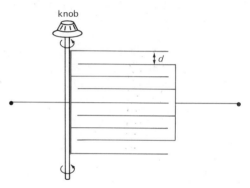

knob

Problem 5

6. The capacitor of Problem 5 with $n = 9$ is charged with a 60-V battery under conditions where its capacitance is a maximum. The battery is disconnected, and the knob is then turned to reduce the area of overlap to 0.1 times its original value. If the gaps between adjacent fixed and movable plates are 1.8 mm wide and the maximum area of overlap is 36 cm², what are the final stored charge and potential difference of the capacitor?

7. Express the electric-field strength between the plates of an ideal parallel-plate capacitor filled with a dielectric material of dielectric constant κ in terms of $\mathscr{E}_0$ and κ, where $\mathscr{E}_0$ is the field strength that would exist with vacuum between the plates.

8. Derive a formula analogous to (24.9) for a

cylindrical capacitor. Find the polarization charge per unit length λ_P in terms of the stored charge per unit length λ and the dielectric constant κ of the material between the cylinders. Express $\mathscr{E}$ in terms of $\mathscr{E}_0$ and κ, where $\mathscr{E}_0$ is the field strength that would exist with vacuum between the cylinders.

9. From the results obtained in Problems 7 and 8 predict the form of the expression for the electric-field strength $\mathscr{E}$ produced by a point charge Q at the origin inside a homogeneous, isotropic dielectric material.

10. The plates of a 0.2-μF parallel-plate capacitor are first charged so that the difference of potential between the plates is 60 V and are then isolated so that no charge can leak off. If the plates are pulled apart so that the separation between the plates is doubled while the plates remain parallel, what will be the potential difference between the plates? What will be the ratio of the magnitude $\mathscr{E}_f$ of the final electric-field strength in the air between the plates to the initial value of $\mathscr{E}$?

11. How much work must be done in separating the plates of the capacitor in problem 10? If the original separation of the plates was 3 mm, what is the magnitude of the average force that must be applied in order to separate the plates?

12. A certain capacitor has a capacitance of 300 pF when the space between the plates is filled by air. If the capacitor is charged so that the difference of potential between the plates is 600 V and is then isolated so that no charge can leak off, what will be the potential difference between the plates if the space between them is filled with oil having a dielectric constant of 2.0? If the capacitor is a parallel-plate capacitor, what will be the ratio of the magnitude of the final electric-field strength between the plates to the initial value of this magnitude when the space between the plates was filled by air?

13. What is the energy initially stored by the capacitor described in the preceding problem? What is the final energy stored by the capacitor after it has been filled with oil? Account for any difference in stored energy.

14. An ideal parallel-plate capacitor has circular plates of radius 5 cm. The plate separation is 2 mm. (a) While in air the capacitor is connected to a battery that establishes a potential difference of 24 V between its plates. What is the resulting electric-field strength between the plates? What are the stored charge and the stored energy? (b) With the battery still connected, the capacitor is immersed in transformer oil of dielectric constant $\kappa = 2.2$. What are the electric-field strength, the stored charge, and the stored energy?

15. Repeat Problem 14(b) for the case where the capacitor is disconnected from the battery before being immersed in the transformer oil. What is the final potential difference between the capacitor plates?

16. A certain capacitor consists of two large parallel plates, initially 0.5 mm apart in air; its capacitance then is 80 μF. It is charged to a potential difference of 500 V by means of a battery. (a) What is the stored energy? (b) The capacitor is constructed so that the plates can be moved apart and remain parallel. The charged capacitor is disconnected from the battery, and the plates are then pushed apart with a glass rod until their separation is 4.0 mm. What is the stored energy of the capacitor after this separation is made? (c) What is the source of the extra energy in (b) as compared with (a)? (d) What is the potential difference across the capacitor after the plates have been separated?

17. A circular parallel-plate capacitor that will have an ideal capacitance of 0.10 μF and will be able to withstand a potential difference of at least 3500 V is to be constructed. The plates are to be immersed in an insulating liquid having dielectric constant 3.2 and

dielectric strength 250 kV/cm. What is the minimum radius that the plates can have?

18. A certain ideal parallel-plate capacitor has a plate separation of 0.1 cm. The space between the plates is filled with a dielectric having $\kappa = 2.2$ and dielectric strength 150 kV/cm. What is the maximum surface charge density that can be stored on either plate? Suppose that the plates are made of copper, which has one conduction electron per atom. How does the number of excess electrons per unit area required to give the maximum negative surface charge density compare with the total number of conduction electrons per unit area in a 0.5 nm thick layer of the plate material?

19. An ideal parallel-plate capacitor has square plates 50 cm by 50 cm separated by a 0.5 mm thick glass slab of dielectric constant $\kappa = 6.2$. What is the energy stored by this capacitor when a potential difference of 24 V is applied across it by a battery? What change in the stored energy occurs if the glass is removed without disturbing the plates while the battery remains connected? What change in the stored energy occurs if the battery is disconnected and then the glass slab is removed? Account for the energy gain or loss in each case.

20. Compare the physical sizes of ideal parallel-plate capacitors having the following dielectrics between the plates: (i) air, $\kappa \approx 1.0$, dielectric strength 30 kV/cm; (ii) polyethylene, $\kappa = 2.3$, dielectric strength 250 kV/cm; (iii) mica, $\kappa = 6.0$, dielectric strength 900 kV/cm. The capacitors are to have the same capacitance and the same breakdown potential difference.

21. A capacitor is composed of two concentric conducting spherical shells. The outer radius of the inner sphere is $r_1 = 7.0$ cm; the inner radius of the outer sphere is $r_2 = 10.0$ cm; each spherical shell is 1.0 cm thick. The space between the spheres is filled with oil of dielectric constant $\kappa = 4.0$ and dielectric strength

120 kV/cm. (a) Show that the capacitance of such a spherical capacitor is given in general by the relation $C = 4\pi\epsilon_0\kappa r_1 r_2/(r_2 - r_1)$. (b) What is the maximum energy that can be stored by this particular capacitor without breakdown of the dielectric?

22. One early type of capacitor called a Leyden jar consists of a glass container coated with metal foil on its inside and outside surfaces. A certain Leyden jar is a cylinder 20 cm tall and 12 cm in diameter (outside dimensions) and has a flat bottom and an open top. It is made of glass that is 3 mm thick and has a dielectric constant $\kappa = 5.5$ and a dielectric strength of 275 kV/cm. The metal foil extends half-way up the sides of the jar. (a) Estimate the capacitance of this Leyden jar. (b) What is the maximum energy that this device can store without breakdown of the dielectric? (c) What is the potential difference between the "plates" of the Leyden jar when this maximum energy is stored?

23. (a) What single capacitor would be equivalent to three capacitors having capacitances of 8 μF, 6 μF, and 4 μF connected in parallel? (b) Repeat for the case where the three capacitors are connected in series.

24. Capacitors can be used in electrical circuits as "voltage dividers" as suggested in the diagram. If point P is maintained at a constant potential of 1200 V, what are the potential differences V_{AB} between the plates of the 1-μF capacitor, V_{BC} between the plates of the 2-μF capacitor, and V_{CD} between the plates of the 3-μF capacitor?

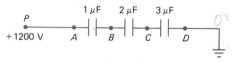

Problem 24

25. How much energy is stored in each of the capacitors considered in Problem 24? What is the ratio of the charge on the plates of

the 3-μF capacitor to the charge on the plates of the 1-μF capacitor?

26. Three capacitors of respective capacitances 6 μF, 15 μF, and 24 μF are connected in parallel between the terminals of a 24-V battery. What are the stored charge, stored energy, and potential difference for each of the capacitors?

27. Derive an expression for the energy stored by an ideal parallel-plate capacitor in terms of the magnitude of the electric-field strength between the plates and the dielectric constant of the material between the plates. It is useful to consider this energy as stored in the electric field. Show that the energy per unit volume stored in the field between the plates of the capacitor is $(\frac{1}{2})\epsilon_0\kappa\mathscr{E}^2$.

28. You are given one 8-μF capacitor, two 6-μF capacitors, and one 4-μF capacitor. What values of equivalent capacitance can be obtained by making various series and parallel combinations of these capacitors? It is not required that all four capacitors be used in every combination.

29. It is easy to make connections of capacitors that cannot be simplified by the simple rules for series and parallel combinations. For example, consider the arrangement shown in the diagram. Is it possible to find a single capacitor that is equivalent to this combination? If so, what is its value?

30. Show that, if capacitor C_5 in the diagram for Problem 29 is removed and replaced by a wire, then the resulting configuration can be described in terms of series and parallel combinations of capacitors. What is the

equivalent capacitance of the new arrangement?

31. You have a large number of 8-μF, 6-μF, and 4-μF capacitors, each rated for a maximum potential difference of 500 V. A 12-μF capacitor that will withstand a potential difference of at least 2000 V is required. Design an arrangement using as few of the available capacitors as possible that will meet these requirements.

32. A 1-μF capacitor is charged to a potential difference of 200 V and a 2-μF capacitor is independently charged to a potential difference of 400 V. The capacitors are then connected by conducting wires, positive plate of each one to the negative plate of the other. What are the resulting potential differences, stored charges, and stored energies for each capacitor? How much of the initial stored electrical potential energy has been converted to other forms of energy?

33. Repeat Problem 32 for the case where the charged capacitors are connected positive plate to positive plate and negative plate to negative plate.

34. A 5-μF capacitor and a 20-μF capacitor are connected in series across a total potential difference of 600 V. The charged capacitors are then disconnected and reconnected positive plate to positive plate and negative plate to negative plate. What are the initial and final stored charges and potential differences for each capacitor?

35. Capacitor $C_1 = 4 \ \mu$F is connected in parallel with the combination of capacitors $C_2 = 3 \ \mu$F and $C_3 = 2 \ \mu$F connected in series. Before being connected, C_2 and C_3 were uncharged and C_1 was charged to a potential difference of 300 V. What will be the stored charge, the potential difference, and the stored energy for each capacitor after the system has come to equilibrium? How much electrical potential energy is converted to other forms of energy?

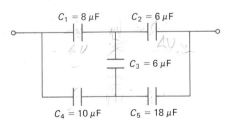

$C_1 = 8 \ \mu$F $C_2 = 6 \ \mu$F

$C_3 = 6 \ \mu$F

$C_4 = 10 \ \mu$F $C_5 = 18 \ \mu$F

Problems 29 and 30

36. Three uncharged capacitors having capacitances of 8 μF, 6 μF, and 4 μF are connected in series across a battery providing a 24-V potential difference. (a) What is the charge stored by the 4-μF capacitor? (b) What is the total energy stored by the three capacitors? (c) The capacitors are disconnected from the battery and reconnected in parallel with their positive plates connected together. What is the potential difference across the parallel combination? (d) What is the total stored energy in the final configuration?

37. A conducting slab of thickness t is inserted between the plates of an ideal parallel-plate capacitor of plate separation d. The conducting slab is oriented with its surfaces parallel to the capacitor plates; it does not touch the capacitor plates. Show that the capacitance when the slab is in place is $C = \epsilon_0 A/(d - t)$.

38. The plates of a certain ideal parallel-plate capacitor have separation d. The space between the plates is filled by two slabs of material, one of dielectric constant κ_1 and thickness d_1 and the other of dielectric constant κ_2 and thickness d_2. What is the ratio of the capacitance of this capacitor to its capacitance with vacuum between the plates? Does the result depend on which dielectric slab is closer to the positive plate?

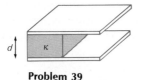

Problem 39

39. A certain ideal parallel-plate capacitor with plate spacing $d = 1.5$ mm has half the volume between its plates filled with a dielectric slab of thickness d and dielectric constant $\kappa = 5.6$, as shown in the diagram. The remainder of the space between the plates is filled with air. The capacitor is at normal laboratory temperature and pressure. A potential difference of 12 V is applied between the plates by a battery. (a) Show that the electric-field strength between the plates is the same in the dielectric and in the air regions. (b) Describe the distribution of surface charge on the capacitor plates. (c) The capacitor is disconnected from the battery and the dielectric slab is then pulled from between the plates. What is the new potential difference between the plates?

40. A certain ideal parallel-plate capacitor with vacuum between its plates has plate separation z. It is charged to a potential difference V by a battery and is then disconnected from the battery. Suppose that the plate separation is increased by an amount dz. (a) What is the change in capacitance dC? (b) What is the change in stored energy dW? (c) By setting the increase in stored energy equal to the work done by an external force in separating the plates without developing any kinetic energy, find the force of electrostatic attraction between the plates. Show that this force per unit area of capacitor plate is $f = \sigma^2/2\epsilon_0$. (d) The magnitude of the electric-field strength at the surface of either plate is $\mathscr{E} = \sigma/\epsilon_0$; the electric-field strength times the charge per unit area is $\sigma\mathscr{E} = \sigma^2/\epsilon_0$. Why is the force per unit area found in part (c) only half this value?

CHAPTER 25

Electric Currents

Up to this point in our treatment of electromagnetism we have been concerned only with electrostatics. The phenomena considered thus far have been interpreted in terms of *charges at rest*. With the present chapter we begin a treatment of phenomena involving *charges in motion*. The time rate of the transfer of electric charge from one place to another is called the *electric current*. Most of the devices employed in modern electrical engineering and technology make use of electric currents. In this chapter we introduce concepts that are important for an understanding of electric currents.

One result of great importance in electrostatics is that inside a conductor $\mathscr{E} = 0$. This result does not necessarily apply when electric currents are present. Electric currents involve the flow of charges through conductors. If a flow of charge through a conductor is to be maintained, $\mathscr{E}$ cannot in general be zero inside the conductor.

When an electric current exists inside a conductor like a wire, the wire becomes warm or even hot. This heating is the result of the dissipation of electrical energy. This dissipation of electrical energy is similar to the dissipation of mechanical energy that occurs when a moving body does work against frictional forces or when there is a flow of a viscous fluid through a pipe. Just as mechanical energy must be supplied by a pump in order to maintain the flow of a viscous fluid through a pipe, electrical energy must be supplied by some device like a battery or generator in order to maintain the flow of electric charges through a wire.

In many important cases there is a simple relationship between the current through a conductor like a wire and the potential difference between its ends. This relationship, known as Ohm's law, states that at a given temperature the ratio of the potential difference to the current is a constant called the *resistance* of the wire. The resistance of a wire depends not only on its length and cross-sectional area but also on the *material* of which the wire is composed. The dependence on the material can be stated in terms of a quantity called the *resistivity* of the material. Although Ohm's law is very useful, it has a limited range of validity and is in no sense a general principle.

Most of our attention in this chapter is devoted to conduction of currents by metals; however, we recall from our studies of chemistry that current can also be conducted by aqueous solutions of electrolytes: acids, bases, and salts.

25.1 ELECTRIC CURRENT

A *current* consists of charges in motion. For many of our applications we shall be concerned with currents in metals; in this case the moving charges are electrons. However, there are important situations involving, for example, electrolytic solutions or ionized gases where the moving charges are both positive and negative objects. In making a quantitative definition of current we must keep in mind situations where different kinds of charges of both signs are in motion.

Imagine an observer who keeps track of the net amount of charge moving through a certain surface. The observer arbitrarily assigns one side of the surface as positive and the other side as negative. To determine the net charge transferred through the surface, the observer counts a positive charge moving from the negative to the positive side as a positive crossing, a positive charge moving from the positive to the negative side as a negative crossing, a negative charge moving from the negative to the positive side as a negative crossing, and a negative charge moving from the positive to the negative side as a positive crossing. These conventions are indicated schematically in Fig. 25.1. In each case, the effect of a positive crossing is to increase the net positive charge on the positive side of the surface. The algebraic sum of all the charge crossings that occur in a time interval Δt gives the net amount of charge ΔQ crossing the surface in this time interval.

We can now make the following definition:

The AVERAGE CURRENT I_{av} through a surface is the net charge ΔQ crossing the surface divided by the time interval Δt during which the charge is transferred. The INSTANTANEOUS CURRENT I is the limit of the average current as the time interval becomes very small:

$$I = \lim_{\Delta t \to 0} \frac{\Delta Q}{\Delta t} = \frac{dQ}{dt} . \qquad \begin{cases} I \text{ in A} \\ Q \text{ in C} \\ t \text{ in s} \end{cases} \qquad (25.1)$$

We shall usually be concerned with macroscopic current. In this case it is understood that in the above limit we consider the time interval to become very small yet remain large enough that *very many* atomic-scale charged particles cross the surface during the time interval. We have encountered analogous limits previously, for example, in the definition of mass density. The unit of current is the coulomb per second. This unit is given the special name *ampere* (A) in honor of the French physicist André Marie Ampère (1775–1836), whose contributions to the theory of electromagnetism will be considered in subsequent chapters. Thus, 1 A = 1 C/s.

We shall often be concerned with currents where the moving charges are confined

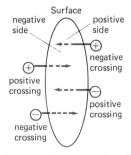

Fig. 25.1 Sign conventions for contributions to the current through a surface from charges crossing the surface.

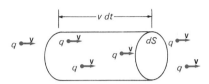

Fig. 25.2 A cylinder of cross section dS is imagined with its axis parallel to the velocity **v** of the particles having charge q.

to well-defined paths such as metallic wires. In this case the surface used to define the current is a cross section of the wire.

We note that we obtain the same current for motion of positive charge in one direction and for motion at the same rate of negative charge in the opposite direction. In nearly all situations the same external effects are observed in either case. It is a well-established convention to represent the sense of a current as the direction that positive charges would move to produce the effects of the current, regardless of whether positive charges or negative charges or both are actually moving. This convention has been incorporated in the SI. Although the direction of the conventional current in a wire is frequently represented by an arrow on diagrams, *current is not a vector quantity*. The current associated with the passage of charge through any surface is a scalar.

Currents cannot, of course, be measured by direct observation of the motions of charged particles. Devices for detecting and measuring currents, call *galvanometers,* generally depend on the magnetic effects produced by the current; we shall consider these magnetic effects in subsequent chapters. The earliest galvanometer, invented by Ampère in 1820, measured current in terms of the torque exerted on a compass needle suspended near the current path.

It is possible to derive a quantitative relation between the current through a small surface and the concentration, charge, and velocity of the moving charged particles that make up the current. Consider a region where there are n particles per unit volume, each having a charge q and moving with an average macroscopic velocity **v.** Imagine a cylinder of cross section dS with its axis oriented parallel to **v,** as shown in Fig. 25.2. The charges moving out through the end of the cylinder in a time interval dt are just those contained at the start of the time interval in a section of the cylinder of length $v\,dt$, as indicated in Fig. 25.2. The number of charges in this section of the cylinder is $nv\,dt\,dS$, and the charge passing through the end of the cylinder in time dt is $dQ = qnv\,dt\,dS$. Thus, at this location the current per unit area of surface perpendicular to the direction of charge motion, which is called the *current density,* is

$$J = dQ/dt\,dS = qnv. \qquad \left\{ \begin{array}{l} J \text{ in A/m}^2 \\ q \text{ in C} \\ v \text{ in m/s} \end{array} \right\}$$

Although current is not a vector, current density can be defined as a vector quantity if we assign to it the direction of the local average charge velocity:

$$\mathbf{J} = qn\mathbf{v}. \quad (Current\ Density) \tag{25.2}$$

If there are several different kinds of charge moving in a region, the resultant current density is the vector sum of terms like (25.2) for each different kind of moving charge. If the resultant current density is known, the current through a surface can be obtained by taking the surface integral of the current density over the surface:

$$I = \iint \mathbf{J} \cdot d\mathbf{S}.$$

In the above discussion we noted that $\mathbf{v}$ is the macroscopic average velocity. This represents an *ordered* motion superimposed on the random thermal motions of the microscopic charged particles. The average velocity associated with the thermal motion is zero since the directions of this motion are random. The magnitude v of the velocity of ordered motion is very small compared with the speed of thermal motion, which for conduction electrons in a metal is the order of 10^6 m/s.

Example.   A copper wire of diameter 1.5 mm carries a current of 2.4 A. What is the speed of ordered motion of free electrons in the wire? Copper has one free electron per atom.

From Table 4.1 the mass density of copper is $\rho_m = 8890$ kg/m³; the atomic mass of copper is 63.54 u. If we consider a volume V of copper, the number of free electrons is the mass $\rho_m V$ divided by the mass per atom since there is one free electron per atom. Thus, the number of free electrons per unit volume is

$$n = \rho_m/\mu = \frac{(8890\ \text{kg/m}^3)(1\ \text{electron/atom})}{(63.54\ \text{u/atom})(1.66 \times 10^{-27}\ \text{kg/u})}$$
$$= 8.43 \times 10^{28}\ \text{electrons/m}^3.$$

The current is $I = \pi r^2 J = \pi r^2 nev$, where r is the radius of the wire and e is the magnitude of the charge of an electron. Thus, $v = I/\pi r^2 ne = (2.4\ \text{A})/\pi(0.75 \times 10^{-3}\ \text{m})^2(8.43 \times 10^{28}\ \text{electrons/m}^3)(1.6 \times 10^{-19}\ \text{C/electron}) = 1.01 \times 10^{-4}$ m/s.

This is surprisingly small; at this rate it requires 10^4 s or 2.8 hr for an electron to travel 1 m through the wire. Because of its smallness, the velocity $\mathbf{v}$ is often called a "drift" velocity.

We must distinguish the drift velocity of individual charges from the rate at which changes in the electrical conditions are propagated. For example, if we close a switch connecting a wire to the terminals of a battery, a potential gradient is established and free electrons are moving under its influence throughout the wire in a very small fraction of a second. Although the individual electrons have only a small drift superimposed on their random thermal motion, the current exists immediately throughout the wire.

25.2 EMF

Maintenance of a steady current requires the presence of a device where nonelectrical energy, for example, chemical energy or mechanical energy, can be converted to electrical potential energy. Such a device is called a source of *EMF* ("ee-em-eff"). This term originally was an abbreviation for "electromotive force," a name that originated when the term force was less precisely defined than now. Because this use of the word "force" is not consistent with out definition of force in mechanics, we shall use only the name provided by the abbreviation EMF.

The points on a source of EMF where electrical connection can be made are called its *terminals;* we shall consider two-terminal devices. When left to itself, a source of EMF maintains an electrical potential difference between its terminals. If a length of metal wire is connected between the terminals, this potential difference is applied between the ends of the wire. The free electrons of the metal move under the influence of the electric field $\mathscr{E}$ associated with the potential gradient along the wire. Thus, a current is established that is directed away from the higher-potential terminal through the wire toward the lower-potential terminal. In a similar way a current could be established by connecting the wire between the plates of a charged capacitor. However, in that case the potential difference between the ends of the wire would steadily decrease as charge flowed, and the current would cease when the capacitor was completely discharged. The distinctive feature of a source of EMF is that it can maintain the potential difference between its terminals nearly constant for a long period even while it is producing a current.

We can now make the following definition:

A SOURCE OF EMF is a device that converts nonelectrical energy to electrical potential energy when a current passes through it from the low-potential (negative) terminal to the high-potential (positive) terminal and converts electrical potential energy to nonelectrical energy at the same rate when the same current passes through it in the opposite direction.

The quantitative measure of the EMF of a source V_E is the *amount of energy transformed per unit charge* passing through the device. Thus, the SI unit of EMF is joule per coulomb or volt.

For an *ideal source of EMF* the potential difference between its terminals is equal to the EMF V_E. When there is a current through a real source, this relationship is altered because of electrical energy dissipation within the source; we shall discuss this in a later section.

If a current I passes through an ideal source of EMF V_E, then by (25.1) the rate at which energy is converted by the source, which is the *power P* converted to electrical form of from electrical form depending on the direction of the current through the source, is given by

$$P = V_E I. \quad (\textit{Ideal Source of EMF}) \qquad (25.3)$$

An ideal source of EMF must furnish the power given by (25.3) in order to maintain a current I in a system of metallic wires.

A *battery* is a device where chemical energy is converted to electrical potential energy and vice versa. When current leaves a battery from its positive terminal and chemical energy is being converted to electrical potential energy, we say that the battery is being *discharged.* When the current is oppositely directed and electrical potential energy is being converted to chemical energy, we say that the battery is being *charged.* In a *storage battery* the chemical energy produced by charging is available for subsequent reconversion to electrical energy. A dry cell is an example of a battery where the chemistry is such that charging does not produce useful chemical energy. The first battery was invented in 1800 by Alessandro Volta (1745–1827) of the University of Pavia in Italy. The so-called "voltaic pile" rapidly became a standard apparatus of scientific research. We shall leave discussion of the internal operation of batteries for courses in physical chemistry.

A *generator* is a device in which mechanical energy is converted to electrical potential energy. It can produce currents in wires connected between its high-potential and low-potential terminals. If current is sent backward through a generator so that electrical potential energy is converted to mechanical energy, the device is called a *motor.* Most common generators and motors involve magnetic effects that will be discussed in later chapters.

In 1822, Thomas Johann Seebeck (1770–1831) of Berlin discovered that a highly stable and reproducible source of low EMF was produced if the two ends of a copper wire were connected to a bar of some other metal and the two resulting junctions were maintained at different temperatures. In such an arrangement thermal energy, supplied by whatever agent maintains the temperature difference, is converted to electrical potential energy. We shall return to a discussion of thermal sources of EMF later in this chapter.

25.3   RESISTANCE: OHM'S LAW

When a potential difference is maintained between the ends of a metallic wire, there is a current in the wire caused by the potential gradient along the wire. In experiments conducted in 1826–1827, the German physicist Georg Simon Ohm (1787–1854) found that the current produced in a copper wire by a Seebeck thermal EMF was inversely proportional to the length of the wire plus a constant and directly proportional to the temperature difference of the Seebeck source. The connection of this relationship with other electrical concepts became clear only as the unifying role of the concept of energy was developed. In 1849, Kirchhoff noted that the essential quantity furnished by the source in Ohm's experiment is the electrical potential difference between the ends of the wire. A modern statement that includes Ohm's results is as follows:

OHM'S LAW: For a given conductor at a given temperature the current produced is directly proportional to the electrical potential difference between the ends of the conductor. The direction of the conventional current is from the high-potential end of the conductor to the low-potential end.

When Ohm's law is stated in this way, the proportionality constant is called the *conductance G* of the conductor, and we can write $I = GV$, where I is the current

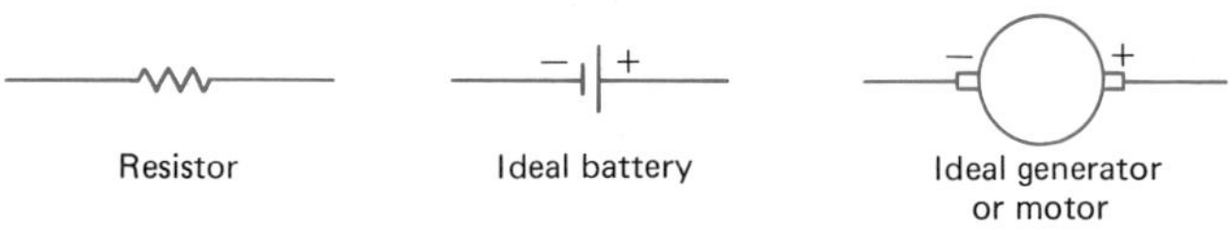

Fig. 25.3 Symbols used in schematic circuit diagrams.

Resistor   Ideal battery   Ideal generator or motor

produced by a potential difference V. In practice, it is more common to use the reciprocal of the conductance $R = 1/G$, which is called the *resistance*, and to write

$$V = IR. \quad \left\{ \begin{matrix} V \text{ in V} \\ I \text{ in A} \\ R \text{ in } \Omega \end{matrix} \right\} \quad (Ohm's \ Law) \qquad (25.4)$$

The SI unit of resistance is the volt per ampere. This unit is given the special name *ohm;* the common symbol used for ohm is the Greek letter capital omega, Ω. Thus, $1 \ \Omega = 1 \ \text{V/A}$.

Ohm's law is not a fundamental principle of physics. It is an empirical relationship that accurately describes the behavior of a given piece of metallic material at a given temperature. We can use (25.4) to define the resistance of a piece of any material, but we then find in many instances that the resistance depends on the applied voltage, sometimes in a complex way.

Most frequently, when considering electrical circuits we shall be concerned with situations where almost all the resistance is associated with certain elements called *resistors* that are electrically connected by wires having resistance that is negligible in comparison. We shall usually apply the approximation of ideal wires that provide definite conducting paths but have zero resistance. By (25.4) the potential difference between the ends of such a wire must be zero; ideal wires are therefore regions of constant potential. In schematic diagrams we shall use single straight lines to represent ideal wires; other symbols used are shown in Fig. 25.3.

The current through a resistor, being from the high-potential end to the low-potential end, is always such that the charges lose electrical potential energy as they pass through the resistor. This energy is converted to heat by inelastic collisions of the conduction electrons with the lattice of the material. When a current passes through a resistor, the net effect is that in each time interval dt an amount of charge dQ is transferred between points having the potential difference V; the loss in electrical potential energy is $V \ dQ$. Thus, the rate at which heat is produced in the resistor is

$$P = V \ dQ/dt = VI.$$

By using (25.4) we can write this as

$$P = I^2R. \quad (Rate \ of \ Heat \ Generation \ in \ a \ Resistor) \qquad (25.5)$$

25.4 RESISTORS IN PARALLEL AND IN SERIES

A combination of resistors can always be replaced by a single resistor that is "equivalent" so far as external connections are concerned. As was discussed for capacitors in Section 24.6, there are two common types of connection for which there are simple formulas for the equivalent resistance.

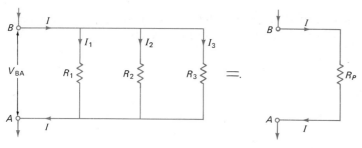

Fig. 25.4   The resistor R_P is equivalent to the three resistors in parallel.

We say that electrical devices are connected in *parallel* if the same potential difference exists across each device. Three resistors connected in parallel are shown in Fig. 25.4. What is the single equivalent resistance R_P that would have the same effect as the parallel combination so far as external connections between points A and B are concerned?

The potential difference across each resistor is V_{BA}. Thus, by using (25.4) for each resistor we obtain $V_{BA} = I_1 R_1 = I_2 R_2 = I_3 R_3$. The current in the external circuit is the sum of the currents in the three resistors: $I = I_1 + I_2 + I_3$. Thus,

$$I = \frac{V_{BA}}{R_1} + \frac{V_{BA}}{R_2} + \frac{V_{BA}}{R_3} = V_{BA}\left(\frac{1}{R_1} + \frac{1}{R_2} + \frac{1}{R_3}\right).$$

But the equivalent resistance R_P must satisfy $I R_P = V_{BA}$, so with $I = V_{BA}/R_P$ we obtain finally

$$\frac{1}{R_P} = \frac{1}{R_1} + \frac{1}{R_2} + \frac{1}{R_3}. \quad (\textit{Resistors in Parallel}) \qquad (25.6)$$

This result is easily extended to an arbitrary number of resistors connected in parallel. We see that the equivalent resistance of a parallel combination is less than the resistance of any one of the individual resistors.

If electrical devices are connected in sequence one after the other along a single conducting path, we say that they are connected in *series*. Three resistors connected in series are shown in Fig. 25.5. What is the single equivalent resistance R_S that would have the same effect as the series combination so far as external connections between points A and B are concerned?

The current through each of the resistors is I. The potential difference between

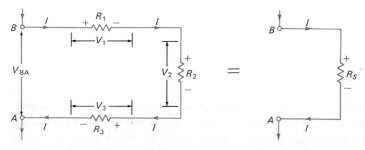

Fig. 25.5   The resistor R_S is equivalent to the three resistors in series.

points B and A is the sum of the potential differences across the three resistors: $V_{BA} = V_1 + V_2 + V_3$. By using (25.4) for each resistor we obtain

$$V_{BA} = IR_1 + IR_2 + IR_3.$$

But the equivalent resistance R_S must satisfy $V_{BA} = IR_S$ or $R_S = V_{AB}/I$, so we obtain finally

$$R_S = R_1 + R_2 + R_3. \quad (Resistors\ in\ Series) \qquad (25.7)$$

This result is easily extended to an arbitrary number of resistors connected in series.

25.5 RESISTIVITY

The resistance of a resistor at a given temperature depends on its size and shape as well as the material of which it is made. For convenient comparison of the conducting abilities of various materials, we need to define a quantity that depends on the material and not on the particular resistor into which it is formed.

Suppose that we make various wires of a given material. If we double the length of a wire, we are in effect putting two equal resistors in series; we conclude from (25.7) that doubling the length of a wire will double the resistance. More generally, we see by this reasoning that the resistance is directly proportional to the length of a wire: $R \propto l$.

For a uniformly distributed current, if we double the cross-sectional area of a wire, we are in effect putting two equal resistors in parallel; we conclude from (25.6) that doubling the area will halve the resistance. Similarly, if we triple the area, we are putting three equal resistors in parallel, and the resistance is reduced to one-third of its original value. We see by this reasoning that in general for a uniformly distributed current the resistance is inversely proportional to the cross-sectional area of a wire: $R \propto 1/A$.

By combining these two results, we have that $R \propto l/A$. The proportionality constant involved in this relation depends only on the *material* of which the wires are composed and is called the *resistivity* ρ:

$$R = \rho l/A. \qquad \begin{cases} R \text{ in } \Omega \\ \rho \text{ in } \Omega \cdot m \\ l \text{ in m} \\ A \text{ in m}^2 \end{cases} \qquad (25.8)$$

Resistivity is a property of the material and depends on the temperature, but it is independent of the particular wire or other shape into which the material is formed. We see from (25.8) that the unit of resistivity is $\Omega \cdot m$. The resistivities of a number of different metals and alloys are listed in Table 25.1. It is unfortunate that the usual symbol ρ for resistivity is also used to represent mass density, charge density, and several other quantities. However, the context in which the symbol ρ is used should keep the particular meaning of the symbol clear.

Table 25.1   Typical Values of the Resistivity ρ and the Temperature Coefficient of Resistivity α for Various Metals and Alloys at 20°C.

Material	ρ (10⁻⁸ Ω · m)	α (10⁻³ K⁻¹)
Aluminum	2.83	4.0
Copper	1.72	3.93
Iron	10	5.0
Lead	22	3.9
Mercury	96	0.88
Platinum	10.5	3.6
Silver	1.59	3.8
Tungsten	5.5	4.5
Constantan (55% Cu, 45% Ni)	49	0.002
Manganin (84% Cu, 12% Mn, 4% Ni)	44	0.000

The variation of resistivity with temperature is sufficiently large for most materials that it must be considered in practical situations. We show in Fig. 25.6 plots of resistivity versus temperature for several different materials. For most metals and alloys the relation between ρ and T is nearly linear over a large temperature range. One can then write to a good approximation that $\rho = A + BT$, where A and B are appropriately chosen constants. It is the usual engineering convention to use the resistivity at 20°C as a reference value and to write

$$\rho = \rho_{20} + \alpha_{20}\rho_{20}(T_C - 20°C). \tag{25.9}$$

In this expression ρ is the resistivity at the Celsius temperature T_C and ρ_{20} is the resistivity at 20°C. The constant α_{20} is called the *temperature coefficient of resistivity*. It is equal to the slope of the ρ versus T curve evaluated at 20°C divided by ρ_{20}:

$$\alpha_{20} = \frac{(d\rho/dT)_{20°C}}{\rho_{20}}.$$

The dimensions of α_{20} are reciprocal kelvins (K⁻¹). Typical values of α_{20} for various metals and alloys are listed in Table 25.1.

We see from Table 25.1 that for most metals the value of α_{20} is about 0.004 K⁻¹. This means that the resistivity changes by about 0.4% for a 1-K temperature change. The resistivity of a metal approximately doubles for a temperature increase of 250 K.

We learned in Section 9.3 that the dimensions of a material change with temperature, obeying a relation similar to (25.9) over a moderate temperature range. However, the magnitudes of relative changes in physical dimensions for metals are only the order of 0.002% to 0.004% for a 1-K temperature change. This is sufficiently small that for most purposes we can neglect changes in dimensions in discussing the dependence on temperature of the resistance of a resistor. We therefore simply multiply (25.9) by l/A and use (25.8) to obtain

$$R = R_{20} + \alpha_{20}R_{20}(T_C - 20°C). \tag{25.10}$$

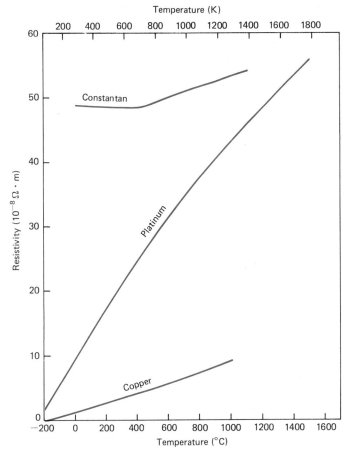

Fig. 25.6 Typical values of the resistivity as a function of temperature for copper, platinum, and constantan. The melting points of these metals are copper, 1083°C; platinum, 1774°C; constantan, 1260°C.

For making precision resistors it is important to use materials having a small temperature coefficient because the presence of a current heats a resistor in accordance with (25.5) and thus raises its temperature. Several alloys, notably constantan and manganin, have been developed for this purpose. These alloys are included in Table 25.1; the relative constancy of ρ with varying T for constantan at moderate temperatures is shown graphically in Fig. 25.6.

The concept of resistivity can be applied to nonmetals. However, because the conduction mechanisms in nonmetals are different from those in metals, resistivity is a less useful parameter. In general, nonmetals do not obey Ohm's law. A material classified as a semiconductor might have resistivity at 20°C of the order of 1–10^3 $\Omega \cdot m$ with a strong dependence on small concentrations of impurities and a large negative temperature coefficient. A material classified as an insulator might have resistivity at 20°C the order of 10^{10}–10^{16} $\Omega \cdot m$ and a large negative temperature coefficient. For such materials the leakage current over the surface may be greater than the current through the bulk of the material, leading to spurious conclusions about the resistivity, particularly if the surface is wet or dirty.

Carbon is an interesting nonmetal that is a fairly good electrical conductor. The resistivity of amorphous carbon at 20°C is about 3.5×10^{-5} $\Omega \cdot m$; its temperature coefficient of resistivity is about -5×10^{-4} K^{-1}.

Because many materials have changes in resistivity with temperature that are large enough to be measured with high precision by use of relatively simple apparatus, resistance is an important thermometric property. Because it is chemically inactive and has an adequately large value of α_{20} over a wide temperature range, platinum is frequently used for resistance thermometers. Carbon and germanium thermometers have seen important use at very low temperatures. High-precision resistance thermometers must be individually calibrated and require more elaborate equations than (25.10) to represent their variation of resistance with temperature.

In 1911, Heike Kamerlingh Onnes (1853–1926) discovered that the resistivity of mercury dropped abruptly to zero as the temperature was lowered past 4.2 K. This phenomenon is known as *superconductivity*. Many metals and alloys have been found to undergo a superconducting transition at temperatures below about 20 K. Since there is no dissipation of energy to heat, a current once started in a superconducting ring will persist indefinitely without requiring any source of EMF to maintain it. There has been a vast amount of experimental and theoretical study of superconductivity, and it has important technical applications. However, discussion of the physics of superconductivity is beyond the scope of this text.

25.6   CONDUCTIVITY AND OHM'S LAW

The formulation of Ohm's law discussed in Sec. 25.3 is appropriate for discussion of the behavior of circuits containing resistors. However, in many situations in the physics of materials it is desirable to use an alternative statement, also known as Ohm's law, that relates the current density **J** and the electric-field strength $\mathscr{E}$ at points inside the conducting material. This statement is as follows: for a given homogeneous, isotropic material at a given temperature the current density **J** at any point is directly proportional to the electric-field strength $\mathscr{E}$ at that point provided the magnitude of $\mathscr{E}$ is not too large. The proportionality constant is called the *conductivity* of the material and is usually represented by the symbol σ. In the form of an equation we have

$$\mathbf{J} = \sigma\mathscr{E}.$$

The SI units of conductivity are $(\Omega\cdot m)^{-1}$.

This statement can be used to derive our earlier equations (25.4) and (25.8). The derivation also shows how the conductivity of a material is related to its resistivity. Consider a specimen of homogeneous material of conductivity σ in the shape of a straight piece of wire or length l and uniform cross-sectional area A. Choose a coordinate system with Z axis along the center of the wire parallel to its length with the ends of the wire at $z = 0$ and $z = l$. Assume that a potential difference V is maintained between the ends of this wire with the high potential end of the wire at $z = 0$. This means that there must be an electric field $\mathscr{E}$ within the wire such that

$$V = \int_{z=0}^{z=l} \mathscr{E} \cdot d\mathbf{l}.$$

For a homogeneous, cylindrical specimen of conductor under steady-state conditions with ends that are equipotential surfaces, the electric-field strength will be a constant parallel to the cylinder axis: $\mathscr{E} = \mathscr{E}\mathbf{k}$; the field $\mathscr{E}$ is directed away from the high potential end of the wire at $z = 0$. Therefore, we have

$$V=\int_0^l (\mathscr{E}\,\mathbf{k})\cdot(\mathbf{k}dz)=\mathscr{E}\int_0^l dz=\mathscr{E}l \quad \text{or} \quad \mathscr{E}=V/l.$$

The current through the wire can be expressed as

$$I=\iint_S \mathbf{J}\cdot d\mathbf{S},$$

where the surface S is a cross section of the wire. With $\mathbf{J} = \sigma\mathscr{E} = \sigma\mathscr{E}\mathbf{k}$ and $d\mathbf{S} = dS\mathbf{k}$, we have

$$I=\iint_S (\sigma\mathscr{E}\mathbf{k})\cdot(\mathbf{k}dS)=\sigma\mathscr{E}\iint_S dS=\sigma\mathscr{E}A \quad \text{or} \quad \mathscr{E}=I/\sigma A.$$

By combining the two expressions we have derived for $\mathscr{E}$ we obtain

$$V/l= I/\sigma A \quad \text{or} \quad V=Il/\sigma A.$$

Comparison shows that this is equivalent to (25.4) with $R = l/\sigma A$. Thus, by (25.8) the conductivity is just the reciprocal of the resistivity,

$$\sigma = 1/\rho.$$

25.7   INTERNAL RESISTANCE OF A SOURCE OF EMF

We noted in Section 25.2 that some energy is dissipated when a current passes through a real source of EMF. This energy dissipation can often be described by ascribing to the source an *internal resistance* r such that the rate of generation of heat when a current I exists through the source is I^2r in accordance with (25.5). Because of the internal resistance, the potential difference between the terminals of a source of EMF differs from V_E when a current is present. To show on a diagram that a device has both EMF and an internal resistance, we can use a representation like that shown in Fig. 25.7. The box is to indicate that the properties r and V_E cannot be separated physically but are both inherent to the device.

Let us represent the difference in potential between the terminals of the source, often called the *terminal voltage,* by V_T. In order to find the value of V_T for a given current I through a source of EMF V_E and internal resistance r, we must distinguish two cases, as indicated in Fig. 25.7. For a generator or a battery on discharge, each element of charge dQ passing through the source *gains* electrical potential energy $dQ\,V_T$. Therefore, the rate at which the source produces electrical potential energy is IV_T. This is equal to the rate at which energy is converted from nonelectrical to

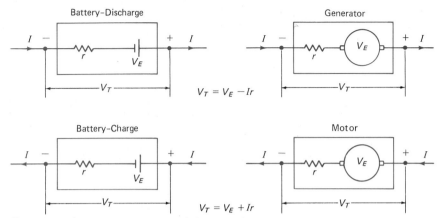

Fig. 25.7 Schematic representation of the internal resistance for a battery on discharge, a generator, a battery on charge, and a motor.

electrical potential form by the source, which by (25.3) is IV_E, minus the rate at which energy is dissipated by the internal resistance. Thus,

$$IV_T = IV_E - I^2r.$$

Upon dividing this relation by I we obtain

$$V_T = V_E - Ir. \quad (\textit{Generator or Battery on Discharge}) \qquad (25.11)$$

For a motor or a battery on charge, each element of charge dQ passing through the source *loses* electrical potential energy $dQ\,V_T$. Therefore, the rate at which energy is delivered to the source is IV_T. This is equal to the rate at which electrical potential energy is converted to nonelectrical form by the source plus the rate at which energy is dissipated by the internal resistance. Thus,

$$IV_T = IV_E + I^2r.$$

Upon dividing this relation by I we obtain

$$V_T = V_E + Ir. \quad (\textit{Motor or Battery on Charge}) \qquad (25.12)$$

25.8   THERMOELECTRICITY

We have already noted the discovery by Seebeck that if wires of two different metals are joined at two junctions and the two junctions are maintained at different temperatures, as suggested in Fig. 25.8, the system acts as a source of EMF. Such a device is called a *thermocouple*. The magnitude and sign of the EMF depend on the particular metals chosen and the temperatures of the junctions. If the temperature of one junction, called the reference junction, is held fixed, the EMF produced may be a rapidly varying function of the temperature of the other junction over a wide

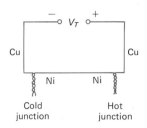

Fig. 25.8 In the Seebeck effect, an EMF is produced when the two junctions between wires of different metals are maintained at different temperatures. The diagram shows the sign of the EMF when the metals are nickel and copper.

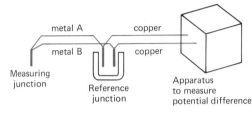

Fig. 25.9 A typical thermocouple circuit.

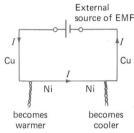

Fig. 25.10 In the Peltier effect, when a current passes through a junction between two metals, the material in the immediate vicinity of the junction becomes heated or cooled. The diagram shows the sign of the effect when the metals are nickel and copper.

range of temperatures. This EMF provides an important thermometric property. In practice, a thermocouple circuit usually consists of three or more metals, as shown in Fig. 25.9.

A second thermoelectric effect, in a sense the inverse of the Seebeck effect, was discovered by the French physicist Jean Charles Anathase Peltier (1785–1845) in 1834. Peltier found that when a current passed through a junction between two metals, the material in the immediate vicinity of the junction was heated or cooled, depending on the direction of the current. This effect is distinct from the general I^2R heating of a current-carrying conductor that is described by (25.5). The rate of heat generation or absorption is proportional to the current and depends on the particular metals and the temperature of the junction. In a circuit like that shown in Fig. 25.10 involving two junctions, one junction tends to become cooler and the other tends to become warmer. If the current is reversed, the roles of the two junctions are reversed. If the junctions are at different temperatures and the current is that due to the Seebeck EMF, then it is the hot junction that tends to be cooled and the cold junction that tends to be warmed by the Peltier effect. If the temperatures of the junctions are to be maintained constant, heat must be supplied continuously at the hot junction and removed from the cold junction.

There is another source of thermal EMF that exists when thermal gradients are present even for a single conducting material. In the design and use of precision electrical apparatus the experimenter must be aware that unplanned temperature differences will produce "thermal EMFs" that might have a deleterious effect on the operation of the equipment.

QUESTIONS

1. In order to specify completely the current in a certain wire, we must state not only the number of coulombs of charge passing a given point of the wire per second but also the direction in which the charge is moving. If both a magnitude and a direction are required, why isn't current a vector quantity?

2. What is the surface to be used in the equation $I = \iint \mathbf{J} \cdot d\mathbf{S}$? Is the integral to be taken over an open surface or a closed surface, or is the equation meaningful for both kinds of surface?

3. If the drift velocity for conduction electrons in a wire is very small, as is illustrated by the example in Section 25.1, why can't we turn off the light switch and jump into bed before the electrons stop moving through the light bulb? After all, the electrons that passed through the switch just *before* we opened it will not reach the light bulb for a number of seconds.

4. EMF is measured in volts. Is EMF the same thing as potential difference? If not, how is the concept of EMF related to the concept of potential difference?

5. Why is the current through a conducting material always directed from the high-potential end of the material to the low-potential end? Can't we make the current go in the opposite direction if we just get a big enough battery?

6. We wish to deliver the greatest possible power to an electric heater using a battery of fixed EMF and negligible internal resistance. Should we choose a low resistance heater coil or a high resistance heater coil? Explain the reason for your choice.

7. In (25.6) and (25.7) we have equations to determine the resistance "equivalent" to a parallel combination of resistors and the resistance "equivalent" to a series combination of resistors, respectively. Explain what is meant by equivalent in this context.

8. A copper coil that is thermally insulated from its surroundings has its temperature increased as current passes through it because of I^2R-heating. Does this cause the power delivered to the coil to increase or decrease if we assume a constant potential difference between the ends of the coil? Repeat for a constant current through the coil.

9. Explain the difference between the terminal voltage and the EMF of a battery. Can these two quantities ever have equal values?

10. When a current exists in a copper wire, are the mean kinetic energies of the conduction electrons greatly increased?

11. Can a current exist in a metal if no potential differences exist in the metal? Explain your reasoning.

12. Why is it difficult to verify Ohm's law for the filament of a light bulb when the bulb is in normal use?

13. On what factors does the resistance of a wire depend?

14. How would you design a platinum *resistance thermometer*?

PROBLEMS

1. The current through a certain surface is 2 A. (a) How much time is required to transfer 1 C of charge through the surface? (b) If the moving charged particles are all electrons, how many electrons cross the surface each second?

2. An automobile battery is guaranteed to deliver 120 ampere-hours without recharging. (a) How many coulombs of charge will the battery deliver? (b) For what length of time can the battery supply a current of 6 A? (c) Suppose that the starter draws 500 A. For what length of time can the battery drive the starter?

3. The mobility B of an ion is the drift speed per unit applied electric-field strength. Under certain atmospheric conditions there is a region where there are 500 positive ions per cm^3 having a mobility of 1.84×10^{-4} $m^2/V \cdot s$ and 480 negative ions per cm^3 having a mobility of 2.00×10^{-4} $m^2/V \cdot s$. Both the positive and the negative ions have charges of magnitude e. There is a downward directed electric field of 100 V/m. What are the magnitude and the direction of the resultant ion current density?

4. A piece of laboratory apparatus draws a current $I = (12 \text{ A}) \sin[2\pi(60 \text{ Hz})t]$ from an electrical outlet, where t is the time in seconds. (a) How many coulombs of charge pass through the apparatus between $t = 0$ and $t = (1/240)$ s; between $t = 0$ and $t = (1/120)$ s; between $t = 0$ and $t = (1/60)$ s? (b) Explain how the current can exist for a finite time and still transfer zero total charge through the apparatus.

5. In a Van de Graaff electrostatic generator charge is "sprayed" onto an endless belt of insulating material by corona discharge at sharp metal points and is carried by the belt to the inside of a hollow metal sphere where it is transferred to the surface of the sphere by a sort of continuously acting Faraday ice-pail experiment. The metal sphere is thereby raised to a high potential relative to ground. At what rate must charge be sprayed onto one side of a belt 50 cm wide traveling at 28 m/s if the current to the metal sphere is to be 1.5×10^{-4} A? What is the average charge per unit area on the belt?

6. In electrostatics we learned that all parts of a conductor are at the same potential and that $\mathscr{E} = 0$ everywhere inside a metallic body. The situation is different when there is an electric current in a conductor. Consider a straight, uniform wire 40 cm long with a resistance of 0.5 Ω that is carrying a current of 12 A. What is the difference in potential between the ends of the wire? What is the magnitude of the average electric-field strength inside the wire?

7. When a charge q is in an electric field $\mathscr{E}$, the charge experiences a resultant force $\mathbf{F} = q\mathscr{E}$ and the charge therefore experiences an acceleration in the direction of $\mathscr{E}$ if there are no other forces acting. In the case of the wire in the preceding problem, what is the acceleration of a conduction electron due to the electric-field strength $\mathscr{E}$? Does the electron's kinetic energy increase by an amount $eV = (1.6 \times 10^{-19} \text{ C})(6 \text{ V}) = 9.6 \times 10^{-19}$ J as it passes from one end of the wire to the other? If not, what becomes of the energy imparted to it by the electric field inside the wire?

8. In Ohm's experiments he used an Ampere-type galvanometer to measure the current I in various lengths l of copper wire of the same cross section A that were attached to a bar of metal at junctions maintained at different temperatures T_1 and T_2. His results could be expressed in the form $I = C_1 (T_2 - T_1)/(C_2 + l)$, where C_1 and C_2 are constants. Discuss the relation of this equation to the statement of "Ohm's law" given in (25.4). What is the significance of the constants C_1 and C_2?

9. A 120-V generator of negligible internal resistance delivers power of 1.5 kW to an electric heater. What current is the generator supplying?

10. An immersion heater brings 1000 cm^3 of water from 10°C to 90°C in 9 min. Assume that 75% of the energy applied by the heater is effective in heating the water. The potential difference applied to the heater coils is

110 V. What is the resistance of the heater coils? How much current does the heater draw? If we wish to heat the water faster, should we use a heater of larger or smaller resistance?

11. A 500-W light bulb and a 100-W light bulb are both designed to operate on a potential difference of 100 V. (a) What are the filament resistances of the two bulbs? (b) What current will each bulb draw if a potential difference of 100 V is applied between the ends of its filament?

12. A certain resistor has a resistance of 8000 Ω and a rating of 4 W. What is the maximum potential difference that should be applied between its terminals? What is the corresponding current?

13. How much energy is dissipated as heat in 10 min by a resistor that draws a current of 0.230 A when a potential difference of 6.0 V is applied between its ends?

14. It is desired to design a 220-V water-cooled electromagnet in which the windings are made of copper tubing cooled by water flowing through the tubing. The windings are to carry a current of 200 A. What flow of water in m³/s is required to carry off all the heat produced by the current in the windings if the water is to enter the windings at 20°C and leave at 75°C?

15. You have three 100-Ω resistors. How many different resistances is it possible to obtain by connecting the resistors in any manner? It is *not* necessary that all the resistors be used in every connection. Sketch the possible connections and calculate the resistance of each combination.

16. Four resistors having resistances of 8, 10, 15, and 18 Ω are connected in series between the terminals of a 60-V battery of negligible internal resistance. Find the potential difference between the ends of each of the resistors and the power dissipated by each resistor.

17. Repeat Problem 16 if the resistors are connected in parallel between the terminals of the battery. What are the currents in each of the resistors?

18. What is the equivalent resistance of the combination of resistors shown in the diagram?

19. If a potential difference of 6 V is applied between points A and B in the diagram, what is the current in each of the resistors?

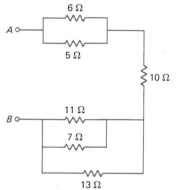

Problems 18 and 19

20. You have a 6-Ω resistor, an 8-Ω resistor, and two 10-Ω resistors. What are the values of the equivalent resistances that can be obtained by making various series and parallel combinations of these resistors? It is not necessary that all four resistors be used in every combination.

21. What is the resistance of a copper bus bar that is 1 cm by 3 cm in cross section and 2 m long if the temperature is 20°C? To what value must the temperature be raised to increase the resistance by 10%?

22. A copper bus bar is 2 cm by 2 cm in cross section and 2 m long at 20°C. Make a quantitative estimate of the percent error that is made in using (25.10) to compute the resistance of the bar at 50°C because of the neglect of the change in the dimensions of the bar. Is the resistance that is computed using (25.10) too high or too low?

23. What is the resistance at 20°C of a continu-

ous steel rail of cross section 45 cm² and length 10 km? By what percent does the resistance change if the temperature drops to 0°C? For this particular steel $\rho_{20} = 17 \times 10^{-8}$ $\Omega \cdot$m and $\alpha_{20} = 4.0 \times 10^{-3}$ K^{-1}.

24. The resistance of a certain resistor is 100.65 Ω at 20°C and is 117.93 Ω at 50°C. What is the average temperature coefficient of resistivity for the material of which the resistor is made over this temperature interval?

25. A certain platinum wire has a resistance of 125 Ω at 20°C. When the wire is placed in an electric furnace, its resistance is found to be 796 Ω. What is the temperature of the furnace?

26. (a) Rods of silver, aluminum, and copper are prepared at 20°C; each rod is 10 m long and has a diameter of 3.0 cm. What are the resistances of the rods? (b) Suppose it is required that the rods all be 10 m long and have the same resistance $R = 3.0 \times 10^{-4}$ Ω. What are their diameters? (c) What are the masses of the rods of part (b)?

27. Repeat part (b) of Problem 26 if it is required that all three rods have a resistance of 3.0×10^{-4} Ω at 50°C.

28. A potential difference V is applied between the ends of a copper wire of diameter d and length l. What are the effects on the resistance of the wire, the mass of the wire, and the drift velocity of electrons in the wire if l is doubled? If d is doubled? If V is doubled?

29. What will be the resistance at 20°C of the tungsten filament of a lamp designed to operate at 2000°C and 150 W when a potential difference of 110 V is applied between the ends of the filament?

30. A copper wire and a silver wire having the same lengths l and the same diameters d are joined end to end. A potential difference V is applied between the two free ends of the composite wire. Write a formula for the current in each wire in terms of l, d, and V.

What fraction of the total potential difference V occurs between the ends of each wire? What is the ratio of the drift speeds of the electrons in the two wires? Assume that silver and copper both have one conduction electron per atom and that both wires are maintained at 20°C.

31. The space between two concentric metal spheres of radii r_1 and r_2, where $r_1 < r_2$, is filled with a semiconducting material of resistivity ρ. (a) Show that the resistance between the spheres is given by $R = (\rho/4\pi)(1/r_1 - 1/r_2)$. (b) If there is a potential difference V between the two spheres, what is the current density at radius r in the semiconducting material? (c) What is the electric-field strength at radius r in the region between the spheres? (d) If $r_1 = 6$ cm, $r_2 = 12$ cm, and $\rho = 2.0$ $\Omega \cdot$m, what is the current between the spheres when the potential difference between them is 6 V?

32. The space between two coaxial metal cylinders of length L and radii r_1 and r_2, where $r_1 < r_2$, is filled with a semiconducting material of resistivity ρ. (a) Show that the resistance between the cylinders is given by $R = (\rho/2\pi L) \ln(r_2/r_1)$. (b) If there is a potential difference V between the two cylinders, what is the current density at radius r in the semiconducting material? (c) What is the electric-field strength at radius r in the region between the cylinders? (d) If $r_1 = 6$ cm, $r_2 = 12$ cm, $L = 20$ cm, and $\rho = 2.0$ $\Omega \cdot$m, what is the current between the cylinders when the potential difference between them is 6 V?

33. The terminal potential difference of a certain battery is 28.5 V when the battery is being charged by a current of 4 A and is 26.1 V when the battery is on discharge and has a current of 3.6 A through it. What are the EMF and the internal resistance of the battery?

34. When a potential difference of 120 V is ap-

plied between the terminals of a certain motor it draws a current of 2.08 A and dissipates energy as heat at the rate of 12.5 W. What is the efficiency of the motor? What is the effective resistance of the motor windings?

35. A 5-Ω resistor is connected between the terminals of a battery of EMF 2 V and internal resistance 0.09 Ω. How much energy does the battery convert from chemical to electrical form in 2 min? How much of this energy appears as heat in the 5-Ω resistor? What happens to the remainder of the energy?

36. In the network shown in the diagram the point P is maintained at a constant potential of 600 V relative to ground. What are the potentials at points A, B, C, D, and E? What are the charges stored by the capacitors?

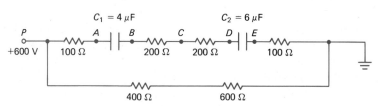

Problem 36

37. For the network considered in Problem 36, how much energy is stored by the capacitors? How much power is dissipated by the resistors in the network?

38. In the network shown in the diagram the point P is maintained at a constant potential of 600 V relative to ground. What are the potentials at points A, B, C, D, and E? What are the charges stored by the capacitors?

39. For the network considered in Problem 38, how much energy is stored by the capacitors? How much power is dissipated by the resistors in the network?

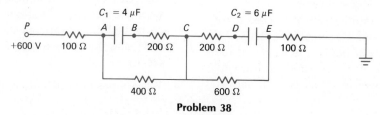

Problem 38

CHAPTER 26

Direct-Current Circuits

A *direct current* is a current that at all times has the same direction. In this chapter we shall consider the *steady* direct currents produced in networks of resistors and sources of constant EMF after transient time-dependent currents associated with the connection of the network and the closing or opening of switches die away. Although we shall consider other kinds of circuit elements in later chapters, we shall now use the term *circuit* to mean a collection of resistors and sources of EMF connected by ideal wires such that there exist one or more *closed conducting paths* around which charge can flow. Such circuits are called *direct-current circuits,* or simply *DC circuits.* Our concern shall be to describe the reasoning by which we can determine what steady currents are produced for a given circuit when the values of the EMFs and the resistances are specified. We shall consider the operation of three of the most important kinds of direct-current measuring instruments. A few of the innumerable practical applications of the analysis of direct-current circuits are described in connection with problems at the end of the chapter.

26.1 SIMPLE CIRCUITS

The simplest kind of circuit is a "load" of resistance R connected between the terminals of a source of EMF V_E. We shall assume that the source has internal resistance r. Such a circuit is shown in Fig. 26.1. Because the terminals of the source having potential difference V_T are connected to the ends of the load resistor, there is a current I from the high- to the low-potential end of the resistor that by Ohm's law satisfies $V_T = IR$. According to the discussion in Section 25.7, the terminal potential difference of a battery on discharge is $V_T = V_E - Ir$. Thus, we have $V_E - Ir = IR$ or

$$I = V_E/(R + r). \tag{26.1}$$

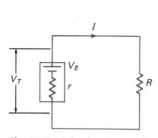

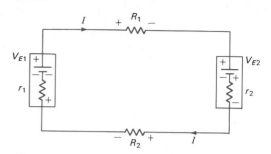

Fig. 26.1 A load resistance R connected between the terminals of a source of EMF.

Fig. 26.2

The electrical power supplied by the source of EMF is $P = IV_E$. By solving (26.1) for V_E and substituting in the power relation, we can write

$$P = I^2(R + r);$$

the electrical power supplied by the source is equal to the sum of the rates at which heat is produced in the two resistors R and r. The power I^2R is regarded as "useful" power delivered to the load resistor, which might well be the "element" in an electric heater; the power I^2r merely heats the battery and serves no useful purpose.

The same reasoning can be used if the load is some combination of resistors that can be reduced to a single equivalent resistor by the rules for series and parallel combinations that were developed in Chapter 25. The equivalent resistance is used in place of R in the above relationships. Once I is known, the currents in the various branches of the resistance combination can be determined in a straightforward way.

26.2 SINGLE-LOOP CIRCUITS WITH SEVERAL SOURCES OF EMF

As the number and arrangement of components in a circuit become more involved, it is advantageous to formalize the ideas we have just used. The procedure for solving a circuit problem can be stated in a step-by-step way that applies to any combination of resistors and sources of EMF. In this section we shall consider circuits having a single conducting path or "loop"; in the following section we shall consider multiple-loop circuits.

As we discuss a general procedure, we shall, as a specific example, apply it to the circuit shown in Fig. 26.2. As a first step, we choose a direction for the current, clockwise or counterclockwise. In some cases, the direction of the actual current will be clear by inspection of the circuit. In other cases, the direction of the current will not be certain until the problem has been solved. Nevertheless, we can arbitrarily *assume* a direction for the current at the onset; so long as we are consistent in using the assumed current, a wrong choice will simply produce a negative value for the current. The magnitude of the current will be correct, so all we have to do is reverse our choice of direction.

Let us assume a clockwise current I in the circuit of Fig. 26.2. We now recall that the current in a resistor is always directed from the high-potential end to the low-potential end. Therefore, our choice of a direction for I establishes which are the high- and the low-potential ends of each resistor. It is helpful to mark on the diagram + signs at the high-potential ends and − signs at the low-potential ends of all the resistors, as has been done in Fig. 26.2. It is most convenient in the analysis to treat the internal resistances of the sources of EMF on the same basis as the other resistances. The high- and low-potential sides of each source of EMF are determined by the way the device is attached in the circuit; these are also marked in Fig. 26.2.

We next recall that for the present steady-current conditions, each point of the circuit has a definite constant potential. In the practical design of circuits it is often advantageous to fix the potential of some point of the circuit and refer all other potentials to that point. Generally this is done by making a connection to the earth or "ground," the potential of which we can take to be zero. The symbol used to indicate a connection to ground is shown in Fig. 26.3.

We are now prepared to write an equation from which the current I can be determined. If we imagine an observer who moves around the loop in *either direction* and keeps track of the potential rises and drops encountered, the total change in potential experienced when the observer returns to the starting point must be zero. In other words, for any trip around the loop the sum of the potential rises must equal the sum of the potential drops. The signs of potential changes are indicated by the plus and minus signs we have marked on Fig. 26.2; the magnitude of the potential difference between the ends of a resistor is given by Ohm's law: $V = IR$; the potential difference between the sides of an EMF is V_E. If we start at the lower left-hand corner of the circuit in Fig. 26.2 and move around the circuit clockwise, we have

$$\text{(Sum of Potential Rises)} - \text{(Sum of Potential Drops)} = 0$$
$$(V_{E1}) - (Ir_1 + IR_1 + V_{E2} + Ir_2 + IR_2) = 0.$$

Upon algebraically rearranging this equation we obtain

$$I = (V_{E1} - V_{E2})/(R_1 + R_2 + r_1 + r_2). \qquad (26.2)$$

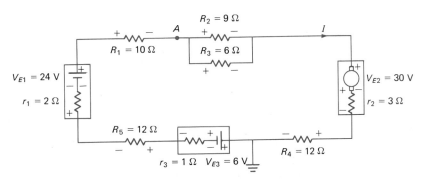

Fig. 26.3 The symbol used to represent a connection to ground.

Fig. 26.4

A little reflection will show that the generalization of (26.2) for an arbitrary single-loop circuit can be stated as follows:

$$I = \left\{ \begin{array}{l} Algebraic \text{ sum of EMFs, counted} \\ \text{as positive if they tend to} \\ \text{send current in the assumed} \\ \text{direction of } I \end{array} \right\} \text{ (divided by) } \left\{ \begin{array}{l} \text{Sum of all} \\ \text{resistances} \\ \text{in the} \\ \text{circuit} \end{array} \right\}. \quad (26.3)$$

Example.   What is the current in the circuit shown in Fig. 26.4? What is the potential of point *A*?

We first replace the parallel resistors R_2 and R_3 by their equivalent: $1/R_P = 1/R_2 + 1/R_3 = 1/9 \ \Omega + 1/6 \ \Omega$, so $R_P = 3.6 \ \Omega$. We assume that the current is clockwise; we can then mark the low- and high-potential ends of all resistors, as shown in Fig. 26.4. When we apply (26.3) to this circuit we obtain

$$I = \frac{V_{E1} - V_{E2} - V_{E3}}{R_1 + R_P + R_4 + R_5 + r_1 + r_2 + r_3}$$

$$= \frac{24 \text{ V} - 30 \text{ V} - 6 \text{ V}}{10 \ \Omega + 3.6 \ \Omega + 12 \ \Omega + 12 \ \Omega + 2 \ \Omega + 3 \ \Omega + 1 \ \Omega} = -0.275 \text{ A}.$$

The minus sign tells us that the actual current is counterclockwise rather than clockwise. This means that the high- and low-potential ends of the resistors are opposite from the markings of Fig. 26.4.

In order to determine the potential of point *A,* we imagine an observer who moves from point A to ground, which is at potential zero, and keeps track of the potential rises and drops encountered. The net potential change experienced in such a trip will give the potential of *A*. Let us move counterclockwise from *A* to ground; the path followed, with the current direction now correctly indicated, is shown in Fig. 26.5. We have

V_A = (Sum of Potential Drops Encountered) − (Sum of Potential Rises Encountered)
  = $(IR_1 + V_{E1} + Ir_1 + Ir_5 + Ir_3) - (V_{E3})$
  = $(0.275 \text{ A})(10 \ \Omega + 2 \ \Omega + 12 \ \Omega + 1 \ \Omega) + 24 \text{ V} - 6 \text{ V} = 24.9 \text{ V}.$

We can confirm that the same result is obtained if the circuit is followed in a clockwise sense from *A* to ground. Try it!

26.3   MULTIPLE-LOOP CIRCUITS: KIRCHHOFF'S RULES

We now extend our analysis to include circuits having more than one closed conducting path. The ideas we use to treat such circuits are just those developed in the preceding section. They are usually expressed as two formal statements known as *Kirchhoff's Rules.*

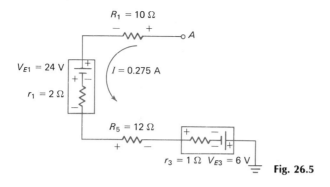

$R_1 = 10 \ \Omega$

$V_{E1} = 24 \ V$

$r_1 = 2 \ \Omega$

$I = 0.275 \ A$

$R_5 = 12 \ \Omega$

$r_3 = 1 \ \Omega \quad V_{E3} = 6 \ V$

Fig. 26.5

KIRCHHOFF'S FIRST RULE: At any junction point in a circuit the total current entering the junction must equal the total current leaving the junction.

A *junction* point is any place where two or more wires meet. We can consider any point on a single conductor as a two-wire junction. At such a point the rule merely says formally that the current has the same value at all points along a single conducting path. We shall apply the rule explicitly to junctions where three or more wires meet. The basis for this rule is that in the circuits we are considering there is no net accumulation or depletion of charge at any point. Therefore, in order to conserve charge the net rate at which charge enters any small volume, such as the volume surrounding a junction point, must equal the net rate at which charge leaves that volume. A capacitor is a place where charge can be accumulated or depleted, depending on whether the capacitor is being charged or discharged; for the present we assume that our circuits have no capacitance.

For our discussion of Kirchhoff's Second Rule it will be convenient to define formally several terms. A *loop* is a closed conducting path in a circuit that passes through no junction point more than once. A *planar circuit* is one that can be drawn on a plane surface in such a way that no branch passes over or under another branch. A *mesh* is a loop of a planar circuit that cannot be subdivided into other loops. The second rule can be stated as follows:

KIRCHHOFF'S SECOND RULE: If an observer moves completely around any loop in a circuit in either direction, the sum of the potential rises encountered must equal the sum of the potential drops encountered.

This rule expresses exactly the reasoning about the uniqueness of the potential of a point that was used in Section 26.2. In order to implement the rule, we assume a direction for the current in each branch of the circuit. As before, we can choose these directions arbitrarily; if an incorrect choice is made, the solution for that current will have the correct magnitude but a negative sign.

A step-by-step technique for applying Kirchhoff's rules to a circuit can now be described. We first assume a direction for the current in each branch of the circuit. Once these current directions are chosen, we can mark the high- and low-potential ends of all the resistors.

We next apply the first rule at the junctions where three or more wires come together. We can express the first rule as an equation by writing that for each junction

$$\Sigma\, I_{\mathrm{i}} \;=\; \Sigma\, I_i. \qquad (26.4)$$
$$\begin{array}{cc}\text{sum of} & \text{sum of}\\ \text{currents} & \text{currents}\\ \text{entering} & \text{leaving}\end{array}$$

If there are n junctions, these applications of the first rule will give only $n - 1$ independent equations; the other equation will be redundant.

The next step is to apply the second rule to $N - (n - 1)$ loops of the circuit, where N is the number of unknown currents, making sure that each branch of the circuit is part of at least one of the loops. For a planar circuit, which we shall assume for our discussion, it is always possible to represent the circuit as $m = N - (n - 1)$ meshes put together like a jigsaw puzzle. The simplest way to obtain the correct number of independent equations from the second rule is to apply the rule to each of these meshes. We shall apply the second rule by writing for each mesh that an observer moving around the mesh in either direction must find

$$\text{(Sum of Potential Rises)} = \text{(Sum of Potential Drops)}. \qquad (26.5)$$

Some people prefer to keep all the EMFs together and all the resistance terms together. We can do this by writing

$$\left\{\begin{array}{l}\text{Algebraic sum of EMFs,}\\ \text{counted as positive if}\\ \text{they tend to send current}\\ \text{in the direction the}\\ \text{observer is traveling}\end{array}\right\} = \left\{\begin{array}{l}\text{Algebraic sum of } IR \text{ products,}\\ \text{counted as positive if the}\\ \text{observer crosses the resistor}\\ \text{in the same direction as the}\\ \text{assumed branch current}\end{array}\right\} \qquad (26.5a)$$

At this point the physics of the problem is completed; there remains a problem in algebra. We have N equations, and we must solve these equations simultaneously for the N currents. Usually the junction equations obtained from the first rule will be relatively simple and can readily be used to eliminate $n - 1$ of the unknowns from the mesh equations obtained from the second rule; this is our first algebraic step. We then have a set of m linear equations, one for each mesh, that involve m unknown currents. We describe below a way to solve these simultaneous equations. The m current values obtained from this solution can then be substituted into the junction equations in order to obtain values for the other currents.

Many readers will be familiar with "Cramer's Rule" for solving a system of simultaneous linear equations. All the equations are written with the unknowns appearing in the same order on the left-hand side and the terms not involving any unknowns collected on the right-hand side. The solution for the ith unknown is then obtained by dividing the determinant formed from the coefficients of the unknowns *into* the similar determinant obtained by replacing the coefficients of the ith column by the column of numbers on the right-hand side of the equations.

Evaluation of the determinants needed for Cramer's Rule becomes unwieldy if there are more than two or three equations. A simple and convenient way to solve a set of m simultaneous linear equations in m unknowns is provided by a method known as Gaussian Elimination. This method is admirably suited for use with a hand calculator. The "first" equation is used to eliminate the "first" variable from the last $m - 1$ equations, then the new "second" equation is used to eliminate the "second" variable from the last $m - 2$ equations, and so on until an equation with only one variable is obtained. This equation is easily solved. The solution is substituted back into the previous equation, which depends on two variables. This equation is then easily solved for the other variable, and the two solutions are substituted back into the next earlier equation, which depends on three variables. This back substitution is continued equation by equation until values are determined for all the variables. The ordering of the equations in the system and of the variables in the equations is arbitrary.

The procedure for applying Kirchhoff's Rules to a multiple-loop circuit is illustrated by the following example.

Example. What are the currents in the branches of the three-loop circuit shown in Fig. 26.6?

We first assume a direction for the current in each branch of the circuit. There

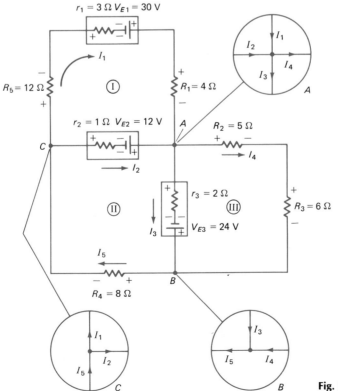

Fig. 26.6

are five branches in the circuit of Fig. 26.6, and the five assumed currents are indicated on the diagram.

Second, once the currents are chosen we can mark the high- and low-potential ends of all the resistors. This has been done in Fig. 26.6.

Third, we apply the first rule at the junctions where three or more wires come together. In our example there are three such junctions, at points A, B, and C on the diagram. We obtain the following equations:

$$\text{junction } A\colon \ I_1 + I_2 = I_3 + I_4; \tag{i}$$
$$\text{junction } B\colon \ I_3 + I_4 = I_5; \tag{ii}$$
$$\text{junction } C\colon \ \ \ \ \ I_5 = I_1 + I_2. \tag{iii}$$

We note that the third equation can be obtained by substituting from the second equation into the first equation; it does not contain independent information.

Fourth, we apply the second rule to the three meshes of the circuit. These meshes are labeled ①, ②, and ③ in Fig. 26.6. We shall imagine moving clockwise around each mesh in turn, starting from point C for meshes ① and ② and from point B for mesh ③. In each case we write

$$(\text{Sum of Potential Rises}) - (\text{Sum of Potential Drops}) = 0.$$

This gives the following equations:

$$\text{Mesh ①: } (V_{E1} + I_2 r_2) - (I_1 R_5 + I_1 r_1 + I_1 R_1 + V_{E2}) = 0,$$

hence

$$I_1(R_5 + r_1 + R_1) - I_2 r_2 = V_{E1} - V_{E2}$$

or

$$(19\ \Omega)I_1 - (1\ \Omega)I_2 = 18\text{ V}. \tag{iv}$$

$$\text{Mesh ②: } (V_{E2} + V_{E3}) - (I_2 r_2 + I_3 r_3 + I_5 R_4) = 0,$$

hence

$$I_2 r_2 + I_3 r_3 + I_5 R_4 = V_{E2} + V_{E3}$$

or

$$(1\ \Omega)I_2 + (2\ \Omega)I_3 + (8\ \Omega)I_5 = 36\text{ V}. \tag{v}$$

$$\text{Mesh ③: } (I_3 r_3) - (V_{E3} + I_4 R_2 + I_4 R_3) = 0,$$

hence

$$I_3 r_3 - I_4(R_2 + R_3) = V_{E3}$$

or

$$(2\ \Omega)I_3 - (11\ \Omega)I_4 = 24\text{ V}. \tag{vi}$$

The physics of the problem is now completed. It remains to solve (i)–(vi) simultaneously for the five unknown currents. We first use (i) and (iii) to eliminate two of the unknowns, say I_4 and I_5, from the other three equations. We have $I_5 = I_1 + I_2$ and $I_4 = I_1 + I_2 - I_3$. When substituted in (iv)–(vi) this produces

$$(19 \ \Omega)I_1 - (1 \ \Omega)I_2 \qquad\qquad = 18 \text{ V}, \qquad\qquad\text{(iv)}$$
$$(8 \ \Omega)I_1 + (9 \ \Omega)I_2 + (2 \ \Omega)I_3 \ = 36 \text{ V}, \qquad\qquad\text{(v$'$)}$$
$$-(11 \ \Omega)I_1 - (11 \ \Omega)I_2 + (13 \ \Omega)I_3 = 24 \text{ V}. \qquad\qquad\text{(vi$'$)}$$

We now use (vi$'$) to eliminate the variable I_3 from (v$'$); this variable is already missing from (iv). We divide through (vi$'$) by 13 and subtract the result from (v$'$) divided by 2. This gives

$$(4.85 \ \Omega)I_1 + (5.35 \ \Omega)I_2 = 16.15 \text{ V}.$$

If we divide through this equation by 5.35 we obtain

$$(0.907 \ \Omega)I_1 + (1 \ \Omega)I_2 = 3.02 \text{ V}. \qquad\qquad\text{(v$''$)}$$

We next use (v$''$) to eliminate the variable I_2 from (iv). If we add (v$''$) and (iv), we obtain an equation involving only I_1:

$$(19.9 \ \Omega)I_1 = 21.0 \text{ V} \quad \text{or} \quad I_1 = 1.06 \text{ A}.$$

Substitution of this result back into (v$''$) gives

$$I_2 = [3.02 \text{ V} - (0.907 \ \Omega)(1.06 \text{ A})]/(1 \ \Omega) = 2.06 \text{ A},$$

and substitution of the results for I_1 and I_2 into (vi$'$) then gives

$$I_3 = [24 \text{ V} + (11 \ \Omega)(1.06 \text{ A}) + (11 \ \Omega)(2.06 \text{ A})]/(13 \ \Omega) = 4.49 \text{ A}.$$

When then obtain from (iii) that

$$I_5 = 1.06 \text{ A} + 2.06 \text{ A} = 3.12 \text{ A}$$

and from (ii) that

$$I_4 = 3.12 \text{ A} - 4.49 \text{ A} = -1.37 \text{ A}.$$

The branch currents are now all determined. The negative value of I_4 indicates that the current in the right-hand branch of Fig. 26.6 is actually in a counterclockwise sense.

26.4   DIRECT-CURRENT MEASURING INSTRUMENTS

We shall next discuss three basic direct-current measuring instruments, the *voltmeter,* the *ammeter,* and the *potentiometer.* In each case we shall assume that the indicating instrument is a galvanometer having a pointer deflection that is directly proportional to the current through the galvanometer itself. A way in which such a galvanometer can be constructed will be described in Chapter 27. A galvanometer has a resistance R_g, and its sensitivity is characterized by the current I_G through the galvanometer or the potential difference $V_G = I_G R_g$ between the galvanometer terminals required to produce full-scale deflection of the pointer. We shall use lowercase subscripts to denote arbitrary values of galvanometer currents and potential differences and upper case subscripts to denote those values that produce full-scale deflection. Galvanometers with a very wide range of sensitivities can be produced; I_G might be the order of microamperes or even less. However, as typical values we can consider R_g of from 10 Ω to 100 Ω and I_G of the order of a few milliamperes.

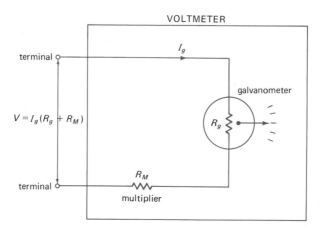

VOLTMETER

terminal

I_g

galvanometer

$V = I_g(R_g + R_M)$

R_g

R_M

terminal

multiplier

Fig. 26.7 A voltmeter is constructed by putting an appropriate multiplier resistor in series with a galvanometer.

Direct-Current Voltmeter

A voltmeter is designed to measure the potential difference between two points in a circuit without significantly altering the currents in the circuit. The voltmeter itself must draw an insignificant current when it is connected between the points in question and therefore must have a *very high resistance* compared with the resistance of the path between the points provided by the circuit. Note, however, that this type of voltmeter does draw *some* current.

In order to construct a direct-current voltmeter we place a high resistance R_M, sometimes called a *multiplier,* in series with a galvanometer, as shown in Fig. 26.7. Suppose that we want a voltmeter having full-scale deflection of the pointer when the potential difference between its terminals is V_F. This means that when the current through the galvanometer is I_G we must have $I_G(R_g + R_M) = V_F$, so the required multiplier resistance is

$$R_M = (V_F/I_G) - R_g. \tag{26.6}$$

Direct-Current Ammeter

An ammeter is designed to measure the current in a branch of a circuit without significantly altering that current. In order to construct a direct-current ammeter, we place a low resistance R_S, called a *shunt,* in parallel with a galvanometer, as shown in Fig. 26.8. The circuit is broken and the ammeter is inserted in series so that the current to be measured passes through the instrument. In order not to disturb the circuit appreciably, the ammeter must have a very low resistance compared with other resistors in the branch where it is connected. Since the parallel combination of R_S and R_g will have an equivalent resistance smaller than either R_S or R_g, this is accomplished if R_S is sufficiently low.

We see from Fig. 26.8 that $I_S R_S = (I - I_g)R_S = I_g R_g$, so

$$I_g = I R_S/(R_g + R_S).$$

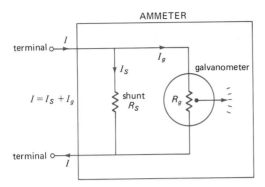

Fig. 26.8   An ammeter is constructed by putting an appropriate shunt resistor in parallel with a galvanometer.

Suppose that we want an ammeter that has full-scale deflection of the pointer when the current through it is I_F. Then we must have

$$I_G = I_F R_S /(R_g + R_S),$$

which upon being solved for R_S yields

$$R_S = I_G R_g /(I_F - I_G).$$

The Potentiometer

A potentiometer is a device for accurately measuring the ratio of two potential differences. If one of these potential differences is the EMF of a battery called a "standard cell," which is the terminal potential difference when the current through the cell is zero, the potentiometer serves for high-precision measurement of potential difference in terms of the EMF of the standard cell.*

The basic circuit of a potentiometer is shown in Fig. 26.9. A current I_0 is provided by a stable source such as a storage battery. The resistor R is made up of fixed resistors and precision slide wires in such a way that the resistances R_S and R_U can be varied continuously and their values read accurately on the dials of the instrument.

To determine the value of an unknown potential difference V_U, we first adjust contact ① until the sensitive galvanometer G reads zero when switch S_1 is closed. Switch S_2 remains open during this adjustment. If G reads zero when S_1 is closed, we have $V_{ES} = I_0 R_S$. We next leave S_1 open and adjust contact ② until the galvanometer G reads zero when switch S_2 is closed. At this setting we have $V_U = I_0 R_U$. Since the storage battery and the resistor R are the same for the two procedures, the value of I_0 is the same for both relations. Upon eliminating I_0 from the equations we obtain

$$V_U = V_{ES} R_U /R_S.$$

---

* A standard cell is intended for use as a secondary standard of voltage, not as a source of electrical energy. It is designed to maintain a very constant EMF over a long period of time provided no appreciable current is ever drawn from the cell and it is not subjected to extremes of temperature or to rough mechanical treatment. The EMF of a Weston cadmium cell is about 1.018 V and will remain constant to about 1 part in 10^5 or better over a time of years if the cell is not abused. The EMF of this cell has a temperature coefficient the order of -40 μV/K.

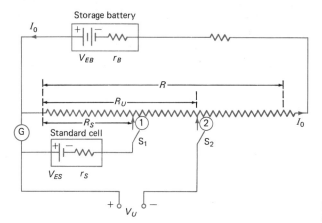

Fig. 26.9 A basic potentiometer circuit.

The value of the unknown potential difference is thus determined in terms of the EMF of the standard cell and the resistances R_U and R_S. Note that it is not necessary to know the value of I_0 or the EMF of the storage battery; all that is required is that V_{EB} and r_B be constant over the time required for a measurement.

When the contacts ① and ② are far from their final settings, there may be significant current through the galvanometer branch of the circuit when S_1 or S_2 is closed. Since excess current can burn out a galvanometer and virtually any current can destroy the calibration of a standard cell, a practical potentiometer must have arrangements to protect these circuit elements.

An important feature of the potentiometer is that *at the final setting where the measurement of V_U is made no current is drawn from the unknown source.* The potentiometer thus allows determination of V_U without, by its presence, disturbing the quantity being measured. A potentiometer can be used to determine accurately the EMF of a thermocouple. (See Section 25.7.) In several of the problems we consider how a potentiometer can be employed to calibrate a voltmeter or an ammeter.

26.5   MEASUREMENT OF RESISTANCE

It is important in an electrical-measurements laboratory to have secondary standards of resistance with which unknown resistances can be precisely compared. A simple, convenient circuit for making such comparisons is the Wheatstone Bridge† shown in Fig. 26.10. The resistors R_A, R_B, and R_C in the figure have known resistances, and at least one of these resistors must be continuously variable over a wide range. In practice all three resistors will usually be variable, although only one may be continuously variable, the others being variable in steps. The resistor R_U is an unknown whose resistance is to be determined. The resistor R_S with sliding contact C is present to protect the galvanometer from excess current.

To determine the value of R_U, the variable known resistors are adjusted until the deflection of the galvanometer G is zero when switches S_1 and S_2 are closed,

---

† This circuit is named for the British physicist Charles Wheatstone (1802–1875), who popularized its use in connection with his experimental verifications of Ohm's law. The circuit was first described by another British scientist, Samuel Christie (1784–1865), in 1833.

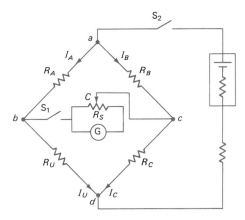

Fig. 26.10 The Wheatstone Bridge circuit.

indicating that there is no current in the branch of the circuit containing the galvanometer. The bridge is then said to be "balanced." Under this condition, we must have $V_{bc} = 0$, which requires that

$$I_A R_A = I_B R_B \qquad (26.8)$$

and also that $I_U R_U = I_C R_C$. Further, since the current in the galvanometer branch is zero, $I_U = I_A$ and $I_C = I_B$, so

$$I_A R_U = I_B R_C. \qquad (26.9)$$

If we divide (26.8) by (26.9) we obtain $R_A/R_U = R_B/R_C$, which can be rearranged to give

$$R_U = R_A R_C/R_B. \qquad (26.10)$$

The value of the unknown resistance R_U is thereby determined in terms of the three known resistances.

In the problems we consider a simple instrument called an *ohmmeter* that can be constructed from a galvanometer, a battery, and a resistor such that the value of the resistance between the terminals of the instrument can with fair precision be read directly from the position of the galvanometer pointer. Time can be saved in bridge balancing if an approximate value of the unknown resistance is first obtained with an ohmmeter.

QUESTIONS

1. How can it be true that we can arbitrarily *assume* a direction for the current in a single-loop circuit when the direction of the current through a battery determines whether it is on charge or discharge?

2. All other things being equal, does the opera-

tion of a circuit depend on which particular point of the circuit is grounded?

3. What difficulties in circuit operation are likely to ensue if two *different* points of the circuit are connected to ground?

4. Do Kirchhoff's rules apply to non-planar cir-

cuits that have an essential three-dimensional structure? If so, why were planar circuits brought into the discussion in the first part of Section 26.3?

5. Is it necessary for all resistors in a circuit to obey Ohm's law in order for Kirchhoff's rules to apply to the circuit?

6. Why must a voltmeter have very high resistance? What determines how high the voltmeter resistance must be in order for a measurement to have a specified accuracy?

7. Why must an ammeter have very low resistance? What determines how low the ammeter resistance must be in order for a measurement to have a specified accuracy?

8. Discuss the advantages and disadvantages of using a potentiometer to measure a potential difference as compared with using a high quality voltmeter.

9. How could a potentiometer be used to mea-sure a current? What auxiliary apparatus would be required?

10. Discuss the advantages and disadvantages of using a Wheatstone bridge for the measure-ment of resistance as compared with using an ohmmeter. (One type of ohmmeter is dis-cussed in connection with Problem 26.39.)

11. If Kirchhoff's first rule did *not* hold at a junction in a network, what would happen?

12. Is there any relation between Kirchhoff's second rule and the line integral relation $\oint \mathscr{E} \cdot d\mathbf{l} = 0$ that we used in electrostatics?

13. Compare the Wheatstone bridge method of measuring resistance with the so-called volt-meter-ammeter method of measuring resis-tance.

14. Show that if we know all EMF's and all resistances in a multi-loop circuit, we can determine the current in every branch of the circuit.

PROBLEMS

1. (a) What must be the value of R_1 in the diagram if the current supplied to the load at the right of line AA is to be 0.250 A? (b) What is the power supplied to the load? (c) What are the currents in the resistors R_2, R_3, and R_4?

2. Show that the maximum power is delivered to the load resistor R in Fig. 26.1 for a given battery when $R = r$. Show that the value of this maximum power is $V_E^2/4r$.

3. A 12-V storage battery has an internal resis-tance of 0.2 Ω. A load resistor of resistance R is to be connected between the terminals of the battery. The resistance R can have

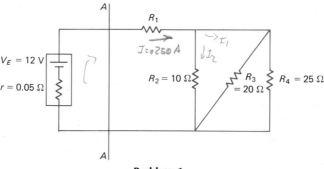

Problem 1

any value from 0 to ∞. (a) What should be the value of R if the current through the resistor is to be a maximum? (b) What should be the value of R if the potential difference between its ends is to be a maximum? (c) What should be the value of R if the power delivered to the resistor is to be a maximum?

4. For the situation of Problem 3, what is the maximum current that the battery can deliver? What is the maximum potential difference that can exist between the ends of the load resistor? What is the maximum power that the battery can deliver to the load resistor?

5. A 24-V generator having an internal resistance of 2.0 Ω is to be used to charge a 12-V battery having an internal resistance of 1.5 Ω. It is desired that the charging current be 0.50 A. (a) What resistance should be placed in series with the battery? (b) What will be the rates of conversion of mechanical energy to electrical energy, of conversion of electrical energy to chemical energy, and of electrical energy dissipation as heat? (c) The current could also be controlled by putting a resistor in parallel with the battery. What resistance should this resistor have? (d) Answer the questions of part (b) for this arrangement. (e) Which arrangement wastes the most energy?

6. A 6-V battery having an internal resistance of 0.75 Ω is driving a load consisting of a motor and a 5-Ω resistor in series. The motor has an internal resistance of 2 Ω and is lifting a 5-kg mass at the steady rate of 1.5 cm/s. What is the current supplied by the battery?

What is the terminal potential difference of the motor?

7. (a) What are the EMF and internal resistance of the single battery that is equivalent so far as external connections are concerned to two batteries of EMFs V_{E1} and V_{E2} and internal resistances r_1 and r_2, respectively, if the batteries are connected in parallel? (b) Evaluate the EMF and internal resistance of the equivalent battery for the particular case where $V_{E1} = 10$ V, $V_{E2} = 12$ V, $r_1 = 0.1$ Ω, and $r_2 = 0.1$ Ω. (c) If the load resistance is 20 Ω, compare the energy dissipated as heat in the equivalent battery with the energy dissipated as heat in the two batteries connected in parallel. (d) Why is the parallel arrangement likely to be an unwise connection?

8. Repeat Problem 7 for the case of two batteries connected in series.

9. A 120-V generator and a 96-V battery, both having negligible internal resistance, are connected in a circuit as shown in the diagram. What is the current through the 40-Ω resistor? What is the current through the 30-Ω resistor? What is the current through the 20-Ω resistor? What is the potential at point P in the diagram?

10. For the situation of Problem 9, how much power is dissipated in the circuit? What fraction of this power is furnished by the generator? What fraction of the power is supplied by the battery?

11. In the circuit shown in the diagram we wish to replace the 40-Ω resistor by another resistor such that the generator will then fur-

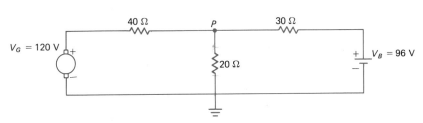

Problems 9–13

nish *all* the current delivered to the 20-Ω resistor. Is this possible? If so, what should be the resistance of the replacement resistor? How much power is delivered to the 20-Ω resistor when this new resistor is inserted in the circuit?

12. In the circuit shown in the diagram we wish to replace the 40-Ω resistor with another resistor such that the battery will then furnish one third of the current delivered to the 20-Ω resistor. What should be the resistance of the replacement resistor? How much power is delivered to the 20-Ω resistor when this new resistor is inserted in the circuit?

13. In the circuit shown in the diagram we wish to replace the 40-Ω resistor with another resistor such that the generator and the battery will then deliver equal amounts of current to the 20-Ω resistor. What should be the resistance of the replacement resistor? How much power is delivered to the 20-Ω resistor when this new resistor is inserted in the circuit?

14. A 12-V battery of negligible internal resistance is connected between points A and B of the resistance network shown for Problem 18 in Chapter 25. Find the current in each of the resistors. How much power is dissipated in each of the resistors? Confirm that the total power dissipated is given by VI, where $V = 12$ V and I is the total current supplied to the resistance network by the battery.

15. If switch S_1 is open so that the 50-Ω resistor R_1 is removed from the circuit shown in the diagram, what is the potential of point C?

16. In the circuit shown in the diagram for Problem 15 switch S_1 is open and battery 1 is replaced by a new battery having the same internal resistance but a larger EMF. It is then found that battery 2 is being charged with a current of 0.500 A. (a) What is the new value of V_{E1}? (b) What is the potential

of point C? (c) Verify that the rate at which battery 1 supplies electrical energy equals the rate at which heat is developed in the load resistors plus the rate at which electrical energy is delivered to battery 2.

17. What are the values of the branch currents for the circuit shown in the diagram for Problem 15 when switch S_1 is closed? Show that the rate at which heat is generated in the load resistors is equal to the net rate at which the batteries develop electrical energy.

18. Explain clearly why one of the equations obtained by applying Kirchhoff's First Rule to the junctions of a multiloop circuit is redundant.

19. Two generators of negligible internal resistance supply current to loads A and B as shown in the diagram. Find the potential differences V_A and V_B and all the unknown branch currents.

20. It is easy to devise connections of resistors that cannot be simplified by use of the rules for series and parallel combinations. Such an arrangement is shown in the diagram. However, an equivalent resistance can be found by determining what single resistor would draw the same current as the combination when they are independently connected between the terminals of a battery. What is the equivalent resistance of the combination of resistors shown in the diagram? What is the equivalent resistance if the 8-Ω resistor is removed? Why are the two results not very different?

21. Repeat Problem 20 if R_1 is replaced by a 50-Ω resistor.

22. For the circuit shown in Fig. 26.6, to what value should R_5 be changed in order to make $I_1 = 0.25$ A?

23. In the circuit shown in Fig. 26.6, suppose that the battery of EMF $V_{E2} = 12$ V is removed and replaced by a resistor. What should be the resistance of this resistor if we want to have $I_4 = -1.55$ A?

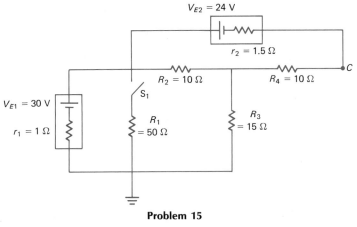

Problem 15

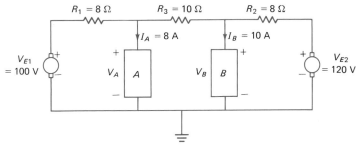

Problem 19

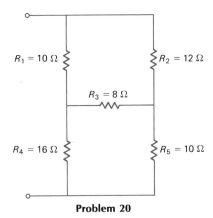

Problem 20

24. In the circuit shown for Problems 15–17, a 12-V battery of internal resistance 0.5 Ω and a 17-Ω resistor are connected in series between point *C* and ground. The positive terminal of the battery is connected to *C*; switch S₁ is closed. Find the currents in all the branches of the circuit.

25. Suppose we have a galvanometer with a resistance of 50 Ω and requiring a current of 5 mA for full-scale deflection. (a) What multiplier resistance should be used to convert the galvanometer into a voltmeter reading 50 V at full scale? 100 V at full scale? (b) What shunt resistor should be used to con-

vert the galvanometer into an ammeter reading 5 A at full scale? 10 A at full scale?

26. Shown in the diagram is a circuit for a multiscale voltmeter having full-scale readings of 3 V, 15 V, and 150 V for the three settings of the switch. If $R_g = 25$ Ω and $I_G = 3$ mA, what are the required values for R_1, R_2, and R_3?

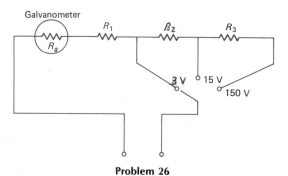

Problem 26

27. Shown in the diagram is a circuit for a multiscale ammeter having full-scale readings of 0.1 A, 1 A, and 10 A for the three settings of the switch. If $R_g = 20$ Ω and $I_G = 2$ mA, what are the required values of R_1, R_2, and R_3?

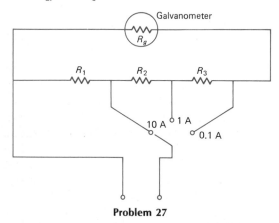

Problem 27

28. The internal resistance of a dry cell increases with age; the EMF is approximately constant at 1.5 V. A dry cell can be tested for aging by measuring the short-circuit current with an ammeter. For a fresh dry cell this current will be about 30 A. What is the correspond-

ing internal resistance of the dry cell? Assume that the ammeter resistance is 10^{-3} Ω. Why would it not be wise to check for aging by measuring the terminal potential difference of the dry cell with a good voltmeter?

29. The diagram shows two arrangements for use of a voltmeter and an ammeter to determine the resistance of a resistor. In either arrangement, if the voltmeter and ammeter were "perfect" instruments that did not disturb the circuit to which they are connected, the resistance would be given by $R = V_M/I_M$, where V_M and I_M are the voltmeter and ammeter readings, respectively. Find an expression for the true resistance in terms of the voltmeter and ammeter readings and the resistances of the voltmeter and the ammeter for circuit A. Show that the simple formula given above is acceptable only if the voltmeter resistance is much larger than the resistance being measured.

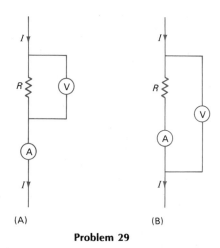

Problem 29

30. Repeat Problem 29 for circuit B. Show that the simple formula $R = V_M/I_M$ is acceptable only if the ammeter resistance is much smaller than the resistance being measured.

31. A voltmeter having a resistance of 1000 Ω is connected across the terminals of an unknown resistor. This combination is connected in series with an ammeter to a source of EMF. When the ammeter reads 0.02 A

the voltmeter reads 4.0 V. What is the resistance of the unknown resistor?

32. The diagram shows an arrangement for calibrating a precision voltmeter by use of a potentiometer. Discuss the operation of this circuit. Why is the resistance R_D called a "voltage divider"? Why is it necessary to require a *steady* DC source? Why is it not likely that one would use this method to calibrate ordinary laboratory voltmeters? What factors determine the accuracy of the calibration?

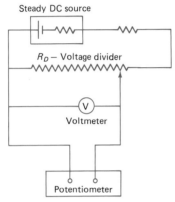

Problem 32

33. The diagram shows an arrangement for calibrating a precision ammeter by use of a potentiometer. Discuss the operation of this circuit. Why is it necessary to require a *steady* DC source? Why is it not likely that one would use this method to calibrate ordinary laboratory ammeters? What factors determine the accuracy of the calibration?

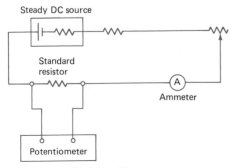

Problem 33

34. Devise a method for measuring precisely the EMF and the internal resistance of a battery. You have voltmeters, ammeters, galvanometers, potentiometers, standard resistors, Wheatstone bridges, and ohmmeters.

35. It is noted in the text that the resistor R_S in Fig. 26.10 is present to protect the galvanometer from excess current. (a) Explain clearly how this resistor protects the galvanometer. Where should the sliding contact C be set at different stages of the measurement? (b) Could this same arrangement be used to protect the galvanometer in Fig. 26.9? If so, draw a diagram showing the modification of the circuit and describe how the sliding contact should be set at different stages of the measurement. (c) Would this arrangement simultaneously protect the standard cell in Fig. 26.9? Discuss. (d) Since the final setting is at zero current through the galvanometer, why not protect the standard cell in Fig. 26.9 simply by putting a very large fixed resistance in series with it?

36. If the Wheatstone Bridge in Fig. 26.10 is balanced when $R_A = 100.0$ Ω, $R_B = 50.0$ Ω, and $R_C = 82.6$ Ω, what is the unknown resistance R_U?

37. For the Wheatstone Bridge of Fig. 26.10 the variable resistor R_C is initially set on 200 Ω, all other resistances being as in Problem 36. The battery has an EMF of 6 V and negligible internal resistance; the resistance in series with the battery is 25 Ω. The galvanometer has a resistance of 20 Ω; the resistance of R_S is 1000 Ω. (a) What is the current through the galvanometer when S_1 and S_2 are closed and the contact C is set all the way to the left? (b) What is the current through the galvanometer when S_1 and S_2 are closed and the contact C is set all the way to the right?

38. A two-wire underwater power cable of length 15,850 m runs across a bay. Each wire has a resistance of 0.3225 Ω per thousand meters. One wire becomes shorted to the lead sheath at some point. In order to determine the loca-

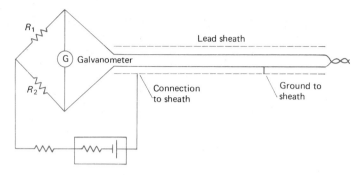

Problem 38

tion of the short, the two wires are connected together at the far end and the bridge circuit shown in the diagram is set up. The bridge is balanced when $R_1 = 15.00$ Ω and $R_2 = 7.63$ Ω. Where is the defect?

39. A basic series-type ohmmeter circuit is shown in the diagram. The galvanometer has a resistance of 27 Ω and requires a current of 1.5 mA for full-scale deflection; the battery has an EMF of 3 V and an internal resistance of 0.05 Ω. The value of the series resistor R_S is chosen so that when points x and y are connected by a wire of negligible resistance, the galvanometer reads full scale; this pointer position is labeled $R = 0$. When there is an open circuit between points x and y the galvanometer shows zero deflection; this pointer position is labeled $R = \infty$. (a) What should be the value of R_S? (b) What resistance R connected between points x and y will cause half-scale deflection of the galvanometer? (c) Quarter-scale deflection? (d) Three-quarter-scale deflection?

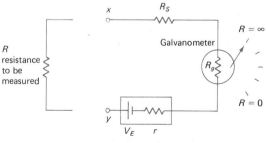

Problem 39

40. Suppose that in the Wheatstone Bridge considered in Problem 36 all the resistors are made of copper and the balance described is attained at 0°C. What is the unknown resistance R_U if the temperature is raised to 100°C? Will the bridge still be balanced at this higher temperature? Explain your reasoning.

Note: The charging and discharging of a capacitor are not instantaneous. The circuit shown in the diagram serves to illustrate the processes involved. A capacitor C, a resistor R, and a source of EMF V_E are connected in a circuit equipped with a key. With the key in position ①, the capacitor eventually receives a charge $Q = CV_E$; with the key in position ②, the charge on the capacitor plates eventually falls to zero.

41. After the key has been in position ① in the diagram for a long time, we shift the key to position ②. With the key in Position ②, the loop equation is $V_C + V_R = 0$; with $I = dQ/dt$ this is $Q/C + R\, dQ/dt = 0$. Solve this equation by separation of the variables Q and t. Remembering that $Q_0 = CV_E$ at $t = 0$ and $Q = 0$ at $t = \infty$, show that the solution can be written in the form $Q = Q_0 e^{-t/\tau}$ with $\tau = RC$. When t is equal to the *time constant* τ, $Q = Q_0/e \approx 0.37Q_0$. Obtain an expression for the current I as a function of time. Make plots of Q, I, and the energy W_C stored in the capacitor as functions of time.

42. For the process of discharge described in Problem 41 with $V_E = 1200$ V, $C = 6$ μF, and $R = 1$ MΩ, compute the values of Q, I, and W_C at $t = 6$ s.

43. After the key has been in position ② for a long time, the charge on the capacitor plates is zero. If we then shift the key to position ①, the loop equation becomes $V_C + V_R = V_E$; with $I = dQ/dt$ this is $Q/C + R\,dQ/dt = V_E$. By separation of the variables Q and t solve the loop equation for Q as a function of time. With $Q = 0$ at $t = 0$ and $Q = CV_E$ at $t = \infty$, show that the solution is $Q = CV_E(1 - e^{-t/\tau})$ with the time constant $\tau = RC$. Obtain an expression for the current as a function of time. Make plots of Q, I, and stored energy W_C as functions of time.

44. With the values of V_E, C, and R listed in Problem 42, find the values of Q, I, and W_C for the charging process described in Problem 43 at time $t = 6$ s after the key has been switched to position ①. What are the initial and final values of the voltage difference V_R between the ends of the resistor and the voltage difference V_C between the plates of the capacitor?

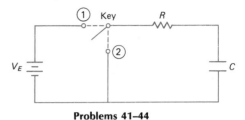

Problems 41–44

CHAPTER 27

The Magnetic Field

Magnetism was known to the ancients in the form of naturally occurring permanent magnets of lodestone (magnetite). The word "magnetism" itself comes from the district of Magnesia in Asia Minor, where the Greeks found an abundance of lodestone. The magnetic compass was in use in China at least by the end of the eleventh century and in Europe 100 years later.

The scientific study of magnetism began with investigations of the properties of permanent magnets. The force and torque that one magnet exerts on another were analyzed; the concept of "magnetic poles" that would have a role in magnetism analogous to that of positive and negative electric charge in electricity was developed, and experiments involving magnets similar to Coulomb's experiment on electrostatic forces suggested that an inverse-square relation describes how the force between two magnetic poles depends on the distance of pole separation. However, there were puzzling differences between the properties of magnetism and of electricity. Every permanent magnet appeared to have two poles of opposite sign. It proved impossible to produce a magnetic charge by simple rubbing, and no way was found to magnetize an object with an excess of one kind of magnetic pole, as could easily be done for electric charge. There was nothing in the field of magnetism corresponding to the behavior of conductors and insulators in electricity.

There was considerable speculation concerning the possibility of some connection between electricity and magnetism; by the end of the eighteenth century the time was ripe for remarkably rapid developments in the understanding of magnetism. The impetus for this period of growth in experimental and theoretical knowledge came in 1820 when Hans Christian Oersted (1777–1851) of the University of Copenhagen announced the observation of forces exerted on a magnet placed in the vicinity of a current-carrying wire. This was the first clear demonstration of a connection between phenomena of electricity and magnetism. Within six years a complete theory of the magnetic effects associated with *steady* currents had been developed; this theory is still in use today. The primary contributors to this development were the French physicists Jean-Baptiste Biot (1774–1862) and Félix Savart (1791–1841), who together investigated the forces exerted by currents on magnets, and André-Marie Ampère, who investigated the forces exerted by one current on another.

The present view is that *all magnetic phenomena are to be explained ultimately in terms of interactions between electric charges in relative motion.* This general idea was proposed by Ampère, but it required the development of modern quantum theory before the proposal could be confirmed in detail. There continues to be serious speculation concerning the possible existence of a free "magnetic pole" that would be the analogue of a particle having an electric charge, and various kinds of experimental schemes have been used to attempt to detect such objects. However, up to the present no convincing evidence for the reality of magnetic poles has been obtained. If such objects do exist, they are very rare in our part of the universe.

27.1 THE MAGNETIC FIELD

In our study of electrostatics we found it convenient to introduce the concept of an electric field. Charges are considered as sources of an electric field $\mathscr{E}$, and other charges in the vicinity respond to the electric field existing at their location. The same kind of viewpoint will be used in our treatment of magnetism. We consider permanent magnets and currents as sources of a magnetic field $\mathscr{B}$. The earth itself is a large magnet; its magnetic field is familiar to anyone who has used a magnetic compass for navigation or orientation. We shall defer to later chapters a discussion of how magnetic fields are related to the various sources that generate them. In the present chapter we shall consider how the strength of the field at a given location can be defined quantitatively and how the interaction of the field with moving charges and with currents can be calculated.

The experimental observations from which the present theory of magnetism evolved concerned forces between pairs of magnets, forces between magnets and current-carrying wires, and forces between pairs of current-carrying wires. However, in making a definition of the magnetic-field strength we shall use the conceptually simpler and theoretically more basic interaction between a magnetic field and a single moving point charge.

In Chapter 21 we discussed the idea of a test charge being small enough that its presence does not disturb the sources of the field being measured. We then defined the electric-field strength $\mathscr{E}$ as the force per unit charge on a test charge *at rest* at the point in question. Suppose that after determining the force on a positive test charge q_0 at rest, we redetermine the force on the test charge when it moves through the same point with various velocities. If the point is close to a magnet or a current-carrying conductor, we would find that the force is different from that when the charge is at rest and that it depends on both the speed and the direction of motion of the test charge. Let **F** be the resultant force on the test charge. The electric force that is measured when the test charge is at rest is $q_0\mathscr{E}$; the force that exists because of the motion of the test charge is $\mathbf{F}_{\mathscr{B}} = \mathbf{F} - q_0\mathscr{E}$.

There is one axis for which $\mathbf{F}_{\mathscr{B}}$ is zero if the velocity **v** of the test charge is parallel to the axis in either direction. We take this axis to define the direction of the magnetic

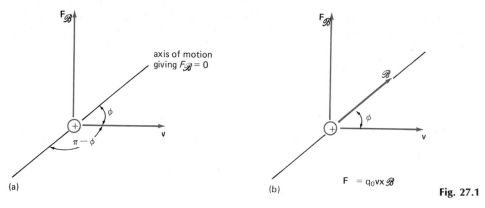

$$F = q_0 v \times \mathscr{B}$$

Fig. 27.1

field $\mathscr{B}$, except that we must still establish which way the $\mathscr{B}$ vector points along the axis. If $\mathbf{v}$ is not along this special axis, we find that $\mathbf{F}_\mathscr{B}$ is perpendicular to the plane formed by the axis and the velocity vector, as shown in Fig. 27.1a. The magnitude of $\mathbf{F}_\mathscr{B}$ is directly proportional to the speed v, the magnitude of the test charge q_0, and the sine of the angle ϕ between $\mathbf{v}$ and the axis giving the direction of $\mathscr{B}$. Since $\sin \phi = \sin(\pi - \phi)$, this does not distinguish one direction along the axis from the other. However, the results of our experiment make the following choice possible. We *define* the magnetic-field strength $\mathscr{B}$ to be such that the force $\mathbf{F}_\mathscr{B}$ that exists because of the motion of the test charge is given by

$$\mathbf{F}_\mathscr{B} = q_0\, \mathbf{v} \times \mathscr{B}. \qquad \begin{Bmatrix} q_0 \text{ in C} \\ \mathbf{v} \ \text{ in m/s} \\ \mathscr{B} \text{ in T} \end{Bmatrix} \qquad (27.1)$$

Here the symbol $\times$ represents the vector product that was defined in Section 7.7. Using the right-hand rule for the direction of the vector product of two vectors, we find that the direction of $\mathscr{B}$ for the situation of Fig. 27.1a must be as shown in Fig. 27.1b. Note that although this procedure uniquely defines the magnetic-field strength $\mathscr{B}$, we cannot "solve" (1) so that it reads "$\mathscr{B}$ equals something." Why?

If we use a negative test charge having the same velocity $\mathbf{v}$, we find that $\mathbf{F}_\mathscr{B}$ has the same magnitude but is reversed in direction. Equation (27.1) holds for both positive and negative charges if we give q_0 an algebraic sign $+$ or $-$.

The dimensions of $\mathscr{B}$ implied by (27.1) are those of force divided by charge times speed. In the SI this unit is $\mathrm{N/C \cdot (m/s)} = \mathrm{kg/C \cdot s}$. This combination is given the special name tesla (T) in honor of Nikola Tesla (1856–1943), an electrical engineer and inventor of Serbian parentage who did much of his work in the United States. We thus measure $\mathscr{B}$ in teslas (T), where $1 \text{ T} = 1 \text{ kg/C} \cdot \text{s}$.

There is no consensus on the name to be used for the field vector $\mathscr{B}$. We have chosen to use terms that parallel those used to describe $\mathscr{E}$.

The *resultant force* acting on a moving test charge q_0 including both electric and magnetic contributions is given by

$$\mathbf{F} = q_0(\mathscr{E} + \mathbf{v} \times \mathscr{B}). \quad (\textit{Lorentz Force}) \qquad (27.2)$$

where $\mathscr{E}$ and $\mathscr{B}$ are the electric- and magnetic-field strengths at the instantaneous position of the charge q_0 where its velocity is **v**. This is often called the Lorentz force equation in honor of the Dutch theoretical physicist Hendrik Antoon Lorentz (1853–1928), who did much to extend and develop classical electromagnetic theory.

27.2   MAGNETIC LINES; MAGNETIC FLUX

A convenient way of visualizing a magnetic field is to use *magnetic lines* that are analogous to the electric lines defined in Chapter 21. A magnetic line is a continuous, directed line that at any point is tangent to the magnetic-field strength $\mathcal{B}$ at the point. In order to represent the magnitude as well as the direction of $\mathcal{B}$, the magnetic lines can be drawn so that the number of lines per unit area through a small-area element oriented perpendicular to the local magnetic-field direction is proportional to the magnitude of the magnetic-field strength $\mathcal{B}$. In regions where $\mathcal{B}$ is large, the magnetic lines are close together; in regions where $\mathcal{B}$ is small, the magnetic lines are far apart. It is not obvious that it is possible to draw a set of continuous lines that meets these requirements. However, a proof of this assertion can be constructed for steady-current sources based on relations that we shall develop in the next chapter.

In contrast to electric lines, there are no magnetic charges on which magnetic lines begin or end. Rather, magnetic lines form *closed loops* or else extend to infinity. Also in contrast to electric lines, the magnetic lines do not represent the direction of the magnetic force on a test charge. Rather, the magnetic force on a test charge as given by (27.1) is perpendicular to the magnetic line at the charge location and to the velocity **v** of the charge.

The flux of a magnetic field through a surface S is defined in the same way as the flux of an electric field through a surface was defined in Chapter 23. As suggested in Fig. 27.2, the flux through an element of surface represented by the vector $d\mathbf{S}$ is $d\Phi_{\mathcal{B}} = \mathcal{B} \cdot d\mathbf{S} = \mathcal{B} \cos \theta \, dS$. For the total flux through the surface S we have

$$\Phi_{\mathcal{B}} = \iint_{S} \mathcal{B} \cdot d\mathbf{S}. \qquad \begin{Bmatrix} \Phi_{\mathcal{B}} \text{ in Wb} \\ \mathcal{B} \ \text{ in T} \\ S \ \ \text{ in m}^2 \end{Bmatrix} \qquad (27.3)$$

As in Chapter 23, the surface S may be either open or closed. However, because there are no magnetic charges on which magnetic lines can begin or end, the magnetic flux through any *closed* surface is zero. Can you prove that this is true?

The SI unit of magnetic flux, which is the $T \cdot m^2$, has its own special name. It is called the weber (Wb) in honor of the German physicist Wilhelm Weber (1804–1891). Thus, 1 Wb = 1 $T \cdot m^2$. The unit Wb/m^2 and the name "flux density" are often used for magnetic-field strength.

27.3   MOTION OF CHARGED PARTICLES IN UNIFORM MAGNETIC FIELDS

The Lorentz force equation (27.2) when combined with Newton's Second Principle $\mathbf{F}_R = m\mathbf{a}$ provides a way to determine the trajectory of a particle of given charge and mass that is released with a given initial velocity in a region where the electric-

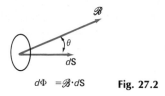

$$d\Phi = \mathscr{B} \cdot d\mathbf{S}$$ **Fig. 27.2**

and magnetic-field strengths are known as functions of position. The velocity $\mathbf{v}$ is always in the direction of the instantaneous motion of the particle. Since by the nature of the vector product the magnetic force $\mathbf{F}_{\mathscr{B}} = q_0 \mathbf{v} \times \mathscr{B}$ is perpendicular to the velocity, we conclude that *the magnetic force can do no work to a charged particle* since there is no force component in the direction of particle displacement. The magnetic force can change the direction of motion of a charged particle, but it cannot transfer energy to or from the particle and therefore cannot directly change the kinetic energy or the speed of the particle.

Consider a positively charged particle of mass m and charge q traveling with a velocity $\mathbf{v}$ that enters a region where there is a *uniform* magnetic field $\mathscr{B}$ directed perpendicular to $\mathbf{v}$, as shown in Fig. 27.3. We assume that this region is suitably evacuated so that the charged particle does not undergo collisions with molecules of air or other material. At point ① where the particle enters the field, the force given by (27.1) is downward in Fig. 27.3, perpendicular to both $\mathbf{v}$ and $\mathscr{B}$. This force can change the direction but not the magnitude of $\mathbf{v}$. At a slightly later time the particle is at point ②, and $\mathbf{F}_{\mathscr{B}}$ has the direction shown, still perpendicular to both $\mathbf{v}$ and $\mathscr{B}$. Since the field $\mathscr{B}$ is assumed uniform and the speed v is not changed by the magnetic force, the forces $\mathbf{F}_{\mathscr{B}1}$ and $\mathbf{F}_{\mathscr{B}2}$ both have the same magnitude $qv\mathscr{B}$.

We learned in Chapter 4 that a force of constant magnitude always perpendicular to the velocity of a particle will cause the particle to move so that its path is a circular arc. The radius R of the arc is determined by the condition that the magnitude of the force is the centripetal force required for motion of a particle of mass m on a circle of radius R with speed v. This condition gives

$$qv\mathscr{B} = mv^2/R,$$

so that

$$R = mv/q\mathscr{B}. \tag{27.4}$$

If a charged particle is somehow introduced into a region of uniform magnetic field far from the edges of the field region and $\mathbf{v}$ is perpendicular to $\mathscr{B}$, the path of

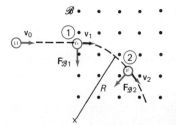

Fig. 27.3 A charged particle entering a region where there is a uniform magnetic field perpendicular to its velocity traverses a circular arc. The dots represent a magnetic field directed up out of the plane of the paper.

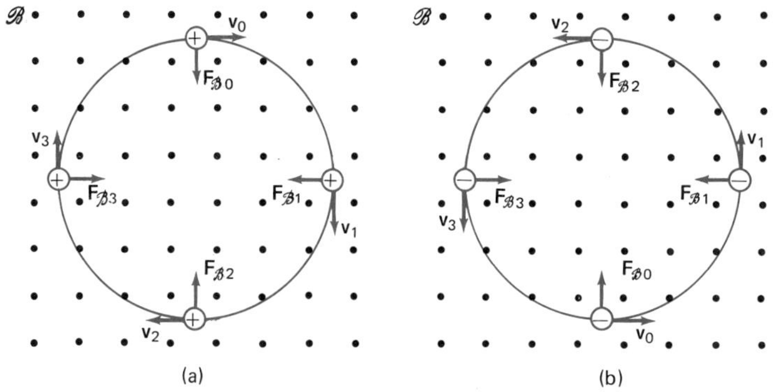

Fig. 27.4 (a) Path of a positive charge moving perpendicularly to a uniform magnetic field. (b) Path of a negative charge moving perpendicularly to a uniform magnetic field. The dots represent a magnetic field directed up out of the plane of the paper.

the particle will be a circle of radius R given by (27.4), as suggested in Fig. 27.4. The time required to make one trip around the circle is

$$T = 2\pi R/v = 2\pi m/q\mathscr{B}, \tag{27.5}$$

and the frequency of the circular motion is

$$f = 1/T = q\mathscr{B}/2\pi m. \tag{27.6}$$

We note that (27.5) and (27.6) do not depend on either the speed v or the radius R. Higher-speed particles go around a circle of larger radius in the same time that lower-speed particles go around a circle of smaller radius.

If the particle has a negative charge, the direction of the force $\mathbf{F}_{\mathscr{B}}$ is reversed. Equations (27.4)–(27.6) still hold if we take the symbol q to represent the magnitude of the charge, but the negative particle traverses a circle in the opposite sense from a positive particle, as shown in Fig. 27.4.

In a more general situation, a charged particle introduced into a region where there is a uniform magnetic field will have a component of its velocity parallel to the field direction. We can resolve the velocity $\mathbf{v}$ of the charged particle into component vectors $\mathbf{v}_{\parallel}$ parallel to $\mathscr{B}$ and $\mathbf{v}_{\perp}$ perpendicular to $\mathscr{B}$, as shown in Fig. 27.5. By (27.1) the magnetic force on the particle is perpendicular to both $\mathscr{B}$ and $\mathbf{v}_{\perp}$ and has magnitude of $qv_{\perp}\mathscr{B}$. If $v_{\parallel}$ were zero, this force would cause the particle to travel in a circle of radius $R = mv_{\perp}/q\mathscr{B}$. The presence of $\mathbf{v}_{\parallel}$ causes a steady motion parallel to $\mathscr{B}$ to be superimposed on the circular motion. The resultant motion follows a helical path wrapped around the magnetic lines, as indicated in Fig. 27.5. The time required for the particle to traverse one turn of the helix is given by (27.5): $T = 2\pi m/q\mathscr{B}$. The distance that the particle moves parallel to the direction of $\mathscr{B}$ in this time and therefore the pitch of the helix is $v_{\parallel}2\pi m/q\mathscr{B}$.

27.4 MOTION OF CHARGED PARTICLES IN SUPERPOSED $\mathscr{E}$ AND $\mathscr{B}$ FIELDS: DETERMINATION OF e/m

As an example of the motions of charged particles in both uniform electric and magnetic fields, we shall consider an experiment of considerable historical importance.

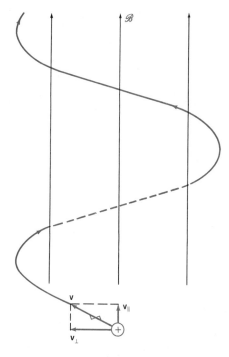

Fig. 27.5   The most general trajectory of a charged particle in a uniform magnetic field is a helical path wrapped around the magnetic lines.

General acceptance of the existence of the electron as a particle of definite charge and mass followed experiments by the English physicist J. J. Thomson (1856–1940) in 1897. Thomson studied the so-called "cathode rays" produced when a large potential difference is applied between the negative cathode C and the positive anode A in an evacuated tube like that shown in Fig. 27.6. The anode A has a small rectangular slot through which the "rays" emitted from the cathode can pass. The screen B is at the same potential as A and has a similar slot. The rays passing through both slots have essentially the same speed, determined by the potential difference between C and A and are traveling in essentially the same direction. If there are no electric or magnetic fields in the region beyond B, the rays travel in a straight line to point P_0, where they reveal their presence by causing a rectangular patch of the glass bulb to fluoresce.

Earlier experiments by Jean Perrin had shown that cathode rays carry negative charge down the tube. Thomson treated the rays as a beam of negatively charged particles of charge $-e$ and mass m. In his experiments, Thomson analyzed the deflection of the beam of particles when it passed through a region where there was a uniform electric field or a uniform magnetic field or both. A uniform electric field directed upward in Fig. 27.6 was obtained by applying a potential difference between

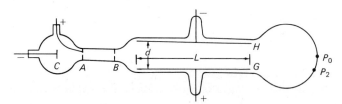

Fig. 27.6   A schematic diagram of Thomson's e/m apparatus.

plates G and H with the upper plate negative. So-called "Helmholtz coils," which we shall describe in the next chapter, were mounted outside the evacuated tube so as to produce a uniform magnetic field directed up out of the paper over the length L of the plates. For the purpose of our analysis we shall assume that the transition between the region of no fields and the region of uniform fields is sharp, and we shall ignore the "fringing" effects that actually exist at the edges of the field region.

In the next paragraphs we shall deduce expressions for the deflection of the beam, first in the presence of a uniform electric field $\mathscr{E}$ and then in the presence of a uniform magnetic field $\mathscr{B}$. In each case our plan is to use the appropriate electric or magnetic force equation plus Newton's Second Principle to determine the coordinates and velocity of the charged particles of the beam at the point P_1 where they leave the field region. Then we use the fact that, in accord with Newton's First Principle, the particles move with constant velocity in the field-free region from P_1 to the end of the evacuated tube to determine the location of the point P_2 where the beam hits the wall of the tube.

When a potential difference V is applied to the plates H and G with plate H negative, the fluorescent spot is found to move to P_2. We shall now determine the deflection y_2 of the fluorescent spot as shown in Fig. 27.7. In order to simplify our computation we shall assume that the end of the evacuated tube is flat rather than rounded. As shown in Fig. 27.7, we choose the X axis to lie along the original beam direction and the Y axis to be perpendiuclar to plates G and H. The electric-field strength that exists between the plates from $x = 0$ to $x = L$ is $\mathscr{E} = (V/d)\mathbf{j}$, and the force on a particle of charge $-e$ due to this field is $\mathbf{F} = -e(V/d)\mathbf{j}$. The particle velocity as it enters the field region is $v_{x0}\mathbf{i}$.

Since there is no force in the X direction, the X component of the particle velocity remains constant as the particle crosses the region between the plates. By Newton's Second Principle $F_y = ma_y = m(dv_y/dt)$ we have for the Y component of the motion that

$$-e(V/d) = m\, dv_y/dt,$$

so $v_y = -(e/m)(V/d)t + c$, where c is a constant of integration. Since at time $t = 0$ when the particle is at the origin we have $v_y = 0$, the constant c must be zero. By the definition of velocity $v_y = dy/dt$; therefore, we have

$$dy/dt = -(e/m)(V/d)t,$$

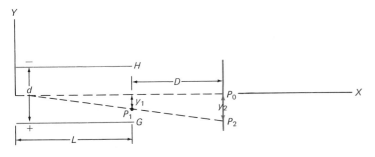

Fig. 27.7 Electric deflection of a negative charged-particle beam.

from which it follows that $y = -(e/m)(V/d)t^2/2$, where we have used the condition $y(t = 0) = 0$ to evaluate the constant of integration.

Since the particle moves with constant velocity $v_{x0}\mathbf{i}$ in the X direction, the time at which it reaches $x = L$ is $t_1 = L/v_{x0}$. Therefore, the coordinates of the particle as it emerges from the field region are $x_1 = L$ and $y_1 = -(e/m)(V/d)(L/v_{x0})^2/2$, and its velocity at this point is $\mathbf{v}_1 = v_{x0}\mathbf{i} - (e/m)(V/d)(L/v_{x0})\mathbf{j}$.

From P_1 to P_2 the particle experiences no force and therefore travels in a straight line with constant velocity. The time required to travel from the edge of the field at $x_1 = L$ to the end of the tube at $x_2 = L + D$ is $\delta t = D/v_{x0}$. It follows from the Y motion between P_1 and P_2 with constant velocity that $y_2 - y_1 = -(e/m)(V/d)(L/v_{x0})\delta t$ or

$$y_2 = -(e/m)(V/d)(L/v_{x0}^2)(D + L/2). \qquad (\textit{Electric Deflection}) \qquad (27.7)$$

An alternative way to produce deflection of the particle beam is to generate a uniform magnetic field $\mathcal{B}$ in the region between $x = 0$ and $x = L$. The deflection under this condition for negative particles of charge $-e$ and mass m when the magnetic field is directed up out of the paper is shown in Fig. 27.8. From the discussion leading to (27.4) we know that the particle trajectory between $x = 0$ and $x = L$ is a circular arc of radius $R = mv_{x0}/e\mathcal{B}$. The center of this arc is on the Y axis, as shown in Fig. 27.8. Can you explain why this is so?

An equation representing the circular path from the origin to P_1 is $R^2 = x^2 + (y - R)^2$, which can be rearranged to read $y = R \pm \sqrt{R^2 - x^2}$. At P_1 we have $x_1 = L$; therefore, the Y coordinate of this point satisfies $y_1 = R \pm \sqrt{R^2 - L^2}$. We can see from Fig. 27.8 that $y_1 < R$, so the minus sign in this expression for y_1 gives the physically acceptable result

$$y_1 = R - \sqrt{R^2 - L^2}.$$

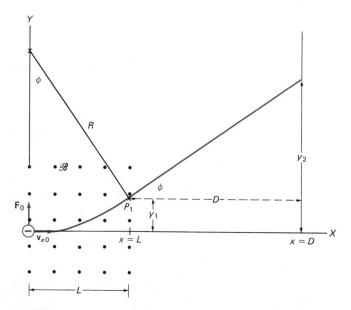

Fig. 27.8 Magnetic deflection of a negative charged-particle beam. The dots represent a magnetic field directed up out of the plane of the paper.

From P_1 to P_2 the particle moves in a straight line with constant velocity. Since the magnetic force can change the direction but not the magnitude of the particle velocity, we know that the particle speed from P_1 to P_2 is just v_{x0}. From the geometrical relations shown in Fig. 27.7 we see that

$$\tan \phi = L/(R - y_1) \quad \text{and} \quad \tan \phi = (y_2 - y_1)/D.$$

Therefore, we have

$$y_2 = DL/(R - y_1) + y_1 = (DL + Ry_1 - y_1^2)/(R - y_1).$$

Upon inserting the value of y_1 determined above we obtain

$$
\begin{aligned}
y_2 &= \frac{DL + R^2 - R\sqrt{R^2 - L^2} - R^2 + 2R\sqrt{R^2 - L^2} - R^2 + L^2}{R - R + \sqrt{R^2 - L^2}} \\
&= \frac{DL + R^2\sqrt{1 - L^2/R^2} - R^2 + L^2}{R\sqrt{1 - L^2/R^2}} \cdot \quad \text{(Magnetic Deflection)}
\end{aligned}
\tag{27.8}
$$

In a practical situation the deflection angle ϕ will be small, and R will be much larger than L. In this case we can simplify our result for y_2 by writing the identity $(1 - L^2/R^2) = (1 - L^2/2R^2)^2 - (L^4/4R^4)$ and neglecting the small quantity $L^4/4R^4$. We then have

$$y_2 \approx \frac{DL + R^2(1 - L^2/2R^2) - R^2 + L^2}{R(1 - L^2/2R^2)} = \frac{DL + L^2/2}{R(1 - L^2/2R^2)} \cdot$$

If we use the relation for R obtained from (27.4) and in the denominator neglect the quantity $L^2/2R^2$ that is small compared with 1, we obtain

$$y_2 \approx (e\mathscr{B}L/mv_{x0})(D + L/2). \quad \text{(Magnetic Deflection)} \tag{27.8'}$$

If we knew the initial speed v_{x0} of the charged particles, we could use (27.7) or (27.8') to determine the ratio e/m from the known geometry of the tube, the measured deflection of the beam y_2, and the magnitude of the electric- or magnetic-field strength. The fact that the fluorescent spot produced by the deflected beam is essentially the same size as that produced at P_0 in the absence of deflecting forces shows that the charged particles all have essentially the same speed when they leave B in Fig. 27.5. In order to determine the magnitude of this speed, Thomson applied the electric and magnetic fields simultaneously and adjusted the field strengths until the beam was undeflected, the fluorescent spot being at the same location P_0 as without any fields. If the beam is undeflected, the resultant force on a charged particle of the beam must be zero. This requires that the electric and magnetic forces, which have opposite directions, be equal in magnitude:

$$e\mathscr{E} = ev_{x0}\mathscr{B} \quad \text{or} \quad v_{x0} = \mathscr{E}/\mathscr{B}. \tag{27.9}$$

A device in which electric and magnetic fields are applied simultaneously in this manner to allow undeviated passage of charged particles of a certain velocity is known as a *velocity selector*.

Thomson used (27.9) together with deflection measurements in (27.7) and (27.8) to determine the value of e/m, which he showed was independent of the metal used for the electrodes and the kind of residual gas in the tube. This marked the beginning of general acceptance of the explanation of cathode rays as being a beam of the charged particles that we now call electrons. The modern value of e/m for electrons is 1.75880×10^{11} C/kg.

Note that throughout our discussion we have not made any reference to gravitational forces. It is easy to show that under typical experimental conditions the deflection of the beam produced by gravitational forces at the surface of the earth is utterly negligible. For simplicity we have also ignored the earth's magnetic field; this must be considered in the design of an actual experiment.

27.5 HALL EFFECT

Direct evidence that a magnetic field exerts a force on the charge carriers in a current-carrying conductor is provided by the results of an experiment first reported by the American physicist E. H. Hall (1855–1938) in 1879. Consider a current I in a flat strip of conductor oriented perpendicular to a uniform magnetic field $\mathscr{B}$ as shown in Fig. 27.9. In the figure we consider both the possibility of positive and the possibility of negative moving charges. In either case, the magnetic force given by (27.1) is directed upward in Fig. 27.9. Thus, for positive moving charges, the top of the conducting strip tends to become positive and the bottom negative, while for negative moving charges these signs are the opposite. A measurement of the Hall potential difference V_H provides a way to determine the sign of the dominant moving charge carriers. Experiment shows that the moving charge carriers in conductors are indeed negative.

As the Hall potential difference develops, there is a separation of positive and negative charges within the metal, and there is an associated electric field $\mathscr{E}_H = V_H/d$ directed from high to low potential. Equilibrium is reached when the resultant

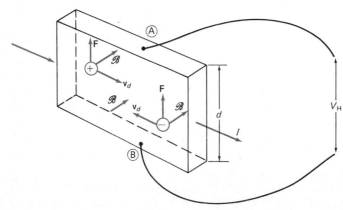

Fig. 27.9 A schematic diagram illustrating the origin of the Hall potential difference V_H.

electromagnetic force $\mathbf{F}_R = \mathbf{F}_{\text{electric}} + \mathbf{F}_{\text{magnetic}}$ on the charge carriers perpendicular to the current direction is zero; this occurs when $|\mathbf{F}_{\text{electric}}| = |\mathbf{F}_{\text{magnetic}}|$, which gives the relation

$$qV_{\text{H}}/d = qv_d\mathscr{B},$$

where q is the charge of the particles moving with drift speed v_d. The current density in the conductor is related to the number of carriers per unit volume n by $I/A = J = nv_d|q|$, where A is the cross-sectional area of the conducting strip. Therefore, we can write

$$V_{\text{H}}/d = (J/n|q|)\mathscr{B} \quad \text{or} \quad n = J\mathscr{B}d/V_{\text{H}}|q|, \tag{27.10}$$

which allows determination of the number of charge carriers per unit volume from measurement of the Hall potential difference.

For metals such as copper, potassium, sodium, and silver that have one conduction electron per atom, the value of n obtained from (27.10) is in reasonably good agreement with the value computed directly from the number of atoms per unit volume. For other metals and for semiconductors our simple drift-velocity picture of the charge carriers is not adequate. A more elaborate model of the material based on quantum mechanics is required for the interpretation of Hall potential difference measurements.

27.6 MOTION OF CHARGED PARTICLES IN NONUNIFORM MAGNETIC FIELDS

A description of the motion of a charged particle is considerably more complicated in a region where the magnetic-field strength varies with position. We shall give a qualitative discussion of one case that has interesting physical applications. Consider a magnetic field that is symmetric about an axis that we take to be the Z axis and varies with position in the manner indicated by the magnetic lines shown in Fig. 27.10. The greater spacing of the magnetic lines in the center of the figure shows that the field strength is smaller in magnitude there than at the left and right edges of the figure where the lines are more closely spaced.

Suppose that at point P_1 of Fig. 27.10 there is a positively charged particle of charge q and mass m having a velocity $\mathbf{v}$ directed down into the paper. As shown in detail in Fig. 27.10b, the magnetic force $\mathbf{F}$ on the particle given by (27.1) has a centripetal component F_c that tends to cause the particle to move on a circular path of radius R about the Z axis and an axial component F_z that accelerates the particle toward the region of lower magnetic-field strength. Since the magnetic force, being always perpendicular to $\mathbf{v}$, cannot change the kinetic energy of the particle, the velocity component perpendicular to the Z axis must decrease in magnitude as the axial component of the velocity increases in magnitude. By (27.4) this will tend to make the radius of the particle's path about the Z axis smaller. However, this tendency is more than compensated by the decrease in $\mathscr{B}$ experienced by the particle as it moves to the right. An analysis that is beyond what we can discuss in this text shows that if the variation of $\mathscr{B}$ over a distance equal to the radius of the particle's path about the Z axis is small, the magnetic flux $\Phi \approx \pi R^2 \mathscr{B}_z$ enclosed by a loop

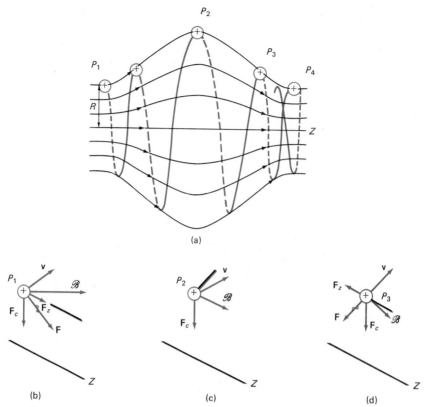

Fig. 27.10   The motion of a charged particle in a nonuniform magnetic field.

of the particle's path is approximately constant. The particle spirals around the surface of a tube of magnetic lines as shown in Fig. 27.10a.

As the particle moves to the right from P_1, the axial acceleration decreases until at P_2 where $\mathscr{B}$ is parallel to the Z axis the axial acceleration is zero. At a point such as P_3 to the right of P_2 the axial acceleration is to the left, as shown in Fig. 27.10d. The velocity component v_z decreases until at P_4 it reaches zero; then the particle begins to spiral back to the left. The particle oscillates back and forth between P_1 and P_4. Because a field of the configuration shown in Fig. 27.10a can trap a charged particle in a definite region of space, the arrangement is called a *magnetic bottle*.

An interesting natural magnetic bottle is provided by the earth's magnetic field. The existence of significant numbers of charged particles spiraling back and forth along tubes of magnetic lines in the earth's magnetic field was first demonstrated by the American physicist J. A. Van Allen (1914–   ) and co-workers in 1958 on the basis of data obtained by instruments carried by rocket-propelled probes and satellites. The nature of the trajectories of such geomagnetically trapped charged particles is shown schematically in Fig. 27.11.

27.7   MAGNETIC FORCE ON A CURRENT ELEMENT

We have noted that among the experimental observations from which the present theory of magnetism evolved were determinations of the forces on current-carrying

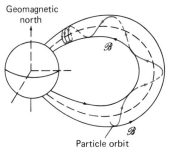

Fig. 27.11 A schematic representation of the motion of a charged particle trapped by the earth's magnetic field. [Adapted from W.G.V. Rosser, *Contemporary Physics* **5**, 198-211 (1964)].

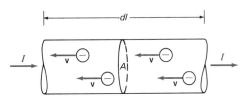

Fig. 27.12 A current element carrying current *I*.

wires caused by magnets or by other currents. We can deduce an expression for the magnetic force on a short segment of current-carrying wire of length *dl*, which we call a *current element,* by considering the magnetic forces on the moving electrons that constitute the current. Because of the interaction of the conduction electrons with the lattice of the metal, the forces on the electrons are transferred to the wire as a whole.

Consider the current element shown in Fig. 27.12 where there are n conduction electrons per unit volume each moving with a drift velocity $\mathbf{v}$ in a wire of cross-sectional area A. Each electron has a charge $-e$; because of the electron drift produced by an EMF there is a current I through the current element in the direction opposite to $\mathbf{v}$. If the current element is in a magnetic field, the force $d\mathbf{F}$ on the current element resulting from the magnetic force (27.1) acting on the individual electrons is $d\mathbf{F} = -enA\,dl\,\mathbf{v} \times \mathscr{B}.$

We introduce a convenient vector representation of the orientation of the current element by defining a vector $d\mathbf{l}$ that has magnitude equal to the length dl of the current element and a direction that coincides with the direction of the current through the current element. We can then write $d\mathbf{F} = enAv\,d\mathbf{l} \times \mathscr{B}.$ In Section 25.1 we showed that env is the magnitude of current density J and $envA$ is the current I through the current element. Thus, we have finally that the magnetic force on the current element is given by

$$d\mathbf{F} = I\,d\mathbf{l} \times \mathscr{B}. \qquad \textit{(Magnetic Force on a Current Element)} \qquad (27.11)$$

The magnetic force on a current element is perpendicular to $\mathscr{B}$ and to $d\mathbf{l}$, as is illustrated in Fig. 27.13.

27.8 MAGNETIC FORCE AND TORQUE ON CURRENT-CARRYING CONDUCTORS

The magnetic force on a current element given by (27.11) cannot be observed in isolation from the rest of the circuit. We shall generally consider situations where there are mechanical forces that act to hold the portion of the circuit that is of interest in a particular geometrical configuration. The resultant magnetic force on this portion of the circuit is then given by the vector sum of the forces $d\mathbf{F}$ given by (27.11) that act on each current element. This sum must extend over all the

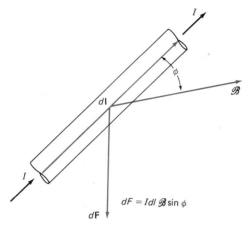

Fig. 27.13 The magnetic force on a current element is perpendicular to $\mathscr{B}$ and to $d\mathbf{l}$.

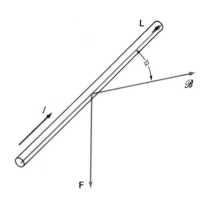

Fig. 27.14 The force on a straight segment of current-carrying conductor in a uniform magnetic field.

current elements making up the portion of circuit being considered. We represent this summation symbolically in the form

$$\mathbf{F} = \int d\mathbf{F} = \int I \, d\mathbf{l} \times \mathscr{B}. \qquad \textit{(Magnetic Force on a Circuit)} \qquad (27.12)$$

In using (27.12) to evaluate the resultant magnetic force we must be sure to use the current I and the magnetic-field strength $\mathscr{B}$ that exist at the particular location of each current element.

We also must think about the "lead wires" that connect the portion of circuit of interest to the battery or generator that is responsible for the current. In some situations the lead wires may be in a region where the magnetic-field strength is negligible. Frequently it is possible to consider the leads to be a pair of wires closely twisted around one another and carrying currents of the same magnitude in opposite directions. Then each current element of one member of the twisted pair is directly beside a current element of the other member of the pair that experiences a force of the same magnitude but in the opposite direction. The resultant magnetic force on the twisted pair is zero.

The simplest kind of extended circuit to which we can apply (27.12) is a single *straight* segment of wire of length L located in a region where there is a *uniform* field $\mathscr{B}$. Since the wire is straight and $\mathscr{B}$ is uniform along its length, the angle ϕ in Fig. 27.13 and the magnitudes $\mathscr{B}$ and I are the same for every current elment, and all the forces $d\mathbf{F}$ are in the same direction. The magnitude of the resultant magnetic force on the wire is

$$F = \int_0^L I\mathscr{B} \sin \phi \, dl = I\mathscr{B} \sin \phi \int_0^L dl = I\mathscr{B}L \sin \phi;$$

the direction of this force is correctly given by the right-hand rule for vector products and this same magnitude is obtained if we write

$$\mathbf{F} = I\,\mathbf{L} \times \mathscr{B}, \qquad (27.13)$$

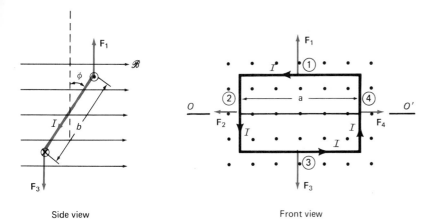

Fig. 27.15   Magnetic forces on the sides of a rectangular current-carrying loop in a uniform magnetic field.

Side view   Front view

where **L** is a displacement vector in the direction of the current from one end of the straight segment of wire to the other end as shown in Fig. 27.14.

Example.   What is the resultant magnetic force on a rectangular circuit having sides of lengths a and b that is oriented at an angle ϕ relative to a uniform magnetic field $\mathscr{B}$ as shown in Fig. 27.15 when the direction of the current I is as shown in the figure? What is the resultant torque due to magnetic forces about the axis OO' shown in the figure?

We use (27.13) four times to determine the magnetic forces acting on the four sides of the rectangle, which are labeled ①, ②, ③, and ④ in Fig. 27.15. The directions of these forces as determined from (27.13) by use of the right-hand rule for vector products are shown in Fig. 27.15. For the magnitudes of these forces we have $F_1 = F_3 = \mathscr{B}Ia \sin 90° = \mathscr{B}Ia$, $F_2 = \mathscr{B}Ib \sin(\pi/2 + \phi) = \mathscr{B}Ib \cos \phi$, and $F_4 = \mathscr{B}Ib \sin(\pi/2 - \phi) = \mathscr{B}Ib \cos \phi$. Thus, $\mathbf{F}_1$ and $\mathbf{F}_3$ have equal magnitudes but are oppositely directed, and $\mathbf{F}_2$ and $\mathbf{F}_4$ have equal magnitudes but are oppositely directed. The *resultant* magnetic force on the rectangular circuit is zero.

Next let us consider the magnetic torque about axis OO' in Fig. 27.15. Forces $\mathbf{F}_2$ and $\mathbf{F}_4$ are parallel to this axis and produce zero torque. The forces on all current elements of side ① have the same lever arm $(b/2) \sin \phi$ about OO'. The forces on all current elements of side ③ have this same lever arm. The torque about OO' produced by these forces is $2(\mathscr{B}Ia)(b/2) \sin \phi = \mathscr{B}IA \sin \phi$, where $A = ab$ is the area enclosed by the circuit. The sense of the torque is such as to turn the circuit so that its area is perpendicular to the direction of $\mathscr{B}$ with side ① uppermost and the magnetic flux $\Phi_{\mathscr{B}}$ enclosed by the circuit is a maximum.

The results found for a rectangular circuit in the above example can be readily extended to any plane current loop, whatever its shape. The computations involve a straight-forward application of (27.11). The conclusion that is reached is that for any plane current loop the resultant force due to a uniform magnetic field is zero and the resultant torque is given by

$$\tau = IA\hat{n} \times \mathscr{B}. \quad \textit{(Torque on Plane Current Loop in a Uniform Magnetic Field)}$$

$$(27.14)$$

The unit vector $\hat{\mathbf{n}}$ is perpendicular to the plane of the loop and directed according to the right-hand rule that when the fingers of the right hand are curved around the loop in the direction of the current the thumb points in the direction of $\hat{\mathbf{n}}$.

27.9 MAGNETIC MOMENT

In considering the resultant magnetic torque on a current loop it is convenient to introduce a vector quantity called the *magnetic moment* $\mathbf{m}$ of the current loop. For a plane current loop enclosing area A we define the magnetic moment to be

$$\mathbf{m} = IA\hat{\mathbf{n}}, \quad \textit{(Magnetic Moment of Plane Current Loop)} \qquad (27.15)$$

where $\hat{\mathbf{n}}$ is the unit vector perpendicular to the plane of the loop that was defined in Section 27.8. If the circuit is composed of N loops of wire each following essentially the same path in space, the total magnetic moment is

$$\mathbf{m} = NIA\hat{\mathbf{n}}. \quad \textit{(Magnetic Moment of N-turn Plane Loop)} \qquad (27.16)$$

Equation (27.14) for the resultant magnetic torque on a plane current loop in a uniform magnetic field can be written

$$\boldsymbol{\tau} = \mathbf{m} \times \mathscr{B}. \quad \left\{ \begin{array}{l} \mathbf{m} \text{ in } A \cdot m^2 \\ \mathscr{B} \text{ in } T \\ \tau \text{ in } N \cdot m. \end{array} \right\} \qquad (27.17)$$

If a current loop is introduced into a magnetic field that is uniform over the area of the loop, we see from (27.17) that the magnetic field exerts a torque on the loop that tends to turn the loop so that its magnetic moment $\mathbf{m}$ is aligned parallel to $\mathscr{B}$. Once $\mathbf{m}$ and $\mathscr{B}$ are aligned, it requires external work to give the loop an orientation so that $\mathbf{m}$ makes an angle ϕ with the uniform field. The *orientational potential energy* of the loop is the work against magnetic torques that must be done by some external agent to give the loop an orientation such that the magnetic moment $\mathbf{m}$ of the loop makes an angle ϕ with the magnetic field $\mathscr{B}$. We shall assume that the magnitude of $\mathbf{m}$ remains constant as the orientation of the loop is changed. We first consider starting from the orientation where $\mathbf{m}$ is parallel to $\mathscr{B}$. From (27.17) the magnitude of the magnetic torque on the loop for an angle ϕ between $\mathbf{m}$ and $\mathscr{B}$ is $\tau = m\mathscr{B} \sin \phi$. The work *against* magnetic forces required to increase the angle ϕ by an amount $d\phi$ is $dW = \tau \, d\phi = m\mathscr{B} \sin\phi \, d\phi$. Therefore, the external work required to bring the loop from $\phi = 0$ to some final orientation with $\phi = \phi_f$ is

$$W = \int_{\phi=0}^{\phi=\phi_f} dW = \int_0^{\phi_f} m\mathscr{B} \sin \phi \, d\phi = -m\mathscr{B} \cos \phi \, \Big|_0^{\phi_f} = -m\mathscr{B} \cos \phi_f + m\mathscr{B}.$$

In making a final definition of the orientational potential energy U_M it is convenient to shift the arbitrary reference level so that U_M is zero when $\phi = 90°$ and $\cos \phi$ is zero. This shift of zero level is accomplished by subtracting the constant quantity

$m\mathcal{B}$ from both sides of the above equation. We then have

$$U_M = -m\mathcal{B}\cos\phi,$$

which has the convenient vector representation

$$U_M = -\mathbf{m} \cdot \mathcal{B}. \qquad (27.18)$$

The potential energy is $-m\mathcal{B}$ when $\mathbf{m}$ and $\mathcal{B}$ are parallel and is $+m\mathcal{B}$ when $\mathbf{m}$ and $\mathcal{B}$ are antiparallel.

Experiment shows that at a given point in a magnetic field a small, plane current loop and a small bar magnet behave in the same way. We can define the magnetic moment $\mathbf{m}$ of a small bar magnet to be a vector directed along the axis of the magnet that is equal to the magnetic moment of a small, plane current loop that would experience the same torque when placed with its magnetic moment in the same orientation at the same location in the same uniform magnetic field. In this discussion, the word "small" means that the magnetic-field strength $\mathcal{B}$ that is of interest does not vary significantly over the area of the loop or the length of the magnet. With this definition of its magnetic moment $\mathbf{m}$, a small bar magnet in a uniform magnetic field experiences zero resultant magnetic force, experiences a magnetic torque given by (27.17), and has a potential energy of orientation given by (27.18).

Example. In the Bohr model of the hydrogen atom, the electron is imagined to move with speed v in a circular orbit of radius R with the proton at the center of the circle, as shown in Fig. 27.16. Deduce an expression for the magnetic moment associated with the electron's orbital motion in terms of its angular momentum.

The angular momentum $\mathbf{L}$ of the electron is $Rm_e v\mathbf{k}$, where m_e is the mass of the electron, and the direction of the Z axis is as shown in Fig. 27.16. (See Section 7.9.) The time required for the electron to make one trip around its orbit is $2\pi R/v$; therefore, the frequency with which it passes any given point on its orbit is $v/2\pi R$. The rate at which charge passes the point in coulombs per second is $I = ev/2\pi R$, where e is the magnitude of the charge of an electron in coulombs; the sense of the current is opposite to the direction of the electron's motion, as is indicated in Fig. 27.16. Therefore, the magnetic moment given by (27.15) is

$$\mathbf{m} = (ev/2\pi R)(\pi R^2)(-\mathbf{k}) = -(evR/2)\mathbf{k}.$$

Since $v\mathbf{k} = \mathbf{L}/Rm_e$, we finally have that

$$\mathbf{m} = -(e/2m_e)\mathbf{L}. \qquad (27.19)$$

The magnetic moment and the angular momentum are oppositely directed for a negative particle. Relation (27.19) between magnetic moment and orbital angular momentum is also obtained from a quantum-mechanical treatment of the orbital motion of a charged particle.

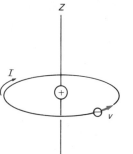

Fig. 27.16

27.10   MOVING-COIL GALVANOMETER

In Section 26.4 we discussed how a galvanometer can be adapted to make a DC ammeter or a DC voltmeter. By far the most common type of modern galvanometer is an instrument in which a coil rotates in the field of a permanent magnet when a current passes through the coil. Such instruments are called d'Arsonval-type after the French biophysicist Arsène d'Arsonval (1851–1940) who invented a moving-coil galvanometer in 1882.

A schematic diagram of a pivoted-coil d'Arsonval-type galvanometer is shown in Fig. 27.17. The coil is supported on hardened steel pivots turning in jeweled bearings. The pole pieces of the permanent magnet and the soft-iron core are shaped so that the vertical sides of the coil are always in a radially directed magnetic field of uniform magnitude. When there is a current I directed down into the paper on the right side of the coil and up out of the paper on the left side of the coil in Fig. 27.17, there is a magnetic torque $2NI\mathcal{B}LR$ on the coil, where N is the number of turns of wire and L is the length of the vertical sides of the coil that is in the field. This magnetic torque causes the coil to rotate clockwise until it is equaled by the resisting counterclockwise mechanical torque of a pair of spiral springs, one above and one below the coil, which also serve as current leads to the coil. These springs are not shown in Fig. 27.17. Since the magnetic torque is proportional to the current and

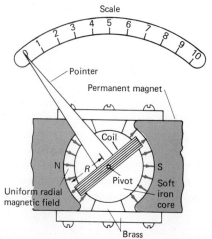

Fig. 27.17   A schematic diagram of a pivoted-coil d'Arsonval-type galvanometer. The diagram shows the equilibrium position for zero current.

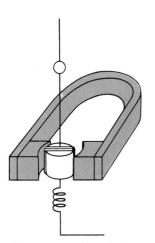

Fig. 27.18 A schematic diagram of a suspended-coil d'Arsonval-type galvanometer.

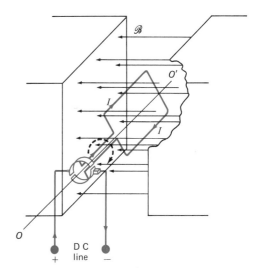

Fig. 27.19 A prototype of a DC motor.

the spring torque is proportional to the angle of rotation from the equilibrium position, the angle of rotation of the pointer is proportional to the current through the coil.

In order to achieve high sensitivity, the spring torque constant must be very low. However, the magnetic torque and consequently the spring torque must be large compared with the frictional torque in the bearings if the instrument is to perform satisfactorily. This limits the highest sensitivity for a pivoted instrument to full-scale deflection for a current of about 1 μA. To reduce friction and allow a lower restoring torque constant, more sensitive instruments of the *suspended-coil* type shown in Fig. 27.18 are needed. Galvanometers of this type can be designed to detect currents smaller than 10^{-10} A.

27.11 DC MOTOR

A simple prototype of a DC motor is illustrated in Fig. 27.19, which shows a single rectangular current loop supported by an arrangement, not shown in the figure, in such a way that it can rotate about the horizontal axis OO' through the center of the loop. The loop is in a uniform magnetic field $\mathscr{B}$ produced by a magnet. When there is a current I in the loop, it experiences a magnetic torque given by (27.17). For the current and field directions shown in Fig. 27.19, this torque causes a clockwise rotation of the loop.

The current is delivered to the loop through a split-ring commutator that causes the current in the loop to reverse in direction as the loop rotates past those positions where the sign of the torque would change. In this way the magnetic torque on the loop always has the same sense, although it varies in magnitude. The torque vanishes when the plane of the coil is normal to the magnetic-field direction and is a maximum when the plane of the coil is parallel to the magnetic-field direction. The torque transmitted to an axle along OO' will fluctuate in time since it is proportional to the sine of the angle ϕ between **m** and $\mathscr{B}$. The motor depends on rotational inertia to carry it through the no-torque position where $\phi = 0$.

A practical motor contains a number of loops arranged at various angles so that only one loop at a time passes through the zero-torque position. Such a motor delivers mechanical energy at a fairly constant torque. It requires a complex commutation system to reverse the current in each loop as the loop passes the zero-torque position.

QUESTIONS

1. Why isn't it possible to solve (27.1) for $\mathscr{B}$? Does (27.1) really provide a definition of a *unique* value for $\mathscr{B}$?

2. Suppose that we propose to carry out a thought experiment in which the electric-field strength and the magnetic-field strength at a certain point will be determined by measuring the force on a known test charge moving with known velocities at the point. If there is no initial knowledge about $\mathscr{E}$ or $\mathscr{B}$, what is the minimum number of measurements that is required? How can we be sure that there are not forces on the test charge that are neither electric nor magnetic, such as gravitational forces?

3. Under what conditions can magnetic lines meet or cross?

4. Are there any circumstances in which a charged particle trajectory can coincide with a magnetic line?

5. Why does the analysis of charged particle trajectories discussed in Section 27.4 provide a way to determine the ratio e/m but not the individual values of e and of m? Could this kind of experiment be redesigned so that e and m are determined individually?

6. In Section 27.7 we consider the magnetic force on the conduction electrons in a short segment of conductor of length dl that is carrying a current I. Discuss the way in which this force on the conduction electrons

leads to a force on the lattice of the conductor itself.

7. How can there be a resultant magnetic force on a current element when the net charge on the current element is zero?

8. Describe a way in which (27.15) could be used as the basis for a definition of the magnetic moment of a nonplanar current loop.

9. How is it possible that work is required to change the orientation of a magnetic moment relative to a magnetic field when we have concluded from (27.2) that a magnetic force cannot do work to a charged particle?

10. Starting from the fact that magnetic lines form closed loops or else extend to infinity, prove that for any *closed* surface the magnetic flux given by (27.3) is zero.

11. If a fixed charge at a given point in space experiences a force, what can we conclude about the nature of the force acting on the charge? If a moving charge experiences a force, what can we conclude about the nature of the force acting on the charge?

12. If no resultant force acts on an electron as it moves through a given region of space, what can we conclude about the electric and magnetic fields in the region?

13. Does a force act on a charged particle moving parallel to an electric field $\mathscr{E}$? Parallel to a magnetic field $\mathscr{B}$? Perpendicular to an

electric field $\mathcal{E}$? Perpendicular to a magnetic field $\mathcal{B}$?

14. How do magnetic lines differ from electric lines?

15. Explain how a d'Arsonval galvanometer works. Given a galvanometer, how can you make (a) a voltmeter and (b) an ammeter?

PROBLEMS

1. Give at least one good reason why we do not simply define the magnetic-field strength so that $\mathcal{B}$ has the same direction as the magnetic force that acts on a moving charged particle.

2. A beam of protons is deflected sidewise in a certain region of space. Could this deflection be caused by an electric field? By a magnetic field? If either type of field could be present, what experiments could you perform to determine which type of field was responsible for the deflection? If only one kind of field could cause the deflection, explain why the other kind of field is not effective in deflecting a proton beam.

3. A particle having a mass of 0.5 g and a charge of $+2.5 \times 10^{-8}$ C is given an initial horizontal velocity of 6.0×10^4 m/s (east) in a vacuum chamber in a laboratory on the earth's surface. What are the magnitude and direction of a resultant magnetic field that will keep the particle moving eastward until it strikes the wall of the chamber? Is the answer unique?

4. An alpha particle having $q = +3.2 \times 10^{-19}$ C and $m = 6.64 \times 10^{-27}$ kg travels in a circular path of radius 0.50 m oriented perpendicular to a uniform magnetic field having $\mathcal{B} = 1.2$ T. What are the speed, kinetic energy, and period of revolution of the alpha particle? Draw a diagram showing the relation between the direction of motion of the alpha particle about the circle and the direction of the magnetic field. Note: An alpha particle is the nucleus of

a helium atom. It consists of two protons and two neutrons bound tightly together and has a charge of $+2e$.

5. An electron ($q = -1.6 \times 10^{-19}$ C, $m = 9.11 \times 10^{-31}$ kg) is accelerated from rest through a potential difference of 15,000 V and is then injected into a region where the magnetic-field strength has magnitude 0.025 T. The velocity of the electron is perpendicular to the direction of the magnetic field. What is the radius of the electron's path? Draw a diagram showing the relation of the direction of circulation of the electron to the direction of $\mathcal{B}$.

6. A proton is injected into a region where the magnetic-field strength is $(0.2 \text{ T})\mathbf{i} + (0.3 \text{ T})\mathbf{j}$. The initial proton velocity is $(1.3 \times 10^4 \text{ m/s})\mathbf{k}$. (a) What is the initial force on the proton? (b) Describe quantitatively the path followed by the proton while in the magnetic-field region.

7. There is a uniform magnetic field perpendicular to the XY plane in the negative Z direction. A positron, an electron, and an alpha particle enter the field traveling in the XY plane in the positive X direction, each particle having the same velocity. (a) What are the relative magnitudes of the radii of the paths followed by the particles? (b) Repeat for a case where the particles have the same kinetic energy. (c) Draw a diagram illustrating the relative orientations of the paths followed by the particles in part (a). Note: A positron has the same mass as an electron but its charge is $+e$

rather than $-e$. The production of positrons will be discussed in Chapter 37. The alpha particle is described in Problem 4.

8. An alpha particle is injected into a region where the magnetic-field strength is $(0.4\text{ T})\mathbf{j}$. The initial velocity of the alpha particle is $(1.5 \times 10^6 \text{ m/s})\mathbf{j} + (0.95 \times 10^6 \text{ m/s})\mathbf{k}$. (a) What is the initial force on the alpha particle? (b) Describe quantitatively the path followed by the alpha particle while in the magnetic-field region. Note: The alpha particle is described in Problem 4.

9. In an e/m experiment using the Thomson apparatus shown in Figs. 27.6 and 27.7 the length of the plates is $L = 6.5$ cm, the plate separation is $d = 1.15$ cm, and the distance from the end of the plates to the (flat) end of the tube is $D = 24$ cm. The electrons have an energy of 10 keV when they pass through the anode A in Fig. 27.6. The electrons enter the plate region midway between the plates. (a) If a potential difference of 175 V is applied between the plates, show that the electrons will not strike either plate. What is the electric deflection of the fluorescent spot at the end of the tube? (b) The potential difference between the deflecting plates is reduced to zero. What magnitude of magnetic-field strength in the region between the plates will give a magnetic deflection equal in magnitude to the electric deflection of part (a)? (c) If a potential difference of 175 V is applied between the plates, what magnitude of magnetic-field strength is required to produce zero deflection of the electron beam? Is this value the same as obtained in (b)? Explain.

10. Can a "velocity selector" operating according to (27.9) be used at a single setting of $\mathscr{E}$ and $\mathscr{B}$ for particles of different charges and masses? If not, explain why not. If so, does the device "select" the same velocity for all different particle charges and masses? Explain your reasoning.

11. The masses of atoms can be compared from determinations of Q/m for ions of known charge Q. A device for making such measurements is called a *mass spectrograph;* one type of mass spectrograph is shown in the diagram. Positive ions of the element being studied are accelerated and a beam of ions traveling in a single direction is produced by slits S_1 and S_2. The beam then passes through a velocity selector that allows ions of speed $v = \mathscr{E}/\mathscr{B}_1$ to pass through slit S_3. Beyond S_3 is a region where the ions move perpendicularly to a magnetic field $\mathscr{B}_2$; the ions in this region traverse a circular arc of radius $R = mv/Q\mathscr{B}_2$ and after turning through 180° strike a photographic plate. (a) Chlorine has two isotopes of masses M and $M + \delta M$. If a beam of chlorine ions all having the same charge Q is analyzed by the mass spectrograph, two traces separated by a distance δx are formed on the photographic plate. Express δM in terms of M, Q, $\mathscr{E}$, $\mathscr{B}_1$, $\mathscr{B}_2$, and δx. (b) The masses of the chlorine isotopes are 34.980 u and 36.978 u. If the ions are singly charged, $\mathscr{B}_2 = 0.45$ T, and the velocity selector passes ions of speed 8.5×10^4 m/s, what is the separation of the two traces on the photographic plate?

12. In a *cyclotron,* which is one kind of device for producing charged-particle beams of high energy, low-energy positive ions are generated at point P midway between two semicircular hollow dee-shaped conductors, as shown in the diagram. The dees are placed in an evacuated chamber between the pole faces of a huge magnet that produces a large field $\mathscr{B}$ perpendicular to the flat faces of the dees. An alternating potential difference of amplitude of the order of 10 kV and frequency of the order of 10 MHz is applied between the dees. This potential difference produces an alternating electric field in the gap between the dees, but the interior of each dee is shielded from the electric field and in the interior

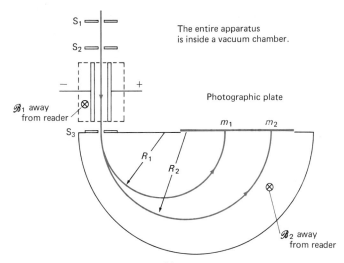

S₁
S₂

The entire apparatus
is inside a vacuum chamber.

−   +

$\mathcal{B}_1$ away
from reader

Photographic plate

m_1 m_2

S₃

R_1
R_2

$\mathcal{B}_2$ away
from reader

Problem 11

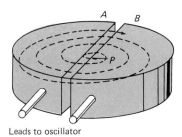

A   B

P

Leads to oscillator
Problem 12

region the ions see only the magnetic field, which causes them to traverse a circular arc. (a) Show that if the frequency of the alternating potential difference is $f = \mathcal{B}Q/2\pi m$, then ions of charge Q and mass m will be *accelerated* across the gap each time they cross the gap. (b) Suppose that $\mathcal{B} = 0.75$ T and protons are being accelerated. If the amplitude of the alternating potential difference is 10 kV, by how much does the proton kinetic energy increase each time it crosses the gap? (c) What is the required frequency of the alternating potential difference? (d) When the proton traverses a path of radius 0.75 m, how many times has it crossed the gap? What is its kinetic energy? (e) How much time is required for a proton to reach a path radius of 0.75 m?

13. In an experiment to measure the Hall potential difference V_H, the contacts (A) and (B) shown in Fig. 27.9 must be exactly opposite one another. Why is this requirement necessary for an accurate measurement of V_H? How might the experimenter determine when this condition is satisfied? Is there any simple way the experimenter can compensate for misalignment without moving the contacts?

14. In a certain Hall-effect experiment the conductor is a copper ribbon 1.5 cm wide and 1.0 mm thick. The ribbon carries a current of 18 A, and the transverse magnetic-field strength is 1.75 T. What value does the theory of Section 5 predict for the Hall potential difference on the basis of one conduction electron per atom for copper?

15. Discuss how the Hall-effect arrangement described in Problem 14 could be used for the determination of the magnitude and direction of an unknown magnetic field.

16. In a Hall-effect experiment, in addition to the Hall electric-field strength $\mathcal{E}_H$ defined in Section 27.5 there is an electric-field strength component $\mathcal{E}_l$ in the direction of the current. Show that $\mathcal{E}_H/\mathcal{E}_l = \mathcal{B}/ne\rho$, where n is the number of charge carriers per unit volume, e is the magnitude of the

charge per charge carrier, and ρ is the resistivity of the material of which the sample is made.

17. A horizontal, straight section of wire 30 cm long carries a current of 40 A eastward through a uniform field of 0.8 T directed northward. What magnetic force acts on this section of wire? What magnetic force would be exerted if the current were directed southward through this magnetic field?

18. A straight piece of wire of length 20 cm carries a current of 3 A horizontally in a northeast direction. This piece of wire is in a region where there is a magnetic field $\mathcal{B} = 0.085$ T (north). What is the magnetic force on the wire?

19. A conducting wire of length 20 cm and mass 4.5 g is suspended by a pair of flexible leads in a horizontal magnetic field directed perpendicular to the wire, as shown in the diagram. The magnitude of the magnetic-field strength is 0.15 T. What magnitude and direction of current in the wire are required to remove the tension in the supporting leads?

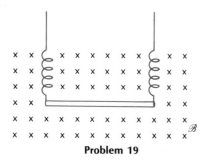

Problem 19

20. Find the magnetic force acting on the section of wire in the magnetic field of Problem 17 if the wire carries the current in a direction 30° south of east; in a direction 60° south of east; vertically upward.

21. A rigid circular loop of wire of radius 5 cm carries a current of 10 A and is situated with the plane of the loop perpendicular

to a uniform magnetic field directed along the axis of the loop as shown in the diagram. The magnetic-field strength has magnitude 0.20 T. Find the magnetic force $d\mathbf{F}$ on each current element of the loop; show the directions of the forces for representative current elements on a diagram. What is the resultant force on the loop due to the magnetic field? What is the tension in the loop?

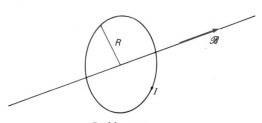

Problem 21

22. A rigid wire carries a current I along an *arbitrary* path from point Ⓐ to point Ⓑ in a *uniform* magnetic field $\mathcal{B}$. Show that the resultant magnetic force on the piece of wire is given by (27.13) if **L** represents the displacement vector from Ⓐ to Ⓑ.

23. What are the magnetic forces on each side of a square conducting loop of side $a = 5.0$ cm lying in the XY plane with one corner at the origin, one side along the $+X$ axis, and another side along the $+Y$ axis if the loop carries a current $I = 26$ A and there is in the region of the loop a magnetic field given by
$\mathcal{B} = [2.0 \times 10^{-5} \text{ T·m}/(x + 0.05 \text{ m})]\mathbf{k}$?
What is the resultant magnetic force on the loop? The current in the side of the loop lying along the X axis is in the direction of increasing x.

24. Two hundred turns of wire are closely wound in a circular coil having a mean radius of 8 cm. If this coil of wire lies horizontally at rest on a flat table and carries a current of 6 A in the counter clockwise sense as viewed from above, what is the magnitude of the magnetic moment of the coil? What is the direction of the coil's magnetic moment?

25. If the coil described in Problem 24 is placed in a uniform magnetic field, no magnetic torque is exerted on the coil when its magnetic moment is directed northward. However, a torque of 1.2 N·m is exerted on the coil when its magnetic moment is directed 30° east of north, and this torque tends to turn the coil's magnetic moment toward the north. What are the magnitude and direction of the uniform magnetic field?

26. How much work must be done against magnetic forces in order to rotate the magnetic moment of the coil described in Problem 25 from directly northward to directly southward in the uniform magnetic field?

27. A small bar magnet is placed in a uniform magnetic field $\mathscr{B} = 0.0996$ T, northward. When the S–N axis of the magnet is oriented in an east–west sense, the magnet experiences a torque of magnitude 4.82 N·m that tends to rotate the magnet so that its N-pole points in the direction of the field. What is the magnitude of the magnetic moment of the bar magnet?

28. If the bar magnet described in the preceding problem is aligned with its N-pole pointing in the direction of the field, how much work is required to rotate the magnet so that its N-pole points in the opposite direction?

29. A nonconducting solid disk of radius R carries a uniform surface distribution of charge σ on its upper surface. The disk is rotating about its axis with angular velocity ω. (a) What is the current due to the charge in a ring on the disk's surface of radius r and width dr? (b) What is the magnetic moment vector $d\mathbf{m}$ of this ring of charge? (c) By integrating the result (b) from $r = 0$ to $r = R$, determine the resultant magnetic moment of the rotating disk. (d) Recalling that the rotational inertia of a uniform disk of mass M and radius R about its axis is $\frac{1}{2}MR^2$, show that the magnetic moment $\mathbf{m}$ of the disk is related to the angular momentum $\mathbf{L}$ of the disk by $\mathbf{m} = (Q/2M)\mathbf{L}$, where Q is the total charge on the disk. Compare this result with (27.19).

30. A coil of arbitrary shape and an arbitrary whole number of turns is to be made from a wire of fixed length L. If a fixed current I is to be passed through the coil, what is the maximum magnitude of magnetic moment that can be obtained?

31. The plane of a rectangular loop of wire of dimensions 5 cm by 8 cm is oriented parallel to a uniform magnetic field of magnitude 0.15 T, the field direction being aligned with the longer side of the loop. The loop carries a current of 10 A. (a) What is the magnetic torque on the loop? Show the direction of this torque on a diagram. (b) What is the *maximum* torque that can be obtained from a single rectangular loop made with the same total length of wire and carrying the same current in this magnetic field?

32. What is the maximum magnetic torque on a circular coil of five turns each of radius 5 cm carrying a current of 5 A in a uniform magnetic field of 0.5 T? What is the magnetic flux through each turn of the coil when the torque is a maximum?

33. The rigid rectangular loop shown in the diagram is initially in the YZ plane and carries a current of $I = 10$ A in the direction shown. The loop is fastened to the Z axis

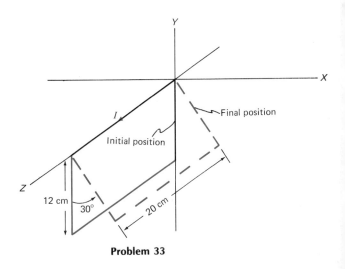

Problem 33

but can rotate about this axis; assume that the friction associated with this rotation is negligible. The wire of which the loop is made has a mass of 0.1 g per cm of length. A uniform magnetic field $\mathscr{B}$ is applied parallel to the Y axis, and the loop swings up through an angle of 30° as shown in the diagram. (a) Does $\mathscr{B}$ point in the positive Y direction or in the negative Y direction? (b) What is the magnitude of $\mathscr{B}$? (c) What is the magnetic flux through the loop in the final configuration?

34. A small coil of magnetic moment **m** is suspended so that **m** is horizontal and parallel to a horizontal magnetic field $\mathscr{B}$. The coil is given a *small* angular displacement about a vertical axis so that **m** makes an angle θ with $\mathscr{B}$ but remains horizontal. If the torsion constant of the suspension is C, what is the period of the oscillations that the coil executes when it is released. Assume that the magnitude of the magnetic moment remains constant during these oscillations. Let $\mathscr{I}$ represent the rotational inertia of the coil about the vertical axis.

35. A 25-turn circular conducting loop of radius 5.0 cm with its center at the origin is pivoted so that it can rotate about the Y axis. The loop is made of copper wire 1 mm in diameter and carries a 17-A current in each turn. The XY plane is horizontal. At the point where the $+X$ axis crosses the loop there is suspended from the loop a 25-g mass. In the region of the loop there is a uniform magnetic field $\mathscr{B}$ in the $+X$ direction. The loop is in equilibrium when it is horizontal. What is the direction of the current in the loop? What is the magnitude of the magnetic-field strength?

36. A certain rigid plane current loop has the shape of an equilateral triangle with sides of length 2.6 cm. The loop is glued to a nonconducting surface that makes an angle of 27° with the horizontal and carries a current of 0.63 A in a counterclockwise sense as seen from above. In the region of the loop there is a vertically downward magnetic field of magnitude 65 μT. What is the orientational potential energy of the loop?

37. The coil of a certain galvanometer is wound of wire of resistance 0.6 Ω/m. Each turn is a rectangle 3 cm long by 2 cm wide. The length of each vertical side of the coil that is in the radial magnetic field is 2.5 cm. The meter is to have a deflection of 1 rad for 1 μA of current and to have a resistance of 30 Ω. The torsion constant of the suspension is 1.25×10^{-7} m·N/rad. How many turns should the coil have? What magnitude of the magnetic-field strength is required?

38. Starting from (27.11), prove that the magnetic torque on a current loop carrying a current I in a uniform magnetic field is independent of the origin about which torques are computed.

39. Consider a plane, circular current loop of radius R in a uniform magnetic field $\mathscr{B}$. Show that without loss of generality we can choose a coordinate system so that the loop lies in the XY plane and $\mathscr{B} = \mathscr{B}_x \mathbf{i} + \mathscr{B}_z \mathbf{k}$. Starting from (27.11), compute the torque on the loop about the origin. You will probably want to use the vector identity $\mathbf{A} \times (\mathbf{B} \times \mathbf{C}) = (\mathbf{A} \cdot \mathbf{C})\mathbf{B} - (\mathbf{A} \cdot \mathbf{B})\mathbf{C}$, where **A**, **B**, and **C** are arbitrary vectors. Show that your result is consistent with (27.17) and (27.15).

Steady Currents as Magnetic Field Sources

In the preceding chapter we defined the magnetic field $\mathscr{B}$ in terms of the force on a moving test charge. We now consider a description of the magnetic fields produced by various kinds of sources. In the present chapter we shall consider how the magnetic-field strength produced by a given array of *steady currents* can be calculated. The analysis for currents that vary in time is more complicated and will be considered in Chapter 32. Throughout this chapter we shall strictly be considering current-carrying conductors or moving charges *in vacuum*. However, the magnetic effects of most materials are not large, and for practical purposes our results hold for currents surrounded by air or by most other materials. By contrast, certain materials such as iron, called *ferromagnetic materials,* have very large magnetic effects and can, in fact, be used to make permanent magnets. We shall defer description of the magnetic properties of materials and of magnets until Chapter 30.

Once the magnetic-field strength produced by a current has been described, it is possible to combine this information with the magnetic force relations of the preceding chapter to describe the magnetic force between two currents. We shall see that the formal definition of the ampere, which is taken in the SI as the additional fundamental unit needed for electromagnetism, is stated in terms of the force between two prescribed currents.

A single moving charged particle is also a source of a magnetic field. We shall consider the nature of this field in the limit of low-magnitude, constant particle velocity. Finally, we shall describe some of the interesting features of the magnetic field produced by the most familiar of all sources, the earth itself.

28.1 PRINCIPLE OF BIOT AND SAVART

Immediately upon learning of the observations of Oersted concerning the force on a magnet produced by a current-carrying wire, Biot and Savart began an investigation in which they determined the force on a suspended magnet due to a long, straight, current-carrying wire. Their results, when expressed in terms of magnetic fields, give the relation to be described in the next section. Biot extended the investigation to consider other configurations of the source current and was led to propose the relation that we shall describe, using modern terminology, in this section.

In any actual situation involving the magnetic field of a current, we observe the field produced by the complete circuit. However, in order to calculate the magnetic-field strength $\mathscr{B}$ produced by a specified current, we imagine the circuit to be divided into a large number of *current elements* $I\,d\mathbf{l}$ of the sort defined in the preceding chapter. Suppose that we want to determine the magnetic-field strength at the point P that is produced by the circuit shown in Fig. 28.1. A typical current element $I\,d\mathbf{l}$ is shown in the figure. We define the vector $\mathbf{r}$ to be the displacement *from* the location of the current element *to* the point P. The contribution $d\mathscr{B}(P)$ to the magnetic-field strength at P due to the single current element $I\,d\mathbf{l}$ is

$$d\mathscr{B}(P) = \frac{\mu_0}{4\pi}\frac{I\,d\mathbf{l}\times\hat{\mathbf{r}}}{r^2}, \qquad \left\{\begin{array}{l} \mathscr{B}\ \text{ in T} \\ I\ \text{ in A} \\ r,dl\,\text{in m} \\ \mu_0\ \text{ in T·m/A} \end{array}\right\} \qquad (28.1)$$

where r represents the magnitude of the vector $\mathbf{r}$ and $\hat{\mathbf{r}}$ is a unit vector in the direction of $\mathbf{r}$.

The proportionality constant $\mu_0/4\pi$ has the *exact* value 10^{-7} T·m/A; this value is exact because it comes directly from the definition of the ampere unit, which we shall consider in Section 28.3. The factor 4π is introduced explicitly in (28.1) so that such factors will not appear in other equations that are used more frequently than (28.1); we recall that the quantity 4π also appears explicitly in the equation representing Coulomb's Principle for the same reason. The constant $\mu_0 = 4\pi \times 10^{-7}$ T·m/A is called the *permeability of free space;* for our present purposes this is merely a name.

We see from (28.1) that the contribution to the magnetic-field strength from a

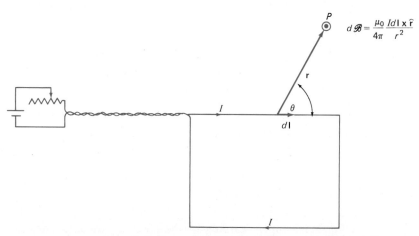

Fig. 28.1 The magnetic-field strength at a point P due to the current element $I\,d\mathbf{l}$.

single current element is proportional to the source current and to the sine of the angle θ between the directions of $d\mathbf{l}$ and $\mathbf{r}$. The dependence on the distance from the current element to the point P is an inverse-square relation. The direction of $d\mathscr{B}$ is perpendicular to both $d\mathbf{l}$ and $\mathbf{r}$.

The resultant field $\mathscr{B}(P)$ at the point P, which is what we could measure by examining the force on a test charge as a function of its velocity $\mathbf{v}$ at P, is obtained by computing the vector sum of the contributions $d\mathscr{B}(P)$ from all the current elements $I\,d\mathbf{l}$ of the circuit. Symbolically we can write

$$\mathscr{B}(P) = \int d\mathscr{B}(P), \tag{28.2}$$

where the integral extends over all the current elements of the circuit. If there are several different source circuits, the resultant field is the vector sum of terms like (28.2) for each of the contributing circuits. The integral $\int d\mathscr{B}(P)$ in (28.2) can be evaluated analytically only for certain geometrically simple circuit configurations.

The assumptions just described that are represented by (28.1) and (28.2) form the basis of the theory of the magnetic-field strength due to *steady currents*. We shall refer to these assumptions as the *Principle of Biot and Savart*. In subsequent sections we shall consider how the magnetic-field strength $\mathscr{B}(P)$ can actually be evaluated for several different circuit configurations.

28.2 MAGNETIC FIELD OF A STRAIGHT SEGMENT OF CURRENT-CARRYING WIRE

As a first application of the Principle of Biot and Savart, we shall consider the magnetic-field strength at a point P located at a perpendicular distance a from a straight segment of wire carrying a steady current I, as shown in Fig. 28.2. We choose a system of coordinates with the X axis through the point P and the Y axis along the wire in the current direction, as indicated in Fig. 28.2; two typical current elements, $I\,d\mathbf{l}$ and $Id\mathbf{l}'$, are shown in the figure. With this choice of coordinates, we have $d\mathbf{l} = dy\,\mathbf{j}$ and $d\mathbf{l} \times \hat{\mathbf{r}} = dy \sin \theta\,(-\mathbf{k})$; the direction of all the vectors $d\mathscr{B}(P)$ given by (28.1) is away from the reader. The magnitude of the resultant field at P as given by (28.2) is

$$\mathscr{B}(P) = (\mu_0 I/4\pi) \int_{-L_1}^{L_2} (\sin \theta / r^2)\, dy.$$

In order to evaluate this integral, we must express the quantities in the integrand in terms of a single variable. It is convenient to choose this variable to be θ. We then have $y = -a\,\mathrm{ctn}\,\theta$, from which it follows that $dy = a\,\csc^2\theta\,d\theta$, and $r = a\csc\theta$. The expression for the resultant magnetic-field strength becomes

$$\mathscr{B}(P) = \frac{\mu_0 I}{4\pi} \int_{\Theta_1}^{\Theta_2} \frac{\sin \theta}{a^2 \csc^2\theta}\, a\,\csc^2\theta\,d\theta \;=\; \frac{\mu_0 I}{4\pi a} \int_{\Theta_1}^{\Theta_2} \sin \theta\,d\theta$$

$$= (\mu_0 I/4\pi a)(\cos \Theta_1 - \cos \Theta_2). \tag{28.3}$$

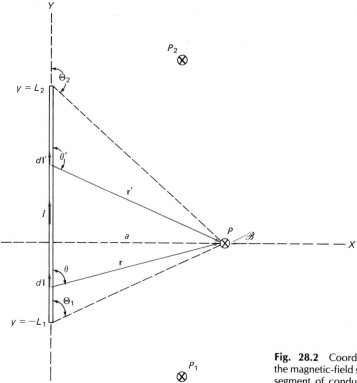

Fig. 28.2 Coordinates for determining the magnetic-field strength due to a straight segment of conductor carrying current I.

The result (28.3) applies to any point P outside the wire, including points like P_1 and P_2 in Fig. 28.2 for which a line drawn perpendicular to the Y axis does not hit the wire itself. The magnetic lines representing the field given by (28.3) form circles about the straight wire in planes perpendicular to the wire, as shown in Fig. 28.3. The sense of these magnetic lines is easily remembered from the following rule:

Grasp the wire with your right hand with your thumb in the direction of the current; your fingers then circle the wire in the direction of the magnetic lines.

In the limit where the ends of the wire are separated by great distances in opposite directions from P compared to the distance a, we have that Θ_1 approaches zero and Θ_2 approaches π. Therefore, in this limit of an "infinitely long" straight wire (28.3) gives the result

$$\mathscr{B}(P) \rightarrow (\mu_0 I/4\pi a)(\cos 0 - \cos \pi) = \mu_0 I/2\pi a. \qquad (28.4)$$

A single segment of straight wire cannot be the complete circuit, but for a very long wire the remainder of the circuit may be so far away from P as not to influence the value of $\mathscr{B}(P)$ significantly. Any circuit composed of straight-wire segments can be handled by applying (28.3) to each segment separately and determining the vector sum of the results.

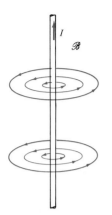

Fig. 28.3 Magnetic lines due to a straight segment of current-carrying conductor.

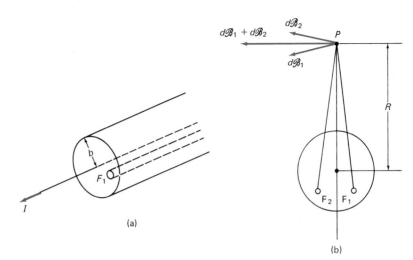

(a)

(b)

Fig. 28.4   (a) Straight wire carrying a current. (b) Cross section of the wire.

Up to now we have assumed that the radius of the current-carrying wire is negligible. If this is not true, then in determining the magnetic-field strength we must consider how the source current is distributed over the cross section of the wire. In order to attack such a problem we can divide the wire into many filaments of negligible radius, apply the Principle of Biot and Savart to find the magnetic-field strength due to a single filament, and superimpose the magnetic fields produced by all the filaments. We shall not attempt to carry through such a computation, but we shall consider one important result obtained from this line of reasoning that will be useful later.

Consider the case of an "infinitely long," straight piece of wire of radius b that carries a current I that is *uniformly distributed* over the cross section of the wire. We divide the wire into many filaments such as F_1 shown in Fig. 28.4a. The field $d\mathscr{B}$ produced by any single filament will have the form given in (28.4) with magnetic lines as shown in Fig. 28.3. This means that the field $d\mathscr{B}_1$ produced by filament F_1 at the point P has the direction shown in Fig. 28.4b. Since the current I is uniformly distributed, the source has cylindrical symmetry about its axis. For any filament F_1 there will be a filament F_2 symmetrically located with respect to the plane containing P and the axis of the wire such that $d\mathscr{B}_1(P) + d\mathscr{B}_2(P)$ is perpendicular to this plane, as shown in Fig. 28.4b. The resultant field at P can be considered as the vector sum of contributions from such pairs of filaments. We conclude that the resultant field $\mathscr{B}(P)$ is perpendicular to the plane containing P and the axis of the wire. This conclusion holds whether P is inside or outside the wire. It follows that the magnetic lines form circles about the axis of the wire just as shown in Fig. 28.3.

Because of the cylindrical symmetry of the source about the axis of the wire and its "infinite" length, the magnitude of the resultant magnetic-field strength $\mathscr{B}(P)$ can depend only on the radial distance R of the point P from the axis of the wire. We shall use these conclusions about the direction and magnitude of $\mathscr{B}$ in Section 28.7.

28.3   DEFINITION OF THE AMPERE

Among the experiments conducted by Ampère on the force between two current-carrying wires was that illustrated in Fig. 28.5. From the results discussed in Section 28.2 for the magnetic field produced by straight segment of wire Ⓐ and the results of the preceding chapter for the force on a current-carrying wire in a magnetic field, we can show that the forces on the segments of the hanging wire Ⓑ are as indicated in Fig. 28.5. Measurement of the angle of rotation of the hanging wire from the vertical when a current I is present allows determination of the mutual force between the two parallel straight segments of current-carrying wire.

An abstraction from this experiment is used in the SI to give a formal definition of the ampere unit of current. Consider two very long, parallel, straight wires separated by a distance a and carrying currents I_1 and I_2, respectively, as shown in Fig. 28.6. At the location of wire ②, wire ① produces a magnetic field $\mathscr{B}_1$ that is away from the reader in Fig. 28.6 and from (28.4) has magnitude $\mathscr{B}_1$ (at 2) $= \mu_0 I_1/2\pi a$. Because of this field, a length L of wire ② experiences a force given by $\mathbf{F}_2 = I_2 \mathbf{L}_2 \times \mathscr{B}_1$. This force is toward wire ① for currents directed as in Fig. 28.6 and has magnitude

$$F_2 = I_2 L \mathscr{B}_1 = L I_2 I_1 \mu_0/2\pi a.$$

Similar considerations show that a length L of wire ① experiences a force of this same magnitude directed toward wire ②. Thus, two parallel wires carrying currents in the same direction attract each other. If the two currents are in opposite directions, the wires repel each other. In either case, the magnitude of the mutual force per unit length between the two wires is

$$F/L = \mu_0 I_1 I_2/2\pi a. \tag{28.5}$$

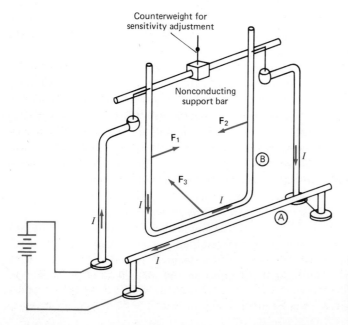

Counterweight for
sensitivity adjustment

Nonconducting
support bar

F_2

F_1

Ⓑ

F_3

Ⓐ

Fig. 28.5 Schematic representation of Ampère's experiment on the force between two current-carrying wires.

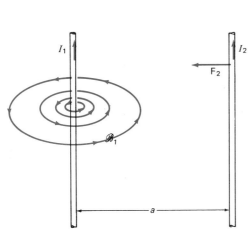

Fig. 28.6

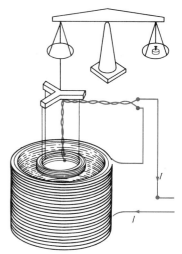

Fig. 28.7 Schematic diagram of an experimental arrangement for determining the force between two current-carrying coils.

The definition of the ampere is based on (28.5).

One AMPERE is that current which, if existing in two long parallel wires 1 m apart, would result in a magnetic force of 2×10^{-7} N per meter of length.

This definition establishes the value of μ_0 as *exactly* $4\pi \times 10^{-7}$ T·m/A. In the SI, the ampere is taken as the fundamental electromagnetic unit to be added to the units of mass, length, time, and temperature. The coulomb and all other electromagnetic quantities are then derived units; for example, 1 C = 1 A·s. This means that the value of ϵ_0 in Coulomb's principle is a matter for experimental determination. The value of ϵ_0 must be that previously given in order to be consistent with the sizes of the newton, the meter, and the coulomb.

Although the case of long, parallel, straight wires is conceptually convenient for stating the formal definition of the ampere, it is not convenient for practical realization of the definition. At standards laboratories like the U.S. National Bureau of Standards, what is actually measured is the force between two geometrically compact coils carrying the same current, as suggested in Fig. 28.7. The coils are carefully designed and constructed so that the dependence of the measured force on the current can be calculated accurately from (28.1) and (28.2) plus $\mathbf{F} = \int I\, d\mathbf{l} \times \mathcal{B}$. In this way a measurement of force serves to determine the current through the coils.

28.4 MAGNETIC FIELD OF A CIRCULAR CURRENT LOOP

As was the case for the computation of the electric-field strength produced by a given charge distribution, the integral (28.2) for the magnetic-field strength $\mathcal{B}$ produced by a current can be evaluated analytically only for circuits that are geometrically relatively simple, and even then frequently only at locations of special geometrical symmetry. For example, the magnetic field produced by a plane circular current loop can be computed easily for a point P on the axis of the loop. However, for points at other locations the integral (28.2) cannot be evaluated in terms of common functions; for such points, we must resort to numerical methods.

In order to determine the magnetic-field strength $\mathscr{B}(P)$ at a point P on the axis of a plane circular current loop of radius a, as shown in Fig. 28.8, we choose a cylindrical coordinate system having its origin at the center of the loop and its $+Z$ axis lying along the axis of the loop in the direction that the right thumb points if the fingers of the right hand are curled around the loop in the current direction. Two current elements $I\,d\mathbf{l}_1$ and $I\,d\mathbf{l}_2$ located at opposite ends of a diameter are shown in Fig. 28.8; these current elements produce at P magnetic-field strengths $d\mathscr{B}_1(P)$ and $d\mathscr{B}_2(P)$ that are given by (28.1). The point P is at the same distance R from all current elements of the loop; $|\mathbf{r}_1| = |\mathbf{r}_2| = R$. Furthermore, the angle between $d\mathbf{l}$ and $\mathbf{r}(P)$ for all current elements is $90°$. Therefore, application of the right-hand rule for vector products shows that $d\mathscr{B}_1$ and $d\mathscr{B}_2$ have the directions shown in Fig. 28.8, and they have the same magnitude

$$d\mathscr{B}_1 = d\mathscr{B}_2 = (\mu_0/4\pi)(I\,dl/R^2).$$

When we compute the vector sum $d\mathscr{B}_1 + d\mathscr{B}_2$, the components perpendicular to the Z axis cancel. Since all current elements of the loop can be considered in pairs in this way, we conclude that $\mathscr{B}(P)$ is directed along the $+Z$ axis. Upon adding the Z components of the contributions to the magnetic-field strength from all the current elements of the circular loop, we obtain

$$\mathscr{B}(P) = \mathbf{k}\int_{\phi=0}^{\phi=2\pi} (\mu_0/4\pi)(I\,dl/R^2)\cos\theta = \mathbf{k}\,(\mu_0/4\pi)(I\cos\theta/R^2)\int_0^{2\pi} a\,d\phi$$

$$= \mathbf{k}(\mu_0/4\pi)(Ia/R^3)(2\pi a) = \mathbf{k}(\mu_0 Ia^2/2R^3). \qquad (28.6)$$

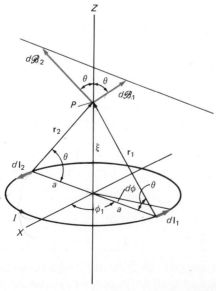

$|\mathbf{r}_1| = |\mathbf{r}_2| = R$ **Fig. 28.8**

This same result holds for points P on both the positive and the negative Z axes.

For points not on the axis of the loop, computation of the magnetic-field strength involves complicated integrals; these integrals can be evaluated numerically. The magnetic lines lying in a plane containing the axis of the loop are shown in Fig. 28.9.

28.5   FAR FIELD OF A MAGNETIC DIPOLE

In Section 27.7 we introduced the magnetic moment of a current loop, which for a plane circuit of N turns each carrying current I and enclosing area A is given by $\mathbf{m} = NIA\hat{\mathbf{n}}$, where $\hat{\mathbf{n}}$ is a unit vector perpendicular to the plane of the circuit and directed so that if the fingers of the right hand are curled in the direction of the current, the thumb points in the direction of $\hat{\mathbf{n}}$. We found that the torque on a current loop in a uniform magnetic field $\mathscr{B}$ is given by $\tau = \mathbf{m} \times \mathscr{B}$. The magnetic field produced by a current loop at distances far from the loop compared with the dimensions of the loop can be expressed in terms of the magnetic moment $\mathbf{m}$ of the loop.

Consider result (28.6) for the magnetic-field strength on the axis of a circular current loop. The magnetic moment of a plane circular loop oriented as shown in Fig. 28.8 is $\mathbf{m} = I\pi a^2 \mathbf{k}$; therefore, (28.6) can be written $\mathscr{B}(P) = (\mu_0/4\pi)(2\mathbf{m}/R^3)$. In the limit that the point P is very far from the loop we have $R^3 \simeq |z_P|^3$. For such points we can write

$$\mathscr{B}(P) \simeq (\mu_0/4\pi)(2\mathbf{m}/|z_P|^3). \tag{28.7}$$

This relation is a special case of a general relation for the magnetic-field strength due to a steady-current loop of magnetic moment $\mathbf{m}$ located at the origin. Let $\mathbf{r}$ represent the position vector of the field point relative to the origin. If the magnitude of $\mathbf{r}$ is large compared with the dimensions of the circuit, then it is possible to show from (28.1) by an analysis that is beyond the scope of this text that

$$\mathscr{B} = \frac{\mu_0}{4\pi}\left(\frac{3m\cos\theta}{r^4}\mathbf{r} - \frac{\mathbf{m}}{r^3}\right), \tag{28.8}$$

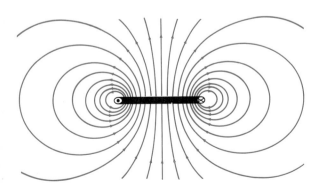

Fig. 28.9   The magnetic lines produced by a circular current loop.

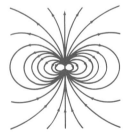

Fig. 28.10   The magnetic lines produced by a current loop of magnetic moment **m.** On the scale of this diagram, the dimensions of the loop are very small. The vector **m** points upward in the diagram.

where θ is the angle between $\mathbf{m}$ and $\mathbf{r}$. The magnetic lines associated with (28.8) lying in a plane containing the magnetic moment $\mathbf{m}$ are shown in Fig. 28.10. Equation (28.8) also holds for the magnetic-field strength at large distances produced by a small bar magnet of magnetic moment $\mathbf{m}$.

For a point on the axis of the circular loop shown in Fig. 28.8 we have $\mathbf{m} = m\mathbf{k}$, $r = |z|$, and $\mathbf{r}\cos\theta = |z|\mathbf{k}$. When these relations are used, we see that (28.8) reduces to (28.7).

Equation (28.8) has the same mathematical form as the electric-field strength at large distances due to a static electric dipole of dipole moment $\mathbf{p}$:

$$\mathscr{E} = \frac{1}{4\pi\epsilon_0}\left(\frac{3p\cos\theta}{r^4}\mathbf{r} - \frac{\mathbf{p}}{r^3}\right). \tag{28.9}$$

This result was considered in Problem 41 of Chapter 22. The magnetic-moment vector $\mathbf{m}$ is often called the *magnetic dipole moment* of the current loop. Although the far fields due to a steady-current loop and a static electric dipole have the same mathematical form, the near fields, close to the respective sources, are very different in the two cases.

28.6 MAGNETIC FIELD OF A SOLENOID

Another arrangement for producing a uniform magnetic field over a region of space is a conducting wire wound into a helical coil of small pitch, as shown in Fig. 28.11. Such an arrangement is called a *solenoid* (Greek: *solen,* a tube). The magnetic-field strength inside a solenoid at a distance far from the ends compared with the lateral dimensions of the helix is extremely uniform. We shall consider a solenoid of length L having N closely spaced circular turns of wire each of radius a. This solenoid closely resembles a line of parallel circular current loops each carrying the same current, and we can determine the magnetic-field strength on the axis of the solenoid to an excellent approximation by making use of (28.6).

We choose the Z axis to coincide with the axis of the solenoid with the positive Z axis in the direction of the field $\mathscr{B}$ on the axis produced by the current in the turns of the solenoid, and we put the origin at the point P where the field strength is to be determined. The solenoid is conceptually divided into segments of width dz, as shown in Fig. 28.12. We treat each segment as a circular current loop of

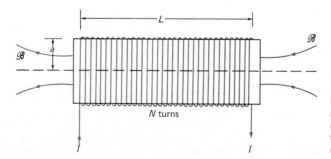

Fig. 28.11 A solenoid. The material supporting the coils has negligible effect on the magnetic field provided it is not ferromagnetic.

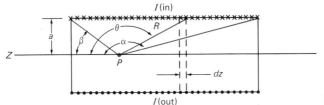

Fig. 28.12

radius a and current $I(N/L)\,dz$, where I is the current in each turn of the solenoid and $N/L = n$ is the number of turns per unit of length along the solenoid axis. From (28.6) the contribution to the magnetic-field strength at P due to a single segment of the solenoid of width dz is

$$d\mathscr{B}(P) = (\mu_0 nI\,dz\,a^2/2R^3)\mathbf{k}.$$

From Fig. 28.12 we see that $a = R\cos(\theta - \pi/2) = R\sin\theta$ and the Z coordinate of the solenoid segment of width dz is $z = R\cos\theta = (a/\sin\theta)\cos\theta = a\,\mathrm{ctn}\,\theta$, from which it follows that $dz = -a\csc^2\theta\,d\theta$. The minus sign appears in this expression because θ decreases when z increases. Upon using these relations in the expression for $d\mathscr{B}(P)$ we obtain

$$d\mathscr{B}(P) = \frac{\mu_0 nIa^2}{2(a\csc\theta)^3}(-a\csc^2\theta\,d\theta)\mathbf{k} = -\frac{1}{2}\mu_0 nI\sin\theta\,d\theta\,\mathbf{k},$$

from which it follows that the resultant field at P is

$$\mathscr{B} = \int_{\theta=\alpha}^{\theta=\beta} d\mathscr{B} = -\tfrac{1}{2}\,\mu_0 nI\mathbf{k}\int_{\alpha}^{\beta}\sin\theta\,d\theta = \tfrac{1}{2}\,\mu_0 nI\,\mathbf{k}(\cos\beta - \cos\alpha). \quad (28.10)$$

This result is not restricted to points inside the solenoid; it holds anywhere on the solenoid axis. If the solenoid is very long, $L \gg a$, and the point P is inside the solenoid far from either end, we have $\beta \to 0$ and $\alpha \to \pi$. This means that

$$\mathscr{B} = \mu_0 nI\,\mathbf{k}. \quad \textit{(At points on the axis well inside a long solenoid)} \quad (28.11)$$

For points not on the axis of the solenoid, determination of the resultant magnetic-field strength from the Principle of Biot and Savart is a much more challenging task. Such computations give results like those illustrated in Fig. 28.13, which shows the magnetic lines lying in a plane containing the solenoid axis for a short solenoid of length equal to twice its diameter. The parallel lines with equal spacing in the center of the solenoid show that the magnetic field is highly uniform in this region. *Equation (28.11) gives the field strength to an excellent approximation over the whole cross section of the interior of the solenoid at points far from either end compared with the solenoid radius.* The relatively large spacing of the magnetic lines outside the solenoid compared with those inside the solenoid shows that the magnitude of the magnetic-field strength $\mathscr{B}$ is small outside as compared with $\mathscr{B}$ inside the solenoid.

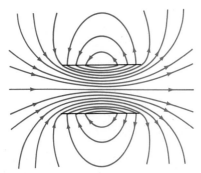

Fig. 28.13 The magnetic lines lying in a plane containing the solenoid axis for a short solenoid of length equal to twice its diameter.

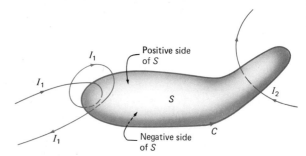

Fig. 28.14 A directed closed curve C bounding a surface S.

28.7   AMPERE'S LINE-INTEGRAL RELATION

In this section we shall describe a relation called Ampere's line-integral relation that plays a role in the analysis of the magnetic fields produced by steady currents similar to that of Gauss's relation in electrostatics. For current distributions having a sufficiently high amount of spatial symmetry, Ampere's relation can be used to determine in a relatively simple way the magnetic-field strength as a function of position.

In order to state Ampere's relation, we consider an arbitrary *directed* closed curve C in space as shown in Fig. 28.14. Like a Gaussian surface, this curve is purely conceptual; it does not necessarily coincide with any physical object. We next need to picture a surface S bounded by the curve C. Imagine a piece of cloth that is glued to the curve C and then trimmed along C without being stretched in any particular way. Any configuration that can be assumed by such a conceptual piece of cloth represents a surface S bounded by the curve C. In many cases it is convenient to think in particular of the surface S that would be defined by a piece of thin rubber sheet that is stretched taut and glued to the curve C. Such a surface is suggested in Fig. 28.14. The surface S is assigned an orientation in the following way. Curl the fingers of the right hand around the curve C in its positive sense; the right thumb then points away from the positive side of the surface S.

Any place where a current-carrying conductor pierces the surface S we say that the associated current *links* the curve C. If the current crosses S going in on the negative side and out from the positive side, we say that the linkage is *positive;* if the current crosses S going in on the positive side and out from the negative side, we say that the linkage is *negative*. In Fig. 27.14 current I_2 links C positively and current I_1 links C *twice* negatively.

In terms of the ideas just described, *Ampere's line-integral relation* can be stated as follows:

The line integral of the magnetic-field strength $\mathscr{B}$ around any closed curve C is equal to μ_0 times the *algebraic* sum of the current linkages of C.

Symbolically we can write this as

$$\oint_C \mathcal{B} \cdot d\mathbf{l} = \mu_0 \, \Sigma I_i, \quad (Ampere's \ Line\text{-}Integral \ Relation) \qquad (28.12)$$

where the terms in the sum on the right-hand side are positive for positive linkages and are negative for negative linkages.

Equation (28.12) can be derived from the Principle of Biot and Savart, but the deviation is beyond the scope of this text. We can use (28.12) to determine an unknown field $\mathcal{B}$ for situations having sufficient spatial symmetry that we can choose curves C along which $\mathcal{B}$ has constant magnitude and the same orientation relative to each path element $d\mathbf{l}$. We shall illustrate this by several examples, but first we shall check (28.12) for the simple case of an "infinitely long" straight wire of negligible radius.

The magnitude of the magnetic-field strength produced by an infinitely long straight wire is given by (28.4); the magnetic lines are circles about the wire as shown in Fig. 28.3. We choose the curve C to be a circle of radius a centered on the wire that coincides with a magnetic line. Then everywhere on C the magnetic-field strength $\mathcal{B}$ is parallel to $d\mathbf{l}$ and has magnitude $\mu_0 I / 2\pi a;$ the line integral of $\mathcal{B}$ around the curve C is

$$\oint_C \mathcal{B} \cdot d\mathbf{l} = \oint_C (\mu_0 I / 2\pi a) \, d\mathbf{l} = (\mu_0 I / 2\pi a) \oint_C dl = \mu_0 I,$$

where in the last step we note that $\oint dl$ is just the length $2\pi a$ of curve C. This result is in agreement with (28.12).

We shall now consider several examples where the distribution of source current has sufficient spatial symmetry that Ampere's relation can be applied in the determination of the magnetic-field strength. Note that in each case we must first make arguments based on symmetry to determine the direction of $\mathcal{B}$ and the coordinates on which the magnitude of $\mathcal{B}$ can depend before we can make effective use of (28.12). Other examples of this sort of reasoning using Ampere's relation are suggested in the problems.

Example. A long, straight wire of radius b carries a current I that is *uniformly* distributed over the cross section of the wire. What is the magnetic-field strength at an arbitrary point outside the wire that is very far from either end of the wire compared to its distance from the wire's axis? What is the magnetic-field strength at a similar arbitrary point inside the wire?

At the end of Section 28.2 we gave an argument showing that in this case the magnetic lines form circles about the axis of the wire as shown in Fig. 28.3 and that the magnitude of the magnetic-field strength can depend only on the radial distance from the axis of the wire. These conclusions about the direction and magnitude of $\mathcal{B}$ indicate that a useful choice of curve C for application of Ampere's relation will be a circle of radius R in the right-hand sense about the wire axis. Everywhere on this circle, $\mathcal{B}$ has the same magnitude $\mathcal{B}(R)$ and is parallel to $d\mathbf{l}$. Therefore, $\oint \mathcal{B} \cdot d\mathbf{l} = \mathcal{B}(R) \oint dl = 2\pi R \mathcal{B}(R)$. If $R > b$, the entire current I links the curve C and (28.12) becomes

$$2\pi R\mathscr{B}(R) = \mu_0 I \quad \text{or} \quad \mathscr{B}(R) = \mu_0 I / 2\pi R,$$

the same result as would be obtained from (28.4) if all the current were concentrated on the wire axis.

If $R < b$, only a portion of the total current I links the path C. Since the current is uniformly distributed over the cross section of the wire, the portion of the current linking the curve C is $\pi R^2 (I/\pi b^2)$. Therefore, for $R < b$ we have from (28.12) that

$$2\pi R\mathscr{B}(R) = \mu_0 R^2 I / b^2 \quad \text{or} \quad \mathscr{B}(R) = \mu_0 IR / 2\pi b^2.$$

A pictorial representation of these results is shown in Fig. 28.15.

Example.   What is the magnetic-field strength produced by the *closely spaced* toroidal winding shown in Fig. 28.16a when the wire carries a current I?

We assume that the windings are sufficiently closely spaced that the pitch of the windings is negligible and there is essentially complete cylindrical symmetry about the vertical axis indicated in Fig. 28.16a. We choose the Z axis to coincide with this symmetry axis. Because of the cylindrical symmetry about the Z axis, the magnitude of the resultant magnetic-field strength $\mathscr{B}(P)$ at an arbitrary point P can depend only on the Z coordinate of P and its radial distance R from the Z axis.

The argument from symmetry that establishes the direction of $\mathscr{B}$ is considerably more difficult to illustrate than for the previous example. We simply note that based on the cylindrical symmetry of the source and the directional properties of (28.1), one can conclude that the magnetic lines are circles about the Z axis.

These conclusions about the magnitude and direction of $\mathscr{B}$ allow us to use Ampere's relation. Clearly a useful curve C to which to apply the relation will be a circle of radius R about the Z axis. Everywhere on such a circle, $\mathscr{B}$ will have the same magnitude and will be parallel to $d\mathbf{l}$. First consider curves like C_1, C_2, C_3, and C_4 in Fig. 28.16b. We can determine the appropriate sense for these curves by considering the field produced by each loop of the windings as

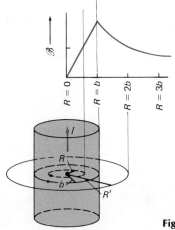

Fig. 28.15

shown in Fig. 28.9. There is no current linking curves C_1, C_2, or C_3. Curve C_4 is linked twice by each loop of the windings, once in the negative sense, and once in the positive sense; the total linkage again is zero. Therefore, Ampere's relation for these curves gives

$$\oint_C \mathcal{B} \cdot d\mathbf{l} = \mathcal{B}(R) \oint dl = \mathcal{B}(R)2\pi R = 0,$$

from which we conclude that $\mathcal{B} = 0$ everywhere outside the toroid windings.

For a curve like C_5 lying inside the toroid windings, each loop of the windings links the curve once in the positive sense. Therefore, Ampere's relation for curve C_5 gives

$$\oint_{C_5} \mathcal{B} \cdot d\mathbf{l} = \mathcal{B}(R) \oint_{C_5} dl = \mathcal{B}(R)2\pi R = N\mu_0 I,$$

where N is the total number of turns of the windings. It follows that

$$\mathcal{B} = \mu_0 NI/2\pi R. \quad \textit{(Inside a Toroid)}$$

This result is much like (28.11) for a long solenoid, but the toroidal field is not uniform across the cross section of the toroid. However, if $b \ll a$ in Fig. 28.16a, the field inside the toroid is approximately uniform.

It is easy to show that the magnetic-field strength outside the singly-wound toroid in the figure is not exactly zero. In the derivation we have neglected the pitch of the windings. However, a curve like C_6 in Fig. 28.16b is linked once by the current I because of the pitch of the windings. Ampere's relation when applied to this curve gives $\oint_{C_6} \mathcal{B} \cdot d\mathbf{l} = \mu_0 I$. This means that $\mathcal{B}$ cannot be zero everywhere

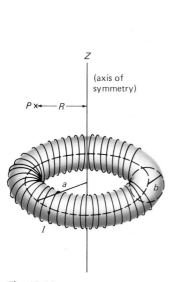

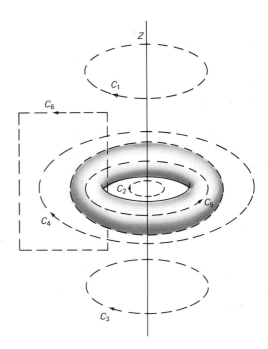

Fig. 28.16

on C_6, but we do not have information about the magnitude and direction of $\mathscr{B}$ that would allow us to evaluate the integral. If the pitch is very small so that the number of turns per unit length is very large, the magnetic-field strength outside the toroid is negligible. How can you use a doubly-wound toroid to make the current linking C_6 zero? Will this make the magnetic-field strength outside the toroid exactly zero?

We shall see later that a closely wound toroidal winding placed on a doughnut of material provides a convenient arrangement for studying the magnetic properties of the material. In this sense the toroid plays a role something like the role played by the parallel-plate capacitor in the study of the electrical properties of materials.

28.8 MAGNETIC FIELD OF A MOVING POINT CHARGE

It was not clear to the early investigators whether the production of a magnetic field by a current-carrying wire was due simply to the motion of charge or whether the material of the conductor played an essential role. The first demonstration of a magnetic field produced by the convection of charge on a moving charged object as opposed to the conduction of charge through a conductor was made by the American physicist Henry Rowland (1848–1901), who detected the exceedingly small magnetic field produced by a rapidly rotating, charged, gilded ebonite disk in 1875. Modern electromagnetic theory and experiment yield expressions for the electric-field strength $\mathscr{E}$ and the magnetic-field strength $\mathscr{B}$ produced by a moving point charge that depend in a nonsimple way on both the velocity and the acceleration of the particle. In the limit when the acceleration of the particle of charge q is negligible and its velocity $\mathbf{v}$ has magnitude much less than the speed of light, these relations reduce to $\mathscr{E} = (q/4\pi\epsilon_0)(\hat{\mathbf{r}}/r^2)$, which is the result obtained from Coulomb's principle of electrostatics, and

$$\mathscr{B} = \frac{\mu_0}{4\pi} q \frac{(\mathbf{v} \times \hat{\mathbf{r}})}{r^2}. \tag{28.13}$$

Equation (28.13) is just what is obtained from (28.1) if we assume that the current I is due to a collection of n particles per unit volume each having charge q and moving with velocity $\mathbf{v}$, as was done in Section 27.5.

Suppose that we have two particles of charges q_1 and q_2 moving with small, steady velocities $\mathbf{v}_1$ and $\mathbf{v}_2$, as shown in Fig. 28.17. By (28.13) and (27.1), the magnetic force on particle ② due to particle ① is

$$\mathbf{F}_{21} = q_2\mathbf{v}_2 \times \left(\frac{\mu_0}{4\pi} q_1 \frac{\mathbf{v}_1 \times \mathbf{r}_{21}}{r_{21}^3} \right),$$

and the magnetic force on particle ① due to particle ② is

$$\mathbf{F}_{12} = q_1\mathbf{v}_1 \times \left(\frac{\mu_0}{4\pi} q_2 \frac{\mathbf{v}_2 \times (-\mathbf{r}_{21})}{r_{21}^3} \right).$$

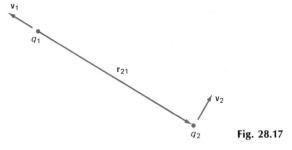

Fig. 28.17

These relations have an unexpected feature. Consideration of several particular cases for the relative orientations of $\mathbf{v}_1$, $\mathbf{v}_2$, and $\mathbf{r}_{21}$ quickly shows that in general $\mathbf{F}_{12}$ is *not* equal to $-\mathbf{F}_{21}$; Newton's Third Principle does not hold for the magnetic interaction between two moving charged particles. For example, in the situation illustrated in Fig. 28.17 we see that $\mathbf{F}_{21} = 0$ since $\mathbf{v}_1 \times \mathbf{r}_{21} = 0$, but $\mathbf{F}_{12}$ does not vanish.

The most important result deduced from Newton's Third Principle was the Principle of Conservation of Momentum, which was discussed in Section 4.12. The consequence of the invalidity of Newton's Third Principle in the magnetic interaction of two moving charged particles is *not* that we must abandon momentum conservation. Rather, a more advanced analysis shows that *the charged particles alone cannot be considered as an isolated dynamical system.* We must include the electric and magnetic fields produced by the charges as part of the system. Energy, linear momentum, and angular momentum are all found to be associated with electromagnetic fields, and the conservation principles for these quantities are obeyed when the contributions of the fields are included in the analysis along with the moving charged particles. Some elementary aspects of these ideas will be considered in Chapter 32.

An analysis shows that when the magnetic interaction of two *complete* circuits carrying *steady* currents is considered by use of (28.1) and (28.2) plus the force relation $\mathbf{F} = \int I \, d\mathbf{l} \times \mathcal{B}$ from Chapter 27, Newton's Third Principle *is* satisfied.

28.9 MAGNETIC FIELD OF THE EARTH

The earth's magnetic field is familiar to anyone who has used a compass. Over most of the earth's surface the horizontal component of this field $\mathcal{B}_H$ points generally northward. The end of a magnetized compass needle that points in the direction of $\mathcal{B}_H$ is called a "north-seeking pole" or often simply an N-pole. The other end of the compass needle is called a "south-seeking pole" or simply an S-pole. This means that the magnetic moment $\mathbf{m}$ of a bar magnet is directed along its axis from its S-pole to its N-pole. The earth's magnetic field has a relatively large downward component throughout most of the northern hemisphere and a relatively large upward component throughout most of the southern hemisphere. A representation of the magnetic lines of the earth's magnetic field is given in Fig. 28.18.

To a useful first approximation the magnetic field at the earth's surface is that due to a simple magnetic dipole as given in (28.8), where the dipole moment $\mathbf{m}$ has a magnitude of about 7.94×10^{22} A·m² and is located very near the center of the earth with its direction inclined at about 11° to the earth's axis of rotation. The

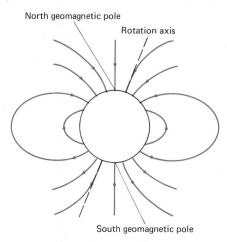

North geomagnetic pole

Rotation axis

South geomagnetic pole

Fig. 28.18 A representation of the magnetic lines of the Earth's magnetic field.

magnitude of the horizontal component of the earth's magnetic field strength varies from about 31 μT at the magnetic equator to zero at the earth's geomagnetic poles; the magnitude of the vertical component varies from zero at the magnetic equator to about 72 μT at the magnetic poles.

Measurements made over the past 400 years show significant changes in both the magnitude and the direction of the magnetic-field strength at the earth's surface. Archeological evidence from the magnetization of ferromagnetic minerals dispersed as small grains in objects such as bricks from pottery kilns and paleological evidence from the magnetization of ferromagnetic minerals dispersed as small grains in rocks indicate that over very long time spans there have been very large variations in the earth's magnetic-field strength. When averaged over times the order of 10 000 years or more, the direction of the earth's magnetic dipole moment has coincided with the earth's rotational axis. The magnitude of the magnetic-field strength at the earth's surface has varied from near zero to more than twice its present value over the past 2.5×10^9 years. The data are widely scattered, and the evidence for any kind of long-term trend is not compelling.

The direction of the earth's magnetic moment relative to its angular momentum has actually undergone repeated reversals at irregular intervals of from hundreds of thousands of years to tens of millions of years. The most recent reversal occurred about 690 000 years ago. The source of the earth's magnetic field thus seems to be a bistable system in a delicate state of balance.

There is general agreement that the earth's magnetic field arises from fluid motions of the electrically conducting core and depends on the phenomenon of electromagnetic induction, which will be discussed in the next chapter. However, consensus does not exist as to the nature of the fluid motions, the source of energy that maintains these motions, or any other details of the source of the earth's field. Several other objects in the solar system have strong magnetic fields. If we let m_E represent the magnetic dipole moment of the earth, Jupiter has a magnetic field associated with a magnetic dipole moment $m_J \simeq 2 \times 10^4 m_E$ and the sun has a magnetic dipole moment $m_S \simeq 3 \times 10^6 m_E$; in both cases there are significant deviations of the field from pure dipole form. The inner planets Mercury, Venus, and Mars have magnetic fields much smaller than that of the earth. Planetary magnetism is an active field of research.

QUESTIONS

1. In (28.1), is $d\mathscr{B}$ perpendicular to $d\mathbf{l}$? Is $d\mathscr{B}$ perpendicular to $\hat{\mathbf{r}}$? Is $d\mathbf{l}$ perpendicular to $\hat{\mathbf{r}}$? What are the physical dimensions of $\hat{\mathbf{r}}$?

2. What is an *ampere*?

3. In our treatment of electrostatics we stated experimental uncertainties for ϵ_0. Why don't we state uncertainties for μ_0?

4. If you need to obtain a *uniform* magnetic field of 2 mT in a cubical volume of space measuring 15 cm on a side, how might you establish such a field?

5. In experiments where the effects of the earth's magnetic field need to be eliminated, *Helmholtz coils* are frequently employed. Helmholtz coils are described in Problem 42. Why are they more effective for the purpose than a single coil?

6. Compare the structures of the *far* fields of electric dipoles and magnetic dipoles. How do their *near* fields differ?

7. How can you use Ampere's line integral relation to show that the magnetic field well inside a long solenoid is uniform and equal to the field on the axis? If this relation for the field held to the very ends of a long solenoid, what would be the magnetic field outside the solenoid?

8. The external field of the closely wound toroid in Fig. 28.16a is not exactly zero if a single winding is used. Why? How could you put on a second layer of winding to make the external field zero?

9. In what sense is a moving charge similar to a current element?

10. What do we mean when we say that the Principle of Biot and Savart forms the basis for the theory of magnetic-field strength due to *steady* currents?

11. No wire can actually be "infinitely long." Under what conditions does (28.4) give a good approximation for the magnetic-field strength due to a current in a straight segment of wire?

12. Rewrite (28.6) in terms of the axial distance ξ of the point P in Fig. 28.8 from the plane of the coil. How is this formula changed if the origin of coordinates is not at the center of the circular loop?

PROBLEMS

1. A long, straight copper wire 4 mm in diameter carries a uniformly distributed current of 9.6 A. What is the magnitude of the magnetic-field strength at the surface of the wire? What is the magnitude of the magnetic-field strength 2 cm away from the center of the wire? What is the magnitude of the magnetic-field strength at the center of the wire?

2. What uniformly distributed current must a long, straight wire of diameter 4.5 mm carry if the magnetic-field strength at a distance of 2.5 cm from the center line of the wire is to have a magnitude of 54 μT?

3. What is the magnetic force on a 10-keV electron due to a long, straight wire carrying a current of 6 A from west to east if the electron is 5 cm above the wire and moving (a) eastward? (b) northward? (c) upward? (d) 20° north of east?

4. At a certain location where magnetic north and true north coincide, the earth's magnetic field has a northward component of 15 μT and a downward component of 52 μT. What error will be produced in the reading of a magnetic compass held at ground level directly below a north–south DC power line

carrying 500 A at a height of 20 m above the ground?

5. What is the resultant magnetic force on the rigid rectangular loop lying in the XY plane as shown in the diagram due to a long straight wire carrying a current I_2 along the Y axis in the negative Y direction? Evaluate the result numerically for the case $I_1 = 1.25$ A, $I_2 = 3$ A, $a = 2$ cm, $b = 4$ cm, $d = 1.5$ cm, and $g = 1.75$ cm.

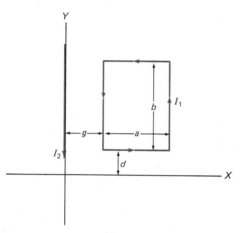

Problem 5

6. Two long, straight wires are parallel to the Z axis. Wire ① carries a current of 6 A in the $+Z$ direction and crosses the X axis at $x = 5$ cm. Wire ② crosses the X axis at $x = 15$ cm. What must be the magnitude and direction of the current in wire ② if the resultant magnetic-field strength on the line parallel to the Z axis through $x = 20$ cm, $y = 0$ is to be zero? What is then the magnetic-field strength at points on the Z axis?

7. In the diagram, I_1 and I_2 represent currents in long, straight wires both directed toward

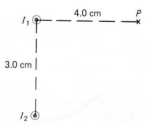

Problem 7

the reader. What is the resultant magnetic-field strength at the point P if $I_1 = 2.0$ A and $I_2 = 3.0$ A?

8. A long, straight wire carrying a current of 50 A is fixed in position at right angles to a uniform external magnetic field having $\mathscr{B} = 2.5 \times 10^{-4}$ T. The wire carries current vertically downward; the external field is directed from west to east. Give a qualitative description of the resultant magnetic-field strength. Determine the locations of the points where the resultant magnetic-field strength is zero.

9. What is the magnetic-field strength at the point P due to the current-carrying wires shown in the diagram?

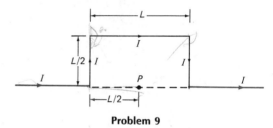

Problem 9

10. What is the magnetic-field strength at the center of a rectangular current loop 8 cm wide by 13 cm long if the loop has 18 turns each carrying a current of 4.6 A?

11. A square loop of side $2a$ lies in the XY plane with its center at the origin and its sides parallel to the X and Y axes. The loop carries a current I counterclockwise as seen from above. Show that the magnetic-field strength due to this loop at an arbitrary point on the Z axis is $[2\mu_0 Ia^2/\pi(z^2 + a^2)\sqrt{2a^2 + z^2}]\mathbf{k}$.

12. Four long, straight, parallel wires each carry a current of 2.5 A in the $-Z$ direction. The wires intersect the XY plane at the four corners of a square of side 3.75 cm. (a) What is the resultant magnetic-field strength at the center of the square? (b) What is the resultant magnetic force on a length L of any one of the current-carrying wires due to the other wires?

13. Repeat Problem 12 for a case where two wires at the opposite ends of a diagonal of

the square carry current in the $-Z$ direction and the two wires at the opposite ends of the other diagonal of the square carry current in the $+Z$ direction.

14. Draw a qualitative representation of the magnetic lines lying in a plane perpendicular to the wires for the systems of Problems 12 and 13.

15. A closely wound circular coil with a mean radius of 5 cm consists of 300 turns of wire. When the current in the windings is 8 A, what is the magnitude of the magnetic-field strength at the center of the coil? If the coil is lying flat on a horizontal table top and the current in the windings is in the CCW sense as viewed from above, what is the direction of the magnetic field at the center of the coil?

16. A magnetic-field strength of magnitude 1mT is desired at the center of a circular coil of radius 8cm. The available wire can safely carry a maximum current of 30 A. How long a piece of wire is required to make the coil?

17. What is the magnetic-field strength at the point P shown in the diagram if the circuit carries a current $I = 8.5$ A, $b = 2$ cm, and $R = 8$ cm?

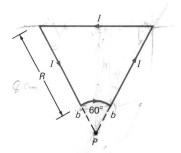

Problem 17

18. What current would be required to produce a magnetic-field strength of magnitude 7.5×10^{-5} T at the center of a circular loop of radius 10 cm? Suppose that we wish to produce a 7.5×10^{-5}-T field with a coil of 10-cm radius, but the only wire available has a resistance of 0.15 Ω/m and can carry a maximum current of 1.0 A. How many turns

of wire are required? What will be the resistance of the coil?

19. A current is sent through a spring made of conducting wire that is hanging vertically with a mass supported from its lower end. Describe what will happen; explain *why* it will happen. Does the result depend on the direction of the current?

20. What is the magnetic-field strength on the axis of the rotating disk of Problem 29 of Chapter 27 at a distance z above the disk?

21. Two coaxial coils, each of radius R, are separated by a distance R. Each coil is composed of 50 closely wound turns of wire, and each carries a current $I = 1.6$ A in each turn in a right-hand sense about the coil axis. What is the magnetic-field strength on the coil axis midway between the coils if $R = 15$ cm?

22. What should be the current in the coils of Problem 21 if the magnetic field produced by the coils is to exactly cancel the earth's magnetic field midway between the coils at a location where the earth's field has a northward component of 15 μT, a downward component of 52 μT, and zero eastward component?

23. Show that the result of Problem 11 for the magnetic-field strength on the axis of a square current loop of side $2a$ is consistent with (28.8) in the limit where $z \gg a$.

24. For the square loop of Problem 11, show that the magnitude of the magnetic-field strength on the X axis in the limit $x \gg a$ is $\mathcal{B} = \mu_0 m/4\pi x^3$, where m is the magnetic moment of the loop. What is the direction of $\mathcal{B}$ on the X axis? Show that this result is consistent with (28.8).

25. A certain long circular solenoid has a radius of 15 cm and carries a current of 0.25 A. What is the number of turns per unit length if the magnetic-field strength far from either end of the solenoid has a magnitude of 8.5×10^{-4} T?

26. What is the magnetic flux through a plane perpendicular to the axis of a long circular

solenoid of radius 3.75 cm wound with 20 turns per cm if a current of 0.25 A is passed through the windings?

27. A solenoid consists of 2600 turns of copper wire wound uniformly on a hollow plastic tube 4 cm in diameter and 80 cm long. What is the magnetic field through the central portion of the solenoid when there is a current of 5 A in the windings? What is the magnetic flux through the central portion of the solenoid?

28. What is the magnitude of the magnetic-field strength on the axis of the solenoid of the preceding problem at a distance of 4 cm outside either end of the solenoid?

29. An observer moves along the axis of the circular solenoid shown in Fig. 28.12 in the vicinity of the left end of the solenoid. Assume that the other end of the solenoid is very far away so that $\alpha \to \pi$. (a) What is the magnetic-field strength on the solenoid axis at the end of the solenoid? (b) How far into the solenoid in terms of the radius a must the observer go before the magnetic-field strength given by (28.10) differs from that given by (28.11) by less than 10%? (c) Make a graph of the magnitude of the magnetic-field strength given by (28.10) divided by the value given by (28.11) for the points along the solenoid axis from five radii from the end outside the solenoid to five radii from the end inside the solenoid.

30. Using the result of Problem 11, find the magnetic-field strength at an arbitrary point on the axis of a square solenoid of side 2a. Show that the limiting case for a point inside and far from either end of the solenoid is again (28.11) as for a circular solenoid.

31. For testing magnetic mines during World War II, large square solenoids were constructed that could be used to apply a uniform magnetic field to the entire mine case. Suppose that such a solenoid is 76 cm square and 7.6 m long and is wound with 1 turn

per cm. Use the result of Problem 30 to compute the magnetic-field strength per ampere of current on the solenoid axis one-half the way from one end of the solenoid to the center of the solenoid. Is the result significantly different from the result given by (28.11)? What order of magnitude of current is required to simulate a ship's field, which is the order of tenths of microteslas?

32. A long, straight wire of radius a carries a uniformly distributed current I. (a) How far from the surface of the wire in terms of the radius a must one go to find the magnetic-field strength reduced to 20% of its value at the surface of the wire? (b) At what distance from the axis of the wire will the magnetic-field strength inside the wire be 20% of its value at the surface of the wire?

33. Suppose that the toroid shown in Fig. 28.16 has $a = 12$ cm and $b = 0.5$ cm, is wound with 1000 turns, and carries a current of 15 mA. What are the maximum and the minimum magnitudes of the magnetic-field strength inside the windings?

34. Verify Ampere's line-integral relation for the two paths shown in the diagram if a long, straight wire carries current I toward the reader at the location indicated.

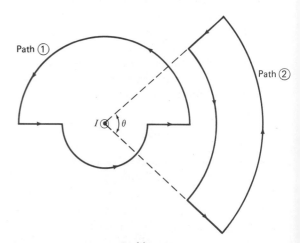

Problem 34

35. A long, straight conducting pipe of inner radius R_1 and outer radius R_2 carries a uniformly distributed current I. Use Ampere's relation to derive expressions for the magnetic-field strength due to the current in the regions $R < R_1$, $R_1 < R < R_2$, and $R > R_2$, where R is the radial distance from the axis of the pipe.

36. A long, straight coaxial cable has an inner conductor of radius R_1 that carries a uniformly distributed current I in one direction and an outer conductor of inner radius R_2 and outer radius R_3 that carries a uniformly distributed current I in the opposite direction from the inner conductor. Use Ampere's relation to derive expressions for the magnetic-field strength due to these currents for the regions $R < R_1$, $R_1 < R < R_2$, $R_2 < R < R_3$, and $R > R_3$, where R is the radial distance from the axis of the cable.

37. For an ideal solenoid, which is well approximated by a real very long closely wound solenoid far from its ends, one can argue from symmetry that $\mathscr{B}$ must be parallel to the solenoid axis inside the solenoid, antiparallel to the solenoid axis outside the solenoid, and cannot depend on the Z coordinate. For points on the axis, $\mathscr{B}$ is given by (28.11). Using these facts about the magnetic field, apply Ampere's relation to paths ① and ② shown in the diagram. The bottom side of each of these paths lies along the solenoid axis. From the result for path ① prove that $\mathscr{B} = 0$ outside the solenoid. From the result for path ② prove that (28.11) holds *everywhere* inside the solenoid.

38. By considering Ampere's relation for a path that circles the outside of a singly-wound solenoid, show that because of the pitch of the windings, $\mathscr{B}$ cannot be exactly zero everywhere outside the solenoid even if the solenoid is arbitrarily long.

39. Two protons are moving near the origin. Compare the magnetic and the electric forces between the protons at a time when one is at $(x, y, z) = (5 \text{ cm}, 0, 0)$ and traveling in the $+Y$ direction with a kinetic energy of 10 keV and the other is at the origin and traveling in the $-Y$ direction with a kinetic energy of 5 keV.

40. Show in detail how (28.13) follows from (28.1) if we assume that the current I is due to a collection of n particles per unit volume each having charge q and moving with velocity **v**.

41. Suppose that we try to develop a theory of magnetic poles by asserting that a needle-shaped bar magnet has a point pole $+q_m$ associated with its N-end and a point pole $-q_m$ associated with its S-end and that the magnitude of the magnetic moment of the magnet is $q_m d$, where d is the length of the magnet. This makes the magnetic moment **m** depend on q_m in the same way that the electric dipole moment **p** depends on the dipole charge q. By comparison of (28.8) and (28.9) deduce the expression for the magnetic-field strength produced by a single point pole and the "Coulomb" relation for the force between point poles.

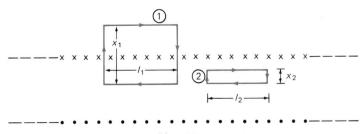

Problem 37

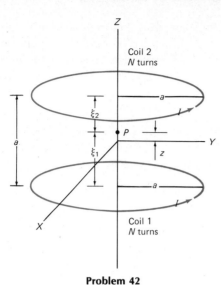

Problem 42

42. The so-called *Helmholtz coils* shown in the diagram consist of two coaxial circular coils of N turns each with planes separated by a distance a equal to their radius. This arrangement gives a remarkably uniform magnetic-field strength over a fairly large volume between the two coils. Illustrate this uniformity by determining $\mathscr{B}$, $d\mathscr{B}/dz$, and $d^2\mathscr{B}/dz^2$ for points on the Z axis. Take the origin midway between the two coils.

CHAPTER 29

Electromagnetic Induction

Following the experiment by Oersted showing that an electric current could produce magnetic effects, Michael Faraday began to search for the converse phenomenon. It was a basic tenet of Faraday's scientific philosophy that every cause and effect has a converse, and he confidently expected that in some fashion magnetism should give rise to electrical effects. He attempted a large number of experiments involving various configurations of magnets and electric currents. In 1831, six years after his first trials, Faraday discovered the essential feature that the magnetic field must be changing in time or the circuit must be moving relative to the magnetic field in order to produce an electrical effect. Faraday was able to show that a large number of experimental arrangements allow a magnetic field to *induce* an EMF in a circuit and thereby give rise to an induced electric current, and he formulated a qualitative explanation of the phenomenon in terms of magnetic lines. The mathematical formulation of Faraday's results was subsequently provided by James Clerk Maxwell.

A number of Faraday's results on electromagnetic induction were discovered independently at essentially the same time by the American physicist Joseph Henry (1797–1878), who later was the first director of the Smithsonian Institution. However, America was so far from the centers of scientific work and communications were so slow that Henry's investigations had little effect on subsequent scientific developments compared with the tremendous impact of Faraday's work.

In this chapter we shall consider the modern formulation of the results of Faraday and Henry on electromagnetic induction. These phenomena allow a magnetic field to act as an intermediary in the operation of generators for the conversion of mechanical energy to electrical potential energy, a process that lies at the heart of the electric power industry. We shall also see that a changing magnetic field is always associated with an induced electric field having properties quite different from those of the electrostatic fields considered previously. This association is basic to the theory of electromagnetic radiation, which we shall consider in Chapter 32.

29.1 MOTIONAL EMF

Consider a straight piece of conducting wire of length L that is moving with a velocity $\mathbf{v}$ in a region where there is a uniform magnetic field $\mathscr{B}$. For simplicity we shall consider a wire segment that is oriented perpendicular to $\mathscr{B}$ and is moving with a velocity $\mathbf{v}$ that is perpendicular to the wire orientation and to $\mathscr{B}$, as is shown in Fig. 29.1. The electric charges of the conductor moving with velocity $\mathbf{v}$ experience magnetic forces given by $\mathbf{F}_{\mathscr{B}} = q(\mathbf{v} \times \mathscr{B})$. The positive charges are bound to the crystal lattice of the conducting material; however, some of the negative charges are "free" conduction electrons that can move relative to the lattice of the material. Under the influence of the magnetic force, the conduction electrons move toward the lower end of the wire in Fig. 29.1.

For a single isolated piece of wire, the motion of the conduction electrons under the influence of the magnetic force does not continue indefinitely even if the region of magnetic field is large. As the electrons move, the lower end of the wire in Fig. 29.1 becomes negative and, because of the depletion of electrons, the upper end of the wire becomes positive. Due to this separation of charge there is an electric field $\mathscr{E}$, and the charges in the wire experience an electric force $\mathbf{F}_{\mathscr{E}} = q\mathscr{E}$. This force is opposite in direction to the magnetic force, and the motion of electrons relative to the wire ceases when the two forces have equal magnitudes: $\mathbf{F}_{\mathscr{B}} = \mathbf{F}_{\mathscr{E}}$, which implies that $\mathscr{E} = v\mathscr{B}$ for the situation of Fig. 29.1.

A more interesting arrangement is obtained if the moving piece of wire is part of a closed circuit, for example as suggested in Fig. 29.2. In this figure there is an applied force $\mathbf{F}_A$ exerted by some external agent that pulls a straight piece of conductor at constant velocity $\mathbf{v}$ along a pair of parallel conducting "rails" that are separated by a distance L. In the region between the rails there is a uniform magnetic field $\mathscr{B}$ directed away from the reader. We assume that the moving conductor maintains an orientation perpendicular to both $\mathbf{v}$ and $\mathscr{B}$. The circuit formed by the moving conductor is completed by a resistor R joined to the ends of the rails by conducting leads. In this case there is not a simple accumulation of negative charge at the bottom and of positive charge at the top of the moving conductor. Rather, electrons are pushed out of the bottom end of the moving conductor and around the circuit, giving rise to the current I indicated in Fig. 29.2. *The conductor moving relative to the*

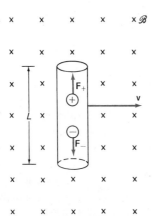

Fig. 29.1 A straight segment of conducting wire moving with velocity $\mathbf{v}$ in a magnetic field $\mathscr{B}$. The symbol x represents a magnetic-field strength vector directed away from the reader.

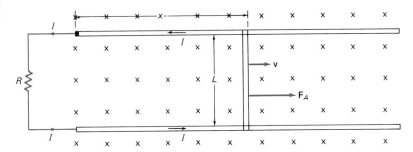

Fig. 29.2 A straight segment of conducting wire is
pulled along a pair of parallel
conducting rails with a velocity **v** by an applied force
F$_A$. There is a uniform magnetic field $\mathscr{B}$ directed away
from the reader; this field is
denoted by the symbol x.

magnetic field acts as a source of EMF. The magnitude of this EMF is the electrical
energy gained per unit positive charge passing through the moving conductor in
the current direction.

For a free electron in the moving conductor having only the velocity **v,** the magnetic
force $-e(\mathbf{v} \times \mathscr{B})$ is directed toward the bottom of Fig. 29.2. However, the resultant
velocity of an electron in the conductor moving with drift velocity $\mathbf{v}_d$ parallel to
the wire axis is $\mathbf{v}_R = \mathbf{v} + \mathbf{v}_d$, and the resultant magnetic force on such an electron
is $\mathbf{F}_{\mathscr{B}} = -e(\mathbf{v}_R \times \mathscr{B}) = -e(\mathbf{v} \times \mathscr{B}) - e(\mathbf{v}_d \times \mathscr{B}) = \mathbf{F}_{\mathscr{B}1} + \mathbf{F}_{\mathscr{B}2}$, as shown in Fig. 29.3.
If $\mathbf{F}_{\mathscr{B}}$ were the only force acting, the electron would curve to the left in Fig. 29.3.
But in addition to $\mathbf{F}_{\mathscr{B}}$ there is a force that arises because of the surface effects that
constrain electrons to remain inside the conductor. It is the existence of such a force
that allows the free electrons to move with the piece of conductor when the applied
force gives it the velocity **v,** and it is because of this force that the external agent
moving the conductor is able to cause work to be done to free electrons in the moving
conductor. The magnetic force, being always perpendicular to the resultant electron
velocity $\mathbf{v}_R$, cannot itself do any work to the electrons. As the sliding wire begins
to move, there is a charge separation as electrons are forced to the left in Fig. 29.3
by the magnetic force. This results in a transverse electric field across the wire as
described for the Hall effect in Section 27.5. An equilibrium is very quickly reached
such that the resultant transverse force on a conduction electron in the sliding wire
is zero. In Fig. 29.3 we represent the nonmagnetic transverse force by $\mathbf{F}_S$, and we
have $\mathbf{F}_S = -\mathbf{F}_{\mathscr{B}2}$.

Suppose that it requires a time Δt for an electron to move from one end of the
sliding wire to the other. The path of the electron is the line *AB* shown in Fig. 29.4.

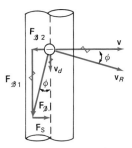

Fig. 29.3 Forces acting on a
conduction electron in the moving wire of Fig. 29.3.

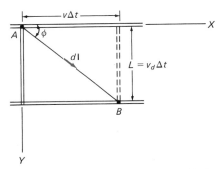

Fig. 29.4 The actual macroscopic path of an
electron as it moves through the sliding wire of
Fig. 29.3 from *A* to *B*.

The work done on an electron during such a trip is $W = \int_A^B (\mathbf{F}_\mathscr{B} + \mathbf{F}_S) \cdot d\mathbf{l}$. As shown in Fig. 29.3, the resultant force $\mathbf{F}_\mathscr{B} + \mathbf{F}_S$ is parallel to the wire axis and has magnitude $F_{\mathscr{B}1} = ev\mathscr{B}$. Therefore, $(\mathbf{F}_\mathscr{B} + \mathbf{F}_S) \cdot d\mathbf{l} = ev\mathscr{B}\, dy$, where the axes are defined in Fig. 29.4, and the work done to an electron moving from A to B is $W = \int_A^B ev\mathscr{B}\, dy = ev\mathscr{B}L$. Electrons moving from A to B give a current in the sense indicated in Fig. 29.2; the EMF associated with the moving wire is $V_E = W/e = v\mathscr{B}L$, and the sense of this EMF is upward in Fig. 29.2.

The current through the resistor R in Fig. 29.2 is such that $IR = v\mathscr{B}L$, or $I = v\mathscr{B}L/R$. We assume that there is negligible work done against frictional forces as the conductor slides along the rails. Then in order for energy to be conserved under steady-state conditions, the rate at which the applied force $\mathbf{F}_A$ does work to the conductor moving with constant velocity $\mathbf{v}$ must equal the rate at which heat is generated in the resistor R, which is $I^2R = v^2\mathscr{B}^2L^2/R$.

The wire moving with velocity $\mathbf{v}$ and carrying a current I experiences a force $\mathbf{F} = I\mathbf{L} \times \mathscr{B}$; this force has magnitude $IL\mathscr{B}$ and is directed to the left in Fig. 29.2. Since the wire moves with constant velocity, the applied force to the right must have this same magnitude: $F_A = IL\mathscr{B}$. The rate at which the applied force does work to the moving wire is, therefore, $F_A v = IL\mathscr{B}v = (v\mathscr{B}L/R)L\mathscr{B}v = v^2\mathscr{B}^2L^2/R$, just the value required for energy conservation.

29.2 FARADAY'S PRINCIPLE OF INDUCTION

In Section 27.2 we defined the magnetic flux through a surface S to be the surface integral of the magnetic-field strength over that surface:

$$\Phi_\mathscr{B} = \iint \mathscr{B} \cdot d\mathbf{S}. \tag{29.1}$$

As an outcome of extensive investigations on the possibility of magnetic phenomena giving rise to electrical effects, Faraday was able to show that the crucial requirement is that the magnetic flux through a surface bounded by a circuit, which is said to *link* the circuit, must be changing in time.

Let us consider again the arrangement shown in Fig. 29.2. At the time when the sliding rod is at position x, the magnetic flux linking the circuit is $\Phi_\mathscr{B} = -xL\mathscr{B}$, where the minus sign appears because we have taken the positive sense of the circuit to be in the counterclockwise direction in the figure and $\mathscr{B}$ is directed away from the reader. The time rate of change of this magnetic flux as the sliding wire moves is $d\Phi_\mathscr{B}/dt = -\mathscr{B}L\, dx/dt = -\mathscr{B}Lv$; thus, the motional EMF found in Section 29.1 is given by $V_E = -d\Phi_\mathscr{B}/dt$.

This conclusion for the circuit shown in Fig. 29.2 is a particular example of a more general result:

FARADAY'S PRINCIPLE OF INDUCTION. There is an EMF induced in a circuit whenever the magnetic flux linking the circuit is changing. This EMF is equal to the negative time rate of change of the magnetic flux linking the circuit. In symbols, Faraday's Principle of Induction has the form

$$V_E = \frac{-d\Phi_{\mathscr{B}}}{dt} = \frac{-d}{dt} \iint \mathscr{B} \cdot d\mathbf{S}. \quad \begin{Bmatrix} V_E \text{ in } V \\ \Phi \text{ in } Wb \\ t \text{ in } s \end{Bmatrix} \quad \begin{array}{l} \textit{(Faraday's Principle} \\ \textit{of Induction)} \end{array} \qquad (29.2)$$

This relation holds whatever the reason for the change in magnetic flux. We can identify two general classes of changes in the magnetic flux linking a circuit. First, there may be changes in the sources of the magnetic-field strength that cause the factor $\mathscr{B}$ in the flux integral (29.1) to vary in time. Second, there may be changes in the size, orientation, or location of the circuit under consideration that cause the surface over which the flux integral (29.1) is computed to vary in time. This second cause of flux change is the situation for the arrangement considered in Section 29.1. In the most general circumstance both kinds of change may occur simultaneously.

If the circuit has N turns of wire each occupying essentially the same location in space, then each turn is linked by the same magnetic flux $\Phi_{\mathscr{B}}$, and each turn has associated with it an EMF given by (29.2). Since the turns of wire follow one another in sequence along the circuit, these EMF's are in series, and the total EMF associated with the N-turn circuit is just N times the EMF associated with a single turn. We can express this by writing

$$V_E = -N\frac{d\Phi_{\mathscr{B}}}{dt} = -N\frac{d}{dt}\iint \mathscr{B} \cdot d\mathbf{S}, \quad \begin{array}{l} \textit{(Faraday's Principle for} \\ \textit{an N-turn circuit)} \end{array} \qquad (29.2')$$

where it is understood that $\Phi_{\mathscr{B}}$ refers to the flux linking a single one of the turns.

If the path bounding the surface S in (29.2) is occupied by a conducting material, the EMF predicted by (29.2) will give rise to a current in the conductor. However, as was first realized by Maxwell, the EMF exists whether or not the path coincides with a wire in which a current can be induced. When we say that the EMF "exists," we mean that there will be net work done on a charged particle that is carried around the path bounding S because of the changing magnetic flux linking that path. This work must be due to forces of electromagnetic origin. However, from the Lorentz force equation a magnetic force $\mathbf{F}_{\mathscr{B}} = q\mathbf{v} \times \mathscr{B}$ is always perpendicular to the particle velocity $\mathbf{v}$ and can do no work to the particle. Maxwell recognized that the induced EMF must be associated with an induced electric-field strength $\mathscr{E}$ such that for a *fixed path* C bounding a fixed surface S we have

$$V_E = \oint_C \mathscr{E} \cdot d\mathbf{l} = \frac{-d}{dt}\iint \mathscr{B} \cdot d\mathbf{S} = -\iint \frac{\partial \mathscr{B}}{\partial t} \cdot d\mathbf{S}, \qquad (29.3)$$

where the differentiation of $\mathscr{B}$ under the integral sign is justified because of the assumption of a fixed surface of integration. Any observer who sees a magnetic-field strength that varies in time will necessarily see associated with it an induced electric-field strength such that (29.3) is satisfied for any fixed closed path C bounding a fixed surface S.

The induced electric-field strength has important differences from the electrostatic-field strength discussed in Chapters 21 and 22 that has as its source charged particles at rest. In Chapter 22 we showed that the electrostatic-field strength $\mathscr{E}_S$ satisfies the relation

$$\oint_C \mathscr{E}_S \cdot d\mathbf{l} = 0 \quad (\textit{Electrostatics}) \tag{29.4}$$

for any closed path C. This is quite different from the behavior displayed in (29.3):

$$\oint_C \mathscr{E} \cdot d\mathbf{l} = \frac{-d\Phi_{\mathscr{B}}}{dt}. \quad (\textit{Induction}) \tag{29.4'}$$

However, since an electric-field strength satisfying (29.4) could be added to the electric-field strength in (29.3) without altering the form of (29.3), we can interpret the symbol $\mathscr{E}$ in (29.3) as representing the resultant electric-field strength due to all sources.

The nonvanishing of the line integral of the induced electric-field strength around a closed path means that the concept of electrical potential cannot be developed for this field as it was for the electrostatic-field strength in Chapter 22. However, we can still consider the difference in electrical energy per unit positive charge between two points connected by *particular paths* such as are provided in a circuit. In order to emphasize the distinction from the electrostatic case where the line integral of the electric-field strength between two points is independent of the path taken between the points, *we shall henceforth use the term "voltage" in referring to the difference in electrical energy per unit positive charge between two points in a circuit.*

29.3   LENZ'S LAW

The sense of the induced EMF given by (29.2) can be determined by application of the sign conventions we have established for magnetic flux. However, it is often convenient to use instead an alternative procedure utilizing a law first formulated by Heinrich Friedrich Lenz (1804–1865) in 1833. We state this law as follows:

LENZ'S LAW.   The induced EMF in a circuit is in such a direction as to *oppose the change* causing it. In particular, the induced EMF is directed such that the current it tends to generate would produce magnetic flux linking the circuit in such a way as to oppose the change in magnetic flux causing the EMF.

When the law is stated in this way, the physical reason underlying the minus sign in (29.2) becomes apparent. If the induced EMF produced a current that generated its own flux in such a way as to increase the change causing the EMF, small random flux variations could feed on themselves and generate huge induced currents.

The best way to learn how to apply Lenz's law is to consider carefully a number of examples of its use. We shall now examine several such examples. In every application of Lenz's law it is essential to remember that it is the *change* in primary magnetic flux linking the circuit that must be opposed by the secondary flux generated by the induced current. The secondary flux will add to or oppose the primary flux depending on whether the primary flux is decreasing or increasing.

In Fig. 29.5 we show a bar magnet falling toward a circuit C with its N-pole down. The magnetic lines of a bar magnet are directed out from its N-pole and in toward its S-pole. The magnetic lines leaving the N-pole are indicated in Fig. 29.5. As the N-pole of the magnet approaches the circuit, the magnetic flux linking the circuit in a downward sense increases. In order to oppose this change in flux, the magnetic flux generated by the current induced in the circuit C must link the circuit in an upward sense, which requires that the induced current in C be counterclockwise as seen from above.

Next consider a circuit C that is moving toward a parallel current-carrying circuit C' as shown in Fig. 29.6. From the orientation of the magnetic lines due to the current I' as shown in Fig. 29.6, we see that the magnetic flux linking C increases to the left in the figure as C approaches C'. In order to oppose this change in flux, the magnetic flux generated by the current induced in circuit C should link this circuit to the right, which requires that the induced current I be in a sense opposite to that of I', as indicated in Fig. 29.6. Another way to think of this particular arrangement is to note that the currents in opposite directions in the parallel loops will repel each other, thereby opposing the motion of loop C that is bringing the circuits closer together. Similar reasoning shows that if C were moving away from C', the induced current I would be in the same sense as I'.

In Fig. 29.7 we show two nearby circuits C and C', with C' carrying a current I'. So long as I' is steady, the magnetic flux due to I' linking C is constant and there is no current induced in C. However, if the switch S is opened, the flux due to I' linking C, which is dominated by the portion of C' between Ⓐ and Ⓑ and therefore links C in the direction toward the reader in Fig. 29.7, drops rapidly to zero. This produces an induced current pulse in circuit C. In order to oppose the change in flux linking C due to I', the magnetic flux generated by the induced current

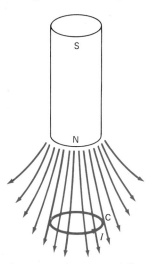

Fig. 29.5 A bar magnet falling toward a circuit C.

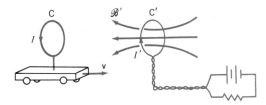

Fig. 29.6 A circuit C moving toward a current-carrying circuit C'. The planes of the two loops are parallel.

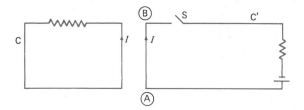

Fig. 29.7

I must also link C in the direction toward the reader which requires that I be counter-clockwise, as indicated in Fig. 29.7. If the switch S is subsequently reclosed, the flux linking C due to I' increases in the direction toward the reader. In order that the flux due to the induced current pulse I oppose this increase, I must now be clockwise in Fig. 29.7, opposite to the direction of the induced current pulse when S is opened.

29.4 AC GENERATOR

The device illustrated in Fig. 29.2 serves to convert mechanical energy to electrical potential energy and hence is a simple *generator*. However, it is not a very practical generator for sustained operation. A prototype of a modern alternating current generator was invented by Faraday in 1851. The basic arrangement for a practical generator is illustrated in Fig. 29.8; a rectangular coil, mounted on a shaft not shown in the diagram, is rotated in a uniform magnetic field as indicated by the dashed circular arrow in the figure. Mechanical energy is supplied by the mechanism causing the coil to rotate, for example, by a water-driven or steam-driven turbine.

As the coil rotates, the magnetic flux linking the circuit changes, and by Faraday's principle there is an induced EMF between terminals A and B that can be used to

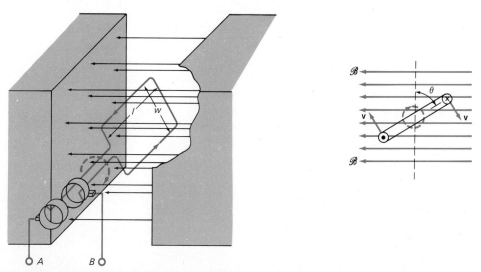

Fig. 29.8 A prototype alternating current generator consisting of a single rectangular coil rotating in a uniform magnetic field. The terminals Ⓐ and Ⓑ make contact through "brushes" with the "slip rings" connected to the ends of the coil wire.

drive a current in an external circuit. The angle θ defined in Fig. 29.8 measures how far the coil has rotated from a vertical orientation. We choose the positive orientation of the path C around the coil to be as indicated by the arrows in Fig. 29.8. The magnetic flux linking the coil is given by

$$\Phi_{\mathscr{B}} = \mathscr{B}wl \cos \theta = \Phi_{max} \cos \theta.$$

We suppose that the coil is rotated with a constant angular velocity $\omega = 2\pi f$ in radians per second so that at any time t we have $\theta = 2\pi ft$. Then according to (29.2) the EMF generated between the terminals A and B is given by

$$V_E = -\frac{d\Phi_{\mathscr{B}}}{dt} = -\frac{d}{dt}(\Phi_{max} \cos 2\pi ft) = 2\pi f\Phi_{max} \sin 2\pi ft. \tag{29.5}$$

Elaborations of this basic sinusoidal generator involving multiple coils all rotating with the same angular velocity have proved very useful in practical engineering applications. We shall discuss circuits with currents produced by sinusoidal alternating EMF's in Chapter 31.

In order to convert the prototype device shown in Fig. 29.8 into a DC generator, we replace the slip rings shown in the figure by a split-ring commutator like that shown in Fig. 27.19. The commutator can be arranged so that terminal A is always positive with respect to terminal B. The EMF between terminals A and B then always has the same sign, but its magnitude fluctuates in time as shown in Fig. 29.9b. Generators can be designed with many coils and a many-segmented commutator so that the resultant EMF is a superposition of many curves like that in Fig. 29.9b but with different phases. The fluctuations are thereby smoothed out and a fairly constant EMF is obtained.

29.5 EDDY CURRENTS

Up to this point we have considered currents induced in well-defined conducting paths provided by wires. In many circumstances, however, one finds relatively large pieces of conducting material moving in magnetic fields or located in a time-varying magnetic field. As a result there are many closed conducting paths in the volume of the material that are linked by a time-varying flux, and in accordance with Faraday's

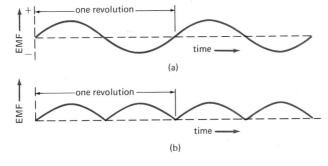

Fig. 29.9 (a) Alternating EMF obtained from the generator of Fig. 29.8. (b) Fluctuating DC EMF obtained by adding a commutator.

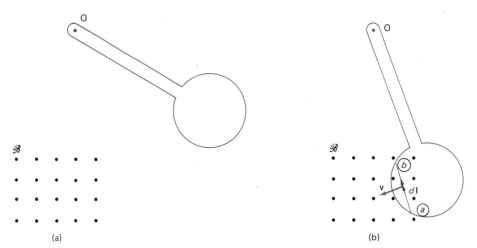

Fig. 29.10 Eddy currents are induced in the conducting disc as the pendulum swings down into the magnetic field $\mathscr{B}$ directed toward the reader. The symbol • is used to represent this field.

principle there are induced currents that circulate in the material. These currents are called *eddy currents* because they form closed loops within the conductor, like eddies within a fluid.

As a simple example of the action of eddy currents, consider the device shown in Fig. 29.10. A magnetic field directed toward the reader exists in the region between the poles of a magnet that is not shown in the figure. A conducting disk is fastened at the end of a rod to form a pendulum that is pivoted at the axis O. The disk is pulled aside and then released so that it swings into the magnetic-field region. As the disk enters the field, an element dl along line ab in the disk is moving relative to the magnetic field $\mathscr{B}$ with velocity **v.** The charges q in dl experience a magnetic force $\mathbf{F} = q\mathbf{v} \times \mathscr{B}$ that is directed toward b for positive charges, and there results an induced current that circulates from a toward b and back through the portion of the disk that is not yet in the field.

Because of the magnetic field $\mathscr{B}$ there is a magnetic force $d\mathbf{F} = I\,d\mathbf{l} \times \mathscr{B}$ directed oppositely to **v** on the electrons constituting the induced current I through $d\mathbf{l}$; the return currents that lie outside the magnetic field do not experience such forces. The result of the interaction of these electrons with the lattice of the material and with the conduction electrons outside the magnetic field region is a braking action on the motion of the disk, as would be expected from the generalized statement of Lenz's law that the induced effect opposes the inducing cause. In fact, in an actual experiment with a reasonably light disk the disk will very rapidly be brought nearly to rest and then will sink slowly to its equilibrium position below the pivot.

Eddy currents are usually unwanted; the I^2R Joule heating associated with these currents constitutes a power loss for the system, and the heat energy produced must be dissipated. In some cases the device can be constructed from many thin sheets or laminations that are separated by nonconducting films so that the circulating eddy currents are confined to a single lamina. In this way the area normal to $\mathscr{B}$ bounded by any conducting path, and therefore the flux linking that path, is made very small, and the induced currents associated with a given flux change are greatly reduced in magnitude.

There are some devices that are specifically designed to take advantage of the existence of eddy currents. For example, in a d'Arsonval-type galvanometer such as described in Section 27.10 the coil and its suspension system form a torsion pendulum. In the absence of damping, such a pendulum would perform oscillations about its equilibrium position when the current through the coils was changed, making the instrument very inconvenient to use. To provide damping, the coil is wound on a light conducting frame. When this frame rotates in the magnetic field, eddy currents are produced that result in a magnetic torque opposing the rotation. The size and shape of the frame are made so as to introduce enough damping to prevent overshooting of the equilibrium position and oscillations but not enough to make the motion of the pointer unduly sluggish. The damping has no effect on the equilibrium position of the pointer because the eddy currents and resulting damping torque are present only when the frame is moving.

29.6 MUTUAL INDUCTANCE

In many important situations we are concerned with the inductive interaction of two circuits that have a fixed geometrical relation to one another. In such a case it is very convenient to introduce a geometrical parameter called the mutual inductance of the circuits. Consider the two circuits shown in Fig. 29.11. Suppose that there is a current I_1 in circuit ①. From the Biot–Savart principle the magnetic-field strength $\mathscr{B}_1$ produced by circuit ① is proportional to I_1. This means that the magnetic flux linking circuit ② due to the field $\mathscr{B}_1$ is also proportional to I_1:

$$\Phi_{21} = \iint \mathscr{B}_1 \cdot d\mathbf{S}_2 = M_{21} I_1. \tag{29.6}$$

If only empty space is involved, which in practice means in the absence of ferromagnetic materials, M_{21} is a constant that depends only on the relative geometry of the two circuits. The constant M_{21} defined by (29.6) is called the *mutual inductance* of circuit ② relative to circuit ①.

We can equally well consider the consequence of a current I_2 in circuit ②. This current will produce a magnetic-field strength $\mathscr{B}_2$ that results in a magnetic flux linking circuit ① that is given by

$$\Phi_{12} = \iint \mathscr{B}_2 \cdot d\mathbf{S}_1 = M_{12} I_2, \tag{29.6'}$$

where M_{12} is the mutual inductance of circuit ① relative to circuit ②.

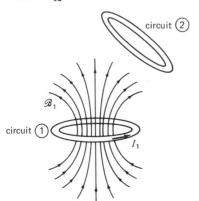

Fig. 29.11 Some of the magnetic lines produced by a current I_1 in circuit ① link a second circuit ②.

The unit of mutual inductance is the weber per ampere. This combination is given the special name *henry* (H) in honor of Joseph Henry:

$$1 \text{ H} = 1 \text{ Wb/A.}$$

In the absence of ferromagnetic material it is possible to show from the Biot–Savart principle that $M_{12} = M_{21}$. Therefore, we represent the mutual inductance of two circuits by the single symbol M. The positive senses of the two circuits are chosen so that M is a positive quantity.

> The **MUTUAL INDUCTANCE** of two circuits in henrys is the magnitude of the magnetic flux linking one of the circuits, in webers, due to a current in the other circuit divided by the magnitude of that current in amperes.

Suppose that there is a current I_1 in circuit ① that is changing in time. As a consequence there will be an EMF V_{E2} induced in circuit ② that by (29.6) and (29.2) is given by

$$V_{E2} = -M\frac{dI_1}{dt}. \quad \left\{ \begin{array}{l} V_{E2} \text{ in V} \\ M \text{ in H} \\ I_1 \text{ in A} \\ t \text{ in s} \end{array} \right\} \quad (29.7)$$

Similarly, a time-varying current in circuit ② produces an induced EMF in circuit ① that is given by

$$V_{E1} = -M\frac{dI_2}{dt}. \quad (29.7')$$

We can give an alternative definition of mutual inductance based on (29.7):

> The **MUTUAL INDUCTANCE** of two circuits in henrys is the magnitude of the EMF induced in one of the circuits, in volts, due to a changing current in the other circuit divided by the magnitude of the time rate of change of that current in amperes per second.

In the presence of ferromagnetic materials, our two definitions are not equivalent because the quantity M in (29.6) may not be independent of the current. In this case it is the second definition that is most useful for circuit theory.

If either circuit has multiple turns, the flux in (29.6) or (29.6') is understood to represent the total flux linkage of the circuit in question for all turns. Therefore, *as the number of turns in either circuit linking the same flux is increased, the mutual inductance of the circuits increases in direct proportion.*

In principle, the mutual inductance of two circuits can be computed from the Biot–Savart principle when the geometric relationship of the two circuits is known. In practice, analytical calculations of mutual inductance are extremely difficult except for certain geometrically simple arrangements. It may make a significant difference in the ease of computation whether one uses (29.6) or (29.6′) to determine the mutual inductance. That is, the flux computation may be simpler when the source current is in one circuit than when it is in the other.

Example. A long closely wound circular solenoid of radius 5 cm is wound with 500 turns per meter. A secondary winding of 250 turns is wrapped around the center of the long solenoid. What is the mutual inductance of the two circuits?

From the discussion in Section 28.6 and Problem 37 of Chapter 28 we know that the magnetic-field strength produced by a current I in a long closely wound solenoid is negligibly small outside the solenoid and is approximately $\mathcal{B} = \mu_0 nI$ everywhere in the interior of the solenoid, where n is the number of turns per unit length. Therefore, the magnetic flux linking each turn of the secondary coil is $\Phi = \mu_0 nI\pi R^2$, where R is the solenoid radius. The total flux linking all turns of the secondary coil is $\Phi_2 = N_2\mu_0 nI\pi R^2 = MI$, so the mutual inductance of the two circuits is

$$M = N_2\mu_0 n\pi R^2 = (250)(4\pi \times 10^{-7}\ \text{T·m/A})(500\ \text{m}^{-1})\pi(0.05\ \text{m})^2$$
$$= 1.23 \times 10^{-3}\ \text{H}.$$

29.7 SELF-INDUCTANCE

The Faraday principle does not require that the source of the time-varying flux be distinct from the circuit in which the induced EMF is produced. Consider again circuit ① in Fig. 29.11. The magnetic-field strength $\mathcal{B}_1$ produced by the current I_1 in circuit ① will result in a flux linking circuit ① that is proportional to I_1. This flux is given by

$$\Phi_{11} = \iint \mathcal{B}_1 \cdot d\mathbf{S}_1 = L_1 I_1, \tag{29.8}$$

where in the absence of ferromagnetic materials L_1 is a constant that depends only on the geometry of circuit ①. The constant L_1 defined by (29.8) is called the *self-inductance* of circuit ①. The unit of self-inductance is again the henry.

The SELF-INDUCTANCE of a circuit in henrys is the magnitude of the magnetic flux linking the circuit, in webers, due to the current in the same circuit divided by the magnitude of that current in amperes.

The self-inductance of a circuit is an inherently positive quantity if the sense of the circuit for computing flux is chosen to agree with the positive direction for current in the circuit.

If the current in a circuit is changing with time, there will be an EMF induced in the circuit that by (29.8) and (29.2) is given by

$$V_E = -L\, dI/dt. \tag{29.9}$$

The minus sign in (29.9) indicates that the induced EMF is in a direction so as to oppose the change in current causing it. If the current I is decreasing, V_E tends to produce current in the same direction as I. If the current I is increasing, V_E tends to produce current in the direction opposite to I. We can give an alternative definition of self-inductance based on (29.9):

> The SELF-INDUCTANCE of a circuit in henrys is the magnitude of the EMF induced in the circuit, in volts, due to a changing current in the same circuit divided by the magnitude of the time rate of change of that current in amperes per second.

It is this definition that we shall extend in Chapter 30 to the case when ferromagnetic materials are present.

Any circuit has some self inductance, but by careful design this can often be made negligibly small. On the other hand, it is often desirable to have relatively large amounts of self-inductance associated with certain locations in a circuit. This can be accomplished by employing an N-turn coil, where N is large. Each turn contributes to the magnetic-field strength $\mathscr{B}$, so the total flux linking each turn is increased by a factor of N over that for a single-turn coil. This means that the induced EMF in each turn is increased by a factor of N. Since the turns are in series, the resultant induced EMF for an N-turn coil is N^2 times the value for a single-turn coil.

If a large number of turns of wire are used, the resistance of the coil will not be negligible. A coil of N turns having both self-inductance L and resistance R is called an *inductor*. The symbols used to represent an inductor in circuit diagrams are shown in Fig. 29.12. Although the inductance L and the resistance R are for clarity shown separately in the diagram, they are in fact physically inseparable, both being properties associated with the coil windings.

The total voltage drop V between the terminals of the inductor in the positive direction of the current is composed of the voltage *rise* V_E due to the induced EMF that is given by (29.9) plus the voltage *drop* due to the resistance that is given by Ohm's law. Thus,

$$V = -V_E + IR = L\,dI/dt + IR. \qquad (29.10)$$

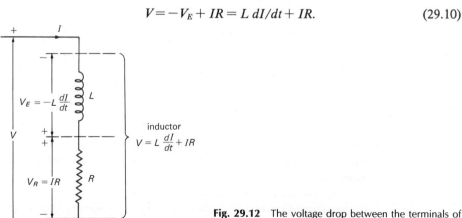

Fig. 29.12 The voltage drop between the terminals of an inductor is composed of the voltage rise due to the induced EMF plus the voltage drop due to the resistance.

When dI/dt and I are positive, the induced EMF is directed opposite to I so as to oppose the current increase, and the voltage drop across the inductor is greater than IR, as is given by (29.10). Similarly, when dI/dt is negative and I is positive, the induced EMF is in the same direction as I so as to oppose the current decrease. The voltage "drop" across the inductor is then less than IR and may in fact be negative thereby indicating a voltage rise, again as correctly described by (29.10).

When dI/dt is positive, work must be done against V_E to move positive charge through the inductor with the conventional current; when dI/dt is negative, work is done by V_E to a positive charge moving through the inductor with the conventional current. Whenever there is a current through the inductor, energy is dissipated as heat because of the resistance of the inductor. The power P_L delivered to the inductor is obtained by multiplying (29.10) by the current I:

$$P_L = IV_L = LI\,dI/dt + I^2R. \tag{29.11}$$

The term I^2R on the right-hand side in (29.11) represents the rate at which energy is dissipated as heat in the inductor. *The term $LI\,dI/dt$ on the right-hand side in (29.11) represents the rate at which energy is stored in the magnetic field of the inductor.*

If the current through an inductor is increased from zero to a final value I_f, the energy stored in the magnetic field of the inductor in a time dt is given by $(LI\,dI/dt)dt$, and the total energy stored by the inductor is

$$W_L = \int_{I=0}^{I=I_f} LI\,dI = \tfrac{1}{2}LI_f^2 \quad (Energy\ Stored\ by\ Inductor). \tag{29.12}$$

If the current is reduced to zero, this energy is delivered back to the circuit.

Example. What is the self-inductance per unit length of a long closely wound solenoid with a circular cross section of radius 5 cm that is wound with 500 turns per meter? What current through the solenoid is required in order that it store a magnetic energy of 0.5 mJ per meter of its length?

As in the example in Section 29.6, the magnetic-field strength inside the solenoid is $\mathcal{B} = \mu_0 nI$ so the magnetic flux linking each turn of the solenoid is $\Phi = \mu_0 NI\pi R^2$, where R is the solenoid radius. Therefore, the total flux linking the turns in a length l of the solenoid is $\Phi_l = ln\mu_0 nI\pi R^2 = LI$, and the self-inductance per unit length of the solenoid is

$$L/l = \mu_0 n^2 \pi R^2 = (4\pi \times 10^{-7}\ \text{T}\cdot\text{m/A})(500\ \text{m}^{-1})^2\,\pi(0.05\ \text{m})^2$$
$$= 2.47 \times 10^{-3}\ \text{H/m}.$$

The energy stored in the magnetic field for a length l of the solenoid is $W_L = \tfrac{1}{2}LI^2 = \tfrac{1}{2}l(L/l)I^2$. Therefore, the current required to store energy 0.5 mJ per meter is

$$I = \sqrt{\frac{2(W_L/l)}{L/l}} = \sqrt{\frac{2(0.5 \times 10^{-3}\ \text{J/m})}{2.47 \times 10^{-3}\ \text{H/m}}} = 0.636\ \text{A}.$$

QUESTIONS

1. What is meant by the term *electromagnetic induction?* Does the use of the word "induction" in this chapter have any relation to its use in Chapter 20?

2. If the magnetic flux through a large copper ring were changing rapidly, a large current would be produced in the ring. If you attached the terminals of a voltmeter to two points on the ring, what would the voltmeter reading? Explain your reasoning.

3. State Lenz's law and give several examples of its application. Lenz's law is similar to a qualitative thermodynamic relation known as the LeChâtelier-Braun law which asserts that if a sudden change is imposed on a thermodynamic system, the system reacts in such a way as to oppose the change. Apply the LeChâtelier-Braun law to the sudden compression of a gas; how does the gas react to oppose the change?

4. Explain carefully how the simple AC generator in Fig. 29.8 can be converted into a simple DC generator. Is the output voltage of the resulting DC generator constant? Are the power outputs of the two generators equal?

5. Give two definitions of the term *mutual inductance.* Under what conditions are the definitions equivalent?

6. Repeat Question 5 for the term *self-inductance.*

7. Why can a large inductor be dangerous? Discuss precautions that are necessary in handling a large inductor.

8. A mechanical engineer and an electrical engineer debate the relative practical importance of the heat engine to modern society compared to electric motors. Which side of the debate would you support? State your case!

9. Explain why it was necessary to assume a *fixed path C* in writing (29.3).

10. Why does the nonvanishing of the line integral of the induced electric-field strength around a closed path mean that the concept of electrical potential cannot be developed for this field as it was for the electrostatic field in Chapter 22?

11. Discuss how a small coil used as described in Problem 29.14 could be utilized to determine *both* the magnitude and the direction of the magnetic-field strength in a certain region.

12. You have a certain length of wire and are to use it to make an N-turn coil, where N is specified. How would you wind the coil to obtain (a) the minimum self-inductance and (b) the maximum self-inductance?

PROBLEMS

1. At a certain location on the equator the earth's magnetic field is $\mathscr{B} = 31$ μT, north. A truck traveling west at 27 m/s carries a thin vertical copper rod 1.25 m long that is attached to the truck by insulating fasteners. What is the induced potential difference between the ends of the rod? Which end of the rod is negative? Assume that the truck itself does not disturb the earth's field.

2. Repeat Problem 1 if the truck is traveling in a direction 27° south of west at 88 km/h.

3. A stiff piece of conducting wire 18 cm long is fastened by insulating supports to the wing of an airplane. The plane flies so that the wire is horizontal and oriented parallel to the east–west axis. At this location the

earth's magnetic field has components of 50 μT downward and 20 μT northward. The plane flies northward at a speed of 180 m/s. What is the induced potential difference between the ends of the wire? Which end of the wire is positive?

4. Repeat Problem 3 for a case where the wire is again horizontal along an east–west axis but the airplane is in a vertical climb at 95 m/s. How should the airplane fly in order for the potential difference between the ends of the wire to be zero?

5. A stiff conducting wire of length 9 cm is rotated about an axis through one end at a constant angular velocity of 15 rad/s. The wire moves in a plane perpendicular to a uniform magnetic field $\mathscr{B} = 0.60$ T. What is the potential difference between the ends of the wire? Which end of the wire is positive?

6. In Fig. 29.2 suppose that $L = 80$ cm, $v = 3$ m/s, $\mathscr{B} = 1.5$ T, and $R = 5$ Ω. (a) What is the current I? (b) What is the magnitude of the applied force F_A? (c) What is the power dissipated in heating the resistor? Verify that this equals the rate at which the applied force does work.

7. Describe in detail how the analysis at the end of Section 29.1 would be changed if the work done against frictional forces as the conductor slides along the rails were *not* negligible.

8. Use Lenz's law to describe qualitatively the variations in the current in circuit ⓑ in the

diagram when the following operations are performed in sequence: (a) Switch S_1 is closed. (b) The sliding contact C is moved downward. (c) Circuit ⓑ is moved to the left toward circuit ⓐ. (d) Circuit ⓑ is moved to the right back to its original position. (e) Switch S_2 is closed. (f) Switch S_1 is opened.

9. A bar magnet is placed on a phonographic turntable with its center at the center of the turntable. The turntable rotates with constant angular velocity. Use Lenz's law to describe qualitatively but in detail the variations in the current induced in a stationary conducting loop situated in a vertical plane at the edge of the turntable.

10. A "harbor loop" is a coil of wire of extensive area laid out on the floor of a harbor entrance to detect the entrance of submarines by means of the voltage induced by the submarine's magnetic field. (a) If the flux through the loop changes at the maximum rate of 0.006 Wb/s as a submarine passes over the side of the loop, what is the maximum EMF induced in a 50-turn loop? (b) If the earth's vertical field can be expected to vary as fast as 0.3×10^{-3} μT/s, what is the maximum area the harbor loop can have if the EMF induced by fluctuations in the earth's field is to be less than 1% of the EMF induced by the submarine in (a)?

11. At time $t = 0$ there exists in a certain region a uniform magnetic field $\mathscr{B}$ directed downward and having magnitude 0.5 T. Starting at $t = 0$ the field magnitude decreases to zero at a uniform rate of 0.01 T/s. What EMF is induced in a horizontal ring of radius 10 cm while the field is changing? What are the magnitude and direction of the steady-state current that an EMF of this magnitude would induce in the ring if the total resistance of the ring is 2.6 Ω?

12. Consider a series circuit with a battery, an inductor, a resistor, and a switch. Will the EMF induced in this circuit be larger when the switch is suddenly closed or when the

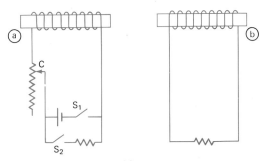

Problem 8

switch is suddenly opened? Explain your reasoning.

13. A uniform magnetic field of magnitude 2.0 T directed away from the reader exists in a region of dimensions 15 cm by 15 cm as indicated in the diagram. A rectangular conducting loop of dimensions 10 cm by 4 cm is moved with a constant velocity $\mathbf{v}$ of magnitude 1.0 m/s through the region where the field $\mathcal{B}$ exists. The plane of the loop remains normal to $\mathcal{B}$. Plot graphs of the magnetic flux through the rectangular loop and the EMF induced in the loop as functions of time. Neglect the effect of any current induced in the loop. Assume that clockwise circulation around the loop is positive and that the leading edge of the loop enters the field region at time $t = 0$. Explain clearly how Lenz's law can be used to find the sense of the induced EMF.

ing in a uniform magnetic field $\mathcal{B} = 2.5$ T. The amplitude of the oscillating EMF induced in the rotating coil is 1.3 V. What is the angular velocity of the rotation?

16. An induction coil such as is used to set off the spark in an automobile sparkplug consists of a primary coil and a secondary coil of many more turns of finer wire, both wound around a straight iron core. The primary normally carries a current, which is broken whenever a spark is desired. If the primary winding has 200 turns and normally carries a current of 4 A, and if this current falls to zero in 0.001 s when the circuit is broken, what must be the mutual inductance if an average EMF of 20 kV is to be induced in the secondary? If the normal current in the primary sets up a total flux of 10^{-3} Wb through any cross section of the core, how many turns are required on the secondary?

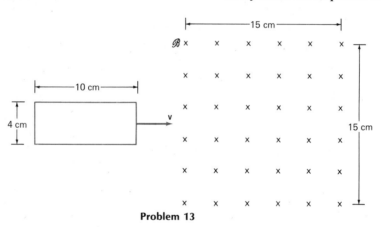

Problem 13

14. A 50-turn coil of area 4 cm² is placed normal to a magnetic field $\mathcal{B}$ and then rapidly moved to a location where $\mathcal{B}_f = 0$. It is determined that 1.5×10^{-4} C of charge pass through a ballistic galvanometer in the circuit to which the coil is connected. The *total* resistance of the circuit is 20 Ω. What is the magnitude of the magnetic-field strength $\mathcal{B}$?

15. The rotating rectangular loop shown in Fig. 29.8 is 12 cm long by 6 cm wide and is turn-

17. A long air-core solenoid has a circular cross-sectional area of 400 cm² and is wound with 30 turns per cm. Around the center of the solenoid is wound a secondary coil of 200 turns of wire. (a) What is the mutual inductance between the solenoid winding and the secondary coil? (b) If the solenoid current changes at the rate of 4 A/s, what EMF is induced in the secondary winding? (c) If the secondary winding is connected to a source of current and the current in this winding

changes at the rate of 4 A/s, what EMF is induced in the solenoid winding?

18. A small square coil of 10 turns and side length 2 cm is completely inside the solenoid of Problem 17 with its plane perpendicular to the axis of the solenoid. What is the mutual inductance of the coil and the solenoid?

19. What is the mutual inductance of the long straight wire and rectangualr loop considered in Problem 5 of Chapter 28 if $a = 2$ cm, $b = 4$ cm, and $g = 2$ mm? The long straight wire can be considered as part of a circuit that is completed very far from the rectangular loop. What is the EMF induced in the rectangular loop because of a time variation of the current in the long straight wire according to the equation $I_2 = (0.50 \text{ A/s})t + 0.15 \text{ A}$?

20. A long straight wire and a rectangular loop are situated as shown in the diagram. The two circuits do *not* make electrical contact where the wire of the loop passes over the long wire. What is the mutual inductance of this arrangement? What will be the direction of the current induced in the rectangular loop if the current in the long straight wire is increasing to the right in the diagram?

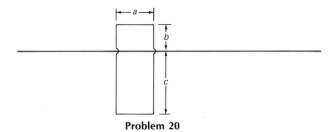

Problem 20

21. The total self-inductance of a closely wound coil of 400 turns is 8 mH. What is the total magnetic flux through *each turn* of the coil when the current is 5.0×10^{-3} A? What is the total energy stored by the inductor when the current has this value?

22. The toroid shown in Fig. 28.16a has a winding of N uniformly spaced turns. Derive an

expression for the self-inductance of the toroid in terms of a, b, and N in the limit where $a \gg b$.

23. What is the self-inductance per unit length of the solenoid considered in Problem 17?

24. For the toroid of Problem 22, if a is 12 cm and b is 2.5 mm, how many turns are required to give a self inductance of 1 mH?

25. The toroid of Problem 22 has a primary winding of 875 turns, a cross section of radius $b = 4$ mm, and a mean ring radius of $a = 16$ cm. A second winding of 35 turns is wrapped on the toroid. What is the mutual inductance of the two windings? What EMF will be induced in the secondary circuit when the current in the primary circuit is changing at a rate of 0.1 A/s? Assume that the secondary circuit contains a very large resistance so that the current induced in this circuit is negligible.

26. Suppose that instead of a circular cross section of radius b as shown in Fig. 28.16a a certain toroid has a cross section that is a square of side b. The mean radius of the toroid ring is a and the toroid has a winding of N uniformly spaced turns. Derive an expression for the self-inductance of the toroid in terms of a, b, and N. Do *not* assume that b is very much smaller than a.

27. If the toroid of Problem 26 has $a = 10$ cm and $b = 2$ cm, how many turns are required to provide a self-inductance of 25 mH?

28. (a) Show that the equivalent self-inductance of two inductors connected in series is

$L_S = L_1 + L_2$ if there is no magnetic coupling between the two inductors; i.e., if the flux linking one inductor due to a current in the other inductor is negligible. (b) Show that under the same condition the equivalent self-inductance of two inductors connected in parallel is $L_P = (1/L_1 + 1/L_2)^{-1}$.

29. How much energy, over and above that dissipated as heat, is required to produce a current of 15 A through a coil of self-inductance 2 mH?

30. A certain inductor has a self-inductance of 8 mH and a resistance of 40 Ω. What is the current through the inductor if the energy stored in the magnetic field of the inductor is 0.5 J?

31. A certain inductor has a self-inductance of 0.01 H and a resistance of 50 Ω. The inductor is connected across the terminals of a 100-V battery of negligible internal resistance. What is the energy stored in the magnetic field of the inductor when the current reaches a steady value?

32. Two circuits ⓐ and ⓑ have self-inductances L_a and L_b, respectively, and have mutual inductance M. Show that if the current in the first circuit is I_a and the current in the second circuit is I_b, then the total energy stored in the magnetic fields of the two circuits is $W = \frac{1}{2}L_a I_a^2 + \frac{1}{2}L_b I_b^2 \pm M I_a I_b$. Discuss the significance of the two possible signs. What determines which sign is applicable in a given situation? Show that this result requires that $M \le \sqrt{L_a L_b}$.

33. Suppose that we try to compute the self-inductance of a circuit by using the Biot–Savart principle to represent the magnetic-field strength $\mathscr{B}$ produced by a current I in the circuit. In particular, consider the flux linking a surface of length l between two parallel long straight wires each carrying a current I as shown in the diagram. Assume that the circuit is completed by wires that are very far from the region shown in the diagram.

Show that the integral for the flux diverges if we assume that the wires have zero radius yet carry finite current. Discuss the complications that ensue if we attempt to use a more realistic model that treats the current as distributed over a wire of finite radius.

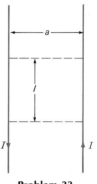

Problem 33

34. Derive an expression for the energy per unit volume stored in the magnetic field of a long closely-wound circular solenoid of n turns per unit length and radius R if there is a current I in the windings. Express the result in terms of the magnitude of the magnetic-field strength inside the solenoid.

35. Repeat Problem 34 for the toroid considered in Problem 22.

36. Prove that (29.2) is dimensionally correct.

37. Prove that H/m are acceptable units for μ_0.

Note: The growth and decay of current in a circuit containing inductance are not instantaneous. The circuit shown in the diagram serves to illustrate the processes involved. A pure inductance L, a resistor R, and a source of EMFV_E are connected in a circuit equipped with a key. With the key in position ①, the current in the circuit eventually reaches the value V_E/R; with the key in position ②, the current eventually drops to zero.

38. After the key has been in position ② for a long time, we switch the key to position ①. With the key in position ①, the loop equa-

tion is $V_L + V_R = V_E$ or $L\, dI/dt + RI = V_E$. By separation of the variables I and t, solve this equation; show that with the conditions $I = 0$ at $t = 0$ and $I = V_E/R$ at $t = \infty$ the solution can be written $I = (V_E/R)(1 - e^{-t/\tau})$, where the time constant is $\tau = L/R$. Express the energy W_L stored in the inductance as a function of time. Make plots of I and W_L as functions of time.

39. With $L = 1$ H, $R = 10\ \Omega$, and $V_E = 250$ V, describe the growth of current when the key in the circuit is switched to position ①. What are the current I and the energy W_L stored in the circuit 0.1 s after the key has been switched to position ①? What are the initial and final values of the voltage differences V_R and V_L?

40. After the key in the circuit has been in position ① for a long time, the current in the circuit has the value V_E/R. When we shift the key to position ②, the loop equation becomes $V_L + V_R = 0$ or $L\, dI/dt + RI = 0$. Solve this equation by separation of the variables I and t. With $I_0 = V_E/R$ at $t = 0$ and $I = 0$ at $t = \infty$, show that your solution becomes $I = I_0 e^{-t/\tau}$ with the time constant $\tau = L/R$. What is the stored energy W_L at time t? Make a plot of I and W_L as functions of time.

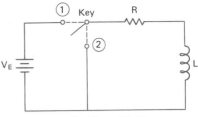

Problems 38–41

41. With the values of V_E, R, and L given in Problem 39, what are the current I and the stored energy W_L at a time 0.1 s after the key has been shifted to position ②?

42. If the plates of a charged capacitor C are connected to the ends of a pure inductance L by wires of zero resistance, the loop equation is $V_L + V_C = 0$. With $V_L = L\, dI/dt$ and $I = dQ/dt$, this equation becomes $L\, d^2Q/dt^2 + Q/C = 0$. Show that a solution of this equation is $Q = Q_0 \cos 2\pi ft$, where Q_0 is the initial charge on the capacitor plates and $f = (1/2\pi)\sqrt{1/LC}$. What is the current in the circuit? Show that the total energy W_L and W_C stored in the circuit remains constant and that energy is transferred back and forth between the electric field of the capacitor and the magnetic field of the inductance. The frequency $f = (1/2\pi)\sqrt{1/LC}$ is called the *resonance frequency* of the circuit.

CHAPTER 30

Magnetic Properties of Matter

Up to this point we have considered only macroscopic currents in wires as sources of magnetic fields. However, we are all familiar with sources of magnetic-field strength where no macroscopic currents are involved. Most of us have enjoyed playing with toys formed from small "permanent magnets" and have observed how they exert forces of attraction and repulsion on one another and can stick to an iron or steel surface. That such permanent magnets are sources of magnetic-field strength $\mathscr{B}$ can be confirmed by observing the effect of their presence on the trajectories of beams of electrons or other charged particles. Permanent magnets see practical use in such devices as galvanometers and loudspeakers. The ability of a "tape recorder" to record information depends on the creation of permanent magnets in the coating on the "magnetic tape."

We are also aware that an unmagnetized iron or steel object will be attracted by a magnet. A less common observation is that materials not sharing the properties of iron and steel are also affected by an applied magnetic field. Careful experiment shows that in an inhomogeneous magnetic field of sufficiently large magnitude some kinds of materials are weakly attracted toward the strongest part of the field; such materials are said to be *paramagnetic*. Other materials are weakly repelled from the strongest part of an inhomogeneous applied magnetic field; such materials are said to be *diamagnetic*. Materials that share the properties of iron of being *strongly* attracted toward the strong part of an inhomogeneous applied magnetic field are said to be *ferromagnetic*. The macroscopic effects of paramagnetic and of diamagnetic behavior are generally small, and for many practical purposes the magnetic properties of such materials can be ignored. Ferromagnetic effects, on the other hand, are not negligible.

In this chapter we shall discuss the properties of diamagnetic, paramagnetic, and ferromagnetic materials and shall consider the microscopic origin of these properties insofar as is possible with a classical description. We shall consider how these kinds of materials respond to an applied magnetic field and how a "magnetized" material can act as a source of magnetic-field strength.

30.1 MAGNETIZATION; MAGNETIC PERMEABILITY

In discussing the dielectric properties of materials in Chapter 24, we found it convenient to consider a slab of the material filling the space between the plates of an
ideal parallel-plate capacitor. In this way all portions of the specimen were subject
to the same electric-field strength $\mathscr{E}$. In discussing the magnetic properties of materials
it is desirable to have a corresponding magnetic arrangement where all portions of
the specimen are subject to the same magnitude of magnetic-field strength $\mathscr{B}$. A
convenient arrangement of this sort is provided by a thin doughnut of material on
which is placed a uniform, closely spaced toroidal winding of the sort considered
in Section 28.7. Consider first the magnetic-field strength in the absence of matter.
If the radius a of the cross section of the doughnut is small compared with the
mean radius R of the doughnut itself, as indicated in Fig. 30.1, the magnetic-field
strength due to a current I in the windings has essentially the same magnitude

$$\mathscr{B}_0 = \mu_0 NI/2\pi R \tag{30.1}$$

everywhere inside the doughnut. Here N is the number of turns of the toroidal winding.
We add the subscript zero in (30.1) to emphasize that this is the field produced by
the current I in the windings in the absence of matter; the result holds strictly for
a vacuum "core" inside the windings.

If there is a core of some material inside the toroidal windings, the material can
become "magnetized" under the influence of the applied field $\mathscr{B}_0$. The resultant magnetic-field strength $\mathscr{B}$ then is a superposition of the applied field $\mathscr{B}_0$ due to the
current in the windings and a field $\mathscr{B}_M$ due to the magnetized material: $\mathscr{B} =
\mathscr{B}_0 + \mathscr{B}_M$. For an isotropic material the magnetic lines of the field $\mathscr{B}_M$ circle the
Z axis inside the doughnut with the same symmetry as the applied field $\mathscr{B}_0$.

The magnetic flux $\Phi_{\mathscr{B}}$ linking any cross section of the toroid in Fig. 30.1 is $\mathscr{B}\pi a^2$.
Changes in this flux and therefore in $\mathscr{B}$ when the current I is changed can be determined by use of a fluxmeter consisting of a second winding on the toroid that is
connected to a ballistic galvanometer, which measures the charge that flows when
a current is induced in the second winding. Such an arrangement is indicated in
Fig. 30.1. By starting from a condition of zero field and using a fluxmeter to measure

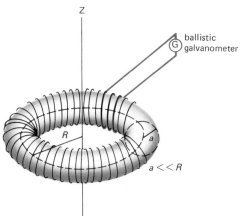

Fig. 30.1 A toroidal winding of N uniformly
spaced turns. A secondary winding connected to
a ballistic galvanometer allows measurement of
changes in $\mathscr{B}$ as I is changed.

the changes in $\mathscr{B}$ when I is changed, we can determine $\mathscr{B}$ for various values of $\mathscr{B}_0$ for a given material. An arrangement like that in Fig. 30.1 for the investigation of the magnetic properties of a material is called a *Rowland ring*. Henry Rowland used such a device to make extensive investigations of various ferromagnetic materials in the early 1870's.

In order to describe the magnetic properties of a material as determined by a Rowland ring experiment, we define the *relative permeability* κ_m of the material to be the ratio of the magnitude of the magnetic-field strength with the material present to the magnitude of the applied field produced by the current in the windings:

$$\kappa_m = \mathscr{B}/\mathscr{B}_0. \quad (\textit{Relative Permeability}) \tag{30.2}$$

For a paramagnetic material κ_m is slightly greater than one, and for a diamagnetic material κ_m is slightly less than one. For a ferromagnetic material, $\mathscr{B}$ is much greater than $\mathscr{B}_0$, but there are also serious complications in the definition of the relative permeability for ferromagnetic materials that we shall consider later in this chapter.

It is the present view that all magnetic fields are due to currents if we include microscopic currents within a single atom or molecule. The general idea that magnetization of a material is due to internal current loops within the material was first proposed by Ampère in 1825. In Chapters 27 and 28 we have discussed the magnetic moment **m** associated with a current loop. There are magnetic moments associated with the internal current loops in a material. The extent to which a material is magnetized is measured quantitatively by the average magnetic moment per unit volume:

The MAGNETIZATION $\mathscr{M}$ of a material is the resultant magnetic moment associated with a macroscopically small volume element divided by the volume of that element.

If the magnetic moment of the jth atom or molecule in a volume V is $\mathbf{m}_j$, the magnetization of the material is

$$\mathscr{M} = \sum_j \mathbf{m}_j/V, \quad \left\{ \begin{array}{l} \mathscr{M} \text{ in A/m} \\ m \text{ in A}\cdot\text{m}^2 \\ V \text{ in m}^3 \end{array} \right\}$$

where the summation extends over all the atoms or molecules in the volume V. It is understood that V is macroscopically very small yet is large enough to contain very many atoms or molecules. Since the units of magnetic moment are $A \cdot m^2$, the units of magnetization $\mathscr{M}$ are A/m.

Although the Rowland ring provides a convenient way to introduce the concept of relative permeability, for typical paramagnetic and diamagnetic materials κ_m is so close to unity that the arrangement is not a practical device for real measurements. Actual determinations of κ_m can be made by measuring the force on a sample of material in an inhomogeneous magnetic field, as suggested in Fig. 30.2. We can understand why there is a resultant force on a current loop in an inhomogeneous magnetic field by considering the special case illustrated in Fig. 30.3. In this figure we show

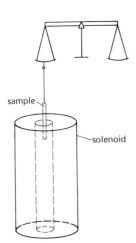

Fig. 30.2 A schematic representation of an arrangement for determining the force on a sample of material in an inhomogeneous magnetic field.

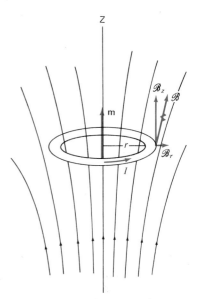

Fig. 30.3 A current loop in an inhomogeneous magnetic field.

a current loop having current I and magnetic moment $\mathbf{m}$ in an inhomogeneous applied magnetic field $\mathscr{B}$ that decreases in magnitude with increasing Z, as is indicated by the spreading of the magnetic lines. We show the magnetic moment $\mathbf{m}$ in the stable orientation of alignment parallel to the applied field $\mathscr{B}$; for any other initial orientation there will be a resultant torque on the current loop tending to rotate its magnetic moment into alignment with $\mathscr{B}$. Note that the field due to the current loop itself is not shown in Fig. 30.3; the loop cannot exert a resultant force on itself.

In Fig. 30.4 we show the force $d\mathbf{F} = I\,d\mathbf{l} \times \mathscr{B}$ on an element $I\,d\mathbf{l}$ of the current loop. For this particular situation where there is symmetry about the Z axis it is easy to see that the resultant force on the current loop will be in the negative Z direction. In general, a current loop with its magnetic moment aligned along the direction of $\mathscr{B}$ will experience a force in the direction of increasing magnitude of $\mathscr{B}$. If $\mathbf{m}$ is reversed with respect to $\mathscr{B}$, which means that the current I is in the opposite direction from Fig. 30.4, the resultant force on the current loop is in the direction of decreasing magnitude of $\mathscr{B}$. We therefore anticipate that the attraction of a paramagnetic or ferromagnetic material to the strong part of a magnetic field is associated with the creation of magnetization parallel to the direction of the applied field, while the repulsion of a diamagnetic material from the strong part of a magnetic field is associated with the creation of magnetization oriented opposite to the direction of the applied field.

In Problem 15 we suggest an argument by which one can show that the resultant force on the current loop in Fig. 30.4 is

$$\mathbf{F} = m \frac{\partial \mathscr{B}_z}{\partial z} \mathbf{k} \qquad (30.3)$$

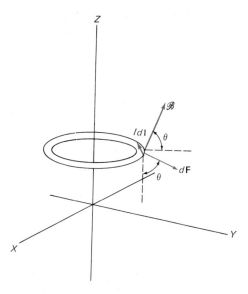

Fig. 30.4 The magnetic force $d\mathbf{F} = I\, d\mathbf{l} \times \mathcal{B}$ on an element $I\, d\mathbf{l}$ of the current loop shown in Fig. 30.3.

provided the radius of the loop is small compared with the distance over which $\mathcal{B}$ varies significantly. The derivative in (30.3) is evaluated at the center of the current loop. In the next section we introduce a relation between magnetization and the applied field that can be used in connection with (30.3) to determine the relative permeability of a paramagnetic or a diamagnetic material.

30.2   MAGNETIC INTENSITY; SUSCEPTIBILITY

Let us now return to the Rowland ring shown in Fig. 30.1. We suppose that the ring material has a magnetization $\mathcal{M}$ of uniform magnitude that circles the Z axis either parallel or antiparallel to $\mathcal{B}_0$. We now ask how the magnetic-field strength $\mathcal{B}_M$ produced by the magnetized material can be computed if the magnetization is known. In order to answer this question, we consider a thin section of the ring of thickness δl as shown in Fig. 30.5. We conceptually divide this section into macroscopi-

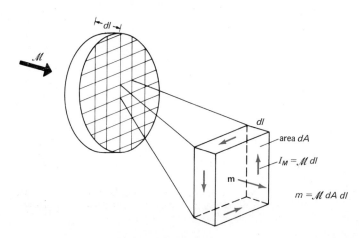

Fig. 30.5 A thin section of a Rowland ring of thickness dl is conceptually divided into macroscopically small pieces. For the purpose of computing $\mathcal{B}_M$ each piece of magnetized material can be replaced by a ribbon of current $I_M = \mathcal{M}\, dl$ about its perimeter.

cally small pieces by the grid indicated in Fig. 30.5. A typical piece of area δA has a magnetic moment $\delta \mathbf{m}$ in the direction of $\mathscr{M}$ of magnitude $\delta m = \mathscr{M} \delta A \delta l$. At distances that are large compared with the dimensions of the piece of material—which for practical purposes means everywhere outside the material—the magnetic-field strength produced by the piece of material of magnetic moment $\delta \mathbf{m}$ depends only on $\delta \mathbf{m}$ and not on the details of the shape of the piece. (See Section 28.5.) Therefore, for the purpose of computing $\mathscr{B}_M$ the small piece of magnetized material can be replaced by a ribbon of current $I_M = \delta m/\delta A = \mathscr{M} \delta l$ about its perimeter, as suggested in Fig. 30.5. A careful analysis that we shall omit shows that this replacement of the magnetized material by an equivalent current distribution also leads to the correct *macroscopic average* magnetic-field strength $\mathscr{B}_M$ *inside* the magnetized material.

Let us now consider the resultant magnetic field produced by the uniformly magnetized slab of the Rowland ring shown in Fig. 30.5. As can be seen in Fig. 30.6, at any *interior* boundary between pieces of the slab we have two equivalent currents in opposite direction that, because the magnetization $\mathscr{M}$ is uniform over the slab, have the same magnitude. The fields produced by these two currents therefore cancel. The resultant magnetic-field strength is just that due to a current $I_M = \mathscr{M} \delta l$ around the surface of the slab, as indicated in Fig. 30.6. Thus, for the purpose of computing $\mathscr{B}_M$ the uniformly magnetized slab of material can be replaced by a surface current directed in a right-hand sense relative to $\mathscr{M}$. The magnitude of this surface current per unit of length measured parallel to $\mathscr{M}$ is equal to the magnitude of the magnetization:

$$I_M/\delta l = \mathscr{M}.$$

We recall that the units of magnetization are A/m, so this relation is dimensionally correct. The complete ring of material in Fig. 30.1 is thus replaced by a surface current distribution either in the same sense or in the opposite sense to the current I in the windings.

The current in the windings establishes a field

$$\mathscr{B}_0 = \mu_0 n I, \quad (\textit{External Currents}) \tag{30.4}$$

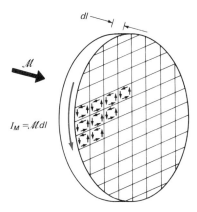

Fig. 30.6 A thin section of a Rowland ring of thickness dl is magnetically equivalent to a current $I_M = \mathscr{M} dl$ around the surface of the section.

where n is the number of turns per unit length around the toroid. Correspondingly, the magnetized material of the ring produces a field

$$\mathscr{B}_M = \mu_0 \mathscr{M}. \quad (\textit{Internal Currents}) \tag{30.5}$$

The resultant magnetic-field strength $\mathscr{B}$ is the vector superposition of the fields represented by (30.4) and (30.5).

It is the usual practice to introduce another vector field represented by the symbol $\mathscr{H}$ that has a particular relation to external conduction currents that we shall mention below. There is no consensus on the name to be used for $\mathscr{H}$; we shall call it the *magnetic intensity*. For the Rowland ring arrangement we can define $\mathscr{H}$ by the relation $\mathscr{H} = \mathscr{B}_0/\mu_0$ so that

$$\mathscr{H} = nI. \quad (\textit{Toroid}) \tag{30.6}$$

We note that the units of $\mathscr{H}$ are A/m, the same as for $\mathscr{M}$.

The resultant magnetic-field strength $\mathscr{B}$ due to the current in the windings and the magnetized material of the Rowland ring as given by (30.5) and (30.6) is

$$\mathscr{B} = \mu_0(\mathscr{H} \pm \mathscr{M}). \quad (\textit{Rowland Ring}) \tag{30.7}$$

Here the symbol $\mathscr{M}$ represents the inherently positive magnitude of the magnetization vector $\mathbf{\mathscr{M}}$. The plus sign holds for paramagnetic materials; the minus sign holds for diamagnetic materials. Both signs are possible for ferromagnetic materials; the complications associated with ferromagnetic materials will be discussed in a later section.

By using (30.2) in (30.7) we obtain

$$\mu_0(\mathscr{H} \pm \mathscr{M}) = \mathscr{B} = \kappa_m \mathscr{B}_0 = \kappa_m \mu_0 \mathscr{H},$$

from which it follows that

$$\mathscr{M} = (\kappa_m - 1)\mathscr{H}.$$

We define the *magnetic susceptibility* χ_m of the material to be

$$\chi_m = \kappa_m - 1 \tag{30.8}$$

so that we have

$$\mathscr{M} = \chi_m \mathscr{H}.$$

The magnetic susceptibility is positive for a paramagnetic material and is negative for a diamagnetic material. The magnetic susceptibilities for *pure* samples of a number of paramagnetic and diamagnetic materials are given in Table 30.1.

Frequently a quantity μ called the *permeability* of the material is introduced by the definition

$$\mu = \kappa_m \mu_0.$$

Table 30.1 Typical Values of the Magnetic Susceptibility χ_m for Diamagnetic and for Paramagnetic Materials at 20°C

Material	χ_m
Bismuth	-16.6×10^{-5}
Copper	-1.0×10^{-5}
Gold	-3.6×10^{-5}
Lead	-1.7×10^{-5}
Mercury	-2.9×10^{-5}
Silver	-2.6×10^{-5}
Aluminum	2.2×10^{-5}
Magnesium	1.2×10^{-5}
Platinum	29.0×10^{-5}
Hydrogen gas (NTP)	-2.1×10^{-9}
Oxygen gas (NTP)	1.9×10^{-6}
Oxygen liquid (90 K)	3.5×10^{-3}

Since κ_m is dimensionless, μ is expressed in the same units as μ_0: T·m/A.

Our discussion in the above paragraphs applies to the specific case of the Rowland ring. The general definition of the magnetic intensity $\mathcal{H}$ can be introduced by consideration of the form of Ampère's line-integral relation when both conduction currents and magnetized matter act as sources of the magnetic-field strength $\mathcal{B}$. It is possible to show that if one defines $\mathcal{H}$ by the relation

$$\mathcal{H} = \mathcal{B}/\mu_0 - \mathcal{M}, \tag{30.9}$$

then Ampère's line-integral relation has the form

$$\oint_C \mathcal{H} \cdot d\mathbf{l} = \Sigma I_C, \tag{30.10}$$

where the term ΣI_C represents the algebraic sum of the external *conduction currents* linking the path C. The value of the corresponding line integral for $\mathcal{B}$ involves both conduction currents and the internal currents representing the magnetized material.

The general relation between magnetization and magnetic intensity is

$$\mathcal{M} = \chi_m \mathcal{H}, \tag{30.11}$$

where χ_m is the same quantity as defined by (30.8). Nonisotropic crystalline materials can have different values of χ_m depending on how $\mathcal{H}$ is oriented relative to the crystal axes; then a more involved relation than (30.11) is required.

We note from (30.9) that in vacuum we have $\mathcal{H} = \mathcal{B}/\mu_0$. In vacuum $\mathcal{H}$ and $\mathcal{B}$ are simply alternative descriptions of the same field.

30.3 DIAMAGNETISM

The phenomenon of diamagnetism was discovered by Michael Faraday in 1845. Faraday found that various materials, notably bismuth, were repelled from the strongest part of an inhomogeneous magnetic field. The terms diamagnetic and paramagnetic were both coined by Faraday. A detailed theory of diamagnetism was provided by the German physicist Wilhelm Weber (1804–1891) in 1852 in terms of Ampère's microscopic current loops and the Faraday induction principle. Diamagnetism is explained by the response of the microscopic molecular or atomic currents of a material to the induced EMF associated with a change in the applied magnetic-field strength. The generation of magnetization directed oppositely to the applied field is thus a manifestation of Lenz's law.

A correct description of the effect of a change in the applied magnetic-field strength on microscopic molecular or atomic currents requires the use of quantum mechanics. However, insight into the process can be obtained by considering the change in magnetic moment when an external field is applied normal to the plane of a circular orbit assumed to be followed by an electron. The *change* in magnetic moment **m** is readily shown to be in a direction opposite to the applied field for both clockwise and counterclockwise revolutions of the electron. This analysis is the subject Problem 16.

Diamagnetism is a property of *all* materials. However, as is suggested by the values in Table 30.1, diamagnetic effects are very small. If a material has paramagnetic or ferromagnetic properties, these will dominate its diamagnetism. The magnetic susceptibility of a diamagnetic material is negative and generally independent of the temperature.

30.4   PARAMAGNETISM

Paramagnetism exists when permanent magnetic moments associated with atomic or molecular currents in a material become aligned parallel to an applied magnetic field. As indicated in Section 27.9; the torque on a magnetic moment **m** due to an applied field $\mathscr{B}$ is $\tau = \mathbf{m} \times \mathscr{B}$. The reason why some atoms have permanent magnetic moments while others do not can be answered only by modern quantum mechanics. The details of the interaction between atomic magnetic moments and an external field also require a quantum-mechanical description.

The atomic magnetic moments responsible for paramagnetism do not have strong electromagnetic interactions with one another. However, the thermal agitation of the material tends to generate a random orientation of magnetic moment directions and thus acts to oppose alignment by the applied field. We can gain some appreciation of the competition between these two effects by the following comparison. The average translational kinetic energy of an ideal-gas molecule at a temperature T is $(3/2)kT$, where k is Boltzmann's constant. Therefore, the quantity kT should represent the order of magnitude of the energy available to an atom in a collision with one of its neighbors. At a typical room temperature of 300 K this energy is

$$W_1 = kT = (1.38 \times 10^{-23} \text{ J/K})(300 \text{ K}) = 4.14 \times 10^{-21} \text{ J}.$$

We compare this thermal energy with the energy $2m\mathscr{B}$ required to turn a magnetic moment **m** from alignment parallel to an applied field $\mathscr{B}$ to alignment antiparallel

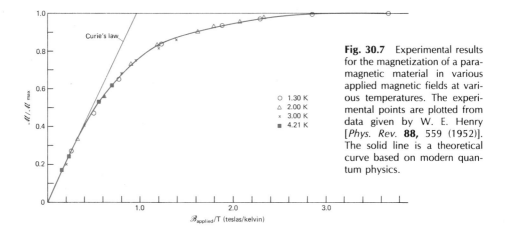

Fig. 30.7 Experimental results for the magnetization of a paramagnetic material in various applied magnetic fields at various temperatures. The experimental points are plotted from data given by W. E. Henry [*Phys. Rev.* **88**, 559 (1952)]. The solid line is a theoretical curve based on modern quantum physics.

to $\mathscr{B}$. (See Section 27.9.) Experiment shows that the quantity $m_B = 9.27 \times 10^{-24}$ J/T represents the order of magnitude of the magnetic moment of an atom having a nonzero magnetic moment. If we consider a relatively large applied field $\mathscr{B} = 1$ T, the energy required to reverse a magnetic moment of magnitude m_B is

$$W_2 = 2m_B\mathscr{B} = 2(9.27 \times 10^{-24} \text{ J/T})(1 \text{ T}) = 1.85 \times 10^{-23} \text{ J}.$$

We see that $W_1/W_2 = 224$; the typical thermal energy available to an atom in a collision is much greater than the energy required to reverse the atomic magnetic moment relative to the applied field. It is therefore not surprising that under ordinary conditions the magnetization due to the alignment of permanent atomic magnetic moments is not large.

A given applied field should be more effective in aligning atomic magnetic moments at low temperatures. This is shown quantitatively by the relation

$$\chi_m = C/T, \quad (Curie's\ Law) \tag{30.12}$$

which was established experimentally by the French physicist Pierre Curie (1859–1906) in 1895. Here C is a constant that depends on the particular paramagnetic material.

Of course, the susceptibility cannot increase indefinitely when T approaches zero as is predicted by (30.12). Actual experimental results for the magnetization of a paramagnetic material together with a theoretical curve based on quantum statistical mechanics are shown in Fig. 30.7. We see that the theory gives an excellent fit to the data. At sufficiently low temperatures and high fields the magnetization becomes *saturated*, approaching a limiting maximum value that corresponds to having all the atomic magnetic moments aligned parallel to the applied field. The Curie law (30.12) corresponds to the straight dashed line shown in Fig. 30.7. Note that deviation from the Curie law occurs only for very high fields and low temperatures.

30.5 FERROMAGNETISM

If iron is used as the material for a Rowland ring experiment, the resultant field $\mathscr{B}$ in the ring may have hundreds or even thousands of times the magnitude of the field $\mathscr{B}_0$ due to the current in the windings alone. Furthermore, in contrast to diamagnetic and paramagnetic materials under normal conditions, the magnetization of the material as deduced from (30.6) and (30.7) is not at all a linear function of $\mathscr{H}$. If we start with zero current in the windings and an iron ring having zero magnetization and determine the increases in the magnitude of the resultant field $\mathscr{B}$ as the current in the windings is increased in small steps, we obtain a "magnetization curve" like that shown in Fig. 30.8. From the points on the magnetization curve in Fig. 30.8 it is possible to use (30.2) and (30.8) to determine values of κ_m and χ_m, but these values vary greatly with $\mathscr{H}$, as is illustrated in Fig. 30.9.

We note from Fig. 30.8 that for sufficiently large values of $\mathscr{H}$ the material undergoes magnetic *saturation*. The magnetization of the material approaches a maximum possible value and further increases in $\mathscr{B}$ arise essentially only from the increases in $\mathscr{B}_0$ associated with increases in the current in the windings.

The nonlinear dependence of $\mathscr{B}$ on $\mathscr{H}$ is not simple. Moreover, if we try to confirm the results by following the changes in $\mathscr{B}$ as the current in the windings is decreased, we discover that *the $\mathscr{B}$ versus $\mathscr{H}$ curve for decreasing I does not retrace the magnetization curve obtained with increasing I. The curve for decreasing I falls above the magnetization curve as shown in Fig. 30.10.* This phenomenon is known as *hysteresis*.

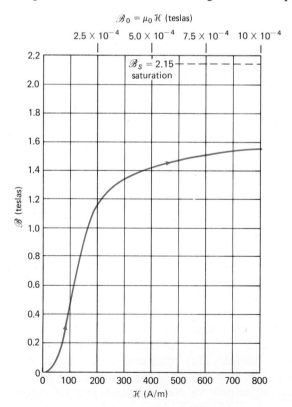

Fig. 30.8 A magnetization curve for a ferromagnetic material.

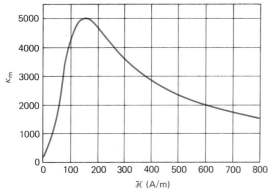

Fig. 30.9 Relative permeability κ_m as a function of $\mathcal{H}$ for the ferromagnetic material of Fig. 30.8.

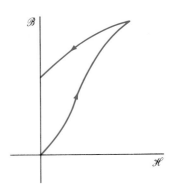

Fig. 30.10 Hysteresis.

When the current in the windings is reduced to zero, the material retains some magnetization and there is a nonvanishing resultant magnetic-field strength $\mathcal{B}$, as is the case for permanent magnets. In general, the resultant magnetic-field strength $\mathcal{B}$ in the material depends not only on the current I in the windings but also on the magnetic history of the material.

Materials that display the properties described in the preceding paragraphs are said to be *ferromagnetic*. Iron is the archetypical ferromagnetic element, but nickel, cobalt, and gadolinium are also ferromagnetic at or near room temperature. There are other elements that become ferromagnetic at lower temperatures. There are also many ferromagnetic alloys, including alloys of elements that are not themselves ferromagnetic. For each ferromagnetic material there is a distinct temperature T_C, called the *Curie temperature*, above which the material ceases to be ferromagnetic. The Curie temperatures for a number of elements are given in Table 30.2. Above these temperatures the materials are paramagnetic.

If ferromagnetic behavior is to be explained on the basis of alignment of atomic magnetic moments, we can see several features that must be part of the explanation. There must be some strong interaction between the atomic magnetic moments that readily locks them into alignment and keeps them aligned against the disordering tendency of thermal motion. This interaction must be sensitive to interatomic spacing and orientation to account for the change from ferromagnetic to paramagnetic behavior at the Curie temperature. The interaction must not depend strongly on the valence electrons because many elements chemically similar to ferromagnetic elements are

Table 30.2 Curie Temperatures for Various Elements

Element	Curie Temperature T_C (K)
Cobalt	1404
Iron	1043
Nickel	631
Gadolinium	293
Dysprosium	85

not themselves ferromagnetic. There must be some limitation on the alignment interaction since every piece of iron we happen to pick up is not strongly magnetized. There must be some feature of the interaction that causes alignment changes induced by an applied field not to be exactly reversible so that hysteresis can be explained.

A satisfactory explanation of the ferromagnetic interaction is provided by quantum theory; there is no classical analogue. A phenomenological theory that covers many features of ferromagnetism but does not explain the nature of the microscopic ferromagnetic interaction was developed in 1907 by the French physicist Pierre Weiss (1865–1940). One important feature of the Weiss theory that is retained in the modern quantum theory of ferromagnetism is the existence of ferromagnetic *domains.*

Weiss introduced the idea that the volume of a ferromagnetic material is divided into regions called domains, each macroscopically small but containing very many atoms. Within a domain, an interatomic interaction causes a spontaneous magnetization to near saturation by locking the atomic magnetic moments into alignment. However, in an "unmagnetized" sample the orientations of the resultant magnetization vectors for neighboring domains are such that the total magnetization of the bulk sample is zero. An applied field causes magnetization of an unmagnetized sample primarily by producing growth in the volume of domains having their magnetization vectors aligned with the applied field and by producing rotation of the direction of the magnetization vectors of domains having their magnetizations in other directions. The magnetization curve of Fig. 30.8 can be considered in terms of three regions. For the lowest values of $\mathcal{H}$, magnetization is dominated by reversible motion of domain boundaries. For intermediate values of $\mathcal{H}$, where most of the magnetization occurs, the magnetization is dominated by irreversible motion of domain boundaries. At the largest values of $\mathcal{H}$, as the magnetization approaches saturation, the magnetization is dominated by sudden rotation or "flipping" of the magnetization directions of domains.

A way of making ferromagnetic domains directly visible for study was developed by the American physicist Francis Bitter (1902–1967) in 1932. In this technique a colloidal suspension of ferromagnetic particles is spread on a carefully prepared surface of the specimen to be studied. Strong local magnetic fields at the domain boundaries cause the colloidal particles to collect there. This produces a pattern on the surface of the specimen that can be seen easily under a microscope. In Fig. 30.11a we show the domains actually observed on the surface of a particular Si-Fe crystal. The arrows have been drawn to indicate the magnetization directions of the domains. In Fig. 30.11b we show schematically how the domains change in size with increasing magnetic field applied in the direction indicated in the figure. The domains having their magnetization in the direction of the applied field grow at the expense of the other domains until at saturation the entire volume is magnetized in the field direction.

30.6   HYSTERESIS

We have noted that a sample that has followed a magnetization curve with increasing $\mathcal{H}$ like that in Fig. 30.8 will not retrace the curve when $\mathcal{H}$ is decreased. If $\mathcal{H}$ is reduced to zero and then is increased in the opposite direction by sending current through the windings in the opposite sense, the magnetic-field strength $\mathcal{B}$ in the

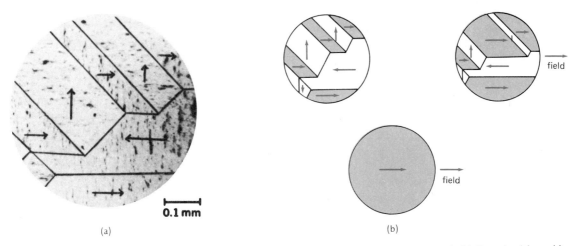

Fig. 30.11 (a) Domain structure observed on the surface of a Si-Fe crystal. (b) Growth of favorably oriented domains as the applied magnetic-field strength is increased.

material can be reduced to zero. If one continues to increase $\mathcal{H}$ in this "negative" direction, the sample becomes magnetized in the direction opposite to the original direction. If the current in the windings is cycled between the same maximum value in opposite directions, the magnetic state of the sample can be made to repeat over and over again a *hysteresis loop* like that shown in Fig. 30.12. The magnitude $\mathcal{B}_R$ of the magnetic-field strength remaining when $\mathcal{H}$ is zero is called the *residual magnetic-field strength*. The magnitude $\mathcal{H}_C$ of the reversed magnetic intensity required to reduce $\mathcal{B}$ to zero is called the *coercive intensity*.

The values of $\mathcal{B}_R$ and $\mathcal{H}_C$ for a hysteresis loop that carries the material to saturation in each direction are called the *remanence* and the *coercivity* of the material, respectively. Values of the remanence and the coercivity for a number of ferromagnetic alloys are given in Table 30.3. A material for a permanent magnet should have a large remanence so that the magnet will be "strong" and a large coercivity so that the magnet is hard to "demagnetize."

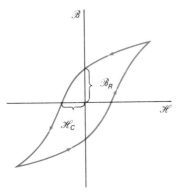

Fig. 30.12 A hysteresis loop for a ferromagnetic material.

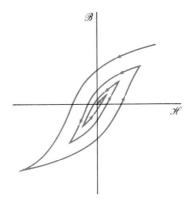

Fig. 30.13 A representation of the demagnetization of a ferromagnetic material.

Table 30.3   Remanence and Coercivity for Ferromagnetic Alloys

Material	Composition	$\mathscr{B}_R$ (T)	$\mathscr{H}_C$ (A/m)
Carbon steel	0.985Fe, 0.01C, 0.005Mn	0.900	4.06×10^3
Cobalt steel	0.536Fe, 0.36Co, 0.058Cr 0.038W, 0.008C	0.975	1.91×10^4
Alnico 2	0.545Fe, 0.125Co, 0.17Ni 0.10Al, 0.06Cu	0.725	4.38×10^4
Alnico 5	0.51Fe, 0.24Co, 0.14Ni 0.08Al, 0.03Cu	1.250	4.93×10^4
Bismanol	0.792Bi, 0.208Mn	0.480	2.90×10^5

The reader may well wonder how it is possible to get the magnetized material back to the initial state where $\mathscr{B}$ and $\mathscr{H}$ are both zero. This can be accomplished by cycling the current in the windings while steadily decreasing the maximum magnitude to which the current is brought in either direction. The magnetic state of the material will then trace out a path like that shown in Fig. 30.13, reaching a point near the origin after a relatively small number of cycles.

There is dissipation of energy as heat due to the irreversible motion of domain boundaries as a material is carried around a hysteresis loop. *The energy dissipated per unit volume of sample per cycle is equal to the area enclosed by the hysteresis loop.* For the case of a Rowland ring this result can be demonstrated as follows. By the Faraday induction principle, the total EMF induced in the windings when the flux in the toroidal ring is changing is

$$V_E = -N \, d\Phi_{\mathscr{B}}/dt = -NA \, d\mathscr{B}/dt,$$

where N is the total number of turns, A is the cross-sectional area of the toroid, and $\Phi_{\mathscr{B}} = \mathscr{B}A$ is the flux linking each turn of the winding. The rate at which work must be done against this EMF by the source maintaining the current I in the windings is

$$dW/dt = -V_E \, I = (NA \, d\mathscr{B}/dt)I.$$

By using (30.6) to express the current in the windings we obtain

$$dW/dt = (NA \, d\mathscr{B}/dt)(\mathscr{H}l/N), \qquad (30.13)$$

where l is the circumference of the toroid. Since Al is the volume of the material in the ring, we have from (30.13) that the increment of energy delivered to the Rowland ring when the magnetic-field strength changes by an increment $d\mathscr{B}$ per unit volume of material is

$$dW = \mathscr{H} \, d\mathscr{B}. \qquad (30.14)$$

It follows directly from (30.14) that when the sample is carried once around the

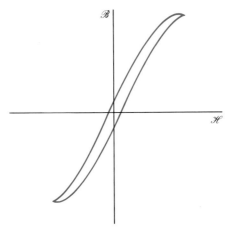

Fig. 30.14 A hysteresis loop for a magnetically soft ferromagnetic material.

hysteresis loop in Fig. 30.12, the net energy delivered per unit volume of material is equal to the area enclosed by the loop.

In the operation of a transformer or a motor there are masses of ferromagnetic material that are continuously carried around a hysteresis loop. In order to minimize power losses due to hysteresis, such materials should be chosen to have small coercivity so that their hysteresis loops will be narrow and enclose a relatively small area. Ferromagnetic materials having small coercivity are said to be *magnetically soft.* An example of a shape of hysteresis loop that can be obtained by proper metallurgical treatment of a suitable material is shown in Fig. 30.14.

30.7 SELF-INDUCTANCE WITH A FERROMAGNETIC CORE

Frequently an inductor is provided with a ferromagnetic core to increase the magnetic flux linking the windings for a given current. In an arrangement such as a Rowland ring where a material of relative permeability κ_m replaces vacuum at all points where a coil generates a magnetic field, the magnetic flux linking the windings for a given current is increased by a factor of κ_m compared with the value for a vacuum core. However, in general, κ_m varies in a complicated way with the current in the windings and the magnetic history of the core material. In such a case we cannot accurately represent the voltage drop across the inductor as simply a constant times dI/dt; the induced EMF and the self-inductance $L=|V_E|/|dI/dt|$ are nonsimple functions of the current and the magnetic history. Fortunately, there are commercially available inductors with ferromagnetic cores of magnetically soft materials having narrow hysteresis loops for which the relative permeability κ_m is both large and approximately constant over the range of currents for which the inductor is designed to operate.

QUESTIONS

1. In research on the electric and magn⁺ic properties of matter what roles are played by the capacitor and the *Rowland Ring?* What special advantages do these devices have?

2. What is meant by the term *magnetization?* How is it related to the magnetic moments of the atoms in a sample of material? What is meant by the term *relative permeability* and in what units is it measured?

3. Use (30.3) to explain why a piece of soft iron is attracted by a permanent magnet.

4. In the magnetic field inside a ferromagnetic material in an electromagnet, which is more important, the field $\mathscr{B}_0$ produced by external currents in the windings or the field $\mathscr{B}_M$ produced by the internal currents associated with the atoms of iron? Discuss carefully.

5. Show from (30.10) that the direction of the vector $\mathscr{H}$ *inside* a permanent magnet is opposite to the direction of $\mathscr{B}$ inside the magnet. Why does a bar magnet tend to become demagnetized when left on a laboratory shelf for prolonged times?

6. Distinguish between *diamagnetism, paramagnetism,* and *ferromagnetism.*

7. Discuss the reasons for the failure of Curie's law as shown in Fig. 30.7.

8. What magnetic properties are important in the selection of materials for permanent magnets? What magnet properties are important in the selection of materials for transformer cores in commercial power systems in which the magnetic field reverses at 60 Hz?

9. As noted in Section 28.9, evidence that the earth's magnetic field has changed in direction has been obtained by studies of minerals containing materials that were magnetized at the time the minerals were formed. Discuss the reasoning involved in these investigations. Similar evidence of changes in terrestrial magnetism during historic times has been obtained in studies of bricks from pottery kilns and other ceramic artifacts. Discuss the reasoning involved in such studies.

10. High-energy charged particles enter the earth's atmosphere from outer space as *cosmic rays.* How would the trajectories of such particles be modified if the earth's magnetic field suddenly vanished?

11. In view of the data given in Table 30.2, is it reasonable to attribute the earth's magnetic field to a permanently magnetized iron-nickel core?

12. How does a magnetic tape recorder work?

PROBLEMS

1. A long cylindrical bar magnet has a uniform magnetization of 5.0×10^5 A/m. What is the magnitude of the magnetic field strength just outside either end of the bar? Hint: Recall the results discussed in Chapter 28 for a solenoid.

2. What is the torque on the bar magnet of Problem 1 if the magnet is 13 cm long, has a cross section of radius 5 mm, and is placed parallel to the X axis in a uniform magnetic field in the Z direction having $\mathscr{B} = (0.095 \text{ T})\mathbf{k}$? Assume that $\mathscr{M}$ is in the positive X direction.

3. A certain sample of iron has a mass density of 7870 kg/m³; when this iron is used for the core in a Rowland ring experiment it is found that the saturation value of the magnetic field strength is 2.15 T and the magnetic intensity required for saturation is 1.6×10^5 A/m. Use this information to determine the approximate magnetic moment of a single iron atom.

4. A large electromagnet in a vacuum chamber has a magnetic field strength of 1.25 T in the gap between its pole faces. What is the magnetic intensity in this region? What would be the magnetization of a small piece of silver placed in this region? Repeat for a small sample of platinum.

5. Explain clearly why a magnet attracts an unmagnetized iron or steel object like a paper clip or a nail.

6. A Rowland ring with a core of Alnico 2 is magnetized to saturation and the current in the windings is then reduced to zero. The ring has a circular cross section of radius 5 mm and a mean ring radius of 15 cm. What is the magnetization of the ring?

7. A certain Rowland ring has a circular cross section of radius 0.5 cm and a mean ring radius of 15 cm. The ring is made of magnetically soft iron having a relative permeability of 5000 and carries a winding of 400 uniformly spaced turns. The iron is initially unmagnetized. What are the magnitudes of $\mathscr{H}$, $\mathscr{M}$, and $\mathscr{B}$ inside the ring after the current in the windings has been increased from zero to 0.5 A?

8. The Rowland ring of Problem 7 has a secondary winding of 28 turns that is connected to a ballistic galvanometer. The total resistance of the secondary circuit is 4.7 Ω. How much charge passes through the galvanometer as the current in the primary winding is increased from zero to 0.5 A?

9. A certain Rowland ring has a square cross section with side length 0.6 cm and a mean ring radius of 14 cm. The ring is made of a magnetically soft material having a relative permeability of 2200 and carries a winding of 450 uniformly spaced turns. The ring is initially unmagnetized and the current in the windings is zero. To what value must the current be raised in order to produce a magnetic-field strength in the ring of 0.75 T? What is then the magnetic flux through a cross section of the ring? To what value must the current be further increased in order to double this flux?

10. Consider the situation of Problem 9 except that the core is made of lead. (a) What is the magnetization of the core when the current in the windings is raised from zero to 1.0 A? (b) What is the magnetic-field strength in the core? (c) If the core were not present, what current would have to be present in a second winding having 150 uniformly distributed turns in addition to the 1.0-A current in the primary windings in order to produce the same magnetic-field strength inside the ring as in (b)?

11. For the Rowland ring of Problem 9 suppose that the current in the windings is increased from zero to 1.0 A. What is the magnetization of the core? What is the surface current per unit length that is equivalent to this magnetization? If the core were not present, how many uniformly distributed turns would have to be added to the windings in order to produce the same magnetic-field strength inside the ring with a current of 1.0 A?

12. Repeat Problem 11 for a case where the core is made of aluminum.

13. Show in detail why (30.14) implies that when a sample of ferromagnetic material is carried once around a hysteresis loop, the net energy delivered per unit volume of material is equal to the area enclosed by the loop.

14. Show that the units of the product $\mathscr{H}\mathscr{B}$ are J/m³ as required by (30.14).

15. The following steps of reasoning can be used to derive (30.3). (a) In Section 27.2 we noted that the magnetic flux through any *closed* surface is zero. Apply this result to a surface in the field of Fig. 30.3 having the form of a coin-shaped cylinder of radius R and thickness Δz oriented as shown in the diagram. Show that the net outward flux from the end surfaces is $\pi R^2[\mathscr{B}_z(z + \Delta z) - \mathscr{B}_z(z)]$ and that through the edge of the surface is $\mathscr{B}_r 2\pi R \Delta z$, where $\mathscr{B}_z$ and $\mathscr{B}_r$ are as shown in Fig. 30.3. (b) Show that in the limit as $\Delta z \to 0$ the statement that the flux through the closed surface is zero implies that $(R/2)(\partial \mathscr{B}_z/\partial z) + \mathscr{B}_r = 0$. (c) Show from $d\mathbf{F} = I\,d\mathbf{l} \times \mathscr{B}$ that the resultant force on the current loop shown in Figs. 30.3 and 30.4 is

$$-2\pi R I \mathcal{B} \cos \theta \mathbf{k} = -2\pi R I \mathcal{B}_r \mathbf{k}$$
$$= 2\pi R I (R/2)(\partial \mathcal{B}_z/\partial z)\mathbf{k}.$$

(d) Show that (30.3) follows directly from this result.

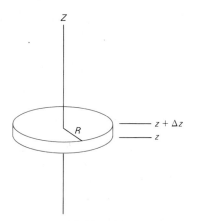

Problem 15

16. The following model provides some insight into the phenomenon of diamagnetism. Consider an electron of charge $-e$ and mass m_e moving in a circular orbit of radius r under the action of a resultant centripetal force $F_0 = m_e r \omega_0^2$. Suppose that a uniform magnetic field $\mathcal{B}$ is applied normal to the plane of the electron orbit and that the radius of the orbit does not change. Show that as a result of the magnetic force $\mathbf{F}_\mathcal{B} = -e\mathbf{v} \times \mathcal{B}$ the angular velocity changes to a value ω satisfying $m_e r \omega_0^2 \pm e r \omega \mathcal{B} = m_e r \omega^2$, where the choice of sign depends on whether the sense of circulation of the electron is clockwise or counterclockwise relative to the direction of $\mathcal{B}$. Which sense of circulation goes with which sign? Show that for $e\mathcal{B}/m_e \ll \omega_0$ one has in good approximation that $\omega = \omega_0 \pm e\mathcal{B}/2m_e$. Show that the magnitude of the change in the magnetic moment associated with the orbiting electron is $\Delta m = r^2 e^2 \mathcal{B}/4m_e$ and that the direction of this change is opposite to the direction of $\mathcal{B}$ whichever the sense of the circulation of the electron.

CHAPTER 31

Alternating Currents

In Section 29.4 we saw how a coil rotating in a uniform magnetic field can produce an EMF that varies sinusoidally in time. In the most general case we can represent such an EMF in the form $V_E = V_{EM} \cos(2\pi f t + \phi)$, where ϕ is a phase factor determined by the state of the oscillation of the generator EMF at time $t = 0$. Almost all power circuits employ sources of sinusoidal EMF. The currents these sources produce are also sinusoidal and have the same frequency f. Such currents are commonly called *alternating currents,* and the circuits in which these currents exist are referred to as AC circuits.

An important reason for the prevalence of AC circuits is the simplicity and efficiency with which alternating voltages and currents can be changed from one amplitude to another by means of a *transformer,* which is a device that operates on the electromagnetic induction principle and has no mechanical moving parts. There is no DC counterpart of the transformer. In the United States, the most common frequency for commercial electrical power is 60 Hz; circuits in aircraft frequently operate at 400 Hz. The type of analysis we shall discuss in this chapter is valid for laboratory circuits at frequencies up to the order of 10^6 Hz, covering the audio and low radio-frequency ranges. At higher frequencies, a circuit description in terms of "lumped," frequency-independent resistance, capacitance, and inductance is less valid, and consideration must also be given to power lost in the form of electromagnetic radiation, which is the subject of the next chapter.

31.1 AC CIRCUITS

In AC circuits the resistance, capacitance, and inductance in the circuit all play important roles in determining the overall circuit behavior. We shall assume that we are dealing with ideal circuit elements that are pure resistors, pure capacitors,

Table 31.1   Summary of Symbols used and Terminal Voltage Relations for Circuit Elements

Circuit Element	Symbol	Terminal Voltage
Resistor, R		$V_R = IR$
Capacitor, C		$V_C = Q/C$
Inductor, L		$V_L = L \, dI/dt$
Sinusoidal EMF		$V_E = V_{EM} \cos(2\pi ft + \phi)$

or inductors having self-inductance and perhaps non-negligible resistance. We assume that these properties are lumped in localized circuit components that are connected by ideal wires of negligible resistance. We further assume that the quantities R, L, and C are all constants independent of the amplitude or frequency of the applied EMF and independent of environmental factors such as the ambient temperature. We also assume that the physical size of our circuit is sufficiently small and the frequency is sufficiently low that to excellent approximation the same current exists in all portions of a series circuit at any instant of time. That is, we assume that all portions of the circuit respond "instantaneously" to changes in the source of EMF rather than allowing time for propagation of a "signal" produced by the change. Since such signals will propagate in the circuit at essentially the speed of light, consideration of delay effects becomes important only for very high frequencies or very great distances. Our assumptions will be violated under various extreme circumstances, but there is a broad range of operating conditions under which our model correctly describes the behavior of circuits.

Resistors, capacitors, and inductors have all been treated in earlier chapters. In Table 31.1 we summarize the results that have already been established and introduce a symbol we shall use to represent a source having sinusoidal EMF. A circuit having a resistor R, an inductor L, and a capacitor C connected in series across a source of sinusoidal EMF V_E is shown in Fig. 31.1. The plus and minus signs indicate the sense of the terminal voltage of the circuit element when this terminal voltage is positive. The positive sense of the current I is chosen so that a positive current is one directed away from the positive terminal of the source of EMF when its terminal voltage is positive. The positive senses of the terminal voltages for the other elements are such that there is a voltage drop in these elements in the positive current direction when these voltages are positive. These sign conventions are the same as we have used in previous discussions of the behavior of resistors, inductors, and capacitors in circuits.

In the following sections we shall first consider separately the behaviors of R, L, and C when an alternating current is supplied to each of them. We shall then consider the behavior of a circuit when all three types of circuit element are present in a simple series combination. In considering the terminal voltages for various types of circuit element, it is convenient to relate them to the current in the element since for a series combination all elements have the same current. Therefore, we assume

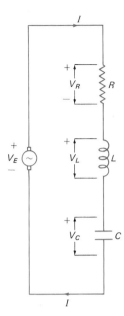

Fig. 31.1 An AC series circuit. The $+$, $-$ signs and the arrows show senses that are taken as positive.

that we have a steady-state alternating current of the form

$$I = I_M \cos(2\pi ft). \tag{31.1}$$

In this chapter we are not concerned with transient effects associated with the development of this steady-state current starting from $I = 0$. We assume that the source of alternating EMF that is responsible for the current was turned on in the very distant past so that all transient contributions to the current have completely died out. This means that we do not have specific initial conditions to impose on the circuit.

31.2 RESPONSE OF A RESISTOR TO A SOURCE OF SINUSOIDAL EMF

If the current (31.1) exists in a resistor of resistance R, Ohm's law says that the voltage drop across the resistor is

$$V_R = IR = I_M R \cos(2\pi ft) = V_{RM} \cos(2\pi ft), \quad \text{(Resistor)} \tag{31.2}$$

where $V_{RM} = I_M R$ is the amplitude of the oscillating voltage. As is illustrated graphically in Fig. 31.2, *the current I in a resistor and the voltage drop V_R across the resistor are in phase.* This means that the current and the voltage have their maxima, their minima, and their zeros at the same times.

At any time t the rate at which energy is being dissipated as heat in the resistor, which is the instantaneous power supplied to the resistor, is

$$P_R = IV_R = RI_M^2 \cos^2(2\pi ft).$$

This quantity is also shown graphically in Fig. 31.2.

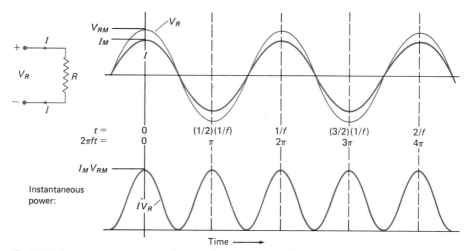

Fig. 31.2　Instantaneous current, voltage, and power for an ideal resistance.

Let T be the period of oscillation associated with the alternating current: $T = 1/f$. In Chapter 3 we defined the *time average* of any time-dependent quantity $F(t)$ over the interval from time t_1 to time t_2 to be

$$\bar{F} = \frac{1}{t_2 - t_1} \int_{t_1}^{t_2} F(t)\, dt.$$

Therefore, the average over a whole number n of cycles of any alternating circuit quantity A has the form

$$\bar{A} = \frac{1}{nT} \int_{t_0}^{t_0 + nT} A\, dt,$$

where n is a positive integer and t_0 is an arbitrary time. This means that for the average power delivered to a resistor we have

$$\bar{P}_R = \frac{1}{nT} \int_{t_0}^{t_0 + nT} R I_M^2 \cos^2(2\pi f t)\, dt = \frac{R I_M^2}{nT} \int_{t_0}^{t_0 + nT} \cos^2(2\pi f t)\, dt.$$

We use the trigonometric identity $\cos^2\theta = \frac{1}{2}(1 + \cos 2\theta)$ to write this as

$$\bar{P}_R = \frac{R I_M^2}{nT} \left\{ \int_{t_0}^{t_0 + nT} \tfrac{1}{2}\, dt + \int_{t_0}^{t_0 + nT} \tfrac{1}{2} \cos(4\pi f t)\, dt \right\}.$$

The second integral in this expression vanishes since in a whole number of cycles, the cosine function has equal numbers of positive and negative excursions each of the same size. Therefore,

$$\bar{P}_R = \frac{R I_M^2}{nT}\, \tfrac{1}{2}\, (t_0 + nT - t_0) = \tfrac{1}{2}\, R I_M^2.$$

Since $V_{RM} = I_M R$, this relation can be written in several alternative ways:

$$\bar{P}_R = \tfrac{1}{2}\, I_M^2 R = \tfrac{1}{2}\, I_M V_{RM} = \tfrac{1}{2}\, V_{RM}^2/R. \quad (Resistor)$$

(31.3)

The relations given in (31.3) are exactly like those for the DC case except for the factor of $\tfrac{1}{2}$. It is common practice to define so-called *effective values* of sinusoidal currents or voltages by the relations

$$I_{\text{eff}} = I_M/\sqrt{2} \quad \text{and} \quad V_{\text{eff}} = V_M/\sqrt{2}.$$

(31.4)

In terms of effective values the power relations (31.3) become

$$\bar{P}_R = I_{\text{eff}}^2 R = I_{\text{eff}} V_{R,\text{eff}} = V_{R,\text{eff}}^2/R.$$

(31.3')

In many cases when alternating currents and voltages are specified without further qualification, it is effective values that are meant. Thus, when we say that a household outlet supples 115 V or 220 V, we are specifying effective values. The corresponding peak values are $\sqrt{2}(115 \text{ V}) = 163$ V and $\sqrt{2}(220 \text{ V}) = 311$ V, respectively. AC measuring instruments are typically calibrated to read effective values. Effective values of sinusoidal quantities represent root-mean-square values of the sort defined in Chapter 15. They are often referred to as "RMS values."

31.3. RESPONSE OF A CAPACITOR TO A SOURCE OF SINUSOIDAL EMF

Suppose that the current (31.1) is acting to charge a capacitor. The voltage across the capacitor at any instant is $V_C = Q/C$. Since $dQ/dt = I$, we have

$$V_C = \frac{1}{C}\int I\, dt = \frac{I_M}{C}\int \cos(2\pi ft)\, dt = \frac{I_M}{2\pi fC}\sin(2\pi ft) + c \,,$$

where c is a constant of integration. After the circuit has been in operation for a long time and steady state is reached, there will be no reason for one direction of the current in the circuit to be favored over the other. If we look at one plate of the capacitor, this plate will spend just as much time negative as it does positive. This means that the time average of the voltage across the capacitor must be zero:

$$0 = \bar{V}_C = \frac{I_M}{2\pi fC}\,\overline{\sin(2\pi ft)} + \bar{c} = 0 + c.$$

This requires that $c = 0$, which means that we have

$$V_C = \frac{I_M}{2\pi fC}\sin(2\pi ft) = \frac{I_M}{2\pi fC}\cos(2\pi ft - \pi/2)$$
$$= V_{CM}\cos(2\pi ft - \pi/2), \quad (Capacitor)$$

(31.5)

where $V_{CM} = I_M/2\pi fC$ is the amplitude of the oscillating voltage across the capacitor. The expressions for I and V_C are shown graphically in Fig. 31.3. We see that as a

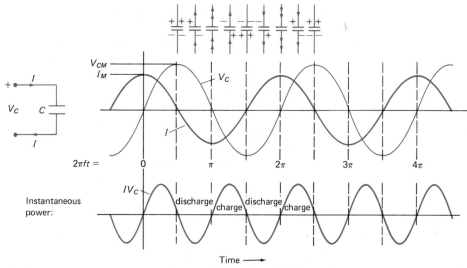

Fig. 31.3   Instantaneous current, voltage, and power for an ideal capacitor.

function of time the peaks and zeros of V_C fall one-quarter cycle *after* the peaks and zeros of I. We say that *the voltage V_C across a capacitor lags the current I to the capacitor by one-quarter cycle or $\pi/2$ radians.*

It is convenient to define a quantity called the *capacitive reactance* by the relation

$$X_C = 1/2\pi fC. \qquad \left\{ \begin{array}{l} X_C \text{ in } \Omega \\ f \text{ in Hz} \\ C \text{ in F} \end{array} \right\} \quad (Capacitive\ Reactance) \qquad (31.6)$$

We then have

$$V_{CM} = I_M X_C \quad \text{and} \quad V_{C,\text{eff}} = I_{\text{eff}} X_C.$$

The units of capacitive reactance are ohms. We note that as the capacitance or the frequency increases, the capacitive reactance decreases.

The instantaneous rate at which energy is delivered to the capacitor is

$$P_C = IV_C = I_M V_{CM} \cos(2\pi ft) \sin(2\pi ft).$$

This quantity is plotted in Fig. 31.3. We see that the instantaneous power is negative as often as it is positive, which implies that

$$\bar{P}_C = 0. \qquad (31.7)$$

The average power delivered to a capacitor by a steady-state alternating current is zero. The energy stored by an ideal capacitor in the part of the cycle when the capacitor is being charged is all returned to the circuit during the part of the cycle when the capacitor is undergoing discharge.

31.4 RESPONSE OF AN INDUCTOR TO A SOURCE OF SINUSOIDAL EMF

We now suppose that the current (31.1) exists in an inductor of self-inductance L. We consider a pure inductance, assuming that the resistance of the coils is negligible. We can take coil resistance into account later by representing an inductor as an inductance and a resistance in series. The voltage drop in a pure inductance is given by $V_L = L\, dI/dt$, from which it follows that

$$V_L = -2\pi f L I_M \sin(2\pi ft) = 2\pi f L I_M \cos(2\pi ft + \pi/2)$$
$$= V_{LM} \cos(2\pi ft + \pi/2), \quad (Inductor) \qquad (31.8)$$

where $V_{LM} = 2\pi f L I_M$ is the amplitude of the oscillating voltage drop in the inductor. The expressions for I and V_L are shown graphically in Fig. 31.4. We see that as a function of time the peaks and zeros of V_L fall one-quarter cycle *before* the peaks and zeros of I. We say that *the voltage drop V_L in an inductance leads the current I in the inductance by one-quarter cycle or $\pi/2$ radians.*

It is convenient to define a quantity called the *inductive reactance* by the relation

$$X_L = 2\pi fL. \qquad \left\{\begin{matrix} X_L & \text{in } \Omega \\ f & \text{in Hz} \\ L & \text{in H} \end{matrix}\right\} \quad (Inductive\ Reactance) \qquad (31.9)$$

We then have

$$V_{LM} = I_M X_L \quad \text{and} \quad V_{L,\text{eff}} = I_{\text{eff}} X_L.$$

The units of inductive reactance are ohms. We note that the inductive reactance increases directly with the frequency and the self-inductance.

The instantaneous rate at which energy is delivered to the inductor is

$$P_L = IV_L = -I_M V_{LM} \cos(2\pi ft)\sin(2\pi ft).$$

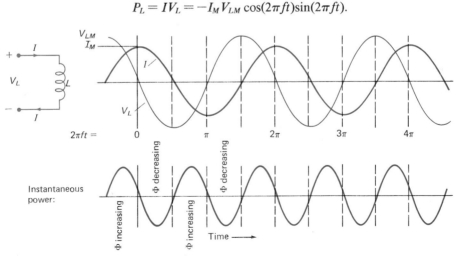

Fig. 31.4   Instantaneous current, voltage, and power for an ideal inductor.

This quantity is plotted in Fig. 31.4. As for the capacitor, we see that the instantaneous power is negative as often as it is positive, which implies that

$$\bar{P}_L = 0. \tag{31.10}$$

The average power delivered to a pure inductor by a steady-state alternating current is zero. The energy stored by an ideal inductor in the part of the cycle when its magnetic field is increasing is all returned to the circuit during the part of the cycle when its magnetic field is decreasing.

31.5   SERIES *RLC* CIRCUIT

We now consider a series circuit containing resistance, inductance, and capacitance to which is connected a source of alternating EMF $V = V_M \cos(2\pi ft + \phi)$. As can be seen from Fig. 31.1, at any instant we have

$$V = V_C + V_R + V_L. \tag{31.11}$$

As we discussed in Section 31.1, at any instant the same current I exists in all the circuit elements. We represent the steady-state alternating current in the form $I = I_M \cos(2\pi ft)$. Then from the results found in the preceding three sections we have

$$V = V_C + V_R + V_L = I_M X_C \cos(2\pi ft - \pi/2) + I_M R \cos(2\pi ft)$$
$$+ I_M X_L \cos(2\pi ft + \pi/2). \tag{31.12}$$

All the terms in this summation have the same frequency, but the terms are not in phase. Simplification of the expression by direct trigonometric manipulation is a messy business. Fortunately, there is an easier way to deal with such summations.

We shall now describe a general graphical method for adding several sinusoidal functions that differ in phase. We shall then apply this method to the particular problem presented by (31.12). Consider the quantity $A = A_M \cos\theta$. We can represent this quantity pictorially as the projection on the X axis of the two-dimensional vector **A** of magnitude A_M shown in Fig. 31.5. Similarly, the quantity $B = B_M \cos(\theta + \phi)$ can be represented as the projection on the X axis of the vector **B** of magnitude B_M shown in Fig. 31.5. Suppose now that we are interested in the sum S of these two quantities:

$$S = A + B = A_M \cos\theta + B_M \cos(\theta + \phi). \tag{31.13}$$

As is shown in Fig. 31.6a, this sum is just the projection on the X axis of the *vector* sum **S** = **A** + **B** of the two vectors defined in Fig. 31.5.

Now suppose that θ increases linearly with time, $\theta = 2\pi ft$, while ϕ remains constant. As time increases, θ increases, and the whole vector diagram of Fig. 31.6a rotates in a counterclockwise direction. However, as is shown in Fig. 31.6b, the *relative* positions of **A**, **B**, and **S** remain unchanged. At any time the quantity S defined in (31.13) is the projection of the rotating vector **S** on the X axis.

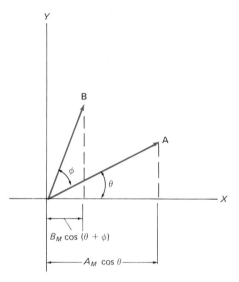

Fig. 31.5

This same construction can be extended in a straightforward way to the summation of an arbitrary number of sinusoidal quantities of the same type as *A* and *B*. Two-dimensional, rotating vectors describing quantities varying sinusoidally in time like the vectors **A, B,** and **S** in Fig. 31.6b are often called *phasors*.

Let us now apply these general ideas to the particular problem presented by (31.12). We see that this is exactly the sort of summation of sinusoidal quantities just described. If we represent the voltage drops V_C, V_R, and V_L by appropriate phasors, evaluation of the sum (31.12) becomes a geometric problem involving vector addition.

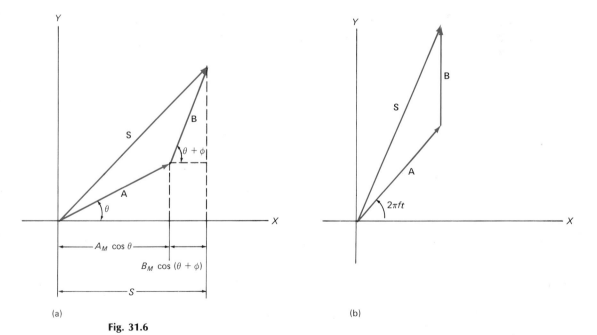

(a)

(b)

Fig. 31.6

Consider first the situation at time $t = 0$. Then (31.12) becomes

$$V = I_M X_C \cos(-\pi/2) + I_M R \cos(0) + I_M X_L \cos(\pi/2).$$

At this instant the phasor diagram representing (31.12) has the form shown in Fig. 31.7a, where we have arbitrarily assumed that $X_L > X_C$. We can represent the current phasor on the same diagram, as is indicated in Fig. 31.7b. Since the current is in phase with the voltage drop across the resistor, the current phasor is in the same direction as $\mathbf{V}_R$. However, the current phasor is not directly involved in the vector sum to give $\mathbf{V}$.

As the time increases, all the phasors shown in Fig. 31.7 rotate counterclockwise together. After a short time t, the phasor diagram has the form shown in Fig. 31.8. The voltage V across the series combination of C, R, and L at any time t is the projection of the phasor $\mathbf{V}$ on the X axis: $V = V_M \cos(2\pi ft + \phi)$. From the geometry of Figs. 31.7 and 31.8 we see that

$$V_M = \sqrt{V_{RM}^2 + (V_{LM} - V_{CM})^2}.$$

Since

$$V_{RM} = I_M R, \quad V_{LM} = I_M X_L, \quad \text{and} \quad V_{CM} = I_M X_C,$$

this can be written as

$$V_M = \sqrt{I_M^2 R^2 + (X_L - X_C)^2 I_M^2} = I_M \sqrt{R^2 + (X_L - X_C)^2}.$$

The quantity

$$Z = \sqrt{R^2 + (X_L - X_C)^2} \quad \text{(Series Impedance)} \tag{31.14}$$

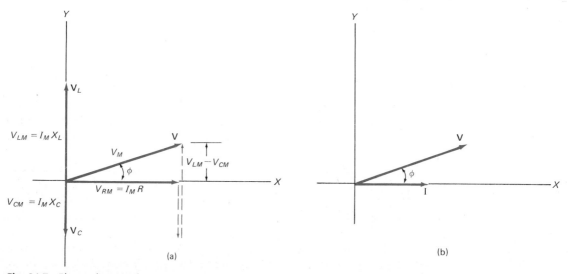

Fig. 31.7   Phasor diagrams for a series RLC AC circuit at time $t = 0$. The diagram represents a case where $X_L > X_C$.

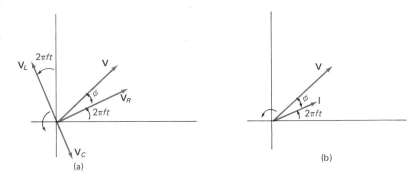

Fig. 31.8 Phasor diagrams for the circuit of Fig. 31.7 at a time $t > 0$. The phasors rotate in a counterclockwise sense about the origin with angular velocity $2\pi f$.

is called the *impedance* of the series circuit. The units of impedance are ohms. In terms of the impedance Z we have

$$V_M = I_M Z, \qquad \left\{ \begin{array}{l} Z \text{ in } \Omega \\ I_M \text{ in A} \\ V_M \text{ in V} \end{array} \right\} \tag{31.15}$$

a relation that has the same form as Ohm's law for a purely resistive circuit. Equation (31.14) for the impedance Z applies only to a series combination of C, R, and L. However, the relation $Z = V_M/I_M$ can be used to *define* the impedance for any circuit.

The phasor diagram could also be developed in terms of effective values rather than maximum values. Since

$$V_{R,\text{eff}} = I_{\text{eff}} R, \qquad V_{L,\text{eff}} = I_{\text{eff}} X_L, \quad \text{and} \quad V_{C,\text{eff}} = I_{\text{eff}} X_C,$$

the result (31.14) is again obtained for Z. In terms of effective values, (31.15) has the form

$$V_{\text{eff}} = I_{\text{eff}} Z. \tag{31.15'}$$

We can also see from Figs. 31.7 and 31.8 that

$$\tan \phi = \frac{V_{LM} - V_{CM}}{V_{RM}} = \frac{I_M(X_L - X_C)}{I_M R} = \frac{X_L - X_C}{R}. \tag{31.16}$$

Thus, we have equations that completely determine the amplitude V_M and the phase angle ϕ for the total voltage drop $V = V_M \cos(2\pi f t + \phi)$ across the series combination of C, R, and L in terms of the resistance and the reactances.

If $X_C > X_L$, the phasor diagram has the form shown in Fig. 31.9. In this case (31.14)–(31.16) still apply, but the numerator in (31.16) is negative, implying that the phase angle ϕ of V relative to I is a *negative* quantity. This means that the voltage V lags the current I rather than leading the current as is the case when $X_C < X_L$.

In the event that one or two of the components R, L, or C are not present in the series circuit, (31.14)–(31.16) still apply with the quantities R, X_L, or X_C for the missing components set equal to zero.

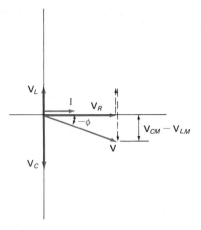

Fig. 31.9 Phasor diagram for a series *RLC* AC circuit at time $t = 0$ for a case where $X_C > X_L$.

The phasor diagram provides a convenient way to represent the concept of relative phase. Imagine an observer sitting on the positive X axis watching the phasors rotate. In describing the relative phase of two phasor quantities, the observer says that a quantity whose rotating phasor passes the X axis first as a function of time *leads* a quantity whose phasor passes the X axis at a later time; the second quantity is said to *lag* the first quantity. The angle of lead or lag is just the angle between the two phasors in the phasor diagram. In Fig. 31.8 the total voltage drop V leads the current I by ϕ radians. In Fig. 31.9 the total voltage drop V lags the current I by $-\phi$ radians. When (31.16) gives a negative value for ϕ, the total voltage lags the current. By inspection of Fig. 31.8 we see that V_L leads the current I by $\pi/2$ radians, V_C lags the current I by $\pi/2$ radians, and V_R is in phase with the current.

We have considered power relations for individual circuit elements in earlier sections. Let us now consider the rate at which energy is delivered to the series combination of C, R, and L by the source of alternating EMF. The instantaneous power supplied by the EMF is $P = VI$. By use of (31.11) we obtain

$$P = VI = V_C I + V_R I + V_L I = P_C + P_R + P_L.$$

Taking the time average of this expression and using (31.3), (31.7), and (31.10), we obtain

$$\bar{P} = \bar{P}_C + \bar{P}_R + \bar{P}_L = 0 + \tfrac{1}{2} I_M^2 R + 0.$$

Although at any instant the capacitor or the inductor may store a large amount of energy, *energy is dissipated only in the resistor.* Energy stored by a capacitor or inductor during one part of the cycle of an alternating current is given back to the circuit in another part of the cycle. Because of the phase difference of π radians between V_L and V_C in a series circuit, when the inductor is storing energy the capacitor is giving up energy, and vice versa.

From the geometry of the phasor diagrams in Figs. 31.8 and 31.9 we see that $\bar{P} = \tfrac{1}{2} I_M^2 R$ can be written as

$$\bar{P} = \tfrac{1}{2} V_M I_M \cos \phi. \tag{31.17}$$

This same result is obtained if we write $P = VI = V_M I_M \cos(2\pi ft + \phi) \cos(2\pi ft)$ and then compute the time average directly. We shall leave the computation of this time average for a problem. The quantity $\cos \phi$ in (31.17) is called the *power factor* for the circuit. If we write (31.17) in terms of effective values, we obtain

$$\bar{P} = V_{\text{eff}} I_{\text{eff}} \cos \phi. \tag{31.17'}$$

Example. A series AC circuit consists of a coil of resistance 100 Ω and self-inductance 0.1 H, a 5-μF capacitor, and a 50-Ω resistor, as shown in Fig. 31.10. The series combination is connected across a source of frequency $f = (1000/2\pi)$ Hz and amplitude 300 V. (a) What is the impedance of the coil? (b) What is the reactance of the capacitor? (c) What is the total impedance of the circuit? (d) Draw a phasor diagram for the circuit at time $t = 0$. What is the phase of the total voltage relative to the current? (e) Draw a second phasor diagram that shows the current and total voltage phasors at a time t such that $2\pi ft = \pi/4$ radians. (f) Does the current lag or lead the total voltage? What does this result mean physically? (g) What are the maximum and effective values of the current? (h) If the current in the circuit is $I = I_M \cos(2\pi ft)$, where $2\pi f = 1000$ s^{-1} and I_M is determined in (g), what is the expression for the total voltage across the series combination as a function of time? What is the effective value of this voltage? (i) What is the voltage drop across the coil as a function of time? (j) What is the average power supplied to the circuit by the source?

(a) The inductive reactance of the coil is given by (31.9):

$$X_L = 2\pi fL = 2\pi(1000/2\pi) \text{ Hz } (0.1 \text{ H}) = 100 \text{ }\Omega.$$

Therefore, by (31.14) the impedance of the coil is

$$Z_{\text{coil}} = \sqrt{R_L^2 + X_L^2} = \sqrt{(100 \text{ }\Omega)^2 + (100 \text{ }\Omega)^2} = 141 \text{ }\Omega.$$

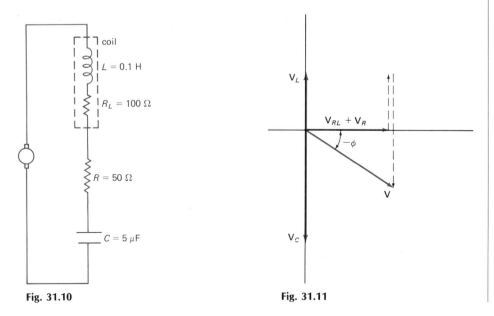

Fig. 31.10   **Fig. 31.11**

(b) The reactance of the capacitor is given by (31.6):

$$X_C = 1/2\pi fC = 1/2\pi(1000/2\pi) \text{ Hz } (5 \times 10^{-6} \text{ F}) = 200 \ \Omega.$$

(c) We can determine the total impedance of the series combination from (31.14) when we note that the total resistance of the series circuit in Fig. 31.10 is $R_L + R$. Thus,

$$Z = \sqrt{(R_L + R)^2 + (X_L - X_C)^2} = \sqrt{(100 \ \Omega + 50 \ \Omega)^2 + (100 \ \Omega - 200 \ \Omega)^2}$$
$$= \sqrt{(150 \ \Omega)^2 + (-100 \ \Omega)^2} = 180 \ \Omega.$$

(d) The phasor diagram for time $t = 0$ is shown in Fig. 31.11. The phase angle ϕ is determined from (31.16):

$$\tan \phi = \frac{X_L - X_C}{R_L + R} = \frac{100 \ \Omega - 200 \ \Omega}{100 \ \Omega + 50 \ \Omega} = \frac{-2}{3},$$

so $\phi = \arctan(-2/3) = -0.588$ radians.

(e) After a time t such that $2\pi ft = \pi/4$ radians, the phasors in Fig. 31.11 have rotated counterclockwise by $\pi/4$ radians. The current phasor is parallel to the X axis at time $t = 0$, so the rotated phasor diagram shown in Fig. 31.12 is obtained for $2\pi ft = \pi/4$ radians.

(f) The current leads the total voltage since the current phasor passes the X axis before the voltage phasor as the phasors rotate in Fig. 31.12. Physically this means that each current maximum occurs earlier in time than the closest voltage maximum.

(g) The current amplitude can be determined from (31.15) by use of the result for Z obtained in (c):

$$I_M = V_M/Z = (300 \text{ V})/(180 \ \Omega) = 1.67 \text{ A}.$$

The effective value of the current is

$$I_{\text{eff}} = I_M/\sqrt{2} = (1.67 \text{ A})/\sqrt{2} = 1.18 \text{ A}.$$

(h) The total voltage is given by

$$V = V_M \cos(2\pi ft + \phi) = (300 \text{ V})\cos[(1000 \text{ s}^{-1})t - 0.588].$$

The effective value of the total voltage is

$$V_{\text{eff}} = V_M/\sqrt{2} = (300 \text{ V})/\sqrt{2} = 212 \text{ V}.$$

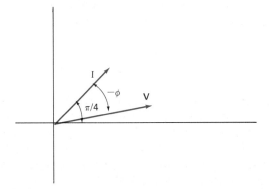

Fig. 31.12

(i) The amplitude of the voltage drop across the coil can be obtained from (31.15) if the coil impedance determined in (a) is used:

$$V_{M,\text{coil}} = I_M Z_{\text{coil}} = (1.67 \text{ A})(141 \text{ }\Omega) = 235 \text{ V}.$$

The phase angle of the coil voltage drop relative to the current can be determined from (31.16) with X_C replaced by zero and R replaced by the coil resistance R_L. Thus,

$$\tan \phi_{\text{coil}} = X_L/R_L = (100 \text{ }\Omega)/(100 \text{ }\Omega) = 1,$$

so

$$\phi_{\text{coil}} = \arctan(1) = \pi/4 \text{ radians}.$$

The coil voltage then is given by

$$V_{\text{coil}} = V_{M,\text{coil}} \cos(2\pi f t + \phi_{\text{coil}}) = (235 \text{ V})\cos[(1000 \text{ s}^{-1})t + \pi/4].$$

(j) The average power supplied to the circuit is

$$\overline{P} = \tfrac{1}{2} I_M^2 (R_L + R) = \tfrac{1}{2} (1.67 \text{ A})^2 (100 \text{ }\Omega + 50 \text{ }\Omega) = 209 \text{ W}.$$

We can easily check that the same result is obtained by use of (31.17):

$$\overline{P} = \tfrac{1}{2} V_M I_M \cos\phi = \tfrac{1}{2} (300 \text{ V})(1.67 \text{ A})\cos(-0.588) = 208 \text{ W},$$

the same result within the accuracy of the computation.

31.6 SERIES RESONANCE

The inductive reactance X_L, capacitive reactance X_C, and impedance Z of a series AC circuit are all functions of the frequency f. In Fig. 31.13 we show a plot of X_C, X_L, R, and Z versus f for a case where $C = 10$ pF, $L = 10$ mH, and $R = 100$ Ω. We note that Z becomes very large as $f \rightarrow \infty$ and as $f \rightarrow 0$, but there is an intermediate frequency at which Z has a minimum value. The frequency at which Z is a minimum is called the *resonance frequency* of the circuit. We see from (31.15) that at the resonance frequency the alternating current will have its greatest amplitude for a given amplitude of the applied alternating voltage.

Examination of (31.14) shows that the minimum possible value of Z as a function of frequency occurs when $X_C = X_L$; under this condition we have $Z_{\text{min}} = R$. The condition $X_C = X_L$ is equivalent to $1/2\pi f C = 2\pi f L$, from which it follows that the resonance frequency is

$$f = 1/2\sqrt{LC}. \quad (\textit{Resonance Frequency}) \tag{31.18}$$

The variations of Z, I_M, and the phase angle ϕ as functions of frequency for $C = 10$ pF, $L = 10$ mH, $R = 100$ Ω, and an applied voltage of amplitude 1.0 V are shown in Fig. 31.14. Note that when $X_L = X_C$, Eq. (31.16) gives $\phi = 0$; *the current and the applied voltage are in phase at resonance.* Although V_{LM} and V_{CM} may individually be relatively large, V_L and V_C are exactly out of phase and at resonance these two voltages cancel in (31.11), leaving $V = V_R$.

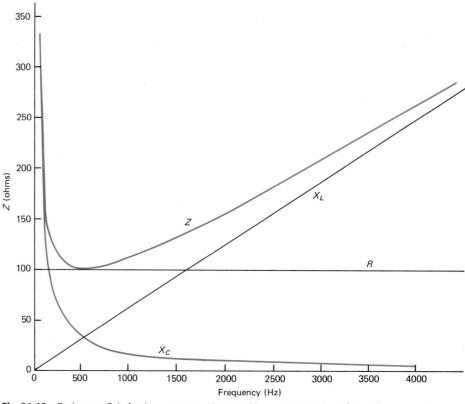

Fig. 31.13 Resistance R, inductive reactance X_L, capacitive reactance X_C, and impedance Z as functions of the frequency for a particular series RLC AC circuit.

The phenomenon of resonance plays an important role in the *tuning* of circuits. This is illustrated in the following example.

Example.   Consider the antenna circuit shown in Fig. 31.15 when a radio wave of frequency $f = 600$ kHz induces a voltage with $V_M = 0.1$ mV between the antenna and ground. The resistance of the circuit is $R = 100$ Ω, the self-inductance is $L = 10$ mH, and the capacitance C is variable. Find the capacitance at resonance. Compute the amplitude I_M of the alternating current in the circuit as a function of the capacitance C.

The capacitance at resonance can be obtained by rearranging (31.13). We have

$$C_{res} = 1/4\pi^2 f^2 L = 1/4\pi^2 (6 \times 10^5 \text{ Hz})^2 (10^{-2} \text{ H}) = 7.04 \times 10^{-12} \text{ F} = 7.04 \text{ pF}.$$

At resonance the impedance of the circuit is $Z_{res} = R = 100$ Ω, and the amplitude of the current is $I_{M,res} = V_M/Z_{res} = 10^{-4}$ V/100 $\Omega = 10^{-6}$ A $= 1.0$ μA. For other values of capacitance the amplitude of the current must be obtained from $I_M = V_M/Z$ with Z given by (31.14). We have

$$I_M = (10^{-4} \text{ V})/\sqrt{(100 \ \Omega)^2 + [2\pi(6 \times 10^5 \text{ Hz})(10^{-2} \text{ H}) - 1/2\pi(6 \times 10^5 \text{ Hz})C]^2}.$$

A graph of I_M versus C as determined from this relation is shown in Fig. 31.15. We note that the current amplitude is large only in the immediate neighborhood

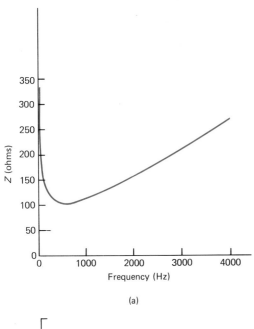

(a)

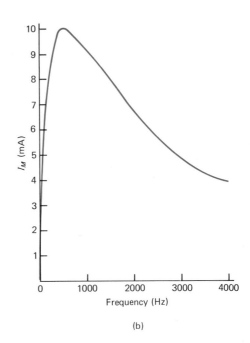

(b)

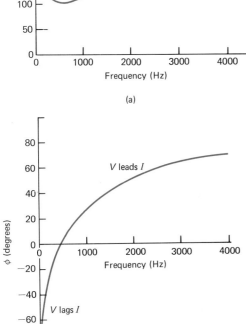

(c)

Fig. 31.14 Impedance Z, current amplitude I_M for an applied voltage $V_M = 1.0$ V, and phase angle ϕ for the series RLC AC circuit of Fig. 31.13.

of C_{res}. The sharpness of the peak in Fig. 31.15 depends on the relative values of X_L and R. We define the width of the peak of a curve like that in Fig. 31.15 to be the horizontal distance between the points where the current amplitude has half its peak value. Some algebraic manipulation shows that the width of the peak in Fig. 31.15 divided by C_{res} varies approximately directly as R/X_L provided $R \ll X_L$. The quantity $\mathcal{Q} = X_L/R$ is called the *quality factor* of the resonant circuit. The greater the quality factor, the sharper the peak in a curve like that in Fig. 31.15.

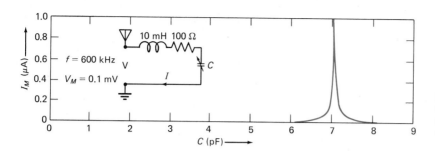

Fig. 31.15 Current amplitude as a function of capacitance for a particular series *RLC* AC circuit. Resonance occurs when $C = 7.04$ pF.

Example. To see how the antenna circuit of a radio can discriminate between stations of different frequencies, repeat the preceding example for cases where the frequency is 580 kHz and 620 kHz.

The values of the capacitance at resonance for these two cases are for $f = 580$ kHz

$$C_{\text{res}} = 1/4\pi^2(5.8 \times 10^5 \text{ Hz})^2(10^{-2} \text{ H}) = 7.53 \times 10^{-12} \text{ F} = 7.53 \text{ pF}$$

and for $f = 620$ kHz

$$C_{\text{res}} = 1/4\pi^2(6.2 \times 10^5 \text{ Hz})^2(10^{-2} \text{ H}) = 6.59 \times 10^{-12} \text{ F} = 6.59 \text{ pF}.$$

The curves of I_M versus C are obtained exactly as in the preceding example except for the changes in frequency. The results for the three frequencies considered are shown in Fig. 31.16. We see that the circuit has significant response to a signal only when the capacitance is in the immediate vicinity of its resonance value for the signal frequency. If the broadcasting stations have frequencies that are sufficiently separated, the circuit can be tuned to respond to a single signal by adjusting a variable capacitor.

Another way to illustrate the tuning property of a series *RLC* circuit is shown in Fig. 31.17, where we plot the current amplitude in the circuit of Fig. 31.15 as a function of signal frequency for a signal amplitude $V_M = 0.1$ mV and a fixed capacitance of $C = 7.04$ pF.

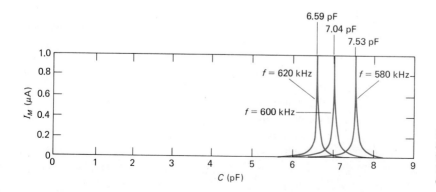

Fig. 31.16 Current amplitude as a function of capacitance for the series *RLC* AC circuit of Fig. 31.15 at three different frequencies.

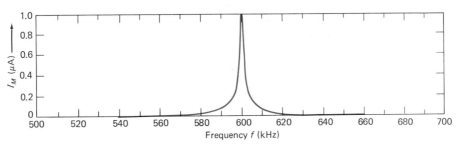

Fig. 31.17 Current amplitude as a function of frequency for the series RLC AC circuit of Fig. 31.15 when $C = 7.04$ pF and $V_M = 0.1$ mV.

31.7 TRANSFORMER

Large currents cannot be transmitted over long distances because of the large power losses in I^2R heating of the conductor. However, the same power can be transmitted by a small current if a correspondingly high voltage is used. In this way the power dissipated in heating the conductor can be reduced to an acceptable value. On the other hand, considerations of safety and technical convenience require that relatively low voltages be used in household and commercial applications. A transformer provides a simple and efficient way in which an alternating voltage can be stepped up in amplitude while the current is simultaneously stepped down in amplitude for transmission. At the end of the transmission line another transformer can be used to step down the voltage for delivery of power to users.

A typical transformer consists of two electrically insulated coils wound on the same iron core, as suggested in Fig. 31.18. The coil to which power is supplied is called the *primary* winding; the coil from which power is taken out is called the *secondary* winding. We assume that the primary winding has N_P turns and the secondary winding has N_S turns. In any real transformer there will be power losses due to I^2R heating of the windings, heating due to eddy currents induced in the core, and hysteresis losses in the core. By using a laminated core made of a material having a narrow hysteresis loop and using low-resistance windings, the efficiency of power transmission for a transformer can be made greater than 99%.

When all its characteristics are taken into account, a transformer is a complicated circuit element. For simplicity we shall consider only an ideal transformer having zero losses and for which all magnetic flux is confined to the ferromagnetic core so that the same flux links both the primary and the secondary windings.

If the switch in the secondary circuit is open so that the secondary current I_S is

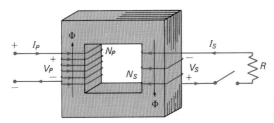

Fig. 31.18 An ideal transformer with a resistive load in the secondary circuit.

zero, all the flux Φ in the core is generated by the primary current I_P. The primary coil acts like a pure inductance in the primary circuit; since we have assumed that both windings have negligible resistance, the primary current lags the voltage V_P across the primary coils by $\pi/2$ radians, and the average power input to the transformer is zero. According to the Faraday induction principle, the primary voltage is

$$V_P = -N_P \, d\Phi/dt. \tag{31.19}$$

Under our assumption that all flux is confined to the core so that the same flux Φ links both windings, the voltage across the secondary coil in the open secondary circuit is

$$V_S = -N_S \, d\Phi/dt \tag{31.20}$$

so that we have at any instant

$$V_S / V_P = N_S / N_P. \tag{31.21}$$

Next let us consider the situation when the switch in the secondary circuit is closed. When the switch is closed, both the primary and the secondary currents generate flux in the core; the resultant flux is a superposition of the two contributions. We shall assume that the voltage V_P applied to the primary coil is fixed by the input circuit. Equations (31.19) and (31.20), and hence (31.21), remain true at every instant; however, the flux Φ is now produced by both currents. By Lenz's law the flux set up by the secondary current tends to oppose the changes in the primary flux and therefore acts to reduce the amplitude of V_P. But we have assumed that V_P is fixed by the input circuit; therefore, the primary current I_P must increase when the switch in the secondary circuit is closed to restore the flux in the core to its original value. Since net power is now being supplied to the secondary circuit, the phase angle ϕ_P between V_P and I_P must now differ from $\pi/2$ radians so that the power factor $\cos \phi_P$ is not zero.

The secondary current I_S and the phase angle ϕ_S between the secondary current and the voltage V_S across the secondary coil depend on the nature of the components in the secondary circuit. For simplicity we shall assume that the load in the secondary circuit is merely a resistor R, as indicated in Fig. 31.18. For a purely resistive load we have $\phi_S = 0$, and the average power delivered to the load is $P_S = V_{S,\text{eff}} I_{S,\text{eff}}$, where $V_{S,\text{eff}} = I_{S,\text{eff}} R$. Under our assumptions of zero losses in the transformer, this must equal the average power supplied by the primary: $\bar{P}_S = \bar{P}_P = V_{P,\text{eff}} I_{P,\text{eff}} \cos \phi_P$.

Circuit equations from which $I_{P,\text{eff}}$ and ϕ_P can be determined can be formulated in a straightforward way in terms of the self-inductances and the mutual inductance of the coils. However, even with our simplifying assumptions these equations are complex, and we shall not consider them here. We merely note that under reasonable operating conditions ϕ_P is close to zero so that we have

$$V_{P,\text{eff}} I_{P,\text{eff}} \approx V_{S,\text{eff}} I_{S,\text{eff}},$$

from which we obtain by use of (31.21) that

$$\frac{N_S}{N_P} = \frac{V_{S,\text{eff}}}{V_{P,\text{eff}}} \approx \frac{I_{P,\text{eff}}}{I_{S,\text{eff}}}. \tag{31.22}$$

This relation illustrates the property discussed at the beginning of this section that when the voltage is stepped up by a transformer, the current is simultaneously stepped down.

QUESTIONS

1. Why is AC used instead of DC in commercial power distribution systems?

2. Why do electrical engineers commonly use effective values of current and voltage?

3. In a *RLC* series circuit consisting of ideal components, at what rate is energy dissipated in the inductance and capacitance?

4. How do the inductive and capacitive reactances of circuit elements depend on frequency?

5. Show that reactance and impedance are properly measured in ohms.

6. What is meant by the *power factor* of an AC circuit?

7. *Resonance* is attained in a series circuit when the inductive and capacitive reactances are equal in magnitude. Why is the word "resonance" used to describe this situation? What is the power factor of a resonant circuit?

6. Why is magnetically soft iron used in the inductors and transformers for AC power circuits? Why are laminated cores used in these circuit elements?

7. Why are high voltages used in long power-transmission lines?

8. Prime movers must be used to operate electric generators. Transmission of electric power always involves "line losses" of electric power. In view of these power losses, why are electric power distribution systems used?

9. Do Kirchhoff's rules as described in Chapter 26 hold for AC circuits? Explain why or why not.

10. If you want to reduce your electric bill, do you want your circuit to have a low power factor or a high power factor, or does it matter? Is there any way to control the power factor for a typical household circuit?

PROBLEMS

1. At what frequency will a 15-mH inductor have a reactance of 100 Ω?

2. At what frequency will a 2.2-μF capacitor have a reactance of 100 Ω?

3. What resistance should be added in series with a 2.2-μF capacitor and a 15-mH inductor of 3.0 Ω resistance in order to give the combination a total impedance of 300 Ω at 400 Hz?

4. A capacitor and a resistor connected in series have a power factor of 0.55 at a frequency of 500 Hz. If the resistance of the resistor

is 22 kΩ, what is the reactance of the capacitor? What is the impedance of the series combination? What is the capacitance of the capacitor?

5. A certain inductor has a resistance of 27 Ω. At a frequency of 175 Hz the voltage across the inductor leads the current through the inductor by 35°. What is the self-inductance of the inductor? What is the reactance of the inductor? What is the impedance of the inductor?

6. The impedance of a certain inductor at 150 Hz is 28 Ω and at 600 Hz is 65 Ω. What are the resistance and the self-inductance of the coil?

7. A certain capacitor of capacitance 2.0 μF has an impedance of 54 Ω when connected to an alternating EMF of frequency 10 kHz. What series resistance is associated with the capacitance in this capacitor?

8. A 60-Hz source of alternating EMF having an effective voltage of 110 V is applied across a series RLC circuit. An AC voltmeter calibrated to read effective values reads 110 V when connected across *any* one of the three circuit elements. Explain how this can be possible. What restrictions does this place on the possible values of R, L, and C?

9. What is the impedance at a frequency of 60 Hz of a 100-Ω resistor, a 0.1-H inductor, and a 20-μF capacitor connected in series? If the effective voltage across the series combination is 181 V, what are the effective voltages across the resistor, the inductor, and the capacitor?

10. Will the voltage across the series combination in Problem 9 lag or lead the current through the combination? What is the angle of lag or lead?

11. A certain series RLC circuit draws an effective current of 75 mA from a 1000-Hz source of EMF having an effective voltage of 35 V. The voltage leads the current. If the effective voltage across the inductor is 57 V and the average power dissipated by the circuit is 12.6 W, what are the values of R, L, and C?

12. A series circuit has an impedance of 50 Ω and a power factor of 0.6 at 60 Hz. The total voltage lags the current. Should an inductor or a capacitor be placed in series with the circuit to raise its power factor? Explain your answer clearly using a phasor diagram. What size of circuit element will raise the power factor to unity?

13. A series circuit has a total resistance of 75 Ω and an impedance of 150 Ω. What is the average power delivered to the circuit by an oscillating EMF having an effective voltage of 120 V?

14. A series circuit consists of a coil of resistance 5.0 Ω and self-inductance 0.5 H and a 100-μF capacitor. These elements are connected to a source of peak voltage 200 V and frequency $(100/2\pi)$ Hz. The current in the circuit has the form $I = I_M \cos 2\pi ft$. Write formulas for the voltage across the capacitor and the voltage across the coil as functions of time.

15. A series RLC circuit consists of a 15.0-Ω resistor, a 95-μF capacitor, and a 4.0-mH inductor of negligible resistance. A source of alternating EMF having an effective voltage of 20 V and variable frequency is applied to the series combination. (a) What is the impedance at a frequency of 60 Hz? (b) At this frequency does the current lag or lead the applied voltage? What is the angle of lag or lead? Draw a phasor diagram. (c) At what average rate is energy dissipated in the circuit? (d) At what frequency is the average rate of energy dissipation the greatest? (e) What is the effective current at this frequency?

16. A series RLC circuit consists of an inductor of resistance 18 Ω and inductance 0.1 H connected in series with a 20-μF capacitor to

a source of alternating EMF of effective voltage 110 V and frequency 60 Hz. What is the effective current in the circuit? What is the phase angle between the current and the applied voltage?

17. For the circuit of Problem 16, what is the average rate at which energy is dissipated by the circuit? How does this power vary if the frequency is slowly increased while the amplitude of the applied voltage is held constant?

18. For the circuit of Problem 16, describe the behavior of the current in the circuit if the capacitance is slowly increased while all other circuit parameters remain constant.

19. A coil having a resistance of 7.5 Ω and a self-inductance of 3.0 mH is connected in series with a 2.2-μF capacitor to a 1000-Hz source of alternating EMF. The effective current in the circuit is 2.0 A. Find the maximum voltage (a) across the coil, (b) across the capacitor, and (c) across the coil and capacitor together. (d) Draw a phasor diagram for the circuit. Does the current lag or lead the applied voltage? (e) What is the power factor of the circuit?

20. For the circuit of Problem 19, write equations for the current, the applied voltage, the voltage across the coil, and the voltage across the capacitor as functions of the time.

21. Describe the behavior of the current in the circuit of Problem 19 if the frequency of the oscillator is slowly increased while its EMF remains constant in amplitude.

22. The current in a series RLC circuit lags the applied alternating EMF. Must one increase or decrease the frequency to bring the circuit to resonance? Explain your reasoning.

23. A variable capacitor is in series with a 0.2-mH inductor. Over what range of values must it be possible to vary the capacitance if we wish to be able to tune the circuit for resonance at any frequency in the AM broad-cast band, which extends from 550 to 1600 kHz?

24. A resistor and a capacitor are connected in *parallel* to an alternating source of EMF. The source voltage is given by $V = V_M \cos 2\pi ft$. Find expressions for the currents through the resistor and through the capacitor as functions of the time. What is the expression for the total current drawn from the source? Draw a phasor diagram representing the applied voltage and the three currents.

25. Using the results of Problem 24, determine what capacitance must be placed in parallel with a 50-Ω resistor in order to draw an effective current of 5 A from a 60-Hz source having an effective voltage of 110 V.

26. Repeat Problem 24 for the case of a capacitor, a resistor, and an inductor of negligible resistance all connected in *parallel.*

27. What is the resonance frequency where the applied voltage and the current drawn from the source are *in phase* for the parallel circuit of Problem 26? Show that the current amplitude for a given amplitude of the applied EMF is a minimum at resonance.

28. Two circuits are in parallel across a pair of leads in a radio set. One circuit has 0.1 μF capacitance and 50 kΩ resistance in series; the other is an inductor of 5 H inductance and 35 Ω resistance. The first circuit is designed to "pass" both audio and radio frequencies; the second circuit is designed to "choke out" radio frequencies. (a) If an audio-frequency signal of effective voltage 50 V at 1000 Hz is applied, what is the effective current in each of the two circuits? (b) If a radio-frequency signal of effective voltage 50 V at 1000 kHz is applied, what is the effective current in each of the two circuits?

29. The energy efficiency of a transformer is 92%. When an effective voltage of 150 V is applied across the primary winding it car-

ries an effective current of 2 A. What is the effective voltage across the secondary winding if an effective current of 0.1 A is drawn from it?

30. A large step-down transformer has an input to the primary winding of 200 kW at 3300 V. If the efficiency of the transformer is 100%, what is the effective secondary current if the secondary winding supplies an effective voltage of 550 V to a resistive load?

31. A transformer on a utility pole has a primary effective voltage of 10 kV, and its secondary circuit delivers an effective voltage of 220 V to an adjacent building. What is the turn ratio of the transformer? If the effective primary current is 5 A, what is the effective secondary current? What average power is delivered to the building? What single resistance is equivalent to the secondary load? Assume an ideal transformer with no losses, a resistive load, and a primary circuit power factor of unity.

32. An AC transmission line 160 km long is made of wire having a resistance of 0.16 Ω/km. (Note that 320 km of wire are required for the round trip.) It is desired to transmit power of 1000 kW from a 2000-V generator. Explain why this is not possible with an effective input voltage of 2000 V. When the effective generator voltage is transformed to 200 kV, the desired power is transmitted. What current exists in the transmission line? What is the resistive load at the end of the line? What fraction of the input power is dissipated because of the resistance of the line itself?

33. A transformer connected to a 120-V, 60-Hz line is used to provide 6 V for ringing a doorbell. The primary has 180 turns, negligible

resistance, and a self-inductance of 0.1 H. How many turns are on the secondary? What effective current and average power are furnished to the primary when the secondary circuit is open (bell is not being rung)? If the primary power factor changes to unity when the secondary circuit is closed and the resistance of the secondary circuit is 24 Ω, what is the effective current in the primary? What average power is supplied by the primary? Assume no transformer losses.

34. Prove that the time average over a whole number of cycles of the quantity $P = VI = V_M I_M \cos(2\pi ft + \phi) \cos(2\pi ft)$ is given by (31.17).

35. Prove that the width of a resonance curve like that in Fig. 31.15 between points where the current amplitude has half its peak value divided by C_{res} varies approximately directly as R/X_L provided $R \ll X_L$.

36. Consider the width of the peak in Fig. 31.17. How would you define the quality factor in this case where frequency f is the independent variable rather than C?

37. Find the value of C in the circuit of Fig. 31.15 that gives the maximum amplitude for the voltage across the capacitor. Express this value in terms of C_{res} and the quality factor $\mathcal{Q} = X_L/R$. What is the maximum voltage amplitude across the capacitor? What is the amplitude of the voltage across the capacitor at resonance?

38. Show that the quality factor of the circuit shown in Fig. 31.15 is equal to 2π times the maximum energy stored by the capacitor divided by the energy dissipated in one cycle, both computed at resonance.

CHAPTER 32

Electromagnetic Waves

In this chapter we are concerned with systems of electric and magnetic fields that propagate through space as *electromagnetic radiation*. Electromagnetic radiation is produced whenever charges undergo accelerated motion. However, the propagation of electromagnetic radiation can be described without specific reference to the source charges that originally generated the radiation. This radiation has many of the properties of mechanical waves that were discussed in Chapter 18. A very important difference is that electromagnetic waves can propagate in vacuum without the presence of any medium in which the disturbance exists.

The "disturbance" for an electromagnetic wave consists of varying electric- and magnetic-field strengths, which both must be present for an electromagnetic wave to exist and which must be considered as a single entity. Quantitative relations satisfied by the electric- and magnetic-field strengths of an electromagnetic wave are obtained from the requirement that they must be consistent with Maxwell's general theory of electricity and magnetism. A detailed investigation of Maxwell's equations is beyond the level of this text. However, we shall describe one form of these equations. Three of the four equations are restatements of relations that we have discussed in earlier chapters. In order to obtain the complete form of the fourth equation we shall have to introduce one new concept, the so-called *displacement current*.

Various kinds of electromagnetic waves are of great importance in many aspects of our lives. Radio waves, television waves, radar, microwaves, radiant heat, light, ultraviolet radiation, and X-rays are all electromagnetic waves, being differentiated by vastly different frequencies and wavelengths. The very different frequencies of these various kinds of electromagnetic waves require that quite different sorts of apparatus be used in their production and detection, but they all have the same basic physical nature. We shall not consider the technical details associated with practical applications of any particular kind of electromagnetic waves. Rather, we shall describe some basic properties shared by all kinds of electromagnetic waves.

A quantitative prediction of the electromagnetic radiation generated by a specified accelerated motion of a source charge can be a complicated calculation. We shall describe in some detail the radiation produced by a particularly simple kind of source, a linear "electric dipole" antenna.

32.1 TIME-DEPENDENT ELECTRIC AND MAGNETIC FIELDS

In our study of electric and magnetic fields we have given primary attention to two kinds of sources. *Static charges* act as sources of electric-field strength according to a relation deduced directly from Coulomb's principle:

$$\mathscr{E} = \frac{1}{4\pi\epsilon_0} \frac{Q}{r^2} \hat{\mathbf{r}}. \tag{32.1}$$

Steady currents act as sources of magnetic-field strength according to the principle of Biot and Savart; for a current element $I\,d\mathbf{l}$ we have

$$d\mathscr{B} = \frac{\mu_0}{4\pi} \frac{I\,d\mathbf{l} \times \hat{\mathbf{r}}}{r^2}, \tag{32.2}$$

and $\mathscr{B}$ for a complete circuit is given by superposition of the contributions $d\mathscr{B}$ from all the elements of the circuit:

$$\mathscr{B} = \int d\mathscr{B}.$$

We note that for both (32.1) and (32.2) the magnitude of the field strength decreases in proportion to the inverse of the square of the distance from the source.

A seemingly reasonable way to try to describe the fields produced by source charges undergoing arbitrary motions would be to continue to use the static-charge and steady-current relations to determine the fields at each instant. This would yield fields with a time dependence generated directly by the motions of the source charges. However, this approach fails for two important reasons. First, the fields do not respond instantaneously to changes in the configuration of the source charges. As the source charges move, the corresponding change in the fields propagates outward from the source with a finite speed c that turns out to be just the "speed of light." At a point P located a distance r from the source, the fields respond to source changes occurring at time t only at the later time $t' = t + r/c$. This *retardation effect* is more important if the source charges move rapidly or the distance of the field point from the source is large.

The second important effect is that when electric or magnetic fields are changing with time, additional fields are necessarily associated with them. In our discussion of the Faraday induction principle in Chapter 29 we learned about one such effect. When the magnetic-field strength varies with time, there is associated with it an induced electric-field strength. As we shall discuss later in this chapter, there is a similar effect for a time-varying electric field. When the electric-field strength varies with time, there is necessarily associated with it a certain magnetic-field strength.

The general expressions for the electric-field strength $\mathscr{E}$ and the magnetic-field strength $\mathscr{B}$ produced by a point-source charge depend in a nonsimple way on both the velocity and the acceleration of the particle. In both expressions there are terms proportional to the magnitude of the acceleration of the source charge that vary directly with the inverse of the first power of the distance r of the field point from the source. The other terms are proportional to higher powers of $1/r$. At large distances from the source only the terms involving $1/r$ are significant; we refer to these terms in the expressions for $\mathscr{E}$ and $\mathscr{B}$ as the *radiation fields*.

32.2 MAXWELL'S EQUATIONS

The diverse phenomena and theories concerning electricity and magnetism were unified, extended, and generalized into a complete theory of electromagnetism by James Clerk Maxwell in the 1860's. The four basic equations of the theory are known as *Maxwell's equations*. In our discussion of electricity and magnetism we have encountered four integral equations involving $\mathscr{E}$ and $\mathscr{B}$ that, after an addition to one equation that we shall discuss below, represent Maxwell's equations for free space in integral form.

The first of these equations is Gauss's relation, which states that the flux of the electric field through any closed surface equals $1/\epsilon_0$ times the total charge inside the closed surface:

$$\Phi_{\mathscr{E}} = \oiint_S \mathscr{E} \cdot d\mathbf{S} = Q_S/\epsilon_0, \quad \textit{(Gauss's Relation)} \tag{32.3}$$

where Q_S is the net total charge inside the closed surface S. Gauss's relation was discussed at length in Chapter 23.

The second equation says that the flux of the magnetic field through any closed surface is zero:

$$\Phi_{\mathscr{B}} = \oiint_S \mathscr{B} \cdot d\mathbf{S} = 0. \tag{32.4}$$

This relation was introduced in Section 27.2. It represents the nonexistence of magnetic charges on which magnetic lines can begin or end.

The third equation represents the Faraday induction principle, which in Equation (29.3) was stated in the form

$$\oint_C \mathscr{E} \cdot d\mathbf{l} = -\iint \frac{\partial \mathscr{B}}{\partial t} \cdot d\mathbf{S}, \quad \textit{(Faraday Induction Principle)} \tag{32.5}$$

where C is a fixed path bounding the open surface S. This equation relates the time variation of the magnetic-field strength to the electric-field strength.

The fourth integral Maxwell equation is related to the Ampère line-integral relation that was introduced in Section 28.7 and states that the line integral of the magnetic-field strength $\mathscr{B}$ around any closed curve C is equal to μ_0 times the algebraic sum of the current linkages of C:

$$\oint_C \mathscr{B} \cdot d\mathbf{l} = \mu_0 \, \Sigma \, I. \quad \textit{(Ampère's Line-Integral Relation)} \qquad (32.6)$$

In the general case the current may not be solely in wires but may for example involve the motions of ions in an electrolyte or a plasma. Therefore, we express the right-hand side of (32.6) in terms of the current density $\mathbf{J}$ defined in Section 25.1:

$$\oint_C \mathscr{B} \cdot d\mathbf{l} = \mu_0 \iint_S \mathbf{J} \cdot d\mathbf{S}, \qquad (32.6')$$

where S is any surface bounded by the curve C as is discussed in Section 28.7.

Maxwell realized that (32.6') is incomplete. In order to identify the difficulty, let us consider the AC circuit shown in Fig. 32.1. For the left-hand side of (32.6') we take the line integral of $\mathscr{B}$ around the closed curve C that circles the wire in a right-hand sense relative to the positive current direction. If we evaluate the right-hand side of (32.6') for the flat surface S_1 shown in Fig. 32.1 we obtain just $\mu_0 I$. However, as was discussed in Section 28.7, the open surface bounded by a closed curve is not unique. The "bag-like" surface S_2 shown in Fig. 32.1 also is bounded by the curve C, but there is no current linking surface S_2 because this surface passes between the plates of the capacitor. If we use surface S_2 to evaluate the right-hand side of (32.6'), the result is zero. Thus, the right-hand side of (32.6') depends on which particular one of the infinity of open surfaces bounded by the curve C is chosen.

Maxwell noted that although there is no conduction current linking S_2, the surface is in a region between the capacitor plates where there is a time-varying electric-field strength. Consider Gauss's relation (32.3) applied to the closed surface $S_1 + S_2$. If Q represents the charge on the capacitor plate that is inside this surface, we have

$$\oiint_{S_1 + S_2} \mathscr{E} \cdot d\mathbf{S} = \iint_{S_1} \mathscr{E} \cdot d\mathbf{S} + \iint_{S_2} \mathscr{E} \cdot d\mathbf{S} = Q/\epsilon_0.$$

We assume that the wire has negligible resistance, so there is a negligible electric field through S_1. Therefore, this relation reduces to

$$\iint_{S_2} \mathscr{E} \cdot d\mathbf{S} = Q/\epsilon_0.$$

If we differentiate this result with respect to time and multiply by μ_0, we obtain

$$\mu_0 \epsilon_0 \iint_{S_2} \frac{\partial \mathscr{E}}{\partial t} \cdot d\mathbf{S} = \mu_0 \frac{dQ}{dt} = \mu_0 I.$$

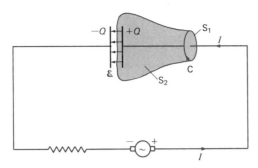

Fig. 32.1 The open surfaces S_1 and S_2 both are bounded by the curve C.

We see that if instead of (32.6') we write

$$\oint_C \mathscr{B} \cdot d\mathbf{l} = \mu_0 \iint_S \mathbf{J} \cdot d\mathbf{S} + \mu_0 \epsilon_0 \iint_S \frac{\partial \mathscr{E}}{\partial t} \cdot d\mathbf{S}, \qquad (32.7)$$

then evaluation of the right-hand side gives $\mu_0 I$ whether we use the surface S_1, in which case the entire contribution comes from the first integral, or the surface S_2, in which case the entire contribution comes from the second integral. Equation (32.7) turns out to be true in general and is the fourth of the integral Maxwell equations. Maxwell named the quantity $\epsilon_0 \partial \mathscr{E}/\partial t$ appearing on the right-hand side of (32.7) the *displacement current.*

Equations (32.3), (32.4), (32.5), and (32.7) are Maxwell's equations in integral form for electromagnetic fields in free space. It is usual to express Maxwell's equations in an alternative form as differential equations involving the partial derivatives of the components of the fields. The differential equations can be derived by mathematical arguments from the integral equations that we have written, but the development is somewhat beyond the mathematical level of this text and we shall omit it.

32.3 ELECTROMAGNETIC RADIATION

By using Maxwell's equations it is possible to predict the time-dependent electric and magnetic fields, and in particular for our present interests the radiation fields, produced by an arbitrarily moving system of source charges. If the source-charge motions consist of oscillations with a definite frequency f, the electric and magnetic radiation fields together constitute an *electromagnetic wave* having the same frequency f that propagates outward from the source. Electromagnetic waves have many of the properties of mechanical waves that were discussed in Chapter 18. The "disturbance" for electromagnetic waves is composed of the electric-field strength $\mathscr{E}$ and the magnetic-field strength $\mathscr{B}$ considered as a single entity. The speed of propagation of electromagnetic waves in vacuum is found to have the same value $c \simeq 3.00 \times 10^8$ m/s for all frequencies. As we shall discuss in the next chapter, "light" is just electromagnetic waves of those frequencies to which the eye is sensitive. Thus, the quantity c represents the speed of light in vacuum. The wavelength λ of an electromagnetic wave in vacuum is given by

$$\lambda = c/f. \qquad (32.8)$$

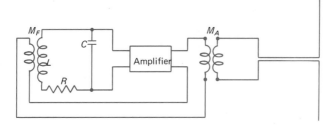

Fig. 32.2 Schematic representation of a circuit that provides continuous current oscillations in a linear antenna.

A circuit in which oscillating currents are generated with the aim of producing electromagnetic radiation having certain characteristics is called an *antenna*. Continuous oscillations in a *RLC* circuit can be maintained by an arrangement like that suggested in Fig. 32.2.

In Fig. 32.2 we show the oscillating capacitor voltage fed into an electronic amplifier that has a large input impedance so that it draws relatively little current from the *RLC* circuit. The output of the amplifier is an oscillating voltage of amplitude much larger than that of the input voltage and a frequency the same as the input frequency. The amplifier is not a passive device; it is a place where electrical energy is continuously supplied to the circuit. Part of the output voltage of the amplifier is fed to the antenna by the mutual inductance M_A. In Fig. 32.2 we show a linear antenna with the oscillating EMF supplied by the mutual inductance M_A applied at its center. The remainder of the output voltage of the amplifier is fed back to the *RLC* circuit by the mutual inductance M_F. This *feedback* loop supplies the energy that sustains the oscillations of the *RLC* circuit. The phase of the EMF produced by the mutual inductance M_F is such as to aid the current in L and hence supply power to the *RLC* circuit.

The oscillating EMF at the center of the antenna arising from the mutual inductance M_A causes an oscillating current in the antenna. These oscillations have a frequency determined by the components of the *RLC* circuit in Fig. 32.2. The oscillating current in the antenna in turn acts as a source of electromagnetic radiation of the same frequency. The detailed characteristics of the radiation depend on the size and shape of the antenna. A particularly simple case occurs for a linear antenna that is short compared with the wavelength of the radiation. The antenna is then equivalent to an electric dipole with a dipole moment **p** that varies sinusoidally with time.

The electric-field strength $\mathscr{E}$ and magnetic-field strength $\mathscr{B}$ generated by an oscillating electric dipole can be determined as functions of time and location in space by a straightforward analysis based on Maxwell's equations that is beyond the level of this book. We shall describe some of the results of this analysis. We choose the Z axis to lie along the dipole. The magnetic lines are circles concentric with and lying in planes perpendicular to the Z axis. The electric lines lie in planes containing the Z axis. In Fig. 32.3 we show the electric lines lying in one such plane at several times in the first half of a cycle of the dipole oscillation. The same diagrams with the directions of all the electric lines reversed represent the electric field at times $t_0 + 0.5T$, $t_0 + 0.635T$, $t_0 + 0.75T$, and $t_0 + 0.875T$, respectively, where T is the period of the dipole oscillation. The pattern of electric lines in three dimensions can be visualized by imagining the diagrams shown in Fig. 32.3 to be rotated about the Z axis.

Very near the dipole the electric-field strength at any instant is essentially the

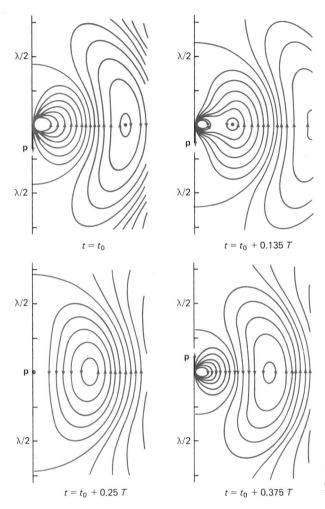

$t = t_0$

$t = t_0 + 0.135\ T$

$t = t_0 + 0.25\ T$

$t = t_0 + 0.375\ T$

Fig. 32.3 Electric lines near an oscillating electric dipole at several times t in the first half of a cycle of oscillation. The oscillation period is T.

same as that produced by a static electric dipole with dipole moment equal to the instantaneous value of the oscillating moment. The electric lines of a static electric dipole are represented in Fig. 32.4. However, as the dipole moment decreases to zero the electric lines do not simply contract and disappear at the origin as they would if the static dipole pattern were strictly followed. Rather, there is a necking down of the lines to form closed loops that then propagate outward from the dipole. If a few of the closed loops are followed out to a distance from the dipole that is large compared with the wavelength $\lambda = c/f$, they appear as suggested in Fig. 32.5. In this figure we also indicate the magnetic lines, which are perpendicular to the plane of the diagram. In this region the radiation fields, which vary with the radial distance r from the dipole in proportion to $1/r$, dominate the behavior of the fields. The radial component of $\mathscr{E}$ becomes negligible and $\mathscr{E}$ approaches being purely transverse to the radial direction. The radiation fields have the characteristics of a sinusoidal wave of frequency f.

The electromagnetic wave generated by the oscillating dipole propagates radially

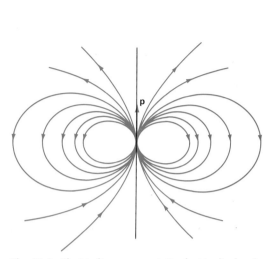

Fig. 32.4 Electric lines near a static electric dipole of dipole moment **p**.

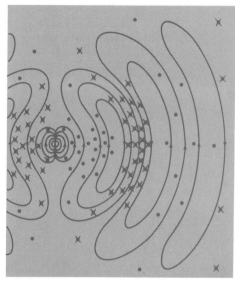

Fig. 32.5 Schematic representation of the electric lines far from an oscillating electric dipole. The magnetic lines form circles about the dipole axis. A dot denotes a magnetic line directed toward the reader and a cross denotes a magnetic line directed away from the reader.

outward from the dipole with speed *c*. Thus, an observer at point P in Fig. 32.5 would see the electric-field strength $\mathscr{E}$ directed first upward, then downward, then upward again, and the magnetic-field strength $\mathscr{B}$ directed first out of the plane of the paper, then into the plane of the paper, then out of the plane of the paper again. The oscillations of the fields $\mathscr{E}$ and $\mathscr{B}$ are *in phase;* their maxima occur at the same times at any given location. The distance between locations of successive maxima at a given time assumes the constant value $\lambda = c/f$.

Let *l* be the length of the dipole antenna and I_0 be the amplitude of the oscillating current in the antenna. Then the radiation fields produced by the oscillating dipole have the forms

$$\mathscr{E}_{\text{rad}} = \frac{2\pi f l I_0}{4\pi\epsilon_0 c^2 r} \sin\theta \, \sin[2\pi f(t - r/c)]\,\hat{\mathbf{e}}_\theta$$

and

$$\mathscr{B}_{\text{rad}} = \frac{\mu_0}{4\pi} \frac{2\pi f l I_0}{cr} \sin\theta \, \sin[2\pi f(t - r/c)]\,\hat{\mathbf{e}}_\phi.$$

(Radiation Fields of Oscillating Electric Dipole)   (32.9)

Here *r*, θ, and ϕ are the usual spherical polar coordinates. The unit vector $\hat{\mathbf{e}}_\theta$ points in the direction of increasing θ for constant *r* and ϕ; the unit vector $\hat{\mathbf{e}}_\phi$ points in the direction of increasing ϕ for constant *r* and θ. These unit vectors are shown in Fig. 32.6 for a particular location P.

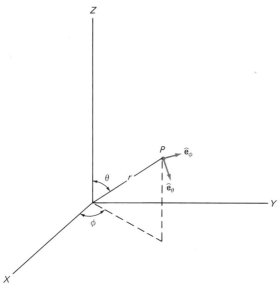

Fig. 32.6 The unit vector $\hat{\mathbf{e}}_\theta$ points in the direction of increasing θ for constant r and ϕ; the unit vector $\hat{\mathbf{e}}_\phi$ points in the direction of increasing ϕ for constant r and θ.

The possibility of the existence of electromagnetic waves was inherent in Maxwell's theory, although Maxwell did not develop the equations relating an oscillating system of source charges to the electromagnetic waves they produce. The first demonstration of radiation of unequivocally electromagnetic origin was made by the German physicist Heinrich Rudolf Hertz (1857–1894) in experiments conducted between 1885 and 1889. Hertz also made significant theoretical developments of Maxwell's theory in predicting the electromagnetic fields generated by particular oscillating sources.

Hertz's source of electromagnetic waves was an unclosed circuit connected to an induction coil. His detector was a simple loop of copper wire with a small gap of adjustable width. The presence of electromagnetic radiation was implied by sparks in the gap of the detector loop that could readily be observed in a darkened room. In his investigations Hertz was able to show that his electromagnetic radiation behaved with regard to interference, diffraction, reflection, refraction, and polarization in a way similar to visible light with allowance for the considerably different wavelength. By setting up standing waves he was able to determine the wavelength of his radiation and use this with the oscillation frequency of his source circuit to show that the velocity of propagation was within the accuracy of the measurements equal to the speed of light.

32.4 PROPERTIES OF ELECTROMAGNETIC WAVES

It is straightforward to show from the differential form of Maxwell's equations that away from source charges and currents the Cartesian components of $\mathscr{E}$ and $\mathscr{B}$ satisfy wave equations that are three-dimensional analogues of Eq. (18.4). By this argument Maxwell was able to show that his theory of electromagnetism was consistent with the existence of fields having the properties of a wave disturbance. Furthermore, the velocity that appears in the wave equation derived from Maxwell's equations for fields in vacuum has the form

$$c = 1/\sqrt{\mu_0 \epsilon_0}. \tag{32.10}$$

We have seen that μ_0 has an exact value of $4\pi \times 10^{-7}$ T·m/A assigned by definition; the value of ϵ_0 is a matter for experimental determination. Maxwell showed that the predicted speed of electromagnetic waves was just the speed of light within the accuracy with which the experimental values of the quantities involved were known. This led to the conjecture, subsequently firmly established, that light is just a particular form of electromagnetic radiation.

The simplest kind of electromagnetic wave is a sinusoidal *plane wave* propagating in a single direction with an amplitude that does not vary with location. From our discussion in Section 18.9 we know that if the electric-field strength represents the disturbance of a plane wave of frequency f and wavelength λ propagating in the X direction, it must have the form

$$\mathscr{E} = \mathscr{E}_M \sin(2\pi ft - 2\pi x/\lambda + \phi). \qquad (32.11)$$

Since both the electric and the magnetic fields are part of the wave disturbance, the magnetic-field strength must satisfy a relation similar to (32.11):

$$\mathscr{B} = \mathscr{B}_M \sin(2\pi ft - 2\pi x/\lambda + \phi'). \qquad (32.12)$$

When it is required that (32.11) and (32.12) simultaneously satisfy Maxwell's equations, a number of additional relations emerge. The fields $\mathscr{E}$ and $\mathscr{B}$ are mutually perpendicular and both are perpendicular to the direction of propagation. These are general results; *electromagnetic waves are transverse*. The speed of propagation $c = f\lambda$ must satisfy (32.10). The oscillations of $\mathscr{E}$ and of $\mathscr{B}$ are *in phase* with relative directions as shown in Fig. 32.7. The amplitudes of the waves represented by (32.11) and (32.12) must have the definite ratio

$$\mathscr{E}_M / \mathscr{B}_M = c, \qquad (32.13)$$

where $\mathscr{E}_M$ is in V/m, $\mathscr{B}_M$ is in T, and c is in m/s.

The wave represented by (32.9) has the form of a *spherical wave,* a type of wave that was also discussed in Section 18.9. Over a localized region at a large distance from the source the variation with r and θ in (32.9) will be negligible, and the wave will essentially be a plane wave. It is readily shown that the fields given by (32.9) have the properties listed above for plane waves.

Electromagnetic waves in vacuum obey the superposition principle stated in Section 18.6. Electromagnetic waves in matter also obey the superposition principle if the field amplitudes are not too large. Quite complicated electromagnetic waves can often be conveniently represented as superpositions of waves of the general form of (32.11) and (32.12) or (32.9). Such superpositions can lead to constructive and destructive

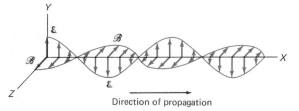

Direction of propagation

Fig. 32.7 Schematic representation of a simple electromagnetic plane wave at a particular time. The direction of propagation is to the right in the diagram.

interference that we described earlier for mechanical waves and shall discuss for light in a later chapter.

32.5 POYNTING VECTOR

An important general result concerning the transfer of energy by an electromagnetic wave was deduced by the British physicist John Henry Poynting (1852–1914) in 1884. Poynting showed that the rate of transfer of energy by an electromagnetic field per unit area normal to the direction of transfer can be represented by a vector **S**, now called the *Poynting vector,* that is defined by

$$\mathbf{S} = \mathscr{E} \times \mathscr{H}. \qquad \left\{ \begin{array}{l} S \text{ in W/m}^2 \\ \mathscr{E} \text{ in V/m} \\ \mathscr{H} \text{ in A/m} \end{array} \right\} \quad (\textit{Poynting Vector}) \qquad (32.14)$$

For electromagnetic radiation in vacuum the Poynting vector becomes $\mathbf{S} = \mathscr{E} \times \mathscr{B}/\mu_0$.

For the plane wave shown in Fig.32.7 we see that the Poynting vector **S** points in the X direction, showing that energy is transferred in the direction of wave propagation. If we use (32.11) and (32.12) with $\phi = \phi'$ and average over a whole number of cycles, we obtain for the average rate of energy transfer per unit area

$$\bar{S} = \mathscr{E}_M \mathscr{B}_M / 2\mu_0.$$

By use of (32.13) and then (32.10) we can write this in the form

$$\bar{S} = \mathscr{E}_M^2 / 2c\mu_0 = c\epsilon_0 \mathscr{E}_M^2 / 2. \quad (\textit{Plane Wave}) \qquad (32.15)$$

These results should be compared with the discussion in Section 18.5 concerning the energy transferred by a mechanical wave.

If we compute the Poynting vector for the radiation fields of an oscillating electric dipole as given by (32.9) and then average over a whole number of cycles, we obtain

$$\bar{\mathbf{S}} = \frac{1}{(4\pi)^2 \epsilon_0} \frac{(2\pi f)^2 l^2 I_0^2}{2c^3 r^2} \sin^2\theta \, \hat{\mathbf{e}}_r, \qquad (32.16)$$

where $\hat{\mathbf{e}}_r$ is a unit vector directed radially outward from the oscillating dipole. Expression (32.16) represents the average rate per unit area at which energy is radiated by the oscillating electric dipole in a direction associated with the angle θ. An element of area on the surface of a sphere of radius r with its center at the origin is $dA = r^2 \sin\theta \, d\theta \, d\phi$, as is shown in Fig. 32.8. Integration of $\bar{S} \, dA$ over ϕ from 0 to 2π and θ from 0 to π shows that the total average power radiated by the oscillating dipole when all directions are considered is

$$\bar{P} = \frac{(2\pi f)^2 l^2 I_0^2}{12\pi \epsilon_0 c^3}. \qquad (32.17)$$

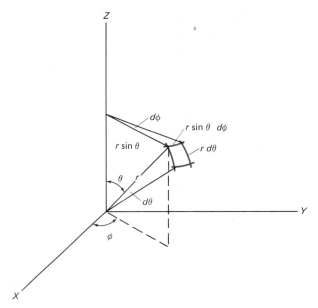

Fig. 32.8 An element of area on the surface of a sphere of radius r with its center at the origin: $dA = r^2 \sin \theta \; d\theta \; d\phi$.

We see that the average power radiated is proportional to the square of the frequency for a given value of I_0. The power is also proportional to the square of the length of the antenna. However, if we attempt to increase the power by increasing the antenna length, we soon violate the assumption that l is much less than the wavelength λ of the electromagnetic wave. Treatment of the radiation from an antenna of arbitrary size can be complicated. The results for a linear antenna are similar to (32.9) but with a more involved dependence on the angle θ.

A case that is important for practical antennas and that can be treated analytically occurs when the length of the antenna is equal to half the wavelength of the electromagnetic waves: $l = \lambda/2$. An analysis that is beyond the level of this text shows that

$$\mathscr{E}_{\text{rad}} = \frac{I_0}{2\pi\epsilon_0 rc} \frac{\cos[(\pi/2)\cos\theta]}{\sin\theta} \sin[2\pi f(t - r/c)] \, \hat{\mathbf{e}}_\theta$$

and   (32.18)

$$\mathscr{B}_{\text{rad}} = \frac{\mu_0 I_0}{2\pi r} \frac{\cos[(\pi/2)\cos\theta]}{\sin\theta} \sin[2\pi f(t - r/c)] \, \hat{\mathbf{e}}_\phi.$$

When the average Poynting vector is constructed for these fields and the integral of $\bar{S} \, dA$ is taken over all directions, we obtain for the average total power radiated by a "half-wave" antenna

$$\bar{P} = (73.1 \; \Omega) I_0^2 / 2.$$ (32.19)

32.6   MICROWAVES

Electromagnetic waves having wavelengths in the range used in radio and television can be generated by antennas with dimensions comparable to the wavelengths involved.

There is, however, a short-wavelength limit that is approached when the wavelength becomes comparable to the size of the components of the electric circuit that supplies energy to the antenna. This limit is reached for wavelengths in the centimeter range. Electromagnetic radiation having a wavelength of this size is called *microwave* radiation.

Microwaves can be generated by setting up standing electromagnetic waves inside *resonant cavities* in conducting bodies in a way that is analogous to the production of sound waves in musical instruments such as organ pipes (Chapter 19). The wavelengths of the microwaves are related to the dimensions of the resonant cavities just as the lengths of sound waves are related to the dimensions of the wind instruments producing them. The energy required to set up the electromagnetic oscillations in the resonant cavities can be supplied by properly directed beams of electrons in ways somewhat analogous to the way in which properly directed jets of air supply the energy to set up acoustical oscillations in wind instruments.

As in the case of the establishment of acoustical oscillations, the detailed mechanisms involved in setting up electromagnetic oscillations in cavities are rather involved and beyond the scope of this book. The basic physical problems involved in microwave production were first solved by the American physicist William Webster Hansen (1909–1949). Two types of modern practical microwave oscillators are called klystrons and magnetrons. The boundary conditions for electromagnetic waves at the walls of metallic cavities are simplified by the fact that at very high frequencies electric currents are confined to the surface layers of metals—the so-called *skin effect*. Because of this, high-frequency electromagnetic fields do not penetrate into the interior of metals, and metals act as good reflectors for electromagnetic waves.

Because metals are good reflectors of microwave radiation, microwaves can be transmitted through hollow metal tubes known as *wave guides*. In order to transmit microwave radiation over long distances, the wave guide from the oscillator terminates with a flared "horn" placed at the focal point of a parabolic metallic reflector that sends out a beam of microwave radiation in a fashion comparable to the way that a beam of light is produced by a searchlight. Microwaves contstitute the boundary between conventional radio and television waves and infrared radiation, which will be treated in the following chapters on light.

QUESTIONS

1. List Maxwell's equations. Describe briefly the nature of the experimental basis for our belief that each of these equations is a valid relation.

2. What is meant by the term *displacement current?* Is this quantity actually a current? Why did Maxwell find it necessary to introduce displacement current in his equations?

3. Figure 32.2 shows a circuit containing capacitance and inductance but no source of EMF attached to the input of an amplifier. Will the circuit oscillate without the presence of a source of EMF? If so, how can the oscillations get started?

4. The expressions in (32.9) for $\mathscr{E}_{rad}$ and $\mathscr{B}_{rad}$ show that these quantities are inversely proportional to the radial distance r from the source. In view of this, what would you predict regarding the relationship between the average power per unit area of wave front and the radial distance from the source?

5. Equation (32.10) gives an expression involving ϵ_0, μ_0, and c. The speed of light c has been

carefully measured. Can both ϵ_0 and μ_0 be determined from measurements of c? Discuss.

6. If the amplitude $\mathscr{E}_M$ of an electromagnetic wave is 1 V/m, what is the magnitude of the associated magnetic field amplitude $\mathscr{B}_M$? In view of the relative magnitudes of $\mathscr{E}_M$ and $\mathscr{B}_M$, which field associated with the wave is likely to have the greater influence on matter?

7. What is the significance of the Poynting Vector?

8. How do the relations between wave intensity and wave amplitude given in (32.15) compare with the corresponding relations for mechanical waves given in Chapter 18?

9. Power is removed from an oscillating circuit equipped with a suitable antenna in the form of electromagnetic radiation. In the light of (32.19), explain why radio engineers speak of the "radiative resistance" of an antenna in contrast to the usually small ohmic resistance of a typical antenna.

PROBLEMS

1. What is the retardation time for electromagnetic signals from a radio antenna that is 200 km from the receiving antenna? Is the retardation effect likely to be important for radio communication on the earth? What is the retardation time for electromagnetic signals from a radio antenna on the moon?

2. What is the wavelength of electromagnetic radiation in vacuum having a frequency of 60 Hz? What can we conclude concerning the applicability of static relations in discussing 60-Hz power circuits?

3. What frequency of electromagnetic radiation has a wavelength of 1.0 m in vacuum?

4. The AM broadcast band extends from 550 to 1600 kHz. What are the wavelengths in vacuum of electromagnetic radiation having these frequencies? What conclusions can be reached about the sizes of radio broadcast antennas?

5. Two kinds of common receiving antennas are (i) a linear antenna, similar to the transmitting antenna shown in Fig. 32.2 and (ii) a "loop" antenna, which is a conductor in the shape of a vertical circle. Consider a plane electromagnetic wave incident on these antennas. The linear antenna responds to the electric-field strength of the wave; the loop antenna responds to the magnetic-field strength of the wave. Use your knowledge of the principles of electricity and magnetism to *explain* these assertions.

6. In Fig. 32.2 we show an electric dipole antenna. Describe a similar arrangement that would produce an oscillating magnetic dipole moment. Discuss the radiation fields that you would expect an oscillating magnetic dipole to produce.

7. Show in detail that (32.13) is dimensionally correct.

8. Show that the radiation fields of an oscillating electric dipole as given by (32.9) have an amplitude ratio satisfying (32.13) at all points in space.

9. Show in detail that (32.14) is dimensionally correct.

10. Suppose that ϕ in (32.11) is zero. Choose ϕ' in (32.12) so that Eqs. (32.11) and (32.12) are consistent with Fig. 32.7.

11. The magnetic-field strength of a certain electromagnetic plane wave has an amplitude of 2 μT. What is the average power per unit area transported by the wave?

12. A typical value of the amplitude of the elec-

tric-field strength for good reception in long-distance, short-wave radio transmission is $\mathcal{E}_M = 100\ \mu V/m$ at the receiving antenna. Assuming that the wave at the receiving antenna is a plane wave, what average power per unit area is passing the antenna? What is the amplitude of the magnetic-field strength associated with the wave?

13. Starting from (32.15), deduce an expression for the average energy per unit volume associated with a plane electromagnetic wave.

14. Electromagnetic standing waves can be set up that are analogous to the mechanical standing waves on a stretched string that were discussed in Section 18.8. Consider a system of electromagnetic standing waves that is set up by reflections of plane waves between two plane, parallel mirrors. Is it possible that the system can be arranged so that at some points there are antinodes of the electric-field strength but nodes of the magnetic-field strength? Explain your reasoning.

15. Derive (32.17) starting from (32.16).

16. What is the "displacement current" associated with a plane wave in vacuum represented by Eqs. (32.11) and (32.12)? Repeat for an electromagnetic wave represented by

(32.9). What are the proper units for displacement current?

17. The average power radiated by an antenna can be represented conveniently by the resistance that would dissipate the same average power as heat. This is called the *radiation resistance*. Show that the radiation resistance of an oscillating electric dipole of length l in vacuum is given by $R = 788(l/\lambda)^2\ \Omega$.

18. Apply (32.7) to the radiation fields given by (32.9) for a case where the curve C is a circle of radius R about the origin lying in the XY plane and the surface S is the hemisphere of radius R bounded by the curve C for which $0 \leq \theta \leq \pi/2$. Show that the right-hand side of (32.7) vanishes for all times t, while the left-hand side does not. Why do the radiation fields (32.9) fail to satisfy (32.7) when we have asserted that (32.7) represents one of the fundamental relations of electromagnetic theory? Why is it permissible to consider only the radiation fields in computing the power radiated by the oscillating dipole?

19. It can be shown that the *complete* expressions for the electric- and magnetic-field strengths for an oscillating electric dipole at the origin of a coordinate system whose Z axis coincides with the dipole axis have the following forms:

$$\mathcal{E} = \frac{2\pi f l I_0}{4\pi\epsilon_0 c^2}\sin\theta\left\{\frac{\sin[2\pi f(t - r/c)]}{r} - \frac{c\cos[2\pi f(t - r/c)]}{2\pi f r^2} - \frac{c^2\sin[2\pi f(t - r/c)]}{(2\pi f)^2 r^3}\right\}\hat{e}_\theta$$

$$-\frac{2\pi f l I_0}{4\pi\epsilon_0 c^2}2\cos\theta\left\{\frac{c\cos[2\pi f(t - r/c)]}{2\pi f r^2} + \frac{c^2\sin[2\pi f(t - r/c)]}{(2\pi f)^2 r^3}\right\}\hat{e}_r$$

$$\mathcal{B} = \frac{2\pi f l I_0}{4\pi\epsilon_0 c^3}\sin\theta\left\{\frac{\sin[2\pi f(t - r/c)]}{r} - \frac{c\cos[2\pi f(t - r/c)]}{2\pi f r^2}\right\}\hat{e}_\phi.$$

Show that these fields do satisfy (33.7) for the curve C and surface S considered in Problem 18.

20. Show that the expressions for $\mathcal{E}$ and $\mathcal{B}$ given

in Problem 19 satisfy Eqs. (32.3) and (32.4) for the case where the surface S is a sphere of radius R with its center at the origin.

21. Show that the expressions for $\mathscr{E}$ and $\mathscr{B}$ given in Problem 19 satisfy (32.5) for the case where the curve C and the surface S are as considered in Problem 18.

22. It is asserted in connection with (32.17) that the average power radiated by an oscillating electric dipole is proportional to the square of the frequency for a given current amplitude I_0. Show that the average power is proportional to the fourth power of the frequency for a given amplitude of the electric dipole moment. Consider the dipole to consist of spheres located at $z = \pm\, l/2$ connected by a wire of negligible capacitance. The charge on the upper sphere is q and that on the lower sphere is $-q$; the electric dipole moment is $\mathbf{p} = q l \mathbf{k}$.

23. A certain radio station emits a total average radiated power of 100 kW from a vertical "half-wave" antenna. What is the amplitude of the current in the antenna?

24. For the situation of Problem 23, what is the amplitude of the electric-field strength of the radiation field at a distance of 10 wavelengths from the center of the antenna for angles with the vertical of $\theta = 90°$, $\theta = 45°$, and $\theta = 0°$? The frequency of the radiation is 580 kHz.

25. Determine the time average Poynting vector for the fields given by (32.18). Make a polar graph of $\bar{S}$ versus θ; discuss the distribution of radiated power as a function of direction outward from the center of the antenna.

26. Two identical half-wave antennas oriented parallel to the Z axis are located at $y = +\lambda/4$ and at $y = -\lambda/4$, respectively. Use the superposition principle to find the radiation fields in the XY plane *far from the origin compared to* λ if the antennas are driven *in phase* with identical current amplitudes I_0. Derive an expression for the time average Poynting vector in the XY plane in terms of the average Poynting vector $\bar{S}_1$ that would describe the radiation for either antenna operating alone. Make a polar graph of the ratio of the magnitude of the Poynting vector in the XY plane to $\bar{S}_1$ versus the angle ϕ of rotation about the Z axis. Discuss the significance of these results.

PART 5

LIGHT

CHAPTER 33

The Nature of Light

The sense of sight provides one of our most important means of observing the universe. Along with the cutaneous sense of hotness and coldness and the sense of hearing, the sense of sight provides direct perception of our immediate environment. The sense of sight provides our *only* direct perception of the distant parts of the universe—the planets, the stars, and even the remote galaxies. However, the sense of sight can be of use to us only when there is *light!*

This part of the book deals with the properties of light and with our uses of light. Since the times of the Greek philosophers, the nature of light has been the subject of speculation. However, in the seventeenth century two major opposing theories developed. Sir Isaac Newton interpreted light in terms of "subtle *particles*" or "corpuscles" that were sent outward from luminous sources; in empty space these tiny particles were supposed to move at enormous speed in straight lines. An opposing theory was proposed by Newton's contemporary, the Dutch physicist Christiaan Huygens (1629–1695); this theory interpreted light in terms of *waves* emitted by luminous sources. Because some type of *medium* is required for wave transmission, it was necessary to assume that otherwise empty space is actually filled with a medium through which light waves can be propagated. Scientists of the nineteenth century called this hypothetical medium the "luminiferous ether." Most of the optical phenomena known at the time of Newton and Huygens could be interpreted equally well in terms of either of these opposing theories.

However, at the very beginning of the nineteenth century, the English physicist Thomas Young (1773–1829) and the French physicist Augustin Jean Fresnel (1788–1827) performed certain optical experiments that could be interpreted *only* in terms of the interference and diffraction of *light waves* of some kind. Later in the century the great theoretician James Clerk Maxwell showed that the *transmission* of light could be interpreted in terms of electromagnetic waves similar to those that we discussed in the preceding chapter. The wavelengths of visible light waves are much shorter than those employed in radio, television, and microwave radar; light waves also have correspondingly higher frequencies. Today we regard light as *visible electromagnetic radiation* with wavelengths in the approximate range 400–800 nanometers (nm). In the present chapter we shall describe one method used for the measurement of the wavelengths of light.

Although the *transmission* of light can be interpreted unambiguously in terms of electromagnetic *waves,* there are certain aspects of the *emission* and *absorption* of light that cannot be fully understood in terms of a simple wave theory. As we shall see in Chapter 36, emission and absorption of light involve *quantum* processes; in certain respects light quanta have particle-like properties. Therefore, we can say today that neither Newton nor Huygens was completely right or completely wrong; light has some wave properties and some particle properties.

In the present chapter and in the next two chapters we shall deal chiefly with properties of light that can be interpreted satisfactorily in terms of *waves.*

33.1   LIGHT SOURCES

Our great natural light source is the sun, a medium-sized star with a surface temperature of approximately 6000 K. The sun thus provides a norm with which other light sources can be compared; because we are accustomed to it, we regard sunlight as "white light." As compared with the sun, the cooler star Betelgeuse appears definitely red and the hotter star Vega definitely blue. The moon gives us light but is not itself a source of light; moonlight reaching the earth is merely sunlight diffusely reflected from the surface of the moon. Similarly, we can see the planets only because sunlight is diffusely reflected from their surfaces. It is today difficult for us to realize that during most of the time that human beings have existed on earth the sun has been the *only* source of light of any practical importance.

The "artificial" light sources that have been developed are of two basic varieties. *Thermal* sources depend on the emission from hot solids such as the carbon particles in the flames of candles and torches or the tungsten filaments in the incandescent electric lights developed by Thomas A. Edison (1847–1931). Electric discharges through gases represent a different kind of source. These *non-thermal* sources include the mercury and sodium arc lamps used for street and highway illumination and also the glow discharges through neon that are widely used for display lighting. The *fluorescent* lights used for indoor illumination employ a discharge through mercury vapor at low pressure; ultraviolet radiation from the mercury vapor strikes a powder coating of the inside of the discharge tube. The powder, known as a phosphor, emits visible light. The color of the light depends on the type of phosphor employed; such a tube can emit apparently white light even though the temperature of the tube remains quite low, and the fluorescent tube is regarded as a non-thermal source. One other familiar non-thermal light source is that of the firefly, which emits light by a process known as *chemiluminescence.*

We now introduce a very convenient concept: the *point source.* Like the "particles" used in mechanics and the "point charges" used in electrostatics, the point source is not really a point in the geometrical sense of the term. Point sources are *small,* but not infinitely small. For certain purposes, we can regard large distant light

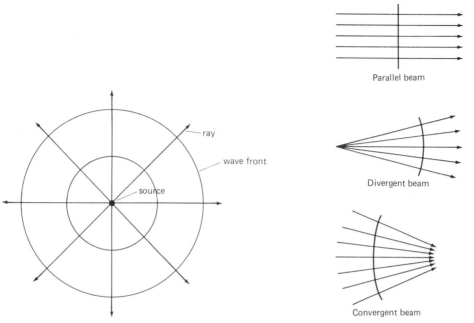

Fig. 33.1 An isotropic point source.   **Fig. 33.2** Light beams.

sources—even enormous sources like stars—as point sources. We can regard real light sources—even extended sources like the sun and like fluorescent light tubes—as consisting of numerous point sources just as we considered an extended body as consisting of particles.

Figure 33.1 shows a diagram of an isotropic point source; i.e., a point source that emits light equally in all directions. Although the diagram in the figure is in a single plane, it represents light traveling outward in all directions with spherical wave fronts spreading radially as the light travels outward from the source. The directions in which the light is traveling are represented by the directed line segments tipped by arrows. These directed lines are called *rays;* rays are not to be regarded as vector quantities. Rays simply indicate the directions in which light is traveling.

From the diagram we note that rays are normal to the advancing wave fronts (Chapter 18). Therefore, when we use rays in optical diagrams of mirrors and lenses, we are also giving information regarding the advancing wave fronts associated with the light. In many situations ray diagrams can be used to give a clearer understanding of optical phenomena than diagrams showing successive positions of advancing wave fronts.

In free space light travels in straight lines. We can easily convince ourselves of this property of *rectilinear propagation* by the casual observation* that sharply defined *shadows* are formed when we interpose an opaque object between a distant point light source and a viewing screen. For example, even when sunlight enters a window on a clear day the shadow of the window frame appears to be sharply defined. Similarly

---

* More careful observation reveals certain interesting complications that we shall discuss in Chapter 35.

the shadow cast by the moon during an eclipse of the sun is sharply defined. Surveyors have great faith in rectilinear propagation; if light did not travel in straight lines, their time and efforts would be wasted!

In describing the transmission of light we shall frequently refer to light *beams,* which are essentially bundles of light rays comparable to the streamtubes that we used in discussing fluid flow. Just as a streamtube is a bundle of streamlines, a light beam is a bundle of rays. When the rays are parallel as in Fig. 33.2a, we refer to the beam as a *parallel beam.* When the rays are spreading out as in Fig. 33.2b, we have a *diverging beam.* When the rays are coming together toward a common point or focus as suggested in Fig. 33.2c, we have a *converging beam.* In each part of Fig. 33.2 we show the advancing wave front, which is plane for a parallel beam and curved for diverging and converging beams.

33.2   SPEED OF LIGHT

The speed of light is so great that in our everyday lives we tend to regard its transmission as instantaneous. For example, when we *hear* the sound from a rapidly moving jet plane we tend to look toward the sky to *see* where the plane "really is." We thus realize that the sound from the plane is transmitted slowly but tend to regard the time required for light transmission as negligible!

The first successful determination of the speed of light was based on astronomical observations. In 1675 the Danish astronomer Olaus Roemer (1644–1710) announced observations leading to a determination of the speed of light; these observations revealed irregularities in the observed times between successive eclipses of Io, the innermost moon of Jupiter. Roemer's argument can be understood from Fig. 33.3, which shows schematically the relative positions of the sun, the earth, Io, and Jupiter. When Io passes behind the planet, it is eclipsed by Jupiter. To simplify our discussion we shall consider Jupiter at rest in its orbit; its orbital motion is slow as compared with the orbital motion of the earth and can easily be taken into account in actual calculations. The observed interval between successive eclipses of Io is 42.5 h when the earth is near A and C in the diagram; at these positions the distance between the earth and Jupiter is not changing. However, the observed interval between Io's eclipses is *greater* than 42.5 h when the earth is at B. Although the motion of Io in its orbit is actually quite regular, at this position the earth is moving away from

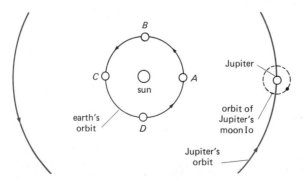

Fig. 33.3 Determination of c from Roemer's observations. Roemer's measurements showed that about 22 min are required for light to travel from A to C in the diagram; what value does this result give for c?

Jupiter, and light from Io has to travel greater distances for successive eclipses. When the earth is at D, the observed time between Io's eclipses is *less* than 42.5 h; at this position the earth is moving toward Jupiter and light from Io has to travel smaller distances for successive eclipses. On the basis of Roemer's comparatively inaccurate observations, one obtains a value of about 224 000 km/s for the speed of light as compared with recent modern measurements of approximately 300 000 km/s.

The first terrestrial measurements of the speed of light employed the round-trip transmission of light over a carefully measured path length D in a measured time t. This gives a value $c = 2D/t$ for the speed of light. The first successful measurement of this kind was reported in 1849 by the French physicist A. H. L. Fizeau (1819–1896), who used the arrangement shown schematically in Fig. 33.4. Light from a source S passing through lens L_1 and reflected from the semitransparent mirror G is brought to a focus F near the rim of the toothed wheel W, which rotates at high speed so that it periodically interrupts the light beam at F and produces a series of brief light pulses. A pulse is sent to the left in the diagram each time the wheel is in such a position that light can pass through a slot between adjacent teeth. The beam passing through the slot is "collimated" or rendered parallel by lens L_2. After the light in the parallel beam has traveled over a path of known length D, it strikes a plane mirror M that returns the light to lens L_2, which again focuses the light at F. If during the time required for the round trip of the light to M the wheel has rotated until the adjacent tooth is at F, the returning light will be intercepted by this tooth.

With the wheel at rest in such a position that light passes through slot 0, the observer at E will see the image of the source formed by light reflected from M; this reflected light passes through the semitransparent mirror to lens L_3 and then to the observer. If the wheel is set in motion with increasing rotational speed, a rotational speed will be reached at which light through slot 0 will be stopped by tooth A; at this same rotational speed light transmitted through slot 1 will be stopped by tooth B on its return trip, and so on. The image of the source will be completely

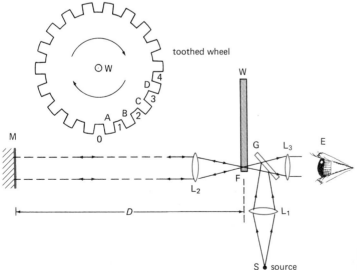

Fig. 33.4 Schematic diagram of Fizeau's apparatus for the determination of c.

"eclipsed" and the observer will see nothing. Further increases in rotational speed will make the image reappear when light transmitted through slot 0 returns through slots 1, 2, . . . , and further eclipses will occur when light transmitted through slot 0 is intercepted by teeth B, C, ... From measured speeds of rotation of the wheel at which successive eclipses and reappearances occur, Fizeau was able to compute the speed of light. The distance D employed by Fizeau was approximately 8.6 km.

In 1850, J. B. L. Foucault (1819–1868) devised a second terrestrial method for determining the speed of light by observation of the displacement of an image formed by light returning to a rotating plane mirror after the light had traversed a known distance. The distances employed in Foucault's experiments were relatively short: 4 m in one experiment and 20 m in another. Although the precision obtained by Foucault was less than that obtained by Fizeau, his work is important in that he measured the speed of light in water as well as air and found that the speed of light in water is less than its speed in air; this result has been predicted on the basis of the wave theory of light but contradicted predictions based on Newton's particle theory.

In both the Fizeau and Foucault methods the time interval required for the round-trip transmission of light over a known path was measured in terms of the mechanical motion of a rotating wheel or a mirror. The most accurate results based on mechanical timers of this type were obtained by the American physicist A. A. Michelson (1852–1931) and his associates, who employed an eight-sided rotating mirror in place of the toothed wheel shown in Fig. 33.4 to provide light pulses and to measure the time for their round-trip passage over carefully measured distances. In one set of experiments, the distance D between the rotating mirror located on Mount Wilson in California and the distant mirror M located on Mt. San Antonio was approximately 35.2 km; this actual distance D was measured by the U.S. Coast and Geodetic Survey in one of the most accurate conventional land surveys ever made. Michelson's results probably cannot be improved by methods employing mechanical devices like rotating wheels and mirrors.

Later experiments have employed electrical methods for the creation of light pulses, for the measurement of the times of round-trip transmission of the pulses and for detection of the reflected pulses. Electrical techniques of timing and detection are superior to the techniques employed in the earlier work.

The presently accepted "best value" for the speed of light in vacuum is

$$c = 2.99792458 \times 10^8 \text{ m/s} \pm 1 \text{ m/s}. \quad \textit{(Speed of Light in Vacuum)} \quad (33.1)$$

This value represents a suitably weighted mean of values obtained by various techniques. This value (33.1) is in agreement with the computed value $c = 1/\sqrt{\epsilon_0 \mu_0}$ given by Maxwell's electromagnetic theory of light; here μ_0 is the defined magnetic permeability of free space and ϵ_0 is the permittivity of free space that can be determined by laboratory experiment. The agreement between the directly measured value of c and the calculated value based on seemingly unrelated electric and magnetic constants gives strong support for the validity of Maxwell's electromagnetic theory of light. In many problems we shall employ the approximate value $c = 3.0 \times 10^8$ m/s.

33.3   MICHELSON INTERFEROMETER

If light does indeed consist of electromagnetic *waves,* it should be possible to determine its wavelengths by means of *interference* effects. We recall from our treatment of sound waves that in order to produce a stationary interference pattern it is necessary to employ wave trains having *coherence;* that is, we must employ two wave trains with a *constant phase relationship* as well as *identical frequencies and wavelengths.* In the case of sound waves it is relatively simple to obtain coherence by employing two loudspeakers operated by a single audio oscillator operating at a constant frequency. The situation is quite different in the case of light waves. Two sodium arcs can be used to produce independent wave trains with identical wavelengths but there is no constant phase relationship between the two wave trains, which are therefore incoherent. The light in the wave train from a sodium arc consists of the superposition of many shorter wave trains emitted by individual atoms; the atoms in one arc are completely independent of the atoms in a second arc. Therefore, it would appear to be impossible to produce stationary interference patterns like those formed by sound waves from two sources. Although this conclusion is correct for most light sources, we can by means of a little cleverness produce interference of light waves by using a single light source and observing the interference pattern produced when the light from a single source reaches an observer *via* two different paths. In accomplishing this bit of optical trickery, we quite literally "do it with mirrors"!

One of the most practically important schemes for producing optical interference is employed in the Michelson interferometer, a simple form of which is shown schematically in Fig. 33.5. Light from an extended source such as a sodium arc strikes a semi-transparent mirror known as a "beam splitter." One-half the light striking the beam splitter traverses path A to a plane movable mirror M_1 and then back to the beam splitter; one-half the light returned to the beam splitter by M_1 is directed toward an observer with the remaining reflected light returning to the source. The other half of the light from the source that strikes the beam splitter is directed along path B to a fixed mirror M_2; one-half the light reflected to the beam splitter by M_2 is returned to the source and the other half is transmitted to the observer. The light reaching the observer thus consists of two superposed wave trains from a single source that have traveled *via* two independent routes. Because they originate from a single source, the two wave trains are coherent and interference can be observed when the two wave trains are superimposed provided the difference in path lengths is not too great.

We note that the light reaching the observer *via* path A has traveled through the glass in the beam splitter three times. In order to make the optical path lengths identical when the actual geometrical distances between the beam splitter and M_1 and between the beam splitter and M_2 are the same, it is necessary to insert a "compensating plate" in path B. The thickness of the compensating plate is equal to the thickness of the glass plate in the beam splitter; the glass used in the beam splitter and the compensating plate has the same optical quality. With the compensating plate in position, the light reaching the observer *via* path B traverses the same thickness of glass as for path A. The use of the compensating plate also makes undesired reflections of light at uncoated glass surfaces the same for the two paths.

When the geometrical distances between the beam splitter and M_1 and the beam splitter and M_2 are equal, the light reaching the observer from any point in the extended source travels identical optical paths. This is the condition for constructive interference and the observer sees a bright field of view. If the distances between the beam splitter and the two mirrors are not equal, the path difference between the two paths depends on the angle with respect to the instrument axis at which

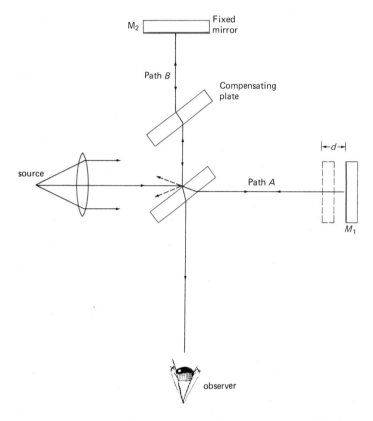

Fig. 33.5 Michelson interferometer: a schematic diagram.

the light traverses the apparatus. With the eye focused to converge parallel light, the observer will see a family of concentric bright and dark rings corresponding to slant paths leading to constructive and destructive interference, as shown in Fig. 33.6a. Calling path A the optical length of the total round-trip passage of light reaching the observer along the instrument axis *via* M_1 and path B the optical length of the total round trip passage of light reaching the observer along the instrument axis *via* M_2, we can state the condition for constructive interference at the center of the pattern of rings in the form

$$|\text{path A} - \text{path B}| = n\lambda, \quad \textit{(Constructive Interference)} \qquad (33.2)$$

where $n = 0, 1, 2, 3, \ldots$. Destructive interference is observed when

$$|\text{path A} - \text{path B}| = (n + 1/2)\lambda, \quad \textit{(Destructive Interference)} \qquad (33.2')$$

where again $n = 0, 1, 2, 3, \ldots$. If we give the movable mirror M_1 a displacement D, the path length difference in (33.2) and (33.2') changes by $2D$. Therefore, if we start with equal path lengths and give the movable mirror a measured displacement D, the observer will note alterations of the center of his field of view from light to

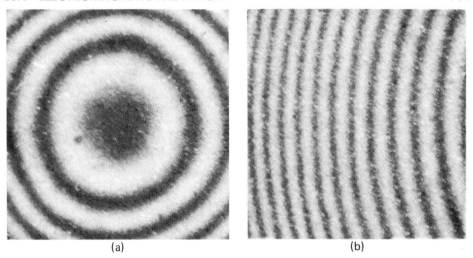

Fig. 33.6 (a) Pattern of fringes observed for the arrangement shown in Fig. 33.5. (b) Pattern of fringes observed when one of the mirrors M_1 or M_2 is slightly tilted.

dark as the displacement is being made. If there are N alterations from bright back to bright while the displacement if being made, we can use (33.2) to write

$$2D = N\lambda.$$

This relation provides a method of determining λ in terms of the measured displacement D; i.e.,

$$\lambda = 2D/N. \tag{33.3}$$

In this way an interferometer can be employed to determine the wave lengths of visible light.

As the Michelson interferometer is actually employed, the mirrors M_1 and M_2 are not perfectly aligned so that the rays shown in Fig. 33.5 traveling along the instrument axis are not exactly perpendicular to their surfaces. If one of the mirrors is tilted very slightly, the observer finds that his field of view consists of a set of alternately bright and dark fringes, as indicated in Fig. 33.6b. As the movable mirror is moved, this set of fringes moves laterally across the field of view. By using a cross hair in a viewing device, the observer can easily count the number of fringes that move past the cross hair while the movable mirror is being displaced. When N bright fringes have moved past the cross hair, (33.3) can be used to determine the wavelength of the light.

We have described the operation of the Michelson interferometer for the case in which *monochromatic radiation*—radiation with single frequency and wavelength—is employed. Most sources emit light with many different wavelengths, which can be measured by other techniques that we shall describe in later chapters.

33.4 ELECTROMAGNETIC RADIATION

The Michelson interferometer provides a highly accurate method of measuring the wavelengths of light throughout the entire *visible spectrum*—the range of wavelengths to which the eye is sensitive. This range extends from approximately 400 nm for violet light to approximately 700 nm for red light. For example, white light from the sun consists of a mixture of spectral colors, which are displayed when sunlight is dispersed by water droplets in a rainbow; white light thus is a superimposition of "all the colors of the rainbow." When the light emitted by a source is resolved or dispersed into its component wavelengths, the resulting pattern of colored light is called the *spectrum* of the source; the appearances of the lights of different wavelengths are referred to as *spectral* colors.

The sensitivity of the human eye is different for different wavelengths. Under conditions of moderate or strong illumination the eye is most sensitive to yellow–green light of wavelength 555 nm. The spectral sensitivity curve of the eye is shown in Fig. 33.7. The wavelengths of the various spectral colors are noted in the figure.

The existence of radiation with wavelengths longer than those of red light was discovered in 1800 by William Herschel (1738–1822), who was able to detect this radiation by means of thermometers placed at various positions in a dispersed spectrum of sunlight. This long-wavelength radiation is termed *infrared* radiation; nearly all of the "thermal radiation" emitted by bodies at temperatures below 800 K is actually infrared radiation. Radiation with still longer wavelengths—*microwaves* and *radio waves*—can be produced and detected by electrical methods.

In 1801, shortly after Herschel's discovery of infrared radiation, radiation having wave- lengths shorter than those of violet light was discovered by J. W. Ritter (1776–1810). This radiation can be detected photographically and by the fluorescence that it produces in various materials. This short-wavelength radiation is called *ultraviolet* radiation. Radiation of still shorter wavelength—*X-rays* and *γ-rays*—was discovered in the closing years of the nineteenth century. The shortest wavelengths are those of γ-rays associated with the "cosmic radiation" produced by high-energy charged particles entering the earth's atmosphere from "outer space."

Electromagnetic radiation of all wavelengths travels with the same speed c in vacuum. The wavelengths and frequencies of all known types of this radiation are listed in Table 33.1. The range of wavelengths and frequencies in this so-called complete *electromagnetic spectrum* is enormous; the ratio of the longest wavelength to the shortest wavelength in this spectrum is 10^{20}! The long wavelengths used in microwave

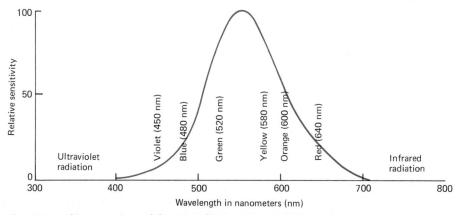

Fig. 33.7 Relative sensitivity of the "typical" human eye to light of various wavelengths.

Table 33.1 Electromagnetic Spectrum

Wavelength (m)		Frequency (Hz)
10^{-15}		3×10^{23}
10^{-14}		3×10^{22}
10^{-13}	Gamma Rays	3×10^{21}
10^{-12}		3×10^{20}
10^{-11}		3×10^{19}
10^{-10}	X-Rays	3×10^{18}
10^{-9}		3×10^{17}
10^{-8}	Ultraviolet	3×10^{16}
10^{-7}		3×10^{15}
10^{-6}	Visible	3×10^{14}
10^{-5}	Infrared	3×10^{13}
10^{-4}		3×10^{12}
10^{-3}		3×10^{11}
10^{-2}	Microwaves	3×10^{10}
10^{-1}		3×10^{9}
1	FM-Radio, TV	3×10^{8}
10		3×10^{7}
10^{2}	AM-Radio	3×10^{6}
10^{3}		3×10^{5}
10^{4}	Maritime Communications	3×10^{4}
10^{5}		3×10^{3}

and radio communications are actually determined by the measurement of the corresponding frequencies in terms of standard frequencies broadcast from such stations as Station WWV associated with the National Bureau of Standards; these standard frequencies are based on the international standard of *time;* wavelengths are then obtained from the relation $\lambda = c/f$. Infrared, visible, ultraviolet, and X-ray wavelengths are determined by measurements involving the international standard of *length.* The frequencies of γ-rays and cosmic-ray photons are determined in terms of their *quantum* properties, which will be discussed in Chapter 36; we note that the wavelength of cosmic-ray photons is comparable with the radius of the atomic nucleus.

In spite of the greatly different wavelengths and frequencies listed in Table 33.1 and in spite of the fact that quite different experimental techniques are employed to detect the seemingly different types of radiation involved, *all* kinds of electromagnetic radiation are basically the same; *all electromagnetic radiation travels in vacuum with speed c.*

Returning to a further consideration of (33.3), we note that the Michelson interferometer itself is employed in establishing the international meter. In writing (33.3) we have expressed λ in terms of a distance D expressed in terms of the meter. The meter itself is defined as $1650763.73\lambda_{\text{Kr}86}$, where $\lambda_{\text{Kr}86}$ is the wavelength in vacuum of the orange light emitted by the rare gas isotope Kr^{86}. The light is produced by an electric discharge in a krypton-filled tube essentially similar to the neon discharge tubes used in display lighting. If we use light from such a tube as the source for a Michelson interferometer operated in vacuum, rearrangement of (33.3) indicates that when the movable mirror is moved steadily by a screw while the observer counts

1650 763.73 fringes, the mirror has moved a distance D of *exactly* 0.5 m. Fortunately, the counting procedure can be automated! By means of the Michelson interferometer, national standardizing laboratories can calibrate metal scales and gauge blocks for use as secondary standards of length. The standard meter itself is *defined* in terms of light waves and therefore is not susceptible to destruction.

33.5   LASERS

Light emitted from most sources like the gas discharge lamps that we have discussed thus far is incoherent in the sense that there is no constant phase relationship between the light waves emitted from one part of the source and light of the same wavelength emitted from another part of the source. For example, a sodium atom near one end of a sodium arc light is completely unaffected by a sodium atom near the other end of the arc. Even though the two atoms are emitting light of the same wavelength, there is no sustained phase relationship between the light waves emitted by the two atoms. We can think of each atom of the source as starting the emission of a wave train and then ending the emission after some extremely short time interval; because the atoms do not start and stop the process of emission at the same times, no sustained phase relationship between the wave trains is possible. We cannot observe interference between two wave trains originating in different parts of the discharge tube and would regard such light as being *incoherent*. In the Michelson interferometer the light emitted by a given atom actually interferes with *itself*.

Another characteristic of the common light sources that we have discussed is that light emitted from them tends to spread out as divergent beams. For example, light from the sun travels radially outward in much the same way as light emitted from the point source shown in Fig. 33.1.

Light emitted from *lasers* behaves quite differently; the light from a laser is remarkably coherent and does not spread appreciably as it travels outward from the laser. The development of the laser is quite recent and has its origin in pioneer work performed in 1952 by the American physicist Charles H. Townes. Although we cannot give a detailed discussion of the processes involved in laser operation until we treat the quantum nature of matter and radiation in Chapter 36, we can at this point present some of the basic ideas involved. Consider the arrangement shown schematically in Fig. 33.8, which shows a tube containing a suitable gas or mixture of gases at low pressure. The gaseous material inside the tube ordinarily has the property of absorbing light of wavelength λ; however, if the gas is excited electrically, it has the property of emitting light of exactly the same wavelength λ. Beyond the ends of the discharge tube in the figure are two plane mirrors M_1 and M_2 separated by

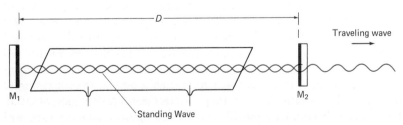

Fig. 33.8   Schematic diagram of a gas laser.

a distance D such that standing waves can be set up between the mirrors by light of wavelength λ. Now suppose that we somehow start a light wave of wavelength λ in the region between the mirrors. If the gas is not excited electrically, the wave "dies out" as the result of absorption of the light by the gas. In this process energy is given up by the light wave to the molecules or atoms of the gas.

Townes devised certain ways of storing energy in the atoms or molecules of the gas by means of an electrical discharge or by illumination from some other light source. When this is properly done, the molecules are "excited" and are able to give up energy to a light wave traversing the region between the mirrors. Therefore, if we start a light wave of wavelength λ in the region between M_1 and M_2 when the molecules are excited, the light wave grows in amplitude; energy is transferred from the molecules to the standing wave between M_1 and M_2 in a process known as *stimulated emission*. The name *laser* itself is merely an achronym for Light Amplification by Stimulated Emission of Radiation. Once this process has started, the material in the tube is said to "lase," and the amplitude of the standing light wave in the tube becomes very large.

The reflecting coating of mirror M_2 at the right end of the tube in Fig. 33.8 is sufficiently thin that some light passes *through* M_2. Some of the light striking the partially reflecting mirror M_2 is thus free to escape. However, the escaping light can be regarded as a part of one of the traveling waves associated with the standing wave between M_1 and M_2. Because this traveling wave is moving from M_1 to M_2, the light beam escaping through M_2 continues to travel in the same direction with little tendency to spread. In this respect the laser is quite different from other light sources.

Light from a laser differs from the light emitted by conventional light sources in another very important way. Whereas the light emitted by one atom in an ordinary gaseous discharge tube has no constant sustained phase relationship with the light emitted by any other atom, the situation is quite different in a laser. Even though the physical dimensions of a laser like that shown in Fig. 33.8 may be very large, all the excited atoms in the tube are giving up energy to the *same* standing light wave between mirrors M_1 and M_2. There is thus a definite phase relation between the light given up to the standing wave by one atom and by the other atoms in the tube. Laser light is therefore highly *coherent*. We can think of the light escaping through M_2 as consisting of a *continuous* wave with constant amplitude and frequency and without any sudden changes in phase. For this reason, laser light can be subjected to intentional modulation in the same way that "carrier waves" from a radio or microwave transmitter can be modulated. The development of the laser has established the basis for a system of *optical communications* that will augment the radio and microwave systems that have been developed earlier.

In Chapter 36 we shall discuss the quantum processes involved in the storage of energy in the atoms in a laser tube in a form that can be given up to the standing waves. For the present we shall merely point out an analogy between the laser and the "singing tubes" that can be used to produce sound waves. By heating the gas in an acoustical resonator tube we can give random thermal energy to the molecules of the gas in one end of the tube. After enough thermal energy has been stored in the molecules, the molecules can give up some of their random thermal energy to the ordered acoustical motion of a standing wave in the tube, and the tube will begin to "sing" at its own characteristic frequency. Whereas the operation of a singing tube is a very simple matter involving heating one end of the tube in the flame of a Bunsen burner, the operation of a laser is considerably more complicated; *all* of the thermal energy added to a singing tube can, in principle, be transformed into acoustical energy; only *some* of the energy added to atoms and molecules can be converted into the radiant energy associated with light waves.

33.6   RADIOMETRY: TRANSMISSION OF ENERGY BY LIGHT WAVES

In Chapter 32 we considered the transfer of energy by electromagnetic waves. The energy W_1 per unit volume associated with a plane light wave is, as in the case of other forms of waves, directly proportional to the square of the amplitude $\mathscr{E}_M$ of the wave: $W_1 \propto \mathscr{E}_M^2$. Because all electromagnetic waves travel at the same speed c in free space, the transmission of a plane light wave with a wave front of 1 m² through space represents the transmission of radiant power per unit area $P/A = W_1 c \propto \mathscr{E}_M^2 c$. The study of the transmission of energy by electromagnetic radiation is a subject called *radiometry,* which we shall now discuss briefly.

The transfer of radiant energy from a source involves the flux F_R of radiation that is properly measured in watts because it represents the flow of energy per unit time. The *radiant intensity of a source* I_R is defined as the radiant flux per steradian (sr):

$$I_R = \frac{\Delta F_R}{\Delta \Omega}, \quad \left\{ \begin{array}{l} I_R \text{ in W/sr} \\ F_R \text{ in W} \\ \Omega \text{ in sr} \end{array} \right\} \quad \textit{(Source Intensity)} \quad (33.4)$$

where ΔF_R is the radiant flux passing through a small solid angle $\Delta \Omega$, as suggested in Fig. 33.9. The radiant source intensity of an isotropic point source is the same in all directions, but the radiant intensity of a real source such as an incandescent light is different in different directions. In specifying the radiant intensity of a real source the viewing direction must be specified.

We now consider the radiation striking a surface. The radiant flux ΔF_R per unit area of surface is an important radiometric quantity E_R called the *irradiance* of the surface and is defined by the relation

$$E_R = \frac{\Delta F_R}{\Delta S}, \quad \left\{ \begin{array}{l} E_R \text{ in W/m²} \\ F_R \text{ in W} \\ S \text{ in m²} \end{array} \right\} \quad \textit{(Irradiance)} \quad (33.5)$$

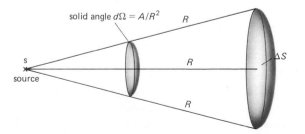

Fig. 33.9 Radiant flux ΔF_R from a source emitted into a solid angle $\Delta \Omega = \Delta S/R^2$.

where ΔF_R is the radiant flux striking a small area of surface ΔS as suggested in Fig. 33.10a. If the irradiance is associated with a beam perpendicular or normal to the surface as shown in Fig. 33.10b, it is sometimes called the "beam intensity." The beam intensity is the radiant power per unit area normal to the direction of propagation and is measured in W/m². Thus, for this case $E_R = P/A \propto \mathscr{E}_M^2 c$. Can you show that the irradiance at the surface in Fig. 33.10a is $\cos \theta$ times the beam intensity?

In making radiometric measurements, we usually employ a "black" receiver that is designed to absorb *all* radiation incident upon it. Absorption of the incident radiant energy increases the thermal energy of the receiver, which is accompanied by an increase in the temperature of the receiver. The increase of the thermal energy can be measured calorimetrically. Thermocouples (Chapter 25) equipped with blackened receivers are frequently employed to give an electrical response proportional to the radiant power absorbed by the receiver. In making absolute measurements, thermocouples and similar radiation detectors must be calibrated calorimetrically.

Studies of radiometry lead to some interesting questions regarding optical interference phenomena: What happens in the case of destructive interference? Does radiant power somehow vanish? The answer is "No!" In interference, the radiant power that disappears from regions of destructive interference is simply shifted to regions of the associated constructive interference in such a way that the total radiant power remains constant. In the case of the fringes seen by the observer in operating a Michelson interferometer (Fig. 33.5), the total radiant power reaching the observer is the same as the radiant power that would have been received if there had been no interference; the radiant power "piles" up in the bright fringes and is depleted from the dark fringes in such a way that total radiant power is conserved.

33.7 PHOTOMETRY

The science of radiometry provides valuable insights into the way that energy is transferred by electromagnetic radiation. However, the information provided by radiometric measurements is useless to the architect or illumination engineer in designing a system for lighting the interior of a house or building or for street or highway illumination at night. Although the radiant flux from a properly operated coal stove

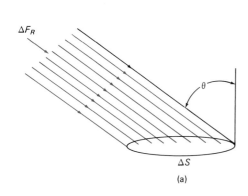

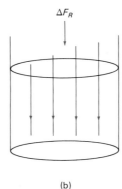

(a)　　　　　　　　　　(b)

Fig. 33.10 Irradiance $E_R = \Delta F_R/\Delta S$.

or from a set of electric pressing irons may be enormous, nobody is able to use this radiant flux to read a book or to *see* nearby objects. In designing a lighting system, engineers are interested only in that portion of radiant flux that can be detected by the human eye, which as indicated in Fig. 33.7 is not equally sensitive to all wavelengths in the visible region. The portion of the total radiant flux that can be detected by the human eye is called the *luminous flux*. In order to measure luminous flux and related quantities, a special set of physical standards and units are needed. These special photometric standards and units have been incorporated into the SI; because they involve *human* physiological and psychological responses, they are not closely related to the other parts of the SI.

There is actually a parallelism between photometry and radiometry. The photometric quantity corresponding to radiant flux is *luminous flux* F_L measured in terms of a special unit called the *lumen* (lm). In defining the lumen, the SI makes use of a standard light source with a luminous source intensity I_L of one *candela* (cd). This standard source consists of an opening of specified size in the wall of a cavity radiator or black body operated at the melting point of platinum (2047 K). As suggested schematically in Fig. 33.11, light travels vertically upward through a small hole at the end of a ceramic tube embedded in platinum inside a thermally insulated vessel; the platinum can be heated by means of the coils of an induction furnace outside the insulated vessel. The light emerging nearly vertically upward from the opening as the platinum solidifies is involved in the definition of the candela. By SI definition

The CANDELA is the luminous intensity of 1/60 cm² of a blackbody at the melting point of platinum. The LUMEN is the luminous flux emitted into a solid angle of one steradian by a point source having a luminous intensity of one candela.

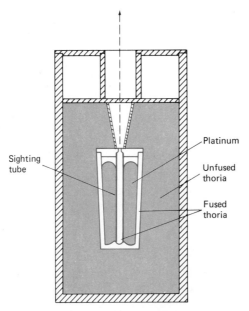

Sighting tube

Platinum

Unfused thoria

Fused thoria

Fig. 33.11   SI standard light source: a schematic diagram.

On the basis of this definition, we can write

$$I_L = \frac{\Delta F_L}{\Delta \Omega} \cdot \left\{ \begin{array}{l} I_L \text{ in cd} \\ F_L \text{ in lm} \\ \Omega \text{ in sr} \end{array} \right\} \quad \textit{(Luminous Source Intensity)} \qquad (33.6)$$

The luminous intensity of a real light source usually depends on the direction from which the source is viewed. If a source radiates isotropically, the total luminous flux from the source is given by the relation: $F_L = 4\pi I_L$.

A third photometric quantity of practical concern to architectural and illumination engineers is the *illumination* or *illuminance* E_L of a surface, which is defined as the luminous flux incident per unit area:

$$E_L = \frac{\Delta F_L}{\Delta S} \cdot \left\{ \begin{array}{l} E_L \text{ in lm/m}^2 \\ F \text{ in lm} \\ S \text{ in m}^2 \end{array} \right\} \quad \textit{(Illumination)} \qquad (33.7)$$

If the surface-area element ΔS is at a distance R from a point source and if the light rays are normal to the surface element, then $\Delta S = R^2 \Delta \Omega$ and we can write

$$E_L = \frac{\Delta F_L}{R^2 \Delta \Omega} = \frac{I_L}{R^2}, \qquad (33.8)$$

which expresses an inverse-square law for illumination.

Light sources are usually compared by means of photometers. With these instruments an observer "matches" the illuminations of a screen illuminated by the two sources; this match is achieved by varying the distances from the sources to the screen; after the illuminations have been made equal the luminous sources are usually compared by making use of (33.8). Sources giving light of different colors cannot be "matched" in this way and are compared by means of a flicker photometer in which a single screen is illuminated by alternated exposures at 5–10 Hz to the two sources; when the observer loses any sensation of flicker as the distance between the sources and the screen is varied, the illuminations the sources are said to be equal.

A connection between radiometric and photometric quantities can be established by means of measurements with monochromatic light. Thus, if yellow–green light with a wavelength of 555 nm is employed, it is found that a radiant flux of 1 W is equivalent to a luminous flux of 680 lm. The ordinates in Fig. 33.7 represent the ratio of the *radiant* flux at 555 nm to the *radiant* flux at other wavelengths required to produce *equal values of luminous flux*. The resulting power ratios were established at the National Bureau of Standards by means of flicker photometers.

QUESTIONS

1. A sharp geometrical shadow is formed when an opaque object is placed between a "point source" and a screen. However, if the opaque object is interposed between an extended source and the screen, only part of the shadow called the *umbra* is "total," and the other part of the shadow called the *penumbra* is only "partial." By drawing rays from various points on the source to the screen show how the umbra and penumbra are produced.

2. Galileo attempted to measure the speed of light by placing observers in towers several kilometers apart. Observer A flashed a signal from a lantern and observer B was supposed to flash an answering signal as soon as A's signal reached him. By measuring the time for such a "round trip" of light over a known distance, Galileo hoped to determine the speed of light. Why did Galileo's attempted measurement fail?

3. Although Foucault's method of determining c gave less accurate results than those of Fizeau, his work was in some respects more important. Why?

4. Explain in detail why it is not possible to observe interference between light waves from two sodium arcs.

5. Explain in detail how the Michelson interferometer can be used to establish the international unit of length. Why is the definition of the meter in terms of light waves preferable to its definition in terms of the carefully preserved standard platinum–iridium bar that was previously used as a standard?

6. What properties do all forms of electromagnetic radiation have in common?

7. Describe the principal ways in which lasers differ from other light sources.

8. Although the "point source" is a useful concept in many situations, point sources are not adequate for detailed treatments of radiometry and photometry. Why? Are there corresponding difficulties in using particles as sources of gravitational fields and in using point charges as sources of electric fields?

9. Discuss the similarities and differences between the concepts of radiant and luminous flux and the concepts of fluid flux, electric flux, and magnetic flux used in earlier chapters.

10. How do the SI special photometric standards and units differ from the other standards and units employed in the SI?

11. What is the connection between photometric and radiometric quantities? Explain in detail how the relative spectral sensitivity curve in Fig. 33.7 could be obtained.

12. The speed of light in vacuum c has now been determined with an accuracy of 1 part in 10^7. Time intervals can be measured even more precisely in terms of the Cs atomic clock. It has been suggested that the international meter be redefined in terms of the distance traveled by light in a measured time interval. What is the approximate time required for light to travel 1 m? If this definition of the meter were adopted, would further improved measurements of c be possible, or would the value of c be fixed by the definition? Explain your reasoning.

PROBLEMS

1. Using the table of astronomical data in the appendix, compute the length of time required for light to travel from the sun to: (1) the earth, (2) Jupiter, and (3) Neptune.

2. A speaker is in a lecture hall 20 m long on a day when the speed of sound is 330 m/s. How long a time is required for the sound of his voice to reach the listeners at the rear of the hall? If his speech is also being broadcast by radio, how far will the radio waves travel in this time?

3. By means of a beam of microwaves an operator in Pasadena, California, transmits a command to a space probe in the vicinity of Jupiter at a time when the probe is 7.2×10^8 km from the earth. How long a time is required for the command to reach the space probe? What is the minimum time after the command is given required for the operator to find whether the command has been carried out?

4. It has been suggested that the international meter be redefined in terms of the *time* required for light to travel a distance of 1 m in vacuum. What is the time required? How might it be measured? What atomic standard would be involved? Discuss the advantages and disadvantages of this proposed change.

5. Astronomers measure distances to the stars in a length unit called the *light year,* defined as the distance traveled by light in one entire year. Express 1 light year in *kilometers.* Express the distance from the earth to the sun in light years.

6. The distance from the earth to the nearest star outside our own solar system is approximately 4 light years. If this nearest star had planets capable of supporting life, how long would be required for an astronaut from one of these planets to reach the earth if he had a space craft capable of maintaining a speed of 33 km/s (approximately three times the speed of escape from the earth)? If the astronaut were 18 years old at the time he left his own planet, how old would he be (a) when he reached the earth and (b) when he returned home after making a round trip to the earth?

7. A pulsed radar set like the one shown in the diagram receives an "echo" signal from an airplane 620 μs after a pulse is transmitted. What is the distance of the plane from the radar station? How long after transmission of a pulse would a radar echo be received from the moon when the moon is 380 000 km from the earth?

8. Microwaves can be used to measure the speed of a moving object by making use of the Doppler effect. A continuous beam of microwaves of frequency f is sent out from a source. If the microwaves are reflected from a moving object approaching or receding at speed v, the frequency f' of the reflected radiation is different because of the Doppler effect. Adapt the arguments that we used in Chapter 19 for sound waves to show that the beat frequency $\Delta f = |f - f'|$ is given by the expression $\Delta f = 2(v/c)f$, where v is very small as compared with c. Note: Actually, treatment of the Doppler effect for electromagnetic radiation is *not* exactly comparable to that for sound waves because there is not an underlying medium with respect to which electromagnetic waves propagate. Electromagnetic waves can propagate in the absence of matter, and the speed of light in vacuum c has the same value for all observers regardless of their motion. However, the *result* obtained in this problem turns out to be the

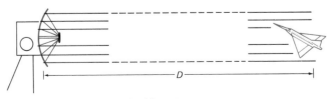

Problem 7

correct limiting value for object speeds v that are much less than c. We shall discuss these matters further in Chapter 37.

9. A microwave transmitter uses radiation of wavelength 10 cm to measure the speed of an automobile on the highway. The observed frequency shift Δf between transmitted and reflected radiation is 456 Hz. What is the speed of the automobile? (See Problem 8.)

10. In the case of the microwave device described in Problem 9, what frequency shift Δf would be produced by an automobile moving at the urban speed limit of 45 km/h? At the highway speed limit of 90 km/h?

11. A continuous microwave radiator using a wavelength of 25 cm is used to measure the speed of approach of an airplane. The Doppler frequency shift is observed to be 325 Hz. What is the approach speed of the plane? (See Problem 8.)

12. When we observe the sun in the sky, we see it at the position it had, relative to the earth, when the light left the sun. What is the angle between this position and the actual position of the sun at the moment we observe it?

13. According to Fig. 33.7, the wavelength of violet light is 450 nm, that of yellow–green light is 555 nm, and that of red light is 640 nm. What are the frequencies of the radiation involved?

14. The wave nature of light sets a limit on the minimum length that can actually be measured visually. If you employed a carefully constructed Michelson interferometer and used orange light emitted by Kr^{86} and were able to observe fringes like those shown in Fig. 33.6 so accurately that a shift in the pattern of one-tenth of a fringe could be detected, what is the minimum displacement D of the movable mirror that you could detect?

15. A Michelson interferometer used with Kr^{86}

light is to be used in the fabrication of a 0.1-mm-thick gauge. How many fringes must an observer count in order to move the movable mirror of the interferometer exactly 0.1 mm?

16. The Michelson interferometer as described in the text employs strictly monochromatic radiation; i.e., light of a definite frequency and definite wavelength. If these conditions are not fulfilled, the pattern of fringes like those in Fig. 33.6 begins to "smear out" as the path difference $2D$ in Fig. 33.5 becomes large. This can be understood by considering the yellow light from a sodium arc light that consists of two nearly equal wavelengths: λ_1 = 589.593 nm and λ_2 = 588.996 nm. (a) From the relation $N\lambda_1 = (N + 1/2)\lambda_2$ find the number N of wavelengths in a wave train of wavelength λ_1 that is equal in length to $(N + 1/2)\lambda_2$. (b) What is the length L of this wave train? If $2D$ in Fig. 33.5 is equal to L, no fringes are observed because the condition for constructive interference for λ_1 gives destructive interference for λ_2. In fact, the fringe pattern will smear out long before $2D$ becomes this large. Because of the Doppler effect and pressure effects in the light source, no atom emits *strictly* monochromatic radiation; in all cases there are limits to usable path differences in interferometers.

17. The light from properly operated gas lasers can under certain circumstances be used in interferometers with path differences as large as several meters. Suppose that a laser emits nominally monochromatic light of wavelength λ = 600 nm and that interference fringes begin to smear out for a path difference $2D = 30$ cm. If we attempt to account for this in terms of two wavelengths λ and $\lambda - \Delta\lambda$ as in Problem 16, what is the value $\Delta\lambda$? Note: There are other factors involved in interference that will be considered in Chapter 35.

18. Energy from the sun reaches the top of the earth's atmosphere at the rate of

1.35 kW/m², a quantity called the solar constant. Compute the total amount of radiant power reaching the earth from the sun. How much solar radiant energy reaches the earth in one day? Recalling that the heat of combustion of gasoline is 48×10^6 J/kg, compute the total mass of gasoline that would give energy equal to that received from the sun in one day.

19. Neglecting reflection by clouds and absorption in the earth's atmosphere, compute the irradiance at points on the earth's surface at latitudes of 0°, 30°, 45°, 60°, and 90° at noon on 21 March when the sun is directly overhead at the equator as shown in the diagram. Use the solar constant defined in Problem 18.

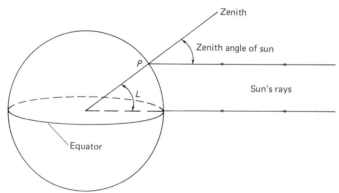

Problem 19

20. An isotropic point source of light emits a total luminous flux of 1256 lumens. What is its luminous source intensity? Calculate the illumination of the inner surface of a sphere of 3-m radius if the point source is at its center.

21. An isotropic point source of light has a luminous intensity of 50 cd. What is the total luminous flux from this source? Calculate the illumination at a point 3 m away from the source if the light strikes the surface on which the point is located (a) perpendicularly and (b) at an angle of 45° from the normal to the surface.

22. A suspended light source has a luminous intensity of 6000 cd when viewed from below. At what distance above a drafting table should this light be suspended in order to provide the recommended illumination of 538 lm/m² immediately below the light?

23. The full moon when directly overhead on a clear night provides an illumination of 0.32 lm/m². Compute the luminous intensity of the moon. How far away from a 60-W tungsten lamp having a luminous intensity of 55 cd must a screen be placed to have the same illumination as that produced by the moon?

24. An incandescent light with a source intensity of 55 cd when viewed from below is 1 m above the surface of a table and is switched on for 6 min. How many lumens reach 1 cm² of surface directly below the lamp while the light is on?

25. A 600-cd light hangs at the center of a cubical room 3 m on an edge and with its walls painted dull black. Assuming that the light emits isotropically, find (a) the total number of lumens striking the floor; (b) the average illumination of the floor; (c) the maximum and minimum values of illumination of the floor.

26. Referring to Problem 25, discuss the modifications that would be produced (a) by paint-

ing the walls and the ceilings white and (b) by covering the walls and ceiling with ideal mirrors.

27. A certain light source emits only light of wavelength 555 nm and radiates at the rate of 0.8 W. What is the total luminous flux from the source? Use Fig. 33.7 to provide an estimate for the luminous flux from a 10-W sodium lamp which radiates light of wavelength 589 nm.

28. The solar constant for the earth as given in Problem 18 is 1.35 kW/m². Calculate the corresponding solar constants for Mercury, Jupiter, and Pluto at their mean distances from the sun.

29. On a day when the speed of sound in air is 345 m/s, a gun is fired 100 m away from an observer. By the time the sound of the shot reaches the observer, how far has the light from the muzzle flash traveled?

30. Using the value 149.5×10^6 km for the radius of the earth's orbit, compare the times be-
tween eclipses of Jupiter's moon Io when the earth is at B and at D in Fig. 33.3 with the time 42.5 h observed when the earth is at A in the figure.

31. Taking 35,386 m as the distance between stations on Mount Wilson and Mount San Antonio in one of Michelson's experiments, find the lowest rotational speed at which the image will again be observed at the cross hairs after the eight-sided mirror has turned through one-eighth of a revolution.

32. Fizeau's apparatus for measuring the speed of light (Fig. 33.4) employed a toothed wheel, the light flash passing out through one slot in the wheel and returning through a later slot. Fizeau used a total light path length of 17.3 km and a wheel with 720 teeth. He found that at every increase in angular speed of the wheel by 1452 rev/min, the light came through to his eye. What value did he obtain for the speed of light?

CHAPTER 34

Reflection and Refraction

In our treatment of mechanical waves in Chapter 18, we pointed out that when a wave strikes the boundary between one medium and a second medium, some of the energy associated with the incident wave is reflected at the boundary and the rest of the energy penetrates the boundary and passes into the second medium. The wave speeds in the two media are different. In the present chapter we apply these ideas to light waves.

Light travels in straight lines through a homogeneous, isotropic medium such as air or vacuum. When a light beam strikes the boundary between two media such as air and glass, some of the light is *reflected* and some is transmitted in a process known as *refraction*. We shall treat these phenomena by tracing *rays*. Treatment of optical phenomena by tracing rays is called *geometrical optics* and represents the simplest approach to many optical problems. Optical engineers use this method in the design of the mirrors and lenses used in optical instruments. However, in making use of this approach we must remember that a ray merely represents the normal to an advancing wavefront. Therefore, when we employ rays we are actually giving information regarding advancing wave trains. We shall discuss the limitations of geometrical optics in the following chapter.

34.1 REFLECTION AT PLANE SURFACES

The reflection of light can be described in terms of two empirical laws that have been known since the times of the Greek philosophers and were clearly stated by Ptolemy of Alexandria:

FIRST LAW OF REFLECTION: The incident ray, the reflected ray, and the normal to the reflecting surface at the point of incidence lie in a single plane.

SECOND LAW OF REFLECTION: The angle of incidence is equal to the angle of reflection.

The meaning of these empirical laws is clarified in Fig. 34.1, which shows the incident ray *IP*, the reflected ray *PR,* and the normal to the surface *NP,* all in a single plane in accord with the first law of reflection. Angle *IPN* between the incident ray and the normal to the reflecting surface at point *P* is called the angle of incidence *i.* Angle *NPR* between the normal and the reflected ray is called the angle of reflection *r.* The second law of reflection states that $i = \angle IPN$ is equal to $r = \angle NPR$. The reflection of a beam of light from a smooth polished surface as suggested in Fig. 34.2 is called *regular reflection* or *specular reflection;* the observer *sees* the original source of light—not the mirror itself.

When a parallel beam of light is incident on a rough or "mat" surface like cement or newsprint, reflection occurs in many directions, as indicated in Fig. 34.3, even though we can apply the laws of reflection to any single ray. Reflection at a rough surface of this kind is called *diffuse reflection.* As a result of diffuse reflection we are able to see nonluminous bodies when light strikes them. The reflected rays from any small portion of a rough surface travel in so many directions that the small area is visible to us in essentially the same manner as a similar small area on the surface of a luminous body. On the other hand, we cannot really *see* a perfect mirror. Diffuse rather than regular reflection is required to make the surface of a nonluminous body visible.

Our distinction between smooth, polished surfaces, and rough surfaces merits further discussion. All surfaces are rough on an atomic scale, but atoms are small (~0.1 nm) as compared with the wavelength of visible light (~500 nm). The dividing line between regular and diffuse reflection depends upon the relationship between the dimensions of the surface irregularities of the reflecting surface and the wavelength of the light being reflected; thus, if the dimensions and spacings of the "hills and valleys" on the reflecting surface are large as compared with the wavelength, the surface is "rough" and diffuse reflection will occur as suggested in Fig. 34.3. However, if the dimensions of the "hills and valleys" are small compared with the wavelength, the surface is regarded as smooth and reflection will be regular as suggested in Fig. 34.2. Therefore, in order to make a good mirror, we must polish a glass or metal surface until its irregularities are small as compared with the wavelength of the light to be reflected. We note that a surface can be rough for light in the visible region of the electromagnetic spectrum but can simultaneously be smooth for microwave radiation. Even a metal window "fly screen" makes a good reflector for microwaves!

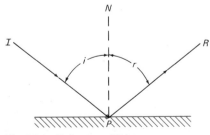

Fig. 34.1 Reflection of light.

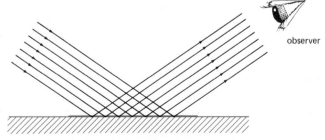

Fig. 34.2 Regular reflection: the observer sees the source.

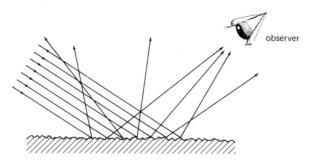

Fig. 34.3 Diffuse reflection: the observer sees the surface.

34.2 PLANE MIRRORS

We now consider the reflection of light by a plane mirror when the light is emitted from a point source near the mirror. In Fig. 34.4 we show three typical rays ①, ②, and ③ coming from the point source O, which we call the *object;* the three rays make angles of incidence i_1, i_2, and i_3 at the surface of the mirror. These rays are reflected from the mirror with angles of reflection $r_1 = i_1$, $r_2 = i_2$, and $r_3 = i_3$, respectively. A fourth ray ④ normal to the mirror is shown reflected with reversed direction. It is a matter of simple geometry to show that all such reflected rays, when extended back of the mirror, will intersect at a common point *I*. The perpendicular distance *IP* behind the mirror from *I* to the reflecting surface is equal to the perpendicular distance *OP* in front the mirror from the object *O* to the reflecting surface.

When an observer places his eye in the position indicated in Fig. 34.4, all the reflected rays that enter his eye *appear* to come from point *I,* and the observer sees a luminous point source, called an *image,* at *I*. Because *I* is located behind the mirror and the rays that seem to come from *I* do not really pass through point *I* at all, *I* is called the *virtual image* of the object *O.*

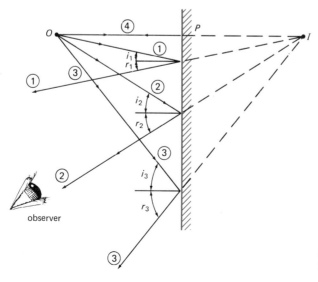

Fig. 34.4 Formation of a virtual object by a plane mirror.

A plane mirror forms a virtual image of a point object. The image is behind the mirror on the normal from the object to the mirror at a distance behind the mirror equal to the distance of the object from the front of the mirror.

If we call the distance from the object to the mirror the *object distance* and the distance from the image to the mirror the *image distance,* we see that for a plane mirror

Image distance = Object distance.

If the object is not a point object, we can treat it as if it were a collection of point objects as indicated in Fig. 34.5. In this figure we show rays from two points *O* and *O'* traced to the observer's eye; for each of these points we could draw several such rays as we did in Fig. 34.4. Consideration of Fig. 34.5 indicates that the eye sees an extended virtual image *II'* of the extended object *OO'* and that each point on the image is as far behind the mirror as the corresponding point on the object is in front of the mirror. Because the arrows representing object *OO'* and image *II'* both point upward in the figure, we regard the image as *upright.* Therefore, we can summarize our discussion by saying that *a plane mirror forms a virtual, upright image whose size is equal to that of the object, with image distance equal to object distance.* These conclusions apply whether the object is self-luminous or is an illuminated object with a diffusely reflecting surface that reflects incident light rays in all directions.

We note that we have shown front surface mirrors in the figures employed thus far. Plane mirrors in common everyday household use are silvered or aluminized on the back surface of plate glass with a protective coating covering the metal so that the reflecting surface is protected from surface scratches and oxidation. The statements made thus far regarding object and image distances are the distances measured from the reflecting surface of the mirror. The thickness of the plate glass used in good back-surface mirrors is usually small as compared with the object and image distances involved in the everyday use of such mirrors.

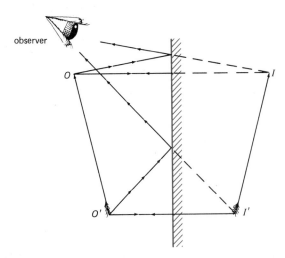

Fig. 34.5 Virtual image of an extended object.

34.3 CONCAVE SPHERICAL MIRRORS: POINT OBJECTS

Spherical surfaces can be easily fabricated by simple grinding and polishing proce-dures and are therefore widely used in optical instruments. A spherical mirror is a mirror whose surface can be obtained by cutting off a portion of a sphere in the manner indicated in Fig. 34.6. The line *MN* represents the cutting plane and the arc *MSN* represents the portion of the sphere to be used as the mirror. The distance *MN* is called the *linear aperture* of the mirror; the angle θ subtended at the center *C* of the original sphere is called the *angular aperture* of the mirror. As we shall soon see, if a spherical mirror is to be of practical use in forming images, its angular aperture θ must be small. The *axis* of a spherical mirror is a line *CS* drawn through the center *C* of the original sphere and the center *S* of the mirror itself. If the *inner* surface of the spherical segment *MSN* is the reflecting surface, the mirror is said to be *concave;* if the *outer* surface is the reflecting surface, the mirror is said to be *convex.* We first consider the properties of concave spherical mirrors.

A concave spherical mirror of small angular aperture can be used to produce a point image *I* of a luminous or illuminated point object *O* placed on the axis of the mirror as suggested in Fig. 34.7a. It is not at all obvious from the figure why the rays from the object *O* to the spherical mirror should be reflected from the mirror surface in such a way that they all pass through the point image *I*. In order to see how the image is formed, consider Fig. 34.7b, which shows a single typical ray *OA* from *O* to some point *A* on the mirror surface; after reflection, this ray traverses path *AI*, where *I* is on the mirror axis. The normal to the mirror surface at point *A* can be constructed by drawing radius *R* from the center of curvature *C* to point *A*. By the second law of reflection, the angle of reflection *r* at point *A* is equal to the angle of incidence *i* at this point.

We now make use of a well-known theorem of plane geometry that asserts that the exterior angle of a triangle is equal to the sum of the opposite interior angles. Applying this theorem to triangle *OAC*, we obtain

$$\beta = \alpha + i \quad \text{or} \quad i = \beta - \alpha.$$

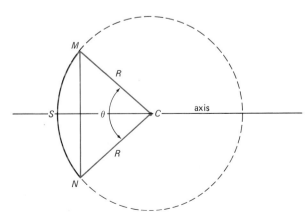

Fig. 34.6 A spherical mirror.

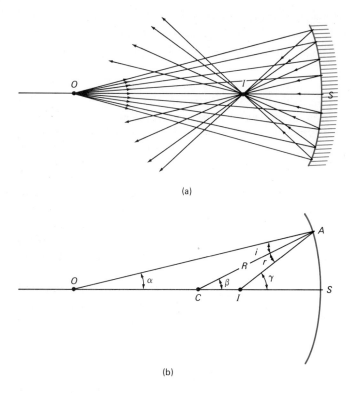

(a)

(b)

Fig. 34.7 Image formation by a concave spherical mirror.

Application of the theorem to triangle CAI gives

$$\gamma = \beta + r \quad \text{or} \quad r = \gamma - \beta.$$

By the second law of reflection, we can set $r = i$ with the result $\gamma - \beta = \beta - \alpha$ or

$$\alpha + \gamma = 2\beta.$$

Angle β in radians equals the arc AS divided by the mirror radius $R = CS$: $\beta = AS/R$. We must now introduce the condition that angles α and γ be small as compared with one radian. If indeed these angles are small, they can be measured to close *approximation* by the ratios

$$\alpha = AS/OS \quad \text{and} \quad \gamma = AS/IS.$$

In the case of small angles the equation $\alpha + \gamma = 2\beta$ becomes

$$\frac{AS}{OS} + \frac{AS}{IS} = 2\frac{AS}{R} \quad \text{or} \quad \frac{1}{OS} + \frac{1}{IS} = \frac{2}{R}.$$

This equation determines IS in terms of known values of OS and R. The distance

IS is thus independent of angle α. Provided angles α and γ are both small, their sum 2β will also be small. Because 2β is the angular aperture of the mirror as defined in Fig. 34.6, the angular aperture of the mirror must also be small if our approximations are to apply. When indeed the angular aperture of the mirror *is* small, distance *IS* in Fig. 34.7b is independent of angle α and *all* rays starting from point *O* on the axis will pass through the *same* point *I* on the axis. Thus, point *I* will be an *image* of the point object *O*. The image formed at *I* in Fig. 34.7 is called a *real image* because the rays from the mirror really do pass through *I*. If an observer's eye is in the position indicated in the figure and he looks toward the mirror, he will see a source of light apparently at *I* if the object *O* is a luminous point. Alternatively, the real image at *I* can be observed by placing a small screen at this position; a small spot of light will appear at *I* on the screen. The introduction of the small screen will cut off some of the rays from *O* before they reach the mirror; however unless *all* the light from *O* is stopped before it reaches the mirror, an image at *I* can still be observed on the screen. A *real* image can be caught on a screen; a *virtual* image can never be observed in this way because light rays never really intersect at a virtual image.

If we call distance *OS* between the object and the mirror the *object distance* and designate it by the symbol *p* and call the distance *IS* between the image and the mirror the *image distance* and designate it by the symbol *q*, the final equation above becomes

$$\frac{1}{p} + \frac{1}{q} = \frac{2}{R}. \quad \textit{(Mirror Equation)} \qquad (34.1)$$

This relation, which is valid when all rays make small angles with the mirror axis, is called the *mirror equation*. We shall now discuss some of the properties of this equation.

First we note that *p* and *q* are symmetric in the equation in the sense that they can be interchanged without altering the validity of the equation. This algebraic symmetry is associated with the geometrical fact that object and image positions can be interchanged in Fig. 34.7. If a point object were placed at point *I* in the figure and rays were drawn *to* the mirror, the rays would be reflected by the mirror to a focus at point *O*. In fact, the rays would be the rays in Fig. 34.7 but with reversed directions.

The mirror equation also tells us that when $p = R$, *q* also equals *R*. This is correct because with a point object at the center of curvature *C* all rays from the object strike mirror at normal incidence and are reflected so that they return to *C*. In other words, the point image coincides with the point object.

Now let us see what happens as the object distance increases. As *p* increases in the mirror equation, *q* decreases. The largest value that *p* can have is ∞; in this case $1/p = 0$ and $q = R/2$. With the point object on the mirror axis at infinite distance, all rays reaching the mirror are parallel, as shown in Fig. 34.8. The image position in this case—the position at which parallel light rays are focused—is called the *principal focus* or *principal focal point* of the mirror. As indicated in Fig. 34.8, the principal focus *F* is located halfway between the mirror surface and the center

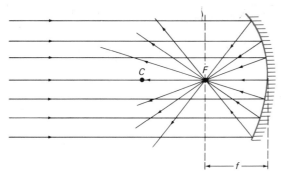

Fig. 34.8 The principal focal point of a concave mirror.

of curvature C. The distance f of the principal focus from the mirror surface is called the *focal length* of the mirror:

$$f = R/2.   \textit{(Focal Length)} \tag{34.2}$$

If the mirror equation (34.1) is rewritten in terms of f, it becomes

$$\frac{1}{p} + \frac{1}{q} = \frac{1}{f}.   \textit{(Mirror Equation)} \tag{34.1'}$$

In view of our earlier discussion of the interchangeability of p and q in the mirror equation, we note that, if we place a point object at principal focus F, the light reflected from the mirror consists of a parallel beam with all rays parallel to the axis. The situation will be similar to that shown in Fig. 34.8 but with all rays reversed in direction. This suggests that we could make a "searchlight" by placing an object at the principal focus of a concave spherical mirror.

Consideration of the mirror equation (34.1') shows that as the object distance p decreases from ∞ to f, the image distance q increases from f to ∞. What happens when the object distance p is less than f—that is, when the object O is "inside the principal focus" between F and the mirror surface? Solution of (34.1') gives a *negative* value of q. We can interpret this as indicating that the image is formed *behind* the reflecting surface and is therefore a virtual image. That this is indeed the case is shown in the ray diagram in Fig. 34.9; an observer with his eye in the position indicated would see an image I behind the mirror. Because there is really no light behind the mirror, the image is virtual.

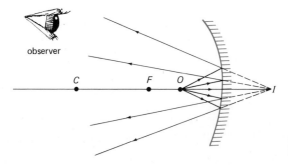

Fig. 34.9 Formation of a virtual image by a concave mirror.

34.4 CONCAVE SPHERICAL MIRRORS: EXTENDED OBJECTS

Thus far we have shown that a concave spherical mirror of small angular aperture will form point images of point objects placed on the axis of the mirror in accord with (34.1). Concave spherical mirrors with small angular aperture can also be used to produce images of extended objects close to the mirror axis provided the rays from the object to the mirror are *paraxial;* that is, provided the rays are nearly parallel to the mirror axis. This limitation to small angles between the rays and the axis forms a condition that must be met if we are to obtain images of extended objects; the object must be close to the axis of the mirror and must subtend only a small angle at the center S of the mirror.

In order to understand how the image of an extended object is formed, consider Fig. 34.10, which shows an object consisting of an arrow OA located at distance p from the center S of a concave spherical mirror of radius R. Because the tail of the arrow A is located on the axis of the mirror, we know from our earlier discussion that the mirror will produce an image of the tail A at point B on the axis at a distance q from the mirror surface given by (34.1). Now consider a ray from O that passes through the center of curvature C of the sphere; because this ray has normal incidence at the reflecting surface at S', it returns through C. If we now draw a second ray from O to the center S of the mirror with an angle of incidence i, it will be reflected at angle $r = i$ and will intersect the first ray at point I. By noting that I is on a line from O through C to the mirror surface at point S', when this line is *paraxial*—nearly coinciding with the mirror axis—we can adapt the arguments leading to (34.1) to show that other rays from O to the mirror will pass through I in Fig. 34.10 and that an image of point O will be formed at this point.

We can also use straightforward geometrical arguments to show that the point I is immediately below point B and hence that a *plane object has a plane image.* The mirror forms a plane image IB of a plane object OA, and the mirror equation (34.1) can be used in locating the image. If the plane object is at infinite distance, its image will lie in the principal *focal plane* of the mirror at a distance $f = R/2$ from the mirror.

We note in Fig. 34.10 that the image IB is an *inverted* image of OA; if arrow OA points upward, arrow IB points downward. If we call the length IB the image

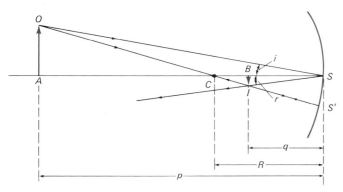

Fig. 34.10 Extended image of an extended object.

size and length OA the object size and note that triangle ISB is similar to triangle OSA, we see that $IB/q = OA/p$ so that

$$\frac{\text{Image size}}{\text{Object size}} = \left| \frac{\text{Image distance}}{\text{Object distance}} \right|. \tag{34.3}$$

We use the absolute value on the right-hand side of the equation because the relation holds for virtual images as well as real images without regard to the sign of q. The ratio of the image size to the object size is called the *enlargement* or *magnification* produced by the mirror. Note that by "sizes" we are referring here to the linear dimensions of image and object and not to their areas.

When we use (34.1) to find the position of the image formed by a spherical mirror and (34.3) to find the size of the image, a better understanding of the process of image formation can be obtained by the graphical construction of *principal-ray diagrams*. Of all the rays that we might draw from an off-axis point on an object to the corresponding point on the image, there are four rays that can be easily traced. These rays, known as *principal rays*, are as follows:

(1) The ray that leaves O parallel to the axis comes back through the principal focus F.

(2) The ray from O that passes through the principal focus F comes back parallel to the axis.

(3) The ray from O that passes through the center of curvature C comes back through C.

(4) The ray from O that strikes the mirror at point S on the axis comes back at an equal angle on the opposite side of the axis.

In Fig. 34.11 these principal rays are drawn for the following cases: (a) the object is between C and F with $f < p < R$, (b) the object is beyond C with $p > R$, and (c) the object is inside F with $p < f$. The four principal rays intersect at the point I of the image in the figure and provide a graphical determination of the position, size, and orientation of the image. Construction of even roughly drawn principal ray diagrams like those in Fig. 34.11 assists in providing an understanding of image formation and furnishes a valuable check on analytical work involving (34.1) and (34.3). Although any two principal rays, accurately traced, serve to locate the image, it is usually safer in making rough diagrams to trace at least three.

34.5   CONVEX SPHERICAL MIRRORS

When a point object is on the axis of a *convex* spherical mirror, the rays from the object clearly diverge after reflection from the mirror surface. This statement is true for any position of the object. However, if the angle of incidence for all the rays is small, an assumption that implies that the angular aperture of the mirror is also small, the reflected rays diverge from a common point as suggested in Fig. 34.12. An observer looking into the convex mirror in Fig. 34.12 sees a virtual image of the object at point I behind the mirror as in the case of a plane mirror.

Similarly, a convex mirror produces a virtual image of an extended object as sug-

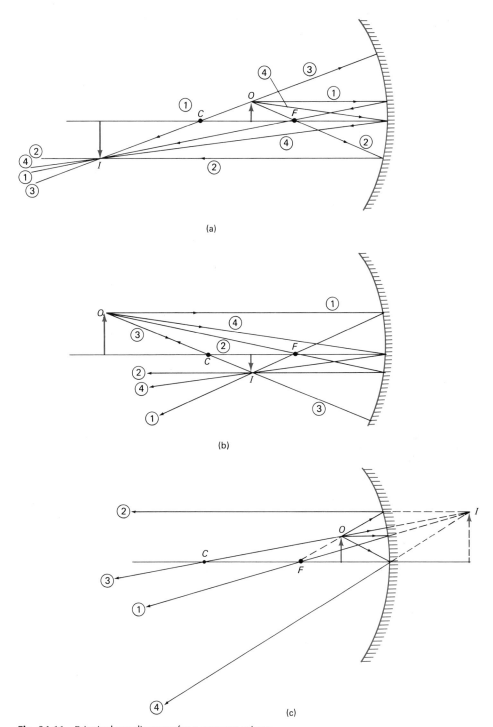

Fig. 34.11   Principal-ray diagrams for a concave mirror.

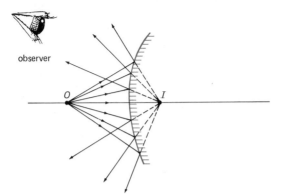

Fig. 34.12 Image formation by a convex mirror.

gested in Fig. 34.13 provided only paraxial rays are involved. The principal focus and the principal focal plane are back of the mirror surface as indicated in Fig. 34.14. A principal-ray diagram for a convex mirror is shown in Fig. 34.15. The mirror equation in the forms (34.1) and (34.1') applies to convex mirrors provided we regard the focal length f and the radius of curvature R as *negative numbers* when we use the equations. Equation (34.3) applies without modification to convex mirrors. All these assertions can be proved by straightforward geometrical arguments that use the laws of reflection and the paraxial ray approximation.

34.6   MIRROR ABERRATIONS: NONSPHERICAL MIRRORS

Our derivation of the mirror equation (34.1) for point objects and point images on the mirror axis was based on the assumption that all angles in Fig. 34.7b are small. This requires that the angular aperture $2\beta = \theta$ of the mirror be small. When the angular aperture of the mirror is *not* small, all rays reflected by the mirror will *not* cross at a common point I. This "shortcoming" of a spherical mirror is known as *spherical aberration* and is illustrated in Fig. 34.16 for a case in which a parallel beam of light from a distant on-axis point object such as a star is incident on a mirror of large angular aperture. The reflected rays from the central portion of the mirror converge at the principal focus F of the mirror. However, as the incident rays strike the mirror at points farther and farther from the mirror axis, the corresponding reflected rays cross the mirror axis farther and farther from F.

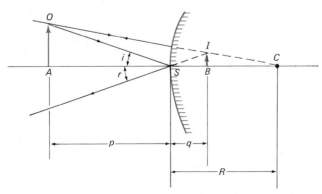

Fig. 34.13 Extended image of an extended object formed by a convex mirror.

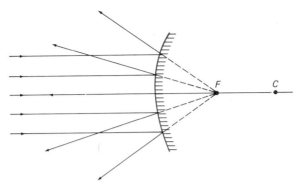

Fig. 34.14 The principal focal point of a convex mirror.

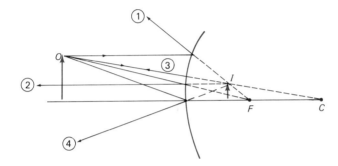

Fig. 34.15 Principal-ray diagrams for a convex mirror.

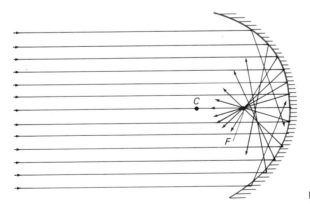

Fig. 34.16 Spherical aberration.

The effects of spherical aberration can be reduced by placing a "diaphragm" or "stop" in front of the mirror to intercept incident rays that are far from the axis before they reach the mirror surface; when a mirror is "stopped down" in this way, only a small central portion of the mirror is used in formation of the image. The effective angular aperture and the effective linear aperture of the mirror are decreased by the stop. As the stop is gradually closed, the image of a star at F becomes more and more nearly a point. However, because with decreasing effective linear aperture the mirror intercepts less and less light from the star, the image at F becomes progressively dimmer.

It is possible to eliminate spherical aberration for distant objects by using a mirror

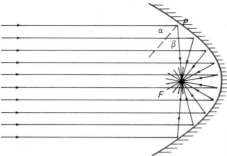

Fig. 34.17 A paraboloidal mirror: Rays parallel to the axis are reflected through the focus *F.*

that is *not* spherical but has the shape of the surface formed when a parabola is rotated about its own axis. Such a mirror, called a *parabolic* or *paraboloidal* mirror, is used in most reflecting telescopes; the parabolic section of such a mirror is shown in Fig. 34.17. It is a geometrical property of the parabola that the normal to the parabola at any point bisects the angle between a line parallel to the axis of the parabola and a line drawn from the focus of the parabola to the point in question. Therefore, the angles α and β at any point P in Fig. 34.17 are equal. Because this equality of angles is also the condition for regular reflection, it follows that any incident light ray parallel to the axis and striking the mirror at an arbitrary point *P* will be reflected through the focal point *F.* Thus, the light from a distant star *on the axis* of the mirror will be imaged as a point at *F.* Paraboloidal mirrors are employed in the reflecting telescopes of all major observatories.

Although paraboloidal mirrors can be regarded as "ideal" for certain limited situations, they are not nearly as useful as spherical mirrors for general purposes involving wide ranges of object and image distances. Although the spherical mirror is "ideal" only for a point object and a point image coinciding at its center of curvature, it is more versatile than other types of mirrors in being able to produce fairly good images of on-axis point objects and is superior to other types in producing fairly good images of off-axis point objects.

In our discussion of the use of spherical mirrors in the formation of images of extended objects, we required that all rays be paraxial. If the rays from an off-axis point object make large angles with the mirror axis, the image formed by the mirror will consist of a bright point with a flared tail like that of a comet; this aberration is called *coma.* Another aberration of spherical mirrors is their failure to form a flat image of a flat extended object; this aberration is called *curvature of field.* There are still other types of aberration. Definitive discussions of aberrations can be found in many specialized optics texts.

34.7 LAWS OF REFRACTION

When light in air strikes the surface of a *transparent* material like water or glass, a considerable fraction of the incident light enters the water or glass. Unless the incident beam is normal to the surface, the light experiences an abrupt change in direction as it passes through the surface. This "bending" of a light ray in passing from one optical medium into another is called *refraction.*

The behavior of a light ray in passing from air into water is shown in Fig. 34.18a.

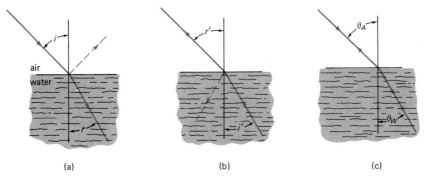

Fig. 34.18 The laws of refraction.

A ray passing from air into water is bent toward the normal to the interface. A ray passing from water into air is bent away from the normal, as shown in Fig. 34.18b. Water is said to be *optically more dense* than air; similarly, glass and most other solids and liquids have greater optical density than air. As indicated in the figure, some light is reflected at the interface; the ratio of the beam intensity of the reflected light to that of the transmitted light depends upon the optical properties of the two media involved and on the angle of incidence.

The behavior of light experiencing refraction at a surface can be described by two empirical laws:

FIRST LAW OF REFRACTION: The incident ray, the refracted ray, and the normal to the surface lie in a single plane.

SECOND LAW OF REFRACTION (Snell's Law): The ratio of the sine of the angle of incidence to the sine of the angle of refraction when light passes from one medium into another is independent of the angle of incidence.

The first law of refraction has been known since the time of the Greek natural philosophers. Formulation of the second law came at a much later date. The Dutch astronomer Willebrord Snell (1591–1626) was the first to discover the second law of refraction, but his discovery was not published until after his death. The second law was discovered independently and first published by the French philosopher René Descartes (1596–1650). The second law is usually called *Snell's law.*

Snell's law for the situation shown in Fig. 34.18a can be written in the form $\sin i / \sin r = \mu_{WA}$, where the constant μ_{WA} is called the index of refraction of water with respect to air. For the case in Fig. 34.18b, Snell's law similarly states that $\sin i' / \sin r' = \mu_{AW}$, where μ_{AW} is the refractive index of air with respect to water. Experiment shows that the path of the refracted ray is completely reversible; thus, if i' in Fig. 34.18b is equal to r in Fig. 34.18a, then r' is equal to i. Hence, we conclude that $\mu_{AW} = 1/\mu_{WA}$. If we let θ_A denote the angle between the normal and the ray in air in Fig. 34.18c and θ_W denote the angle between the normal and the ray in water, Snell's law becomes

$$\frac{\sin \theta_A}{\sin \theta_W} = \mu_{WA}. \quad \textit{(Snell's Law)} \qquad (34.4)$$

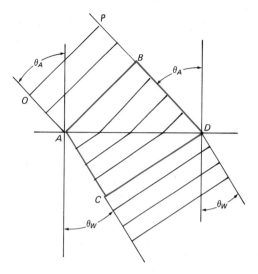

Fig. 34.19 Representation of a parallel beam of light passing from air into water.

Refraction can be interpreted in terms of differences between the speed of light as measured in various optical media. Consider Fig. 34.19, which shows a parallel beam of light passing from air into water, where observation shows that it continues as a parallel beam of increased width. Rays *OA* and *PB* are normal to an advancing plane wave front, various positions of which are shown in the figure. When the plane wave front is at *AB*, ray *OA* enters the water along *AC* while ray *PB* continues a distance *BD* in air. At *CD* the wave front is entirely in water. In Fig. 34.19 $\angle BAD = \theta_A$ because the sides of the angles are mutually perpendicular; similarly, $\angle ADC = \theta_W$. Therefore, Snell's law becomes

$$\mu_{WA} = \frac{\sin \theta_A}{\sin \theta_W} = \frac{\sin BAD}{\sin ADC} = \frac{BD/AD}{AC/AD} = \frac{BD}{AC}.$$

We note that in time Δt, light has traveled a distance $BD = v_A \Delta t$ in air while light has traveled a distance $AC = v_W \Delta t$ in water, where v_A and v_W are the speed of light in air and water, respectively. Substituting these expressions for *BD* and *AC* in the last equation, we obtain

$$\mu_{WA} = v_A / v_W. \qquad (34.5)$$

Equation (34.5) states that the index of refraction of water with respect to air is equal to the ratio of the speed of light in air to the speed of light in water. Foucault's direct measurements of v_A and v_W gave results that agreed with optical measurements of μ_{WA} from (34.4). Foucault's results thus supported the wave theory of light but were in disagreement with predictions based on Newton's particle theory of light. On the particle theory, refraction was explained in terms of an increase in the normal component of the velocity of light particles as they passed from a rare medium like air into a dense medium like water; the particle theory thus led to the prediction $v_W > v_A$, a prediction proved invalid by Foucault's experiments.

Because the speed of light in vacuum is greater than the speed of light in any transparent material medium, it is convenient to refer the refractive indices of all transparent optical media to vacuum.

The ABSOLUTE INDEX OF REFRACTION of any optical medium is defined as the index of refraction of the medium relative to vacuum.

Thus, on the basis of (34.5) we can express the absolute index of refraction μ_M of any transparent optical medium M in the form

$$\mu_M = c/v_M, \qquad (34.6)$$

where c is the speed of light in vacuum and v_M is the speed of light in the medium. The absolute index of refraction of a medium is called simply the *index of refraction* or the *refractive index* of the medium.

The refractive indices for various gases, liquids, and solids are listed in Table 34.1. The values in the table are the refractive indices for yellow light of wavelength 590 nm; as we shall see, μ_M has a slight dependence on wavelength. Because the indices of typical gases are so nearly equal to 1, it is possible in many situations to approximate them by unity.

Table 34.1. Indices of Refraction for Yellow Light of Vacuum Wavelength 590 nm

Gases at NTP	
Dry air	1.00029
Carbon dioxide	1.00045
Liquids at 20°C	
Benzene	1.501
Carbon disulfide	1.642
Carbon tetrachloride	1.461
Ethyl alcohol	1.354
Water	1.334
Solids at 20°C	
Diamond	2.419
Fluorite	1.434
Glass (typical values)	
Crown	1.517
Commercial plate	1.523
Light flint	1.574
Dense flint	1.656
Quartz (fused)	1.458
Plastics	
Nylon	1.53
Polyethylene	1.52
Polystyrene	1.59

The relative index of refraction μ_{WA} appearing in (34.5) can now be expressed in terms of the absolute indices of air and water as follows:

$$\mu_{WA} = \frac{v_A}{v_W} = \frac{(c/\mu_A)}{(c/\mu_W)} = \frac{\mu_W}{\mu_A}.$$

Substitution of this expression for μ_{WA} in (34.4) gives

$$\sin \theta_A / \sin \theta_W = \mu_W / \mu_A \quad \text{or} \quad \mu_A \sin \theta_A = \mu_W \sin \theta_W.$$

This expression can be generalized to apply to the passage of light through the interface in either direction between any two optical media I and II as suggested in Fig. 34.20:

$$\mu_I \sin \theta_I = \mu_{II} \sin \theta_{II}, \quad \text{(Snell's Law)} \tag{34.7}$$

where μ_I and μ_{II} are the absolute refractive indices of the media I and II, respectively, and θ_I and θ_{II} are the angles between rays and normals in media I and II, respectively. Equation (34.7) is the most useful mathematical form in which to remember Snell's law.

34.8 EQUIVALENT OPTICAL PATH IN A TRANSPARENT MEDIUM

On the basis of (34.6) we can express the speed of light in any transparent optical medium in the form

$$v_M = c/\mu, \tag{34.6'}$$

where μ is the refractive index of the medium. Because the speed of light changes when light passes from one medium to another, we can well ask how the frequency and the wavelength of light change at an interface. At an interface between vacuum and glass, light in vacuum approaches the interface at a speed greater than the speed of the light in glass as it leaves the interface. Do the light waves tend to "pile up" at the interface?

We can answer this question by recalling our discussion of sinusoidal mechanical waves (Chapter 18). We recall that the frequency of the sinusoidal waves emitted by a source depends only on the properties of the source and that the speed of transmission for a given type of wave depends only on the medium. These same

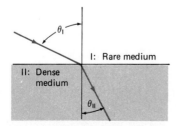

Fig. 34.20 Snell's law: $\mu_I \sin \theta_I = \mu_{II} \sin \theta_{II}$.

considerations apply to light waves. For example, a sodium atom in a sodium arc light emits yellow light of a characteristic frequency f. In vacuum, light travels at speed c; because $f\lambda = c$, the wavelength of sodium light in vacuum is given by $\lambda = c/f$. When a wave train of sodium light passes from vacuum into a glass plate, the speed of the light changes to $v_G = c/\mu_G$, where μ_G is the refractive index of the glass. Because the frequency f of the light depends only on the source and so does not change, the *wavelength* of the light must change as it enters the glass. Thus, inside the glass $f\lambda_G = v_G = c/\mu_G$. Writing the relations for vacuum and glass in the form $f\lambda = c$ and $f\lambda_G = c/\mu$, we can express the quantity λ_G/λ in the form

$$\frac{\lambda_G}{\lambda} = \frac{1}{\mu_G} \quad \text{or} \quad \lambda_G = \frac{\lambda}{\mu_G}. \tag{34.8}$$

Thus, we conclude that the wavelengths of light waves decrease when they pass from vacuum or air into a dense optical medium. For example, for yellow sodium light $\lambda = 590$ nm in vacuum but in dense flint glass with $\mu_G = 1.656$, the wavelength of sodium light is only $\lambda_G = (590 \text{ nm})/1.656 = 356$ nm. The frequency of the light $f = v_G/\lambda_G = (c/\mu_G)/(\lambda/\mu_G) = c/\lambda$ remains unchanged. No waves "pile up" at the interface!

In dealing with the lengths of optical paths through a medium, it is sometimes convenient to introduce the concept of an *equivalent optical path* in vacuum. The ideas involved are presented in Fig. 34.21, which shows schematically a sinusoidal light wave passing from vacuum through a glass plate and then back into vacuum. The wavelength changes from λ in vacuum on the left to λ_G as the light enters the glass and then back to λ as the light reemerges from the glass into the vacuum at the right. *The equivalent optical path length corresponding to the real path length l in the glass is the length of the path in vacuum that contains the same number of wavelengths.* Because $\lambda_G = \lambda/\mu_G$, the length of the equivalent optical path in vacuum will be longer than l by a factor μ_G; thus, for the situation shown in Fig. 34.21,

$$\text{Equivalent optical path} = \mu_G l. \tag{34.9}$$

We shall find the concept of equivalent path lengths useful when we discuss optical interference in thin films.

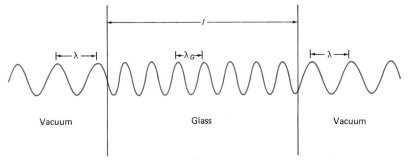

Fig. 34.21 The wavelength of light in glass is less than the wavelength in vacuum.

34.9   TOTAL INTERNAL REFLECTION

At this point let us return to a consideration of Fig. 34.20, which shows a reversible ray crossing the interface between a rare optical medium I and a dense medium II. When light in the rare medium travels across the interface into the dense medium, the rays representing its direction of propagation for non-normal incidence are bent toward the normal to the interface. There is no limitation on angle θ_I in Fig. 34.20. Although an increasingly greater fraction of the incident light is reflected as θ_I increases, some light will enter the denser medium even for values of θ_I approaching 90°.

As indicated in Fig. 34.22, this is not the case for light traveling from the dense medium into the rare medium. The figure shows light rays from a point source S in the dense medium. For small values of θ_{II} greater than 0° each ray is bent away from the normal as it passes from dense medium II into the rarer medium I. However, with increasing values of θ_{II} we reach a value $\theta_{II} = \theta_C$ for which θ_I has its maximum value of 90°. The angle $\theta_{II} = \theta_C$ is called the *critical angle*. For any value of θ_{II} in Fig. 34.22 greater than the critical angle, *no* light will cross the interface into an extended rarer medium; *all* the light reaching the interface with incident angles θ_{II} greater than the critical angle will be reflected. For all values of $\theta_{II} > \theta_C$, the surface acts as a perfect reflector; we say that there is *total internal reflection*.

The value of the critical angle θ_C can be determined by substitution in (34.7) with $\theta_I = 90°$ and $\theta_{II} = \theta_C$. The result is

$$\sin \theta_C = \mu_I / \mu_{II}. \quad \textit{(Critical angle)} \tag{34.10}$$

For the common case where the rare medium is air with $\mu_I \cong 1$, the value of the critical angle reduces to $\sin \theta_C = 1/\mu_{II}$. The value of θ_C thus decreases as the refractive index μ_{II} increases. At a water–air interface, the critical angle is 48.6°. At a diamond–air interface, the critical angle is only 24.4°. Note that *the critical angle of incidence always occurs inside the denser medium.* The relatively high refractive index and consequent small critical angle for diamond allow a diamond to be cut in such a way that much of the light that enters the face of the diamond is totally reflected several times and finally emerges directed back toward an observer. A properly cut diamond therefore "reflects" light like a high-quality mirror, giving the gem its property of "sparkle" or "brilliance."

Because total internal reflection is really *total*, it furnishes the basis for a perfect

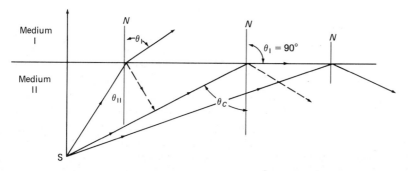

Fig. 34.22   Internal reflection: For $\theta_{II} > \theta_C$ all light is reflected.

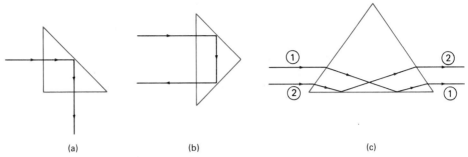

Fig. 34.23 Total internal reflection in prisms.

mirror that can be used in various ways in optical instruments. Figure 34.23 shows how prisms employing total internal reflection can be used to change the direction of a light beam through 90° in part A and through 180° in part B. Part C of the figure shows how a prism can be used to "turn a light beam upside down"; the beam emerging from the prism is inverted with respect to the entering beam because ray ① that entered at the top of the beam emerges at the bottom of the beam. Reflecting prisms are used in binocular "field glasses."

Total internal reflection is also used effectively in the design of "light guides" or "light pipes" like the one shown in Fig. 34.24. Light entering such a pipe at one end remains confined in the pipe by total internal reflection and emerges at the other end provided there are no sharp bends in the pipe and provided the walls of the pipe are smooth. Such pipes can be fabricated from glass or clear plastics. The lateral dimensions of such a pipe can be very small. If the light from a laser is focused at one end of a small glass fiber, it will emerge at the other end. Such a fiber can be used as a guide for the coded laser beams employed in optical communication systems. Light guides of this kind are much smaller than the metal waveguides used for microwaves and are indeed much smaller than the copper wires used in conventional telephone systems.

Total internal reflection is also the phenomenon involved in what is termed *fiber optics*. Once inside a smooth pipe like the one shown in Fig. 34.24, light does not emerge until it reaches the other end of the pipe. If a large number of fibers, each of which acts as a light guide, are gathered into a bundle like the one shown in Fig. 34.25, the bundle can be used by an observer to get indirect views of objects that cannot be conveniently viewed directly.

34.10 THIN LENSES

The refractive properties of transparent materials like glass can be used to design lenses capable of producing images. Lenses consist of transparent materials with polished surfaces, at least one of which is curved. The commonest type of simple lens has two surfaces that can be considered as parts of spheres as suggested in Fig. 34.26; the line passing through the centers of the spheres is called the *lens axis*. We shall consider lenses made of dense optical materials like glass that are to be used in air, for which $\mu_A \cong 1$. We shall limit our treatment to "thin lenses," for which the lens thickness t in Fig. 34.26 is small compared with radii R_1 and R_2.

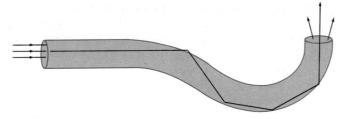

Fig. 34.24 A light guide employs total internal reflection.

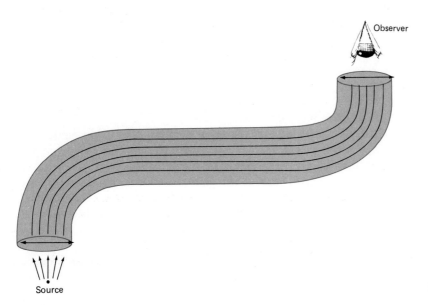

Fig. 34.25   Fiber optics.

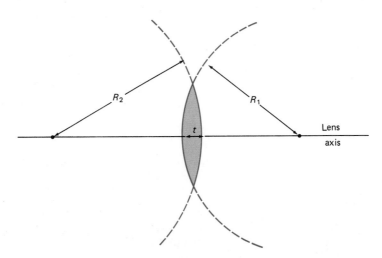

Fig. 34.26

Lenses are classified as *converging* or *diverging* on the basis of their effects on incident light rays parallel to the axis, as suggested in Fig. 34.27. A lens thicker at the center than at the edges tends to *converge* parallel light rays; a lens thinner at the center than at the edge tends to *diverge* parallel light rays.

A converging lens produces a point image I of a luminous or illuminated point object O located on the lens axis, as suggested in Fig. 34.28a. In Fig. 34.28b, a typical ray is shown leaving a point object O located on the lens axis at a distance p from the lens; after passing through the lens the ray crosses the lens axis again at a distance q from the lens. Figure 34.28c shows the refraction of the ray at the first surface of the lens, where it passes from air into the lens material, which has refractive index μ. By Snell's law, we can write $\sin i_1 = \mu \sin r_1$, where i_1 is the angle of incidence in air and r_1 is the angle of refraction in glass. If i_1 and r_1 are sufficiently small, we can write $i_1 = \mu r_1$ because for small angles the sine of an angle is nearly equal to the angle itself measured in radians. By considering the exterior angles of the triangles in Fig. 34.28c, we can write

$$i_1 = \theta + \alpha \quad \text{and} \quad r_1 = \alpha - \gamma.$$

Furthermore, because $i_1 = \mu r_1$, we can write

$$\theta + \alpha = \mu(\alpha - \gamma). \qquad (34.11)$$

Figure 34.28d shows the refraction at the second surface, where the incident ray inside the glass has angle of incidence i_2 and the refracted ray in air has angle of

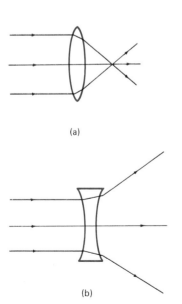

Fig. 34.27 Converging and diverging lenses.

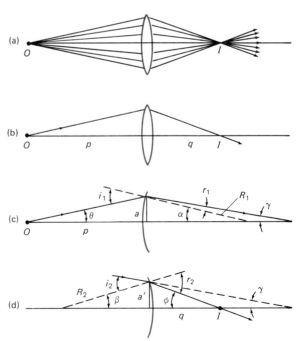

Fig. 34.28 Formation of a real image of a point object on the lens axis.

refraction r_2. Snell's law states that $\mu \sin i_2 = \sin r_2$ at the second surface; for small angles this reduces to $\mu i_2 = r_2$. Considerations of the triangles in Fig. 34.28d along with Snell's law leads to

$$\beta + \phi = \mu(\beta + \gamma). \tag{34.12}$$

By adding (34.11) and (34.12) we obtain

$$\theta + \alpha + \beta + \phi = \mu(\alpha + \beta)$$

or

$$\theta + \phi = (\mu - 1)(\alpha + \beta). \tag{34.13}$$

If we assume that the lens thickness is negligible compared with p, q, R_1, and R_2, it does not matter from what point in the lens we measure p and q; furthermore, for a thin lens a in Fig. 34.28c and a' in Fig. 34.28d can be considered equal. Then by considering all angles in (34.13) to be sufficiently small to replace their sines or tangents, we can write the following approximations for the angles:

$$\theta = a/p, \quad \phi = a/q, \quad \alpha = a/R_1, \quad \text{and} \quad \beta = a/R_2.$$

Substitution of these values in (34.13) and division of both sides of the equation by a gives the *lens equation**

$$\frac{1}{p} + \frac{1}{q} = (\mu - 1)\left(\frac{1}{R_1} + \frac{1}{R_2}\right), \quad \textit{(Lens Equation)} \tag{34.14}$$

where p is the object distance, q is the image distance, and R_1 and R_2 are the radii of curvature of the first and second lens surfaces, respectively.

Because there is nothing unique about the particular ray shown in Fig. 34.28b, relation (34.14) predicts the same value of q for *all* rays coming from the point object O to the lens provided all angles involved are small. We conclude that all such rays pass through point I. Hence, point I is a real image of the point object.

If we have a point object on the lens axis at infinite distance from the lens, the lens forms a point image at the principal focus F of the lens at focal distance f from the lens. We can find the focal length of the lens by setting $p = \infty$ in (34.14) and noting that for this situation the image distance q is by definition equal to f. The result is

$$\frac{1}{f} = (\mu - 1)\left(\frac{1}{R_1} + \frac{1}{R_2}\right). \quad \textit{(Lensmaker's Equation)} \tag{34.15}$$

---

* The lens equation has been derived on the assumption that the same material—air or vacuum—is on both sides of the lens. It does not apply to a glass lens in the wall of an aquarium tank, where air is on one side of the lens and water is on the other side. In a case of this kind, (34.14) would have to be modified.

This equation is called the *lensmaker's equation* because it determines the combination of radii of curvature that an optical technician must use in fabricating a lens having a desired focal length.

Substitution of the value of $1/f$ given by (34.15) into the lens equation (34.14) gives the lens equation in the convenient form

$$\frac{1}{p} + \frac{1}{q} = \frac{1}{f}, \quad \textit{(Lens Equation)} \tag{34.16}$$

which is mathematically similar to the mirror equation (34.1′).

Unlike a mirror, a lens is "two-sided," and light can pass through it in either direction. Because (34.15) is symmetric with respect to R_1 and R_2, the image-forming properties are identical for light traveling in the two directions. As shown in Fig. 34.29, a parallel beam approaching a lens from the left is brought to a focus at point F while a parallel beam of light approaching a lens from the right is brought to a focus at F'. Thus, the lens has two principal foci F and F' on opposite sides of the lens. Equation (34.15) assures us that the distance from F to the lens is equal to the distance from F' to the lens. The focal length f of the lens is the same for light traveling through it in either direction. Because light rays are reversible, we can obtain a parallel beam of light by placing a luminous point object O at either focus, as is shown in Figs. 34.29a′ and 34.29b′.

34.11   THIN LENSES: OBJECTS AND IMAGES OF FINITE SIZE

We have derived (34.14) and (34.16) for a point source on the lens axis; the same relations can be shown to apply for objects slightly off the axis provided the angles of incidence at the first surface of the lens are small. Because objects of finite size can be regarded as collections of point sources, the lens can provide an image of an object of finite size provided all angles of incidence at the lens are small and provided all rays are close to the axis of the lens. For a flat object of finite size in a plane perpendicular to the axis at a distance p from the lens, the image is also flat

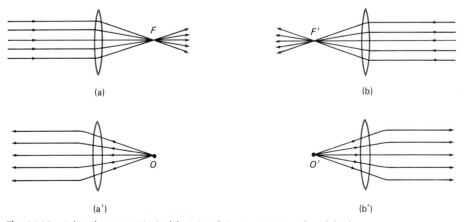

(a)   (b)

(a′)   (b′)

Fig. 34.29   A lens has two principal foci F and F' on opposite sides of the lens.

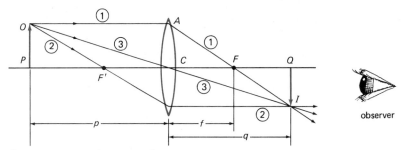

Fig. 34.30 Principal rays: a real image.

and is located in a parallel plane at a distance q from the lens given by (34.14).

In order to understand how such images are formed, consider an object OP and construct the following numbered principal rays that are shown in Fig. 34.30:

(1) The ray that leaves O in a direction parallel to the lens axis and after refraction by the lens passes through principal focus F.

(2) The ray that leaves O and passes through principal focus F' and after refraction by the lens is parallel to the lens axis.

(3) The ray from O that passes without deviation through the optical center of the lens.

Principal ray 3 is defined by a straight line from O through point C, which is called the *optical center* of the lens. The surface of the lens where ray 3 enters the lens is parallel to the surface of the lens where ray 3 leaves the lens; because the lens is "thin" there is no appreciable lateral displacement of the ray. All rays through C pass through the lens without deviation; all rays passing through the lens above C are bent downward and all rays passing through the lens below C are bent upward in a diagram like the one in Fig. 34.30. After passing through the lens, all three principal rays intersect at a common point I, as can readily be proved from Fig. 34.30. Point I is a real point image of the point source O. Similar principal rays can be drawn from other points on OP to corresponding points along the line IQ, which is an extended image of the extended object OP. Remember that there are many rays from point O to point Q and that the principal rays are merely rays that are easily traced. In solving problems involving lenses it is always desirable to make principal-ray diagrams. We note from similar triangles OPC and IQC in Fig. 34.30 that the enlargement or magnification is given by the expression

$$\frac{\text{Image size}}{\text{Object size}} = \left|\frac{\text{Image distance}}{\text{Object distance}}\right|, \tag{34.17}$$

where the image size is simply the *length* of the image IQ and the object size is the *length* of the object OP.

For an object of finite size at infinite distance, the lens forms an image in the principal *focal plane* of the lens at a distance f from the lens.

34.12 LENS EQUATION

By employing the proper sign conventions, we can use (34.14) and (34.16) for all types of thin lenses. In the case of the lensmaker's equation (34.14), we regard R_1

and R_2 as positive for convex surfaces and negative for concave surfaces. If the sum $1/R_1 + 1/R_2$ is positive, the focal length f of the lens in (34.15) is positive, which indicates that the lens is a converging lens; if the sum $1/R_1 + 1/R_2$ is negative, the focal length is negative, which indicates that the lens is a diverging lens.

Consider the lens equation (34.16) for a *converging lens*. If the object distance p is greater than the focal length f of the lens, the image distance q as given by the lens equation is also greater than f, and the image is real. As shown in the principal-ray diagram in Fig. 34.30, the image is inverted. The image size as given by (34.17) may be greater than, equal to, or smaller than the size of the object.

If the object distance p from a converging lens is less than the focal length f of the lens, the image distance q as given by (34.16) is negative, a result indicating that the image is *virtual*. The situation is shown by the principal-ray diagram in Fig. 34.31, in which the principal rays *seem* to intersect at I to the left of the lens. An observer on the right would see an enlarged virtual image on the opposite side of the lens. As indicated in the diagram, the virtual image is erect and enlarged.

When the object is at a distance $p = f$ from a converging lens, (34.16) shows that $q = \infty$. This means that following their passage through the lens all rays from a given point on the object are parallel, and no image is formed because the parallel rays never intersect.

Now let us examine the properties of a *diverging lens*, a lens that is thinner at the center than at the edges and that is characterized by a negative value of f in (34.16). In Fig. 34.32a we show a parallel beam of light approaching the lens from the left; after passing through the lens the beam diverges. The diverging rays leaving the lens seem to come from the focal point F at the left of the lens on the same side of the lens as the incident beam. Similarly, a parallel beam approaching the diverging lens from the right diverges as it passes through the lens and seems to come from the focal point F' on the right side of the lens. Comparison of Fig. 34.32 with Fig. 34.29 shows that the positions of F and F' for a diverging lens are the reverse of those for a converging lens.

Because f is negative for a diverging lens and the object distance p is positive for a real object, the numerical value of q given by (34.16) must be *negative*. This means

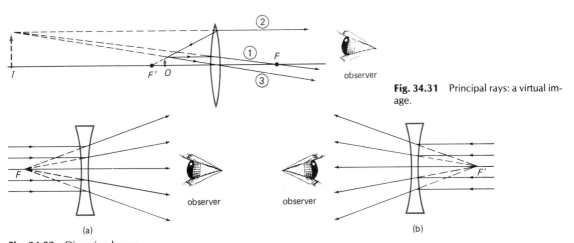

Fig. 34.31 Principal rays: a virtual image.

(a)   (b)

Fig. 34.32 Diverging lenses.

that a diverging lens cannot produce a real image of a real object; the image is always virtual. This conclusion is confirmed by the principal ray diagram in Fig. 34.33. For any real object, a diverging lens always forms a virtual, erect image that is smaller than the object.

A diverging lens cannot be used to produce a parallel beam of light from a diverging incident beam as can a converging lens. A diverging lens can, however, produce a parallel beam when the incident beam converges in the manner shown in Fig. 34.34. A beam from the left converging toward point F' is rendered parallel by the lens; a beam from the right converging toward F is rendered parallel by the lens. In any case involving converging incident beams, points of convergence behind the lens are called *virtual objects*. In using the lens equation (34.16) to describe such situations, we must regard the distance from a virtual object to the lens as a negative number.

To conclude our treatment of thin spherical lenses, we can give the following summary. The lens equation

$$\frac{1}{p}+\frac{1}{q}=\frac{1}{f}$$

(34.16)

applies to all lenses with the following sign conventions:

$$\text{Object distance } p \text{ is } \begin{cases} + \text{ for a real object} \\ - \text{ for a virtual object} \end{cases},$$

$$\text{image distance } q \text{ is } \begin{cases} + \text{ for a real image} \\ - \text{ for a virtual image} \end{cases},$$

$$\text{focal length } f \text{ is } \begin{cases} + \text{ for a converging lens} \\ - \text{ for a diverging lens} \end{cases}.$$

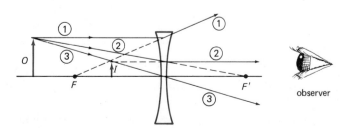

Fig. 34.33 Principal ray diagram for a diverging lens.

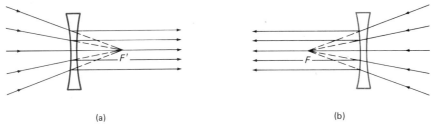

Fig. 34.34 Rays directed toward the principal focus behind a diverging lens become parallel after passing through the lens.

Image size can always be determined from (34.17), in which the algebraic signs of p and q are eliminated. We can best determine whether the image is erect or inverted by means of a principal-ray diagram.

As in the case of spherical mirrors, lenses with spherical surfaces do not produce perfect images. Rays parallel to the axis that strike the lens at points far from the axis do not pass through the principal focus defined for rays close to the axis; this defect, called *spherical aberration,* can be minimized by the use of a diaphragm to "stop down" the lens so that only a small portion close to the axis is employed. Failure to meet all the approximations made in our derivation of the lens equation leads to further aberrations like *coma* and *curvature of field* when objects of finite size are employed. As in the case of spherical aberration, the effects of these other aberrations can be reduced by "stopping down" the lens, but with a resulting decrease in the brightness of the image. Further discussion of lens aberrations can be found in advanced texts dealing with optics.

Another type of aberration, encountered with lenses but not with mirrors, is called *chromatic aberration.* This aberration results from the fact that the refractive index μ appearing in the lensmaker's equation (34.15) does not have exactly the same value for light of different wavelengths. Therefore, if a luminous point object that emits white light is placed on the axis of a simple lens, the image forms colored images at points that do not coincide. Chromatic aberration causes images of white extended objects to "show color" at their edges. We shall give further consideration to chromatic aberration later in this chapter.

34.13 COMBINATION OF LENSES

In nearly every practical optical instrument, more than one lens is employed; therefore, we need to discuss lens combinations. If light from an object passes through two lenses, one after the other, the combined action of the two lenses can be determined by treating the image produced by the first lens as the object for the second lens. If the first lens produces an image in front of the second lens, the first image is regarded as a *real object* for the second lens. This situation is shown in Fig. 34.35, where object and image distances for each lens are indicated. Principal-ray diagrams are useful in determining the image positions even though all principal rays may not actually be present in the cone of rays leading from the first object to the final image.

If the image I_1 that would have been formed by the first lens is located *behind*

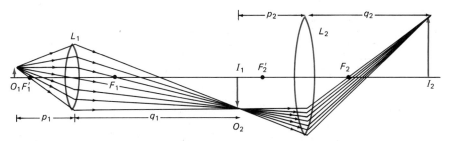

Fig. 34.35   A lens combination: the image formed by the first lens is a real object for the second lens.

the second lens as in Fig. 34.36, it must be treated as a *virtual object* for the second lens. The first lens would have formed an image at I_1 if the light beam had not been intercepted by the second lens. In finding the position of the final image I_2 formed by the second lens, we must regard the object distance p_2 as a negative number when we make substitutions in the lens equation (34.16). In Fig. 34.36, we note that the converging beam that leaves the first lens is made still more convergent by the second lens so that the final image I_2 is actually formed between the second lens and its principal focus F_2.

34.14   DISPERSION: ACHROMATIC LENSES

The index of refraction μ in (34.6) is not the same for all wavelengths. For most common optical media it is slightly greater for violet light than for red light. As a result, rays of violet light are bent more than rays of red light as they pass from air ($\mu \cong 1$) into a denser optical medium, as suggested in Fig. 34.37.

If a ray of white light strikes the water surface in Fig. 34.37 at the same angle of incidence as the red and violet rays, it splits after passing through the surface into a group of colored rays with a violet ray at one boundary and a red ray at the other. The white light is said to be *dispersed*. Such dispersion can be observed when a narrow beam of sunlight strikes the surface of the water in an aquarium tank.

In a famous experiment Newton brought a pencil of sunlight through a shutter into a darkened room, where the light entered a glass prism as shown schematically in Fig. 34.38. The colored rays leaving the prism could be displayed on a screen in a pattern that Newton termed a *spectrum*. The modern interpretation is to regard the incident white light as consisting of a complex wave that can be resolved into

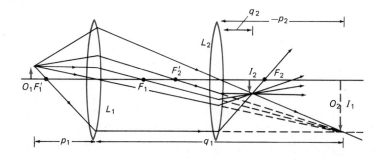

Fig. 34.36   A lens combination: the image formed by the first lens is a virtual object for the second lens.

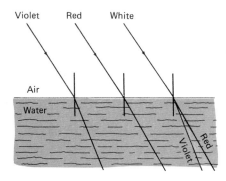

Fig. 34.37 Dispersion.

components of different wavelengths and frequencies corresponding to different spectral colors. The prism serves to separate the wave trains of different wavelengths as indicated in the figure. We note that the prism separates the wave trains of different wavelengths but provides no direct measurements of either wavelength or frequency. The wavelengths listed in the figure have been determined by means of interferometers or other related devices.

The refractive indices μ_R, μ_Y, and μ_B of several optical materials for wavelengths in the red, yellow, and blue regions of the spectrum are listed in Table 34.2. A glance at the numbers in Table 34.2 is sufficient to give us an understanding of chromatic aberration. Because of the factor $\mu - 1$ in the lensmaker's equation (34.15), the focal length of a simple lens is slightly different for different colors. If a parallel beam of white light from a distant point object strikes a simple lens as in Fig. 34.39a, a set of colored images will be formed at slightly different points on the lens axis; in the figure we designate positions R, Y, and B of the red, yellow, and blue images corresponding to the colors of the light listed in Table 34.2. The principal focal point of the lens is different for different colors. The separation of the red and blue images depends on the difference $\mu_B - \mu_R$ for the optical material involved; for lenses of equal focal length for yellow light, the separation of the red and blue foci is greater for flint glass than for crown glass because $\mu_B - \mu_R$ is greater for flint glass. For a lens of either material the principal focus for yellow light lies between the principal foci for red and blue light.

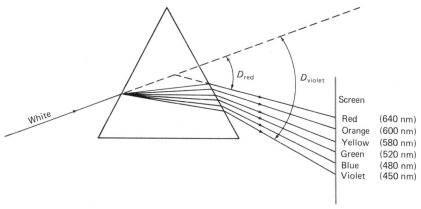

Fig. 34.38 White light is dispersed into spectral colors by a prism.

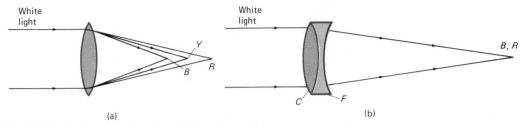

Fig. 34.39 (a) Chromatic aberration. (b) An achromatic lens.

Table 34.2.   Refractive Indices at 20°C

Material	Refractive Index for Wavelength in Vacuum		
	λ_R (red) 656.3 nm	λ_Y (yellow) 589.3 nm	λ_B (blue) 486.1 nm
Water	1.3312	1.3330	1.3372
Carbon disulfide	1.6182	1.6276	1.6523
Crown glass (typical)	1.5145	1.5172	1.5240
Flint glass (typical)	1.6221	1.6270	1.6391

By constructing a compound lens from two simple lenses of different materials such as crown glass and flint glass, we can make the red and blue images coincide as in Fig. 34.39b. When such a lens has been constructed, we find that the images for colors of intermediate wavelengths also nearly coincide at the common principal focus for red and blue. Such a two-component lens is called an *achromatic* doublet*.

QUESTIONS

1. Can the empirical laws of reflection be explained in terms of Newton's particle theory of light? Can they be explained in terms of the wave theory of light?

2. Which type of reflection—regular or diffuse—is of more practical importance to you in your daily life?

3. By considering waves spreading spherically outward from a point source and striking a plane mirror, show that the mirror forms a virtual image of the source. By graphical methods show that the distance from the virtual image to the mirror surface is equal to the distance from the source to the mirror surface.

4. When we draw optical ray diagrams, what information are we giving about wave fronts?

5. What are the approximations that are made in deriving the mirror equation (34.1)?

6. If we place a small object slightly "inside" the focal plane of a concave mirror (between the focal plane and the mirror surface), where will the image be formed? If we place the object just "outside" the focal plane of the mirror, where will the image be formed?

* From the Greek: without color.

What are the enlargements or magnifications in the two cases?

7. Why could Snell's Law not have been formulated by the early Greek philosophers?

8. How can Snell's Law be explained on the basis of Newton's particle theory of light? How can Snell's Law be explained on the basis of the wave theory of light? Why do we now accept the wave theory? What evidence do we have that was not available to Newton?

9. How can you define the absolute index of refraction of a medium in terms of the speed of light transmission in the medium?

10. What is meant by the term *equivalent optical path?* Why is a compensating plate used in a Michelson interferometer (Sec. 33.3)?

11. Why does the *critical angle* of incidence always occur inside the denser medium?

12. A ray of light strikes the glass bottom of an empty aquarium tank. How does the angle of refraction inside the glass change when the tank is filled with water?

13. What approximations are made in the derivation of the lens equation (34.16)?

14. Chromatic aberration is involved in lenses but not in mirrors? Why?

15. An observer faces a mirror on the north wall of a room and points eastward with his right hand. Show that the image formed by the mirror is upright but points eastward with his left hand. If the mirror reverses right and left, why doesn't it reverse up and down? If a clock is placed in front of the mirror, in which sense—CW or CCW—do the hands of the image of the clock rotate?

16. Light does not really pass through points on a virtual image. Is it possible to take a photograph of a virtual image? If so, describe how; if not, explain why not.

17. As indicated in Fig. 34.19, a beam of light broadens when it passes from air into water. What effect does this have on the illumination of objects below the surface of the water? Is the conservation-of-energy principle violated?

18. When monochromatic light passes from air into water, its speed of transmission and its wavelength change but its frequency remains the same. How is this possible?

19. On a clear day a diver below the surface of a clear-water pool looks upward. What is the color of the sky as observed by the diver? Give reasons for your conclusion.

20. The French mathematician Pierre de Fermat (1601–1665) showed the equivalent path length *actually* tranversed by light in traveling from one point to another is a minimum as compared with other conceivable neighboring paths that might have been followed. Note that a minimum equivalent path length also implies a minimum time of transmission. Show that this relation, called "Fermat's principle," is consistent with rectilinear propagation and with the laws of regular reflection and the laws of refraction.

PROBLEMS

Note: In working these problems, take the refractive index of air to be unity. Take other indices of refraction from Table 34.1.

1. A woman is 1.6 m tall and wishes to purchase a plane mirror just long enough to enable her to see a full-length image of herself. How long should the mirror be?

2. In sensitive instruments like the one used in the Cavendish experiment (Sec. 9.1) and Coulomb's experiment (Sec. 20.4) the twist of a thin fiber is measured by reflecting a

narrow beam of light from a small mirror attached to the fiber to a scale that can be mounted at a distance of several meters from the fiber. Show that when the fiber is twisted through angle θ the reflected light beam turns through the angle 2θ. If such a fiber twists through an angle of 5.7°, what will be the displacement of the light beam along a scale mounted at a distance of 2 m from the mirror?

3. Show by means of a ray diagram that if two adjacent walls of a rectangular room are mirror surfaces, an observer can see three images of himself and of all other objects in the room.

4. An observer stands between two large plane mirrors that are joined at the edge to include an angle of 60°. Show that the observer can see five images of herself.

5. Two adjacent walls of a rectangular room consist of plane mirrors. Show by tracing rays that a horizontal parallel light beam headed toward the corner of the room will be reversed in direction when it is reflected.

6. Two adjacent walls and also the ceiling of a rectangular room with a horizontal ceiling consist of mirrors. Show that a parallel light beam headed toward the mirrored corner of the room will be reversed in direction when it is reflected. Note that by the laws of reflection when a beam of light is reflected at a surface its tangential component of velocity is unchanged and its normal component of velocity is reversed. "Corner reflectors" of this type are useful in providing "land marks" for airborne radar systems and provide the basis for the "retrodirective reflectors" used for guidance in night driving on highways.

7. An illuminated object 4 cm tall is located 30 cm away from a concave mirror with a radius of curvature of 40 cm. Find the image distance, size, and character (real or virtual, erect or inverted). Sketch the principal-ray diagram.

8. An illuminated object 4 cm tall is placed at a distance of 50 cm from a concave mirror with a radius of curvature of 40 cm. Find the image distance, size, and character. Sketch the principal-ray diagram.

9. An illuminated object 4 cm tall is placed 10 cm away from a concave mirror with a radius of curvature of 40 cm. Find the image distance, size, and character. Sketch the principal-ray diagram.

10. A luminous object is placed on the axis of a concave mirror with a radius of curvature of 40 cm. Find the positions of the image when the distance between the object and the mirror has the following values: ∞, 80 cm, 40 cm, 20.2 cm, 19.8 cm, 10 cm, and 1 cm. What happens when the point object is exactly 20 cm from the mirror?

11. A concave spherical mirror has a radius of curvature of 60 cm. How far from this mirror should you place an object if you wish to produce a real image twice as long as the object? to produce a virtual image twice as long as the object?

12. How far from a concave mirror with a radius of curvature of 60 cm should you place a luminous object if you wish to produce a real image half as tall as the object? a virtual image half as tall as the object?

13. Let R be the radius and f the focal length of a concave spherical mirror. Five possible object positions are: (1) $p > R$, (2) $p = R$, (3) $R > p > f$, (4) $p = f$, and (5) $f > p > 0$. Which of these positions give (a) an inverted image smaller than the object, (b) an inverted enlarged image, (c) an inverted image equal in size to the object, (d) an "image at infinity" (really no image at all), (e) an erect image equal in size to the object, (f) an erect enlarged image, (g) a real image, and (h) a virtual image?

14. An object is placed at a distance x in front of a concave mirror with a focal length of 10 cm. What are the least and greatest values

of x for which (a) the image is real? (b) the image is erect? (c) the image is larger than the object?

15. An object 4 cm tall is placed on the axis at a distance of 50 cm from a convex mirror with a radius of curvature of 40 cm. Find the image distance, size, and character.

16. An object 4 cm tall is placed on the axis at a distance of 10 cm from a convex mirror with a radius of curvature of 40 cm. Find the image position, size, and character.

17. How far from a convex mirror with a radius of curvature of 40 cm should you place an object if you wish to produce an image half as tall as the object?

18. When an object is placed 30 cm away from a convex mirror, a virtual image one-third as tall as the object is formed. Find the focal length and the radius of curvature of the mirror.

19. A ray of light in air strikes a water surface at an angle of incidence of 30°. What is the angle of refraction in the water? Show a diagram.

20. A ray of light in air strikes the surface of a diamond at an angle of incidence of 60°. What is the angle of refraction in the diamond? Show a diagram.

21. If a ray of light in water strikes the surface of a diamond at an angle of incidence of 30°, what is the angle of refraction in the diamond?

22. A small stone is 2 m below the surface of a pool of clear water. What is the apparent depth of the stone noted by an observer who sees the stone by means of a cone of light leaving the water surface in a direction that makes an average angle of 30° with the normal to the water surface? Show that the apparent depth of the stone as viewed vertically from above is equal to its actual depth divided by the refractive index of water.

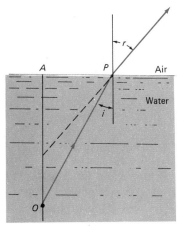

Problem 22

23. A cylindrical metal cup is 6 cm in diameter. An observer looks over the rim at such an angle α that he can just see the far edge of the bottom when the cup is empty. When the cup is filled with water, the observer without moving his eye can just see a spot at the center of the bottom. What is the depth of the cup?

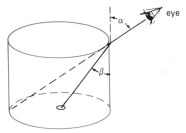

Problem 23

24. What are the speeds of light in water, carbon tetrachloride, and plate glass? If light waves of sodium arc light have a wavelength of 590 nm in vacuum, what are the wavelengths of sodium light in water, carbon tetrachloride, and plate glass? What are the frequencies of sodium light waves in air, water, carbon tetrachloride, and plate glass?

25. A rectangular glass aquarium tank contains a 3-cm layer of water floating on top of a 4-cm layer of carbon tetrachloride. If a light ray in air strikes the water surface at an angle of incidence of 45°, what are the angles of

refraction in the water, in the carbon tetra-chloride, and in the plate glass bottom of the tank? (The index of refraction of the glass is 1.53.) Draw a ray diagram.

26. What is the wavelength of sodium light in diamond if its wavelength in vacuum is 590 nm? What is the speed of sodium light in diamond?

27. A ray of light in glass with a refractive index of 1.57 strikes the surface of the glass at an angle of incidence of 30°. What is the angle of refraction in air? For a ray of light in glass making an angle of 39.6° at the surface, what would be the angle of refraction in air?

28. A slab of flint glass with an index of refraction of 1.65 has a small bubble a short distance below the surface. A dime (diameter 1.75 cm) placed on the surface of the glass is just large enough to prevent the bubble from being seen from above. How far down is the bubble?

29. A double convex lens of crown glass has surfaces with radii of curvature of 40 cm and 50 cm, respectively. What is its focal length?

30. What is the radius of curvature of the curved surface of a plano-convex crown-glass lens if the lens has a focal length of 43 cm?

31. An object 4 cm tall is placed near the axis of a thin converging lens at a distance of 33.3 cm from the lens. If the focal length of the lens is 20 cm, where will an image be formed and what will be the size of the image? Sketch a principal-ray diagram.

32. How far from a lens with a focal length of 30 cm should you place an object if you wish to produce (a) a real image equal in size to the object and (b) a virtual image equal in size to the object?

33. A converging lens has a focal length of 10 cm. Determine the image distances when an object is placed at the following distances from the lens: 25 cm, 20 cm, 15 cm, 10 cm, and 5 cm.

34. Locate the images produced by a converging lens of focal length f when an object distance p has the following values: (1) $p > 2f$, (2) $p = 2f$, (3) $f < p < 2f$, (4) $p = f$, and (5) $p < f$.

35. An object 2 cm tall is placed near the axis at a distance of 10 cm from a diverging lens of -10 cm focal length. Where will an image be formed? What will be the size of the image? Sketch a principal-ray diagram.

36. A diverging lens has a focal length of -10 cm. Locate the image produced when an object is at the following distances from the lens: 30 cm, 20 cm, 15 cm, 10 cm, and 5 cm.

37. A crown-glass converging lens has a focal length of 20 cm when used in air. What is the focal length of the lens if it is completely immersed in water and used in "underwater optics"? Hint: Review the derivation of (34.14).

38. If the lens in Problem 37 is used in a water-tight camera with air on one side of the lens and water on the other side, what is its focal length? Hint: Review the derivation of (34.14).

39. Two converging lenses are placed 10 cm apart. The focal length of the first lens is 20 cm and that of the second lens is 30 cm. If a luminous object is placed on the common axis 40 cm in front of the first lens, where will the final image be formed? Make a principal-ray diagram for each lens.

40. A converging lens with a focal length of 10 cm is placed 20 cm in front of a diverging lens with a focal length of -10 cm. If an object is placed 40 cm in front of the converging lens, where will the final image be formed? Show a principal-ray diagram for each lens.

41. Show that the focal length f_{comp} of the two-component compound lens formed by two thin lenses in contact is given by the relation

$1/f_{comp} = 1/f_1 + 1/f_2$, where f_1 and f_2 are the focal lengths of the component thin lenses. Two plano-convex converging lenses are placed in contact. If the focal lengths of the lenses are 40 and 50 cm, what is the focal length of the resulting compound lens? Show a principal-ray diagram for an object 60 cm away from the first lens.

42. (a) Using the equation derived in Problem 41, show that the condition for achromatism of the compound lens in Fig. 34.39 is

$$\frac{1}{(f_{comp})_R} = \frac{1}{(f_{comp})_B}$$

or   (i)

$$\frac{1}{f_{CR}} + \frac{1}{f_{FR}} = \frac{1}{f_{CB}} + \frac{1}{f_{FB}},$$

where the subscripts C and F refer to the crown- and flint-glass components, while R and B refer to red and blue light. (b) Show by substitution of the refractive indices of Table 34.2 in the lensmaker's equation that for any crown-glass lens the focal lengths for red and blue light are related by

$$f_{CR} = (0.5240/0.5145)f_{CB} = 1.0185f_{CB},\ \ (ii)$$

while for any flint glass lens,

$$f_{FR} = (0.6391/0.6221)f_{FB} = 1.0273f_{FB}.\ \ (iii)$$

(c) Show by substitution of (ii) and (iii) in (i) that the condition for achromatism is $f_{FR} = -1.467f_{CR}$ and that the focal length of the compound lens is $f_{comp} = 3.102f_{CR}$.

43. If you wish to use flint glass and crown glass to construct a converging achromatic lens with a focal length of 50 cm, what should be the focal length for red light of the crown-glass component of the lens? The focal length for red light of the flint glass component?

44. If you wish to use crown glass and flint glass to construct a diverging achromatic lens with a focal length of −50 cm, what should be the focal length for red light of the crown-glass component? Of the flint-glass component?

NOTE: *Complex optical instruments can be considered as combinations of the following simple instruments: (1) the camera, which utilizes a lens to form real images of distant objects; (2) the projector, which uses a lens to form an enlarged, real image of a nearby well-illuminated object; and (3) the simple microscope, a lens of short focal length used to produce an enlarged virtual image of a nearby object. These simple instruments are considered in the following problems:*

45. A photographic camera has a lens with a focal length of 6 cm. When this camera is used to photograph a tree 50 m away, an inverted image of the tree that is 8 mm high is formed on the photographic film, which is located in the focal plane of the lens. How tall is the tree?

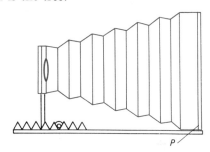

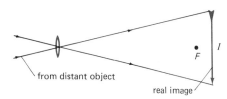

Problem 45. The camera.

46. A photographic slide measuring 30 mm by 30 mm is used in a slide projector equipped with a lens having a focal length of 20 cm. If the viewing screen to be used is 1.5 m by 1.5 m, what should be the distance between the lens and the screen? What is the ratio of the area of the screen to the area of the slide? Why must the slide be brilliantly illuminated?

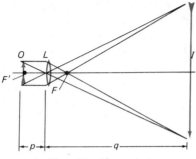

Problem 46. The projector.

47. A lens with a focal length of 1 cm is used as a simple microscope. How far from the lens should a jeweler place a small object 2 mm long in order to produce a virtual image at a distance of 25 cm from the lens? What is the length of the image? The distance of 25 cm is regarded as the *distance of most distinct vision* for the human eye. What is the angle subtended by the image at the jeweler's eye when the image is at this distance?

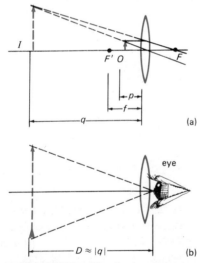

Problems 47–48. The simple microscope.

48. The continued use of the simple microscope in the manner described in the preceding problem would produce eyestrain because in its relaxed state the human eye produces clear images of *distant* objects. At what distance from object should the jeweler in the preceding problem place the object in order to produce an image at infinite distance? What angle at the jeweler's eye would be subtended under this condition?

NOTE: *The magnifying power of an optical instrument is defined as the ratio of the angle α_I subtended at the observer's eye by the image to the angle α_O subtended by the object when it is viewed directly in "the most favorable manner."*

49. What is the magnifying power of the simple microscope in the preceding problems when the image is formed 25 cm away from the lens? When the image is formed at infinite distance? What angle is subtended by the object when it is viewed in the most favorable manner; i.e., at the *distance of most distinct vision?*

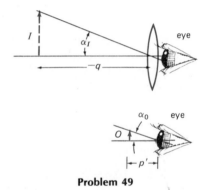

Problem 49

50. A jeweler needs a lens to provide a magnifying power of 10. What should be the focal length of such a simple microscope? If the jeweler uses this lens to observe an object having an area of 1 mm², what is the area of the image?

NOTE: *A compound microscope is a combination of two lenses of short focal length. The objective lens, placed close to the object to be viewed, acts as a projector to produce an enlarged real image. The eyepiece acts as a simple microscope to produce an enlarged virtual image, which is viewed by the observer. The maximum magnifying power is achieved when the final virtual image is at the distance of most distinct vision; however, when the ob-*

server makes prolonged use of the microscope, he usually adjusts it to produce the final image at infinite distance.

51. A compound microscope has an objective lens with a focal length of 0.5 cm and an eyepiece with a focal length of 2 cm. What is the maximum attainable magnifying power when the lenses are 10 cm apart?

54. How can a compound microscope be used to produce a real image of the object being observed? If the image is formed on a screen 25 cm beyond the eyepiece, what is the ratio of image size to object size if the magnifying power of the microscope is 50 when a *virtual* image is formed at infinite distance? What would be the ratio of the maximum illumina-

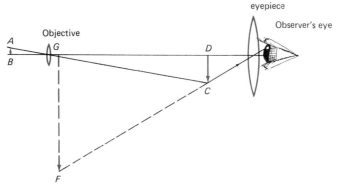

Problems 51–54. The compound microscope.

52. If the objective of a microscope has a focal length of 5 mm, where should the object be placed in order that the objective produce an enlargement of 100 diameters? What should be the focal length of the eyepiece in order to provide an overall magnifying power of 2000 for the microscope when the final image is 25 cm from the eyepiece?

53. A compound microscope has an objective with a focal length of 5 mm and an eyepiece with a focal length of 8 mm. How far apart should these lenses be in order to obtain a magnifying power of 500 when the final image is "formed at infinity"?

tion of the screen to the illumination of the object? Draw a ray diagram.

NOTE: *The astronomical telescope is a combination of two lenses. The objective lens has a long focal length and acts as a camera to produce a real image of the stars to be viewed. The eyepiece has a short focal length and acts as a simple microscope to view the real image produced by the objective. The objective has a large diameter in order to collect as much light as possible.*

55. Show that when an astronomical telescope is adjusted to produce a final image at infinite

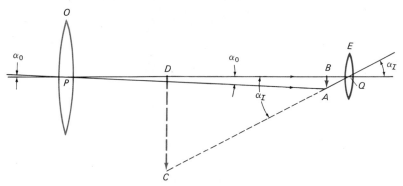

Problems 55–59.   The astronomical telescope.

distance from the eyepiece, its magnifying power is given by the relation M.P. = f_O/f_E, where f_O is the focal length of the objective and f_E is the focal length of the eyepiece.

56. A telescope at the Yerkes Observatory has an objective lens with a diameter of 102 cm and a focal length of 19.8 m. What is the magnifying power (Problem 55) of the Yerkes telescope when it is used with an eyepiece of focal length 2.54 cm and when the final image is at infinity?

57. On a certain day the illumination from the sun is 86,000 lm/m² at the earth's surface. Recalling that the sun's diameter subtends an angle of 0.5°, find the illumination of the sun's image formed in the focal plane of the telescope at the Yerkes Observatory described in Problem 56.

58. A high-school boy looks at the result of Problem 55 and resolves to build a telescope with a magnifying power equal to that of the Yerkes telescope described in Problem 56. Forthwith, he purchases a long pipe, a lens 10 cm in diameter with a focal length of 19.8 m, and an eyepiece with a focal length of 2.54 cm. After mounting the lenses at the ends of the long pipe, the boy sets out to test his telescope. What value does he obtain for the magnifying power of his telescope? In spite of his apparent success, the boy is disappointed because his telescope is not *"really as good"* as the Yerkes instrument. Why?

59. The apparent angular separation of two stars is 4° as observed with the Yerkes telescope described in Problem 56. What is the angular separation of these stars as viewed directly in the sky? What would be the apparent angular separation of these stars as viewed with the Yerkes telescope when an eyepiece with a focal length of 1.27 cm is being used? when an eyepiece with a focal length of 0.635 cm is being used?

NOTE: *The astronomical telescope is unsuitable for terrestrial use because the final virtual image is inverted. One type of simple terrestrial telescope utilizes an erecting lens* E', *as shown in diagram A, the sole function of which is to invert the image formed by the objective. Because the use of an erecting lens makes a simple terrestrial telescope inconveniently long, totally reflecting prisms are usually employed in prism binoculars as suggested in diagram B.*

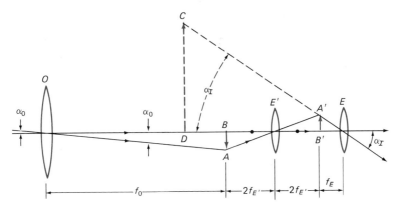

Diagram A. The terrestrial telescope.

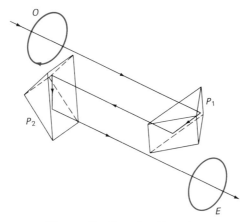

Diagram B. The prism binocular.

60. An astronomical telescope has an objective with a focal length of 30 cm and an eyepiece with a focal length of 1 cm. In order to convert this telescope into a terrestrial telescope, an erecting lens with a focal length of 12 cm is installed. Neglecting the thickness of the lenses, find the overall length of the telescope. Show a principal-ray diagram for each lens. Is it possible to shorten the telescope by positioning the erecting lens so that it produces a magnified image in the focal plane of the eyepiece?

61. Diagram B is a schematic drawing showing the arrangement of lenses and prisms used in one component of a set of prism binocular "field glasses." By tracing four rays parallel to the axis of the objective lens show that prism P_1 gives a right-to-left reversal of the beam and that prism P_2 produces a vertical up-down reversal of the beam.

CHAPTER 35

Physical Optics

In our earlier discussions of the *rectilinear propagation* of light through homogeneous media, the *reflection* of light when it strikes a boundary between two media, and the *refraction* of light when it travels from one medium into another, we made use of light *rays*. Although rays are normal to advancing wave fronts, we have not had to base our discussions on detailed considerations of the wave nature of light. The treatment of reflection and refraction in terms of light rays is called *geometrical optics* and is valid only when rectilinear propagation is involved.

In the present chapter we shall discuss optical phenomena known as *interference* and *diffraction* that can be interpreted *only* in terms of waves. The treatment of optical phenomena directly in terms of waves is known as *physical optics*. As pointed out in our discussion of sound waves, interference can be observed when wave trains from two coherent sources reach an observer or when wave trains from a single source reach an observer after traversing two different paths. Diffraction involves a change in the direction of propagation of a wave train as it passes some obstacle. Diffraction of sound waves is a matter of common experience. Audible sound waves do not travel in straight lines and can easily "bend around the corners of obstacles"; for example, sound waves spread after passing through an opening in a wall. Diffraction of light waves can be observed when light travels past small obstacles or through narrow openings with dimensions comparable with the wave length of light.

Interference and diffraction phenomena are characteristics of all kinds of waves— both transverse and longitudinal. In this chapter we shall also discuss optical *polarization,* a phenomenon that can be readily interpreted *only* on the basis of transverse waves. Polarization thus indicates that visible *light waves* are *transverse waves*.

35.1 YOUNG'S EXPERIMENT

After controversy for more than 100 years between adherents of the Newtonian particle theory of light and followers of the wave theory of Huygens, the English

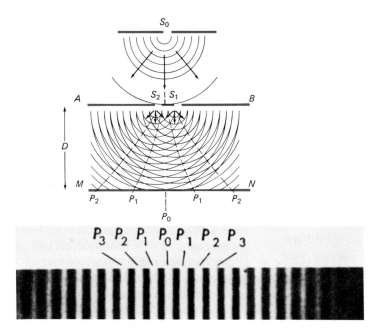

Fig. 35.1 Young's experiment.

scientist Thomas Young (1773–1829) performed experiments in 1802–1803 that demonstrated unambiguously that wave characteristics are involved in the transmission of light. Young's most famous experiment employed an arrangement of the type shown schematically in Fig. 35.1. If monochromatic light of wavelength λ passes through a narrow vertical slit S_0 to two closely adjacent vertical slits a distance d apart, vertical alternately light and dark fringes can be observed on a screen located at a distance D behind slits S_1 and S_2. Because slit S_0 acts as a single source illuminating S_1 and S_2, light waves spreading beyond S_1 and S_2 are coherent, and we thus have the conditions for interference of the kind that we discussed in detail in connection with sound waves (Section 18.10). If the difference in the path lengths S_1P and S_2P to a given point P on the screen is $n\lambda$, where n is an integer, the light waves interfere constructively at P and a bright fringe is observed. However, if the difference in the path lengths S_1P and S_2P is $(n + 1/2)\lambda$, the light waves interfere destructively at P and a dark fringe is observed. For point P_0 on the screen $S_1P_0 = S_2P_0$ and a bright fringe is observed.

In contrast to the interference of acoustical waves considered earlier, the spacing of the interference fringes in Young's optical experiment is given by a very simple expression because in any practical situation the distance D to the screen in Fig. 35.1 is enormous as compared with the separation d of slits S_1 and S_2 and with the wavelength λ of the light waves: $D >> d >> \lambda$. The simple expression can be obtained directly from our earlier more general expression as was done in obtaining (18.25).

The approximate expressions for the fringe locations can also be obtained directly from Fig. 35.2 when we note that under the experimental conditions the angle θ is very small and S_1P and S_2P are almost parallel. Then the distance S_2A in the figure is to a good approximation the difference in the path lengths S_2P and S_1P, and we have $\tan \theta = y/D$ and $\tan \theta \simeq \sin \theta \simeq S_2A/d$. This leads to the following expression for the positions of the bright and dark fringes on the screen:

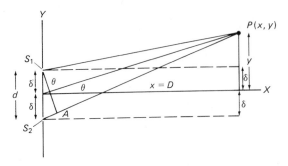

Fig. 35.2

$$y = \pm n \frac{\lambda D}{d}, \qquad \textit{(Bright Fringes)}$$

$$y = \pm (n + \tfrac{1}{2}) \frac{\lambda D}{d}. \quad \textit{(Dark Fringes)}$$

(35.1)

Because all the slits involved are narrow, the fringe pattern on the screen in Young's experiment is extremely dim even when observed in a well-darkened room. We also note that two optical phenomena are actually involved; the *interference* pattern is produced as a result of the spreading of light by *diffraction* as it passes through slits S_1 and S_2. In Fig. 35.1 light reaches S_1 and S_2 from S_0 because of diffraction. We shall discuss diffraction later in this chapter. The importance of Young's experiment is that it for the first time demonstrated compelling evidence of the existence of light *waves* by showing that the wave phenomena of diffraction and interference can be observed for light.

A somewhat later experiment by the French physicist Augustin Jean Fresnel (1788–1827) served to demonstrate clearly the *interference* of light waves in a somewhat different manner by means of the arrangement shown in Fig. 35.3. Two plane front-surface mirrors M_1 and M_2 meet each other along a straight line K. The two mirrors are inclined toward each other at an extremely small angle. At a distance of a few centimeters from the mirrors a narrow slit S_0 is set up in such a way that it is parallel to the line of intersection K of the mirrors. Slit S_0 is illuminated from behind by a sodium arc or some other source of monochromatic radiation so that light passing through the slit S_0 strikes both mirrors and is reflected as indicated in the figure.

Slit S_0 is imaged by mirror M_1 at S_1, and light appearing to diverge from S_1 strikes the screen in the region between A and A' in the diagram. Similarly, mirror M_2 forms a virtual image of S_0 at S_2; light appearing to diverge from S_2 strikes the screen in the region between B and B'. Thus, the portion of the screen between A and B' receives light from both virtual images, S_1 and S_2. By use of the two mirrors we have produced two "sources" S_1 and S_2 having not only identical frequencies but also a definite phase relationship. Therefore, the region on the screen between A and B' receives light from two coherent "sources" and the conditions for interference are fulfilled. The interference results in a set of alternately bright and dark fringes on the screen; these interference fringes are parallel to line K and slit S_0.

Note that the length of any light path from S_0 to mirror M_1 to any point on the screen is the same as the length of the straight line from S_1 to the point. Similarly, the length of the light path from S_0 to M_2 to any point on the screen is the same

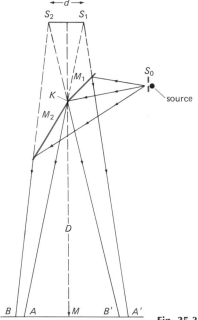

Fig. 35.3 Fresnel's double-mirror experiment.

Fig. 35.4 Fringes observed in the fresnel double-mirror experiment.

as the distance from S_2 to the same point. Therefore, the interference fringes on the screen will be formed in the same manner as that described for Young's experiment. If the separation of "sources" S_1 and S_2 is d and the distance to the screen is D, the relations given in (35.1) will apply. A photograph of a set of fringes obtained by a Fresnel arrangement is shown in Fig. 35.4.

We note that in Young's experiment and in the Fresnel double-mirror experiment light from a single monochromatic source like a sodium arc passes through a slit S_0 to form two sources S_1 and S_2 that are coherent. The wave trains from S_1 and S_2 to the screen not only have identical wavelengths but also have definite phase relationships. If each of the slits S_1 and S_2 is illuminated by a different sodium arc or other "ordinary" monochromatic source, no interference pattern can be seen on the screen because there is no definite phase relationship between the two wave trains reaching the screen. Whereas it is relatively easy to control the phase relations between two sources of sound waves (Chapter 18), phase relations between ordinary sources of light waves cannot be controlled. However, it is possible to employ two separate lasers operating at the same frequency to produce interference patterns for extremely brief periods of time before relative changes in phase occur. In order to produce an interference pattern with two sources for a given time interval, the two sources must *remain* coherent during the entire observation time interval involved.

35.2   INTERFERENCE IN THIN FILMS

Optical interference phenomena are produced by the reflection of light from thin transparent films. The colors observed involved in thin films such as soap bubbles, thin layers of oil on water, and thin layers of oxide on metal surfaces are familiar to everyone. Such films are usually observed by reflection of white light, and the colors are due to the interference of light waves reflected at the front and back surfaces of the films.

The reflection involved is regular reflection. In order to understand how interference is produced, consider Fig. 35.5 which shows two parallel rays ① and ② originating from the same point of a monochromatic source like a sodium arc being reflected from the front and back surfaces of a soap film and proceeding to an observer's eye; the distance from the source to the film and distance from the film to the eye are very large as compared with the thickness of the soap film. If the wave trains along the two rays are in phase at P and Q, their phase differences at P' and Q' will depend on the difference in the optical paths ① between P and P' and ② between Q and Q'. Ray ① follows the route PRP' in air, for which the refractive index is $\mu_A = 1$. Ray ② follows the route QSQ' in the soap film, which has a refractive index μ_W nearly equal to that of water.

As we pointed out earlier in Chapter 34, the optical path length through any medium is the length of the path in vacuum that would contain the same number of wavelengths as does the actual path through the medium. Because λ_m in the medium is equal to λ_{vac}/μ, the optical path length through any medium is the product of μ for the medium and the geometrical length of the path through the medium. In the case of the soap film in Fig. 35.5, optical path ① through air is simply PRP' and optical path ② is $\mu_W(QSQ')$. Therefore, the difference in optical path lengths for the two rays is

$$P_② - P_① = \mu(QSQ') - PRP', \qquad (35.2)$$

where we take the refractive index of air as unity and represent the refractive index of water simply as μ.

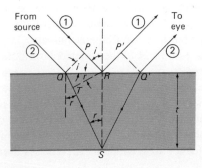

Fig. 35.5 Optical paths for reflection by a thin film.

From Fig. 35.5, we see that $QS = QT + TS = QR \sin r + t \cos r$, where t is the film thickness. Since by Snell's law, $\mu \sin r = \sin i$, we can write $\mu QS = QR \sin i + \mu t \cos r$. From this last relation and the fact that $QS = SQ'$, we see that the optical path difference (35.2) has the value

$$P_{②} - P_{①} = 2\mu t \cos r = 2t\sqrt{\mu^2 - \mu^2 \sin^2 r} = 2t\sqrt{\mu^2 - \sin^2 i}. \qquad (35.3)$$

For near-normal incidence, this expression approaches

$$P_{②} - P_{①} = 2\mu t. \quad \textit{(Normal Incidence)} \qquad (35.3')$$

On the basis of our earlier discussions of interference we might jump to the hasty conclusion that constructive interference occurs in a thin film when the path difference $P_{②} - P_{①}$ is equal to a whole number of wavelengths. However, we must recognize that light coming to the observer in Fig. 35.5 reaches him as a result of two *reflections* that may or may not involve phase changes. We recall from our earlier discussion of reflection of waves on a string in Section 18.7 that there is no phase change when such waves are reflected at a boundary between two media if the speed of propagation in the second medium is greater than the speed in the first medium. Because the speed of light in any optical medium is $v = c/\mu \leq c$, where μ is the refractive index of the medium, we expect by analogy that there is no phase change for waves reflected at the back surface of the film in Fig. 35.5. However, our earlier discussion of waves on a string showed that if the speed of propagation in the second medium is less than that in the first medium, there is a phase change of π radians in the waves as they are reflected. In the case of light, we anticipate that waves reflected from the front surface of the water film in Fig. 35.5 experience a phase change of π radians. One kind of direct optical evidence for this phase change is cited in Problem 5. This phenomenon can also be verified experimentally by observing a soap film in air as the film becomes very thin and bursts. As the thickness t of the film in Fig. 35.5 approaches zero, the waves reflected from the front and back surfaces have essentially zero optical path difference but differ in phase by π radians, and destructive interference occurs. The soap film thus becomes black just before the film breaks. This can easily be verified by watching a soap bubble in daylight. The soap bubble exhibits various colors due to constructive interference of various wavelengths present in the incident white light but becomes black at the place where the film is thinnest just before the bubble bursts.

If in addition to the phase difference arising from the optical path difference there is a phase difference of π radians between the wave trains associated with their reflections from the two surfaces of the film, there is *destructive interference* when the optical path difference $P_{②} - P_{①}$ is equal to $n\lambda$, where $n = 0, 1, 2, 3 \ldots$; this is the case for the soap film in air. In this situation, constructive interference occurs when the optical path difference is $P_{②} - P_{①} = (n + \frac{1}{2})\lambda$, where $n = 0, 1, 2, 3 \ldots$. If there is no phase difference between the wave trains associated with their reflections from the two surfaces of the film, the reverse relationship between interference and optical path difference results. Thus, for a thin layer of oil with $\mu = 1.51$ on the upper surface of a flat plate of flint glass with $\mu = 1.60$, constructive interference will be observed as the film thickness t approaches zero.

When there is a thin layer of air between glass plates, interference can be observed when the film is illuminated by monochromatic light and is observed by reflection. In this case constructive interference is observed when the optical path difference between waves reflected at the front and the back of the film is $(n + \frac{1}{2})\lambda$ and destructive interference is observed when the path difference is $n\lambda$. This phenomenon is used to test glass surfaces for flatness. If two optically flat glass surfaces are slightly separated at one edge and the other edge is in contact, there is a wedge-shaped layer of air between the two surfaces. The interference pattern formed when the film is illuminated by monochromatic light and viewed by reflection consists of a set of parallel fringes like the ones shown in the photograph in Fig. 35.6a. When a nonflat glass surface is in contact with a flat glass surface, the observed interference pattern is like the one shown in Fig. 35.6b. Interference is used in routine tests carried out in optical fabrication plants.

Several points should be noted in connection with our discussion. (a) The observer in Fig. 35.5 focuses his eye on the *film* and not the reflected image of the source. (b) Because of the way in which we have calculated path differences in films, the value of λ to be used in establishing constructive or destructive interference is the wavelength of light *in vacuum*. (c) No energy disappears when interference occurs in a thin film; in parts of the film where reflection is a maximum, transmission of light through the film is a minimum, and in parts of the film where reflection is a minimum, transmission is a maximum.

Example. A thin layer of oil with refractive index 1.5 floats on the surface of water on a pavement following a rain storm. The oil layer appears to be yellow green to an observer who views it at near-normal incidence. What is the minimum thickness of an oil layer that can produce this effect?

Because the film is viewed at near-normal incidence, the optical path difference through the oil film is given by (35.3'): $P_{②} - P_{①} = 2\mu t = 2(1.5)t$. Because the index of refraction of oil is greater than the refractive index of water, which is 1.33, there will be a phase difference of π radians between wave trains reflected from its upper and lower surfaces associated with the different natures of those

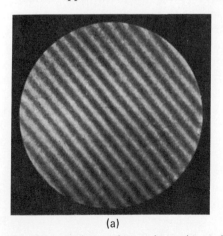

(a)

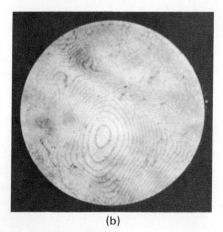

(b)

Fig. 35.6 Interference fringes observed in air films between glass plates.

reflections; therefore, constructive interference will occur for $P_{②} - P_{①} = (n + \frac{1}{2})\lambda$. Recalling that the wavelength of yellow–green light is approximately 550 nm, we can write: $2\mu t = (n + \frac{1}{2})\lambda$ or $t = (n + \frac{1}{2})\lambda/2\mu$. For the thinnest film, $n = 0$ and $t = \lambda/4\mu = (550 \text{ nm})/4(1.5) = 91.7$ nm. Reflection maxima will also be obtained for film thicknesses of $t = 1.5\lambda/2\mu = 275$ nm; $t = 2.5\lambda/2\mu = 458$ nm; $t = 3.5\lambda/2\mu = 642$ nm, etc. Sunlight contains light of all visible wavelengths, but it is easily shown that the thin oil film produces constructive interference only for yellow–green light.

35.3 FRESNEL DIFFRACTION: FRINGED SHADOWS

As light travels through free space, it travels in straight lines. However, when the advancing wave front in a light beam strikes an obstacle or a narrow opening, there is some spreading of the light into regions where it would not enter if propagation were strictly rectilinear. This spreading of a light beam is called *diffraction* and is an inherent characteristic of wave phenomena. A general quantitative treatment of diffraction presents serious mathematical difficulties, but there are two limiting cases that can be easily treated in terms of rather simple schemes first proposed by Huygens and later elaborated by Fresnel.

The first of these two limiting cases, called *Fresnel diffraction,* produces *fringed shadows* of small openings and small obstacles. The general effects involved are illustrated in the schematic diagram shown in Fig. 35.7, which shows a parallel light beam approaching a slit S in an opaque screen called the *diffraction screen.* The broad incident beam is characterized by plane wave fronts. If its transmission remained rectilinear as the light passes through the slit S, the shadow of the diffraction screen formed on a nearby observation screen would be a sharply defined *geometrical shadow.* The entire observation screen would be dark except for a bright, sharply outlined region in the center of the screen, which we can call the "bright shadow" of the slit S. The width of the geometrical shadow of the slit would be exactly equal to the width w of S and would be independent of the distance D between the diffraction and observation screens. Careful experiments with narrow slits S show that the shadow of the slit is *not* sharp but is "fuzzy"; this fuzzy shadow is called the *diffraction*

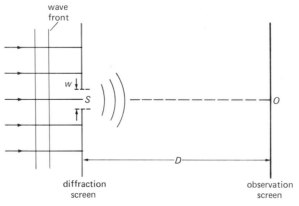

Fig. 35.7 Fresnel diffraction.

pattern of the slit. The appearance of this diffraction pattern is strongly dependent on the width w of the slit and the distance D between the screens. We attribute the pattern to the spreading of the narrow portion of the incident light beam that has passed through slit S. This spreading is shown schematically in Fig. 35.7 by the nonplanar wave fronts in the region between the diffraction and observation screens. The center of the diffraction pattern of the slit is always at point O on the observation screen where the center of the geometrical shadow of the slit would be formed if propagation were rectilinear.

The variation of the diffraction patterns obtained with slits of different widths w for a fixed distance between D between the diffraction screen and the observation screen is demonstrated in the photographs in Fig. 35.8. Figure 35.9 shows the variation in the diffraction pattern of a narrow slit of fixed width w as the distance D between the screens is varied. The top panel (a) in Fig. 35.9 shows the relative illumination E_L across the observation screen when the screens are nearly in contact; in this case the width of the diffraction pattern is just the one that would be expected on the basis of rectilinear propagation. Panel (b) of Fig. 35.9 shows the pattern observed when the distance D between the screens is 3 cm; note that the pattern is slightly wider and shows some evidence of fringes. Panel (c) shows the diffraction pattern observed when the distance D between the screens is 20 m; note that the width of the diffraction pattern in panel (c) is enormous as compared with the width of the

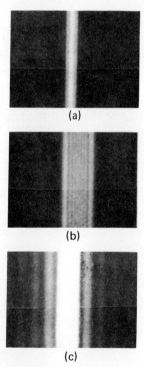

Fig. 35.8 Photograph of the Fresnel diffraction pattern of a single slit with screen at same distance D. (a) Wide slit; (b) narrower slit; (c) extremely narrow slit.

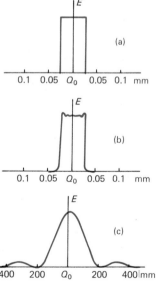

Fig. 35.9 Illumination in the Fresnel diffraction patterns of a slit 0.05 mm wide as observed at different distances D. (a) $D = 1$ mm; (b) $D = 4$ cm; (c) $D = 20$ m. Note abscissa scales.

slit itself. The major features of the Fresnel diffraction pattern in panel (c) are similar to those of Fraunhofer diffraction patterns that we shall discuss in the next section.

Explanations of diffraction were first based on an early hypothesis formulated by Christiaan Huygens to account for the way in which light waves are propagated. According to Huygens' hypothesis, *every point on an advancing wave front can be considered as a source of secondary wavelets which spread out spherically in a homogeneous medium; a later position of the advancing wave front is given by the envelope of these secondary wavelets.* The application of Huygens' hypothesis to spherical waves in free space can be understood by consideration of Fig. 35.10a. If W_1 is a wave front spreading out from a point source at speed c, then according to the Huygens hypothesis every point on this wave front is to be considered as the source of a secondary wavelet whose radius after t seconds would be ct. The position of the primary wave front W_2 at this later time is given by the forward envelope of the secondary wavelets.

In the case of the unobstructed *plane* wave front W_1 shown in Fig. 35.10b, the envelope of the secondary wavelets would also be an unobstructed *plane* wave front W_2. In this way a broad parallel beam of light would be transmitted through space without any changes in direction. However, if the plane wave front encounters an obstruction like the slit S in Fig. 35.7, only points on the portion of the wave front entering the slit set up secondary wavelets, and the forward envelope of these wavelets is not plane. Hence, the wave advancing through the slit tends to spread, as suggested in Fig. 35.7.

Although Huygens' hypothesis provides a more or less satisfactory qualitative explanation of diffraction, it does not provide a quantitative method of predicting the distribution of illumination in diffraction patterns. However, on the basis of certain additional assumptions Fresnel was able to calculate the distribution of illumination in diffraction patterns of various kinds. Kirchhoff later showed that most of the detailed assumptions made by Fresnel could be justified from quite general wave properties without making any special *ad hoc* assumptions.

The general ideas employed by Fresnel involve the assumption that the amplitude $\mathscr{E}$ of the light wave at any point P on a wave front is the resultant of the contributions of wavelets sent out by all points on the wave front when it was at some earlier position. In particular, he assumed that the contribution $d\mathscr{E}_2$ to the amplitude of a point such as P_2 on wave front W_2 in Fig. 35.10 due to an element dS_1 on wave front W_1 in Fig. 35.10 could be expressed in terms of the area dS_1, the amplitude $\mathscr{E}_1$ at dS_1, and the path between dS_1 and P_2. The resultant amplitude $\mathscr{E}_2$ at point

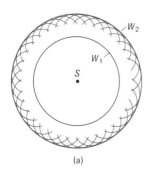

(a)

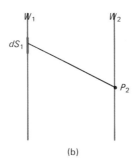

(b)

Fig. 35.10 Huygens' wavelets: (a) for a spherical wave front and (b) for a plane wave front.

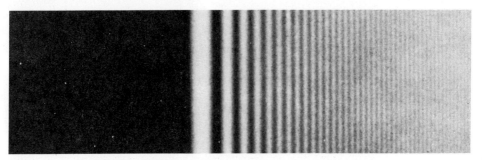

Fig. 35.11   Fresnel diffraction pattern of a straight edge.

P_2 is equal to the integral $\int d\mathscr{E}_2$, where the limits of integration include contributions from the entire surface S_1 of the advancing wave front at W_1. In carrying out the integration, account must be taken that the wavelets from different elements dS_1 do not arrive in phase when they reach point P_2. Fresnel devised methods of carrying out the necessary integrations for advancing wave fronts W_1 that are interrupted by diffraction screens like the one in Fig. 35.7 and obtained results for the amplitude $\mathscr{E}_2$ at various points in the diffraction pattern. Because the illumination E_2 at point P_2 is proportional to $\mathscr{E}_2^2$, the results of Fresnel's integration procedure could be compared with observed diffraction patterns and were found to be in satisfactory agreement.

As one other example of a Fresnel diffraction pattern we show in Fig. 35.11 the shadow of a straightedge such as that of a razor blade. Instead of the sharply defined geometrical shadow to be expected on the basis of rectilinear propagation, the photograph shows the screen illumination gradually decreasing as we proceed from the geometrical-shadow edge into the dark portion of the screen and shows a series of fringes of varying illumination as we proceed from the edge of the geometrical shadow toward the bright part of the screen where the illumination is uniform.

Although we shall not attempt to formulate or evaluate the Fresnel integral, we note that the relative value of the amplitude $\mathscr{E}_2$ at point P_2 at the edge of the geometrical shadow in Fig. 35.12 can be computed easily. The contribution $d\mathscr{E}_2$ due to a typical surface element dS_1 of the advancing plane wave front W_1 can be stated in terms of dS_1, $\mathscr{E}_1$, and the displacement between dS_1 and P_2. Since the lower half of W_1 is eliminated by the obstruction, the limits of integration cover only half the total area S_1 of the advancing wave front W_1. Therefore, the value of the amplitude $\mathscr{E}_2$ at point P_2 is half the value that would have been obtained if the obstruction had not

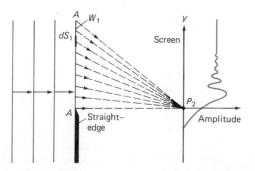

Fig. 35.12   Fresnel diffraction by a straight edge.

been present. Because the illumination E_2 of the screen at point P_2 is proportional to $\mathscr{E}_2^2$, the illumination at point P_2 is one-fourth of the illumination that would be attained in the absence of the obstruction. The illumination at points within the geometrical shadow decreases steadily as more and more of the contributions of the wavelets from W_1 are eliminated by the obstruction.

Above point P_2 on the screen the amplitudes vary with distance from the edge of the geometrical shadow because of the successive elimination of in-phase and out-of-phase wavelets by the obstruction. However, at sufficiently large distances above P_2 the illumination becomes equal to that to be expected in the absence of the obstruction. The centers of the bright fringes occur at distances y above the geometrical-shadow edge; y is given approximately by the relations

$$y = \sqrt{\lambda D},\ \sqrt{3\lambda D},\ \sqrt{5\lambda D},\ \ldots,$$

where λ is the wavelength of the light and D is the distance from the straightedge to the screen. If $\lambda = 490$ nm and $D = 1$ m, the first three bright fringes occur at approximately $y = 0.7$, 1.2, and 1.5 mm above the edge of the geometrical shadow.

35.4 FRAUNHOFER DIFFRACTION: FRINGED IMAGES

The other limiting case of diffraction involves the *fringed image* of a light source that is formed when light from a distant source passes through an aperture of some kind and then is imaged by a lens; this type of diffraction is called *Fraunhofer diffraction* because it was first investigated intensively by the German physicist Joseph Fraunhofer (1787–1826). In contrast to the Fresnel diffraction pattern, which is in essentials merely a fringed shadow of the aperture itself, a Fraunhofer diffraction pattern is a *fringed image* of a source as viewed through the aperture. The nature of the Fraunhofer diffraction pattern depends on the size and shape of the aperture limiting the beam reaching the lens that forms the image.

Fresnel diffraction is observed when the distance between the diffraction screen and the observation screen is finite; no lenses are needed. Fraunhofer diffraction is observed when a parallel light beam from a distant source is incident on the diffraction screen and a converging lens located between the diffraction and observation screens is used to form an *image of the source* on the observation screen. The *fringed image of the source constitutes the Fraunhofer diffraction pattern.*

A simple arrangement for observing the Fraunhofer diffraction pattern of a slit is shown in Fig. 35.13. Monochromatic light passes through a source slit S to lens L_1

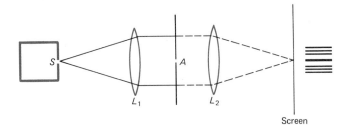

Fig. 35.13 Arrangement for observing the Fraunhofer diffraction pattern of a single slit A. The lens produces an image of the line source S on the screen.

Fig. 35.14 Photograph of the Fraunhofer diffraction pattern produced by a single slit.

that renders the beam parallel. In the absence of the slit aperture A, the parallel light beam formed by lens L_1 reaches a second lens L_2 that produces a sharp real image of the source slit on the screen. When slit A is inserted parallel to S, a diffraction pattern is observed on the screen. The bright central portion of the diffraction pattern is at the same location as the original image of slit S but is considerably broader. If the aperture slit A is narrow, several bright and dark fringes appear on the screen on each side of the central image. The width of the central fringe and the spacing of the fringes are determined by the width of slit A. The width of the central fringe on the screen is approximately twice that of the other fainter bright fringes, as indicated in Fig. 35.14.

The explanation of the observed diffraction pattern is fairly simple because only plane wave fronts reaching lens L_2 are focused on the screen. The simplified drawing in Fig. 35.15a is useful in understanding the observed diffraction patterns; in this figure the magnitude of the angle θ is highly exaggerated, with Δp drawn large for clarity. The lines ① represent the paths traversed in the forward direction by secondary Huygens wavelets from the two edges of the slit. Because the light approaching the slit consists of a parallel beam, the original wave front is plane and all sources of Huygens wavelets in the slit are in phase. Therefore, the secondary wavelets traversing paths ① and all parallel paths in the forward direction are in phase: the lens L_2 produces a bright central image in the forward direction; this bright image of source

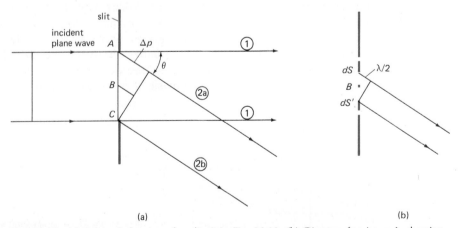

Fig. 35.15 (a) Enlarged drawing of a slit A in Fig. 36.13. (b) Diagram for $\Delta p = \lambda$ showing elements in the upper and lower halves of the slit for which the path difference is $\lambda/2$.

slit S is the central component of the diffraction pattern. The illumination on other parts of the screen depends on the differences in path lengths traversed by secondary waves from different parts of the slit in accordance with the Fresnel assumptions discussed in the previous section. If we are interested in the illumination on the screen at a point for which a line drawn from the slit to the screen makes angle θ with lines ① drawn in the forward direction, we must consider Huygens wavelets that leave slit A at angle θ in Fig. 35.15. Lines ②a and ②b represent paths traversed by such secondary wavelets. We note that path ②a is longer than path ②b by an amount Δp. If this path difference is $\Delta p = \lambda$, we can divide the slit into two zones AB and BC as suggested in the figure; for every element dS in the upper zone there is a corresponding element dS' in the lower zone for which the path lengths of the wavelets differ by $\lambda/2$ as indicated in Fig. 35.15b. Thus, the contributions of all elements in the upper zone and the contributions of all elements in the lower zone cancel in pairs when they are brought together on the screen by the lens. The resulting amplitude of the actual light waves at this point on the screen is zero and hence the illumination is zero. Therefore, at the angle θ for which $\Delta p = \lambda$ there is a region of zero intensity or a *dark fringe* on the screen. Similar reasoning shows that dark fringes are observed for angles at which $\Delta p = 2\lambda, 3\lambda, 4\lambda, 5\lambda, \ldots$. Therefore, complete cancellation occurs for angles θ such that $\sin \theta = n\lambda/a$, where a is the width of the aperture slit and n is an integer.

The situation is different when Δp in Fig. 35.15a is equal to an odd number of half wavelengths. For example, consider the case for which $\Delta p = 3\lambda/2$. We can divide the slit into three zones; for every element dS in one of the zones there is an element dS' in the adjacent zone such that the path lengths traversed by the Huygens wavelets differ by $\lambda/2$. Therefore, when the wavelets are brought together by the lens, the wavelets from two of the three zones completely cancel. However, wavelets from the third zone do not cancel, and a bright fringe or illumination maximum appears on the screen. Similar arguments show that bright fringes occur when $\Delta p \cong 5\lambda/2, 7\lambda/2, 9\lambda/2, \ldots$. The illumination at the centers of the bright fringes decreases rapidly as we go away from the central bright fringe. Because the first dark fringe occurs for $\Delta p = \lambda$ and $\Delta p = 0$ gives the central maximum, the distance between the centermost dark fringes is twice that between succeeding dark fringes. Therefore, the width of the central bright fringe is twice that of the other bright fringes; this can be seen from the photograph shown in Fig. 35.14.

Figure 35.16 shows the way in which light from the aperture slit is focused on the screen by lens L_2. The angle θ at which light is focused on the screen can be stated in terms of Δp in Fig. 36.16 by $\sin \theta = \Delta p/a$. Since parallel light beams are

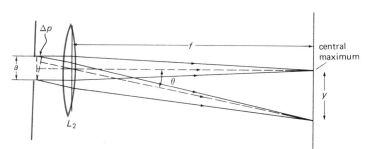

Fig. 35.16 Formation of a Fraunhofer diffraction pattern on the screen. The lens forms an image of the source.

focused on the screen by the lens L_2, the distance from the aperture slit to the screen must be the focal length f of the lens. Parallel light making a small angle θ with the axis of the lens will be focused at point y for which $\tan \theta = \pm \, y/f$ as shown by the dashed rays drawn through the optical center of the lens in Fig. 35.16. Because θ is small for all parts of the observed diffraction pattern, both $\sin \theta$ and $\tan \theta$ are approximately equal to the angle θ in radians. Hence, we can replace $\sin \theta$ and $\tan \theta$ by θ and write

$$\frac{\pm y}{f} = \frac{\Delta p}{a} \quad \text{or} \quad y = \pm \left(\frac{\Delta p}{a} \right) f. \tag{35.4}$$

In the case of the arrangement in Fig. 35.16, bright fringes are centered at values of y given by $\Delta p \cong 0, \, 3\lambda/2, \, 5\lambda/2, \, 7\lambda/2, \, \ldots$ and dark fringes occur at values of y given by $\Delta p = \lambda, \, 2\lambda, \, 3\lambda, \, \ldots$.

We note that a complete treatment of double-slit interference as considered in Section 35.1 would involve simultaneous description of the interference between waves propagating through the two slits and diffraction at each slit as treated in this section. The illumination of the interference fringes is modulated by the illumination function of the single-slit diffraction pattern shown in Fig. 35.14.

Note that the larger the aperture a, the narrower is the central illumination maximum. If the source slit S in Fig. 35.13 were actually a line, we could make the central illumination maximum on the screen as narrow as we pleased by increasing the width a of the aperture slit. However, we cannot make the aperture width a greater than the linear aperture of the lens L_2 itself. When the screen containing the aperture slit is completely removed in Fig. 35.13, the lenses themselves provide an aperture a and there is still a diffraction pattern on the screen.

The calculation of the diffraction pattern produced by a circular aperture is similar in essentials to that for a slit aperture. However, because the details of the calculation are considerably more complicated, we shall merely state the results. When an ordinary lens is used to produce an image of a point source such as a star, the lens does not produce a point image even if there are no aberrations. Because of its finite aperture, the lens produces a diffraction pattern consisting of a circular central region of maximum illumination surrounded by alternately dark and bright rings corresponding to the outer diffraction fringes that we have discussed for a slit source viewed through an aperture slit. In the case of the circular diffraction pattern produced by the lens, the radius r of each fringe is given by

$$r = (m\lambda/D)f, \tag{35.5}$$

where D is the diameter or linear aperture of the lens and f is its focal length. Bright rings have their illumination maxima for values of r given (35.5) with $m = 0, \, 1.635, \, 2.679, \, 3.699, \, 4.710, \, \ldots$ and dark fringes have radii given by (35.5) with $m = 1.220, \, 2.233, \, 3.238, \, 4.241, \, \ldots$. The radius of the first dark fringe occurs when the angular separation θ of the fringe from the center of the central maximum is radians is $\theta = 1.22 \, \lambda/D$.

Example.   An achromatic lens 4 cm in diameter and with a focal length of 1 m produces an image of a star. What is the radius of the first dark ring in the Fraunhofer diffraction pattern of the star?

Here the diameter D of the lens itself gives the diameter of the circular aperture. Taking $\lambda = 550$ nm as the wavelength (yellow–green), we use (35.5) to obtain $r = (1.22)(5.5 \times 10^{-7}$ m$)(1$ m$)/(4 \times 10^{-2}$m$) = 1.68 \times 10^{-5}$ m or 0.0168 mm. This ring would be marginally visible to the unaided eye and could easily be observed through a simple microscope, which could be used to study the entire diffraction pattern.

35.5   RESOLVING POWER OF OPTICAL INSTRUMENTS

The magnifying power of an astronomical telescope (see Problem 55 in Chapter 34) is given by the ratio of the focal length of the objective to the focal length of the eyepiece: M.P. $= f_O/f_E$. It would appear that with a given objective the magnifying power could be increased without limit by using eyepieces of shorter and shorter focal length. If anything to be gained by thus increasing the magnifying power?

The eyepiece is merely a simple microscope used to examine the images of distant objects that are formed in the focal plane of the objective. The images are in the last analysis simply diffraction patterns formed by the objective, the diameter of which is the diffraction aperture. In the case of a star, the diffraction pattern is of the type that we have just discussed—a bright circular central region of maximum illumination surrounded by a set of alternately dark and bright rings such as is shown in Fig. 35.17a. Little is to be gained in forming a larger and larger virtual image of

 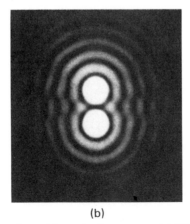 

| (a) | (b) | (c) |

Fig. 35.17 Fraunhofer diffraction patterns formed by a circular aperture. (a) Diffraction pattern for a single point source. (b) Diffraction pattern for two point sources. (c) Diffraction pattern for two point sources at the Rayleigh limit of resolution.

such a diffraction pattern by using eyepieces of shorter and shorter focal length. As a result of Fraunhofer diffraction, the objective lens of a telescope forms a "fuzzy image," of a distant star, and magnification of the fuzzy image by means of a simple microscope cannot reduce the fuzziness. The wave nature of light thus sets ultimate limits on the useful magnifying power attainable with a telescope.

A more meaningful ultimate limitation on the usefulness of a telescope is called its *resolving power,* a quantity that is a measure of the telescope's ability to distinguish point objects when they are close together. For example, in the case of two stars that are seemingly close together in the sky, the telescope objective produces not two point images but two circular diffraction patterns. For stars with small angular separations in the sky, the two diffraction patterns may overlap as in the photograph shown in Fig. 35.17b. The resolving power of an optical instrument is usually defined as $1/\theta_{\min}$, where $\theta_{\min}$ is the minimum angular separation of two point objects that can be distinguished as two sources instead of a single source. One useful way of stating $\theta_{\min}$ that was suggested by the English physicist Lord Rayleigh (1842–1919) has been widely accepted and is in general use. According to the *Rayleigh criterion,* two point objects can just be distinguished by an optical instrument if their angular separation is such that the central maximum in the diffraction pattern of one of the images formed by the instrument's objective is separated from the central maximum in the diffraction pattern of the other by a distance equal to the radius of the first dark ring in the diffraction patterns. This situation is illustrated in the photograph in Fig. 35.17c; objects with smaller angular separation could not be resolved.

On the basis of (35.5), we have for the objective lens or mirror of a telescope that $\theta_{\min} = r/f = 1.22\lambda/D$, where r is the radius of the first dark ring and f is the focal length of the objective. This value also gives the minimum angular separation θ in radians of two stars that can just be resolved. (See Fig. 35.18.) Thus,

$$\theta_{\min} = 1.22\lambda/D, \quad \text{(Rayleigh's Criterion)} \tag{35.6}$$

where D is the diameter of the telescope objective, and for the visual use with white light λ has a nominal value of 500 nm. On the basis of this value of $\theta_{\min}$, the resolving power of a telescope can be expressed as

$$\text{Resolving power} = 1/\theta_{\min} = D/1.22\lambda. \quad \text{(Resolving Power)} \tag{35.6'}$$

We note that the resolving power of a telescope depends only on the diameter of the objective. The focal lengths of the eyepiece and objective are not involved at

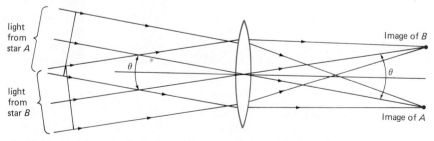

Fig. 35.18   Angular separation of two stars.

all. Although a conveniently large magnifying power is desirable, it has no real bearing on the ultimate performance of an astronomical telescope.

We note that the resolving power stated in (35.6′) represents an ultimate value that involves the wave nature of light itself. Any aberrations in the lenses or mirrors of a telescope will reduce the value of the instrument's resolving power. Convection currents of the air in the vicinity of the telescope as well as fluctuations in pressure or temperature along the optical path through the atmosphere also serve to limit the actually attainable resolving power of a telescope.

The ultimate resolving power of a microscope is also limited by the wave nature of light. The ratio D/λ also appears in the expression for the resolving power of a microscope, where D is the diameter of the objective. However, in the case of a microscope, we have some control of the wavelength λ of the radiation used to illuminate the object. If ultraviolet light is used to illuminate the object, the resolving power of a microscope can be increased because ultraviolet light has shorter wavelengths than visible light. It is necessary, of course, to use a photographic film or a fluorescent screen to observe the image in an ultraviolet microscope.

Example. At closest approach the moon is 357 000 km from the earth. Using the Rayleigh criterion, compute the separation of the two lunar craters that can just be resolved (a) by a small telescope with an objective 25 cm in diameter and (b) by the 508-cm reflecting telescope at Mt. Palomar.

According to the Rayleigh criterion, the minimum angular separation of point sources that can be resolved is $\theta_{min} = 1.22\lambda/D$. For the small telescope, $\theta_{min} = (1.22)(5 \times 10^{-7} \text{ m})/(2.5 \times 10^{-1}\text{m}) = 2.44 \times 10^{-6}$ rad. The distance d between two points on the moon's surface with this angular separation is $d = R\theta_{min}$, where R is the radial distance to the moon. Thus, $d = (3.57 \times 10^8 \text{ m})(2.44 \times 10^{-6} \text{ rad}) = 8.71 \times 10^2$ m or 0.871 km. For the large Mt. Palomar telescope, $\theta_{min} = 1.22 (5 \times 10^{-7} \text{ m})/(5.08 \text{ m}) = 1.20 \times 10^{-7}$ rad, and $d = (3.57 \times 10^8 \text{ m})(1.20 \times 10^{-7} \text{ rad}) = 42.8$ m.

35.6 DIFFRACTION GRATING

The diffraction grating, invented by Fraunhofer, provides a clear-cut demonstration of the nonrectilinear propagation of light and its interpretation in terms of the wave theory of light. A diffraction grating is a diffraction screen containing a large number of very narrow parallel slits uniformly spaced with separations comparable with the wavelength of light. The device produces very sharp diffraction maxima at large diffraction angles. A transmission grating can be formed by ruling grooves on glass with a diamond cutting edge moved by a very carefully constructed "ruling engine," which serves to maintain even spacings between the grooves. The clear places between the grooves act as the narrow slits in the grating. Reflection gratings can be ruled in similar fashion by making grooves on metal surfaces. Once a good reflection grating has been produced, it can be used as a "master grating" from which inexpensive replicas can be fabricated by "printing" grooves on a layer of plastic material. Since

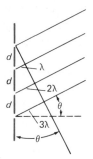

Fig. 35.19   Several slits in a diffraction grating.

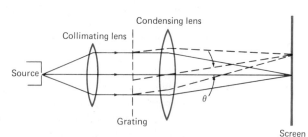

Fig. 35.20   A diffraction grating with a collimating lens and condensing lens.

the development of the laser, it has been possible to use optical interference effects to guide the ruling engine in maintaining equal spacings between the lines or grooves on the grating. Gratings can also be made by photographing the diffraction patterns produced by the interference of coherent wave trains from laser sources.

The action of a grating can be understood by a consideration of Fig. 35.19, which shows a few adjacent slits in a large transmission grating. With a parallel beam of light approaching the grating from the left, a plane wave front reaches the grating so that the initial wave disturbance has the same phase at all the slits shown. Under this condition all secondary waves traveling through the grating in the forward direction at $\theta = 0$ are in phase; this results in a central maximum in the diffraction pattern produced by the grating. In certain other directions secondary waves are also in phase at a plane wave front; these directions depend on the wavelength λ of the light and the distance d between the narrow slits in the grating. One of these directions is denoted by θ in the figure. At this angle the lengths of the paths traversed by secondary waves from adjacent slits differ by an amount equal to the wavelength of the light. Hence, a converging lens can be used to produce a bright image of the original light source on an observation screen in its focal plane. Examination of Fig. 35.19 shows that the angle θ is given by $\sin \theta = \lambda/d$.

Figure 35.20 shows a slit S illuminated by a light source. Light emerging from this slit reaches a "collimating lens" that produces the parallel light beam that strikes the grating. Light passing through the grating strikes a "condensing lens" that produces images of the source slit on an observation screen. The central image in the diffraction pattern is formed by light traveling through the grating in the forward direction with $\theta = 0$. So-called *first-order* images of the source slit will be formed at angles θ_1 for which $\sin \theta_1 = \lambda/d$ on each side of the central image; only one of these first-order images is indicated in Fig. 35.20.

Consideration of Fig. 35.19 indicates that secondary waves from the slits can also provide constructive interference in other directions θ for which the path lengths of the secondary waves from adjacent slits differ by 2λ, 3λ, 4λ, ... The directions θ_n in which diffraction maxima can be produced are given by the general relation

$$\sin \theta_n = n\lambda/d, \tag{35.7}$$

where $n = 0, 1, 2, 3, 4, \ldots$. The central image on the screen is formed for $n = 0$ in (35.7). The diffraction maximum with $n = 1$ is called the *first-order* image, that for $n = 2$ is called the *second-order* image, etc. Light of all wavelengths emitted by the source is focused in the central image. If the source emits light of different wavelengths, a line for each wavelength λ will be displayed on the observation screen for the first and higher orders. The display of a "line" for each wavelength on the screen is called the *spectrum* of the source. Each spectral line is merely a colored image of the entrance slit.

Because the spacing d between the narrow slits is established when the grating is made and because angles θ are readily measured, a grating can be used to determine the wavelengths of the light emitted by a source. Gratings are incorporated in commercially available instruments called spectrometers or spectrographs that can be used in the systematic studies of the spectra of sources of various types.

Example. A grating having 10,000 lines/cm is used to study the spectrum of a sodium arc light that is used to illuminate the slit of a spectrograph similar to the device shown in Fig. 35.20. When a photographic plate is inserted at the observation-screen position in Fig. 35.20, a single spectral line is observed in first order at an angle $\theta_1 = 36.2°$. What is the wavelength of sodium light? What is its frequency?

The grating space d is 10^{-4} cm = 1000 nm. The wavelength involved can be determined from (35.7): $\lambda = d \sin \theta_1 = (1000 \text{ nm})(\sin 36.2°) = 590$ nm. The frequency f of the light can be obtained from the relation $f = c/\lambda$. Use of the approximate value $c = 3.0 \times 10^8$ m/s gives $f = (3.0 \times 10^8 \text{ m/s})/(5.9 \times 10^{-7} \text{ m}) = 5.08 \times 10^{14} \text{ s}^{-1} = 5.08 \times 10^{14}$ Hz. Note: The yellow light from a sodium arc actually consists of a mixture of light of two nearly equal wavelengths and frequencies. A good spectrograph or spectrometer would show the corresponding spectral lines as a "closely spaced doublet" in the observed spectrum.

35.7 POLARIZATION

Whereas interference and diffraction are phenomena characteristic of both longitudinal and transverse waves, the phenomenon of *polarization can be interpreted only in terms of transverse waves*. In the case of longitudinal mechanical waves, the motions of the particles of the medium are parallel to the direction of wave propagation and thus can show no asymmetry about this direction. However, in a simple transverse mechanical wave the particles of the medium move at right angles to the direction of propagation and thus their motion is asymmetric with respect to the direction of wave propagation. The plane in which the motion of the particles takes place is called the plane of polarization; for example, the plane of polarization of the sinusoidal wave shown in Fig. 18.5 of is the XY plane.*

Whenever there is a lack of symmetry around an axis in the direction of propagation of a wave, we say that the wave is *polarized*. Polarization can occur only for transverse

* Although electromagnetic waves involve simultaneously varying $\mathscr{E}$ and $\mathscr{B}$, the electric field $\mathscr{E}$ interacts more strongly with matter than does the accompanying magnetic field $\mathscr{B}$. Therefore, in our discussion of polarization we specify only the orientation of $\mathscr{E}$; $\mathscr{B}$ is always perpendicular to $\mathscr{E}$.

waves. A light wave can be polarized; we conclude that light waves are transverse waves.

The production of polarized light by *selective absorption* ("dichroism") is exhibited by the crystals of certain minerals like *tourmaline* and by crystals of certain organic compounds. Unfortunately, most large specimens of tourmaline are colored and large dichroic crystals of organic compounds cannot be readily produced. However, in 1935 the American inventor Edwin H. Land (1909–   ) developed a method of embedding small needle-shaped dichroic crystals of quinine iodosulfate in a sheet of clear plastic in such a way that their crystal axes are aligned in a common direction. The resulting sheet of material, first marketed under the trade name of *polaroid,* is now called a "polarizing plate." With the development of polaroid, it became possible to produce broad beams of polarized light for many practical uses.

When a beam of light from an ordinary source such as an incandescent lamp passes through a polarizing plate, the intensity of the light beam is reduced by about 50%. The human eye can detect no essential difference between the incident light and the transmitted light except for a change in observable beam intensity. However, if light transmitted by the first polarizing plate, called the *polarizer,* is viewed through a second polarizing plate, called the *analyzer,* pronounced changes in beam intensity can be observed. These changes depend on the relative orientations of the polarizer and the analyzer plates, which are illustrated in Fig. 35.21. If we assign to the plates certain "polarization axes," which can be arbitrarily set parallel to the long dimensions of the plates in the diagram, we have a way of describing the phenomena shown in the diagram. When the polarization axes of polarizer and analyzer are parallel, nearly all the light transmitted through the polarizer is also transmitted through the analyzer. With an acute angle θ between their polarization axes, some of the light transmitted by the polarizer is absorbed by the analyzer. The fraction of light transmitted by the polarizer that is absorbed in the analyzer gradually increases as the angle θ is increased. When the axes of the polarizer and analyzer are perpendicular to each other, no light at all is transmitted. With $\theta = 90°$, we say that the polarizer and analyzer are "crossed."

A wave explanation of the phenomena shown in Fig. 35.21 is given schematically in Fig. 35.22 A beam of ordinary light consists of a transverse wave involving "disturbances" $\mathscr{E}$ that are perpendicular to the direction of wave propagation. At a given location in the beam, the periodic variations of $\mathscr{E}$ are all in a plane perpendicular to the direction of propagation; however, in an ordinary light wave there is no preferred orientation of $\mathscr{E}$ in any direction in this plane. The transverse wave associated with the beam is actually the superposition of many sinusoidal waves; these sinusoidal waves originate in different atoms in the light source; because the atomic emissions are independent, the vibrations of $\mathscr{E}$ occur in all possible directions in planes perpendicular to the direction of wave propagation. In Fig. 35.22 we show schematically a beam of ordinary light approaching a polarizer from the left; Fig. 35.22a below this

(a)

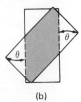

(b)

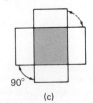

(c)

Fig. 35.21 Transmission of light through two polarizing plates.

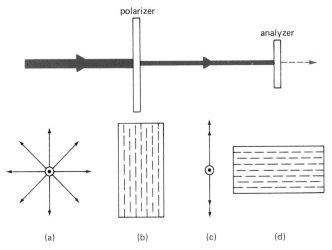

polarizer

analyzer

(a)   (b)   (c)   (d)

Fig. 35.22 Transmission of light through a polarizer and analyzer.

beam indicates that vibrations of $\mathscr{E}$ have all orientations in a plane perpendicular to the beam.

However, the electric-field vectors involved can be resolved into components parallel to any two axes normal to the direction of propagation. Thus, if a beam of ordinary light is approaching the reader along the Z axis as shown in Fig. 35.23a, the vibrations of $\mathscr{E}$ take place in all directions perpendicular to the Z axis, including those shown. We can resolve the oscillating vector $\mathscr{E}$ of each vibration into components parallel to the X and Y axes. The whole unpolarized light wave can be considered as equivalent to two light waves, one with vibrations parallel to the X axis and the other with vibrations parallel to the Y axis, as suggested in Fig. 35.23b.

The incident beam strikes the polarizer in Fig. 35.22. Figure 35.22b indicates that the polarizer is set to transmit light waves involving vertical vibrations of $\mathscr{E}$ but to absorb light having horizontal vibrations of $\mathscr{E}$; the light transmitted through the polarizer is said to be *plane polarized* and in Fig. 35.22c has only vertical vibrations of $\mathscr{E}$. The *plane of polarization* is the plane containing an axis in the direction of propagation in which the vibrations of $\mathscr{E}$ take place.

When an unpolarized monochromatic light beam passes through a polarizer, the plane-polarized beam emerging from the polarizer has half the intensity of the unpolarized beam because vibration components perpendicular to the polarization axis of the polarizer have been eliminated by absorption in the polarizer. If $\mathscr{E}_1$ is the amplitude of the plane-polarized beam emerging from the polarizer, the amplitude $\mathscr{E}_2$ transmitted by an analyzer with its polarization axis inclined at angle θ to the plane of polarization

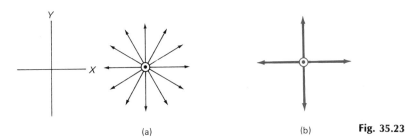

Y

X

(a)   (b)   **Fig. 35.23** is $\mathscr{E}_2 = \mathscr{E}_1 \cos \theta$, just the amplitude of the component of $\mathscr{E}_1$ along the polarization axis of the analyzer. Because the intensity of a wave is proportional to the square of the wave amplitude, the intensity I_1 of the wave emerging from the analyzer is equal to $I_1 \cos^2 \theta$, where I_1 is the intensity of the wave emerging from the polarizer.

In Fig. 35.22d, the analyzer is set to absorb vertically polarized light and transmit horizontally polarized light. Because there is no horizontally polarized light reaching the analyzer, no light at all is transmitted. The polarizer and analyzer are "crossed" and $\cos \theta = 0$. In our discussion of Fig. 35.22 we have assumed that both polarizer and analyzer are "perfect" or "ideal"; however, when a pair of real polarizing plates are crossed, a small amount of light usually manages to leak through!

Example.   Four polarizing plates are stacked so that the polarization axis of each plate is turned 30° clockwise with respect to the polarization axis of the preceding plate, the last plate therefore being "crossed" with respect to the first. What fraction of the intensity of an incident unpolarized light beam emerges from the stack?

The first plate transmits one-half of the incident intensity. Each succeeding plate transmits a fraction $\cos \theta$ of the wave amplitude or a fraction $\cos^2 \theta$ of the wave intensity. Because $\cos 30° = \sqrt{3}/2$ and $\cos^2 30° = 3/4$, the fraction of the beam intensity transmitted by the stack is

$$1/2 \cdot 3/4 \cdot 3/4 \cdot 3/4 = 27/128 = 0.211$$

or 21.1% of the incident intensity. Note that if we removed two plates from the center of the stack, no light at all would be transmitted! Explain.

The invention of the polarizing plate made it possible to produce polarized light beams in a very convenient way. However, selective absorption is not the only method of producing polarized light. Perhaps the simplest method of polarizing light was discovered in 1808 by the French scientist Etienne Louis Malus (1775–1812), who discovered that light reflected at non-normal incidence from the polished surface of

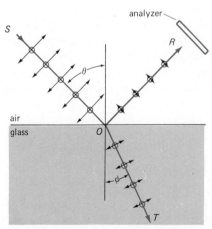

Fig. 35.24 Partial polarization by reflection.

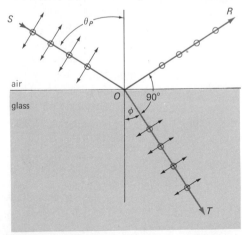

Fig. 35.25 Complete polarization by reflection at Brewster's angle θ_P.

a nonmetallic material like glass is partially polarized. Consider an unpolarized incident parallel light beam striking a glass surface as suggested by the light ray *SO* in Fig. 35.24. At such a surface there is a reflected beam, described in Fig. 35.24 by the ray *OR,* and a refracted beam, described in Fig. 35.24 by *OT.* If we examine the reflected light by means of an analyzer placed at the indicated position, we find that the reflected light is partially polarized in such a way that light associated with vibrations parallel to the surface and perpendicular to the plane of incidence is more highly reflected than light associated with vibrations in the plane of incidence. The plane of incidence is the plane of the paper in Fig. 35.24. When the angle of incidence at a glass surface is about 57°, the reflected beam is completely polarized, as suggested in Fig. 35.25. This angle is called the *polarizing angle* for glass and is designated as angle θ_P in the figure. At this angle approximately 8% of the incident light flux is reflected at a glass surface; all the reflected light is plane polarized. The light in the refracted beam, parallel to ray *OT* in the figure, is partially polarized because it has been depleted of light having vibrations perpendicular to the plane of incidence.

David Brewster (1781–1868) first noted that when light is incident at the polarizing angle, the reflected ray and the refracted ray are exactly 90° apart as shown in Fig. 35.25. Brewster's discovery enables us to derive a very simple relation between the polarizing angle and the refractive index of a medium. Snell's law for the case involved states that $\sin \theta_P = \mu \sin \phi$, where ϕ is the angle of refraction; the angle of reflection is equal to angle θ_P by the law of refraction. Because the reflected ray and the refracted ray are 90° apart, we can write

$$\theta_P + \phi + 90° = 180° \quad \text{or} \quad \theta_P + \phi = 90°.$$

Because θ_P and ϕ are thus complementary angles, $\sin \phi = \cos \theta_P$. Substituting $\cos \theta_P$ for $\sin \phi$ in Snell's law, we obtain

$$\mu = \sin \theta_P / \cos \theta_P = \tan \theta_P. \quad \textit{(Brewster's Law)} \tag{35.8}$$

Brewster's law enables us to calculate the polarizing angle in terms of the refractive index of any medium. For this reason the polarizing angle θ_P is frequently called *Brewster's angle.*

The phenomenon of selective reflection can be used to construct a fairly effective polarizer by mounting a stack of thin glass plates inside a tube as indicated in Fig. 35.26. When a beam of light strikes the stack of plates at the polarizing angle θ_P, some of the light with vibrations perpendicular to the plane of incidence is selectively reflected at the surface of each plate, whereas light with vibrations in the plane of

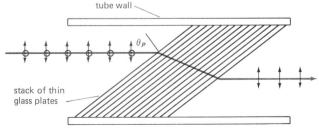

Fig. 35.26 Polarizer constructed from a stack of glass plates. The polarization is never complete.

Fig. 35.27 Radiation from a laser equipped with Brewster-angle windows is polarized.

incidence is selectively transmitted through each plate. By using a large number of plates we can obtain a transmitted light beam with vibrations predominantly in the plane of incidence. The reflected light can be effectively absorbed by the blackened wall of the mounting tube. Although the light transmitted through the stack of plates is never completely plane polarized, a stack of a large number of plates gives approximately complete polarization and can be used for many purposes as a polarizer or analyzer.

The light emitted from "ordinary sources" like the sun, flames, electric arcs, electric discharges through gases, and incandescent filaments is unpolarized. However, this is not necessarily the case for lasers, in which there is usually strong tendency toward polarization. In the case of a laser involving a gas discharge, light polarized in a selected plane can be produced by the scheme shown in Fig. 35.27. By equipping the discharge tube with windows mounted at the Brewster angle, light polarized perpendicular to the plane of the diagram is selectively removed from the "cavity" provided by the mirrors at the ends of the tube, while light polarized parallel to the plane of the diagram is transmitted by the windows. Because light with the perpendicular polarization is systematically removed, standing waves having this polarization do not build up in the cavity. Light emerging through the mirror at the right is therefore plane polarized, as suggested in the figure.

35.8   DOUBLE REFRACTION

Certain noncubic crystals like quartz or calcite have some rather interesting optical properties. If we place a polished calcite crystal on the printed page of a book and try to read a word through the crystal, we see not one printed word but two words slightly displaced from each other. If we place a polarizing plate on top of the calcite crystal and rotate the plate, we can for a certain orientation of the plate see only one of the two printed words; if we rotate the plate through 90° about an axis normal to the page, we see the other word. This property of calcite is called *double refraction*.

The property of double refraction can be understood from the schematic diagram in Fig. 35.28, which shows a ray of unpolarized light entering the lower surface of a crystal at normal incidence. One of the refracted rays proceeds through the crystal without deviation as would be expected from Snell's law; this ray is called the *ordinary ray* and is labeled O in the figure. The other ray experiences a sudden deviation to the right as it enters the crystal and then emerges from the upper surface along a normal to the surface; this second ray is called the *extraordinary ray* and is labeled E in the figure. By using a polarizing plate as an analyzer for the light emerging from the upper surface of the crystal, we find that light associated with the two rays has different planes of polarization as suggested in the figure. If we remove the analyzer and rotate the crystal about a vertical axis along the incident ray, we find that the extraordinary ray rotates in a circular path about the ordinary ray.

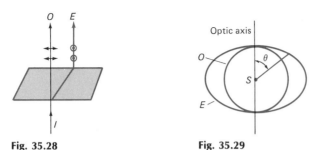

Fig. 35.28   Fig. 35.29

The phenomenon of double refraction can be interpreted on the wave theory of light if we assume that within the crystal light waves associated with the ordinary ray travel with equal speeds in all directions, whereas the light waves associated with the extraordinary ray travel with different speeds in different directions. This model is shown schematically in Fig. 35.29, which shows wave fronts emerging from a hypothetical point source S located inside a doubly refracting crystal. One wave front labeled O spreads spherically from S in quite *ordinary* fashion. However, the other wave front labeled E spreads from the source S in *extraordinary* fashion as an ellipsoid; because its speed varies with the angle θ in the figure, the E rays, representing the direction in which the energy of the E vibrations is transmitted, are not even normal to the advancing E wave front! In one *direction* in the crystal, corresponding to $\theta = 0$ in Fig. 35.29, the speeds of the O waves and E waves are equal; this direction is called the *optic axis* of the crystal and is indicated by the dotted line in the figure. It should be emphasized that the term "optic axis" refers to a *direction* within the crystal and not to a single line; thus any line parallel to the dotted line in Fig. 35.29 could also represent the optic axis. The speeds of E waves and O waves are the same when they travel parallel to the optic axis and differ by the greatest amount when they travel in a direction perpendicular to the optic axis.

The propagation of light in a doubly refracting crystal can be described in terms of Huygens wavelets provided we use spherical wavelets for the ordinary wave and ellipsoidal wavelets for the extraordinary wave. When a plane wave strikes at normal incidence a crystal cut with its optic axis perpendicular to the surface, as indicated in Fig. 35.30a, the wave fronts of E and O polarization remain together as the light travels through the crystal. If the plane wave enters a crystal cut at some angle θ to the optic axis as in Fig. 35.30b, there is a lateral displacement of the wave fronts inside the crystal as indicated by the rays; the O and E wave fronts emerging from the crystal are no longer in phase with each other. If a plane wave enters the face of a crystal cut like the one shown in Fig. 35.30c in a direction perpendicular to the optic axis, there is no lateral displacement of the E and O rays in the crystal but the wave fronts of the emerging plane waves with E and O polarization are not in phase with each other. If the E and O wave fronts of the same phase emerging from a crystal like the one in Fig. 35.30c are separated by a distance of $\lambda/4$, where λ is the vacuum wavelength of the light, the crystal is called a *quarter-wave plate;* if they are separated by $\lambda/2$, the crystal is called a *half-wave plate.*

Because of the phase difference between the E wave fronts and the O wave fronts emerging from a doubly refracting crystal, plane-polarized light entering the crystal

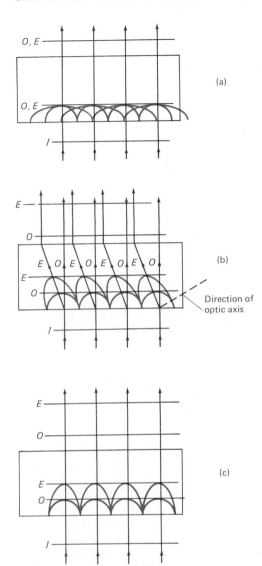

Fig. 35.30 Passage of a parallel light beam through a doubly refracting crystal. In (a) the beam is parallel to the optic axis; in (b) the beam makes an arbitrary angle with the optic axis; in (c) the beam is perpendicular to the optic axis.

may no longer be plane polarized when it leaves the crystal. The doubly refracting material splits the incident plane-polarized light into two plane-polarized components that become progressively farther out of phase for greater distances of propagation through the material. If we assume monochromatic incident light, the resultant electric field of the wave emerging from the doubly refracting material is a superposition of two perpendicular oscillations of the same frequency with relative amplitude and phase difference that depend on the orientation of the optic axis of the material relative to the initial polarization and propagation directions and on the thickness of the doubly refracting material traversed. For light traveling in the Z direction, the components of the electric-field strength for the emerging wave at a fixed location have the form $\mathscr{E}_x = \mathscr{E}_1 \cos 2\pi ft$ and $\mathscr{E}_y = \mathscr{E}_2 \cos (2\pi ft + \delta)$. One can show that under these conditions the terminus of the resultant electric-field strength vector at

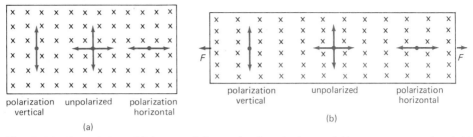

Fig. 35.31 Transmission of light toward the reader through sheets of (a) isotropic material and (b) anisotropic material.

a given location moves in an ellipse in a plane perpendicular to the direction of propagation. Such light is called *elliptically polarized light.*

For a quarter-wave plate, the phase difference between the electric-field components of the emerging wave is $\delta = \pm \pi/2$ radians. If the optic axis of the quarter-wave plate makes an angle of 45° with the plane of polarization of the incident light, the amplitudes $\mathscr{E}_1$ and $\mathscr{E}_2$ are equal. The emerging light is then *circularly polarized;* the terminus of the resultant $\mathscr{E}_R$ vector at a fixed location moves in a circle. A circularly polarized light beam is never completely absorbed by an analyzer. Why?

Some understanding of double refraction can be obtained from the atomic models shown in Fig. 35.31. We first emphasize that light is a form of electromagnetic radiation and that the "vibrations" in the light waves are really oscillations of the electric field $\mathscr{E}$ associated with the waves. When light traverses a sheet of homogeneous material in which the atoms are evenly spaced as suggested in Fig. 35.31a, the electric field $\mathscr{E}$ interacts with the atoms in the material in the same way for vertical and for horizontal vibrations. Because the speed of light transmission through a material is determined by these interactions, the speed of transmission of vertically and horizontally polarized light is the same. If, however, we distort the sheet of material by stretching it as in Fig. 35.31b, the lateral separation of its atoms becomes greater than their vertical separation. Therefore, vertical electric fields and horizontal electric fields interact with the atoms quite differently, and vertically polarized and horizontally polarized light beams will travel at different speeds through the distorted sheet, which is therefore doubly refracting.

Whenever a homogeneous material like a clear plastic is subjected to stresses, the strained regions of the material become doubly refracting. If we place an unstrained piece of plastic between two "crossed" polarizing plates serving as polarizer and analyzer as in Fig. 35.32a, no light is transmitted through the analyzer. However, if strains are produced in the piece of plastic, the plastic becomes doubly refracting; light transmitted through the strained material has its polarization altered and some light can pass through the analyzer. By constructing clear plastic models of the structural members to be used in the construction of buildings or machines, engineers can use an arrangement like the one shown in Fig. 35.32 to map the internal strains set up in the structural members when they are subjected to external forces. A photograph of a strained model of this type is shown in Fig. 35.32c. Engineers find these techniques, called *photoelasticity,* quite useful. Glassblowers frequently employ arrangements similar to the one in Fig. 35.32 to detect strains in glassware.

Because doubly refracting materials like other optical materials are dispersive, the

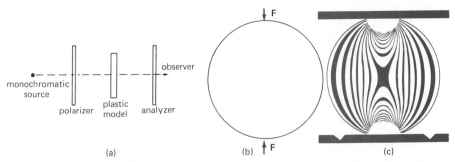

Fig. 35.32   (a) Schematic diagram of a photopolariscope. (b) Stress of a plastic model. (c) Photograph of the stressed model as viewed through the polariscope.

speeds of transmission of *O* waves and *E* waves in doubly refractive materials depend upon the wavelength of the incident light. The separation of the emerging *O* and *E* wave fronts in Fig. 35.30c is different for different wavelengths. Therefore, if we place a sample of clear colorless doubly refracting material between the polarizer and the analyzer in Fig. 35.32a and use an incandescent filament as the light source, the sample may appear to be brightly colored as the observer views it through the analyzer. If the observer rotates the analyzer, the color of the sample appears to change.

35.9   SCATTERING OF LIGHT

When a light beam traverses a path through a medium in which particles are suspended, the light beam becomes visible from the side; for example, if a narrow beam of sunlight enters a darkened room through a small hole in a window shade, its path is plainly visible if there are dust particles in the air. This type of "scattering" by relatively large particles is due largely to reflection of light at the surfaces of the particles.

However, if the suspended particles are so small that their diameters are comparable with the wavelengths of the incident light, a different type of scattering process occurs. This type of scattering involves not ordinary surface reflection but a kind of diffraction in which each particle in the light path behaves as if it were a secondary light source. The intensity of the scattered light beam varies inversely as the fourth power of the wavelength. Hence, if white light enters the medium in which small particles are suspended, more of the light near the violet end of the spectrum is scattered at right angles to the incident beam than is light near the red end of the visible spectrum. For violet light with a wavelength of 450 nm, eight times as much light is scattered as for red light of wavelength 750 nm because $(750/450)^4 \approx 8$. Therefore, a narrow beam of white light traversing a suspension of small particles appears bluish when viewed from the side because a preponderance of the scattered light is of short wavelength; it appears reddish when viewed along the beam in the direction of the source because less of the red and orange light has been scattered out of the beam. This effect can be noted when tobacco smoke is viewed in sunlight; the smoke appears blue-gray but its shadow has a reddish-gray tint.

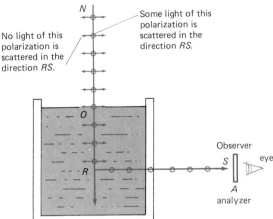

Fig. 35.33   Polarization of light by scattering.

The red color of the sun at sunrise and sunset is due to selective scattering by small particles in the air near the earth's surface and to scattering produced by small local variations in the molecular density of gases in the atmosphere. When the sun is at the horizon, the sunlight reaching an observer at the earth's surface has an effective path that is nearly 50 times as long as the path traversed by light moving vertically downward through the atmosphere. This longer path accentuates the effects of scattering by molecules and by small particles. The blue color of the sky can also be explained in terms of scattering. Just as the directly transmitted sunlight appears reddish because light at the blue end of the spectrum is scattered out of the beam, when we look away from the sun we see this selectively scattered blue light and the sky appears blue.

Examination of scattered light by use of a polarizing plate employed as an analyzer shows that light scattered by small particles is plane polarized. In order to determine the plane of polarization, consider the arrangement shown in Fig. 35.33. A beam of unpolarized light *NO* enters a liquid at normal incidence. If the liquid holds fine particles in suspension, some of the light will be scattered to an observer along path *RS*. By rotating the analyzer, the observer finds that the light reaching him is plane polarized with its electric-field vibrations $\mathscr{E}$ perpendicular to the plane of the paper, as indicated in the diagram. None of the light of the incident beam having its electric-field vector in the plane of the paper is scattered in the direction *RS* because the scattered wave must be transverse. The light is scattered by the particles without any change in the orientation of the electric-field vibrations. Similarly, blue light from the sky is polarized. It is completely plane polarized when the incident sunlight is scattered through an angle of 90° as in Fig. 35.33.

Optical scattering can be successfully accounted for in terms of classical electromagnetic theory. The particle responds to the wave's electrical oscillations $\mathscr{E} = \mathscr{E}_0 \sin (2\pi ft)$ by acquiring a varying dipole moment of the form $\alpha \mathscr{E}_0 \sin (2\pi ft)$, where α is the polarizability of the particle. Its varying dipole moment serves as the source of secondary waves.

QUESTIONS

1. What properties do light waves and sound waves have in common? What optical phenomenon indicates that they are basically different?

2. Does Young's experiment (Fig. 35.1) involve only diffraction, only interference, or both diffraction and interference? Answer this question for Fresnel's double-mirror experiment (Fig. 35.3). What is the difference between interference and diffraction?

3. A freshly prepared aluminum surface quickly becomes covered by a thin chemically inert layer of aluminum oxide Al_2O_3. Why is thin-film interference not observed at the surface of a front-surface aluminized mirror?

4. When a soap bubble in air becomes extremely thin, it becomes black just before it bursts. From this observation alone what can you conclude about the phase changes that occur at the two surfaces of the film? What additional information is provided by the Lloyd single-mirror experiment described in Problem 5?

5. A film of ethyl alcohol ($\mu = 1.354$) is on the surface of a flat plate of glass ($\mu = 1.523$). If this film is illuminated with sodium light, what will be its appearance as its thickness approaches zero because of evaporation?

6. Place two fingers a few centimeters in front of your eye and view the sky through the opening between your fingers. If you bring your fingers closer and closer together so that they nearly touch, the bright opening between your fingers appears to be crossed by dark lines parallel to your fingers. Explain why this occurs.

7. On a dark night, if you view a distant street light through a tightly stretched linen handkerchief, you will see not a single point source but a pattern of point sources. If you rotate the stretched handkerchief in front of your eye, the pattern rotates. Explain this phenomenon.

8. How do Fresnel and Fraunhofer diffraction differ?

9. Is coherence important in reflection? In refraction? In interference? In photometry? In radiometry? Give reasons for your conclusion in each case.

10. When a lens is coated by a thin layer of oxide to reduce reflection, what becomes of the radiant energy that was previously reflected? Does the oxide coating become hot as a result of absorption of the previously reflected light?

11. According to Prob. 34.55, the magnifying power of an astronomical telescope is given by the ratio f_O/f_E, where f_O is the focal length of the telescope objective and f_E is the focal length of the eyepiece. It would appear to be possible to increase the magnifying power almost without limit by using eye-pieces of smaller and smaller focal length. Why is it not possible to improve the ultimate performance of a telescope merely by increasing its magnifying power?

12. Give two reasons why it is desirable to make the objective lens or mirror of a telescope as large as possible. In all the largest astronomical telescopes, the objective consists of a parabolic mirror rather than an achromatic lens. What are some practical reasons for the use of mirrors rather than lenses as telescopic objectives at observatories?

13. If you had a *single* polarizing plate, is there any way in which you could determine its "polarization axis?"

14. The phenomenon of polarization was well known to Newton, who believed that it gave evidence that light particles were "different in their sides." Discuss this point of view.

How would you refute Newton's theory of polarization?

15. Can light inside glass be polarized by reflection at a glass–air interface?

16. If we regard light rays as mere indications of the direction of propagation, we can always make use of ray diagrams. What unusual features are involved if we attempt to describe the behavior of light in Fig. 35.29 in terms of rays?

17. If you placed a quarter-wave plate between two polarizing plates, what changes in intensity would you observe as you rotated the analyzer?

18. Why is the light from the clear sky polarized even when there are no dust particles in the air?

19. In the discussion of thin-film interference (Section 35.2) it is stated that the observer in Fig. 35.5 focuses his eye to view the *film* and not the reflected image of the source. Why is this important?

20. Why must the film be considered in Section 35.2 be *thin*? Won't the equations be just as valid for a "thick" film?

21. Why would one make a polarizer by using a stack of thin glass plates as in Fig. 35.26 to produce approximately complete polarization of the transmitted beam when with a *single* reflection at Brewster's angle we can produce complete polarization of the reflected beam?

PROBLEMS

1. A narrow slit S_0 used in a repetition of Young's experiment is illuminated by yellow light with a wavelength of 589 nm. If the separation of the source slits S_1 and S_2 (Fig. 35.1) is 0.2 mm and if the perpendicular distance to the screen is 3.0 m, what is the distance y from the central bright fringe to the nearest bright fringes on either side?

2. If monochromatic light of a different color is used in the experiment described in Problem 1, the distance between the central bright fringe and the nearest bright fringe on either side is observed to be 10.0 mm. What is the wavelength of the light?

3. In a Fresnel double-mirror experiment the separation of the virtual source slits S_1 and S_2 (Fig. 35.3) is 0.2 mm, the distance D to the screen is 70 cm, and the fringe separation on the screen is 1.75 mm. What is the wavelength of the monochromatic light used in the experiment?

4. In our derivation of (35.1) we made use of the diagram given in Fig. 35.2. In this figure, we show an angle θ subtended at a point midway between S_1 and S_2 such that $\tan \theta = y/D$. From (35.1) show that for the $n = 1$ bright fringe this implies that $\lambda/d = \tan \theta$. Is this really the case? What *geometrical* approximations are being made when we use (35.1)?

5. An interference experiment somewhat similar to Fresnel's double-mirror experiment is the so-called Lloyd single-mirror experiment performed with the arrangement shown schematically in the diagram, where the mirror is actually a flat glass surface. On the screen in the region where beams from the real source slit S and the virtual source slit S' overlap, interference fringes are observed. However, the central fringe in the pattern is a *dark* fringe in contrast to the central bright fringe obtained in the Fresnel double-mirror experiment. Why? Give a detailed explanation.

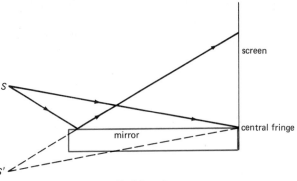

Problem 5

6. Interference between light from separate independent lasers can be detected if the observation is made in a sufficiently brief period of time. Suppose that two such lasers emit light of wavelength 600 nm and that fast instrumental observations show that interference patterns can be detected if the observation is made in a time less than 5 ns. What is the approximate length of the wave trains that remain coherent? Approximately how many waves are there in each such wave train?

7. If we assume that the "response time" of the eye in observing interference patterns is 0.1 s, what should be the approximate minimum length of the wave trains from the lasers mentioned in Problem 6 in order for interference to be observed directly? Approximately how many wavelengths would be involved in the wave trains?

8. In discussing interference in films, why is it necessary to insist that the films be *thin?* Yellow light from sodium vapor is not actually monochromatic, but consists of two wavelengths: 589.0 nm and 589.6 nm. What is the minimum thickness of a soap film ($\mu = 1.33$) in air that would appear bright for one of these wavelengths and dark for the other when the film is viewed by reflected light at near-normal incidence?

9. A soap film 672 nm thick is illuminated by white light and viewed by reflection at near-normal incidence. What wavelength gives constructive interference? What is the color of the film?

10. A thin layer of oil with a refractive index of 1.45 covers a plate of dense flint glass. If the thickness of the film is 400 nm, what is the color of the film when it is illuminated by white light and is viewed by reflection at angles near the normal to its surface?

11. The flatness of the surfaces of glass plates are tested by placing two such plates in contact along one edge, separating the other edge by a thin sheet of metal of thickness *d,* and observing the interference pattern when the thin air film between the plates is viewed by reflected monochromatic light. The arrangement is shown in the diagram. Show that if the plates are perfectly flat, a set of straight, parallel, uniformly spaced fringes will be observed when the air film is viewed by reflected light at angles near the normal to the plates. Obtain an expression for the

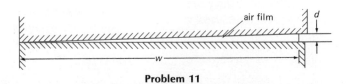

Problem 11

spacing of the fringes in terms of the plate separation d, the plate width w, and the wavelength λ of the light.

12. Explain how a nonreflecting coating can be applied to a glass plate. In some art galleries paintings are covered by glass plates coated in this way. The glass plates are very effective in eliminating "glare" due to undesirable reflection when the paintings are viewed from points directly in front but are less satisfactory when the paintings are viewed at oblique angles. Why?

13. In an arrangement similar to the one shown in Fig. 35.13 a lens with a focal length of 60 cm is used to form a diffraction pattern of a slit 0.3 mm wide. Calculate the distance on the screen from the center of the central maximum to the center of the first dark band and to the center of the next bright band when the slit is illuminated by yellow light with $\lambda = 589$ nm.

14. A parallel light beam like the one in Fig. 35.13 with wavelength 546 nm is incident on a slit 1 mm wide. If a lens with a focal length of 200 cm is mounted just behind the slit and the light is focused on a screen, what will be the distance on the screen from the central maximum of diffraction pattern to (a) the first minimum, (b) the first maximum, and (c) the third maximum? If the slit width were decreased to 0.5 mm, what would be the effect on the diffaction pattern?

15. In the Fraunhofer diffraction pattern of a single slit the distance from the first minimum on one side of the central maximum to the first minimum on the other side is 6.75 mm. If the wavelength of the light employed is 546 nm and the lens used to form the diffraction pattern has a focal length of 90 cm, what is the width of the slit?

16. In discussing the production of interference fringes by Fresnel's double-mirror technique (Fig. 35.3), we specified that slit S_0 be "narrow" so that the diffraction pattern of the slit on the screen will be very broad. Assuming that the distance D in Fig. 35.3 is suffi-

ciently large for the Fraunhofer treatment to apply to the diffraction pattern, discuss the effects of diffraction on the observed interference pattern. If the width of S_0 is 0.146 mm, the distance D is 90 cm, and the distance d is 0.75 mm, what is the appearance of the interference pattern observed for light of wavelength 546 nm?

17. If a slit like the one in Fig. 35.13 is illuminated by *white* light, the diffraction pattern consists of a bright central maximum on the screen with a few light and dark fringes on either side. However, as one proceeds outward from the central maximum the difference between the screen illumination at the bright and dark fringes decreases rapidly, so that the diffraction pattern appears to "smear out." Explain this effect.

18. What is the limit of angular resolution of the Mount Palomar telescope which employs as its objective a mirror 5 m in diameter? Use Rayleigh's criterion. What is the resolving power of this telescope?

19. What is the theoretical angular limit of resolution of the Yerkes telescope, which employs an objective lens 1 m in diameter? What is the resolving power of the Yerkes telescope?

20. When the moon is 360,000 km from the earth, what is the minimum separation of two craters on the lunar surface for them to be resolved by the Yerkes telescope described in Problem 19?

21. The pupil of the human eye is approximately 2 mm in diameter under conditions of moderate illumination. Considering the eye as a telescope, compute the eye's limit of angular resolution. What is the maximum distance of a scale from the eye at which millimeter markings on the scale can just be resolved? Is the resolving power of the eye greater at twilight or in the bright sunshine of high noon?

22. If a microscope is used with violet light ($\lambda = 450$ nm), how does its resolving

power compare with its resolving power when red light ($\lambda = 640$ nm) is being used?

23. A transmission grating has 5000 lines/cm. Calculate the angular deviation of the second-order image for sodium light of wavelength 589 nm when a parallel beam of light strikes the grating at normal incidence. Show a diagram.

24. When a parallel beam of sodium light $\lambda = 589$ nm strikes a transmission grating at normal incidence, the grating produces a diffraction pattern in which the third-order maximum appears at an angle of 60° away from the central image. What is the distance between lines on the grating?

25. Plane monochromatic waves of wavelength 500 nm are incident normally on a plane transmission grating having 5000 lines/cm. Find the angles at which the first-, second-, and third-order diffraction maxima appear.

26. A coarse transmission grating consists of a set of slits of width 1200 nm; the distance between the centers of adjacent slits is 2400 nm. When a beam of light of wavelength 600 nm strikes the grating at normal incidence, the first-order and third-order diffraction orders are observed, but the second-order is absent. Explain. Hint: Remember that each slit has a diffraction pattern of its own.

27. A transmission grating consists of slits 800 nm wide; the distance between the centers of adjacent slits is 2400 nm. Which grating diffraction orders are eliminated? How would the situation differ if the slits were only 400 nm wide? (See hint in Problem 26.)

28. Show that two perfect polarizing plates with axes making an angle θ with each other transmit $(1/2) \cos^2\theta$ of the beam intensity of an incident unpolarized beam.

29. Three perfect polarizing plates are stacked. The first and third are crossed; the one between them has its axis at 45° to the other two. Find the fraction of the beam intensity

of an incident unpolarized beam that is transmitted by the stack. How would this transmission of the stack be affected if the middle plate were continuously rotated between the outer two plates? Discuss.

30. Find the fraction of the intensity of an incident unpolarized beam that would be transmitted by the following stacks of perfect polarizing plates: (a) Four polarizing plates with the angle between the axes of successive plates equal to 30°. (b) Seven polarizing plates with the angle between the axes of successive plates equal to 15°.

31. Calculate the values of Brewster's angle for water, for crown glass, and for flint glass. Verify that the angle between the reflected ray at the Brewster angle and the refracted ray is in each case equal to 90°.

32. Show that the "partially plane-polarized" light reflected when a plane-polarized beam of light is incident at angles other than Brewster's angle at the surface of a transparent medium is actually elliptically polarized. What is the situation for an unpolarized incident beam? Explain how the plane-polarized light beam reflected at Brewster's angle can be used to establish the actual orientation of the "axis" of a polarizing plate.

33. Light of wavelength 550 nm is normally incident on a sheet of crystal quartz cut with its face parallel to the optic axis. The refractive index of quartz for one polarization is 1.553 and for the other 1.544. What are the two wavelengths of light in the crystal?

34. Determine the minimum thickness of a quarter-wave plate of quartz and the corresponding thickness of a half-wave plate of quartz for light having a wavelength of 550 nm in vacuum. (See Problem 33.)

35. Two polarizing plates are crossed. What happens when a half-wave plate is inserted between the polarizing plates? What happens when a quarter-wave plate is inserted between the polarizing plates? Discuss.

PART 6

MODERN PHYSICS

CHAPTER 36

Quantum Physics

This part of the book will be somewhat different. Whereas the previous parts of the book have presented basic principles of physics, this part, which deals with *modern quantum and relativistic physics* must, of necessity, be more descriptive and incomplete.

Earlier parts of this book have dealt with *mechanics, heat, sound, electromagnetism, and light:* what is known as *classical physics.* In terms of classical physics, the behavior of *matter on a macroscopic scale* under the conditions normally encountered on earth can be readily understood; predictions based on the classical principles of mechanics, thermodynamics and electromagnetism are valid when applied to macroscopic systems. Classical physics forms the basis on which most of engineering and much of laboratory science rests. Although we have on occasion made use of atomic and molecular models in gaining further insight into some of the macroscopic mechanical and thermal phenomena being discussed, most our treatment of the mechanical and thermal properties of matter would have been valid without the introduction of these models. Similarly, our treatment of electromagnetism would have been valid even if we had made no mention of electrons; in fact, at the time when the basic principles of electromagnetism were being formulated by Faraday and Maxwell, the existence of the electron had not been established.

In sharp contrast to classical physics, *modern quantum physics* deals with the properties of *matter on a microscopic scale;* i.e., on an atomic or subatomic scale. During the present century the science of physics has become divided and even subdivided into specialized fields such as atomic physics, molecular physics, solid-state physics, nuclear physics, and high-energy or elementary-particle physics. In a text of this kind it is impossible to treat each of these subjects. Instead, we shall merely discuss some of the development of the two new *theories* that account for the properties of matter on a microscopic scale. These two theories serve as guides to the understanding and interpretation of results obtained in the new specialized fields of physics.

Although we know from earlier chapters that an atom consists of an extremely small but massive positive nucleus surrounded by electrons, the electrons in their motions around the nucleus do not obey the laws of classical physics. The motions of these subatomic particles must be treated in terms of what is called *quantum mechanics*. In the present chapter we shall present some of the steps that led to the development of quantum mechanics, which had to be invented to replace classical theories in dealing with small particles like electrons and atoms. We shall not present the basic principles of modern quantum mechanics, which require more space for their elucidation than we have available.

The final chapter of the book deals with Einstein's theory of special relativity. We shall show how Einstein's theory led to predictions of previously unknown and unsuspected relations between mass and energy that have formed the basis of much of nuclear and high-energy physics.

The development of quantum physics and the development of relativistic physics are two of the greatest intellectual achievements of the 20th century. These two developments have led not only to a better understanding of the nature of the universe but also to the development many new technological processes and many practical devices like the transister, the laser, and the nuclear reactor. Any serious student of physical science or engineering will undoubtedly wish to pursue further studies of quantum and relativistic physics.

36.1 SPECTROSCOPY

The phenomena of reflection, refraction, and polarization of light can be interpreted reasonably satisfactorily in terms of electromagnetic waves. We now turn from these phenomena associated with transmission of light to a consideration of *emission* and *absorption*. Classical predictions regarding the emission and absorption of light by atoms and molecules have proved unsatisfactory.

The wavelengths present in a given beam of light can be measured by means of a grating mounted in an instrument of the type shown schematically in Fig. 36.1. Light from the source being investigated passes through a slit S, located in the focal plane of the collimating lens L_1 that is used to produce a parallel or collimated beam of light. The light in the collimated beam reaches the transmission grating G.

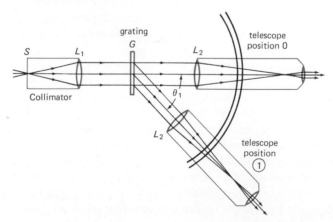

Fig. 36.1 A grating spectrograph.

Some of the light passes straight through the grating without deviation. The objective lens L_2 of the telescope at position O forms an image of the entrance slit; because light reaching the telescope consists of a parallel beam, the image is formed in the principal focal plane of the objective lens. This *central image* in the diffraction pattern has the same location for all wavelengths. If the source emits monochromatic light of wavelength λ, the *first-order* image of the slit will be formed by the telescope after it has been moved through the appropriate angle θ_1: $\sin \theta_1 = \lambda/d$, where d is the distance between adjacent slits on the grating. If the source emits light of several different wavelengths, images of the slit are formed in first order at a different value of θ_1 for each wavelength. Similarly, the telescope objective will form an image of the slit in various orders n for which $\sin \theta_n = n\lambda/d$. Because the "grating space" d was established when the grating was fabricated, the wavelengths in the spectrum can be determined directly from the relation $\lambda = d \sin \theta_n/n$ when the angle θ_n is measured.

Provided they are equipped with suitable detectors, spectrographs like that in Fig. 36.1 can be used to record infrared and ultraviolet spectra as well as visible spectra. Most of the grating spectrographs employed in research actually make use of reflection gratings. Instruments employed for use in the infrared region employ front-surface mirrors instead of lenses. In the ultraviolet and infrared, glass lenses cannot be employed because of the absorption of glass in these regions.

The spectrum of a source may consist of several or many spectral lines; such spectra are called *line spectra*. A "spectral line" does not really correspond to a single wavelength but represents the radiant power in a narrow band of wavelengths $\Delta\lambda$ centered at the nominal wavelength λ of the line. The linewidth $\Delta\lambda$ depends on the nature of the source.

Emission spectroscopy involves the systematic measurement of the radiant power per unit wavelength interval emitted under various conditions by various materials and the determination of relationships between the observed spectra and properties of the materials. The first *systematic* program of spectroscopy was initiated at Heidelberg in the 1860's by the physicist Kirchhoff and his colleague in chemistry R. W. Bunsen (1811–1899). They established some interesting empirical relationships between the properties of chemically pure materials and their characteristic spectra. We shall now summarize some of the results obtained by Kirchhoff and Bunsen and by later workers in studies of emission spectra.

Under conditions of low pressure, *the atoms of each chemical element have a characteristic line spectrum.* These spectra consist of numerous lines scattered through the spectrum in no easily recognized patterns. The simplest characteristic atomic spectrum is that of hydrogen shown in Fig. 36.2; the lines are unevenly spaced, but seem to converge to a limit in the near ultraviolet.

Under conditions of low pressure, *the molecules of each diatomic and polyatomic chemical compound have a characteristic band spectrum.* For some relatively simple compounds a typical band consists of numerous closely spaced lines that can be resolved from one another; the spectrum of cyanogen, CN, in the visible region is shown in the spectrogram of Fig. 36.3. For more complex molecules the emission bands may have little or no observable line structure.

When an opaque solid such as iron or tungsten is heated to incandescence, it has a continuous spectrum. At increasingly high pressure, the emission lines of atomic

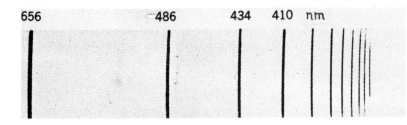

Fig. 36.2 A photograph of the emission spectrum of atomic hydrogen in the visible region. Such a photograph can be obtained by placing film in the focal plane of lens L_2 in Fig. 37.1.

or molecular gases become increasingly broad and at enormous pressures continuous spectra are observed.

No satisfactory explanation of the observed relations between the excited source and the characteristic line and band spectra emitted can be obtained on the basis of classical physics.

When a beam of light passes through a material, some of the light is absorbed. The absorption by a homogeneous material can be described by a simple relationship known as Lambert's law after Johann Heinrich Lambert (1728–1777), although it was actually first stated by the French scientist Pierre Bouguer (1698–1758) in 1729. We assume that the change dI in the intensity of the beam as it passes through a thin layer of thickness dx is proportional to the intensity I of the beam and to dx, and depends on the properties of the medium; that is, $dI = -\alpha I\ dx$, where dI is negative because the beam intensity decreases. The quantity α is called the absorption coefficient of the medium. Integration leads to the expression

$$I = I_0 e^{-\alpha x},$$

where I_0 is the intensity of the incident beam and I is the intensity of the beam after the light has traveled a distance x through the absorbing medium. It turns out that I, I_0, and α depend on the wavelength of the radiation involved, so that Lambert's relation can be written more properly in the form

$$I(\lambda) = I_0(\lambda)e^{-\alpha(\lambda)x}. \quad (Lambert's\ Law) \tag{36.1}$$

The experimental problem of absorption spectroscopy is the determination of $\alpha(\lambda)$ as a function of λ.

An experimental arrangement for absorption spectroscopy is shown schematically in Fig. 36.4. Light from an incandescent source is directed by lenses or mirrors through an empty absorption cell to the entrance slit S of a spectrograph, which maps the continuous emission spectrum $I_0(\lambda)$ versus λ of the source. Then the absorp-

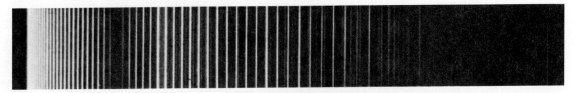

Fig. 36.3 Emission spectrum of a molecule.

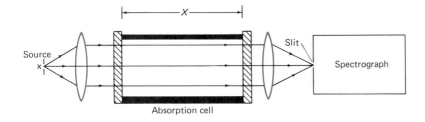

Fig. 36.4 Experimental arrangement for absorption measurements.

tion cell is filled with the homogeneous absorbing medium and the resulting spectrum $I(\lambda)$ versus λ is mapped by the spectrograph. The ratio $I(\lambda)/I_0(\lambda)$ gives the fractional transmission of the material in the cell; from this the Lambert absorption coefficient $\alpha(\lambda)$ can be obtained.

Kirchhoff and Bunsen along with others concluded that the absorption spectra of chemical elements vaporized in atomic form at low pressure are characterized by *absorption lines,* that molecules are characterized by *absorption bands,* and that opaque solids have *continuous absorption spectra.* Comparison of observed absorption and emission spectra revealed that many of the characteristic absorption lines or bands coincided with the characteristic emission lines or bands of the same material.

36.2 BLACKBODY RADIATION

By considering a small body in *thermal equilibrium* inside a cavity, Kirchhoff showed that the ratio of the spectral radiant emittance $R(\lambda)$ of the body to its spectral absorption coefficient $\alpha(\lambda)$ for radiation in the wavelength range λ to $\lambda + d\lambda$ at any temperature is equal to the spectral radiant emittance $R(\lambda)_{BB}$ of a blackbody at the same temperature. Thus,

$$R(\lambda) = \alpha(\lambda)R(\lambda)_{BB}. \quad \textit{(Kirchhoff's Radiation Principle)} \quad (36.2)$$

Therefore, if the spectral radiant emittance of a blackbody at a given temperature is known for all wavelengths, the spectral radiant emittance of any other body at this same temperature can be calculated in terms of its spectral absorption coefficient at this temperature.

We must emphasize that Kirchhoff's radiation principle applies only to *thermal radiation;* that is, the radiation that a body emits by virtue of its own temperature. For example, it applies to the radiation emitted by a hot tungsten filament in a light bulb but does not apply to radiation from the fluorescent tube of a modern light fixture or to the radiation emitted by a firefly as a result of chemiluminescence.

In view of Kirchhoff's radiation principle, a great deal of attention was devoted to experimental measurement of the emission spectrum of a blackbody. In a long series of careful, painstaking experiments the German physicists Otto Lummer (1860–1925) and Ernst Pringsheim (1859–1917) and others determined the form of the $R(\lambda)_{BB}$-versus-λ curves for blackbodies at different temperatures. Examples of these blackbody radiation curves are shown in Fig. 36.5. Several features of these curves should be pointed out.

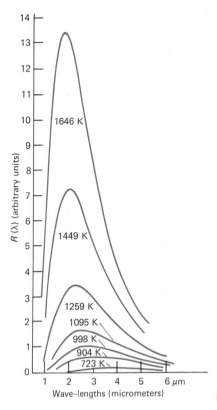

Fig. 36.5 Blackbody radiation curves.

First of all, the curves never cross. At every wavelength λ the radiant emittance $R(\lambda)_{BB}$ for one temperature is higher than $R(\lambda)_{BB}$ for all lower temperatures. Second, the wavelength λ_{max} at which $R(\lambda)_{BB}$ is a maximum shifts toward shorter wavelengths as the temperature is increased; in fact, there is a relation called Wien's displacement law which states that

$$T\lambda_{max} = \text{constant.} \quad \textit{(Wien's Displacement Law)} \quad (36.3)$$

This was established in 1893 by Wilhelm Wien (1864–1928), who devoted a great deal of attention to interpretations of the blackbody radiation curves. Third, we note that the total radiant emittance R_{BB} for a given temperature equals the area under the appropriate curve in Fig. 36.5. However, R_{BB} is also given by the Stefan–Boltzmann law (Chapter 14): $R_{BB} = \sigma T^4$. Therefore,

$$\int_0^\infty R(\lambda)_{BB}\, d\lambda = \sigma T^4. \quad \textit{(Stefan–Boltzmann Law)} \quad (36.4)$$

All attempts to derive the observed blackbody radiation curves from classical physics have resulted in failure. Wien derived a semiempirical classical expression that gave $R(\lambda)_{BB}$ in fair approximation for short wavelengths but failed at long wavelengths. Lord Rayleigh (1842–1919) derived a quite different classical expression that gave $R(\lambda)_{BB}$ in fair approximation for long wavelengths but failed for short wavelengths.

Beginning with the Wien and the Rayleigh expressions for $R(\lambda)_{BB}$, the German theoretical physicist Max Planck (1858–1947) in 1900 obtained the following formula that gives a completely satisfactory description of the experimental results:

$$R(\lambda)_{BB} = \frac{2\pi hc^2}{\lambda^5 (e^{hc/\lambda kT} - 1)}, \quad \textit{(Planck's Radiation Law)} \qquad (36.5)$$

which gives $R(\lambda)_{BB}$ in W/m² · m when λ is the wavelength in *meters*, $c = 2.997\,925 \times 10^8$ m/s is the speed of light, $k = 1.3805 \times 10^{-23}$ J/K is *Boltzmann's constant*, $h = 6.6256 \times 10^{-34}$ J·s is *Planck's constant*, and $e = 2.718\,28$ is the base of natural logarithms.

The validity of the Planck formula (36.5) seems to be perfect. However, its original formulation seems to have involved some lucky guesses along with the introduction of a new constant h, which had never been needed before. Having recognized that his new law was in excellent agreement with experiment, Planck set about to find a theoretical basis for it and within a few weeks succeeded. It follows from (36.2) that in thermal equilibrium the density of the radiant energy of a given wavelength λ or frequency f inside an enclosure does not depend on the nature of the bodies inside the enclosure. Planck chose one of the simplest possible models for these bodies: harmonic oscillators. He then showed that (36.5) can be derived in a systematic way from classical electromagnetic theory and thermodynamics if one makes the following *assumption:* An oscillator vibrating with frequency f can take on only one of the energy values $E_0, 2E_0, 3E_0, \ldots$, where $E_0 = hf$. Thus, in deriving the correct blackbody radiation law, Planck found it necessary to introduce the concept of a *quantum of energy $E_0 = hf$*, which represents the smallest amount of energy that an oscillator with frequency f can emit or absorb. The need for introducing such a quantum of energy was a complete contradiction to the laws of classical physics, which place no restriction on the amount of energy an oscillator can emit or absorb.

The introduction of this new concept therefore amounts to the formulation of a new principle of physics now called:

PLANCK'S QUANTUM PRINCIPLE: Radiation of frequency f can be emitted or absorbed only in a discrete quantity or quantum $E_0 = hf$.

36.3 PARTICLE NATURE OF RADIATION

One of the first scientists to recognize that Planck's principle had initiated a new era in physics was the youthful Albert Einstein, then a patent examiner in the Swiss Patent Office, who was nearly unknown to other scientists of the time. In 1905 Einstein published the first paper in which Planck's principle was given serious consideration. A part of his paper was concerned with the frequency distribution of radiant energy inside an enclosure of volume V under equilibrium conditions. We can understand some of the ideas involved by considering N particles inside a box of volume V. If we have a single molecule in the box, the probability of this particle being inside some small volume ΔV within the box is simply $\Delta V/V$. If the box contains N independent particles, the probability of *all* the particles being in the smaller volume is $(\Delta V/V)^N$.

In his 1905 paper Einstein considered the distribution of the radiant energy inside an enclosure of volume V in thermal equilibrium at temperature T. If $E(f)$ represents the total radiant energy associated with radiation of frequency in the range f to $f + df$, Einstein found that for $hf \gg kT$ the probability P of *all* the radiant energy being in some smaller volume ΔV inside the enclosure is given by the relation

$$P = (\Delta V/V)^{E(f)/hf}. \qquad (36.6)$$

Comparison of this result with the result stated above for particles in a box indicates that the exponent $E(f)/hf$ is analogous to the number N of particles in the box. In view of this analogy, Einstein proposed that the total radiant energy $E(f)$ inside the enclosure was simply the sum of the energies hf of light quanta inside the enclosure. In other words, he proposed that

$$E(f) = Nhf, \qquad (36.7)$$

where N is the total number of quanta inside the enclosure. This is a very important concept and indicates that the electromagnetic field inside an enclosure is quantized. Planck himself did not like this idea; although he himself had proposed that energy could be added to or removed from the field in quanta hf, he preferred to regard the radiation itself as composed of continuous classical waves.

In view of the phenomena of interference and diffraction, we know that light does indeed have wave properties. In 1909 Einstein made a more general study of energy fluctuations inside an isothermal enclosure at a temperature T. If E represents the amount of energy inside some small region of the enclosure of volume ΔV associated with radiation in the frequency range f to $f + df$, the simplest measure of energy fluctuations is given by

$$\overline{(\Delta E)^2} \quad \overline{(E - \bar{E})^2} ,$$

where the bars denote time averages. Einstein showed that

$$\overline{(\Delta E)^2} = hf\bar{E} + \bar{E}^2/Z, \qquad (36.8)$$

where $Z = 8\pi\Delta V f^2 \, df/c^3$. The term $hf\bar{E}$ is the value $\overline{(\Delta E)^2}$ would have if the radiation actually consisted entirely of particles with energy hf. This is so because by the use of (36.7) we can set $\overline{\Delta E^2} = (hf)^2 \, \overline{\Delta n^2}$, where n is the number of light particles in the small region being considered, and a straightforward statistical argument can be used to show that $\overline{\Delta n^2} = \bar{n}$ so that $\overline{\Delta E^2} = (hf)^2\bar{n} = hf\bar{E}$. The term $\bar{E}^2/Z$ can be shown to be the value that $\overline{(\Delta E)^2}$ would have if the radiation consisted entirely of waves. Therefore, (36.8) can be expressed in the form

$$\overline{(\Delta E)^2} = \overline{(\Delta E)^2}_{\text{particles}} + \overline{(\Delta E)^2}_{\text{waves}}. \qquad (36.8')$$

Equation (36.8') is a statement of what is called *wave–particle duality*.

In view of (36.8) and (36.8′) we have to conclude that light has *some* particle properties and *some* wave properties. For radiation of low frequency and long wavelength, consideration of (36.8) indicates that the wave properties are dominant. For radiation of high frequency and short wavelength the particle properties are dominant in (36.8). The particle properties of radiation of very high frequency are so pronounced that the entities possessing quantum energy *hf* are usually called *photons*. The terms *quantum* and *photon* are frequently used as synonyms to denote "light particles." The term *photon* was initially proposed by the American chemist G. N. Lewis (1875–1946).

36.4 THE PHOTOELECTRIC EFFECT

The conduction electrons remain inside a metal because of a surface potential barrier V_s. If the temperature of the metal is raised sufficiently high, some of the electrons acquire sufficient energy to penetrate the barrier and escape. However, electrons can escape from a cold metal when it is illuminated with ultraviolet light. This phenomenon is known as the *photoelectric effect* and was discovered in 1887 by Heinrich Hertz, who noticed that a spark would jump more readily between two charged metal spheres when their surfaces were illuminated by light from another spark. On the basis of classical physics, it was predicted that the kinetic energy of the escaping electrons should depend on the intensity of the radiation striking the surface, but experiments showed that this classical prediction was invalid.

The photoelectric effect was treated in Einstein's 1905 paper. In his treatment of the problem, Einstein proposed that a quantum model must be used to treat the ejection of electrons from a metal by a light beam. When a photon strikes the surface of a metal, its entire energy $E = hf$ is delivered to a *single* conduction electron within the metal, where the conduction electrons have essentially constant potential energy. After acquiring the photon energy, the electron inside the metal has increased kinetic energy; if the electron is moving toward the surface, its newly acquired energy allows it to escape provided its acquired energy *hf* is equal to or greater than the energy required for the electron to move through the potential barrier at the surface. If eV_s represents the energy required for the most energetic electrons of the metal to move through the surface, then the Einstein photoelectric equation embodying these ideas is

$$hf = (1/2)mv_{max}^2 + eV_s, \tag{36.9}$$

where v_{max} is the maximum speed of electrons *after* the escape through the surface of the metal. Other electrons escaping through the surface may have smaller speeds of escape. In the next decade R. A. Millikan, who began his work as a doubter of the whole idea, conducted a set of definitive experiments that fully confirmed the validity of the theory proposed by Einstein.

In his experiments Millikan illuminated a clean metallic surface in an evacuated enclosure with light of different frequencies and determined the "retarding potential" required to prevent the ejected electrons from reaching a second nearby electrode inside the enclosure.

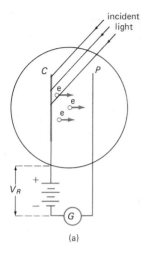

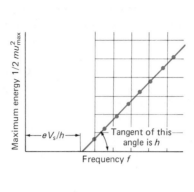

Fig. 36.6 Photoelectric effect: (a) Schematic diagram of apparatus. (b) Plot of Millikan's results.

(a)

(b)

A schematic diagram of Millikan's experimental arrangement is given in Fig. 36.6a. When the test electrode C was illuminated by light of sufficiently high frequency, electrons ejected produced a current between C and the nearby plate electrode P. By applying the retarding potential V_R, Millikan was able to reduce the current; the minimum value of V_R' required to reduce the current to zero provided a measure of the maximum kinetic energy of electrons escaping from the metal: $(1/2)mv_{max}^2 = eV_R'$. Figure 36.6b gives a plot of Millikan's results; in this figure $(1/2)mv_{max}^2$ as determined by the retarding potential V_R' is plotted as a function of the frequency f of the incident light. The data display the linear relation expected from (36.9):

$$(1/2)mv_{max}^2 = hf - eV_s. \qquad (36.9')$$

The "work function" or surface barrier is given by $V_s = hf_T/e$, where f_T is the threshold frequency of light just able to cause electrons to emerge from the metal. The slope of the curve in the figure is equal to Planck's constant h. Millikan's careful experiments fully confirmed the validity of Einstein's predictions.

The *number* of electrons ejected from a metal-like electrode C in Fig. 36.6a is determined by the number of photons striking the metal. For a fixed value of V_R the current between electrodes P and C is found to be proportional to the intensity of the light beam striking C. Therefore, the intensity of the light beam is determined by the number of photons transferred per unit time. Regardless of beam intensity, the maximum kinetic energy of the ejected electrons is that given by (36.9').

36.5   SPECIFIC HEAT CAPACITY OF SOLIDS

In Chapter 16 (Problem 20) we pointed out that at room temperature the heat capacity per kilomole C_V has a value of approximately $3R$ for most chemically pure metals. Experiment shows that C_V for these metals becomes less than $3R$ as the temperature is decreased and becomes very small at extremely low temperatures. Because classical theory predicts the value of $3R$ for all temperatures, the observed variation of C_V with temperature constituted a puzzle.

In 1907 Einstein supplied a solution to the problem by employing quantum considerations. If Planck's quantization of the energy of a harmonic oscillator is correct, this quantization ought to have an important bearing on the heat capacities of solids, which are associated with atoms vibrating about equilibrium positions in the crystal lattice. On the basis of classical physics, each atom vibrates as a three-dimensional oscillator with average thermal energy kT associated with each of the three modes of oscillation; the total average thermal energy of each atom is thus $3kT$. The thermal energy of one kilomole would thus be $U = N_A 3kT = 3RT$, where N_A is Avogadro's number. The classical value of the heat capacity per kilomole is $C_V = dU/dT = 3R$, which is the actual value at high temperatures but not at low temperatures.

In his approach to the problem, Einstein chose an extremely simple model of a solid in which the atoms have three-dimensional oscillation about their equilibrium positions at a single frequency f_0. Einstein proposed that each of the three independent modes of oscillation is represented by a quantized Planck oscillator with allowed energies of $E_0 = hf_0$, $2E_0$, $3E_0$, . . . , etc. He showed that the average thermal energy of a three-dimensional oscillator of this type is given by the expression

$$E_{AV} = \frac{3hf_0}{e^{(hf_0/kT)} - 1}.$$

The thermal energy per kilomole of a solid of this type is given by $U = N_A E_{AV}$, where N_A is Arogadro's number, and the heat capacity per kilomole is $C_V = dU/dT$. From the value of E_{AV} given above we find that C_V has the following value:

$$C_V = 3R \left(\frac{hf_0}{kT}\right)^2 \frac{e^{hf_0/kT}}{(e^{hf_0/kT} - 1)^2}. \tag{36.10}$$

The value of C_V as given by this equation approaches $3R$ as the ratio hf_0/kT becomes very small; thus at sufficiently high temperatures the value of C_V given by (36.10) is the same as the value given by classical physics. However, as the value of hf_0/kT increases, C_V becomes less than $3R$ and approaches 0 as $T \rightarrow 0$ K. This variation of C_V is shown in Fig. 36.7, where C_V is plotted as a function of kT/hf_0.

Although Einstein's model of a solid is admittedly too crude, particularly in using a single frequency f_0 to describe all the vibrations of the atoms in the solid, the form of the curve shown in Fig. 36.7 is in general agreement with experimental results. The value of C_V does indeed approach zero at absolute zero. More realistic models of solids have been developed by theorists and have given results in general agreement with Einstein's value as given in (36.10) and in better agreement with experiment.

36.6 EMPIRICAL SPECTROSCOPIC RELATIONSHIPS

The spectroscopists in the closing decades of the 19th century and the first decades of the 20th century were amassing enormous quantities of new information regarding the emission and absorption spectra of atoms. We have indicated that the atomic spectra of the elements consist of large numbers of lines. There are no frequency

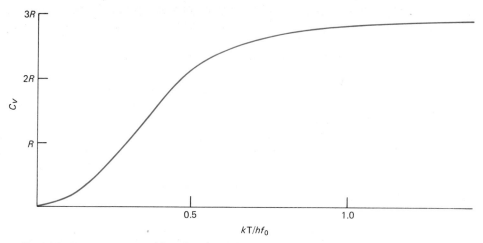

Fig. 36.7 Heat capacity per kilomole as given by Einstein's quantum theory.

sequences of the type to be expected from harmonic oscillators or other classical oscillating systems; much time and effort was spent in looking for such sequences, all to no avail. The first successful empirical relationship between the observed lines in an atomic spectrum was discovered in 1885 by Johann Jakob Balmer (1825–1898). Balmer found that the frequencies of the lines of hydrogen in the visible region (Fig. 36.2) can be given by a simple equation of the form $f = cR(1/4 - 1/n^2)$, where $n = 3, 4, 5, 6, \ldots$; c is the speed of light in vacuum; and R is a constant now called the Rydberg constant that has the value 10 967 758 m^{-1}. Balmer actually wrote his formula in terms of wavelengths rather than frequencies. Johannes Robert Rydberg (1854–1919) was a Swedish scientist who made major contributions to the mathematical organization of atomic spectral data. The frequencies of the lines in the hydrogen series in Fig. 36.2, now called the *Balmer series,* converge to a limit $cR/4$ as n becomes very large.

The success of Balmer's empirical equation in expressing the frequencies of the visible lines of hydrogen by a simple formula led to the search for other sets of hydrogen lines in other parts of the electromagnetic spectrum on the basis of tentative predictions based on Balmer's formula. This search was successful and led to the discovery of the following sets of hydrogen lines, which have been named after their discoverers:

Series	Equation	Spectral Region
Lyman	$f = cR(1/1^2 - 1/n^2)$ with $n = 2, 3, 4, \ldots$	Ultraviolet
Balmer	$f = cR(1/2^2 - 1/n^2)$ with $n = 3, 4, 5, \ldots$	Visible
Paschen	$f = cR(1/3^2 - 1/n^2)$ with $n = 4, 5, 6, \ldots$	Infrared
Brackett	$f = cR(1/4^2 - 1/n^2)$ with $n = 5, 6, 7, \ldots$	Infrared
Pfund	$f = cR(1/5^2 - 1/n^2)$ with $n = 6, 7, 8, \ldots$	Infrared
Humphreys	$f = cR(1/6^2 - 1/n^2)$ with $n = 7, 8, 9, \ldots$	Infrared

These series encompass the entire hydrogen spectrum as it has been observed in the laboratory; additional series of hydrogen lines have been observed in the microwave and radio regions by radio astronomers, who have studied the spectrum of the hydrogen in interstellar space. Note that a single empirical value of R is used in all the equations given above.

We note that all the hydrogen-atom spectral frequencies can be expressed as differences between quantities of the form cR/n^2 and cR/m^2, where n and m are integers. These quantities are called spectral *term values*. Spectroscopists began to look for term values in the spectra of other atoms. It was found that the enormous numbers of lines in the spectrum of any atom can be expressed as the differences between a much smaller number of term values that can be determined empirically for the atom in question. The term values for other atoms cannot be expressed quite so simply as those for hydrogen, but in many cases they can be written in the form $cR/(n + \alpha)^2$, where n is an integer, α is an empirical constant, and R is very nearly the same for all atoms.

36.7 BOHR'S THEORY OF STATIONARY STATES: RADIATIVE TRANSITIONS

Einstein's success in applying quantum theory to problems that were insoluble in terms of classical physics could not long be ignored by other physicists. In 1913 the young Danish theoretical physicist Niels Bohr (1885–1962) applied quantum considerations to the interpretation of atomic spectra. Ernest Rutherford (1871–1937) had in 1911 demonstrated that an atom has a small nucleus of mass nearly equal to that of the entire atom and with a charge $+Ze$ and that the positive nucleus was surrounded by Z electrons in orbital motion of some kind around the nucleus. However, on the basis of classical physics an atom of this kind is inherently unstable; because of their accelerated motion, the electrons emit radiation and spiral in toward the nucleus.

Bohr proposed that atoms can exist in any one of a set of *stationary energy states* without emitting radiation. According to Bohr's hypothesis, radiation is emitted or absorbed by an atom only when it makes a radiative transition from one stationary state to another. Thus, if levels E_m and E_n in Fig. 36.8 represent two stationary states, when radiation is absorbed the atom undergoes a transition from the initial state of lower energy E_m to the state of higher energy E_n; similarly, if the atom is initially excited and in the upper state E_n, it can reach the state of lower energy E_m by the emission of radiation.

According to Bohr's theory, such transitions involve the absorption or emission of a photon of energy $E = hf_{mn}$ equal to the difference between the energies of the stationary energy levels:

$$hf_{mn} = E_m - E_n \quad \textit{(Bohr's Frequency Relation)}. \tag{36.11}$$

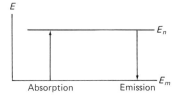

Fig. 36.8 Radiative transitions between stationary energy states.

Although this relation represented a bold assumption when it was first proposed, it remains valid today even after many subsequent developments in quantum physics.

The empirical spectroscopic *term values* discussed in Section 36.6 can be readily interpreted in terms of Bohr's frequency relation. The energies of the allowed stationary states of an atom are simply h multiplied by the empirical term values; the quantum energy of the photon emitted or absorbed when a radiative transition occurs is simply the difference between energies of the stationary states involved. On this basis, we can construct an *energy-level diagram* for hydrogen of the type shown in Fig. 36.9. The horizontal lines represent allowed energy levels of the atom. The energy E_n of each level is simply $-hcR/n^2$, where n is called the quantum number of the level and takes the integral values $n = 1, 2, 3, 4, \ldots$. The energy is negative because, following the usual convention of electrostatics, we take the zero of potential energy to correspond to infinite separation of the proton and electron. The energy $hf_{nn'}$ of the photon emitted or absorbed in a radiative transition between levels n and n' is the difference between E_n and $E_{n'}$. The observed spectral series are indicated in the diagram. Because the difference in energy between the lowest level E_1 and the other levels is large as compared with kT at room temperature, nearly all hydrogen atoms in thermal equilibrium at room temperature are in the lowest level E_1, which is called the *ground state* of the atom. In thermal equilibrium at temperature T the number of atoms in an upper level E_n is given by the Boltzmann relation (Chapter 15) $N_n = N_1 e^{-(E_n - E_1)/kT}$, where N_1 is the number in the ground state E_1.

Because only the lowest energy level E_1 has an appreciable population at room

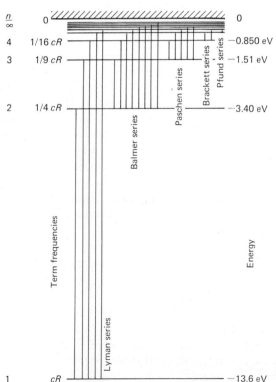

Fig. 36.9 Energy-level diagram for the hydrogen atom.

temperature, only the Lyman series will be observed in the absorption spectrum of cold hydrogen atoms. However, if the hydrogen is in an electrical discharge tube, the energies of some of the atoms will be raised to the upper "excited states" E_2, E_3, E_4, ... Various hydrogen series appear in the resulting emission spectrum as the atoms make downward radiative transitions to the lower levels as in the energy-level diagram in Fig. 36.9. The general ideas involved in Bohr's interpretation of the spectrum of atomic hydrogen worked equally well when applied to the spectra of other atoms for which empirical term values had been determined.

36.8 BOHR'S MODEL OF THE HYDROGEN ATOM

Although Bohr's ideas regarding the existence of stationary atomic energy states and radiative transitions between them proved basically correct, there was no way to account for the existence of these states in terms of classical physics or in terms of the quantum physics known in 1913. In order to provide some understanding of the problem, Bohr proposed a simple model of the hydrogen atom in which the electron moved in classical circular orbits around the proton—subject to *one additional arbitrary condition introduced to quantize the motion.* Although the Bohr model has been superceded, we can still learn something by examining its properties.

Bohr's quantum assumption was that the total orbital angular momentum L of the atom was restricted to integral multiples of $h/2\pi$; thus,

$$L_n = nh/2\pi. \quad \textit{(Bohr's Quantum Condition)} \tag{36.12}$$

Because $L = pr = mvr$, this quantum condition imposes certain restrictions on the orbital speed v of the electron and the radius of its orbit around the central proton. These restrictions result in definite allowed values E_n of the atomic energy states. Bohr's quantum condition gives the correct energies for the allowed states in hydrogen and also gives a value for the radius r_1 of the electron orbit when the atom is in its ground state E_1 that is in general agreement with the sizes of atoms and molecules based on the kinetic theory of gases.

Let us first compute the allowed values of the atomic radius of hydrogen. The magnitude of the Coulomb force of *attraction* between a proton of charge $+e$ and an electron of charge $-e$ separated by a distance r is

$$F = \frac{1}{4\pi\epsilon_0} \frac{e^2}{r}.$$

For an electron of mass m moving in a circular orbit of radius r about the proton, we can equate this force to the mass m of the electron times the centripetal acceleration $a_c = v^2/r$. Thus, $F = mv^2/r = m^2v^2r^2/mr^3 = p^2r^2/mr^3 = L^2/mr^3$. Here $p = mv$ is the momentum of the electron and $L = mvr$ is the angular momentum of the atom; we are ignoring any motion of the relatively massive proton that serves as the nucleus of the atom. Substituting these values along with (36.12) in the equation $F = ma_c$, we obtain

$$\frac{1}{4\pi\epsilon_0}\frac{e^2}{r_n^2} = \frac{L^2}{mr_n^3} = \frac{n^2h^2/4\pi^2}{mr_n^3} = n^2\left(\frac{h^2}{4\pi^2mr_n^3}\right).$$

Solution of this equation for the allowed values of r_n gives

$$r_n = n^2\left(\frac{\epsilon_0 h^2}{\pi m e^2}\right). \tag{36.13}$$

Substituting the known values of ϵ_0, h, e, and m, we obtain

$$r_n = n^2(5.292 \times 10^{-11} \text{ m}) = n^2(0.052\ 92 \text{ nm}).$$

For $n = 1$, the radius r_1 of the Bohr atom is thus about 0.05 nm and is in agreement with the size of the hydrogen atom to be expected on the basis of kinetic theory. The radii of the allowed electron orbits are given by n^2r_1 and thus take the values $r = r_1$, $4r_1$, $9r_1$, $16r_1$, etc. The size of the atom increases rapidly as the atom becomes excited, as indicated in Fig. 36.10.

We now turn to a computation of the energies associated with these orbits. Taking the arbitrary reference level of potential energy as zero when the distance between the proton and the electron is infinite, we write the potential energy of the atom in the form predicted by classical electrostatic theory:

$$E_P = -\frac{1}{4\pi\epsilon_0}\frac{e^2}{r}. \tag{36.14}$$

The kinetic energy of the atom is merely that of the electron in its orbital motion: $E_K = (1/2)mv^2$. However, we can write $(1/2)mv^2 = (1/2)m^2v^2r^2/mr^2 = (1/2)L^2/mr^2$. Thus, introducing Bohr's quantum condition (36.12), we can write

$$E_K = \frac{1}{2}\frac{L_n^2}{mr_n^2} = \frac{1}{2}\frac{n^2h^2/4\pi^2}{m(n^4\epsilon_0^2h^4/\pi^2m^2e^4)} = \frac{me^4}{8n^2h^2\epsilon_0^2}.$$

Entering the allowed values r_n in (36.14), we obtain

$$E_P = -\frac{me^4}{4\ n^2h^2\epsilon_0^2}.$$

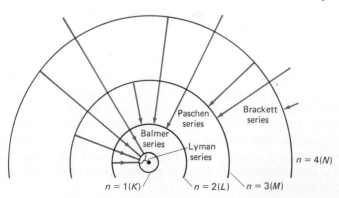

Fig. 36.10 Bohr model of the hydrogen atom.

The total energy of the atom in state n is, therefore,

$$E_n = E_P + E_K = -\frac{1}{n^2}\left(\frac{me^4}{8\,h^2\epsilon_0^2}\right) = -\frac{2.180 \times 10^{-18}}{n^2}\,\text{J}.\qquad (36.15)$$

Comparison of (36.15) with the value $E_n = -hcR/n^2$ based on the empirical relations discovered by Balmer shows that the empirical value of the Rydberg constant can be *calculated* in terms of e, m, h, and ϵ_0; the agreement between the calculated and observed values of R is nearly perfect. Thus, Bohr's model gives results in nearly perfect agreement with the known facts about the *spectrum* of hydrogen and also provides an acceptable size for the atom.

Although Bohr's simple model sufficed to interpret nearly all of the then known features of the hydrogen spectrum, it proved impossible to extend the theory to atoms containing more than one electron. In attempting to apply Bohr's ideas to other systems, Arnold Sommerfeld (1868–1951) and others extended the treatment to include elliptical orbits for the electrons. This involved the introduction of more quantum numbers. One puzzling feature was that not all transitions between all energy levels were actually observed; some transitions were regarded as "allowed" and others as "forbidden" according to *selection rules* which had to be introduced on an empirical basis. Although the Bohr–Sommerfeld model was satisfactory in some respects, in view of all the quantum numbers and selection rules introduced on an *ad hoc* basis, it had become a complicated contraption by the time it was replaced by modern quantum mechanics in the late 1920's.

There are several additional features that should be mentioned. When emitting atoms are placed in a magnetic field, their spectra undergo certain modifications; in general, single lines are split into several components when the source is in a magnetic field. This phenomenon, known as the Zeeman effect after its discoverer Pieter Zeeman (1865–1943), indicates that atoms have certain magnetic properties as a result of the motion of the electrons. As we have seen in Section 27.9, the magnetic moment of a particle of charge q and mass m in orbital motion is equal to $q/2m$ times the angular momentum associated with the orbital motion. Therefore, the magnetic moment associated with an electron in the first Bohr orbit has the magnitude

$$m_\text{B} = (e/2m)(h/2\pi) = eh/4\pi m \quad \textit{(Bohr Magneton)}.$$

This value, called the Bohr magneton, represents a convenient unit in terms of which atomic magnetic moments can be measured. The actual magnetic moments of atoms are of this order of magnitude.

Certain patterns in the spectra of atoms made it necessary to conclude that the electron has an intrinsic angular momentum and magnetic moment in addition to the angular momentum and magnetic moment associated with its orbital motion. This inherent angular momentum was interpreted as due to *electron spin* and amounted to $(1/2)(h/2\pi)$—just half the angular momentum associated with an electron in the first Bohr orbit. However, it was found that the magnetic moment of the spinning electron was anomalously large and amounted to one Bohr magneton. The concept of intrinsic electron spin was successfully introduced by G. E. Uhlenbeck (1900–) and S. Goudsmit (1902–1978) in 1925.

36.9   EINSTEIN'S TRANSITION PROBABILITIES

Bohr's hypothesis that radiation occurs only in transitions between stationary energy states raised questions regarding the nature of the interaction between matter and radiation. In 1917 Einstein reported the results of a study of the interpretation of emission and absorption in terms of quantum physics. He considered radiative transitions between two energy levels E_n and E_m of the atoms of a gas in thermal equilibrium inside a blackbody cavity. He first considered the *probabilities* of emission and absorption in processes induced by the radiation field, as suggested in Fig. 36.11. The probability P_1 of absorption of a quantum in a short time interval dt he assumed to be given by a relation $P_1 = u(f)B_{nm}\, dt$ and that of emission stimulated or induced by the presence of the radiation to be $P_2 = u(f)B_{mn}\, dt$, where $u(f)$ is the energy per unit volume in the cavity associated with the frequency interval f to $f + df$ and B_{nm} and B_{mn} are constants that depend on the type of atom being considered. He showed that in agreement with classical theory the probabilities of induced emission and absorption should be equal; that is, $B_{nm} = B_{mn}$.

However, although the probabilities P_1 and P_2 are equal, the number of radiating transitions occurring depends on the numbers of atoms N_m and N_n in the upper and lower energy states. In thermal equilibrium at temperature T, N_m and N_n are not equal but are related by the Boltzmann factor:

$$N_m = N_n e^{-(E_m - E_n)/kT}.$$

Therefore, the numbers of absorption processes and induced emission processes taking place per unit time are given by

$$u(f)B_{nm}N_n \quad \textit{(Absorption)}$$

and

$$u(f)B_{nm}N_n e^{-(E_m - E_n)/kT}. \quad \textit{(Induced Emission)}$$

(36.16)

Because the rate of absorption as given by (36.16) is greater than the rate of induced emission, the number of atoms N_m in the upper state will increase with time; in other words the temperature of the gas inside the cavity will increase. Clearly, thermal equilibrium cannot be maintained if absorption and induced or stimulated emission are the only processes involved.

Einstein argued that another radiative process called *spontaneous emission* must be invoked. He assumed that the probability P_3 of such a process occurring in time

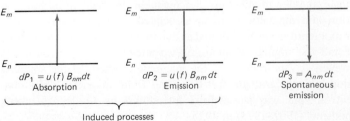

$$E_m \qquad\qquad E_m \qquad\qquad E_m$$

$$E_n \qquad\qquad E_n \qquad\qquad E_n$$

$$dP_1 = u(f)\,B_{nm}dt \qquad dP_2 = u(f)\,B_{nm}dt \qquad dP_3 = A_{nm}dt$$

Absorption   Emission   Spontaneous emission

Induced processes

Fig. 36.11   Absorption and emission processes.

dt is given by the relation $P_3 = A_{nm} \, dt$, where A_{nm} is a constant that depends on the type of atom being considered, and the number of processes taking place per unit time is given by the expression

$$A_{nm} N_m = A_{nm} N_n e^{-(E_m - E_n)/kT}. \quad \text{(Spontaneous Emission)} \quad (36.17)$$

In order for the gas to remain in thermal equilibrium, the total number of emission processes occurring per unit time must be equal to the total number of absorption processes occurring per unit time: $(P_2 + P_3)N_m = P_1 N_n$. On the basis of these considerations, Einstein deduced an expression for $u(f)$. In order that his expression agree in the high- and low-frequency limits with the expressions associated with the Wien and Rayleigh radiation laws, Einstein concluded that

$$A_{nm} = \gamma f^3 B_{nm}, \quad (36.18)$$

where $\gamma = 8\pi h/c^3$ is merely a constant, and

$$E_m - E_n = hf \quad \text{or} \quad f = (E_m - E_n)/h.$$

In the absence of external fields due to electromagnetic radiation of frequency f, an atom can radiate *only* by spontaneous emission. The number of absorption processes and therefore the number of stimulated-emission processes occurring per unit time are directly proportional to the radiant power associated with the electromagnetic waves of frequency f that may be present. In view of the presence of f^3 in (36.18) the coefficient A_{nm} is much larger for transitions involved in the ultraviolet and X-ray regions than for transitions in the infrared and visible regions of the electromagnetic spectrum. Although Einstein's use of the coefficients A_{nm} and B_{nm} provided insight into the nature of the interactions between matter and radiation that are involved in emission and absorption, his theory provided no basis for the calculation of these coefficients in terms of atomic properties. This type of calculation became possible only after the development of modern *quantum mechanics.*

There are, however, several topics covered in Einstein's 1917 paper that merit further comment. First of all, he was able to provide a sound theoretical basis for the relation $hf = E_m - E_n$, which Bohr had introduced as an hypothesis. Second, he showed that when an atom or molecule emits a photon, the photon travels in a definite direction. In the process of spontaneous emission, there is no preferred direction for the photons; thus, in spontaneous emission an excited gas emits photons in all directions. However, in the process of stimulated or induced emission the emitted photons travel only in the same direction as the electromagnetic wave that induces the emission. Third, he showed that in addition to energy hf a photon possesses momentum

$$p = hf/c = h/\lambda, \quad \text{(Momentum of Photon)} \quad (36.19)$$

where λ is the wavelength of the radiation in vacuum. Equation (36.19) is interesting in emphasizing the duality that is characteristic of electromagnetic radiation; it gives the momentum p of the photon, which in many ways resembles a *particle,* in terms

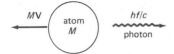

Fig. 36.12 An atom recoils when a photon is emitted.

of the *wave* properties of the radiation involved. Note that as shown schematically in Fig. 36.12, an emitting atom of mass M experiences a recoil when a photon is emitted; in accord with the conservation-of-momentum relation,

$$MV_{\text{recoil}} = h/\lambda. \tag{36.20}$$

The emitting atom thus furnishes not only the photon's energy $hf = E_m - E_n$ but also the photon's momentum h/λ. Although the recoil momentum MV_{recoil} is small for light of wavelengths in the visible region and the associated recoil kinetic energy of the atom can thus be ignored, it becomes important for shorter wavelength radiation.

36.10 LASERS

We are now in a position to add to the discussion of lasers that was begun in Chapter 33 by showing how it is possible to store energy in a medium in a form that can be given up coherently to a light wave in the manner discussed earlier. Consider the three energy-level system shown schematically in Fig. 36.13. If we have a large number of atoms or molecules characterized by such an energy-level system, we know that under conditions of thermal equilibrium the numbers of such units in the excited states E_1 and E_2 are smaller than the number N_0 in the ground level in accord with the Boltzmann factor:

$$N_1 = N_0 e^{-(E_1 - E_0)/kT} \quad \text{and} \quad N_2 = N_0 e^{-(E_2 - E_0)/kT}.$$

Therefore, such a collection of molecules or atoms will absorb radiation of frequencies $f_{01} = (E_1 - E_0)/h$ and $f_{02} = (E_2 - E_0)/h$, from an incident beam.

Suppose, however, that we have a situation where the Einstein transition probabilities are such that A_{01} and A_{12} and thus B_{01} and B_{12} are large as compared with A_{02} and B_{02}. Under these conditions, if we irradiate a sample of the material with light of frequency f_{01}, some atoms or molecules in excited state E_1 will rapidly make radiative transitions to excited state E_2. However, because A_{02} is smaller than the other transition

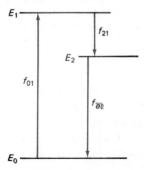

Fig. 36.13 Three energy levels employed in a laser.

probabilities, atoms or molecules in state E_2 will less rapidly make transitions to the ground state E_0. Therefore, if we "pump" the system with radiation of frequency f_{01}, the number N_2 of atoms or molecules in state E_2 will become greater than its thermal equilibrium value. If the rate of pumping is sufficiently large, N_2 eventually becomes greater than the number N_0 of atoms or molecules in the ground state. If light of frequency f_{02} strikes a sample having a "population inversion" $N_2 > N_0$ of this kind, the sample will give up energy to the electromagnetic field as a result of *induced emission* involving the Einstein coefficient B_{02}. Therefore, the amplitude of the light waves inside the cavity shown in Fig. 33.8 will grow in the manner discussed earlier. The material inside the cavity will "lase" at frequency f_{02}.

It is not always necessary to use radiative pumping. Population inversions can be produced by many methods. Under proper conditions an electrical discharge in a sample of gas can be used to produce a population inversion $N_2 > N_0$. Whenever a population inversion occurs in a sample of solid, liquid, or gas, energy is stored in the sample in a form that makes laser action possible.

36.11   DE BROGLIE'S HYPOTHESIS: THE WAVE NATURE OF MATTER

By 1925 it became apparent that the structure of atoms with two or more electrons could not be understood in any satisfactory manner on the basis of the Bohr–Sommerfeld models. The beginning of a new approach was furnished by Louis de Broglie (1892–   ) in his doctoral dissertation at the University of Paris in 1924. Noting that electromagnetic radiation has a wave–particle duality, de Broglie proposed that a similar duality might well apply to material particles like the electron. In particular, in analogy to (36.19) which gives a relation between wavelength λ and momentum p for photons, de Broglie suggested that the electron might also be characterized by a wavelength λ given by the relation

$$\lambda = h/p, \quad \text{(de Broglie Wavelength)} \tag{36.21}$$

where p is the magnitude of the electron's momentum mv. If this hypothesis is correct, interference and diffraction effects should be observed for electrons.

The only evidence of interference that de Broglie could cite at the time was a kind of intra-atomic interference. By comparison of (36.21) with Bohr's quantum condition (36.12), he found that the circumference of each allowed orbit in the Bohr model of the hydrogen atom contained an even number of electron wavelengths. Thus, we have from (36.12) that $mv = nh/2\pi r_n$, and from (36.21) that $mv = h/\lambda$; setting these expressions for mv equal to each other, we obtain

$$2\pi r_n/\lambda = n. \tag{36.22}$$

The circumference of the nth Bohr orbit is thus equal to n electron wavelengths λ. Although this result is interesting, it was considered to give little valid evidence that the electron actually possesses wave characteristics.

However, valid evidence was soon forthcoming. According to (36.21) an electron with an energy of 100 eV has a wavelength of 0.123 nm. This wavelength is comparable with the wavelengths of X-rays, which it was known can be diffracted by the three-dimensional grating structure of crystals. This immediately suggested that a beam of electrons would experience diffraction when reflected from the surface of a crystal or transmitted through a very thin crystal. In 1927 electron diffraction of this type was observed independently by C. J. Davisson (1881–1958) and L. H. Germer (1896–1971) in America and by G. P. Thomson (1892–1975) in Britain. The observed electron-diffraction patterns gave full confirmation of de Broglie's hypothesis as stated in (37.21).

Consideration of (37.21) indicates that the de Broglie wavelengths of macroscopic particles are too small to give rise to observable diffraction phenomena even with a crystal grating. As a consequence, the wave nature of particles larger than those of "atomic size" has never been detected. If the wavelength of a particle as given by (36.21) is much less than the radius of the atomic nucleus $r \approx 10^{-15}$ m, its wave nature can be completely ignored because it can never be observed; the motion of such a particle is that predicted on the basis of classical Newtonian mechanics—provided its speed is small compared with the speed of light.

Both microscopic particles and radiation have some properties that we ordinarily ascribe to *particles* and other properties that we ordinarily ascribe to *waves*. The particle properties of a radio-frequency photon are not apparent because the energy and momentum of a photon of this frequency are so small that a single photon cannot be readily detected; only a large number of such photons can be detected. The wave properties of a macroscopic body like a moving billiard ball are not apparent because its wavelength is undetectably small. In the X-ray region of the electromagnetic spectrum, the radiation exhibits both wave and particle properties; X-rays can be diffracted by a crystal grating but behave like particles when scattered by free electrons. In the extremely high-frequency γ-ray region, the radiation displays only particle properties; the wavelengths are too small to be observable by diffraction or interference. Slowly moving electrons, protons, and neutrons have detectably large wavelengths, so these elementary *particles* have some observable wave properties in addition to their readily observed particle properties.

Beginning in 1925, Erwin Schrödinger (1887–1961) and Werner Heisenberg (1901–1976) took over the de Broglie hypothesis and used it in the formulation of the modern *quantum mechanics* that enables us to determine the properties of atoms and molecules from certain general equations without the necessity of introducing any *ad hoc* hypotheses. Although the formulations proposed by Schrödinger and Heisenberg appear quite different mathematically, it has been demonstrated that they are merely different statements of the same general principles. The basic principles of quantum mechanics are sufficiently different from anything we have discussed thus far that serious detailed treatment of quantum mechanics must be postponed for courses where a significant amount of time can be devoted to the subject.

36.12   APPLICATIONS OF QUANTUM MECHANICS

Although we shall not attempt to describe the results in detail, quantum mechanics not only accounts not only for the structure of atoms but also for all details of atomic spectra including the *ad hoc* selection rules introduced by Sommerfeld. Emission and absorption spectra in the visible and near ultraviolet result from transitions between energy levels involving the outermost electrons, while X-ray spectra are produced by transitions between energy levels that involve the electrons closest to the nucleus. Quantum mechanics also gives a satisfactory account of the valence forces that connect atoms in molecules. Molecular emission and absorption in all regions of the spectrum are accounted for as transitions between energy levels associated with different electronic configurations along with discrete energy levels associated with quantized vibrational and rotational motions of the molecules.

Once atomic and molecular structure was clearly understood, quantum mechanics provided a method of treating the microscopic structure of solids. Of special importance has been a valid theory of electrical conduction in metals and in semiconductors. The specific heats of solids can now be calculated on the basis of quantum mechanical considerations.

The positive nucleus of an atom consists of Z protons along with $(A - Z)$ neutrons, where Z is the atomic number of the element and A is a mass number that is nearest to the atomic weight listed for the isotope of the atom in atomic mass units. Although all forces involved in the extranuclear structure of the atom are *electromagnetic forces,* there are other nonelectromagnetic *strong forces* of attraction between neutrons and protons, collectively called *nucleons,* inside the nucleus; these strong nuclear forces of attraction between nucleons are necessary for the stability of the nucleus, which otherwise would be unstable because of electromagnetic forces of repulsion between the protons. In addition to the strong nuclear forces, there are other nonelectromagnetic *weak forces* that are important in accounting for the emission of β particles (electrons) from unstable nuclei. Once the potential energy E_P has been determined in terms of the electromagnetic and the strong and weak nuclear forces, the allowed nuclear energy levels can be calculated. The emission of γ rays is accounted for in terms of radiative transitions between these levels. Quantum mechanics is thus satisfactory for interpreting the structure of the atomic nucleus and for the emission and absorption of γ radiation.

The application of quantum mechanics to solid-state problems has resulted in the development of many practical devices such as the transistor and various devices for the detection of electromagnetic radiation. Another very important device based on quantum physics is the laser.

QUESTIONS

1. What evidence can you cite for believing that electrons are constituent parts of atoms? What is the evidence for the existence of the atomic nucleus? (Look up descriptions of the Rutherford scattering experiment.)

2. One of the early classical models of the atom proposed by J. J. Thomson consisted of a matrix of positive charge in which electrons were embedded. (See Problem 23.19.) What kind of hydrogen spectrum would you predict on the basis of this Thomson model?

3. After Rutherford's discovery of the nucleus, it was assumed that the hydrogen atom consisted of a proton around which an electron moved in a classical orbit under the influence of a central Coulomb force. Recalling that the electron would supposedly emit electromagnetic radiation as a result of its centripe-

tal acceleration, what kind of hydrogen spectrum would you predict on the basis of this model?

4. Can Kirchhoff's radiation principle (36.2) be applied to a neon display sign? To the filament of a tungsten light bulb? To the phosphor coating of a fluorescent lighting unit? To a firefly? Give reasons for your answers.

5. Lambert's law (36.1) provides a description of the absorption of electromagnetic radiation. What becomes of the radiant energy once it has been absorbed?

6. Despite his success with the quantum principle stated in Section 36.2, Max Planck was reluctant to regard the radiant energy inside an enclosure as *quantized*. Why do you suppose this was so? What were Albert Einstein's views on this subject?

7. Discuss the wave–particle duality introduced in Section 36.3. Is the particle aspect of radiation more important for X-radiation or for visible light?

8. On the basis of Einstein's theory of the photoelectric effect, show that the number of electrons ejected per unit time from a metal is proportional to the intensity of the incident radiation.

9. Discuss the respects in which Bohr's theory of stationary energy states is a repudiation of classical physics.

10. According to Bohr's *correspondence relation*, the low frequencies involved in transitions between energy levels characterized by high quantum numbers correspond to classical predictions. (See Problem 36.20.) Discuss why there must be a definite relation of this sort between quantum physics and classical physics.

11. How does radiation due to spontaneous emission differ from radiation due to induced emission? Which emission process is more important to the operation of a laser?

12. Because a photon has momentum as well as energy, an atom emitting a photon experiences *recoil* and therefore acquires kinetic energy. Why? Because of this recoil, the total energy $E_n - E_m$ involved in a radiative transition is shared by the photon and the emitting atom. How does the fraction of the total energy $E_n - E_m$ that is associated with the atom depend on the value of $E_n - E_m$ and on the mass of the atom?

13. Why are strong nonelectromagnetic forces required for the stability of the atomic nucleus?

PROBLEMS

1. What is the angular separation of the red ($\lambda = 656.3$ nm) and the blue ($\lambda = 486.1$ nm) light emitted by hydrogen when a parallel beam of light is used at normal incidence and a transmission grating with 5000 lines/cm is employed in the second order? If a telescope objective lens with a focal length of 120 cm is used with the grating as in Fig. 36.1, what will be the separation of the red and blue hydrogen lines on a photographic plate located in the focal plane of the telescope objective?

2. If sodium light ($\lambda_1 = 589.0$ nm and $\lambda_2 = 589.6$ nm) were used with the grating spectrograph in Problem 1, what would be the plate separation of the two components of this "doublet" when observed in the first order? In the second order?

3. Experiment shows that the constant in Wien's displacement law is 2.898×10^6 nm·K. At what wavelength λ_{max} does a blackbody radiation curve like the ones

in Fig. 36.5 have its maximum when the temperature of the blackbody is 27°C?

4. Find the value of λ_{max} for blackbodies at the following temperatures: 600 K, 1200 K, 2400 K, 4800 K, 9600 K. (See Problem 3.)

5. The maximum λ_{max} in the observed radiation curve for the sun is 480 nm. What would be the temperature of a blackbody having this value of λ_{max}? (See Problem 3.)

6. The melting point of tungsten is 3673 K. What is the value of λ_{max} for a blackbody at this temperature? (See Problem 3.) Why does the light from an incandescent lamp appear "orange" as compared with "white" sunlight?

7. Astronomical studies show that λ_{max} for the red star Betelgeuse is 960 nm and λ_{max} for Vega is 240 nm. If we regard the sun as a blackbody with a surface temperature of 6000 K and maximum emission at 480 nm, what corresponding surface temperatures do we obtain for Betelgeuse and Vega?

8. Show from the empirical relationships stated in Section 36.6 that each series in the hydrogen spectrum converges to a high-frequency limit as n → ∞. What are these limits for each series?

9. By differentiating Planck's radiation law (36.5) and setting $dR(\lambda)/d\lambda = 0$, derive Wien's displacement law $\lambda_{max}T = $ constant.

10. On the basis of classical physics the average thermal energy a three-dimensional harmonic oscillator is $3kT$. Compare the minimum energy $E_0 = hf$ for a Planck oscillator with the classical value of the average thermal energy of an oscillator at $T = 300$ K with f having the following values: 10^6 Hz (radio waves), 10^{10} Hz (microwaves), 10^{13} Hz (infrared), 10^{15} Hz (visible), and 10^{18} Hz (X-rays). For what frequency f would $E_0 = 3kT$?

11. For equal total energy $E(f)$ inside a large cavity of volume V, show that for

$hf \gg kT$ the probability of finding all of the radiant energy in a small part ΔV of the cavity is greater for X-rays ($f = 10^{19}$ Hz) than for visible light ($f = 10^{15}$ Hz).

12. The maximum of the radiation curve $R(\lambda)$ versus λ for the sun occurs at 480 nm. What is the frequency of this radiation? What is the energy of a single quantum of this radiation?

13. Show that Planck's constant $h = 6.63 \times 10^{-34}$ J·s can be expressed in eV·s. What is the value of h in these units?

14. Find the frequencies of the first three lines of the Lyman series of hydrogen. The lines of the Lyman series converge toward a limit; what is the frequency of this limit?

15. When ultraviolet light of 300 nm wavelength strikes a zinc surface in vacuum as in Fig. 36.6a, a "retarding potential" of 0.5 V must be applied to keep the most energetic electrons from reaching the collector. Determine the work function of the zinc, the wavelength of the photoelectric threshold, and the retarding potential required for light of 200 nm wavelength.

16. On the basis of Einstein's relation (36.10) for the heat capacity per kmole of a solid, show that C_V is small for $hf_0 \gg kT$ and is $3R$ for $hf_0 \ll kT$. What is the value of C_V when $hf_0 = kT$? Discuss a method of selecting the frequency f_0 for a given solid.

17. One of the vibrational absorption bands of the CO_2 molecule has a central frequency of approximately 2×10^{13} Hz and involves transitions between the ground state of the molecule and the excited level involved. What is the ratio of the population of this excited level to the population of the ground state at 300 K?

18. (a) Show from (36.12) and (36.13) that the orbital speed of the electron in the first orbit of the Bohr model of the hydrogen atom is approximately equal to $c/137$. (b) Using

(36.15) verify that the expression in parentheses in this equation is indeed equal to hcR, where R is the Rydberg constant given in Section 36.6.

19. What is the frequency of revolution of the electron in the first orbit of the Bohr atom? In the second orbit? According to classical theory, the frequency of the light emitted or absorbed by an electron moving in a circular orbit is equal to the frequency of the orbital motion; what is the actual frequency of the first line of the Lyman series of hydrogen?

20. According to what is known as "Bohr's Correspondence Principle," the predictions based on quantum considerations correspond to classical predictions when low frequencies are involved. In order to demonstrate this, repeat Problem 19 for the electron's orbital frequency in the 50th and 51st Bohr orbits and for the actual frequency corresponding a radiative transition between these levels.

21. What is the recoil velocity of a hydrogen atom when it emits a photon corresponding to the first line in the Lyman series, which has a frequency of 2.47×10^{15} Hz? What fraction of the total energy released is associated with the recoiling atom?

22. Compute the de Broglie wavelength of an electron, a proton, and an α-particle He^{2+} having the following kinetic energies: 1 eV, 10 eV, and 100 eV. The distance between atoms in a crystal is of the order of 10^{-10} m; which of particles involved in your computation could be used effectively in diffraction studies of crystals?

23. Compute the de Broglie wavelength of (a) an electron, (b) a proton, and (c) an α-particle when each has a thermal kinetic energy $3kT/2$ at room temperature $T = 300$ K.

CHAPTER 37

Relativistic Physics

In this chapter we show how classical mechanics has to be modified in order to account correctly for the behavior of bodies moving at speeds that are comparable with the speed of light. These modifications are based on the work of Albert Einstein and form the basis of what is called *relativistic physics*. Einstein's development of the theory of special relativity in 1905 and the theory of general relativity in 1916 constitutes one of the major intellectual achievements of the twentieth century. These theories not only removed some of the philosophical weaknesses of Newtonian mechanics but also provided valid predictions of physical phenomena that were entirely unknown at the time the theories were formulated.

In our earlier discussion of Newton's Principles (Chapter 4), we gave a brief discussion of *inertial frames* of reference. By the term inertial frame we mean a reference frame in which Newton's principles are valid. The simplest requirement for such a frame is that a particle in the frame have constant velocity when not acted upon by forces; in other words, if the First principle applies in a given reference frame, the frame involved is an inertial frame. Newton also showed that any frame moving at constant velocity with respect to a given inertial frame is also an inertial frame. This result formed the basis of the *Newtonian principle of relativity*: If the laws of mechanics are applicable in one frame of reference, they also apply in any frame moving at constant velocity with respect to the first.

Newton believed it possible to find a system at *absolute rest* with respect to space itself. He also believed that the time measurements involved in the formulation of his principles concerned *absolute time* in the sense that it "flowed steadily" for all observers—a sort of universal time that was the same throughout the universe. In his critical examination of Newtonian mechanics published in 1883, Ernst Mach rejected these ideas of absolute space and absolute time because definite operational procedures could not be specified for their verification. With regard to motion, Mach pointed out that the only motion that can be attributed to a particle is its motion relative to other matter in the universe and not relative to space itself. Mach's insistence on the description of definite operations performed by observers was highly important to physical science and formed the basis of the *thought experiments* later employed so successfully by Einstein.

Although it appeared on the basis of Mach's work to be impossible to specify absolute motion with respect to space itself, the development of Maxwell's electromagnetic theory of light seemed to open the possibility of establishing an absolute frame of reference fixed to the "medium" through which light is propagated. We recall that on the basis of Maxwell's theory the speed of light is $c = 1/\sqrt{\mu_0 \epsilon_0}$, where μ_0 is the permeability and ϵ_0 is the permitivity of *free space*. We shall begin our discussion by noting some of the attempts to measure the motion of bodies relative to the "medium" in which light waves are propagated. The results of these experiments have an important bearing on Einstein's theories of relativity.

37.1   SPEED OF LIGHT

An early hypothesis regarding the speed of light was that light travels with a constant speed relative to its source just as a bullet moves with a muzzle velocity relative to the gun from which it is fired. This hypothesis is negated by the fact that the two components of a "double star" are observed to move in regular orbits about their common center of mass; these orbits are those to be expected on the basis of gravitational forces on the assumption that light from each of the stars travels to us at the same speed. The observed motion of the double star would be much more complicated if the speed of light emitted by the star approaching the earth at speed v were $c + v$ and the speed of light emitted by the star leaving the earth at speed v were $c - v$. The definitive analysis of double-star data was given by the Dutch astronomer Willem de Sitter (1872–1934) in 1913.

The favorite hypothesis for many decades was that there was an *absolute frame of reference* relative to which light travels at speed c. This frame of reference was believed to be filled with a hypothetical medium called the *luminferous ether* through which light waves were propagated. On this hypothesis, an observer moving relative to the absolute frame would observe different light speeds for light transmitted in different directions through the ether, just as a boat moving in a river with a definite speed relative to the water has different speeds relative to an observer on the bank that depend on whether the boat is headed upstream, downstream, or across the stream. The ether hypothesis was disproved in a brilliantly designed and executed experiment first performed by A. A. Michelson in 1881 and repeated with improved accuracy by Michelson and E. W. Morley in Cleveland, Ohio, in 1887. In their "ether drift" experiment, Michelson and Morley set up a Michelson interferometer mounted on a millstone floated in mercury so that its orientation in space could be varied by rotating the interferometer. If the ether hypothesis had been correct, and if the laboratory had an absolute velocity **v** with respect to the ether, the interference pattern should have changed as the interferometer was rotated. Actually, no change at all was observed even though the arrangement was sufficiently sensitive to observe effects $\frac{1}{40}$ the size of those produced by a speed relative to the ether equal to the orbital speed of the earth. Later experiments with improved sensitivity have shown that no motion of the earth relative to the ether can be observed even though relative speeds of the order of as little as 30 m/s could have been detected. These results indicate that absolute motion relative to a hypothetical lumiferous ether cannot be detected.

In view of the results obtained by Michelson and Morley and of the results of numerous related experiments, we are forced to conclude that *the speed of light through empty space is the same in all directions and does not depend on the relative motion of the source and the observer who makes the measurements.*

37.2 PRINCIPLE OF SPECIAL RELATIVITY

Although H. A. Lorentz and others attempted by various schemes to explain the negative results obtained in the speed-of-light experiments just described, it remained for Albert Einstein to develop a new system of physics that incorporates them in a natural way. This system of physics has proved to be valid in situations where classical physics fails but reduces to classical Newtonian physics in the situations for which Newtonian physics has proved valid. Einstein's article of 1905 contains a statement now called the

PRINCIPLE OF SPECIAL RELATIVITY: The basic principles of physics that are valid in one frame of reference are equally valid in any frame of reference in motion at constant velocity relative to it. There is no way of determining an absolute velocity; only relative velocities can be measured.

This statement represents a generalization of Newtonian relativity to include not only the laws of mechanics but also the laws of electromagnetism as formulated by Maxwell; also included is the assertion that the establishment of any absolute frame of reference of the kind envisaged by Newton is impossible. The impossibility of determining absolute motion is consistent with the earlier conclusion of Mach.

Coupled with this statement of relativity, Einstein incorporated into his new theory as a basic tenet the results that we have seen are obtained in measurements of the speed of light:

Any observer will always measure the same value c for the speed of light in empty space relative to himself, regardless of the direction of the light beam involved and regardless of the velocity of the source of light.

The acceptance of the constancy of the speed of light as measured by any and all observers gives the speed of light c a preferred status in the theories developed by Einstein. As we shall see later, no material particle can have a speed as great as c; the speed of light thus represents an ultimate speed that cannot be exceeded.

The statement of the principle of relativity given above is sometimes called the *principle of invariance* of physical laws. Einstein concluded that the laws of electromagnetism as formulated by Maxwell were indeed correctly invariant and that they give a value $c = 1/\sqrt{\mu_0\epsilon_0}$ for light transmission; however, the Newtonian principles of mechanics require revision in order to make them invariant.

In his revision of the laws of mechanics to make them invariant, Einstein conducted numerous *thought experiments* that led to results that sometimes seem to be inconsistent with "common sense" and with any "physical intuition" that we may have developed on the basis of classical physics. Actually, Einstein's modifications of Newtonian mechanics become important only for objects moving at speeds comparable with the speed of light, and with objects of this kind we have little or no everyday experience on which to base common sense or physical intuition.

We shall now see how our familiar concepts of length, time, and mass must be modified in the light of Einstein's principles. In doing this we shall make use of some thought experiments involving an observer α in one reference frame and a second observer β in another reference frame moving with constant velocity $\mathbf{v}$ relative to the first frame. We assume in each case that the observer is equipped with instruments with which locations and times of events can be determined relative to the observer's frame of reference. In order to simplify matters we shall consider two reference frames with origins at O_A and O_B having the X_A, Y_A, Z_A axes of frame O_A parallel to the X_B, Y_B, Z_B axes of frame O_B. The axes will be chosen so that the relative velocity of the frames is parallel to the X_A and X_B axes.

37.3   RELATIVE NATURE OF TIME

The measurement of times and time intervals involves the concept of *simultaneity,* which we have assumed implicitly in our treatment of Newtonian mechanics. However, two events that are regarded as simultaneous by one observer may not be simultaneous to another observer. This fact is clearly demonstrated by one of Einstein's thought experiments.

Consider a railway car moving at constant velocity along a track as suggested in Fig. 37.1. Two lightning bolts strike opposite ends of the car and leave marks on the ground. Assume that the two strokes appear to be simultaneous to an observer α located on the ground just beside the center of the car because light pulses from the strokes travel equal distances to him and reach him at the same time. However, consider the situation from the point of view of observer β who is aboard the moving car. Because he is moving away from the mark on the ground at the left and toward the mark on the ground at the right in the figure, light from the bolt at the right reaches him before it reaches observer α and light from the bolt at the left reaches him after it reaches observer α. Thus, observer β receives the light pulse from the

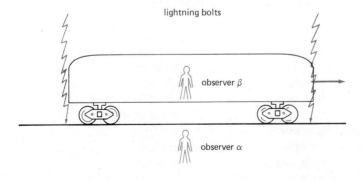

lightning bolts

observer β

observer α

Fig. 37.1   Relativity of simultaneity.

bolt that strikes the right end of the car before he receives the light pulse from the bolt that strikes the left end of the car. But the two ends of the car are equidistant from β; observer β concludes that the two bolts struck at equally distant points but that the light pulses from these points reached him at different times. Therefore, β must assert that the bolts did not strike the two ends of the car simultaneously. Thus, the two observers disagree. There is no basis for saying that one observer is "right" and the other is "wrong"; each observer is correct in his own frame of reference.

Time *intervals* between the same events also depend on the relative motion of observers of the events. Consider in Fig. 37.2 an observer β at rest in reference frame B, which has velocity **v** relative to frame A in which observer α is at rest. Observer β sends a light pulse to a mirror M located a distance d away from him and measures the time interval required for the pulse to travel to the mirror and back. The time interval measured by β between two events—in this case the departure and return of the light pulse—at the *same location* in his own frame is called a *proper time interval.* The proper time interval between the departure and return of the light pulse is given by the simple expression

$$\Delta t_0 = 2d/c. \tag{37.1}$$

However, to observer α in frame A, with respect to which the departure and return of the light pulse occur at different locations, the total path length traversed by the light pulse is not $2d$ but is $2l$ as indicated in Fig. 37.2c, where

$$l = \sqrt{d^2 + (v\Delta t/2)^2}$$

and Δt is the transit time of the pulse as measured by observer α. From (37.1) we note that $d = c\Delta t_0/2$. Furthermore, the time interval Δt as measured by α is $2l/c$. Therefore, we can write

$$\Delta t = \frac{2}{c}\sqrt{\left(\frac{c\Delta t_0}{2}\right)^2 + \left(\frac{v\Delta t}{2}\right)^2}. \tag{37.2}$$

By squaring both sides of (37.2) and solving for Δt, we obtain the relation

$$\Delta t = \frac{\Delta t_0}{\sqrt{1 - v^2/c^2}}. \tag{37.3}$$

This relation gives an extremely important result. If observer β measures the proper time interval Δt_0 between two events at the same location in his own frame of reference,

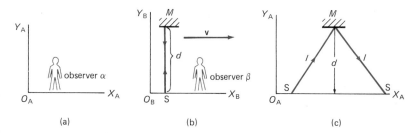

Fig. 37.2 (a)–(b) Frame B moves a velocity **v** *relative* to a frame A. (c) Light path as seen by an observer in frame A.

observer α in a different frame moving at velocity $\mathbf{v}$ relative to the first frame measures a time interval Δt between the two events that is larger than Δt_0 by the factor given in (37.3). It is left as a problem to show that reversing the roles of α and β and allowing α to send out the light flash to a mirror at rest with respect to reference frame A and thus measure a proper time interval Δt_0 has no influence on (37.3); in the case of reversed roles observer β would obtain the value Δt given in (37.3).

The result given in (37.3), which is known as *time dilation,* can be generalized. When two observers equipped with identical "clocks" are moving with relative velocity $\mathbf{v}$, each of the observers will measure the same proper interval τ_0 between events such as the "ticks" of his own clock at rest in his own frame. However, each of the observers will measure time intervals τ between events at a single location in the other's frame, events such as the "ticks" of the other's clock. The relation between time intervals τ and τ_0 is just that given by (37.3):

$$\tau = \tau_0/\sqrt{1 - v^2/c^2}. \quad \textit{(Time Dilation)} \tag{37.4}$$

The result is that each of the observers thinks that the other observer's clock is too slow; i.e., the time between ticks of the other observer's clock is too long. Because only the square of the magnitude of the relative velocity v^2 appears in (37.3) and (37.4), it makes no difference whether the relative velocity is one of approach or separation.

37.4 RELATIVE NATURE OF LENGTH

Just as the time interval between two events depends on the reference frame of the observer, so also the distance between two points in space depends on the reference frame of the observer. Consider an observer β in reference frame B in Fig. 37.3, which is moving in the X direction at velocity $\mathbf{v}$ relative to frame A in which observer α is at rest. Observer β sends a light pulse along a rod of proper length l_0 parallel to the direction of relative motion. By *proper length* we mean that the ends of the rod between which the length is measured are *at rest with respect to the observer*. At the end of the rod is a plane mirror that reflects the light pulse back to its source. The proper time interval Δt_0 as measured by β for the transmission and return of the light pulse is $\Delta t_0 = 2l_0/c$ or

$$c = \frac{2l_0}{\Delta t_0}. \tag{37.5}$$

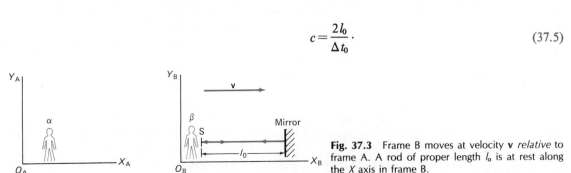

Fig. 37.3 Frame B moves at velocity $\mathbf{v}$ *relative* to frame A. A rod of proper length l_0 is at rest along the X axis in frame B.

The time required for the transmission and return of the pulse as observed by observer α is Δt, which differs from Δt_0 by the relation given in (37.3). In order to infer the length l of the moving rod relative to his frame of reference, observer α reasons as follows. A time Δt_1 is required for the light pulse traveling at speed c to get from the source to the mirror M at the far end of the rod of length l that is receding at speed v, where $c\Delta t_1 = l + v\Delta t_1$ or $\Delta t_1 = l/(c - v)$. A time Δt_2 is required for the light pulse to return from the mirror to the source where $c\Delta t_2 = l - v\Delta t_2$ or $\Delta t_2 = l/(c + v)$. Therefore, the total time as measured by α for the light pulse to go to the mirror and return is

$$\Delta t = \frac{l}{c - v} + \frac{l}{c + v} = \frac{2cl}{c^2 - v^2} = \frac{2l}{c} \frac{1}{(1 - v^2/c^2)},$$

from which it follows that

$$c = \frac{2l}{\Delta t} \frac{1}{(1 - v^2/c^2)}. \tag{37.6}$$

Setting the expressions for c in (37.5) and (37.6) equal to each other and making use of (37.3), we find that

$$l = l_0\sqrt{1 - v^2/c^2}. \tag{37.7}$$

Therefore, the length of the rod l measured by α is less than the proper length l_0 of the rod as determined by β in his own frame where the rod is at rest.

The result in (37.7) can be generalized in the following way. Any measuring rod of proper length l_0 as determined by an observer at rest with respect to the rod has a shorter length l as measured by another observer moving at velocity $\mathbf{v}$ with respect to the rod *in a direction parallel to the length of the rod*. Thus, to the observer in motion at velocity $\mathbf{v}$ relative to the rod, the length l is

$$l = l_0\sqrt{1 - v^2/c^2}. \quad \textit{(Lorentz–Fitzgerald Contraction)} \tag{37.8}$$

This relation is called the *Lorentz–Fitzgerald contraction* because the Irish physicist G. F. Fitzgerald (1851–1901) in 1889 made the suggestion, elaborated by Lorentz in 1895, that the null result of the Michelson–Morley experiment could be explained if the length of any material object contracted by the fraction $\sqrt{1 - v^2/c^2}$ in the direction of its motion through the ether. We note that the contraction or shrinkage of an extended body is observed only for the dimensions of the body that are parallel to $\mathbf{v}$; other dimensions are unchanged.

37.5 RELATIVE NATURE OF MASS

The principle of momentum conservation asserts that the total momentum of an isolated system is constant. Thus, when two particles collide, their total momentum following collision is equal to their total momentum prior to collision provided there

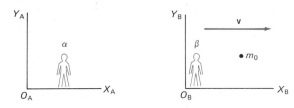

Fig. 37.4 Frame B moves at velocity **v** *relative* to frame A. A particle of proper mass m_0 is at rest in frame B.

are no interactions between the collision pair and other bodies. The momentum-conservation principle forms an important part of relativistic mechanics, but in using this principle we must alter some of our classical ideas regarding momentum.

Consider a particle in Fig. 37.4 at rest in reference frame B, which moves at velocity **v** in the X direction relative to reference frame A. Observer β in frame B can determine the *proper mass* or *rest mass* m_0 of the particle in his own system. In order for the momentum-conservation principle to apply when this particle has collisions with other particles, observer α in frame A must assign the particle a momentum

$$\mathbf{p} = \frac{m_0 \mathbf{v}}{\sqrt{1 - v^2 c^2}} \quad \text{(Momentum)} \tag{37.9}$$

instead of the momentum $m_0\mathbf{v}$ that would be employed in classical Newtonian mechanics. A derivation of (37.9) from Einstein's relativity principles is rather lengthy, and we shall omit it.

However, we note that observer α in Fig. 37.4 can still express the momentum of the particle in the form $\mathbf{p} = m\mathbf{v}$, provided he makes the assumption that the *mass* of a particle is not constant as in Newtonian mechanics. Instead, observer α must express the mass m of the particle in Fig. 37.4 in the form

$$m = \frac{m_0}{\sqrt{1 - v^2/c^2}}, \quad \text{(Mass)} \tag{37.10}$$

where m_0 is the *rest mass* or *proper mass* of the particle.

We see that the adoption of Einstein's Principle of Special Relativity along with the tenet regarding the constancy of the speed of light leads to a modification of our ideas regarding the fundamental mechanical quantities of *length, mass, and time.* These quantities no longer have absolute values but have values that depend on the motions of bodies relative to observers. If a measuring rod has a proper length l_0 as determined by an observer in a frame in which the rod is at rest, the length l determined by another observer moving at relative velocity **v** parallel to the length of the rod is given by (37.8). If τ_0 is a proper time interval as determined by a clock at rest in one frame of reference, the time interval τ as observed by an observer moving at velocity **v** relative to the clock is given by (37.4). Finally, a body with proper mass m_0 moving at velocity **v** relative to an observer has mass m given by (37.10). It should be emphasized that the velocity **v** in these relations is the *relative velocity.* Neither the observer nor the object being observed can be regarded as absolutely at rest; only their relative motion has physical significance.

37.6 RELATIVISTIC KINEMATICS

In order to understand some of the results of applying relativistic principles to kinematics, consider the two frames of reference A and B shown in Fig. 37.5. The origins of the two coordinate systems O_A and O_B coincide at time $t = 0$ and the B frame is moving to the right in the figure at relative velocity $\mathbf{v}$ in the X direction.

First let us consider the classical treatment of the motion. Classically, time is a universal independent variable such that $t_A = t_B = t$. Under this classical assumption, we can write for the location of a particle P

$$x_A = x_B + vt, \quad y_A = y_B, \quad z_A = z_B. \quad \text{(Galilean Transformation)} \quad (37.11)$$

This transformation of coordinates is called the *Galilean transformation*. Now we can write the relation between the components of the velocity $\mathbf{u}_A$ of particle P as observed by α and the components of the velocity $\mathbf{u}_B$ of the same particle P as observed by β:

$$
\begin{aligned}
u_{Ax} &= dx_A/dt = dx_B/dt + v = u_{Bx} + v, \\
u_{Ay} &= dy_A/dt = dy_B/dt \quad\;\; = v_{By}, \\
u_{Az} &= dz_A/dt = dz_B/dt \quad\;\; = u_{Bz}.
\end{aligned}
\quad (37.12)
$$

The inverse relations are easily seen to be $u_{Bx} = u_{Ax} - v$, $u_{By} = u_{Ay}$, and $u_{Bz} = u_{Az}$. Now consider the case where the moving particle is a photon moving at speed c in frame B so that $u_B = c$; in this case (37.12) leads to the prediction that

$$u_{Ax} = c + v. \quad (37.13)$$

This result is in disagreement with experiments, which show that the speed of light is c for all observers and is in disagreement with Einstein's principle of relativity.

The correct transformation of coordinates that must be used in connection with Fig. 37.5 is called the *Lorentz transformation* because Lorentz discovered in 1903 that Maxwell's equations are invariant under this transformation, whereas they are not invariant under the Galilean transformation. The Lorentz transformation takes account of (37.4) and (37.8), which imply that both time and lengths in the direction of relative motion are different for observers α and β. The Lorentz transformation is as follows:

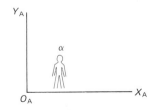
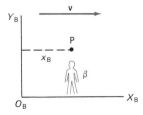

Fig. 37.5 Transformations of velocities. Both observers describe the motion of a particle P.

$$\left.\begin{array}{l} x_A = \dfrac{x_B + vt_B}{\sqrt{1 - v^2/c^2}}, \\[3mm] y_A = y_B, \quad z_A = z_B, \\[3mm] t_A = \dfrac{t_B + vx/c^2}{\sqrt{1 - v^2/c^2}}. \end{array}\right\} \quad (\textit{Lorentz Transformation}) \qquad (37.14)$$

These equations can be derived directly from Einstein's postulates, but the argument is somewhat lengthy. From the Lorentz transformation equations, it can be shown that the correct relations between the components of the velocity $\mathbf{u_A}$ of particle P in Fig. 37.5 as observed by α and the components of the velocity $\mathbf{u_B}$ of the same particle P as observed by β are

$$u_{Ax} = \frac{u_{Bx} + v}{1 + u_{Bx}v/c^2}, \quad u_{Ay} = \frac{u_{By}\sqrt{1 - v^2/c^2}}{1 + u_{Bx}v/c^2}, \quad u_{Az} = \frac{u_{Bz}\sqrt{1 - v^2/c^2}}{1 + u_{Bx}v/c^2}. \quad (37.15)$$

The corresponding expressions for the velocity $\mathbf{u_B}$ of the particle observed by β in the B frame are

$$u_{Bx} = \frac{u_{Ax} - v}{1 - u_{Ax}v/c^2}, \quad u_{By} = \frac{u_{Ay}\sqrt{1 - v^2/c^2}}{1 - u_{Ax}v/c^2}, \quad u_{Bz} = \frac{u_{Az}\sqrt{1 - v^2/c^2}}{1 - u_{Ax}v/c^2}. \quad (37.15')$$

Now consider the form of (37.15) for small values of v and u_B for which $u_B v \ll c^2$; this restriction leads to the result $u_{Ax} = u_{Bx} + v$, which is just the classical value given in (37.12). Similarly, for $u_A v \ll c^2$, (37.15') reduces to $u_{Bx} = u_{Ax} - v$. Thus, in the case of velocities small compared with the speed of light, the relativistic equations of kinematics reduce to the familiar classical equations.

Now let us examine (37.15) for the case in which the particle is a photon for which $u_{Bx} = c$. In this case (37.15) gives

$$u_{Ax} = \frac{c + v}{1 + cv/c^2} = \frac{c^2(c + v)}{c^2 + cv} = \frac{c^2(c + v)}{c(c + v)} = c.$$

Similarly, for a photon in A having $u_{Ax} = c$, (37.15') gives

$$u_{Bx} = \frac{c - v}{1 - cv/c^2} = \frac{c^2(c - v)}{c^2 - cv} = \frac{c^2(c - v)}{c(c - v)} = c.$$

Therefore, observers α and β measure the same value c of the speed of light regardless of their relative motion, as required by Einstein's theory of relativity.

An interesting and important application of the relativistic kinematical considerations that we have just discussed is to the Doppler effect for electromagnetic radiation. Consider a monochromatic light source S at rest in frame B, which moves at velocity $\mathbf{v}$ relative to frame A in Fig. 37.6. If f_s is the proper frequency of the source as measured by observer β, its period τ_s as measured by β is $\tau_s = 1/f_s$. Because of

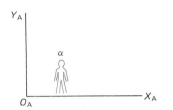
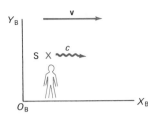

Fig. 37.6 A monochromatic light source S is at rest relative to frame B. Light has speed c for *all* observers.

the time-dilation relation (37.4), the period τ of the source as measured by α in frame A is $\tau = \tau_s/\sqrt{1-v^2/c^2}$ and its corresponding frequency is $f = f_s\sqrt{1-v^2/c^2}$. However, because the source is receding from observer α with a speed v as it oscillates, the wavelength λ of the radiation reaching α, which is the distance between successive wave crests as measured with respect to frame A, is given by the expression $(c+v)/f$. Because the radiation moves with speed c, the number of waves reaching α per unit time, which is the frequency f_A that he will observe, is given by

$$f_A = \frac{c}{\lambda} = \frac{cf}{(c+v)} = \frac{cf_s\sqrt{1-v^2/c^2}}{c+v} = \frac{f_s\sqrt{c^2-v^2}}{c+v}. \tag{37.16}$$

Noting that $\sqrt{c^2-v^2} = \sqrt{(c+v)(c-v)}$ and that $c+v = \sqrt{(c+v)(c+v)}$, we can write

$$f_A = f_s\sqrt{\frac{c-v}{c+v}} \quad \text{(Relative Separation)} \tag{37.17}$$

for the frequency of the light actually observed by α in frame A.

If the relative velocity v is one of approach, the final expression in (37.16) is

$$f_A = f_s\frac{\sqrt{c^2-v^2}}{c-v} = f_s\frac{\sqrt{(c+v)(c-v)}}{\sqrt{(c-v)(c-v)}}$$

and thus

$$f_A = f_s\sqrt{\frac{c+v}{c-v}}. \quad \text{(Relative Approach)} \tag{37.17'}$$

Note again that no absolute motion can be specified. Astronomers on earth can use measurements of the Doppler effect to specify the velocity of a star or galaxy relative to themselves, but absolute motion has no meaning in relativistic physics.

37.7 RELATIVISTIC DYNAMICS

In his critical examination of the principles of classical physics in the light of his principle of relativity, Einstein found the laws of electromagnetism formulated by Maxwell to be acceptable. However, observers moving relative to each other will measure different values of electric-field strength $\mathscr{E}$ and magnetic-field strength $\mathscr{B}$.

To an observer at rest in a given frame of reference, a charge at rest in the same frame has a purely electric field $\mathcal{E}$. However, an observer in motion relative to the first frame sees the charge in motion and attributes both an electric field $\mathcal{E}$ and a magnetic field $\mathcal{B}$ to the same charge. In another situation one observer may observe a charged particle moving through a magnetic field and will observe that the particle has an acceleration that he correctly attributes to a magnetic force. However, a different observer relative to whom the charge is momentarily at rest will correctly attribute the acceleration to an electric force.

As we have noted, Einstein found that the Newtonian principles were in need of revision. In relativistic mechanics, Newton's First Principle applies without modification; there exist frames of reference with respect to which an isolated particle not acted on by forces has constant velocity. Newton's Second Principle is found to be acceptable when it is expressed in terms of the particle's momentum:

$$F = \frac{d\mathbf{p}}{dt},$$

provided the momentum $\mathbf{p}$ is expressed in the form given in (37.9). Thus, the Second Principle assumes the form

$$F = \frac{d}{dt}(m\mathbf{v}) = m\frac{d\mathbf{v}}{dt} + \mathbf{v}\frac{dm}{dt}, \quad \textit{(Newton's Second Principle)} \quad (37.18)$$

where m has the value $m = m_0/\sqrt{1 - v^2/c^2}$ given in (37.10). Because $d\mathbf{v}/dt = \mathbf{a}$, the first term $m\,d\mathbf{v}/dt$ on the right-hand side of (37.18) resembles the simple form of the second principle as we first introduced it in Chapter 4; however, we must remember that m in (37.18) is not constant but depends on the magnitude of the particle's velocity. It should be noted that for $v \ll c$, the relativistic form of the second principle reduces to $\mathbf{F} = m_0\mathbf{a}$, so that our earlier form of the second principle does apply to a particle moving at a speed that is small as compared with the speed of light. The second term $\mathbf{v}\,dm/dt$ on the right-hand side of (37.18) assumes increasing importance as the magnitude v of the particle velocity approaches the speed of light. As v becomes very large, the major effect of a resultant force $\mathbf{F}$ in the direction of motion is to increase the mass of a particle rather than to accelerate the particle. As v approaches c, the mass of the particle approaches ∞, so that the acceleration of the particle approaches zero. In the limit $v = c$, the mass of the particle would become infinite.

In the relativistic form of the second principle, the effectiveness of a resultant force in accelerating a particle depends on the direction of the force $\mathbf{F}$ with respect to the velocity $\mathbf{v}$ of the particle. We shall consider the two special cases in which $\mathbf{F} \perp \mathbf{v}$ and $\mathbf{F} \parallel \mathbf{v}$. If $\mathbf{F} \perp \mathbf{v}$, the magnitude of the particle's velocity does not change and the acceleration is thus centripetal; (37.18) takes the form

$$F = ma = m\frac{v^2}{R} = \frac{m_0}{\sqrt{1 - v^2/c^2}}\frac{v^2}{R}, \quad (\mathbf{F} \perp \mathbf{v}) \quad (37.18')$$

where R is the radius of the particle's path. Except for the dependence of mass on speed, this expression is similar to the classical Newtonian result.

If the resultant force $\mathbf{F}$ is parallel to the particle velocity $\mathbf{v}$, (37.18) becomes

$$F = ma + v\frac{dm}{dt} = ma + v\frac{dm}{dv}\frac{dv}{dt} = \left(m + v\frac{dm}{dv}\right)a.$$

From (37.10), we obtain

$$\frac{dm}{dv} = \frac{m_0}{(1 - v^2/c^2)^{3/2}}\frac{v}{c^2} = \frac{mv/c^2}{(1 - v^2/c^2)}. \qquad (37.19)$$

Substitution of this result in the original equation leads to

$$F = \frac{ma}{(1 - v^2/c^2)} = \frac{m_0 a}{(1 - v^2/c^2)^{3/2}}. \qquad (\mathbf{F} \parallel \mathbf{v}) \qquad (37.18'')$$

For particles moving at speeds comparable with the speed of light, the resultant force required to produce a given acceleration is enormous as compared with the classical Newtonian value $F = m_0 a$.

The form taken by the second principle in relativistic mechanics seems rather complicated. However, Newton's Third Principle is found to apply without modification for mechanical interactions in collisions. This makes it possible to derive the momentum-conservation principle from the third principle along with the second principle in its general form $\mathbf{F} = d\mathbf{p}/dt$. *The principle of the conservation of momentum is valid in relativistic mechanics.*

Experimental verification of the relations given in (37.9) and (37.10) was obtained shortly after the publication of Einstein's initial paper in 1905. In a series of experiments concluded in 1906 by Wilhelm Kaufmann (1871–1947) and in experiments performed with greater accuracy in 1908 by A. H. Bucherer (1863–1927), measurements were made of the curvature of the paths of β-particles in magnetic fields; it was found that the curved paths agreed with predictions based on (37.18'). The variation of mass with particle speed is given by the curve in Fig. 37.7, which shows a plot of m/m_0 as a function of v/c. The points shown on the curve represent experimental results obtained by Kaufmann and by Bucherer in their experiments with electrons. The validity of the predictions embodied in (37.18') has been established in numerous experiments.

37.8 RELATIVISTIC ENERGY RELATIONS

We now turn to a consideration of energy in terms relativistic mechanics. Just as in Newtonian mechanics, the element of work done by a force is given by the relation $dW = \mathbf{F} \cdot d\mathbf{r}$. Therefore, if we allow a resultant force $\mathbf{F}$ to act on a particle of mass m_0 when it is initially at rest in an inertial reference frame, the kinetic energy E_K

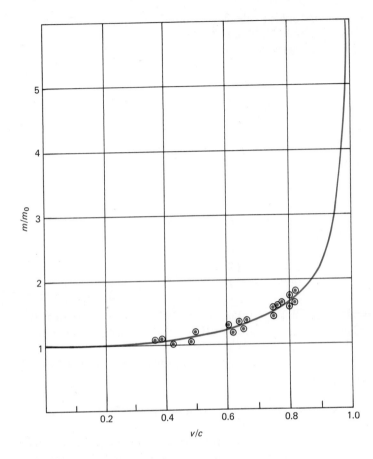

Fig. 37.7 Experimental results for electron mass as a function of speed. The solid curve is computed from (37.10).

of the particle is equal to the line integral $\int \mathbf{F} \cdot d\mathbf{r}$. Because of the form of (37.18) it is desirable to evaluate the integral in a somewhat indirect way:

$$E_K = \int \mathbf{F} \cdot d\mathbf{r} = \int \mathbf{F} \cdot (d\mathbf{r}/dt)dt = \int \mathbf{F} \cdot \mathbf{v}\, dt \qquad (37.20)$$

since $\mathbf{v} = d\mathbf{r}/dt$. This integral must be taken over the path traversed by the particle as it starts from rest and attains speed v. Using (37.18), we see that

$$\mathbf{F} \cdot \mathbf{v} = m\frac{d\mathbf{v}}{dt} \cdot \mathbf{v} + \mathbf{v} \cdot \mathbf{v}\frac{dm}{dt} = m\frac{d\mathbf{v}}{dt} \cdot \mathbf{v} + v^2\frac{dm}{dt} \qquad (37.21)$$

since $\mathbf{v} \cdot \mathbf{v} = v^2$. We can simplify this expression by use of the following differentiation:

$$\frac{d(v^2)}{dt} = \frac{d}{dt}(\mathbf{v} \cdot \mathbf{v}) = \frac{d\mathbf{v}}{dt} \cdot \mathbf{v} + \mathbf{v} \cdot \frac{d\mathbf{v}}{dt} = 2\frac{d\mathbf{v}}{dt} \cdot \mathbf{v}.$$

Hence, the first term on the right in (37.21) reduces to

$$m \frac{d\mathbf{v}}{dt} \cdot \mathbf{v} = \frac{1}{2} m \frac{d}{dt}(v^2) = mv \frac{dv}{dt}$$

and (37.21) becomes

$$\mathbf{F} \cdot \mathbf{v} = mv \frac{dv}{dt} + v^2 \frac{dm}{dt} = \left(mv \frac{dv}{dm} + v^2 \right) \frac{dm}{dt}. \qquad (37.21')$$

The value of dv/dm can be obtained from (37.19); insertion of this value in (37.21') leads to the simple expression

$$\mathbf{F} \cdot \mathbf{v} = c^2 \, dm/dt. \quad \textit{(Power)} \qquad (37.21'')$$

Substituting this value of $\mathbf{F} \cdot \mathbf{v}$ in (37.20), we obtain the relativistic expression for the kinetic energy of a particle:

$$E_K = \int c^2 (dm/dt) \, dt = c^2 \int_{m_0}^{m} dm = (m - m_0) c^2,$$

where m_0 is the rest mass of the particle and m is the mass of the particle as it moves with speed v. This equation expresses the mathematically simple relation:

> The KINETIC ENERGY of a particle is equal to c^2 times the difference between its mass and its rest mass:

$$E_K = (m - m_0) c^2. \quad \textit{(Kinetic Energy)} \qquad (37.22)$$

This expression states that a material particle with rest mass m_0 would have infinite kinetic energy if its speed were equal to the speed of light. Because (37.20) indicates that we would have to do an infinite amount of work to give a particle infinite energy and because (37.18'') indicates that an infinitely large force would be required, we conclude that no material particle having non-zero rest mass can move with the speed of light. *All material particles move at speeds less than the speed of light.*

What about photons? In our discussion of quantum physics we indicated that photons have certain particle-like properties and possess energy $E = hf$. If we regard this energy as being "kinetic" in nature, (37.22) might appear to present difficulties involving infinite energy. However, we note that a photon has zero rest mass; (37.22) does not apply to photons. To all observers a photon must move with speed c. The "particles" of electromagnetic radiation are *not* material particles!

Because we have seen in earlier chapters that the classical expression $E_K = (1/2)m_0 v^2$ is valid for particles moving at speeds $v \ll c$, we should expect E_K as given in (37.22) to reduce to the classical expression for small speeds. We can show that it does so by writing (37.22) in the form

$$E_K = m_0 \left[(1 - v^2/c^2)^{-1/2} - 1 \right] c^2$$

and expanding the term by $(1 - v^2/c^2)^{-1/2}$ by use of the binomial theorem. The resulting expression is

$$E_K = m_0 \left[\left(1 + \frac{1}{2}\frac{v^2}{c^2} + \frac{3}{8}\frac{v^4}{c^4} + \cdots \right) - 1 \right] c^2$$

$$= \frac{1}{2} m_0 v^2 \left[1 + \frac{3}{4}\frac{v^2}{c^2} + \cdots \right].$$

Thus, if v^2/c^2 is small as compared with unity, the correct relativistic expression (37.22) for the kinetic energy does indeed reduce to the classical expression $E_K = (1/2)m_0 v^2$.

37.9   MASS–ENERGY RELATIONS

Einstein regarded (37.22) as an expression of the idea that energy and mass as merely different manifestations of the same physical quantity "mass–energy" with c^2 representing a "conversion factor" giving a relation between joules and kilograms in the SI system that we have employed. Thus, on the basis $E = \Delta mc^2$ in (37.22) we can write the mass–energy equivalents

$$1 \text{ kg} \sim 8.987 \times 10^{16} \text{ J}, \quad 1 \text{ J} \sim 1.113 \times 10^{-17} \text{ kg}.$$

At the time that Einstein proposed this view, scientists accepted not only a conservation-of-energy principle but also a conservation-of-matter principle, which was amply supported by experimental evidence dating from the time of Lavoisier, who had demonstrated that in every chemical reaction the mass of the reaction products was equal to the mass of the initial reactants. If the mass of a body is actually changed when energy is added, why had this not been detected by the careful chemists? The answer to this question is found in the extremely small value of the mass–energy conversion factor 1.113×10^{-17} kg/J. As can be readily seen from the mass–energy equivalents given in Table 37.1, the mass changes involved in ordinary thermal and chemical effects are too small to be measured by even the most careful chemist with the best chemical balance ever produced. For example, if we heat 1 kg of water from 0°C to 100°C, the mass of the water changes by only 5×10^{-12} kg—much too small to measure!

Table 37.1   Mass–Energy Equivalents

Mass–Energy Equivalents	kg	u	J	MeV
1 kilogram~	1	6.025×10^{26}	8.987×10^{16}	5.610×10^{29}
1 atomic mass unit~	1.660×10^{-27}	1	1.492×10^{-10}	931.5
1 joule~	1.113×10^{-17}	6.705×10^{9}	1	6.242×10^{12}
1 million electron-volts~	1.783×10^{-30}	1.074×10^{-3}	1.602×10^{-13}	1

Table 37.2 Rest Energies of Particles

Particle		Mass (u)	Energy (MeV)[a]
Electron		0.000 549	0.511
Atomic mass unit u		1.0000	931.50
Proton	^1_1H	1.0073	938.3
Neutron	^1_0n	1.0087	939.6
Deuteron	^2_1H	2.0141	1 876
Helium	^4_2He	4.0026	3 728
Carbon	$^{12}_6C$	12.0000	11 178
Calcium	$^{40}_{20}Ca$	39.962	37 224
Iron	$^{56}_{26}Fe$	55.935	52 103
Bismuth	$^{209}_{83}Bi$	208.980	194 660
Uranium	$^{235}_{92}U$	235.044	218 940
	$^{238}_{92}U$	238.051	221 740

[a] Computed on Basis of 1 u = 931.50 MeV

Despite extensive experimental evidence supporting separate conservation principles for mass and for energy, Einstein proposed the following generalized interpretation of (37.22):

$$mc^2 = m_0c^2 + E \qquad \text{(Conservation of Mass–Energy)}$$

Total Energy = Rest Energy + Energy Added. (37.23)

The term m_0c^2 he regarded as a rest energy that is associated with a body at rest as a result of its existence. The rest energies of several atomic particles are listed in Table 37.2. If we add energy E in any form to this rest energy, we increase the total energy and we increase the mass of the body from m_0 to m.

The first clear and unambiguous evidence of the validity of Einstein's views regarding mass–energy equivalence was obtained more than a quarter century after his initial paper appeared. In 1932 Carl D. Anderson (1905–) observed that when an energetic photon entered a thin lead plate, two charged particles emerged from the other side of the plate. One of the emerging particles was found to be an ordinary electron. Measurement of the path of the second particle in a magnetic field showed that it had the same mass as an electron but had a *positive* charge; it is therefore called a *positron*. What Anderson had observed was the *creation of matter*. The energy hf of the photon had been transformed into two particles:

$$(hf)_{\text{photon}} \rightarrow (m_0c^2 + E_K)_{\text{electron}} + (m_0c^2 + E_K)_{\text{positron}}. \qquad \textit{(Creation)} \quad (37.24)$$

Because the rest energies m_0c^2 of the electron and positron are each equal to 0.511 MeV, this creation process—known as *pair production*—can occur only for photons with energy $hf \geq 1.022$ MeV. We note that energy and electric charge are both conserved in the process of pair production; the initial photon has zero electric charge and the net charge of the pair $+e$ and $-e$ is also zero. In order for momentum to be conserved, the process must take place in the vicinity of a nucleus like that of the lead atom; recoil of the nucleus is necessary to satisfy simultaneously the conditions for conservation of energy and momentum. Numerous subsequent experiments with X-rays under controlled conditions have verified that a definite threshold energy of 1.022 MeV does exist for the pair-production reaction (37.24) and that the probability of pair-production increases rapidly as the photon energy is increased above this threshold.

Left to itself, the positron is a stable particle, but it is extremely rare in our part of the universe. The reason for this is that in traversing ordinary matter a positron is ultimately *annihilated* by the following process:

$$(m_0c^2)_{\text{positron}} + (m_0c^2)_{\text{electron}} \rightarrow 2(hf)_{\text{photons}}. \quad \textit{(Annihilation)} \qquad (37.25)$$

It is observed that *two* photons appear as a result of the annihilation process; each photon has an energy of approximately 0.5 MeV, which indicates that the electron and positron have little kinetic energy when they are annihilated. Hence, the kinetic energy terms have been omitted from the expression. The two photons travel in opposite directions, each with a momentum having a magnitude of hf/c. (In some cases three photons are produced, but in this case also momentum and energy are conserved.) Thus, momentum is conserved in the annihilation process without the presence of a third particle as was the case in the creation process, where a heavy nucleus serves as a "silent partner" in the reaction.

The discovery that particles like the electron and positron can be created by a photon and can be annihilated by producing photons gave strong support for Einstein's interpretation of (37.22) in the generalized form given in (37.23).

37.10 NUCLEAR BINDING ENERGIES: NUCLEAR ENERGY RELEASE

Relativity provides an understanding of the stability of the atomic nucleus. If M_0 is the mass of a stable nucleus as measured by a mass spectrograph, the rest energy of the nucleus is given by the relation $E_0 = M_0c^2$. In order for a nucleus to be stable its rest energy must be less than the rest energy of the protons and neutrons (collectively called nucleons) making it up. If a nucleus contains Z protons, the total rest energy of the protons is $E_p = Zm_pc^2$, where m_p is the rest mass of a single proton. If the mass number of the nucleus is A, it contains $A - Z$ neutrons, so that the total rest energy of its neutrons is $E_n = (A - Z)m_nc^2$, where m_n is the rest mass of a single neutron. The nucleus is stable if $E_p + E_n > E_0$. The stability of the nucleus is measured by a quantity called its *binding energy* E_B, where E_B is the difference between the rest energy of the nucleons and the rest energy of the nucleus. The binding energy is equal to the energy that we would have to supply in order to break up the nucleus into its constituent nucleons. Thus,

$$E_B = \{[Zm_p + (A - Z)m_n] - M_0\}c^2. \qquad (37.26)$$

The nuclear binding energy increases with increasing mass number A—but not quite linearly. A quantity of more significance than E_B is the binding energy per nucleon E_B/A. A plot of this quantity as a function of mass number A is shown in

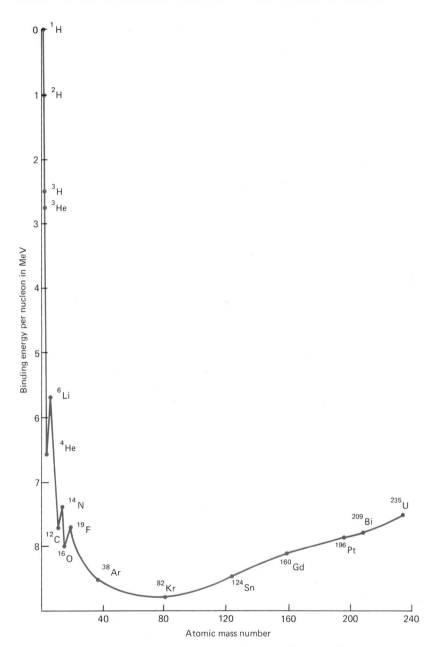

Fig. 37.8 The binding energy per nucleon as a function of mass number.

Fig. 37.8. The quantity E_B/A is plotted downward so that the most stable elements are represented by the lowest part of the curve. The most stable elements are in the range $A = 40$ to 120. As compared with nuclei in this range, extremely heavy elements with $A > 220$ are rather unstable and light elements with $A < 12$ are very unstable.

It is believed that the energy of the sun is associated with nuclear reactions in which light nuclei combine to form heavier nuclei with the release of the binding energy. Such a reaction is called a *fusion* reaction. In order for a nuclear reaction of this kind to proceed, the reacting nuclei must have sufficient energy in order for them to approach each other to within distances of the order of the nuclear radius $r \sim 10^{-15}$ m. In order for this to occur, the temperature must be enormous. The net result of a set of reactions believed to be prominent in the sun is the combination of four hydrogen nuclei to form a single stable helium nucleus. This set of reactions in the sun takes place slowly and requires many, many years; the sun is "burning" at a slow but fairly steady rate and is definitely not exploding!

Because the energy release in thermonuclear fusion reactions is enormous compared with chemical reactions, much attention has been devoted to the possibility of producing large-scale controlled fusion reactions on earth, where fossil fuels are being rapidly depleted but where normal hydrogen and its isotopes are abundant. Thus far, no completely successful results have been attained. The only use of thermonuclear fusion reactions on earth that has been possible thus far is in the "hydrogen bomb"; in this device, the enormous temperatures required can be produced for a few microseconds before the enormous release of energy by fusion blows the device apart.

We note in Fig. 37.3 that energy could also be produced by causing the nuclei of very heavy elements to "split" into nuclei of elements of smaller atomic mass. Beginning in 1934, Enrico Fermi (1901–1954) and his collaborators began a systematic study of the neutron capture reactions that occur when slow neutrons having the thermal energy $(3/2)kT$ characteristic of ordinary room temperature enter the nuclei of various elements. In 1939 Otto Frisch (1904–1979) and Lise Meitner (1878–1968), then refugees in Copenhagen and Stockholm, and their colleagues Otto Hahn (1879–1968), and F. Strassmann (1902–   ) in Berlin showed that neutron capture by $^{235}_{92}U$ resulted in the "splitting" or *fission* of the $^{235}_{92}U$ nucleus into nuclei of smaller atomic mass along with several neutrons. One such reaction is*

$$^{235}_{92}U + ^1_0n \rightarrow ^{144}_{56}Ba + ^{89}_{36}Kr + 3^1_0n. \quad \text{(Fission Reaction)}$$

The so-called fission products normally include one "heavy fragment" like $^{144}_{56}Ba$ and one "light fragment" like $^{89}_{36}Kr$. Fission products are not stable because their nuclei have too many neutrons to be stable nuclei with the atomic numbers involved. The fission products are therefore radioactive and attain stability only after a series of β decays. Careful measurements show that the total average energy release per fission that is available for thermal energy of material particles is about 200 MeV.

Because two or three neutrons are produced during each fission process, it is apparent that provided enough fissionable material is available, nuclear "chain reactions" are possible on a scale suitable for power production. How this is possible is demonstrated schematically in Fig. 37.9. In Fig. 37.9a, a single neutron produces fission of a $^{235}_{92}U$ nucleus in a block of uranium metal and three neutrons are released along with the fission fragments. All the neutrons are "lost" either by escape from the block of metal or through radiative capture by $^{238}_{92}U$ or some impurity that may be present. Hence, the reaction is not self-sustaining.

* In these expressions, the superscript gives the total number of nucleons (neutrons plus protons) and the subscript gives the number of protons in the nucleus.

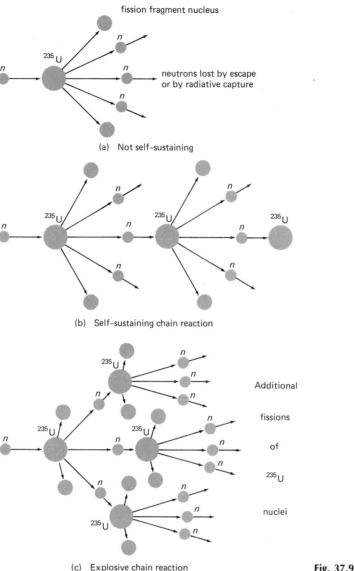

fission fragment nucleus

neutrons lost by escape
or by radiative capture

(a) Not self-sustaining

(b) Self-sustaining chain reaction

Additional

fissions

of

^{235}U

nuclei

(c) Explosive chain reaction

Fig. 37.9

If we increase the size of the block of uranium and surround it by water or by graphite that can slow down some of the initially fast neutrons so that they are more effective in producing the desired fission process, we can produce the situation shown in Fig. 37.9b. In this situation only two neutrons are "lost" and the third produces another fission process; the chain reaction is just self-sustaining. This is the situation to be desired in the nuclear reactors used for power production. The mass of a piece of uranium just large enough to maintain self-sustaining fission chains is called the *critical mass.*

In Fig. 37.9c we have a chain reaction that involves high "multiplication" in which every neutron released in one fission process produces the additional fission of another

$^{235}_{92}$U nucleus. Assuming three neutrons per fission, we would expect 3^N fissions in the Nth "generation" in the chain. Recalling that approximately 200 MeV of energy is released in each fission process, we see that an enormous amount of energy would be produced in an extremely short time—just the situation to be desired in a bomb. In an "atomic bomb" a subcritical mass of highly enriched $^{235}_{92}$U or $^{239}_{94}$Pu is rapidly compressed by conventional high explosives into a highly *supercritical mass* in which enormous amounts of energy are released before the bomb blows itself apart.

37.11 RELATIVISTIC PHYSICS

The principles of relativity formulated by Albert Einstein have given us a completely new view of the universe and have provided predictions of phenomena that were completely unknown at the time when the principles were first formulated. They have provided the basis for an understanding of nuclear physics and for the development of a new branch of engineering—nuclear engineering—as well as much applied science. It is possible that the continuing developments of the relativistic quantum mechanics will give even further and deeper insights into the nature of the universe. Still other types of technology may well develop.

For proper historical perspective we are at present perhaps really too close in time to the development of the two great theories of the century: relativity and quantum mechanics. Just as a person in 1700 really had no understanding of how Newtonian mechanics would alter history or as a person in 1890 could not foresee the practical applications that would result from Maxwell's theory of electromagnetism, so we today are not able to estimate the true significance of relativity and quantum theories for the future. However, we *can* say this: The 20th century is an exciting time for a scientist or engineer to be alive. *Much exciting work remains to be done!*

QUESTIONS

1. According to Mach's conclusion, the only motion that can be attributed to a particle is its motion relative to other matter in the universe. Why wasn't the inertial frame used by Newton in his formulation of his theory of motion acceptable to Mach?

2. Observer β at rest in frame B observes light of proper frequency f_0 and proper wavelength λ_0 emitted from a source at rest in his own frame. Observer α at rest in frame A, which is approaching frame B at a speed of $0.8c$, observes the same light but with frequency $f > f_0$ and wavelength $\lambda < \lambda_0$. What is the speed of light measured by α for light from the source in frame B?

3. When informed that the light coming to him from a source approaching him at speed $0.9c$ moves at the same speed c as light from a source at rest, a nonscientist says: "That statement is contrary to common sense!" How can you reply to this statement? What is "common sense"?

4. What is meant by the *principle of invariance?* What kinds of things are "invariant," and what kinds of things are "relative"?

5. If the fundamental physical quantities *mass, length,* and *time* are all "relative," how is it possible to establish a set of standards in terms of which the fundamental quantities can be measured?

6. Observer β at rest in frame B characterizes the field of a charge at rest in his own frame in terms of a purely electrostatic field. How would the field of this charge be characterized by observer α at the origin of frame A if frame B is approaching him at speed v?

7. Isn't there a severe contradiction of logic in the conclusion at the end of Section 37.3 that each observer sees the other's clock as running too slow? How can this be possible?

8. Is Newton's Second Principle valid in relativistic mechanics? Discuss.

9. Does Newton's Third Principle apply to the emission of photons? When an atom on the sun emits a photon that is absorbed by an atom on the earth, momentum is transferred from the atom on the sun to the atom on the earth. Can the emission and absorption be regarded as "action and reaction" in the sense of these terms in the statement of Newton's Third Principle? Discuss your reasoning.

10. Can the rest energy $E_0 = m_0c^2$ of a particle be regarded as a form of "internal energy"?

11. Is the Principle of Conservation of Energy valid in relativistic physics?

12. There are neutral particles known as *neutrinos* that apparently move with the speed of light. What can you say about the rest mass of a neutrino?

13. Conservation of electric charge is observed in creation and annihilation processes like those described by (37.24) and (37.25). With the development of large modern accelerators, it has become possible to create *negative protons*. What minimum total energy is required for the creation of a negative proton?

14. Following the discovery of the positron and the negative proton, there has been speculation as to the existence of "reversed matter" or "antimatter" in which negative nuclei are surrounded by positrons. If such matter does indeed exist in distant parts of the universe, is there any optical method by which we can verify its existence? If a piece of anitmatter in the form of a meteorite struck the earth, what would happen?

15. We now recognize four basic types of forces: gravitational, electromagnetic, and the strong and weak nuclear forces. Which type is of most important in astronomy? Which type is involved in what we have called elastic forces? Which type is responsible for chemical reactions? Which type is of most importance in nuclear physics? Discuss the basis of your answers.

PROBLEMS

1. Two reference frames A and B initially coincide with no relative motion. Then the frames acquire a relative velocity of separation **v** for 2 hr as measured by A, a relative velocity of approach of the same magnitude for 2 h as measured by A and after a total elapsed time of 4 h coincide at rest. Can observers α and β, by comparing notes, decide which frame has actually been in motion?

2. In Fig. 37.2 equip observer α with a light source and mirror and let him measure the time required for transmission and reflection of a light pulse. By looking at the process from the standpoint of observer β derive (37.3).

3. At what relative velocity must two frames move for an observer in one frame to observe a clock in the other frame to have a period of 2 s if the proper period of the clock is 1 s?

4. In Fig. 37.3 let observer α do a time-of-flight

experiment for photons along a rod of proper length l_0 and back in his own frame A. By looking at the experiment from the point of view of β, derive (37.7).

5. Find the magnitude of the velocity of an object with rest mass m_0 if its mass as determined by an observer is $2m_0$, $10m_0$, $100m_0$.

6. An object of uniform density ρ_0 has proper dimensions Δx_0, Δy_0, and Δz_0 as determined by an observer at rest relative to the object. What are the dimensions of this object as determined by an observer in a second frame moving at velocity $\mathbf{v}$ in the X direction relative to the first frame? What is the density of the object as determined by the second observer?

7. Observer α in system A places light sources S_1, S_2, S_3, and S_4 at the corners of a square frame at rest in A in the $X_A Y_A$ plane with sides parallel to the X_A and Y_A axes, as shown in the diagram. The sides of the frame have proper length l_0. If system A has a velocity $v = 0.8c$ in the X direction relative to system B, what is the area enclosed by the frame as determined by observer β at rest at the origin of system B? Recalling that time is required for light to travel from the sources to observer β, discuss the shape of the frame as *seen* by β at any instant. Does the shape of the frame as observed by β change as system A passes system B?

8. Observer β in frame B determines the velocity of a particle in his own frame moving in the X direction as $u_{Bx} = 0.5c$. What is the velocity u_{Ax} of the particle as determined by observer α if frame B is moving with speed $v = 0.5c$ in the X direction relative to frame A? What value would observer α compute for u_{Ax} if he employed the Galilean transformation (37.12)?

9. Repeat Problem 8 for a case in which frame B is moving with speed $v = 0.5c$ in the $-X$ direction relative to frame A.

10. Repeat Problems 8 and 9 for a case when observer β sees a particle moving at velocity $u_{By} = 0.5c$ in the Y direction in his own frame.

11. What values u_{Bx} would be determined by observer β in Problems 8 and 9 if observer α determines a value $u_{Ax} = 0.5c$ for a particle moving in the X direction in his own frame? Repeat for a case where observer α determines a value $u_{Ay} = 0.5c$ for a particle moving in the Y direction in his own frame.

12. An astronomer observes a sodium absorption line with a wavelength of 600 nm as a result of absorption by sodium atoms in the outer atmosphere of a star. The corresponding wavelength of sodium light as determined in the laboratory is 589 nm. What conclusions can the astronomer draw regarding the motion of the star relative to his observatory?

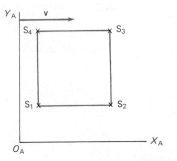
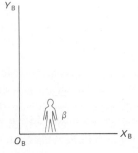

Problem 7

13. An astronomer finds that the light coming to him from a star is characterized by dark absorption lines that have frequencies that are 40% greater than the atomic lines of the elements involved as measured in the laboratory. The astronomer tries to account for this observed Doppler shift by assuming classically (a) that the star is approaching him at velocity v_1 and then (b) that he is approaching the star at velocity v_2. See Problem 33.8. Compare his values of v_1 and v_2 with the correct relativistic value of relative velocity v.

14. A stream of hydrogen atoms is directed down an evacuated tube in which the atoms move at a speed equal to $0.5c$. The hydrogen atoms are excited by electrons so that they emit light. An observer viewing the light emitted at right angles to the direction of the stream finds that even though the atoms have no radial motion relative to his spectrograph, the frequencies of the emission lines are not those emitted by hydrogen atoms in an ordinary discharge tube. Explain this so-called *transverse Doppler effect* and give an estimate of the fractional change in the frequency of each emission line.

15. Suppose that a 1-kg object were moving due northward at a velocity of $0.8c$. What would be the magnitude of the object's acceleration if it were subjected to a resultant force of 1 N directed (a) due westward, (b) due northward, and (c) due northwest?

16. What is the ratio of a particle's actual kinetic energy to the classical value of its kinetic energy if the particle is moving at a speed $0.6c$? At a speed of $0.8c$?

17. What is the minimum energy of a photon required to produce an electron–positron pair? If the annihilation of such a pair results in the production of two oppositely directed photons, what is the minimum energy of each of the photons?

18. An antiproton has the same rest mass as a proton but a charge of $-1e$. What is the minimum energy that must be available to create a proton–antiproton pair?

19. The shapes of atomic nuclei can be studied by means of the diffraction of the de Broglie waves associated with rapidly moving electrons having wavelengths comparable with the radius of the nucleus $\sim 10^{-15}$ m. Electrons can be accelerated to energies of 20 GeV by means of a large linear accelerator at Stanford University. Show that these electrons are satisfactory for use in such diffraction experiments.

NOTE: *In Problems 20–23 use data listed in Table 37.2.*

20. A deuteron ${}^2_1$H consists of a proton and a neutron. What is the total binding energy of the deuteron? What is its binding energy per nucleon?

21. Compute the total binding energies for each of the isotopes listed in Table 37.2. Compute the binding energy per nucleon for each of the isotopes listed in Table 37.2.

22. How much energy is released when four protons combine to form one ${}^4_2$He nucleus in the sun? How much energy is released when 4 kmol of protons combine to form 1 kmol of helium?

23. Thermal energies measured on earth indicate that the sun radiates energy at the rate of 1.2×10^{34} J per year. If all of this energy comes from hydrogen fusion to produce helium, how much mass does the sun lose per year? At this rate, how long would its mass last? Could the sun really continue to radiate at this rate until its mass is exhausted?

24. Taking 200 MeV as the average energy released in the fission of a single ${}^{235}_{92}$U nucleus, compute the number of fissions occurring

each second in a nuclear reactor operating at a power level of 4 MW. How much does the total mass of such a reactor decrease in one day?

25. The fuel value of coal is measured by the "heat of combustion" of the coal in J/kg or kcal/kg. Using 200 MeV as the energy release per fission, compute the corresponding "heat of fission" for pure $^{235}_{92}U$ in these units. To how many kg of coal (7500 kcal/kg) is 1 kg of $^{235}_{92}U$ equivalent in fuel value?

APPENDIX

I. THE GREEK ALPHABET

α	A	alpha	ι	I	iota	ρ	P	rho
β	B	beta	κ	K	kappa	σ	Σ	sigma
γ	Γ	gamma	λ	Λ	lambda	τ	T	tau
δ	Δ	delta	μ	M	mu	υ	Y	upsilon
ϵ	E	epsilon	ν	N	nu	ϕ	Φ	phi
ζ	Z	zeta	ξ	Ξ	xi	χ	X	chi
η	H	eta	o	O	omicron	ψ	Ψ	psi
θ	Θ	theta	π	Π	pi	ω	Ω	omega

II. USEFUL MATHEMATICAL RELATIONSHIPS

A. Algebra

Quadratic formula: If $ax^2 + bx + c = 0$, then

$$x = \frac{-b \pm \sqrt{b^2 - 4ac}}{2a}.$$

Binomial expansion:

$$(1 + x)^n = 1 + nx + \frac{n(n-1)}{2!} x^2 + \frac{n(n-1)(n-2)}{3!} x^3 + \cdots, \quad x^2 < 1.$$

Exponential expansion:

$$e^x = 1 + x + \frac{x^2}{2!} + \frac{x^3}{3!} + \frac{x^4}{4!} + \cdots.$$

B. Geometry

Circle of radius R: circumference $= 2\pi R$, area $= \pi R^2$.
Sphere of radius R: surface area $= 4\pi R^2$, volume $= \frac{4}{3}\pi R^3$.
Pythagorean theorem: $x^2 + y^2 = r^2$. (See Fig. A.1.)

C. Trigonometry

Trigonometric functions: (See Fig. A.1.)

$$\sin \phi = y/r \qquad \cos \phi = x/r$$
$$\tan \phi = y/x \qquad \cot \phi = x/y$$
$$\sec \phi = r/x \qquad \csc \phi = r/y$$

$$\sin(\alpha \pm \beta) = \sin \alpha \cos \beta \pm \cos \alpha \sin \beta$$
$$\cos(\alpha \pm \beta) = \cos \alpha \cos \beta \mp \sin \alpha \sin \beta$$

D. Differential Calculus

The differential calculus deals with rates of change. The general ideas involved can be gathered from a simple problem of kinematics. Suppose an observer finds that the position x of a particle moving along the X axis can be expressed as a function of the time t by the relation

$$x = 3.00 + 0.50t + 0.20t^2, \tag{A.1}$$

where the dependent variable x is in m and the independent variable t is in s. This

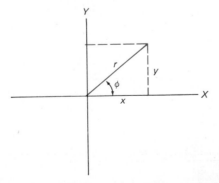

Fig. A.1

relation is graphed in Fig. A.2a. Our problem is to determine the instantaneous velocity v_x of the particle at any time t.

First, let us show in detail how the instantaneous velocity at some particular time such as $t = 2$ s can be obtained. We begin by determining the average velocity $\bar{v}_x = \Delta x/\Delta t$ for time intervals Δt of various lengths all of which begin at $t = 2$ s. For each time interval Δt we can determine the corresponding displacement Δx from (A.1) and can thereby construct the following table:

Time Interval	Δt (s)	Δx (m)	$\bar{v}_x = \Delta x/\Delta t$ (m/s)
2 to 4 s	2.000	3.400	1.700
2 to 3 s	1.000	1.500	1.500
2 to 2.5 s	0.500	0.700	1.400
2 to 2.2 s	0.200	0.268	1.340
2 to 2.1 s	0.100	0.132	1.320
2 to 2.05 s	0.050	0.0655	1.310
2 to 2.01 s	0.010	0.0130	1.300
2 to 2.005 s	0.005	0.0065	1.300
2 to 2.001 s	0.001	0.0013	1.300

We note that as the time interval Δt becomes smaller and smaller, the ratio $\Delta x/\Delta t$ ceases to change as the time interval is decreased. We say that the ratio $\Delta x/\Delta t$ approaches the limiting value 1.300 m/s. The instantaneous velocity v_x at $t = 2$ s is equal to the limiting value of this ratio as Δt becomes arbitrarily small. Geometrically, the limiting value of the ratio $\Delta x/\Delta t$ is the *slope* of the line shown in Fig. A.2a that is tangent to the x versus t curve at the point where $t = 2$ s.

We now generalize this idea. If x is a dependent variable depending in some way

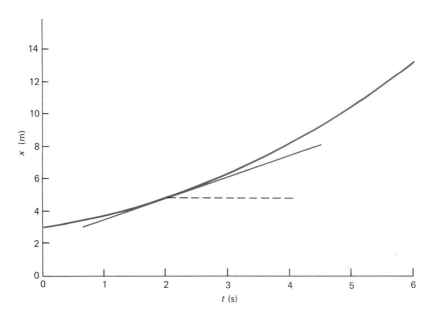

Fig. A.2(a)

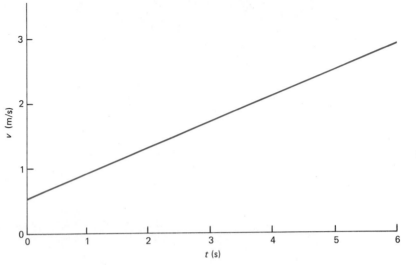

on the independent variable t, then the limiting value of the ratio $\Delta x/\Delta t$ as Δt becomes arbitrarily small is called the *derivative dx/dt* of x with respect to t:

$$\frac{dx}{dt} = \lim_{\Delta t \to 0} \frac{\Delta x}{\Delta t}.$$

The values of the derivatives of various functions can be determined by the methods of calculus. Tables of derivatives appear in calculus textbooks. A short table of useful derivatives is given below.

For the simple functional relationship given in (A.1), we can obtain a general expression for the instantaneous velocity v_x as follows:

$$v_x = \frac{dx}{dt} = \frac{d}{dt}(3.00 + 0.50t + 0.20t^2) = 0.50 + 0.40t. \tag{A.2}$$

By substituting $t = 2$ s in (A.2) we obtain for the instantaneous velocity at this time the value $v_x = 1.30$ m/s, in agreement with the result obtained in the table that was constructed above. In Fig. A.2b, we give a plot of $v_x = 0.50 + 0.40t$ as a function of time. We see that the v_x versus t curve is a straight line of constant slope. Therefore, the average acceleration $\bar{a}_x = \Delta v_x/\Delta t$ is the same at all times t and for all values of Δt. The instantaneous acceleration a_x is simply equal to the constant value of $\bar{a}_x$, which is easily determined from (A.2). In terms of the derivative of (A.2), we have

$$a_x = \lim_{\Delta x \to 0} \frac{\Delta v_x}{\Delta t} = \frac{dv_x}{dt} = \frac{d}{dt}(0.50 + 0.40t) = 0.40 \text{ m/s}^2.$$

E. A Short Table of Derivatives

In keeping with common mathematical notation, arbitrary functions are represented by f and g, and the independent variable is represented by x. The symbol a is used to represent a constant.

$$\frac{d}{dx}(af) = a\frac{df}{dx} \qquad\qquad \frac{d}{dx}(f+g) = \frac{df}{dx} + \frac{dg}{dx}$$

$$\frac{d}{dx}(fg) = f\frac{dg}{dx} + g\frac{df}{dx} \qquad \frac{d}{dx}\left(\frac{f}{g}\right) = \frac{g\,df/dx - f\,dg/dx}{g^2}$$

$$\frac{d}{dx}(x^n) = nx^{n-1} \qquad\qquad \frac{d}{dx}\left(\frac{1}{x}\right) = \frac{-1}{x^2}$$

$$\frac{d}{dx}(e^x) = e^x \qquad\qquad \frac{d}{dx}(\ln x) = \frac{1}{x}$$

$$\frac{d}{dx}\sin x = \cos x \qquad\qquad \frac{d}{dx}\cos x = -\sin x$$

$$\frac{d}{dx}\tan x = \sec^2 x \qquad\qquad \frac{d}{dx}g[f(x)] = \frac{dg}{df}\frac{df}{dx} \quad (Chain\ Rule).$$

F. Partial Derivatives

When a function f is given in terms of several independent variables such as x and y, the partial derivative $\partial f/\partial x$ of the function with respect to the independent variable x is the derivative that we obtain with respect to this variable when we treat the other independent variable y as a constant. In Fig. A.3 we show a surface representing the values of some function $f(x,y)$ for values of the independent variables x and y lying in the first quadrant. The partial derivative $\partial f/\partial x$ at the point P on this surface is just the slope of the line AB that is tangent to the surface at P and lies in a plane perpendicular to the Y axis. Similarly, the partial derivative $\partial f/\partial y$ at the point P is the slope of the line CD that is tangent to the surface at P and lies in a plane perpendicular to the X axis.

This idea is readily extended to an arbitrary number of independent variables. As an example, consider a rectangular solid lying in the first octant with three of its edges aligned with the axes of a rectangular coordinate system and one corner at the origin. The volume of the rectangular solid is $V = xyz$, where x, y, and z are

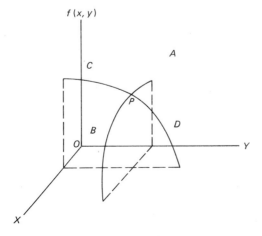

Fig. A.3

the lengths of its edges. The partial derivatives of the volume with respect to each of the independent variables in turn are

$$\frac{\partial V}{\partial x} = yz, \quad \frac{\partial V}{\partial y} = xz, \quad \text{and} \quad \frac{\partial V}{\partial z} = xy.$$

The *total differential* of a function $f(x,y,z)$ of three independent variables is the change df in the function when the independent variables are given very small, independent increments dx, dy, and dz. It can be shown that the total differential is given by the following expression:

$$df = \frac{\partial f}{\partial x} dx + \frac{\partial f}{\partial y} dy + \frac{\partial f}{\partial z} dz. \tag{A.3}$$

G. Integral Calculus

The integral calculus can be approached from the problem of determining the area under a curve like the one in Fig. A.4, which shows the values of a function f of the independent variable x. An approximate value of the area A_{N0} between the curve and the X axis for the region bounded by the coordinates x_0 and x_N can be obtained by dividing the region into n narrow rectangles as shown in Fig. A.4 and summing the areas of the rectangles. We have chosen rectangles such that the upper right corner of each rectangle is on the curve f. The area of the ith rectangle is $f_i \Delta x_i$, and the approximate area under the curve is obtained by summing the areas of all the rectangles from $i = 1$ to $i = n$:

$$A_{N0} \simeq f_1 \Delta x_1 + f_2 \Delta x_2 + f_3 \Delta x_3 + \cdots + f_n \Delta x_n = \sum_{i=1}^{n} f_i \Delta x_i.$$

By increasing the number n of rectangles and reducing their widths Δx_i, we can approximate the area A_{N0} more and more closely. The limit of the above summation

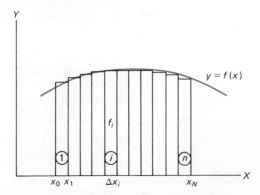

Fig. A.4

obtained by allowing $n \to \infty$ in such a way that $\Delta x_i \to 0$ for all the rectangles gives the exact area A_{N0} and defines the definite integral of $f(x)$ from x_0 to x_N:

$$A_{N0} = \lim_{\substack{n \to \infty \\ \Delta x \to 0}} \sum_{i=1}^{n} f_i \Delta x_i = \int_{x_0}^{x_N} f(x)\, dx. \tag{A.4}$$

The mathematical operation represented by (A.4) is inverse to the operation of differentiation. In order to see this, consider the integral of the function f as a function of its upper limit. We define a new function $\phi(x)$ by the relation

$$\phi(x) = \int_{a}^{x} f(t)\, dt, \tag{A.5}$$

where a has some fixed value and the independent variable x now represents the upper limit of the integration process. The derivative of the function $\phi(x)$ is given by

$$\frac{d\phi}{dx} = \lim_{\Delta x \to 0} \frac{\Delta \phi}{\Delta x},$$

where $\Delta \phi$ is the change in the function ϕ when the independent variable changes from x to $x + \Delta x$. By consideration of (A.4) and Fig. A.4 we see that $\Delta \phi$ is just the area of one additional rectangle of width Δx added to the right in Fig. A.4: $\Delta \phi = f(x + \Delta x) \Delta x$. Therefore, we have

$$\frac{d\phi}{dx} = \lim_{\Delta x \to 0} \frac{f(x + \Delta x)\Delta x}{\Delta x} = f(x). \tag{A.6}$$

The function ϕ defined by (A.5) is said to be an *antiderivative* of the function f. Since we can add any constant to ϕ without changing its derivative, the antiderivative of a function is not unique. So-called "Tables of Integrals" give lists of antiderivatives of various functions f. A constant c, called a *constant of integration*, can be added to any antiderivative obtained from such a table. A short table of useful antiderivatives is given below.

If an antiderivative ϕ of a function f is known, the definite integral of f given in (A.4) can be obtained very simply. Consideration of (A.4), (A.5), and the interpretation of a definite integral as the area under a curve as shown in Fig. A.4 leads to the conclusion that

$$\int_{x_0}^{x_N} f(x)\, dx = \phi(x_N) - \phi(x_0). \tag{A.7}$$

H. A Short Table of Integrals

The symbols f and g represent arbitrary functions of the independent variable x. The symbol a is used to represent a constant.

$$\int a\,dx = ax \qquad\qquad \int af(x)\,dx = a\int f(x)\,dx$$

$$\int [f(x)+g(x)]dx = \int f(x)\,dx + \int g(x)\,dx \qquad \int x^n\,dx = \frac{x}{(n+1)},\quad n\neq -1$$

$$\int \frac{dx}{x} = \ln|x| \qquad\qquad \int e^{ax}\,dx = \frac{1}{a}e^{ax}$$

$$\int \sin(ax)\,dx = -\frac{1}{a}\cos(ax) \qquad \int \cos(ax)\,dx = \frac{1}{a}\sin(ax)$$

$$\int \tan(ax)\,dx = -\frac{1}{a}\ln|\cos(ax)| \qquad \int \sin^2(ax)\,dx = \frac{x}{2} - \frac{\sin(2ax)}{4a}$$

$$\int \cos^2(ax)\,dx = \frac{x}{2} + \frac{\sin(2ax)}{4a} \qquad \int \frac{dx}{a^2+x^2} = \frac{1}{a}\arctan\left(\frac{x}{a}\right)$$

$$\int \frac{dx}{a^2-x^2} = \frac{1}{2a}\ln\left|\frac{x+a}{x-a}\right| \qquad \int \frac{dx}{\sqrt{a^2-x^2}} = \arcsin\left(\frac{x}{a}\right)$$

$$\int \frac{dx}{\sqrt{x^2-a^2}} = \ln|x+\sqrt{x^2-a^2}| \qquad \int \frac{dx}{\sqrt{x^2+a^2}} = \ln|x+\sqrt{x^2+a^2}|$$

III. THE INTERNATIONAL SYSTEM OF UNITS

A. Names and Symbols of SI Units

Quantity	Name of Unit	Symbol
SI Base Units		
length	meter	m
mass	kilogram	kg
time	second	s
electric current	ampere	A
thermodynamic temperature	kelvin	K
luminous intensity	candela	cd
amount of substance	mole	mol
SI Derived Units		
area	square meter	m^2
volume	cubic meter	m^3
frequency	hertz	$Hz = s^{-1}$
mass density (density)	kilogram per cubic meter	kg/m^3
speed, velocity	meter per second	m/s
angular velocity	radian per second	rad/s
acceleration	meter per second squared	m/s^2
angular acceleration	radian per second squared	rad/s^2
force	newton	$N = kg\cdot m/s^2$
pressure (mechanical stress)	pascal	$Pa = N/m^2$
dynamic viscosity	newton-second per square meter	$N\cdot s/m^2$

Quantity	Name of Unit	Symbol
SI Derived Units		
work, energy, quantity of heat	joule	$J = N \cdot m$
power	watt	$W = J/s$
quantity of electricity	coulomb	$C = A \cdot s$
potential difference, EMF	volt	$V = W/A$
electric field strength	volt per meter	V/m
electric resistance	ohm	$\Omega = V/A$
capacitance	farad	$F = A \cdot s/V$
magnetic flux	weber	$Wb = V \cdot s$
inductance	henry	$H = V \cdot s/A$
magnetic flux density (field strength)	tesla	$T = Wb/m^2$
magnetic intensity	ampere per meter	A/m
entropy	joule per kelvin	J/K
specific heat capacity	joule per kilogram kelvin	$J/(kg \cdot K)$
thermal conductivity	watt per meter kelvin	$W/(m \cdot K)$
SI Supplementary Units		
plane angle	radian	rad
solid angle	steradian	sr

B. Definitions of SI Base Units

ampere (A) The *ampere* is that constant current which, if maintained in two straight parallel conductors of infinite length, of negligible circular cross section, and placed 1 meter apart in vacuum, would produce between these conductors a force equal to 2×10^{-7} newton per meter of length.

candela (cd) The *candela* is the luminous intensity, in the perpendicular direction, of a surface of 1/600,000 square meter of a blackbody at the temperature of freezing platinum under a pressure of 101,325 newtons per square meter.

kelvin (K) The *kelvin,* unit of thermodynamic temperature, is the fraction 1/273.16 of the thermodynamic temperature of the triple point of water.

kilogram (kg) The *kilogram* is the unit of mass; it is equal to the mass of the international prototype of the kilogram. (The international prototype of the kilogram is a particular cylinder of platinum-iridium alloy which is preserved in a vault at Sèvres, France, by the International Bureau of Weights and Measures.)

meter (m) The *meter* is the length equal to 1,650,763.73 wavelengths in vacuum of the radiation corresponding to the transition between two specified energy levels of the krypton-86 atom.

mole (mol) The *mole* is the amount of substance of a system which contains as many elementary entities as there are carbon atoms in 0.012 kg of carbon 12. The elementary entities must be specified and may be atoms, molecules, ions, electrons, other particles, or specified groups of such particles.

radian (rad) The *radian* is the plane angle between two radii of a circle which cut off on the circumference an arc equal in length to the radius.

second (s) The *second* is the duration of 9,192,631,770 periods of the radiation corresponding to the transition between two specified energy levels of the cesium-133 atom.

steradian (sr) The *steradian* is the solid angle which, having its vertex in the center of a sphere, cuts off an area of the surface of the sphere equal to that of a square with sides of length equal to the radius of the sphere.

IV. ASTRONOMICAL DATA

Earth

Radius: mean . . . . 6371 km = 3959 mi

equatorial . . . . 6378 km = 3963 mi

polar . . . . 6357 km = 3950 mi

Distance from sun: mean . . . . . . 149.5×10^6 km = 92.9×10^6 mi

aphelion . . . . 152.1×10^6 km = 94.5×10^6 mi

perihelion . . 147.1×10^6 km = 91.4×10^6 mi

Period of rotation . . . . 86 164 s = 1 sidereal day = 23.94 h

Radiation from sun at

earth's mean distance . . . . 1.35 kW/m²

Moon

Radius . . . . 1 741 km = 1 082 mi

Distance from earth: mean . . . . . 384 400 km = 239 000 mi

apogee . . . . 407 000 km = 253 000 mi

perigee . . . 357 000 km = 222 000 mi

Period of revolution

= period of rotation . . . . 27.322 d

Mass . . . . 7.343×10^{22} kg

Mean density . . . . 3.33 Mg/m³

Sun

Radius . . . . 696 500 km = 432 200 mi

Mass . . . . 1.987×10^{30} kg

Mean density . . . . 1.41 Mg/m³

Planets	Distance from Sun (10⁶ km)			Period of Revolution (d)	Mean Radius (km)	Mass[a] (10²⁴ kg)	Mean Density (Mg/m³)
	Mean	Aphelion	Perihelion				
Mercury	57.9	69.8	46.0	88.0	2 420	3.167	5.46
Venus	108.1	109.0	107.5	224.7	6 261	4.870	4.96
Earth	149.5	152.1	147.1	365.2	6 371	5.975	5.52
Mars	227.8	249.2	206.6	687.0	3 389	0.639	4.12
Jupiter	777.8	815.9	740.7	4 333	69 900	1900	1.33
Saturn	1426	1508	1348	10 760	57 500	568.9	0.71
Uranus	2868	3007	2737	30 690	23 700	86.9	1.56
Neptune	4494	4537	4459	60 190	21 500	102.9	2.47
Pluto	5908	7370	4450	90 740	2 900	5.37	5.50

[a] Excluding satellites.

V. PHYSICAL CONSTANTS

The values given in the following table are from E. Richard Cohen and B. N. Taylor, *J. Phys. Chem. Ref. Data* **2**, 633 (1973). The numbers in parentheses represent one standard-deviation uncertainties in the last digits of the quoted value.

Quantity	Symbol	Value	Units
Speed of light	c	$2.99792458(1.2) \times 10^8$	m/s
Permeability of vacuum	μ_0	$4\pi \times 10^{-7}$	H/m
Permittivity of vacuum	$\epsilon_0 = 1/\mu_0 c^2$	$8.85418782(7) \times 10^{-12}$	$C^2/J \cdot m$
Gravitational constant	G	$6.6720(41) \times 10^{-11}$	$N \cdot m^2/kg^2$
Elementary charge	e	$1.6021892(46) \times 10^{-19}$	C
Planck constant	h	$6.626176(36) \times 10^{-34}$	$J \cdot s$
Boltzmann constant	k	$1.380662(44) \times 10^{-23}$	J/K
Stefan-Boltzmann constant	σ	$5.67032(71) \times 10^{-8}$	$W \cdot m^2/K^4$
Avogadro constant	N_A	$6.022045(31) \times 10^{26}$	$kmol^{-1}$
Atomic mass unit	u	$1.6605655(86) \times 10^{-27}$	kg
Gas constant	R	$8.31441(26) \times 10^3$	$J/kmol \cdot K$
Bohr magneton	$\mu_B = eh/4\pi m_e$	$9.274078(36) \times 10^{-24}$	J/T
Faraday constant	F	$9.648456(27) \times 10^7$	C/kmol

Rest Masses of Particles

Particle	(u)	(kg)	(MeV)
electron	0.00054858026(21)	$9.109534(47) \times 10^{-31}$	0.5110034(14)
proton	1.007276470(11)	$1.6726485(86) \times 10^{-27}$	938.2796(27)
neutron	1.008665012(37)	$1.6749543(86) \times 10^{-27}$	939.5731(27)
deuteron	2.013553229(22)	$3.3436370(86) \times 10^{-27}$	1875.628(5)
alpha particle	4.001506191(48)	$6.6447631(86) \times 10^{-27}$	3727.409(11)

energy equivalent of one atomic mass unit: 931.5016(26) MeV
standard atmosphere: 101325 Pa
standard gravitational acceleration: 9.80665 m/s²
thermochemical kilocalorie: 4184 J

VI. TABLES OF CONVERSION FACTORS

Angle	°	′	″	rad	rev
1 degree =	1	60	3600	1.745×10^{-2}	2.778×10^{-3}
1 minute =	1.667×10^{-2}	1	60	2.909×10^{-4}	4.630×10^{-5}
1 second =	2.778×10^{-4}	1.667×10^{-2}	1	4.848×10^{-6}	7.716×10^{-7}
1 radian =	57.30	3438	2.063×10^5	1	0.1592
1 revolution =	360	2.16×10^4	1.296×10^6	6.283	1

Length	m	km	in.	ft	mi
1 meter =	1	10^{-3}	39.37	3.281	6.214×10^{-4}
1 kilometer =	1000	1	3.937×10^4	3281	0.6214
1 inch =	0.0254	2.54×10^{-5}	1	0.0833	1.578×10^{-5}
1 foot =	0.3048	3.048×10^{-4}	12	1	1.894×10^{-4}
1 statute mile =	1609	1.609	6.336×10^4	5280	1

1 angstrom = 10^{-10} m
1 X-unit = 10^{-13} m
1 nautical mile = 1852 m = 1.1508 mi = 6076.10 ft
1 astronomical unit = 149.5×10^6 km
1 fermi = 10^{-15} m
1 Bohr radius = 5.291 67 $\times 10^{-11}$ m
1 light year = 9.4600×10^{12} km
1 parsec = 3.084×10^{13} km

1 fathom = 6 ft
1 yard (yd) = 3 ft
1 rod = 16.5 ft
1 mil = 10^{-3} in.
1 league = 3 nautical miles

Area	m^2	cm^2	ft^2	$in.^2$
1 square meter =	1	10^4	10.76	1550
1 square centimeter =	10^{-4}	1	1.076×10^{-3}	0.1550
1 square foot =	9.290×10^{-2}	929.0	1	144
1 square inch =	6.452×10^{-4}	6.452	6.944×10^{-3}	1

1 square mile = 27 878 400 ft^2 = 640 acre
1 circular mil = 7.854×10^{-7} $in.^2$
1 acre = 43 560 ft^2
1 barn = 10^{-28} m^2
1 hectare = 10 000 m^2 = 2.471 acre

Volume	m^3	cm^3	ft^3	$in.^3$
1 cubic meter =	1	10^6	35.31	6.102×10^4
1 cubic centimeter =	10^{-6}	1	3.531×10^{-5}	0.06102
1 cubic foot =	2.832×10^{-2}	28320	1	1728
1 cubic inch =	1.639×10^{-5}	16.39	5.787×10^{-4}	1

1 U.S. fluid gallon = 4 quarts = 8 pints = 128 fluid ounces = 231 $in.^3$
1 British Imperial gallon = the volume of 10 lb of water at 62°F = 277.42 $in.^3$
1 liter = 1000 cm^3

Mass	g	kg	lb	slug	ton
1 gram =	1	0.001	0.002 205	6.852×10^{-5}	1.102×10^{-6}
1 kilogram =	1000	1	2.205	6.852×10^{-2}	1.102×10^{-3}
1 pound (avoirdupois) =	453.6	0.4536	1	3.108×10^{-2}	0.0005
1 slug =	1.459×10^4	14.59	32.17	1	1.609×10^{-2}
1 ton-mass =	9.072×10^5	907.2	2000	62.16	1

1 avoirdupois pound = 16 avoirdupois ounces = 7000 grains = 0.453 592 37 kg
1 troy or apothecaries' pound = 12 troy or apothecaries' ounces
$\qquad\qquad\qquad$ = 0.8229 avoirdupois pound = 5760 grains
1 long ton = 2240 lb = 20 cwt
1 metric ton = 1000 kg = 2205 lb
1 atomic mass unit (u) = 1.6604×10^{-27} kg
1 stone = 14 lb
1 carat = 0.2 g
1 hundredweight (cwt) = 112 lb
1 pennyweight (dwt) = 24 grains

Time	y	d	h	min	s
1 year =	1	365.2	8.766×10^3	5.259×10^5	3.156×10^7
1 day =	2.738×10^{-3}	1	24	1440	86 400
1 hour =	1.141×10^{-4}	4.167×10^{-2}	1	60	3600
1 minute =	1.901×10^{-6}	6.944×10^{-4}	1.667×10^{-2}	1	60
1 second =	3.169×10^{-8}	1.157×10^{-5}	2.778×10^{-4}	1.667×10^{-2}	1

1 sidereal day = period of rotation of earth = 86 164 s
1 year = period of revolution of earth = 365.242 198 79 d

Density	slug/ft³	lb/ft³	lb/in.³	kg/m³	g/cm³
1 slug per ft³ =	1	32.17	1.862×10^{-2}	515.4	0.5154
1 pound per ft³ =	3.108×10^{-2}	1	5.787×10^{-4}	16.02	1.602×10^{-2}
1 pound per in.³ =	53.71	1728	1	2.768×10^4	27.68
1 kg per m³ =	1.940×10^{-3}	6.243×10^{-2}	3.613×10^{-5}	1	0.001
1 gram per cm³ =	1.940	62.43	3.613×10^{-2}	1000	1

Speed	ft/s	km/h	m/s	mi/h	knot
1 foot per second =	1	1.097	0.3048	0.6818	0.5925
1 kilometer per hour =	0.9113	1	0.2778	0.6214	0.5400
1 meter per second =	3.281	3.6	1	2.237	1.944
1 mile per hour =	1.467	1.609	0.4470	1	0.8689
1 knot =	1.688	1.852	0.5144	1.151	1

1 knot = 1 nautical mile/h

Force	dyne	kgf	N	p	pdl
1 dyne =	1	1.020×10^{-6}	10^{-5}	2.248×10^{-6}	7.233×10^{-5}
1 kilogram-force =	9.807×10^5	1	9.807	2.205	70.93
1 newton =	10^5	0.1020	1	0.2248	7.233
1 pound =	4.448×10^5	0.4536	4.448	1	32.17
1 poundal =	1.383×10^4	1.410×10^{-2}	0.1383	3.108×10^{-2}	1

1 kgf = 9.806 65 N
1 p = 32.173 98 pdl

Pressure	atm	inch of water	cm Hg	Pa (N/m²)	lb/in.²
1 atmosphere =	1	406.8	76	1.013×10^5	14.70
1 inch of water[a] =	2.458×10^{-3}	1	0.1868	249.1	0.03613
1 cm mercury[a] =	1.316×10^{-2}	5.353	1	1333	0.1934
1 pascal =	9.869×10^{-6}	0.004 105	7.501×10^{-4}	1	1.450×10^{-4}
1 pound per in² =	6.805×10^{-2}	27.68	5.171	6.895×10^3	1

[a] Under standard gravitational acceleration, and temperature of 4°C for water, 0°C for mercury.

1 bar = 10^5 Pa   1 torr = 1 mm Hg
1 cm of water = 98.07 Pa   1 ft of water = 62.43 p/ft²

Energy	Btu	ft · p	J	kcal	kWh
1 British thermal unit =	1	777.9	1055	0.2520	2.930×10^{-4}
1 foot-pound =	1.285×10^{-3}	1	1.356	3.240×10^{-4}	3.766×10^{-7}
1 joule =	9.481×10^{-4}	0.7376	1	2.390×10^{-4}	2.778×10^{-7}
1 kilocalorie =	3.968	3086	4184	1	1.163×10^{-3}
1 kilowatt-hour =	3413	2.655×10^6	3.6×10^6	860.2	1

1 kcal = 2.612×10^{22} eV
1 erg = 10^{-7} joule
1 horsepower-hour = 1.980×10^6 ft · p

Power	Btu/h	ft · p/s	hp	kcal/s	kW	W
1Btu/h =	1	0.2161	3.929×10^{-4}	7.000×10^{-5}	2.930×10^{-4}	0.2930
1 ft · p/s =	4.628	1	1.818×10^{-3}	3.239×10^{-4}	1.356×10^{-3}	1.356
1 horsepower =	2545	550	1	0.1782	0.7457	745.7
1 kcal/s =	1.429×10^4	3087	5.613	1	4.184	4184
1 kilowatt =	3413	737.6	1.341	0.2390	1	1000
1 watt =	3.413	0.7376	1.341×10^{-3}	2.390×10^{-4}	0.001	1

1 ton (refrigeration) = 12 000 Btu/h

Electric Charge	abC	C	statC
1 abcoulomb (1 emu) =	1	10	2.998×10^{10}
1 coulomb =	0.1	1	2.998×10^{9}
1 statcoulomb (1 esu) =	3.336×10^{-11}	3.336×10^{-10}	1

1 ampere-hour = 3600 C

Electric Current	abA	A	statA
1 abampere (1 emu) =	1	10	2.998×10^{10}
1 ampere =	0.1	1	2.998×10^{9}
1 statampere (1 esu) =	3.336×10^{-11}	3.336×10^{-10}	1

Electric Potential	abV	V	statV
1 abvolt (1 emu) =	1	10^{-8}	3.336×10^{-11}
1 volt =	10^{8}	1	3.336×10^{-3}
1 statvolt (1 esu) =	2.998×10^{10}	299.8	1

Electric Resistance	abohm	Ω	statohm
1 abohm (1 emu) =	1	10^{-9}	1.113×10^{-21}
1 ohm =	10^{9}	1	1.113×10^{-12}
1 statohm (1 esu) =	8.987×10^{20}	8.987×10^{11}	1

Capacitance	abf	F	μF	statF
1 abfarad (1 emu) =	1	10^{9}	10^{15}	8.987×10^{20}
1 farad =	10^{-9}	1	10^{6}	8.987×10^{11}
1 microfarad =	10^{-15}	10^{-6}	1	8.987×10^{5}
1 statfarad (1 esu) =	1.113×10^{-21}	1.113×10^{-12}	1.113×10^{-6}	1

Inductance	abH	H	mH	statH
1 abhenry (1 emu) =	1	10^{-9}	10^{-6}	1.113×10^{-21}
1 henry =	10^{9}	1	1000	1.113×10^{-12}
1 millihenry =	10^{6}	0.001	1	1.113×10^{-15}
1 stathenry (1 esu) =	8.987×10^{20}	8.987×10^{11}	8.987×10^{14}	1

Magnetic Flux	Mx	kiloline	Wb
1 maxwell (1 line or 1 emu) =	1	0.001	10^{-8}
1 kiloline =	1000	1	10^{-5}
1 weber =	10^{8}	10^{5}	1

Magnetic Field Strength $\mathscr{B}$	G	kiloline/in²	T	mG
1 gauss (line per cm²) =	1	6.452×10^{-3}	10^{-4}	1000
1 kiloline per square inch =	155.0	1	1.550×10^{-2}	1.550×10^{5}
1 tesla =	10^{4}	64.52	1	10^{7}
1 milligauss =	0.001	6.452×10^{-6}	10^{-7}	1

$1 \text{ T} = 1 \text{ Wb/m}^2$

Magnetomotive Force	abA-turn	A-turn	Gi
1 abampere-turn =	1	10	12.57
1 ampere-turn =	0.1	1	1.257
1 gilbert =	7.958×10^{-2}	0.7958	1

Magnetic Intensity $\mathscr{H}$	abA/cm	A/in.	A/m	Oe
1 abampere-turn per centimeter =	1	25.40	1000	12.57
1 ampere-turn per inch =	3.937×10^{-2}	1	39.37	0.4947
1 ampere-turn per meter =	0.001	2.540×10^{-2}	1	1.257×10^{-2}
1 oersted =	7.958×10^{-2}	2.021	79.58	1

Mass-energy Equivalents	kg	u	J	MeV
1 kilogram ~	1	6.025×10^{26}	8.987×10^{16}	5.610×10^{29}
1 atomic mass unit ~	1.660×10^{-27}	1	1.492×10^{-10}	931.5
1 joule ~	1.113×10^{-17}	6.705×10^{9}	1	6.242×10^{12}
1 million electron-volts ~	1.783×10^{-30}	1.074×10^{-3}	1.602×10^{-13}	1

ANSWERS FOR ODD-NUMBERED PROBLEMS

CHAPTER 1

1. 4.02×10^7 m; 5.15×10^{14} m², 1.10×10^{21} m³
3. $\pi/6$, $\pi/4$, $\pi/3$, . . . , etc.
5. 0.25 rad;   14.3°;   0.0398 rev
7. (1) 5 m, 53.1°;   (2) 5 m, 126.9°;   (3) 5 m, 233.1°;   (4) 5 m, 306.9°
9. (1) 1.73 m, 54.7°, 45.0°;   (2) 1.73 m, 54.7°, 54.7°, 54.7°
11. (1) 60°, 120°;   (2) 10 m, 60° or 120°, 35.3°;   (3) 7.07 m, 5.00 m, ± 5.00 m
13. (1) 2π m;   (2) 1.61×10^8 m²;   (3) 5.15×10^{14} m³
15. −1.07 m, 1.83 m, 1.51 m
17. 1.08 m, 283°, −0.84 m
19. 1.714 rad, 0.627 rad, 0.965 rad
21. 1.14 m, 299°, 1.48 m
23. 2.72 m, 42.7°, 70.4°, 126.0°
25. 4.91×10^{-2} m³
27. 87.7 cm³;   263 cm³
29. 1.44, 2.08

CHAPTER 2

1. 10 km in a direction 36.9° north of east
3. $D_x = 34.6$ km; $D_y = 20.0$ km
5. $D = 5.38$ m; $\alpha = 68.2°$, $\beta = 56.1°$, $\gamma = 42.0°$
7. For Problem 5, $2\mathbf{i} + 3\mathbf{j} + 4\mathbf{k}$;   For Problem 6, $2\mathbf{i} + 2\mathbf{j} - 2\mathbf{k}$
9. 6.96 km, 6.96 km, 1.74 km; $\alpha = 45.9°$, $\beta = 45.9°$, $\gamma = 80°$
11. 4.58 m; $\alpha = 29.2°$, $\beta = 77.4°$, $\gamma = 64.1°$
13. $(4.58 \text{ m})\hat{\mathbf{D}}$; $\hat{\mathbf{D}} = 0.873\mathbf{i} + 0.218\mathbf{j} + 0.437\mathbf{k}$
15. $\mathbf{r} = (3 \text{ m})\mathbf{i} + (4 \text{ m})\mathbf{j} + (5 \text{ m})\mathbf{k} = (7.07 \text{ m})\hat{\mathbf{r}}$, $\hat{\mathbf{r}} = 0.424\mathbf{i} + 0.566\mathbf{j} + 0.707\mathbf{k}$
17. 1.54×10^4 km; 9.81×10^3 km
19. 3.12 km
21. 28.3 m, northward

23. 26.9 m;   26.9 m;   −10 m;   −15 m;   −20 m
25. 3.6 m; $D_x = 2$ m; $D_y = 3$ m
27. (a) (3 m)i + (2 m)j + (1 m)k; (b) (−1 m)i + (4 m)j + (−5 m)k;
     (c) (−4 m)i + (2 m)j + (−6 m)k
29. (4 m)i;   (2 m)i + (3 m)j;   (6 m)i + (3 m)j
31. 8.26 m, 22.7 m, 6.47 m;   D = (−8.26 m, −22.7 m, 33.5 m);   41.3 m
33. 4.76 m at 30.8° south of west
35. 0.694, −0.586, 0.417
37. 81 cm;   −0.802, 0.519, −0.296
39. 2.90 m;   0.829, −0.092, −0.552

CHAPTER 3

1. 68 km/h;   48.2 km/h, 41.6° north of east
3. 222 km, 22.5° north of east;   22.2 km/h, 22.5° north of east;   24 km/h
5. 96.6 km/h;   26.8 m/s
7. $v_x = 1.73$ m/s; $v_y = 1.00$ m/s;   (2 m/s)v̂;   0.866i + 0.500j
9. $v_{BW} − v_{WE}$; $v_{BW} + v_{WE}$
11. 36.9°;   4.0 km/h;   1 h
13. 2 m/s², eastward;   −4 m/s², eastward or 4 m/s², westward
15. 20 m/s;   100 m;   10 m/s
17. 9.8 m/s, 19.6 m/s, 29.4 m/s, downward;   4.9 m, 19.6 m, 44.1 m, downward;   5.71 s;
     28.0 m/s, downward;   9.8 m/s², downward
19. 100, 200, 300, 400, 500 m, eastward;   4.9, 19.6, 44.1, 78.4, 122 m, downward
21. 3.06 s;   45.9 m;   0 m/s;   9.8 m/s², downward
23. 4.5 m/s²
25. 465 m/s, 403 m/s, 233 m/s, 0
27. 1670 km/h, 1450 km/h, 837 km/h in a westward direction
29. (a) 20 min, 50 min, 70 min;   (b) 28.3 min, 40.7 min, 69.0 min;   (c) 25.4°, 22.1 min,
     41.1 min, 63.2 min
31. 1.22×10^4 m; 8.49×10^4 m;   9.8 m/s²
33. 6.5 m/s;   2.0 m/s
35. 2, 6.5, 8, 6.5, 2, −5.5, −16 m/s
37. 6, 3, 0, −3, −6, −9, −12 m/s²
39. 4.3 s;   No. Why?
43. 16.4 m/s;   v = (10.6 m/s)i + (12.5 m/s)j
45. ā = (1.6 m/s²)i + (2.0 m/s²)j
47. v = $(6 − 4t + 0.6t^2)$i + $(4 + 6t − 0.9t^2)$j + $(4 + 8t − 1.2t^2)$k

CHAPTER 4

1. 0.25 kg
3. 2 m/s², east;   10 m/s, east;   25 m, east
5. 4.29 m/s²;   8580 N
7. 8580 N, opposite in direction to car's acceleration;   0. Why?
9. 2 m/s², eastward at an angle of 36.9° above the horizontal
11. 495 N
13. 2250 N
15. 0.50;   0.25

17. (a) 84.9 N; 49.0 N; 4.9 m/s²; (b) 32.0 N; 3.2 m/s²
19. 10 kg · m/s², 50 kg · m/s, 25 m/s, all eastward
21. 2.45 kg · m/s, 30.6 N, both upward
23. 0; 0; 800 kg · m/s, east; 800 kg · m/s, west; 0.4 m/s, west; 4.0 m, west
25. 1 s; 0.49 N
27. $x = x' + V_{0x}t + \frac{1}{2}A_xt^2$; $v_x = v'_x + V_{0x} + A_xt$; $a_x = a'_x + A_x$, $y = y'$, $v_y = v'_y$, $a_y = a'_y$ where the primed quantities are measured in the $X'Y'$ frame
29. 4.50 N; 2.42 N; 0.889 s; 1.21 s; 5.87 m/s
31. 2.0 m/s²; 2400 N; 0.204
33. 465 m/s; 0.0338 m/s²; 0.0676 N
35. 2.99×10^4 m/s; 5.96×10^{-3} m/s²; 3.56×10^{22} N
37. 370 cm³
39. 0; 0; 20,000 kg · m/s, westward; 20,000 kg · m/s, eastward
41. 22 m/s, eastward; 20,000 kg · m/s, eastward; 340 m, eastward
43. 48,000 kg · m/s, westward; 240,000 N, westward
45. 9.5 kg · m/s; 2.0 kg · m/s²; 2.0 N
47. (3.36 kg · m/s)i + (8.88 kg · m/s)j; (−0.32 N)i + (1.44 N)j
49. (15.4 kg · m/s)i + (12.2 kg · m/s)j + (4.7 kg · m/s)k; (4.2 N)i + (1.6 N)j − (0.4)k
51. 1.6 N; 5.2 kg · m/s; 1.3 N; 19.2 m; 4.8 m/s; 2.4 kg · m/s

CHAPTER 5

1. 10 N, to the right; 10 N
3. 0.577
5. 24.2 m/s
7. 42.6°
9. 6.02 m/s²; Impossible. Why?
11. 14.3 N, 17.6 N
13. 5.7 N, 11.3 N
15. 0.743 m
17. 16.7°; 7.07 N; 5.22 N
19. 1.86 m/s; 3.46 m/s²; 6.93 N; 20.8 N
21. 1.09 m/s²; 21.8 N
23. (1) 6.53 m/s², 6.53 N; (2) 5.23 m/s², 9.14 N
25. (1) 1.69 kg; (2) 0.913 m/s², 15.0 N
27. 0.286; 1.40 m/s²
29. 4670 km
31. $9.54 \times 10^{-4}R$
33. 2.10 m
35. $r_{c.m.} = (0.900$ m, 0.012 m, 0.585 m)
37. $M \cdot L^3 \cdot T^{-2}$; kg · m³/s² = N · m²
39. $v_0\sqrt{2h/g}$
41. 0, 0, (3/8)R

CHAPTER 6

1. 520 J
3. 0.848 m/s, eastward; 360 J
5. 2.35×10^5 J; 19.8 m/s
7. 64 N; 0.544

9. 61.0 J; 8.72 N; 0.629
11. 0.544
13. 45.9 m; 21.2 m/s
15. (1) 3.61 m/s; (2) 2.80 m/s; 15.7 J
17. 1.49 m/s, eastward; 0; 596 J
19. 8.75 m/s, eastward; 3.38×10^5 J
21. 6 m/s, eastward; 12 m/s, eastward; 64 J
23. 18.1 m/s, west; 1.9 m/s, east; 0.18
25. 131 W
27. 7.35×10^5 W; 0.708
35. 24.2 m/s; 17.2 m/s; 20.8 m/s
37. 50 cm; 75 cm; 50 cm; 75 cm
39. The values of h_{max} for the three chains are 50 cm, 25 cm, and 12.5 cm
41. 1 m, 93.8 cm, 84.0 cm, 79.8 cm
43. 3.13 m/s; 29.4 N
45. $2.5R$; $\sqrt{gR}$; $\sqrt{5gR}$
53. 0.496 m/s at 8.1° north of east

CHAPTER 7

1. 36 rad/s, CCW; 216 rad, CCW
3. 31.7 rad/s, CCW; 7.93 s; 15.8 rad/s, CCW
5. 10 m/s; 252 m/s²
7. 24 J; 3.6 N · m, CCW; 6.67 rad, CCW
9. 0.18 kg · m²; 324 J; 12.7 m/s
11. 0; 36 W; 72 W
13. $l/3.46$; $l/1.73$
15. 0.6 rad/s², CCW; 1.2 rad/s², CCW
17. 0.467 m/s²; 2.80 N
19. 0.350 m/s²; 9.45 N; 5.08 N
21. 1.6 N · m · s, CW; 0.4 rad/s, CW
23. 5.0 rad/s; 40 N · m
25. 19.6 N · m; 19.6 N; 19.6 N; 0
27. 2.05 rad/s, CCW
29. 10 rad/s; 20 J
33. 1.414; 1.155
35. 0.96 N · m; 3.24 kg · m²/s; 13.1 J
37. rad/s$^{1/2}$, $k/(2t^{1/2})$; $-k/(4t^{3/2})$; No. Why?
39. $2v_0$; $2mv_0^2$; $8mv_0^2/R_0$
47. (−1,7,5); 3; (0,−5,−5); −5

CHAPTER 8

1. 85 cm; 54.9 N
3. 15.7 N; 43.1 N
5. 40,000 N; 1.88 m in front of the rear axle
7. 97.9 N; 97.9 N; 60°
9. 61.2 cm
11. 80 N; 62.5 cm

13. Center, 4 m/s²; left end, 16 m/s²; right end, −8 m/s²
15. 7.35 m/s²; 14.7 m/s²; 1.22 N
17. 3.27 m/s²; 8.00 m/s
19. 1.15 m/s² to the right; 28.8 N to the left
21. 173.2 J; 115.5 J; 57.7 J
23. 4.63 m/s²; 401 N
25. 2.5 m/s²; 0
27. A: 1.00 m/s², 0 N; B: 0.75 m/s², −0.75 N; C: 0.50 m/s², −1.50 N; D: 0.25 m/s², −2.25 N
29. 21.3 rad/s
31. 19.6 m/s²
33. $h = \frac{5}{4}D$
35. $F_A = 19.6$ N; $F_B = 19.6$ N; $F_D = 39.2$ N
41. 8.79×10^{-3} m/s²
43. 1.40 m/s²; 11.2 N; 16.8 N
45. 0.891 m/s²; 10.7 N; 17.8 N
51. 399 N, 659 N; 149 N; ±344 N at an angle of 30.3° with the horizontal

CHAPTER 9

1. 3.52×10^{22} N; 0.0059 m/s²
3. 6.81×10^{-7} N
5. 3.6×10^8 m; No. Why?
7. 1.75×10^{18} N; 3.52×10^{22} N for sun; 1.98×10^{20} N for moon
9. 1.62 m/s²; 25.9 m/s²; 784 N; 130 N; 2070 N
11. 2.46 m/s²; 6.26×10^7 J
13. 6.26×10^8 J; 11.2 km/s
15. 4.22×10^7 m; 3.07×10^3 m/s
17. 0, 1.96, 3.93, 5.89, 7.86, 9.82, 5.01, 3.03, 0.61, 0 m/s²
19. $U = (GM_E/2R_E)(r^2/R_E^2 - 1)$ for $0 < r < R_E$; for $r > R_E$ the result is given in (9.31)
21. 10.7 km/s; 11.7 km/s; 11.2 km/s
25. $U_0 = -(3/2R_E)GM_E$

CHAPTER 10

1. 653 N/m; 0.294 J
3. 980 N/m; 1.02 cm
5. 625 N/m
7. 13.75 N · m/rad; 17.0 J
9. 0.78 mm; 2.6×10^{-4}; 2.86×10^7 N/m²
11. 0.412 mm; 3.74×10^7 N/m²; 1.87×10^{-4}
13. -9.52×10^{-3} liter; 4.76×10^{-3}; 4.76×10^{-10} m²/N
15. 297 m · N/rad; 3.15×10^8 N/m²; 7.68×10^{-3}
17. 109 kg
19. 2.8×10^4 N
23. $k = M_Y A/l$
25. $\rho_{av} = 0.318$
27. 8.17×10^6 N/m²; 7.43×10^{-5}; 1.22×10^7 N/m²; 6.12×10^{-5}
29. 10.2 m/s²

33. 0.643 J

37. 0;   9.0 m/s²

39. $S = (F/l^2)[(1 + \sin \phi)/\cos \phi]$

41. 2.6 mm

43. -9.3×10^{-11} m²

45. 3.96 m · N;   0.021 rad;   189 m · N/rad;   0.0416 J

CHAPTER 11

1. 2.94×10^7 N; 2.94×10^4 Pa; 1.47×10^4 Pa

3. 1.96×10^5 Pa; 2.02×10^5 Pa

5. 1.96×10^3 N; 1.33×10^4 J

7. 0.922;   0, why?

9. 121 kg

11. 1.001×10^5 Pa;   10.2 m; 8.01×10^7 N

13. 2.94×10^5 Pa; 3.95×10^5 Pa;   20.7 m

15. 15.9 m/s;   0.636 m/s; 1.26×10^5 Pa

17. 0.171 m³/s

25. 3.53×10^5 Pa;   26.6 m/s

27. 360 N; 6.48×10^4 J

29. 10.2 m/s²;   15.2 m/s²;   23.5 m/s²

33. 2.58×10^4 N

37. $v_T = mg/\mathscr{R}$

39. 65.6 m/s², upward

41. 1.2×10^{-4} m/s;   30 m/s;   120 m/s;   480 m/s; 2.8×10^3 m/s; 9.9×10^4 m/s

43. 2.8×10^5

47. 9.14×10^3 kg

49. 37.5 m/s

CHAPTER 12

1. 6 cm;   2.49 Hz;   0.402 s

3. 5 Hz;   493 N/m;   24.7 N

5. 3.10 kg;   12.8 cm

7. 3.84 J;   3.92 m/s;   3.39 m/s

9. $E_2/E_1 = 4$; $v_{2max}/v_{1max} = 2$

13. 0.433 Hz;   2.31 s

15. 0.174 Hz;   5.74 s;   5.92 J

17. 0.24840 m

19. 0.498 Hz;   0.610 Hz;   0.352 Hz

21. 0.516 Hz;   0.932 m

23. $(1/2\pi)\sqrt{g/2R}$; $2R$

25. $(1/2\pi)\sqrt{2g/3R}$

27. 63.2 N/m;   0.0229 W

29. 2.24, 1.58, 1.29, 0.707, 0.500, 0.316 Hz

31. 5.06×10^3 s or 84 min; 1.97×10^{-4} Hz;   7.9 km/s;   9.8 m/s²

33. 1.004;   1.002

39. $x = (0.14$ m$)[\cos 2\pi(3$ Hz$)t]$, $y = (0.14$ m$)[\sin 2\pi(3$ Hz$)t]$;   1.99 N;   14.2 N/m

49. 3.7 cm

CHAPTER 13

1. 5.0 mm; 1.0 cm
3. 0.68 mm; 1.02 mm; 2.04 mm; 98 cm²; 1.47×10^3 cm³
5. 161°C; No, why?; No, why?
7. 7.28 cm³; 5.28 cm³
9. 1.86 cm³
15. −136.5°C; −183°C
17. $\Delta V/V = (1.2 \times 10^{-6}$ Cdeg$^{-1})\Delta T$; 1.00012
19. 76.2 cm of mercury
23. 75.9 cm of mercury
25. 7.54×10^4 N
27. 5.03×10^3 atm
29. 0.684 s/h; fast
31. 0.036%; larger
35. 18°C

CHAPTER 14

1. 6.36×10^{-2} kcal/K; 34°C
3. 13.2 kcal; 16.6°C
5. 25.1°C; 0°C
7. 73.0°C; 31.7 g
9. 2914 kcal; 0.013; 0.109; 0.137; 0.740
11. 2.30×10^4 J; 5.50 kcal
13. 5.58 kW
15. 11.8 N; 4.5 N
17. 1.77×10^3 kcal; 2.06 kW
19. −6.17°C; 226 kcal; 263 W
21. 1.70 m
27. 4.48×10^{26} W
29. 0.625; 0.375; 30 W/m²
31. 1.49 kW/m²; 403 K
35. 1.30 cm/h
37. 0.223

CHAPTER 15

1. 0.0446 kmol; 2.69×10^{25} molecules
3. 6.63×10^6 Pa; 6.53×10^6 Pa
5. 2.09×10^5 J; 3.13×10^5 J
7. 1.22×10^5 J; 0
9. 149 kcal; 6.23×10^5 J
11. 248 kcal; 6.23×10^5 J; 4.16×10^5 J
13. 38.9 kcal; 1.63×10^5 J; 0
15. 8.25×10^6 J; 8.25×10^6 J
17. 1070 K; 85.6 atm
21. 6.21×10^{-21} J; 517 m/s
23. 0.798
25. 6.42×10^{-4} m/s

27. 2.69×10^{25} molecules; 2.026×10^5 Pa
29. 7.99 km
31. 64.5 kg; 13.4×10^{26}
33. 7.71 m³
35. 1.52×10^5 J; 1.27×10^3 J; 1.27×10^3 J; 273 K
41. 0.6, 0.4; 0, 1.0
43. 89.1 cm of mercury
45. 14.5 atm
47. 0.27 atm; 3228 atm
49. $(\Delta V/V)^N$; $(1/2)^N$

CHAPTER 16

1. 755 mm
3. 9.84 m
5. 15.35 atm; the cylinder contains only liquid water; fluid. Why?
7. 0.01°C
9. 0.590
11. 677.1 kcal/kg; 3.33×10^5 J; 2.37×10^6 J
13. 775 cm³; 69.7 mg
15. 467 mm of mercury
17. 50.5%; 11.6 g/m³
19. 1.17 kg/m³; 1.15 kg/m³
23. 11.2%
25. Approximately 9°C
29. Approximately 10.5°C
31. 5.1×10^6 Pa; −0.4°C; about 22°C; about 265°C

CHAPTER 17

1. 8.10×10^6 J
3. 0.575; 4.81×10^3 J
5. 39.9 kcal; 3.97; No. Why?
7. 0.268; 373 W; 273 W
9. 364 K; 546 K; 1092 K; 5460 K
11. 667 J; 667 J
13. 3.10×10^5 J
15. 0.236; 0.116
17. 14.1 J; 84.5 J; 155 J
19. -1.21×10^4 J/K
21. 105 J; 837 W; 27.1 kg
23.

	A → B	B → C
Q	5.41×10^5 J	0
W	5.41×10^5 J	9.76×10^5 J
ΔU	0	-9.76×10^5 J

	C → D	D → A	Whole cycle
Q	-2.71×10^5 J	0	2.70×10^5 J
W	-2.71×10^5 J	-9.76×10^5 J	2.70×10^5 J
ΔU	0	9.76×10^5 J	0

25. 991 J/K, 0, −991 J/K, 0, 0
27. 1.23×10^3 J/K
29. 0.034; 0.068; 0.102; 0.136
31. 2.03×10^5 J; 1.01×10^5 J; 1.01×10^5 J;   800 K;   200 K; $A \rightarrow B$, $D \rightarrow A$;
    $B \rightarrow C$, $C \rightarrow D$
33. 2.49×10^6 J; 9.8×10^5 J
35. 15.3×10^5 J

CHAPTER 18

1. 143 m/s;   71.5 m/s
3. 29.4 m/s
5. Decreased;   67.6 m/s;   30 m/s
7. 2.4 m/s;   48 m
9. 0.0020 m;   9.55 Hz; 100π m; 3×10^3 m/s;   positive X direction;
    $v_p = 0.120 \cos(60t - 0.02x + \pi/4)$; $v_p(\text{max}) = 0.120$ m/s
11. 0.80 s;   1.25 Hz;   99.0 m/s;   79.2 m;
    $Y = (0.008 \text{ m})\sin[(7.85 \text{ Hz})t - (0.0793 \text{ m}^{-1})x]$;
    $Y = (0.008 \text{ m})\sin[(7.85 \text{ Hz})t - (0.0793 \text{ m}^{-1})x - \pi/2]$
13. 0.00274 m
15. 9.14 W, 8.54 W, 0.61 W
17. 200 Hz;   49
19. (a) 87.4 Hz;   1.21;   yes. (b) 148.6 Hz;   yes;   41.5 N.   (c) yes;   2.72 mm
21. $Y = -(0.02 \text{ m})\sin[(1.57 \text{ m}^{-1})x]\cos[(82.3 \text{ Hz})t]$
27. (b) 1.91 J;   (c) 5.0 mm
29. 0.853 m;   1.72 m

CHAPTER 19

1. (a) 0.184 m, 331 m/s, 1.76×10^{-6} m;   (b) 8.42×10^{-5};   (d) 1.99×10^{-2} m/s
3. 107 m;   4.4 s
9. $v = \sqrt{P/\rho} = \sqrt{kT/\mu}$;   15.5%
11. Rod wave;   446 m;   0.22 s
13. 28.1 Hz, 56.2 Hz, 84.3 Hz, 112.4 Hz;   4.32%
15. 8.25 m;   4.125 m
17. 2.06×10^3 Hz, 9; 1.03×10^3 Hz, 10
19. 334 m/s
21. 25 cm;   75 cm;   two
23. 43.5 beats in 10 s
25. 225 Hz;   112 Hz
27. 1.64 m;   1.53 m;   224 Hz, 197 Hz
29. 1173 Hz;   1036 Hz
31. 4.95×10^4 Hz
33. (b) 59.8;   (c) 2.79×10^{-4};   (d) 2.79×10^{-4}. All ratios have the water quantity in the numerator
35. 19.1 dB
37. 5.00 μW; 1.84×10^{-3} Pa; 2.29×10^{-10} m;   79.4 m

CHAPTER 20

1. 7.81×10^{-5} N; 7.81×10^{-7} N; 1.95×10^{-11} N;   0.500 N
3. 2.22×10^{-4} N; 2.22×10^{-4} N;   8.48 cm
5. $(-3.46 \times 10^{-3}$ N)i $+ (2.59 \times 10^{-3}$ N)j
7. $(-8.64 \times 10^{-4}$ N)i $+ (6.48 \times 10^{-4}$ N)j
9. $(-3.46 \times 10^{-3}$ N)i $+ (8.59 \times 10^{-3}$ N)j; $(-3.46 \times 10^{-3}$ N)i $+ (-3.41 \times 10^{-3}$ N)j
11. 25.6 N; 1.53×10^{28} m/s²
13. 1.84 m
17. $\mathbf{F} = (1/4\pi\epsilon_0)(Q^2/2a^2\, d^2)\{1 - [1 + (1/4a^2)]^{-3/2}\}\mathbf{k}$
19. 0
21. -19.54×10^{-7} C; -7.68×10^{-7} C; $+7.68 \times 10^{-7}$ C
23. $Q/2$
25. $1.25 \times 10^{11}, 2.81 \times 10^{11}$; $3.54 \times 10^{-13}, 7.96 \times 10^{-13}$; 2.64×10^{-6} N;
    4.59×10^{-7} N (repulsion)
27. Repulsion; 2.52×10^{13}
31. 5.75 N (In what direction?)
33. 3.52 N toward the center of the pentagon
35. 46.6 cm from Q_1 in the direction toward Q_2
37. 5.09 m
39. $(-4.30$ m/s²)k

CHAPTER 21

1. $(1.60 \times 10^{-4}$ N)i
3. 6.39×10^4 N/C radially outward; 6.39×10^4 N/C radially inward
5. $(-4.55 \times 10^3$ N/C)i; $(-4.55 \times 10^3$ N/C)i
9. $(1.37 \times 10^4$ N/C)j; $(-1.37 \times 10^4$ N/C)j
15. $(-7.05 \times 10^5$ N/C)i $+ (0.58 \times 10^5$ N/C)j
17. -1.41×10^{-6} C
19. 2.02×10^4 N/C, downward
21. 1.78×10^7 N/C at 76.0° above the line joining P and Q_2
23. $\mathbf{F} = 0$; $\tau_z = 0$
25. $\mathbf{F} = 0$; $\tau_z = 2.30 \times 10^{-9}$ m · N
27. 4.9 N/C, upward
29. 1.11×10^{-2} N
31. $18.7° \le \phi \le 20.4°$
33. $\mathbf{F} = 0$; $\tau_z = 6.07 \times 10^{-8}$ m · N
37. (b) $(1/4\pi\epsilon_0)(Q/z^2)\mathbf{k}$
39. $\mathscr{E}(\mathbf{r}) = 0$

CHAPTER 22

1. 7.50×10^5 V; B; -1.50 J; $+1.50$ J
3. On a sphere with center at Q and radius 1.00 m;   on a sphere with center at Q and
   radius 1.22 m; 8.38×10^{-3} J; -4.19×10^{-3} J
5. 8.44×10^{-4} V;   higher
7. $V_P = 10$ V $- (168$ V/m$)x_P$
9. 0;   900 V, -900 V;   0, 0

13. 2700 V, 2700 V; 2280 V, 2280 V
15. 18,000 V; 7.2×10^{-3} J
17. 0; 1.35×10^{-6} J
19. 244 V; $+1.00 \times 10^{-8}$ C
21. 73.9 V; -73.9 eV
23. (b) $(1/4\pi\epsilon_0)(-q/z - 2dq/z^2)$; (c) $(1/4\pi\epsilon_0)(2qd^2/z^3)$
27. $V_P = Q/4\pi\epsilon_0 R$
29. -0.436 J
31. 0.122 J
39. 4.34×10^{-5} eV/molecule

CHAPTER 23

7. 5.33×10^{-7} C; 3.33×10^{12}; 1.47×10^{-13}
9. $\mathscr{E} = 0$ for $r > a$; $\mathscr{E} = \hat{r}Q(1 - r^3/a^3)/4\pi\epsilon_0 r^2$ for $0 < r < a$
11. $(8.24 \times 10^3 \text{ V/m})\hat{r}$
13. $\rho(r) = 2\mathscr{E}\epsilon_0/r$
15. $(Q_A + Q_B)/4\pi\epsilon_0 r$; $Q_A/4\pi\epsilon_0 r + Q_B/4\pi\epsilon_0 B$; $Q_A/4\pi\epsilon_0 A + Q_B/4\pi\epsilon_0 B$
17. 4.80×10^3 V; 1.20×10^4 V
19. $k = e^2/4\pi\epsilon_0 R^3$; 6.57×10^{15} Hz
25. $\mathscr{E} = \hat{\rho}\lambda/2\pi\epsilon_0\rho$; 2.59×10^{-8} C/m
27. $(180 \text{ V/m})\mathbf{k}$; $-(180 \text{ V/m})\mathbf{k}$

CHAPTER 24

1. 5.69×10^{-12} F; 5.53×10^4 V; 3.50×10^{-4} C/m²
3. 2.42×10^{-11} F/m; 3.05×10^{-8} C/m; 1.92×10^{-5} J/m; 4.91×10^{-5} J
7. $\mathscr{E}_0/\kappa$
11. 3.60×10^{-4} J, 0.12 N
13. 5.40×10^{-5} J, 2.70×10^{-5} J
15. 5.45×10^3 V/m; 8.34×10^{-10} C; 4.54×10^{-9} J; 10.9 V
17. 15.7 cm
19. 7.89 μJ; -6.62 μJ; 41.1 μJ
21. 3.30 J
23. 18 μF; 1.85 μF
25. 0.214 J, 0.107 J, 0.071 J; 1
29. 10.0 μF
33. 333 V; 6.67×10^{-4} C; 3.33×10^{-4} C; 5.54×10^{-2} J; 11.1×10^{-2} J; 1.4×10^{-2} J
35. C_1: 9.23×10^{-4} C, 231 V, 0.107 J; C_2: 2.77×10^{-4} C, 92.3 V, 1.28×10^{-2} J;
C_3: 2.77×10^{-4} C, 138 V, 1.92×10^{-2} J; 0.041 J
39. (c) 39.6 V

CHAPTER 25

1. 0.5 s; 1.25×10^{19}
3. 3.01×10^{-12} A/m² downward
5. 1.5×10^{-4} C/s; 1.07×10^{-5} C/m²

7. 2.63×10^{12} m/s^2
9. 12.5 A
11. 20 Ω, 100 Ω;   5 A, 1 A
13. 828 J
15. 7;   33.3 Ω, 50 Ω, 66.7 Ω, 100 Ω, 150 Ω, 200 Ω, 300 Ω
17. 60 V for all resistors;   7.5 A, 6 A, 4 A, 3.33 A;   450 W, 360 W, 240 W, 200 W
19. $I_6 = 0.171$ A, $I_5 = 0.205$ A, $I_{10} = 0.376$ A, $I_{11} = 0.110$ A, $I_7 = 0.173$ A,
    $I_{13} = 0.093$ A
21. 1.15×10^{-4} Ω;   45.4°C
23. 0.378 Ω;   −7.94%
25. 1511°C
27. $d_{Ag} = 2.74$ cm; $d_{Al} = 3.67$ cm; $d_{Cu} = 2.86$ cm
29. 7.83 Ω
31. (b) $J = (V/\rho r^2)/(1/r_1 - 1/r_2)$;   (c) $\mathscr{E} = r_1 r_2 V/r^2(r_2 - r_1)$;   (d) 4.52 A
33. 27.2 V;   0.316 Ω
35. 94.3 J;   92.6 J
37. 0.432 J;   1360 W
39. 0.350 J;   300 W

CHAPTER 26

1. 42.7 Ω;   3.00 W;   0.132 A, 0.0658 A, 0.0526 A
3. 0;   ∞;   0.2 Ω
5. 20.5 Ω;   12.0 W, 6.0 W, 6.0 W;   2.49 Ω;   135 W, 6.0 W, 129 W
7. $V_E = [(r_1 r_2)/(r_1 + r_2)][V_{E1}/r_1 + V_{E2}/r_2]$, $r = r_1 r_2/(r_1 + r_2)$;   11 V, 0.05 Ω;   0.0150 W,
   20.0 W
9. 1.57 A;   1.29 A;   2.86 A;   57.2 V
11. 5.00 Ω;   461 W
13. 47.5 Ω;   150 W
15. 6.18 V
17. 1.425 A, 0.724 A, 0.572 A, 1.577 A, 0.854 A
19. 37.2 V, 38.8 V;   7.85 A, 10.15 A, 0.154 A
21. 14.0 Ω;   16.5 Ω
23. 6.36 Ω
25. 9950 Ω, 2.00×10^4 Ω; 5.00×10^{-2} Ω, 2.50×10^{-2} Ω
27. 4.00×10^{-3} Ω; 3.61×10^{-2} Ω;   0.368 Ω
29. $R = V_M R_V/(I_M R_V - V_M)$
31. 250 Ω
37. 0; 7.12×10^{-3} A
39. 1.97×10^3 Ω;   2000 Ω;   6000 Ω;   667 Ω

CHAPTER 27

3. 3.27 T, north
5. 1.65×10^{-2} m
7. $R_e = R_p$, $R_\alpha/R_e = 3.64 \times 10^3$; $R_e = R_p$, $R_\alpha/R_e = 42.7$
9. 1.35 cm; 2.57×10^{-4} T
11. $\delta M = (Q\mathscr{B}_2\mathscr{B}_1/\mathscr{E})\delta x$;   3.9 mm
17. 9.6 N, upward;   0

19. 1.47 A from left to right in the diagram
21. $\mathbf{F}_R = 0$; $T = 0.10$ N
23. $(3.60 \times 10^{-4}$ N$)(-\mathbf{j})$, $(2.60 \times 10^{-4}$ N$)\mathbf{i}$, $(3.60 \times 10^{-4}$ N$)\mathbf{j}$, $(5.20 \times 10^{-4}$ N$)(-\mathbf{i})$; $(2.60 \times 10^{-4}$ N$)(-\mathbf{i})$
25. 0.0996 T, north
27. 48.4 A·m²
29. $dI = r\omega\sigma\,dr;$ $d\mathbf{m} = \pi r^3 \omega\sigma\,dr\,\mathbf{k};$ $\mathbf{m} = (\pi R^4 \omega\sigma/4)\mathbf{k}$
31. 6.00×10^{-3} m·N; 6.34×10^{-3} m·N
33. positive Y direction; 9.05×10^{-3} T; 1.09×10^{-4} Wb
35. clockwise as seen from above; 3.67×10^{-3} T
37. 500; 0.500 T
39. $\tau = I\mathcal{B}_x\pi R^2\mathbf{j}$

CHAPTER 28

1. 9.6×10^{-4} T; 9.6×10^{-5} T; 0
3. 2.28×10^{-16} N (up); 0; 2.28×10^{-16} N (west); 2.14×10^{-16} N (up)
5. $(-9.14 \times 10^{-7}$ N$)\mathbf{i}$
7. 2.09×10^{-5} T at 20.2° to the left of the vertical in the diagram
9. $\sqrt{2}\mu_0 I/\pi L$ (away from the reader)
13. (a) 0; (b) $F/L = 2.36 \times 10^{-5}$ N/m directed away from the center of the square
15. 3.02×10^{-2} T; vertically upward
17. 3.47×10^{-5} T away from the reader
21. 4.80×10^{-4} T
25. 27.1 turns/cm
27. 0.0204 T; 2.56×10^{-5} Wb
29. $\frac{1}{2}\mu_0 I$; $1.33a$
31. 1.27×10^{-4} T/A
33. 2.61×10^{-5} T; 2.40×10^{-5} T
35. 0; $(\mu_0 I/2\pi R)(R^2 - R_1^2)/(R_2^2 - R_1^2)$; $\mu_0 I/2\pi R$
39. $F_{\mathscr{E}} = 9.20 \times 10^{-26}$ N (repulsion); $F_{\mathscr{B}} = 1.38 \times 10^{-30}$ N (repulsion)

CHAPTER 29

1. 1.05×10^{-3} V; upper end
3. 1.62×10^{-3} V; west
5. 3.64×10^{-2} V
11. 3.14×10^{-4} V; 1.21×10^{-4} A, clockwise
15. 72.2 rad/s
17. 3.02×10^{-2} H; 0.121 V; 0.121 V
19. 1.92×10^{-8} H; 9.60×10^{-9} V
21. 10^{-7} Wb; 10^{-7} J
23. 0.452 H/m
25. 1.92×10^{-6} H; 1.92×10^{-7} V
27. 5.58×10^3
29. 0.225 J
31. 0.02 J
35. $\mathscr{B}^2/2\mu_0$

39. $I = (25 \text{ A})(1 - e^{-(10 \text{ s}^{-1})t})$;   15.8 A, 125 J;   initial: $v_R = 0$, $v_L = 250$ V;   final: $v_R = 250$ V, $v_L = 0$

41. 9.20 A;   42.3 J

CHAPTER 30

1. 0.314 T

3. 1.83×10^{-23} A · m²

7. 212 A/m; 1.06×10^6 A/m;   1.33 T

9. 0.530 A; 2.70×10^{-5} Wb;   1.06 A

11. 1.12×10^6 A/m; 1.12×10^6 A/m; 9.90×10^5 turns

CHAPTER 31

1. 1060 Hz

3. 261 Ω

5. 1.72×10^{-2} H;   18.9 Ω;   33.0 Ω

7. 53.4 Ω

9. 138 Ω;   131 V;   49.4 V;   174 V

11. 168 Ω;   0.121 H; 4.91×10^{-7} F

13. 48.0 W

15. (a) 30.4 Ω, (b) 1.06 radians lead, (c) 6.49 W, (d) 258 Hz, (e) 1.33 A

17. 23.4 W

19. (a) 57.4 V, (b) 205 V, (c) 153 V, (d) lead, (e) 0.139

23. 49 to 419 pF

25. 1.08×10^{-4} F

27. $f = 1/2\pi \sqrt{LC}$

29. 2.76 kV

31. 2.2×10^{-2};   227 A;   49.9 kW;   0.969 Ω

33. 9;   3.18 A;   0;   0.0125 A;   1.5 W

CHAPTER 32

1. 6.67×10^{-4} s, 1.3 s

3. 3.0×10^8 Hz

11. 478 W/m²

13. $\epsilon_0 \mathscr{E}_M^2/2$

23. 52.3 A

25. $\bar{S} = \dfrac{I_0^2}{8\pi^2\epsilon_0 r^2 c} \dfrac{\cos^2[(\pi/2)\cos\theta]}{\sin^2\theta} \, \hat{e}_r$

CHAPTER 33

1. 498 s (8.3 min);   2593 s (43 min);   14,980 s (4 h 10 min)

3. 40 min;   1 h 20 min

5. 9.47×10^{12} km; 15.8×10^{-6} light years

7. 93.0 km;   2.54 s
9. 82.1 km/h
11. 146 km/h
13. 6.66×10^{14} Hz; 5.40×10^{14} Hz; 4.68×10^{14} Hz
15. 330
17. 6×10^{-4} nm
19. 1.35;   1.16;   0.954;   0.675;   0 kW/m²
21. 628 lm;   5.55 lm/m²;   3.93 lm/m²
23. 4.73×10^{16} cd;   13.0 m
25. (a) 400π lm;   (b) 140 lm/m²;   (c) 267 lm/m², 51.3 lm/m²
27. 544 lm
29. 8.70×10^{7} m
31. 3.33×10^{3} rad/s

CHAPTER 34

1. 80 cm
7. 60 cm;   8 cm
9. −20 cm;   8 cm
11. 45 cm;   15 cm
15. −14.3 cm;   1.14 cm
17. 20 cm
19. 22.1°
21. 16.0°
23. 3.52 cm
25. 32.0°, 28.9°;   27.5°
27. 51.7°;   90°
29. 43.0 cm
31. 50 cm beyond lens;   6 cm
33. 16.7, 20, 30, ∞, and −10 cm
35. −5 cm from lens;   1 cm
37. 75.4 cm
39. 15 cm behind the second lens
41. 22.2 cm
43. 16.12 cm;   −23.79 cm
45. 6.7 m
47. 0.961 cm;   5.2 cm;   0.21 rad
49. 26, 25;   0.008 rad
51. 206
53. 9.3 cm
57. 3.0×10^{6} lm/m²
59. 5.13×10^{-3} degrees;   8.0°;   16.0°

CHAPTER 35

1. 8.84 mm
3. 500 nm
7. 3×10^{7} m; 5×10^{13}
9. 510 nm;   green

11. spacing $= w\lambda/2d$

13. 1.18 mm;   1.77 mm

15. 0.146 mm

19. 6.1×10^{-7} rad; 1.64×10^{6}

21. 3.05×10^{-4} rad;   3.28 m. At twilight;   why?

23. 36.1°

25. 14.5°, 30.0°, 48.6°

29. 1/8

31. 53.1°, 56.6°, 58.9°

33. 354, 356 nm

CHAPTER 36

1. 12°;   250 mm

3. 9.66 μm (infrared)

5. 6040 K

7. 3000 K, 12 000 K

13. 4.14×10^{-15} eV·s

15. 3.63 V;   342 nm;   2.57 V

17. 0.041

19. 6.58×10^{15} Hz; 8.22×10^{14} Hz; 2.46×10^{15} Hz

21. 3.26 m/s; 5×10^{-9}

23. 6.23×10^{-9} m; 1.45×10^{-10} m; 7.3×10^{-11} m

CHAPTER 37

3. $0.866c$

5. $0.866c$; $0.995c$; $0.99995c$

7. $l_0^2\sqrt{1 - v^2/c^2}$

9. 0;   0

11. 0,0; $0.8c$, $1.0c$; $-0.5c$, $-0.5c$; $0.5c$, $0.5c$

13. $0.286c$; $0.4c$; $0.324c$

15. 0.6 m/s²;   0.216 m/s²;   0.451 m/s²

17. 1.022 MeV;   0.511 MeV

23. 1.34×10^{17} kg/g; 1.49×10^{13} years;   No. Why?

25. 8.21×10^{13} J/kg; 1.96×10^{10} kcal/kg;   2 600 000 kg

INDEX